*Chemistry
of the
Amino Acids*

VOLUME 2

Chemistry of the Amino Acids

JESSE P. GREENSTEIN
and MILTON WINITZ

Laboratory of Biochemistry,
National Cancer Institute,
National Institutes of Health,
Public Health Service,
United States Department of Health,
Education, and Welfare

John Wiley and Sons, Inc.   New York   London   Sydney

Copyright © 1961 by John Wiley & Sons, Inc.

All Rights Reserved. This book or any part thereof must not be reproduced in any form without the written permission of the publisher.

**Library of Congress Catalog Card Number: 61-6474
Printed in the United States of America**

Contents

Part III Organic Chemical Aspects (*Continued*)

CHAPTER 10 CHEMICAL PROCEDURES FOR THE SYNTHESIS OF PEPTIDES 763

Introduction
1. Nomenclature and Structure 763
2. Some Naturally Occurring Peptides 771
3. Historical Considerations 776

Classical Methods of Peptide Synthesis
4. Condensations Involving α-Amino Acids or Their Ester Derivatives 782
5. The Diketopiperazine Method 793
6. Acylamino Acid Chlorides and Azides in Peptide Synthesis 804
7. The α-Haloacyl Halide and Related Methods 808
8. The Azlactone Method in the Synthesis of Saturated and Unsaturated Peptides 823
9. Properties of Dehydropeptides and Their Preparation via the Condensation of Amides or Nitriles with α-Keto Acids 843
10. The N-Carboxy-α-amino Acid Anhydride Method 860
11. The Thio-thiazolidone Method 876

Synthetic Peptide Methods Involving Selectively Removable Acyl Blocking Groups
12. General Considerations 883

MASKING OF THE AMINO FUNCTION
13. p-Toluenesulfonyl Group   886
14. The Carbobenzoxy and Related Groups   887
15. Phthalyl Group   901
16. Trityl Group   907
17. Trifluoroacetyl Group   911
18. The Phenylthiocarbonyl and Related Groups   916
19. o-Nitrophenoxyacetyl and Chloroacetyl Groups   920
20. Formyl Group   920
21. Benzylsulfonyl Group   922

MASKING OF THE CARBOXYL FUNCTION
22. Amino Acid Methyl and Ethyl Esters   925
23. Amino Acid Benzyl Esters   928

PROCEDURES FOR COUPLING ACYLAMINO ACIDS WITH AMINO ACIDS, PEPTIDES, OR ESTER DERIVATIVES THEREOF
24. Types of Coupling Procedures   943
25. Considerations of Optical Purity   945
26. Azide Method   949
27. Acid Chloride Method   965
28. Mixed Carboxylic Acid Anhydride Procedure   970
29. Mixed Carboxylic-Carbonic Acid Anhydride Method   978
30. Phosphate Anhydrides of Amino Acids and Acylamino Acids   982
31. Methods Involving Substituted Phosphite Ester Intermediates   988
32. Sulfuric Acid Anhydride Method   996
33. Phosphazo Method   999
34. Phosphorus Oxychloride Method   1006
35. N-Carbonyl-α-amino Acid Ester Method   1011
36. Carbodiimide Method   1016
37. N-Acyl-5-oxazolidone Method   1024
38. Active Ester Method   1027
39. Methods Applicable to Amino Acid Residues with Secondary Functional Groups   1048
40. Physical Constants of Acylated Peptide Esters   1108
41. Preparation and Physical Constants of Acylated Amino Acid and Peptide Amides   1110

CONTENTS

42. Preparation and Physical Constants of Acylated Peptides (Free Acids) 1158
    REMOVAL OF N-ACYL BLOCKING SUBSTITUENTS
43. Preparation and Physical Constants of Peptides, Peptide Esters, Peptide Amides, and Amino Acid Amides 1187
44. Catalytic Hydrogenolysis 1189
45. Chemical Reduction 1239
46. Hydrolytic and Non-hydrolytic Cleavage with Acid 1243
47. Alkaline Hydrolysis and Hydrazinolysis 1249
48. Special Cleavage Methods 1252
49. An Approach to the Determination of the Optical Purity of Peptides 1254
    PREPARATION OF SELECTED DERIVATIVES
50. Glutamine and Asparagine 1257
51. O- and N-Phosphoamino Acids and Peptides 1260
52. Benzoylamino Acids 1266
    References 1268

Part IV   General Analytical Procedures

CHAPTER 11   COLORIMETRIC METHODS 1299
1. Introduction 1299
2. Photometric Ninhydrin Method 1301
3. Copper Complex Method 1312
   References 1316

CHAPTER 12   MANOMETRY AND TITRIMETRY 1318
1. Oxidative Degradation of the Amino Acids 1318
2. Reaction with Ninhydrin 1320
3. Reaction with N-Bromosuccinimide 1331
4. Reaction with Nitrous Acid 1332
5. Titrimetric Methods 1340
   References 1343

CHAPTER 13   ISOTOPE DILUTION 1345
1. The Single-Isotope Technique 1345
2. The Double-Isotope Dilution Technique 1348
   References 1349

CHAPTER 14 MICROBIOLOGICAL ASSAY METHODS 1350

1. Introduction 1350
2. Growth Conditions for Lactic Acid-Producing Bacteria 1351
3. Assay Organisms 1354
4. Assay Procedure 1357
5. Evaluation of Method 1361
   References 1364

CHAPTER 15 CHROMATOGRAPHY 1366

1. Introduction 1366
2. Partition Chromatography 1371
3. Paper Chromatography 1376
4. Desalting 1392
5. Color Reactions 1394

   ILLUSTRATIVE EXAMPLES OF THE SCOPE OF QUALITATIVE PAPER CHROMATOGRAPHY

6. The Problem of the Natural Occurrence of Norleucine 1398
7. The Problem of the Natural Occurrence of β-Hydroxyglutamic Acid 1399
8. Discovery of Butyrine, β-Aminoisobutyric Acid, Methylhistidine, and Felinine 1400
9. Discovery of α-Aminoheptylic Acid 1405
10. Discovery of α,ε-Diaminopimelic Acid 1406
11. Discovery of γ-Methyleneglutamine and Related Compounds 1407
12. Discovery of α-Aminopimelic Acid 1409
13. Discovery of γ-Hydroxyglutamic Acid 1410
14. Discovery of Pipecolic Acid 1411
15. Discovery of γ-Aminobutyric Acid 1412
16. Discovery of N-Methyl-α-amino Acids 1414
17. Discovery of L-Allohydroxyproline 1415
18. Discovery of Lanthionine 1416
19. Cyclic Imino Acids 1417
20. Tissue Extractives 1418
21. Thyroid Hormone Intermediates and Autoradiography 1425
22. Procedures for Paper Chromatography 1427
23. Determination of Optical Configuration of Amino Acids 1433

CONTENTS

24. Starch Columns 1434
25. Countercurrent Distribution 1440

   ADSORPTION CHROMATOGRAPHY

26. Charcoal Column Chromatography 1447
27. Earlier Work on Ion Exchange Resins 1452
28. Displacement Chromatography with Ion Exchange Resins 1456
29. Elution Analysis with Ion Exchange Resins 1461
30. Use of Ion Exchange Chromatography in the Resolution of Amino Acids 1477
31. Isotope Effects in Ion Exchange Chromatography 1479
32. Peptides 1479
33. Ionophoresis 1495
34. Ion Exchange Paper Chromatography 1500
    References 1500

CHAPTER 16   SEQUENTIAL ANALYSIS OF PEPTIDES 1512

1. Early Studies on Partial Hydrolysates of Proteins 1512
2. Carnosine, Anserine, and Glutathione 1521
3. More Exact Studies on Partial Hydrolysates of Proteins by the Use of Chromatographic and Other Techniques (Silk, Wool, and Lysozyme) 1524
4. Procedures for Terminal Amino Acid Analysis 1537

   N-TERMINAL SEQUENCES (PEPTIDES)
   N-TERMINAL SEQUENCES (PROTEINS)
   C-TERMINAL SEQUENCES
   PROBLEMS OF PARTIAL HYDROLYSIS

5. Sequences in Peptides 1626
6. The Amino Acid Sequences in Insulin 1665
   References 1673

CHAPTER 17   SPECTROPHOTOMETRY 1688

1. Ultraviolet Absorption Spectra 1688
2. Infrared Absorption Spectra 1695
3. Infrared Spectra of Diastereomeric Amino Acids 1706

4. Infrared Spectra of Corresponding Optically Active and Racemic Amino Acids   1710
5. Aqueous Phase Infrared Spectroscopy   1714
6. Raman Spectra   1716
7. Spectral Changes and Ionization   1719
References   1722

CHAPTER 18 OPTICAL ROTATION   1724

1. General Aspects   1724
2. Mineral Acid to Amino Acid Ratios   1727
3. Influence of the Disulfide Bond on Optical Rotation   1730
4. Procedure for Optical Rotation Measurements   1731
References   1733

CHAPTER 19 DETERMINATION OF OPTICAL AND STERIC PURITY   1734

1. General Considerations   1734
2. The Use of Oxidases and Decarboxylases   1738
3. Criteria of Purity Suggested by the National Research Council   1742
4. A Brief Recapitulation   1748
References   1749

Part V   Enzymes in Amino Acid Technology

CHAPTER 20 ENZYMES INVOLVED IN THE DETERMINATION, CHARACTERIZATION, AND PREPARATION OF THE AMINO ACIDS   1753

1. Introduction   1753
2. Mammalian Tissue Acylases   1754
3. Preparation and Properties of Renal Acylase I   1755
4. Renal Acylase II   1767
5. Pancreatic Carboxypeptidase   1767
6. Acylases in Microorganisms   1770
7. Renal Amidase   1778
8. Renal D-Amino Acid Oxidase   1782
9. L-Amino Acid Oxidase   1789

CONTENTS

10. Amino Acid Decarboxylases of Bacterial Origin   1793
11. Arginase   1807
12. Aminopeptidase   1808
    References   1812

TRANSLATIONS OF FOREIGN QUOTATIONS   1816a

INDEX (see Volume 3)

PART III

Organic Chemical Aspects (continued)

chapter *10*

Chemical Procedures for the Synthesis of Peptides

INTRODUCTION

1. Nomenclature and Structure. The class of compounds composed of amino acid units chemically bound one to the other through amide linkages, with the elimination of the elements of water, forms the most exhaustively studied of all amino acid derivatives. They may be represented by

—NH·CHR·CO$_2$H + NH$_2$·CHR'·CO— → —NH·CHR·CO ··· NH·CHR'·CO— + H$_2$O

where the characteristic amide linkage concerned with the union of the α-amino or α-imino group of one amino acid with the α-carboxyl of another is referred to as a *peptide bond* (dotted line). Compounds which include linkages of this type are commonly designated *peptides* or *polypeptides*, terms early fabricated by Emil Fischer (1) in imitation of the nomenclature conventionally employed with the carbohydrates:

Den namen Polypeptide habe ich vorgeschlagen für die Produkte, die durch amidartige Verkettung von Aminosäuren entstehen, und deren einfachster Vertreter das Derivat des Glykocolls, das sogenannte Glycylglycin,

NH$_2$CH$_2$CO—NHCH$_2$CO$_2$H

ist. Nach der Anzahl der in ihnen enthaltenen Aminosäuren sollen sie als Di-, Tri-, Tetra-Peptide usw. unterschieden werden. Diese Bezeichnung ist einerseits der Nomenklatur der Kohlehydrate nachgebildet, anderseits is darin das alte Wort Pepton verwertet, denn ich habe von Anfang an erwartet, und ich bin durch alle nachfolgenden Beobachtungen in dieser Überzeugung bestärkt worden, dass diese künstlichen Produkte den natürlichen Peptonen sehr nahe verwandet sind, mit anderen Worten, dass die Peptone im wesentlichen ein bisher untrennbares Gemisch von Polypeptiden sind.[40]

Thus, peptides or polypeptides may be considered polymers of amino acids which are united *via* amide bonds to form chains which incorporate as few as two or as many as several thousand *amino acid residues*. A segment of a hypothetical peptide chain may be depicted

$$\begin{array}{c}
\text{H} \quad \text{O} \quad \text{R}^2 \quad \text{H} \quad \text{O} \quad \text{R}^4 \quad \text{H} \quad \text{O} \\
| \quad \| \quad | \quad | \quad \| \quad | \quad | \quad \| \\
\text{N} \quad \text{H} \quad \text{C} \qquad \text{C} \quad \text{N} \quad \text{H} \quad \text{C} \qquad \text{C} \quad \text{N} \quad \text{H} \quad \text{C} \\
\diagdown \diagup \diagdown \diagup \diagdown \diagup \diagdown \diagup \diagdown \diagup \diagdown \diagup \diagdown \\
\text{C} \qquad \text{N} \quad \text{H} \quad \text{C} \qquad \text{C} \qquad \text{N} \quad \text{H} \quad \text{C} \qquad \text{C} \\
| \quad | \quad \| \quad | \quad | \quad \| \\
\text{R}^1 \quad \text{H} \quad \text{O} \quad \text{R}^3 \quad \text{H} \quad \text{O} \quad \text{R}^5
\end{array}$$

Like polymers which incorporate two, three, and four amino acid residues are known as di-, tri- and tetrapeptides respectively, etc.

Although the realization that proteins are composed of amino acids had its inception as early as 1820 with the isolation of glycine from gelatin hydrolysates by Braconnot (2), it remained for Hofmeister (3) and Fischer (1) independently to postulate, some eighty years later, that the chemical union of these amino acids in the protein molecule was mediated through peptide linkages. As a consequence of such hypothesis, the protein molecule could, in its simplest form, be regarded as a linear polypeptide (I) of $x + 2$ residues wherein R represents a side chain of diverse composition, i.e., alkyl, aryl, heterocyclic, etc. A portion of the considerable body of evidence which has

$$\text{NH}_2\text{CHRCO}-(\text{NHCHRCO})_x-\text{NHCHRCO}_2\text{H}$$
$$\text{I}$$

since accumulated in support of the polypeptide nature of proteins is briefly summarized in the following: (*a*) The characteristic purple color induced by the peptide bond in alkaline copper sulfate solution ("biuret reaction"), although very pronounced with proteins, becomes decreasingly so with decreasing size of the polypeptide chain and, consequently, with the lesser number of peptide bonds; (*b*) although the number of titratable amino and carboxyl groups in the intact protein is relatively small, a marked increase in these groups, which appear in nearly equal number, results upon complete hydrolysis; (*c*) proteolytic enzymes which catalyze the hydrolysis of proteins to amino acids induce the cleavage of synthetic peptides in like manner; (*d*) partial acid hydrolysis of proteins leads to the liberation of small peptides whose chemical structure may be ascertained; (*e*) infrared and X-ray analyses of proteins reveal the presence of the characteristic peptide bond found in smaller synthetic peptides of known composition; and (*f*) a parallel behavior is revealed by proteins and synthetic peptides upon their sequential degradation with various chemical agents.

Proteins are present in every living cell and are possessed of the most diverse

CHEMICAL PROCEDURES FOR SYNTHESIS OF PEPTIDES

biochemical activities. They may appear, for example, as enzymes, genes, virus, and hormones, and they compose a major portion of muscle, tendon, skin, and hair. Although little more than twenty different kinds of amino acids, all of the L-configuration, have thus far been demonstrated as protein constituents, a single protein may none the less contain several hundreds or even thousands of residues. Qualitative and quantitative differences in their amino acid composition, as well as differences in the arrangement of residues in the peptide chains, in the nature and number of lateral bonds between chains, and in the looping of chains, make theoretically possible countless numbers of distinct kinds of proteins which may exist in a multiplicity of structural conformations. X-ray analysis has, for example, represented one such conformation of the polypeptide chain of the protein molecule as a helical or spiral structure which contains 3.7 amino acid residues per turn of helix, with the pitch of the helix being about 5.4 A. (4); such postulated structure is shown in projection in Figure 10-1. In any event, proteins differ from smaller open-chain polypeptides not only in that they embody a much larger variety of amino acid residues, but also because they possess a molecular weight of at least 10,000, an arbitrary figure which roughly corresponds to the lower limit of ability to be retained by cellophane on dialysis (5). Otherwise, differences in the general physical and chemical properties between peptides and proteins show a direct correlation to molecular size.

Nomenclature. The designations conventionally employed in peptide nomenclature are stated in the following I.U.P.A.C. rule (6):

Radicals derived from amino acids which have trivial names ending in *ine* by removal of OH from all —CH(NH$_2$)CO$_2$H and related groups will be named by replacing the ending *ine* with *yl*.

Examples: glycyl (from glycine), tyrosyl (from tyrosine), cystyl (from cystine).

The following names do not conform to this rule but are recommended: asparaginyl (from asparagine), glutaminyl (from glutamine), cysteinyl (from cysteine), tryptophyl (from tryptophan).

The corresponding radicals derived from aspartic acid and glutamic acid will be called aspartyl and glutamyl.

Use of such nomenclature is more fully elaborated in Table 10-1.

Since amino acid residues of the general type —NH·CHR·CO— are to all intents and purposes considered acyl substituents, their identification in any given peptide is denoted by the order in which they occur from the terminal amino end of the peptide chain. In addition, the configuration of each amino acid residue is designated by the small capital L or D prefix. As illustrative of this nomenclature scheme, the tetrapeptide which incorporates an N-terminal L-alanine residue followed by a glycine, an L-asparagine, and

766 CHEMISTRY OF THE AMINO ACIDS

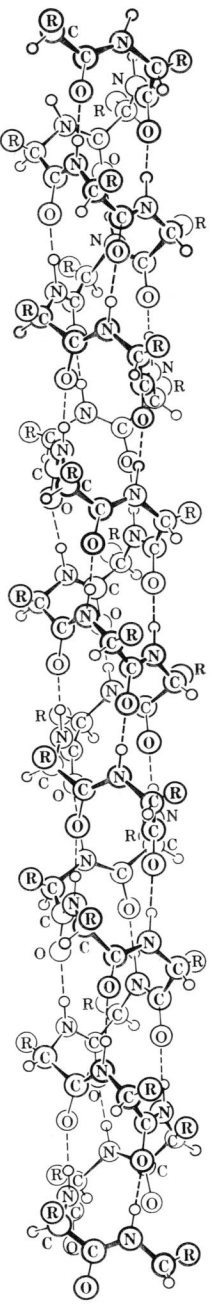

Figure 10–1. Drawing of the 3.7 residue helix. Pauling, L., *Record Chem. Progr.*, **12,** 155 (1951).

a D-alanine residue, as represented structurally by (II), may be denoted L-alanylglycyl-L-asparaginyl-D-alanine.

$$NH_2CH(CH_3)CO-NHCH_2CO-NHCH(CH_2CONH_2)CO-NHCH(CH_3)CO_2H$$
II

The number of stereoisomers theoretically possible for a peptide of known sequence may be given as 2^n, where n refers to the number of asymmetric centers. With the single exception of glycine, the α-carbon atom of all amino acids which have thus far been demonstrated to be components of naturally occurring peptides and proteins is asymmetric. Additional centers of asymmetry may be found in several other amino acids, such as the diasymmetric "isoleucines," "hydroxyprolines," and "threonines." In consequence of such asymmetry, a variety of configurational combinations becomes feasible in a peptide of known amino acid sequence. This type of stereoisomerism may be illustrated with leucylalanylserine which, since it contains three centers of asymmetry, may possess 2^3, or eight, theoretically possible optical isomers. These are depicted in the following:

A.	L-L-L	L-D-D	L-L-D	L-D-L
B.	D-D-D	D-L-L	D-D-L	D-L-D
	III	IV	V	VI

where the A and B forms of any given pair are optical antipodes and each pair (III to VI) of themselves represent one of four possible racemic modifications.

Abbreviated Names. From the above, it becomes readily apparent that the routine use of conventional peptide nomenclature could become quite cumbersome in those instances wherein more than only a few amino acid residues are involved. In an attempt to alleviate this difficulty, Brand (7) proposed the adoption of abbreviated names. Thus it was recommended that the first three letters of the name of a given amino acid be employed to denote the —NH·CHR·CO— portion of that amino acid, e.g., Gly and Ala for a glycine and an alanine residue, respectively. As illustrative of the use of such abbreviations, an empirical representation of Gly$_2$AlaLeu could be made for the peptide designated glycylleucylglycylalanine. A more complete and precise depiction of this compound as H·Gly·Leu·Gly·Ala·OH can be made in consequence of the general adoption of a later convention whereby, in those cases for which the sequence of amino acid residues is known, the appropriate symbols may be arranged in proper order and joined by a period (cf. 8). If residues derived from asparagine, glutamine, cysteine, or half-cystine are involved, these are generally represented as Asp-NH$_2$, Glu-NH$_2$, CySH, and CyS-, respectively. Functional derivatives of amino acid residues, such as γ-ethyl glutamate and S-benzylcysteine, could in analogous manner be depicted by Glu-OEt and CyS-Bz, while

TABLE 10-1
Radical Designations and Abbreviated Names of α-Amino Acids

Parent Amino Acid	Radical Name	Formula	Abbreviated Name
Alanine	Alanyl	$CH_3CH(NH_2)CO-$	Ala
Arginine	Arginyl	$NH_2C(=NH)NH(CH_2)_3CH(NH_2)CO-$	Arg
Asparagine	Asparaginyl	$NH_2OCCH_2CH(NH_2)CO-$	Asp-NH_2
Aspartic acid	Aspartyl	$HO_2CCH_2CH(NH_2)CO-$	Asp
Aspartic acid	β-Aspartyl	$-OCCH_2CH(NH_2)CO_2H$	β-Asp
Aspartic acid	Aspartoyl	$-OCCH_2CH(NH_2)CO-$	–
Cysteine	Cysteinyl	$HSCH_2CH(NH_2)CO-$	CySH
Cystine	Cystyl	$[-SCH_2CH(NH_2)CO-]_2$	(CyS—)$_2$
Glutamine	Glutaminyl	$NH_2OCCH_2CH_2CH(NH_2)CO-$	Glu-NH_2
Glutamic acid	Glutamyl	$HO_2CCH_2CH_2CH(NH_2)CO-$	Glu
Glutamic acid	γ-Glutamyl	$-OCCH_2CH_2CH(NH_2)CO_2H$	γ-Glu
Glutamic acid	Glutamoyl	$-OCCH_2CH_2CH(NH_2)CO-$	–
Glycine	Glycyl	$CH_2(NH_2)CO-$	Gly
Histidine	Histidyl	$HC{=\!=}CCH_2CH(NH_2)CO-$ $\quad\mid\qquad\mid$ $\;N\qquad NH$ $\;\;\searrow\;\;\swarrow$ $\;\;\;CH$	His

Hydroxylysine	Hydroxylysyl	NH$_2$CH$_2$CH(OH)CH$_2$CH$_2$CH(NH$_2$)CO—	Hylys
Hydroxyproline	Hydroxyprolyl	NHCH$_2$CH(OH)CH$_2$CHCO—	Hypro
Isoleucine	Isoleucyl	CH$_3$CH$_2$CH(CH$_3$)CH(NH$_2$)CO—	Ileu
Leucine	Leucyl	(CH$_3$)$_2$CHCH$_2$CH(NH$_2$)CO—	Leu
Lysine	Lysyl	NH$_2$(CH$_2$)$_4$CH(NH$_2$)CO—	Lys
Methionine	Methionyl	CH$_3$SCH$_2$CH$_2$CH(NH$_2$)CO—	Met
Norleucine	Norleucyl	CH$_3$(CH$_2$)$_3$CH(NH$_2$)CO—	Nleu
Norvaline	Norvalyl	CH$_3$(CH$_2$)$_2$CH(NH$_2$)CO—	Nval
Ornithine	Ornithyl	NH$_2$(CH$_2$)$_3$CH(NH$_2$)CO—	Orn
Phenylalanine	Phenylalanyl	C$_6$H$_5$CH$_2$CH(NH$_2$)CO—	Phe
Proline	Prolyl	NHCH$_2$CH$_2$CH$_2$CHCO—	Pro
Serine	Seryl	HOCH$_2$CH(NH$_2$)CO—	Ser
Taurine	Tauryl	NH$_2$CH$_2$CH$_2$SO$_2$—	Tau
Threonine	Threonyl	CH$_3$CH(OH)CH(NH$_2$)CO—	Thr
Thyronine	Thyronyl	HO—⟨C$_6$H$_4$⟩—O—⟨C$_6$H$_4$⟩—CH$_2$CH(NH$_2$)CO—	Thy
Tryptophan	Tryptophyl	(indole)CH$_2$CH(NH$_2$)CO—	Try
Tyrosine	Tyrosyl	*p*-HOC$_6$H$_4$CH$_2$CH(NH$_2$)CO—	Tyr
Valine	Valyl	(CH$_3$)$_2$CHCH(NH$_2$)CO—	Val

structural isomers, such as the leucine, isoleucine, and norleucine residues, are accordingly represented by Leu, Ileu and Nleu. Abbreviations which are commonly assigned to some of the more common amino acids are given in Table 10–1.

Classification of Peptides. On the basis of structural considerations, peptides may be classified according to whether they occur in *normal* or *abnormal* peptide linkage and possess *open chains* or are *cyclic*. Such classification is given in what follows:

(*a*) *Normal, open-chain* peptides contain x molecules of amino acid which are bound in peptide linkage via their α-amino or α-carboxyl groups, or both, with the elimination of $x - 1$ molecules of water, e.g.,

$$NH_2CHR^1CO_2H + NH_2CHR^2CO_2H + NH_2CHR^3CO_2H + NH_2CHR^4CO_2H \rightarrow$$
$$NH_2CHR^1CO-NHCHR^2CO-NHCHR^3CO-NHCHR^4CO_2H + 3H_2O$$

Since the terminal residues of peptides of this type contain either a free α-amino or α-carboxyl group, they exist as dipoles. Such polypeptides may occur as straight chains, wherein only a single terminal α-amino and α-carboxyl group is present, e.g., glycylalanylglycine, or as branched chains, wherein the occurrence of several terminal α-amino and α-carboxyl groups result from the presence within the molecule of a diaminodicarboxylic acid, such as cystine, which may serve as a bridge between the two peptide chains. Although most proteins thus far examined appear to be normal, open-chain polypeptides of the type described above, the available evidence is not yet sufficiently adequate to exclude completely the existence of amide linkages which involve the side-chain acidic functions of aspartic or glutamic acids, or the basic functions of arginine, lysine, or histidine.

(*b*) In *normal, cyclic polypeptides*, x molecules of the component amino acids are united in peptide linkage through their respective α-amino and α-carboxyl groups with the elimination of x molecules of water. In peptides of this type, the possession of acidic or basic properties is dependent upon the presence of the requisite functional groups in the side chains of the amino acid residues involved, inasmuch as free α-amino and α-carboxyl groups are lacking. The simplest members of this class of compounds are represented by the 2:5-diketopiperazines (IX), which may be regarded as condensation products of two amino acids (VII and VIII) with the loss of two molecules of water. A somewhat larger member of this class of compounds is exemplified by the cyclodecapeptide antibiotic, gramicidin S.

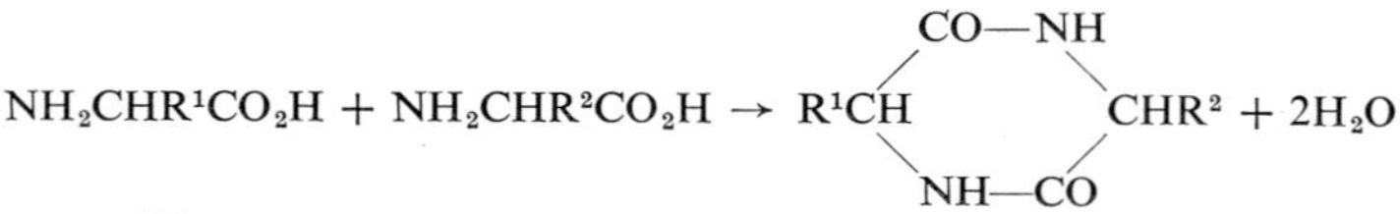

$$NH_2CHR^1CO_2H + NH_2CHR^2CO_2H \rightarrow R^1CH\begin{matrix}CO-NH\\ \\NH-CO\end{matrix}CHR^2 + 2H_2O$$

VII　　　　　　VIII　　　　　　　　IX　　　　　　X

(c) Polypeptides in *abnormal peptide linkage* include those compounds wherein the amide bond which unites the component amino acids does not involve both an α-amino and an α-carboxyl group. Such linkages may or may not implicate α-amino acids exclusively. Thus amide bonds associated with the side-chain carboxyl of glutamic or aspartic acid, or the ω-basic functions of lysine, arginine, or histidine, belong to this category, as do bonds concerned with the amino or carboxyl groups of such non-protein amino acids as β-alanine. ε-Glycyllysine (XI) and γ-glutamylglycine (XII) are representative of the former type, whereas the latter is exemplified by carnosine, i.e., β-alanylhistidine (XIII). Frequently both normal and abnormal peptide linkages reside within the same molecule, as in glutathione (γ-glutamylcysteinylglycine).

$$NH_2CH_2CO-NH(CH_2)_4CHNH_2 \atop \quad\quad\quad\quad\quad\quad\quad\quad\quad CO_2H$$
XI

$$NH_2CH(CH_2)_2CO-NHCH_2CO_2H \atop \quad CO_2H$$
XII

$$NH_2CH_2CH_2CO-NHCHCH_2C\!-\!-\!-\!-\!N \atop \quad\quad\quad\quad\quad\quad\quad\quad CO_2H \;\; CH \quad\;\; CH \atop \quad\quad\quad\quad\quad\quad\quad\quad\quad\quad\quad\quad\; NH$$
XIII

2. Some Naturally Occurring Peptides. A large number of simple, open-chain polypeptides has been isolated *in vitro* through the partial acid hydrolysis and enzymic degradation of proteins, especially since the advent of paper and ion exchange chromatography. *In vivo* enzymic cleavages of proteins which arise from tissue autolysis, bacterial action, digestive processes, and the like undoubtedly result in the generation of a large variety of peptides of similar nature. Peptides of related structure have also been detected in blood plasma in relatively small amounts, and in red blood corpuscles, muscle, liver and other tissues, as well as in urine in somewhat larger amounts. The natural occurrence of peptides of this type may, in the main, be attributed to the fact that they represent either the end products of protein metabolism or some transitory stage in the interconversion of amino acids and proteins. Other naturally occurring peptides, however, appear to possess a more clearly defined physiological role as coenzymes, hormones, or antibiotics, and presumably serve to create a more optimal environment for the parent organism. Table 10–2 lists several such peptides the structures of which have been more or less definitely established. The existence within these compounds of either abnormal peptide linkages or amino acid residues of unusual structure, constitution, or configuration conceivably imparts to the molecule an exceptionally high degree of resistance

TABLE 10-2
Naturally Occurring Acylamino Acids, Peptides, and Related Compounds

Compound	Formula	Original Source and Synthesis
Glutathione (γ-L-glutamyl-L-cysteinylglycine)	$\text{HO}_2\text{CCHCH}_2\text{CH}_2\text{CO—NHCHCO—NHCH}_2\text{CO}_2\text{H}$, with NH_2 and CH_2SH side groups	Yeast, muscle, liver (9–12)
Pteroyl-L-glutamic acid (α = 1) (L. casei factor)	[pteridine–CH$_2$NH–C$_6$H$_4$–CO–NHCHCO$_2$H–(CH$_2$)$_2$–CO$_2$H]	Liver (13, 14)
Pteroyl-tri-L-glutamic acid (α = 3) (fermentation factor)	[pteroyl–CO–NHCHCO$_2$H–(CH$_2$)$_2$–CO–]$_x$	Fermentation liquor of *Corynebacterium* (15, 16)
Pteroyl-hepta-L-glutamic acid (α = 7)		Yeast (17, 18)
γ-L-Glutamyl-S-methyl-L-cysteine (and the sulfoxide thereof)	$\text{HO}_2\text{CCHCH}_2\text{CH}_2\text{CO—NHCHCO}_2\text{H}$, with NH_2 and CH_2SCH_3 (and $\text{CH}_2\text{S(—O)CH}_3$)	Dry lima beans (19, 19a) (*Phaseolus lunatus* L.)
L-Pyroglutamyl-L-glutaminyl-L-glutamine	pyroglutamyl—CO—NHCHCO—NHCHCO$_2$H with (CH$_2$)$_2$CONH$_2$ side chains	*Pelvetia fastigiata* (20, 20a) (brown marine algae)
Eisenine (L-pyroglutamyl-L-glutaminyl-L-alanine)	pyroglutamyl—CO—NHCHCO—NHCHCO$_2$H with (CH$_2$)$_2$CONH$_2$ and CH$_3$	*Eisenia bicyclis* Setchell (brown marine algae) (21, 22)
γ-Glutamylvalylglutamic acid	$\text{HO}_2\text{CCHCH}_2\text{CH}_2\text{CO—NHCHCO—NHCHCO}_2\text{H}$ with NH$_2$, CH(CH$_3$)$_2$, CH$_2$CH$_2$CO$_2$H	*Juncus conglomeratus, J. effusus, J. filiformis* (22a)
Acetylamino acids	$\text{CH}_3\text{CO—NHCHRCO}_2\text{H}$	
L-Glutamic acid	R = CH$_2$CH$_2$CO$_2$H	Beef liver extract (23, 24)
L-Aspartic acid	R = CH$_2$CO$_2$H	Cat brain (25)
Phenacetylamino acids	$\text{C}_6\text{H}_5\text{CH}_2\text{CO—NHCHRCO}_2\text{H}$	
Glycine	R = H	Dog and rabbit urine (26)
L-Glutamine	R = CH$_2$CH$_2$CONH$_2$	Human and ape urine (27)
L-Ornithine	R = CH$_2$CH$_2$CH$_2$NH—COCH$_2$C$_6$H$_5$	Hen excreta (28)
Benzoylamino acids	$\text{C}_6\text{H}_5\text{CO—NHCHRCO}_2\text{H}$	
Glycine	R = H	Mammalian urine (29, 30)
L-Ornithine	R = CH$_2$CH$_2$CH$_2$NH—COC$_6$H$_5$	Bird excreta (31, 32)

Mercapturic acids $CH_3CO-NHCHCO_2H$ $\quad\quad\quad\quad\quad\quad\; CH_2SR \quad R = C_6H_4Br, C_6H_4Cl,$ etc.	Human urine (33, 34)
Ergot alkaloids Ergotamine (R = H, R' = $CH_2C_6H_5$) Ergosine (R = H, R' = $CH_2CH(CH_3)_2$) Ergocristine (R = CH_3, R' = $CH_2C_6H_5$) Ergocryptine (R = CH_3, R' = $CH_2CH(CH_3)_2$) Ergocornine (R = CH_3, R' = $CH(CH_3)_2$)	*Claviceps purpurea* (35–37) (rye ergot)
Fumaryl-DL-alanine $\quad HO_2CCH=CHCO-NHCH(CH_3)CO_2H$	*Penicillium resticulosum* (38)
Lycomarasmin $\quad\quad\quad\quad\quad\quad\; \overset{CH_2CONH_2}{\underset{OH}{}}$ (?) $\quad\quad\quad\quad\quad\quad HO_2CC(CH_3)-NHCH_2CO-NHCHCO_2H$	*Fusarium lycoperspici* (39–41a) (phyto-pathogenic fungus)
Biocytin (ε-biotinyl-L-lysine)	Yeast (42, 43)
Carnosine (R = R' = H) Anserine (R = CH_3, R' = H) Ophidine (R = H, R' = CH_3) $\quad NH_2CH_2CH_2CO-NHCHCH_2\!\!-\!\!\overset{\displaystyle NR^a}{\underset{\displaystyle N}{\overset{\displaystyle\Vert}{C}}\!\!-\!\!\overset{\displaystyle CR'}{}}\atop CO_2H\;CH$	Muscle extract (44–47) Goose muscle (48–51) Snake muscle (52–54)
Glycocholic acid	(Bile cf. 55)
Ophthalmic acid (L-γ-glutamyl-L-α-amino-*n*-butyrylglycine) $\quad\;\;\overset{\displaystyle NH_2}{}\quad\quad\;\;\overset{\displaystyle CH_2CH_3}{}$ $HO_2CCHCH_2CH_2CO-NHCHCO-NHCH_2CO_2H$	Calf lens (56, 57)

TABLE 10-2 (continued)

Compound	Formula	Original Source and Synthesis
Norophthalmic acid (L-γ-glutamyl-L-alanylglycine)	HO$_2$CCHCH$_2$CH$_2$CO—NHCHCO—NHCH$_2$CO$_2$H with NH$_2$ and CH$_3$ substituents	Calf lens (58)
Hypertensin I (angiotonin)	H·Asp·Arg·Val·Tyr·Val·His·Pro·Phe·His·Leu·OH[a] H·Asp·Arg·Val·Tyr·Ileu·His·Pro·Phe·His·Leu·OH[a]	Rabbit renin on ox serum (59, 60) Hog renin on horse serum (61–63)
Hypertensin II (active form)	H·Asp·Arg·Val·Tyr·Ileu·His·Pro·Phe·OH[a]	Plasma enzyme on hypertensin I (horse) (62, 63)
L-Leucyl-L-proline anhydride	CHCH$_2$CH(CH$_3$)$_2$ (64) cyclic structure	Adrenal cortex (65) Cocoon of silkworm (66)
Phalloidin	(cyclic peptide structure)	*Amanita phalloides* (67–69) (poisonous mushroom)
Etamycin[c]	(complex cyclic depsipeptide structure)	*Streptomyces griseus* (69a)

CHEMICAL PROCEDURES FOR SYNTHESIS OF PEPTIDES

Gramicidin S — cyclo(L-Orn·L-Leu·D-Phe·L-Pro·L-Val·L-Orn·L-Leu·D-Phe·L-Pro·L-Val) — *Bacillus brevis* (70–73)

Tyrocidin A — cyclo(L-Orn·L-Leu·D-Phe·L-Pro·L-Phe·D-Phe·L-Asp-NH$_2$·L-Glu-NH$_2$·L-Tyr·L-Val) — *Bacillus brevis* (74–76)

Polymyxin B — cyclo(L-Thr·D-Phe·diamino-L-But·L-Leu·diamino-L-But·L-Thr·diamino-D-But·diamino-L-But·(γ-N-d-6-methyloctan-1-oyl)(diamino-L-But)$_2$] — *Bacillus polymyxa* (77, 78)

Amidomycin (composed of D-valine and D-α-hydroxy-isovaleric acid residues, where R = CH(CH$_3$)$_2$) — *Streptomyces* (79)

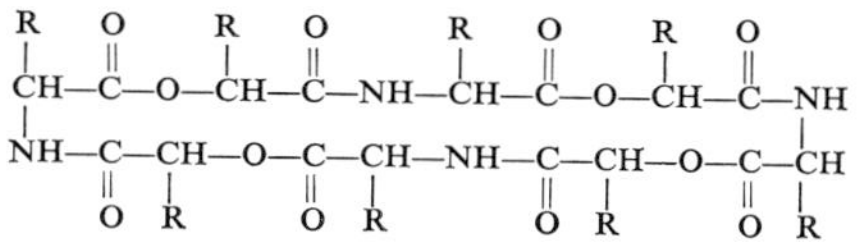

$$\begin{array}{c} \text{R} \quad \text{O} \quad \text{R} \quad \text{O} \quad \text{R} \quad \text{O} \\ -\text{CH}-\text{C}-\text{O}-\text{CH}-\text{C}-\text{NH}-\text{CH}-\text{C}-\text{O}-\text{CH}-\text{C}-\text{NH} \\ \text{NH}-\text{C}-\text{CH}-\text{O}-\text{C}-\text{CH}-\text{NH}-\text{C}-\text{CH}-\text{O}-\text{C}-\text{CH}- \\ \text{O} \quad \text{R} \quad \text{O} \quad \text{R} \quad \text{O} \quad \text{R} \end{array}$$

Oxytocin — H·CyS·Tyr·Ileu·Glu-NH$_2$·Asp-NH$_2$·CyS·Pro·Leu·Gly·NH$_2$[a] — Posterior pituitary gland (80–84)

Vasopressin (beef) — H·CyS·Tyr·Phe·Glu-NH$_2$·Asp-NH$_2$·CyS·Pro·Arg·Gly·NH$_2$[a] — Posterior pituitary gland (85)

Vasopressin (hog) — H·CyS·Tyr·Phe·Glu-NH$_2$·Asp-NH$_2$·CyS·Pro·Lys·Gly·NH$_2$[a] — Posterior pituitary gland (86–89)

Benzylpenicillin —

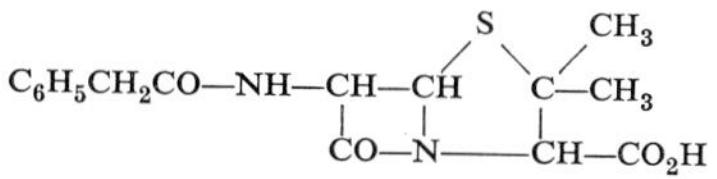

$$\text{C}_6\text{H}_5\text{CH}_2\text{CO}-\text{NH}-\text{CH}-\text{CH} \begin{array}{c} \text{S} \\ \end{array} \begin{array}{c} \text{CH}_3 \\ \text{C} \\ \text{CH}_3 \end{array} \\ \qquad\qquad\qquad \text{CO}-\text{N}-\text{CH}-\text{CO}_2\text{H}$$

— *Penicillium notatum* (90, 91)

Cycloserine (oxamycin) —

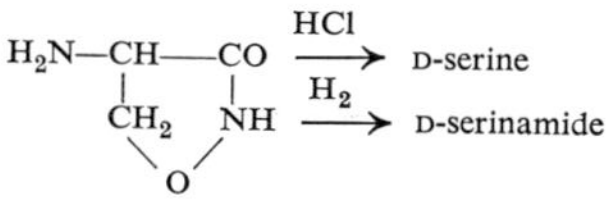

$$\text{H}_2\text{N}-\text{CH}-\text{CO} \xrightarrow{\text{HCl}} \text{D-serine} \\ \quad\;\; | \qquad\quad | \\ \quad\text{CH}_2 \;\;\; \text{NH} \xrightarrow{\text{H}_2} \text{D-serinamide} \\ \qquad \backslash \;\; / \\ \qquad\;\; \text{O}$$

— *Streptomyces orchidaceous* (92, 93)

[a] All residues are of the L-configuration.
[b] See Section 16–5.
[c] The amino acid composition is given as follows: 3-hydroxypicolinic acid, L-threonine, D-leucine, D-allohydroxyproline, sarcosine, L-β-N-dimethylleucine, L-alanine, and L-α-phenylsarcosine.

to the hydrolytic action of the proteolytic enzymes which it ordinarily may encounter.

3. Historical Considerations. From a purely fundamental point of view, synthetic peptides may serve as substrates in the investigation of the specificity and mode of action of proteases and peptidases, and as models for studies on the constitution, physical properties, and chemical reactions of proteins. Convenient techniques of peptide synthesis therefore become a vital tool in the elucidation of knowledge of protein structure and function. Alternatively, when considered from a practical point of view, these same techniques may be utilized not only for the unequivocal demonstration of the constitution and structure of such naturally occurring substances as the polypeptide antibiotics, hormones, and coenzymes, but also may be employed for either the commercial production of these compounds *per se* or for the formulation of suitable analogs thereof. A host of related compounds, with varying degrees and shades of biological activity, thereby becomes potentially available.

Preparation of Macromolecular Polypeptides. Contemporary investigations in the field of synthetic peptide chemistry may be viewed as proceeding primarily along two parallel lines, namely, the synthesis of the smaller crystalline polypeptides of well-defined character, and the preparation of amorphous macromolecular polypeptides, comparable in dimension to that of protein molecules, but of indefinite composition. Experimental research along the latter line had its inception in the early 1870's and was based on the assumption that the amino acids which constitute the protein molecule are linked together via amide bonds which implicate the α-carboxyl group of one amino acid and the α-amino group of the next. Such studies, initiated by Schaal (94) in 1871 and extended by Grimaux (95) some ten years later, involved the condensation of aspartic acid and asparagine to a mixture of polymeric products which exhibited a positive biuret reaction reminiscent of that demonstrated by proteins. That a solution of glycine ethyl ester in dry ether, on standing, deposits a substance which shows a like biuret reaction was noted by Curtius (96, 97) in 1883. Comparable polymeric products were secured by Schiff (98) in 1897 through the thermal decomposition of free aspartic acid. Still other related investigations during the same decade were announced by Schützenberger (99) on the condensation of various amino acids with urea upon heating in the presence of phosphoric pentoxide, by Lilienfeld (100) on the polymerization of mixtures of amino acid esters as induced by a variety of condensation agents, and by Balbiano and Trasciatti (101) on the transformation of glycine in hot glycerol solution into a horn-like, water-insoluble polymer. Especially noteworthy among these early investigations, and one which was to provide the groundwork for a major portion of future work in this province, was that of Leuchs (102) which, in 1906, showed that amino acids, as their N-carboxyanhydride derivatives, could be induced to polymerize under certain conditions.

Despite the superficial resemblance of the polymeric substances secured by the above techniques to the protein molecule, research in this direction was not encouraged. It soon became apparent that each individual polymeric unit which constituted the polymeric mixture was not necessarily of exactly the same chain length as every other unit. Aside from this apparent lack of definite chemical constitution, the substances secured were amorphous, highly insoluble in water, and generally intractable, properties which were not conducive to their ready characterization. All these adverse properties of polymeric mixtures presented a formidable barrier to their serious consideration as protein models. The current attitude of the day toward such substances was reflected, and no doubt strongly influenced, by a statement by Fischer and Forneau (103) in 1901:

[Alle] sind amorphe, schwer charakterisierbare Substanzen, über deren Struktur man ebensowenig wie über den Grad ihrer Verwandtschaft mit den natürlichen Proteinstoffen etwas sagen kann. Will man auf diesem schwierigen Gebiete zu sichern Resultaten kommen, so wird man zuerst eine Methode finden müssen, welche es gestattet, successiv und mit definierbaren Zwischenstufen die Moleküle verschiedener Aminosäuren anhydridartig aneinander zu reihen.[41]

In a somewhat milder and more poetic mood, Fischer later (1) deplored what to him was essentially a brutal and hasty synthetic reaction, and stated

eine derartige Synthese [polymerization] ... [ist] einem Reisenden [zu] vergleichen, der im Schnellzug ein Land durcheilt und hinterher kaum etwas darüber berichten kann," whereas, "Ganz anders gestaltet sich die Lage, wenn die Synthese gezwungen ist, schrittweise vorzugehen und das Molekül Stufe für Stufe aufzubauen.... Dan gleicht sie dem Fussgänger, der Schritt für Schritt mit gespannter Aufmerksamkeit sich den Weg sucht, der viele Wege erproben muss, bis er den rechten gefunden hat. Der lernt auf seiner langen, mühsamen Wanderung nicht allein die Geographie und Topographie des Landes gründlich kennen, sondern wird auch mit der Sprache und Kultur seiner Bewohner vertraut. Wenn er schliesslich sein Ziel erreicht hat, so ist er imstande sich in jedem Winkel des Landes zurecht zu finden, und wenn er ein Buch darüber schreibt, so wird dies anderen Leuten auch möglich sein.[42]

In this appealing barrage by the most gifted chemist of the era, the seeming interment of the early amino acid polymerization procedures was pronounced, and future efforts concentrated, rather, on the development of techniques which would permit the stepwise synthesis of peptide chains from the component amino acids.

Although scant effort was devoted to the polymerization of amino acids from 1906 to 1947, a few highly significant investigations none the less did appear during this period. Among these might be cited the studies of Wessely

(104), which contributed to the elucidation of the mechanism by which N-carboxyanhydrides of amino acids (Leuchs' anhydrides) undergo polymer formation, and those of Frankel and Katchalski (105–107) and of Pacsu and Wilson (108–110), which were concerned with the production of polyamino acid esters from the corresponding amino acid and peptide esters. In 1947, however, a resurgence of interest in macromolecular polypeptides as protein models occurred. This was influenced, to a large extent, by the brief announcement of Woodward and Schramm (111) that the preparation of the more complex linear peptides could be effected through a refinement of the Leuchs' (102) procedure, as well as by the introduction of new physical and chemical methods for the analysis of such polymers. A wave of investigations relating to such aspects as the kinetics and mechanism of polymer formation, the production of water-soluble polymers, and the susceptibility of polyamino acids to the action of proteolytic enzymes has since appeared. These aspects have been fully detailed in an admirable review by Katchalski (112), and a comprehensive treatise by Bamford, Elliott, and Hanby (113).

In the synthetic production of macromolecular polypeptides, the monomers generally employed in the polymerization procedure may be single pure amino acid, dipeptide, or tripeptide derivatives, or heterogeneous mixtures thereof. The former group of substances gives rise in the polymer to a single kind or, at best, two or three different kinds of amino acid residues which recur as periodic units along the polymer chain. Where heterogeneous mixtures are employed as the monomers, however, a greater diversity of amino acid residues may be incorporated into the polymeric chain, but these appear in neither definite, controllable, nor predictable sequence. Since proteins are macromolecules composed of a large variety of amino acid residues of varying degrees of complexity but very probably of definite sequence, the problem of protein structure becomes much more complicated than that derived from studies on synthetic macromolecules alone. Despite these obvious shortcomings, studies on the solubility, X-ray diffraction, infrared absorption, and behavior toward proteolytic enzymes of these synthetic polymers should, nevertheless, serve at least partially to illuminate the physical structure, chemical reactions, and biological behavior of the native proteins.

Stepwise Synthesis of Peptides. Synthesis of the first crystalline, well-characterized peptide derivative from the component amino acids can be traced to Curtius (114) who, in 1882, reported that the action of benzoyl chloride on silver glycinate yielded, among other products, the N-substituted dipeptide, benzoylglycylglycine. Some twenty years later, Fischer and Forneau (130) announced a preparation of the corresponding free dipeptide through the partial acid hydrolysis of 2:5-diketopiperazine. This report immediately plunged Fischer and Curtius into sharp controversy relating to the question of priority, the former alleging that, although the latter had undoubtedly prepared a peptide derivative of well-defined character, the method of synthesis employed lacked general applicability. This induced Curtius (115–119), in 1902, to resume his investigations on the synthesis of various benzoylated peptide derivatives. A number of such peptides were produced by the condensation of the azide derivatives of benzoylated amino acids or of peptides with other amino acids. It is significant, however, that all efforts to regenerate the free amino moiety by the selective removal of the benzoyl group led, in addition, to complete hydrolysis of the labile peptide bonds. Thus, although credit for the first synthesis of a peptide derivative undoubtedly belongs to Curtius, synthesis of the first free peptide by a general method should be attributed to Fischer and Forneau.

Although a variety of simple peptides could be prepared through the hydrolysis of substituted 2:5-diketopiperazines, Fischer soon became aware of several severe limitations possessed by this method, not the least of which was its inherent applicability to the preparation of dipeptides only. A search for more satisfactory methods led Fischer (120), in 1903, to attempt an approach analogous to that employed by Curtius (115–119) for the preparation of benzoylated peptide derivatives. Such approach involved the conversion of the free amino acid to its corresponding carboethoxy- or carbomethoxy-derivative which, in turn, was converted to the acid chloride and coupled with an amino acid ester to yield the acyldipeptide ester. Upon subsequent saponification, the free acid of the acylated dipeptide was derived. However, as with the earlier experiences of Curtius, attempts to secure the free peptide by preferential hydrolysis of the acyl masking substituent proved unsuccessful. Consequently, efforts were concentrated on the development of alternative approaches for the synthesis of peptides, and the search for an easily removable acyl blocking group was temporarily abandoned.

In 1903, Fischer and Otto (121) described a procedure which utilized α-haloacyl substituents as blocking groups for amino acids *in lieu* of the afore-mentioned carbalkoxy group and were thereby enabled to circumvent the implication of a final hydrolytic step in the synthesis of peptides. Thus, during the final step of the reaction sequence, the conversion of the α-haloacyl substituent into the N-terminal amino acid residue of the peptide chain could be effected by the action of aqueous or alcoholic ammonia. With both this and the earlier diketopiperazine method at his disposal, Fischer and his collaborators not only envisioned synthetic peptide structures which resembled, in character, the protein molecule itself but, indeed, also succeeded in the synthesis of an octadecapeptide aimed at the fulfillment of this goal (cf. 122). However, such striking synthetic achievement of itself emphasized the unfortunate limitations of these earlier methods, for the restriction of the composition of the latter peptide solely to leucine and glycine residues typified their virtually exclusive application to peptides incorporating only the simplest of the amino acids. In general, these peptides were devoid of such reactive radicals as the guanidino nucleus of arginine, the ε-amino group of lysine, the imidazole ring of histidine, and the ω-carboxyl groups of glutamic and aspartic acids, all of which contribute in part to the free reactive groups of the natural proteins. Fischer's vision of a synthetic protein was still far from a reality.

With the death of Fischer in 1919, no general method of peptide synthesis had yet been formulated that would permit the incorporation of the more complex amino acids into the peptide chain. During the 1920's, however, the development of azlactones as peptide intermediates by Bergmann (123–125) and his collaborators resulted in the preparation of a few peptides which contained acidic and basic amino acid residues but which again provided no general method of peptide synthesis. The feeling persisted that the latter aim could be achieved if a suitable, readily removable acyl blocking group could be found, despite the earlier failures alluded to above. In fact, Fischer (126) had himself further investigated acyl substituents which could be removed by other than hydrolytic means and reported, in 1915, that the action of a mixture of warm phosphonium iodide and hydriodic acid led to a reductive fission of a *p*-toluenesulfonyl ("tosyl") group united in amide linkage with an amino acid. Although it remained for Schoenheimer (127), eleven years later, to employ the latter reaction for the final reductive removal of the tosyl group in the synthesis of several simple peptides, further exploitation of this blocking group for the synthesis of the more complex peptides was forestalled because of the rather severe conditions involved in its cleavage.

The thirty-year search for a satisfactory acyl blocking group in peptide synthesis finally bore fruit, in 1932, with the ingenious development of the "carbobenzoxy method" by Bergmann and Zervas (128). Introduction of this outstanding method truly ushered in the modern age of peptide chemistry and permitted ready access to some of the more complex peptides which had hitherto been unattainable. In brief, the method relied upon the initial condensation of benzyloxycarbonyl ("carbobenzoxy") amino acids, via the classical azide or acid chloride procedures, with other amino acids to yield the corresponding carbobenzoxy peptide. Conversion of the latter compound to the free peptide could be accomplished by scission of the carbobenzoxy moiety through catalytic hydrogenation in the presence of palladium black. In such manner the acyl group could be easily and quantitatively removed under extremely mild conditions, and the free peptide thus liberated without danger of rupture to the sensitive peptide bonds. A fuller discussion of this procedure will be given in the appropriate section below. It should suffice to note here, however, that, since its inception, the original Bergmann-Zervas procedure, together with later modifications thereof, has been employed in the synthesis of some several hundred different peptides which have embodied all varieties of the protein-bound amino acids. It remains even today the most universally applicable of all the available peptide synthesis procedures.

With a potentially limitless variety of synthetic peptides as enzyme substrates now at their disposal, Bergmann and his collaborators launched a classical series of investigations aimed at the classification of peptidases and proteases according to the specific peptide linkages which they cleave. Although such small synthetic substrates unquestionably differ quite markedly from the macromolecular polypeptides encountered *in vivo*, the belief has none the less prevailed that the susceptibility of these synthetic model compounds toward the action of different proteases reflects, in large part, the behavior exhibited by the protein molecule itself. There can be little doubt that such studies have indeed provided important information toward the elucidation of protein structure and have laid the groundwork upon which contemporary studies on protease-substrate relations are founded. It is therefore unfortunate that detailed consideration of this work does not fall within the scope of the present volume. However, a considerable portion of this area has been described in several excellent reviews (129–133) (cf. Chapter 16).

During the 1940's, the discovery of many antibiotics and other natural products of polypeptide structure markedly stimulated studies aimed at improvements in existing methods, as well as the development of newer methods of peptide synthesis. Not only were alternative methods for the removal of the carbobenzoxy and tosyl groups uncovered, but the introduction of several other important blocking groups, such as the phthaloyl, formyl, triphenylmethyl (trityl), and trifluoroacetyl groups, was effected as well. Additional effort too was expended upon the development of more satisfactory coupling procedures than was provided by the classical acid chloride or azide procedures, and a number of simplified coupling procedures which involved mixed anhydrides with organic and inorganic acids, "activated esters," and "carbodiimide" intermediates, among others, were evolved. That such activity has indeed been fruitful is attested to by the successes achieved in the synthesis of several important natural polypeptides as gramicidin S, oxytocin, and vasopressin, as well as in the variety of syntheses now known for glutathione. Whether the methods now available will suffice for the stepwise preparation of the infinitely more complex labile protein molecule, however, can at present only be open to conjecture. Despite this extreme measure of uncertainty, investigations are currently being effected in various laboratories throughout the world which are aimed at the synthesis of molecules of protein nature, such as insulin, whose structure has hitherto been elucidated by degradation studies (Chapter 16). There can be little doubt that Fischer's dream of a synthetic protein molecule has come at least one step closer to a reality.

Scope of This Chapter. The synthetic procedures which have been employed for the preparation of peptides are treated in the sections below with an eye toward presenting them both in their proper historical perspective and according to the chemical relationship they bear to each other. At least partial fulfillment of the latter objective could be achieved by categorizing the procedures on the basis of whether or not the final step invokes the selective cleavage of an acyl blocking substituent. The procedures have, accordingly, been classified under "Classical Methods of Peptide Synthesis" and "Synthetic Peptide Methods Involving Selectively Removable Acyl Blocking Groups." Inasmuch as the former section will include studies which have been pursued up to the present day, such classification should of course be considered quite arbitrary. However, true chronological sequence within each section will be adhered to wherever practicable. Additional sections of the chapter will deal with the preparation of peptides which incorporate the specific protein-derived amino acids, as well as synthetic procedures which have been employed for several individual peptides of biological importance.

CLASSICAL METHODS OF PEPTIDE SYNTHESIS

4. Condensations Involving α-Amino Acids or Their Ester Derivatives.

Principle. That the formation of a simple fatty acid amide results from the reaction of a primary or a secondary amine with a fatty acid ester has long been known. However, if both the amino and the ester moiety reside within the same reactant molecule, as in an α-amino acid ester, then the condensation product (III) which results from the union of two molecules (I and II), since it too is reactive by virtue of its free amino and ester groups, may undergo still further condensation with another molecule of reactant (I) or of product (III). Repetition of such process, known as a *condensation polymerization*, proceeds with the formation of the corresponding *condensation polymer*. The linear molecules (V) so produced show a character-

$$NH_2 \cdot CHR \cdot CO_2Et + NH_2 \cdot CHR \cdot CO_2Et \rightarrow NH_2 \cdot CHR \cdot CO - NH \cdot CHR \cdot CO_2Et + EtOH$$
$$\text{I} \qquad\qquad \text{II} \qquad\qquad \text{III} \qquad\qquad \text{IV}$$

$$x NH_2 \cdot CHR \cdot CO_2Et$$

$$NH_2 \cdot CHR \cdot CO-(NH \cdot CHR \cdot CO)_x-NH \cdot CHR \cdot CO_2Et \qquad\qquad \begin{array}{c} CO-NH \\ RCH \quad HCR \\ NH-CO \end{array}$$
$$\text{V} \qquad\qquad\qquad\qquad\qquad\qquad \text{VI}$$

istic recurring unit and, owing to the loss of $x + 1$ molecules of alcohol during their formation, differ markedly in composition from the reactant molecules from which they arise. Their molecular size may be limited to large extent by the occurrence of ring formation. Thus, whenever the formation of a five- or a six-membered ring is possible, this reaction will generally compete quite successfully with linear polymer formation under the usual reaction conditions. Since the production of the six-membered 2:5-diketopiperazine ring (VI) from the intermediate dipeptide ester (III) becomes entirely conceivable in the present situation, the choice of experimental conditions will govern the predominance of either the linear or the ring compound. It should be pointed out that the course of the reaction may be altered under special conditions. In this connection, for example, the use of highly dilute solutions may result in the production of large rings.

Aside from ring formation, still other factors may limit the molecular size of polymers. These include, among others, the accidental multilation of the reactive terminal groups, or a marked decrease in concentration of available reactive groups as the reaction proceeds. Additionally, since an increase in viscosity accompanies an increase in polymer size, the mobility and, therefore, the rate of reaction of the molecules are decreased. The implication of other factors which may affect polymer size has been ably discussed by Marvel and Horning (134).

Polymerization of α-Amino Acids or Their Ester Derivatives. The first recorded attempt to join α-amino acids in peptide linkage was reported by Kohler (135) in 1865. This attempt involved the heat-induced self-condensation of glycine in a stream of hydrogen chloride gas and resulted in the formation of a product composed principally of 2:5-diketopiperazine. A like effort to condense α-amino acids by Schaal (94), some six years later, led him to heat aspartic acid as well as asparagine in an atmosphere of carbon dioxide. This condensation yielded a mixture of products which was subsequently shown by Grimaux (95) to consist, in the main, of two biuret-positive polymeric products of undefined chemical constitution. Comparable polymerization of aspartic acid was effected in 1897 by Schiff (98) who, after heating the free amino acid at 190–200° and then treating the residual mass with boiling water, was presumably able to identify tetra- and octaaspartic acids among the other products of the reaction mixture. Comparable treatment of DL-aspartic acid by Kovacs, Könyves, and Pusztai (136) in 1953 led to the ultimate isolation of a water-soluble polyaspartic acid incorporating some 71 amino acid residues and an accompanying suggestion that these residues were combined in peptide linkage via their β-carboxyl groups. However, in reactions of this type, the possibility of the implication of either or both of the carboxyl groups in peptide formation cannot be precluded. Mixtures of polymers containing residues united both through the α- and β-carboxyl functions of aspartic acid thereupon become a distinct possibility here.

That the esters of α-amino acids may similarly undergo transformation to the corresponding polymers, as well as to diketopiperazines, was initially reported by Curtius (96) in 1883. Curtius observed that glycine ethyl ester (VII), when moist, undergoes spontaneous conversion to 2:5-diketopiperazine (VIII) and to a substance later identified (97) as the tetrapeptide derivative, triglycylglycine ethyl ester (IX). The latter compound, referred to as "biuret base" because it exhibited a strong purple-violet biuret reaction,

$$NH_2CH_2CO_2Et \xrightarrow{H_2O} \underset{VIII}{\underset{CO-NH}{CH_2 \overset{NH-CO}{\diagup\diagdown} CH_2}} + \underset{IX}{NH_2CH_2CO-NHCH_2CO-NHCH_2CO-NHCH_2CO_2Et}$$

was precipitated almost exclusively over a period of several weeks from a solution of glycine ethyl ester in dry ether. Some seventeen years later, Balbiano and Trasciatti (101) effected a similar polymerization of glycine upon heat treatment of its glycerol solution, a reaction suggested by Maillard (137) to involve the transitory formation of glyceryl esters of the amino acid. That the main product was the 2:5-diketopiperazine was indicated by both Maillard (137) and by Meyer and Go (138). The former investigator demonstrated, in addition, that the mixture of polymeric products formed during this reaction revealed the presence of a tetramer and a hexamer, in addition to a horny, water-insoluble polymer. Indication that the latter compound resembled polyglycine esters arose as a consequence of the admirable studies of Frankel and Katchalski (105, 106), and of Baniel, Frankel, Friedrich, and Katchalski (139), who repeated and extended the earlier observations of Curtius with the methyl, ethyl, isobutyl, octyl, dodecyl, hexadecyl, octadecyl, β-naphthyl, and cholesteryl esters of glycine. With the lower alkyl esters, a number of polyglycine esters of varying chain length (10 to 35 glycine residues), in addition to the products formerly observed by Curtius (96, 97), were secured. Polymerization of the higher alkyl esters, on the other hand, appeared to proceed without concomitant formation of diketopiperazine.

Aside from glycine and several of its derivatives, the polymerization of amino acids apparently occurs with some difficulty, and several unsuccessful attempts to polymerize the free α-amino acids by heating in glycerol solution have been reported (101, 140). Although the polymerization (XII) (10–16 residues) of alanine ethyl ester (X) was successfully accomplished by Frankel and Katchalski (107), such polycondensation was effected only after several weeks *in vacuo* at 25–80°. Alanine anhydride (XI) formation accompanied the reaction. Like treatment of a number of other amino acid esters led

$$\underset{X}{\underset{|}{NH_2\overset{CH_3}{\underset{|}{C}}HCO_2Et}} \rightarrow \underset{XI}{\underset{CO-NH}{CH_3CH \overset{NH-CO}{\diagup\diagdown} CHCH_3}} + \underset{XII}{NH_2\overset{CH_3}{\underset{|}{C}}HCO-(NH\overset{CH_3}{\underset{|}{C}}HCO)_{8-10}-NH\overset{CH_3}{\underset{|}{C}}HCO_2Et}$$

to the formation and identification of the corresponding 2:5-diketopiperazines as the only isolable products, if reaction indeed occurred. Such reactions

TABLE 10-3

Polycondensation Products of Some α-Amino Acid Esters (112)

Derivative	Condensation Products	Ref.
DL-Alanine ethyl ester (b.p. 48° at 11 mm.)	Tetraalanine ethyl ester; 10–16 polyalanine ethyl ester; alanine anhydride	107
L-Arginine methyl ester	α,δ-Bisguanidino-*n*-valeric acid anhydride + ornithine methyl ester	141, 142
L-Aspartic acid diethyl ester	2:5-Diketopiperazine-3:6-diacetic acid diethyl ester (heating in the presence of zinc chloride)	143
L-Aspartic acid dimethyl ester	2:5-Diketopiperazine-3:6-diacetic acid dimethyl ester (heating to 100°)	144
L-Cystine dimethyl ester	Decomp. at normal temp.	145
Glycine methyl ester	Glycine anhydride; tetraglycine methyl ester; 18–30-polyglycine methyl ester	105
Glycine ethyl ester	Glycine anhydride; tetraglycine ethyl ester ("biuret base"); 12–20 polyglycine ethyl ester	107
L-Histidine methyl ester	Histidine anhydride (heating to 100°)	141
DL-Isoleucine ethyl ester (b.p. 90–92° at 15 mm.)	Distills without decomp.	146
L-Leucine ethyl ester (b.p. 83.5° at 12 mm.)	Distills without decomp.	147
DL-Leucine ethyl ester (b.p. 83.5° at 12 mm.)	Distills without decomp.	148
DL-Lysine methyl ester	"Lysine anhydride" DL-3-aminohomopiperidone + lysyl peptides	141, 149
ε-N-Carbobenzoxy-L-lysine methyl ester	ε,ε′-Dicarbobenzoxylysine anhydride (heating to 100°)	150
DL-Phenylalanine ethyl ester (b.p. 143° at 10 mm.)	Distills without decomp.	151
DL-Serine methyl ester	Serine anhydride (at 35–40°)	141
L-Tyrosine ethyl ester (m.p. 108–109°)	Tyrosine anhydride (heating to 180°)	151
DL-Valine ethyl ester (b.p. 63.5° at 8 mm.)	Valine anhydride (at room temp.)	152

apparently proceeded with the preliminary condensation of two molecules of the amino acid ester (XIII), followed by an intramolecular cyclization of the intermediate dipeptide ester (XIV) so derived to the corresponding diketopiperazine (XV). Data for several of the amino acid esters which have been subjected to such treatment have been tabulated by Katchalski (112) and are reiterated in Table 10–3. Note should be made that the marked facility with which dipeptide esters undergo internal condensation was early observed by Fischer and Forneau (103) with glycylglycine ethyl ester.

$$NH_2CHRCO_2R' \rightarrow NH_2CHRCO\text{---}NHCHRCO_2R' \rightarrow \begin{array}{c} NH\text{---}CO \\ RCH \quad\quad HCR \\ CO\text{---}NH \end{array}$$

XIII　　　　　　　　　　XIV　　　　　　　　　　XV

In contradistinction to the above, those amino acids which contain an ω-amino group, e.g., α,β-diaminopropionic acid, isoserine, or lysine, undergo facile dipeptide ester formation without concomitant anhydride production upon heat treatment of their corresponding esters (141). Such behavior might well be due to the participation of the ω-amino group in the condensation reaction, thereupon making the generation of the six-membered anhydride ring impossible, as in the following:

$$2NH_2CH_2(CH_2)_xCH(NH_2)CO_2CH_3 \rightarrow NH_2CH_2(CH_2)_xCH(NH_2)CO\text{---}NHCH_2(CH_2)_xCH(NH_2)CO_2CH_3$$
XVI　　　　　　　　　　　　　　　　　XVII

Thus Adamson (149) pointed out that a preparation obtained by Fischer and Suzuki (141) from the autocondensation of lysine methyl ester and described by them as "lysine anhydride" was, in actuality, a mixture composed of some 40% of the volatile intramolecular anhydride of lysine (3-aminohomopiperidone) and 60% of non-volatile lysine peptides. Unequivocal synthesis of lysine diketopiperazine was subsequently effected by Katchalski, Grossfeld, and Frankel (150) through the employment of N^ε-carbobenzoxylysine methyl ester, wherein the reactive ε-amino group of the lysine residue was blocked. Situations analogous to the above could presumably arise, in addition, from implication of the ω-carbonyl groups in condensation reactions involving esters of aspartic and glutamic acids.

In connection with the above, the ill-fated history of synthetic "arginylarginine" becomes of interest here. Although this compound, which was characterized as the picrate and nitrate derivatives, was presumed by Fischer and Suzuki (141) in 1905 to have arisen from the autocondensation of L-arginine methyl ester, such presumption was nevertheless qualified by certain reservations. Thus, not only did a Dumas nitrogen analysis of the substance reveal values which were too high, but also prolonged treatment of the material with hot concentrated hydrochloric acid resulted in no regeneration of free arginine, a fact which cast some doubt upon its alleged peptide nature. Despite these observations, Edlbacher and Bonem (153), some twenty years later, reported that the "arginylarginine" of Fischer and Suzuki was completely hydrolyzed upon heating with 25% sulfuric acid for 14 hours, and that the free amino acid could be recovered from the hydrolysate in nearly quantitative yield as its picrolonate derivative. In addition, the "arginylarginine" exhibited formol-titratable nitrogen values which were in good agreement with those theoretically expected for this compound, while the action of arginase upon this substance resulted in the liberation of some 20–21 % of the total nitrogen as urea. The major arguments barring definite assignment of the arginylarginine structure, tentatively proposed by Fischer and Suzuki, were thereby seemingly removed. However, a disturbing element crept into the picture in 1927 with the announcement by Kossel and Staudt (154) that, in contradistinction to the results of Edlbacher and Bonem, not only did they fail to observe any arginine formation upon prolonged treatment of "arginylarginine" with hot sulfuric acid, but also that the picrolonate derivative of arginine described by the latter investigators was in actuality the corresponding derivative of unhydrolyzed "arginylarginine." Just one year later, Waldschmidt-Leitz, Schäffner, Schlatter, and Klein (155) reported that an original preparation of Fischer and Suzuki was completely insusceptible to the hydrolytic action of either trypsin-kinase or intestinal erepsin and thus supported the previous doubt about the peptide nature of this substance. Such doubt was resolved during the same year by a classical study of Zervas and Bergmann (142), which unequivocally demonstrated that the autocondensation of arginine methyl ester (XVIII) to the corresponding dipeptide ester (XIX) is rapidly succeeded by a disproportionate cleavage of the latter compound into ornithine methyl ester (XXI) and an anhydride of α,δ-diguanidinovaleric acid (XX). It was the latter compound which constituted the controversial "arginylarginine" of

$$
\begin{array}{cccccc}
NH_2 & NH_2 & NH_2 & NH_2 & & \\
| & | & | & | & & NH_2 \\
C{=}NH & C{=}NH & C{=}NH & C{=}NH & & | \\
| & | & | & | & & +(CH_2)_3 \\
NH & \rightarrow NH & NH & \rightarrow NH & & | \\
| & | & | & | & NH & CHNH_2 \\
(CH_2)_3 & (CH_2)_3 & (CH_2)_3 & (CH_2)_3 & \| & | \\
| & | & | & | & CNH & CO_2CH_3 \\
CHNH_2 & CHCO{-}{-}{-}NHCH & CHNH{-}{-}{-}{-}CNH & & \\
| & | & | & | & & \\
CO_2CH_3 & NH_2 & CO_2CH_3 & CO{-}{-}{-}{-}{-}{-}{-}{-}{-}| & & \\
\text{XVIII} & \text{XIX} & & \text{XX} & & \text{XXI}
\end{array}
$$

Fischer and Suzuki. It is somewhat ironical that, although an authentic sample of arginylarginine has only recently been synthesized (Section 10-39), reference to this peptide as an arginase-susceptible substrate has hitherto appeared frequently in published investigations and reviews.

Polymerization of Higher Peptide Esters. Higher peptide esters share the tendency of amino acid and dipeptide esters to undergo condensation polymerization, although this tendency diminishes with increased chain length and necessitates more drastic conditions. Such use of higher peptide esters was initially described in 1906 by Fischer (156), who secured pentaglycylglycine in good yield upon heating diglycyclglycine methyl ester

(XXII) at 100°, followed by saponification of the hexapeptide ester (XXIII)

$$NH_2CH_2CO—NHCH_2CO—NHCH_2CO_2CH_3 \xrightarrow{100°} NH_2CH_2CO—(NHCH_2CO)_4—NHCH_2CO_2CH_3$$
$$\text{XXII} \qquad\qquad\qquad\qquad\qquad\qquad\qquad \text{XXIII}$$

isolated from the polymeric mixture so derived. A lesser amount of water-insoluble material, presumed to be the dodecapeptide ester, was also isolated. Comparable behavior was shown by the methyl ester of leucylglycylglycine and alanylglycylglycine (157). That the condensation reaction may be induced to proceed with the formation of a polymer which contains on the average as many as 96 amino acid units was reported some years later by Pacsu and Wilson (109, 110), who studied the methyl esters of glycyl-, alanyl- and leucylglycylglycine at 100–110°. The same investigators (109), in addition, reaffirmed the earlier observation of Abderhalden and Fodor (158) that a methanolic solution of glycylglycylglycine methyl ester yields the insoluble hexapeptide methyl ester upon standing at room temperature. The kinetics of this reaction, at 0°, 25°, and 60°, has been studied by Rees, Tong, and Young (159).

Brockmann, Tummes, and von Metzsch (160) have indicated that condensation reactions involving tripeptide esters need not necessarily proceed with the exclusive formation of linear polymers. Thus a cyclic tri- and hexapeptide could be isolated from a methanolic solution of glycylalanylphenylalanine methyl ester (XXIV; R = CH$_3$, R' = CH$_2$C$_6$H$_5$) containing either ammonia or piperidine. Origin of the former product (XXVI) could presumably be traced to an intramolecular cyclization of the reactant tripeptide ester (XXIV), whereas the latter cyclic product (XXVII) was formed subsequent to an intermolecular condensation of two molecules of reactant (XXIV) to yield the intermediate hexapeptide ester (XXV). These results are compatible with an earlier suggestion by Ruggli (161), that a

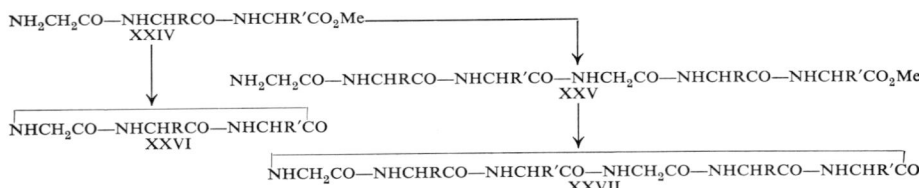

cyclic product could arise from a reaction which normally proceeded with the formation of polymeric products if the distance which separated the molecules in solution was greater than that which separated both ends of a given molecule. Thus dilution could potentially impede an intermolecular condensation reaction to an extent that would result in the favored formation of cyclic products.

In point of historical perspective, it is of interest to here take note of the report by Fischer (157) that, contrary to an earlier claim of Curtius (97), neither triglycylglycine methyl ester nor the corresponding ethyl ester

CHEMICAL PROCEDURES FOR SYNTHESIS OF PEPTIDES 789

exhibited any tendency to polymerize upon being heated at 100°. Such conflict was seemingly resolved by the report of Sluyterman and Veenendaal (162) that the former ester, after a prolonged induction period at 100°, undergoes a methyl group migration from oxygen to nitrogen atom with the concomitant production of free triglycylglycine, as well as its N-methyl and N,N-dimethyl derivatives. Condensation polymerization, with the formation of polyglycine esters, was reported (163) at higher temperatures. However, a later communication by Brockmann and Musso (164) indicated that triglycylglycine methyl ester underwent no apparent change at 125° for 4 days, although the production of the free tetrapeptide and other decomposition products was noted at yet higher temperatures. In conformity with these results, Rydon and Smith (165) showed that triglycylglycine ethyl ester yields the free tetrapeptide as the only product after 12 hours at 135°. These investigators noted in addition that, although the di- and tripeptide ethyl esters of glycine polymerize quite readily, little or no polymerization of the tetra-, penta-, and hexapeptide ethyl esters occurs up to 37 hours at elevated temperatures. Previous data by Frankel and Katchalski (105, 107) demonstrated, however, that polyglycine and polyalanine esters, containing an average of 13 to 30 amino acid units, can condense to yield polymers embodying 23 to 110 units upon heating at 100–130° for periods ranging from 9 to 34 days. More facile condensation was noted with the methyl esters than with the ethyl esters of the peptides (105, 165).

In view of the seeming inconsistencies among various investigations with respect to the thermal polymerization of tetrapeptide and higher polypeptide esters, still further study is required before any definite statements concerning the degree of polymerization exhibited by these compounds can be made. A summary of the polycondensation products reported in several such studies is given in Table 10–4.

The peculiar behavior exhibited by proline peptides in condensation reactions compels further elaboration here. As has been pointed out by Edsall (167), the conformation of a molecule which incorporates either a proline or a hydroxyproline residue is influenced by the relative inflexibility of the two atoms of the pyrrolidine ring attached to the two adjacent atoms of the peptide chain. In consequence, polypeptides which contain these residues (XXIX) are unable to assume the fully extended conformation of those wherein such residues are lacking (XXVIII), a phenomenon which could result in the distortion of helical conformations and cause the chain to

TABLE 10–4
Polycondensation Products of Some Peptide Esters

Reactant	Temp. and Time of Heating	Condensation and Decomposition Products	Ref.
Glycylglycine ethyl ester	78° (20 hr.) or rm. temp. (18 mo.)	Glycine anhydride; tetraglycine methyl ester	165
Diglycylglycine ethyl ester	135° (12 hr.)	Hexa- and nonaglycine ester; high polymers (trace)	165
	105° (1 mo.)	Hexaglycine ester; higher polymers (main product)	165
Diglycylglycine methyl ester	100°	Hexaglycine ester; amorphous, water-insoluble fraction	156
	100° (9 days)	Polyglycine methyl ester; trace of sarcosine	163
	102–130° (20 days)	6–96 Polyglycine ester	108, 109
	105° (1 mo.)	High polymers	165
	108° (20 hr.)	Hexa- and nonaglycine ester; high polymers	165
	100°	"Cyclic octaglycine anhydride"	97
Triglycylglycine ethyl ester	135° (12 hr.)	Tetraglycine	165
	20° (14 days)	No reaction	164
Triglycylglycine methyl ester	100° (29 days)	Polyglycine methyl ester; small peptides; sarcosine; N,N-dimethylglycine	162
	125° (4 hr.)	No reaction	164

Triglycylglycine methyl ester	140° (4 hr.)	Tetraglycine (60% reaction)	164
	160° (4 hr.)	Brownish coloration; tetraglycine	164
	180° (4 hr.)	Black coloration; tetraglycine; glycine (traces)	164
	185° (25 min.)	Polyglycine methyl ester; trace of sarcosine	163
	205° (5 min.)	Black coloration; no ninhydrin positive material remaining	164
Tetraglycylglycine ethyl ester	124° (17.5 hr.)	Pentaglycine (trace)	165
	163° (17 hr.)	Pentaglycine (4% reaction)	165
Pentaglycylglycine ethyl ester	124° (17 hr.)	Hexaglycine (trace); higher polymers (trace)	165
	163° (37 hr.)	Hexaglycine (trace); higher polymers (trace)	165
Pentaglycylglycine methyl ester	102–130° (21 days)	96-Polyglycine methyl ester; smaller peptide esters	16
16-Polyglycine ethyl ester	100° (34 days)	30-Polyglycine ethyl ester	105
20-Polyglycine ethyl ester	100° (34 days)	42-Polyglycine ethyl ester	105
30-Polyglycine methyl ester	130° (9 days)	110-Polyglycine methyl ester	105
L-Alanylglycylglycine methyl ester	100°	Hexapeptide ester; amorphous polymer	157
DL-Alanylglycylglycine methyl ester	80–110° (32 days)	Poly-DL-alanylglycylglycine methyl ester (water-soluble)	110
	110° (4 days)	Glycine anhydride; 6–42 residue polymers	166
13-Poly-DL-alanine ethyl ester	150°	23-Poly-DL-alanine ethyl ester	107
DL-Leucylglycylglycine methyl ester	100–110° (11 days)	Poly-DL-leucylglycylglycine methyl ester (water-soluble)	110

bend back upon itself. In any event, it has been shown that, unlike other dipeptides under comparable conditions, dipeptides containing a proline or a hydroxyproline residue exhibit a marked propensity toward intramolecular cyclization with the formation of the corresponding 2:5-diketopiperazines (168, 169). Extension of this phenomenon to the ethyl esters of several di-, tri- and tetrapeptides embodying a proline residue has been reported by Rydon and Smith (170). Intramolecular cyclization to glycylproline anhydride (XXXI), without accompanying linear polymerization, was observed upon either heating glycyl-L-proline ethyl ester (XXX) at $105°/10^{-3}$ mm. for 15 hours, or else permitting it to stand *in vacuo* at room temperature overnight. Conversion of prolylglycine ethyl ester (XXXII) to the same product could be effected in like manner, as well as by allowing the ester to stand in ethanolic triethylamine solution at room temperature for a period of 2 weeks. Comparable investigation of the three possible tripeptide

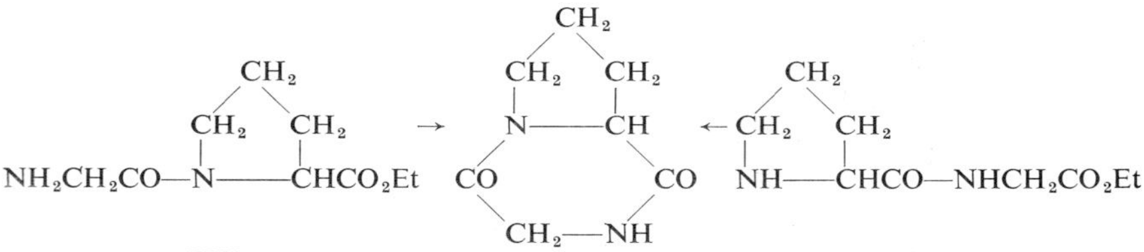

ethyl esters containing one L-proline and two glycine residues gave complex mixtures containing the anhydride (XXXI), 2:5-diketopiperazine, and some polymeric material. On the other hand, the tetrapeptide, prolyldiglycylglycine ethyl ester, exhibited no apparent tendency toward inter- or intramolecular reaction after being heated at $95°/10^{-3}$ mm. for 20 hours. In an extension of this study by Smith (170), it was noted that during the storage of a solution of glycyl-DL-prolylglycine ethyl ester in anhydrous ethanolic triethylamine at room temperature over a period of two years, a small amount of crystalline product deposited which was removed periodically by filtration and subsequently identified as the cyclic tripeptide, *cyclo*-glycylglycyl-DL-prolyl. Glycylprolylglycine, glycine, glycylproline anhydride and presumably some hexapeptide ethyl ester were among the products identified in the ethanolic mother liquors.

Controlled Ester Condensations. From the previous discussion it becomes readily apparent that the employment of controlled polycondensation reactions involving amino acid or peptide methyl or ethyl esters for the general synthesis of peptides of given structure is infeasible. Such is the case, not only in view of the difficulties encountered in securing homogeneous peptides of required chain length, but also because the introduction of different amino acid residues into the peptide chain, in a predetermined sequence, is virtually uncontrollable. An early but fruitless attempt was made by Fischer (171) to utilize condensation reactions of this type for the preparation of peptides of known sequence. This attempt involved the heat-induced condensation of ethyl carboethoxyglycylglycinate (XXXIII) and DL-leucine ethyl ester (XXXIV; R = C_4H_9) to give ethyl carboethoxyglycylglycyl-DL-leucinate (XXXV; R = C_4H_9). This method was quickly

$$C_2H_5OCO\text{—}NHCH_2CO\text{—}NHCH_2CO_2Et + NH_2CHRCO_2Et \rightarrow$$
$$\text{XXXIII} \qquad\qquad \text{XXXIV}$$

$$C_2H_5OCO\text{—}NHCH_2CO\text{—}NHCH_2CO\text{—}NHCHRCO_2Et$$
$$\text{XXXV}$$

abandoned, however, owing to the extremely poor yields of product obtained, as well as to the complications inherent in further elongation of the peptide chain by a similar procedure.

A few isolated examples nevertheless do exist whereby the controlled condensation of methyl or ethyl esters may be employed for the synthesis of well-defined peptides. Among these might be cited the preparation of hexaglycine ester from the condensation of two molecules of triglycine methyl ester by heating (156, 165) in the absence of solvent or in methanol solution (109, 158), as well as the classical Curtius synthesis (97) of tetraglycine ester from glycine ethyl ester in anhydrous ether.

Evaluation of the Method. Although the synthesis of small peptides of predetermined sequence via ester condensation procedures is impracticable except in certain rare instances, the method has been somewhat more successfully employed for the preparation of amino acid polymers of various sizes. However, preparation of the larger polypeptides generally requires the use of high temperatures, a condition which is quite drastic and often leads to marked decomposition of both reactant and product. Where optically active reactants are employed, the danger of racemization also exists. In addition, the reactivity of the methyl and ethyl esters employed as monomers is generally influenced both by the nature of the side chains of the component amino acids and by the initial chain length, conditions which restrict the constitution as well as the size of the resultant polymeric products. The present availability of other polymerization techniques which do not impose these limitations, such as the N-carboxyanhydride procedure (Section 10-10), has consequently resulted in the obsolescence of the ester condensation method.

5. The Diketopiperazine Method. *Principle.* The 2:5-diketopiperazines (III) may be considered combinations of two amino acids (I and II) connected, one to the other, in peptide linkage with the loss of two molecules of water. Complete acid or alkaline hydrolysis of these compounds should normally proceed with regeneration of the two component amino acids (I and II).

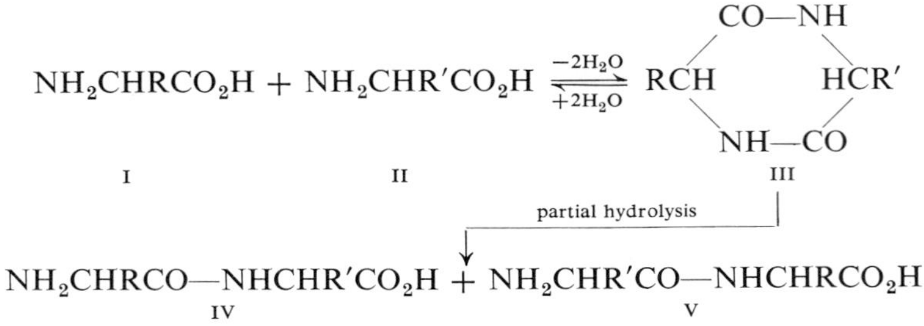

$$NH_2CHRCO_2H + NH_2CHR'CO_2H \underset{+2H_2O}{\overset{-2H_2O}{\rightleftarrows}} \begin{matrix} & CO-NH & \\ RCH & & HCR' \\ & NH-CO & \end{matrix}$$

I　　　　　　　II　　　　　　　　　　　　　　III

partial hydrolysis

$$NH_2CHRCO-NHCHR'CO_2H + NH_2CHR'CO-NHCHRCO_2H$$

　　　　IV　　　　　　　　　　　　V

Partial hydrolysis of the diketopiperazine ring should, on the other hand, be expected to produce a mixture of two dipeptides (IV and V) in a ratio which would be governed by the relative rates with which each of the two amide bonds of the reactant (III) is cleaved. If conditions conducive to this type of selective hydrolysis could be found, a general method of dipeptide synthesis might be evolved. Such was the rationale undoubtedly applied by Fischer and Forneau (103) in their initial synthesis of glycylglycine (VII) via the partial acid hydrolysis of 2:5-diketopiperazine (VI).

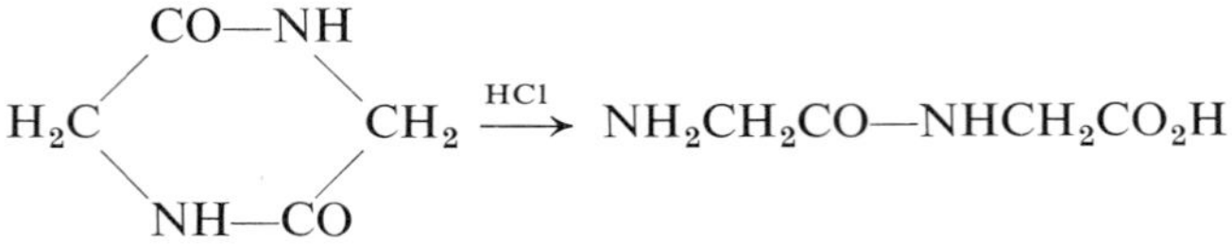

$$\begin{matrix} & CO-NH & \\ H_2C & & CH_2 \\ & NH-CO & \end{matrix} \xrightarrow{HCl} NH_2CH_2CO-NHCH_2CO_2H$$

　　　　　VI　　　　　　　　　　　　　　VII

Symmetrical or *homogeneous* diketopiperazines are those in which the constituent amino acid residues are of the same chemical structure but may be of unlike optical configuration. Dependent upon such configuration, these compounds may generally exist in three different stereoisomeric forms, i.e., two optically active *cis* forms and one optically inactive *trans* form. This is exemplified by the stereoisomeric forms of alanine anhydride:

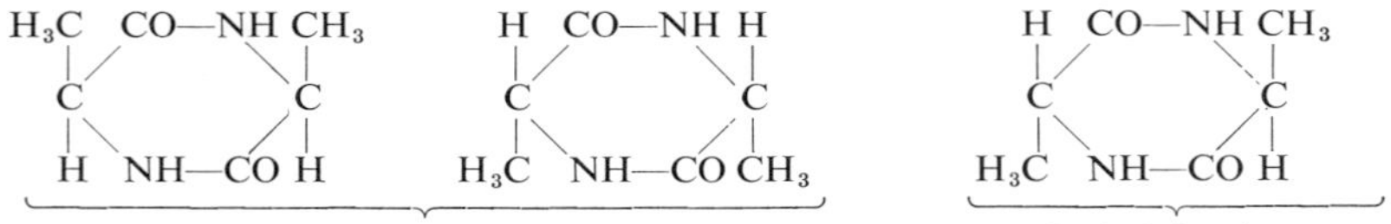

$$\begin{matrix} H_3C & CO-NH & CH_3 \\ C & & C \\ H & NH-CO & H \end{matrix} \qquad \begin{matrix} H & CO-NH & H \\ C & & C \\ H_3C & NH-CO & CH_3 \end{matrix} \qquad \begin{matrix} H & CO-NH & CH_3 \\ C & & C \\ H_3C & NH-CO & H \end{matrix}$$

　　　　　　Optically active　　　　　　　　　　　Optically inactive

where each of the former two compounds is composed of residues of like configuration whereas the latter compound incorporates both an L and a D residue. Controlled acid or alkaline hydrolysis of either of the optically active diketopiperazines, if unaccompanied by racemization, would thereupon result in the formation of an optically active dipeptide. Comparable treatment of the internally compensated inactive form would, on the other hand, give rise to a racemic modification constituting L-alanyl-D-alanine and its antipode, D-alanyl-L-alanine.

Unsymmetrical or *mixed* diketopiperazines differ from the above in that they are composed of amino acid residues of unlike chemical composition. If each of the constitutent residues contains only a single asymmetric center, then four optically active stereoisomers may theoretically exist. These may be generalized as follows:

        Optically active *cis* forms   Optically active *trans* forms

where each pair of *cis* forms or *trans* forms, respectively, constitutes a racemic modification. Partial hydrolysis of any given optical form would, in the absence of preferential bond cleavage, lead to the production of two dipeptides (IV and V) which differ in their amino acid residue arrangement.

Preparation of 2:5-Diketopiperazines. "Leucinimide" or leucine anhydride (VIII) was described by Bopp (172) in 1849 and is the earliest known member of this class of compounds. Preparation of this substance was effected by

$$\begin{array}{c} \text{CO—NH} \\ CH_3CHCH_2CH \diagup \quad \diagdown CHCH_2CHCH_3 \\ | \qquad \diagdown \quad \diagup \qquad | \\ CH_3 \qquad NH—CO \qquad CH_3 \\ \text{VIII} \end{array}$$

Hesse and Limpricht (173) in 1860, and by Kohler (135) in 1865, by heating the parent amino acid in a stream of carbon dioxide and hydrogen chloride, respectively; essentially the same procedures were later employed for the synthesis of the corresponding anhydrides of alanine (174), phenylalanine (175), sarcosine (176), and phenylglycine (177). Still more recently, the simple expedient of heating free glycine (IX) in ethylene glycol at 174–176° has resulted in a convenient synthesis of glycine anhydride (X) in some 62% yield (178, 179).

$$NH_2CH_2CO_2H \xrightarrow[\Delta]{\text{ethylene glycol}} H_2C \diagup\!\!\!\!\begin{array}{c}CO—NH\\ \\NH—CO\end{array}\!\!\!\!\diagdown CH_2 \xleftarrow{H_2O} NH_2CH_2CO_2Et$$

    IX   X   XI

Illustrative procedure 10–1. Glycine anhydride (X) (179). A mixture containing 700 g. of technical glycine and 3500 ml. of technical ethylene glycol is heated for 50 min. at 174–176° with continuous stirring in a 5-l. round-bottom flask. The mixture is cooled for 20 hr. in the refrigerator, the suspension centrifuged, and the brown crystalline precipitate washed on a Büchner funnel with absolute methanol (1500 ml. total volume) until the washings are nearly colorless. The brown-colored 2:5-diketopiperazine (about 320 g.) is dissolved in 2.2 l. of boiling water and the solution cooled overnight in the refrigerator. The suspension is filtered and the light-brown crystals are washed with absolute methanol (500 ml.) and dried in air. The product (about 250 g.) is dissolved in 2.5 l. of boiling water, the solution decolorized with 20 g. of charcoal, and the suspension filtered on a steam-heated Büchner funnel. If the filtrate is yellow, the decolorization procedure is repeated using 5 g. of charcoal. The colorless filtrate is cooled overnight in the refrigerator, the suspension filtered, and the crystals are washed in turn with 100 ml. of ice water, 80 ml. of 50% methanol, and 80 ml. of absolute methanol. The yield is 210 g. (40%) of air-dried, pure white 2:5-diketopiperazine. An additional 22% of the product may be obtained from the pooled filtrates.

With the exception of the procedure described above, the preparation of 2:5-diketopiperazines directly from the component amino acids has proved generally unsatisfactory. An alternative route, announced by Curtius and Goebel (180) in 1888, depended upon somewhat more facile conversions involving ester derivatives of amino acids. Such a method was initially applied to the production of glycine anhydride (X) from an aqueous solution of glycine ethyl ester (XI) at room temperature. The rate of transformation of ester to anhydride, as Abderhalden and Suzuki (181) showed later, is highly dependent upon the degree of steric hindrance imposed by the ester radical, and it becomes slower with a progressive increase in the size of the latter group (Table 10–5). A decrease in rate with increasing size of the aliphatic side chain of the amino acid residue was observed by Fischer and Suzuki (141, 151). Thus, although little or no apparent conversion of the ethyl ester derivatives of alanine, aminobutyric acid, leucine, α-amino-*n*-caproic acid, phenylalanine, or tyrosine to the corresponding diketopiperazines occurred in aqueous solution, such transformations were none the less readily effected at 150–180° in a sealed vessel. The symmetrical diketopiperazines of histidine (141), serine (141), proline (182), and β-ethyl aspartate (143), among others, were also prepared from their respective esters. Similar procedures proved unsuccessful with glutamic acid, however, owing to the preferential intramolecular cyclization of diethyl glutamate (XII) to ethyl α-pyrrolidone carboxylate (XIII). Since a spontaneous transformation

$$\underset{\text{XII}}{\underset{|}{\text{CH}_2\text{CH}_2\overset{|}{\text{CHCO}_2\text{Et}}}}\overset{\text{CO}_2\text{Et} \quad \text{NH}_2}{} \rightarrow \underset{\text{XIII}}{\underset{|}{\text{CH}_2\text{CH}_2\overset{|}{\text{CHCO}_2\text{Et}}}}\overset{\text{CO}\text{———}\text{NH}}{} + \text{EtOH}$$

of amino acid esters to the corresponding diketopiperazines is effected in the dry state, prolonged storage of these compounds as the free base should be generally avoided. The relative ease with which some esters, such as

TABLE 10–5
Rate of Transformation of Various Glycine Esters into 2:5-Diketopiperazine upon Storage in the Solid State (181)

Ester Derivative	Days of Storage At 37°	Days of Storage At 18°	Per Cent Diketopiperazine Formed
Glycine methyl ester[a]	2		99.4
		2	88.8
Glycine ethyl ester	2.7		54.2
	5.7		92.2
		5.7	54.5
Glycine *n*-propyl ester	2.7		39.2
	5.7		96.5
		6	47.2
Glycine isopropyl ester	5.7		18.1
	14		71.6
		14	14.8
Glycine *n*-butyl ester	2.7		41.5
	6		92.8
		8	50.5
Glycine isobutyl ester	2.7		41.5
	5.7		97.2
		7.7	45.7
Glycine *n*-amyl ester	2.7		63.1
	6		100.8
		6	64.4
Glycine isoamyl ester	2.7		49.0
	6		87.8
		6	59.0
Glycine benzyl ester	3		20.2
	10		36.0
		10	22.8

[a] After 2 hr. at 37°, the conversion to 2:5-diketopiperazine was essentially complete.

L-serine methyl ester, undergo anhydride formation upon storage in the dry state is emphasized by the procedure below.

Illustrative procedure 10–2. L-Serine anhydride (183). A suspension of 2 g. of finely powdered L-serine in 60 ml. of dry methanol is rapidly saturated with a stream of dry hydrogen chloride gas, during which time solution is effected. The clear solution is concentrated under reduced pressure at a temperature not exceeding 40°, the residual crystalline mass covered with 30 ml. of dry methanol, and the hydrogen chloride treatment repeated. After concentration to dryness, the crude product is taken up in the minimal amount of dry methanol at room temperature, and the L-serine methyl ester hydrochloride precipitated as glistening white crystals by the careful addition of dry ether. Yield, 82%; m.p. 163–167° (dec.). One gram of the ester hydrochloride is converted to the free base by dissolving it in 10 ml. of dry alcohol and neutralizing with the exact amount (7.3 ml.) of a 2% solution of sodium in dry methanol. Removal of sodium chloride is achieved by adding 20 ml. of dry ether, cooling in an ice bath for 15 min., and filtering off the precipitate. Concentration of the filtrate to dryness under reduced pressure yields free L-serine methyl ester as a colorless oil. This compound, upon standing at room temperature for 12–15 hr., is completely converted to a crystalline mass of L-serine anhydride which, after washing with a small amount of ethanol, is secured in some 66% yield. Recrystallization is accomplished by dissolving the material in the ten fold quantity of hot water to which twice the volume of ethanol is subsequently added. M.p., 247° (dec.); $[\alpha]_D^{25} = -67.5°$ (2.2% in water).

That the lactones of certain amino acids exhibit a marked tendency toward diketopiperazine formation was observed by Fischer and Leuchs (184) in 1902. Thus α-amino-γ-valerolactone (XV), secured by the action of ethanolic-HCl on α-amino-γ-hydroxyvaleric acid (XIV), was shown to undergo a rapid and spontaneous conversion to the diketopiperazine (XVI) upon standing at room temperature. The process presumably involved the preliminary polymerization of two molecules of amino acid lactone (XV)

$$\underset{\text{XIV}}{\overset{\text{OH} \quad \text{CO}_2\text{H}}{\text{CH}_3\text{CHCH}_2\text{CHNH}_2}} \rightarrow \underset{\text{XV}}{\overset{\text{O}——\text{CO}}{\text{CH}_3\text{CHCH}_2\text{CHNH}_2}} \rightarrow \underset{\text{XVI}}{\overset{\text{OH} \qquad \text{CO—NH} \qquad \text{OH}}{\text{CH}_3\text{CHCH}_2\text{CH} \diagdown \diagup \text{CHCH}_2\text{CHCH}_3 \atop \text{NH—CO}}}$$

to yield a transitory dipeptide lactone intermediate, succeeded by an intramolecular cyclization of the latter compound. The occurrence of a similar phenomenon with yet other γ-hydroxy amino acids is highly probable.

Since each of the afore-mentioned methods leads solely to the formation of homogeneous molecules, resort must be made to dipeptide esters or α-haloacylamino acid ester precursors for the preparation of mixed diketopiperazines. The first such compound (XIX), described by Fischer and Otto (121) in 1903, was obtained by the action of alcoholic ammonia on chloroacetylalanine ethyl ester (XVII). That the latter compound initially

$$\underset{\text{XVII}}{\text{ClCH}_2\text{CO—NHCH(CH}_3\text{)CO}_2\text{Et}}$$

$$\text{NH}_3 \swarrow \qquad \qquad \searrow 2\text{NH}_3$$

$$\underset{\text{XVIII}}{[\text{NH}_2\text{CH}_2\text{CO—NHCH(CH}_3\text{)CO}_2\text{Et}]} \rightarrow \underset{\text{XIX}}{\overset{\text{CO—NH}}{\text{CH}_3\text{CH} \diagdown \text{CH}_2 \atop \text{NH—CO}}} \leftarrow \underset{\text{XX}}{[\text{NH}_2\text{CH}_2\text{CO—NHCH(CH}_3\text{)CONH}_2]}$$

undergoes a transitory conversion to either the dipeptide ester (XVIII) or amide (XX) is strongly suggested by the relative ease with which such compounds as glycylglycine ethyl ester (103), leucylalanine ethyl ester (157), glycylvaline methyl ester (185), glycylglycinamide (186), and glycylphenylalaninamide (186) are transformed into their respective diketopiperazines merely upon standing at room temperature in alcohol, alcoholic ammonia, or aqueous solution. Certain free dipeptides also exhibit a marked tendency to pass over into diketopiperazines, although at elevated temperatures (187, 188). Such intramolecular condensation tendencies of dipeptides, as well as derivatives thereof, have been exploited to separate this class of compounds from mixtures which contain the higher polypeptides (Chapter 16).

Utilization of the ready intramolecular condensation tendencies of dipeptide esters has permitted the synthesis of several complex diketopiperazines which incorporate a cystine residue in combination with either glutamic acid, aspartic acid, or tyrosine (189). Of particular interest was the preparation of bisanhydro-L-cystinyl-L-cystine (XXIII), a tricyclic molecule secured by the cyclization of L-cysteinyl-L-cysteine ethyl ester (XXI) in ethanolic NH_3 at 0°, followed by oxidation in aqueous solution of the crystalline dithiol piperazine intermediate (XXII) so derived. The molecular structure of

$$\underset{\text{XXI}}{HSCH_2\overset{NH_2}{\overset{|}{C}}HCO-NH\overset{CO_2Et}{\overset{|}{C}}HCH_2SH} \quad \underset{}{SCH_2\overset{CO-NH}{\underset{NH-CO}{\diagdown\diagup}}CHCH_2S}$$

$$\downarrow EtOH-NH_3$$

$$\underset{\text{XXII}}{HSCH_2\overset{CO-NH}{\underset{NH-CO}{\diagdown\diagup}}CHCH_2SH} \overset{H_2O_2}{\longrightarrow} \underset{\text{XXIII}}{SCH_2\overset{CO-NH}{\underset{NH-CO}{\diagdown\diagup}}CHCH_2S}$$

(XXIII) is of some theoretical interest since it incorporates a 16-membered heterocyclic ring in addition to two diketopiperazine rings. X-ray examination of this compound in Astbury's laboratory (190) revealed the crystals to be monoclinic, the unit cell having the dimensions a, 11.15 A.; b, 5.9 A.; c, 12.5 A.; and $\beta = 90°$. The number of molecules per unit cell was 2. Preliminary calculations revealed that the piperazine rings are about 6.25 A. apart, and are probably not flat but puckered into the chair form. The double-ring molecule behaves optically almost exactly like two separate molecules related to each other by a dyad screw axis. Description of the crystalline diketopiperazine of L-homocysteine has also appeared (191). Unlike the L-cysteine analog (189), however, oxidation of this compound yielded an insoluble, high molecular weight polymer of homocystine anhydride (XXIV).

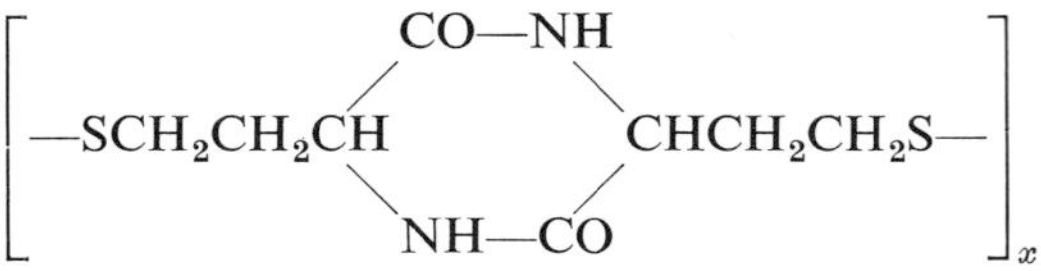

$$\left[-SCH_2CH_2CH \begin{array}{c} CO-NH \\ \diagup \quad \diagdown \\ \diagdown \quad \diagup \\ NH-CO \end{array} CHCH_2CH_2S- \right]_x$$

XXIV

Hydrolysis of 2:5-Diketopiperazines. The first successful partial hydrolysis of the 2:5-diketopiperazine ring was accomplished by Abenius and Widman (192), in 1888, via the action of hydrochloric acid on the symmetrical 1:4-ditolyl derivative (XXV; R = $CH_3C_6H_4-$). Some thirteen years later,

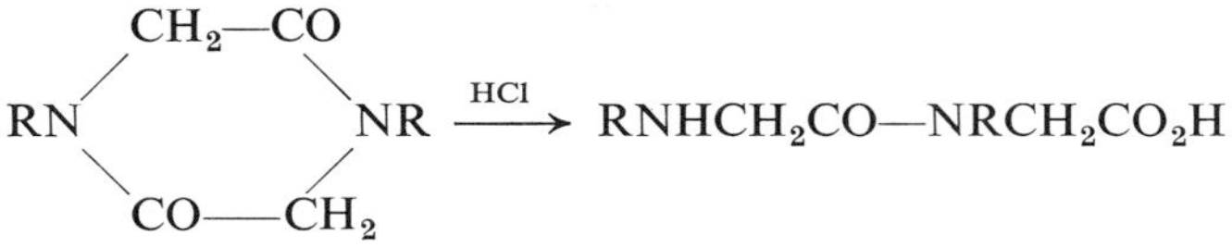

$$RN \begin{array}{c} CH_2-CO \\ \diagup \quad \diagdown \\ \diagdown \quad \diagup \\ CO-CH_2 \end{array} NR \xrightarrow{HCl} RNHCH_2CO-NRCH_2CO_2H$$

XXV　　　　　　　　　　　XXVI

a cleavage was described by Fischer and Forneau (103) who, after only briefly warming the corresponding unsubstituted diketopiperazine (XXV; R = H) with strong hydrochloric acid, noted the precipitation of glycylglycine hydrochloride from the rapidly cooled solution. Upon conversion of the latter compound to the free dipeptide (XXVI; R = H) with alkali or silver oxide, the synthesis of the first well-defined peptide was achieved. Comparable treatment of glycine anhydride (XXVII) with alcoholic HCl resulted in the ready formation of glycylglycine ethyl ester hydrochloride (XXVIII). Use of the precursor anhydride for the preparation of the latter compound as well as the free dipeptide is detailed below (procedure 10–3).

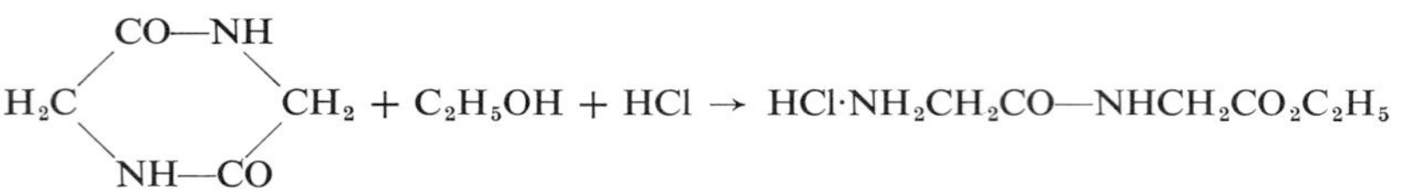

$$H_2C \begin{array}{c} CO-NH \\ \diagup \quad \diagdown \\ \diagdown \quad \diagup \\ NH-CO \end{array} CH_2 + C_2H_5OH + HCl \rightarrow HCl \cdot NH_2CH_2CO-NHCH_2CO_2C_2H_5$$

XXVII　　　　　　　　　　　　　XXVIII

Extension of the above reactions to 2:6-alkyl substituted diketopiperazines by Fischer (171) one year later could be accomplished only through the use of conditions more drastic than those employed previously. The conversion of leucine anhydride to the corresponding dipeptide, for example, required a half hour of heating in concentrated hydrobromic acid, while decomposition of alanine anhydride by prolonged heating with either aqueous or alcoholic hydrochloric acid proceeded with the formation of highly impure products. Histidine anhydride and tyrosine anhydride, on the other hand, appear to be completely resistant to the hydrolytic action of acids. Surprisingly, however, the homogeneous diketopiperazine ring of L-cysteine (193) is hydrolyzed to the optically active dipeptide (XXX) by the action of cold, concentrated hydrochloric acid with a facility that can

$$\underset{\text{XXIX}}{\underset{\text{NH—CO}}{\overset{\text{CO—NH}}{\text{HSCH}_2\text{CH}}}\diagdown\text{CHCH}_2\text{SH}} \xrightarrow{\text{HCl}} \underset{\text{XXX}}{\text{HSCH}_2\overset{\text{NH}_2}{\text{CH}}\text{CO—NH}\overset{\text{CO}_2\text{H}}{\text{CH}}\text{CH}_2\text{SH}}$$

be equaled only by the analogous compound of glycine (103). Such a phenomenon is presumably explicable on the basis of a distinct labilizing influence exerted on the diketopiperazine ring by the mercaptan groups. In this connection, it is of interest to note that bisanhydrocystinylcystine (XXIII) exhibits a marked resistance to the action of concentrated hydrochloric acid and, on prolonged boiling, is converted to cystine exclusively.

The difficulties encountered in the acid hydrolysis of several of the diketopiperazines impelled Fischer (194) in 1905 to subject these compounds to the hydrolytic action of normal alkali. With the latter medium, both glycine anhydride (194) and alanine anhydride (195) could be readily converted to their corresponding dipeptides at room temperature, in 15 to 20 minutes for the former, and within several hours for the latter. On the other hand, the corresponding anhydrides of both histidine (141) and α-amino-*n*-butyric acid (196) required some 1 to 3 days for a comparable reaction to take place, whereas a marked resistance to hydrolysis was exhibited by the leucine derivative (194) even during this increased period of time. Ease of hydrolysis with alkali is, as in the case of strong acid, undoubtedly governed by the nature of the amino acid participating in the ring, those residues with the longer hydrocarbon chains forming the more stable rings (141). Although an increase in temperature results in an accelerated rate of hydrolysis, such condition imposes less selectivity and thus is usually accompanied by the added undesirable cleavage of the resulting dipeptides to the free amino acids.

Despite the greater facility with which diketopiperazines are generally cleaved in alkaline than in acid solution, use of the former medium is limited because of the extensive racemization which is commonly observed in the dipeptides isolated from partial alkaline hydrolysates of optically active diketopiperazines. This phenomenon, initially observed with alanylalanine (195) derived from the alkaline cleavage of L-alanine anhydride, was subsequently shown to occur with the anhydride of L-tyrosine (197) as well. The knowledge that such racemization was due, in the main, to the action of alkali on the optically active diketopiperazine rather than upon the liberated dipeptide arose from the systematic studies of Levene, Steiger, and Marker (198). In symmetrically constituted anhydrides composed of two optically active amino acids, the extent of racemization was found to increase with the increased stability of diketopiperazine in alkaline solution. Thus, whereas the action of $0.2N$ sodium hydroxide on

L-alanine anhydride for 48 hours at 25° was accompanied by some 80% racemization, the comparable experiment with L-alanyl-L-alanine indicated no loss of optical activity, even upon prolonged contact with alkali. Of related interest is the complete and rapid racemization of L-leucine anhydride in alkali under conditions which lead to no concomitant cleavage of the diketopiperazine ring. Bergmann, Zervas, and Köster (199) had previously demonstrated that an aqueous solution of the diketopiperazine of D-phenylalanyl-L-arginine, as the free base, underwent 50% autoracemization in only 19 minutes, a phenomenon which may presumably be attributed to the marked basicity of the guanidino group.

In the hydrolysis of mixed diketopiperazines, added complications are imposed by the possibility that ring opening may proceed in two different ways:

$$\begin{array}{c} CH_2-CO \\ / \quad \quad \backslash \\ NH \quad \quad NH \\ \backslash \quad \quad / \\ CO-CH-C_4H_9 \\ \text{XXXI} \end{array} \quad \xrightarrow{(b)} \quad (a)\ NH_2CH_2CO-NHCH(C_4H_9)CO_2H \quad \text{XXXII}$$

$$\xrightarrow{(b)} \quad (b)\ NH_2CH(C_4H_9)CO-NHCH_2CO_2H \quad \text{XXXIII}$$

Thus hydrolytic cleavage of glycylleucine anhydride (XXXI) was found to yield a disproportionate mixture of the difficultly separable dipeptides, glycylleucine (XXXII) and leucylglycine (XXXIII) (197). That the hydrolysis sometimes favors the formation of only a single peptide was demonstrated by Bergmann and Tietzman (200) who, upon acid hydrolysis of L-prolyl-L-phenylalanine anhydride, secured L-prolyl-L-phenylalanine exclusively. However, experience has indicated that the latter instance is probably more representative of the exception than of the rule.

Evaluation of the Method. From the above, several severe limitations of the use of diketopiperazines in a general method of peptide synthesis become immediately apparent. Primary among these is the exclusive applicability of the method to the synthesis of dipeptides. Added to this are the difficulties encountered in satisfactorily hydrolyzing diketopiperazines in either acid or alkali under standardized conditions, as well as in the loss in optical activity which almost invariably accompanies the implication of the latter medium. Finally, the two dipeptides which may result from the cleavage of mixed diketopiperazines not only occur in unpredictable proportion, but also often pose seemingly insurmountable fractionation problems. These deficiencies have led to a replacement of the method, virtually in its entirety, by later, more satisfactory ones. Nevertheless, the method remains of historical interest as the first source of well-defined peptides.

Illustrative Peptide Synthesis. The diketopiperazine method, although replaced almost entirely for the synthesis of peptides by later procedures,

CHEMICAL PROCEDURES FOR SYNTHESIS OF PEPTIDES

still provides one of the most practical routes to glycylglycine (XL), the simplest of all peptides. This compound, as well as glycylglycine ethyl ester hydrochloride (XXXVIII), is readily prepared from 2:5-diketopiperazine (XXXVII) by the classical Fischer and Forneau (103) procedure:

$$HCl \cdot NH_2CH_2COOC_2H_5 \xrightarrow{(C_2H_5)_3N} NH_2CH_2COOC_2H_5 + (C_2H_5)_3N \cdot HCl$$
$$\text{XXXIV} \qquad\qquad \text{XXXV} \qquad \text{XXXVI}$$

$$\begin{array}{c} H_2C \begin{array}{c} CO-NH \\ \\ NH-CO \end{array} CH_2 \\ \text{XXXVII} \end{array} \xrightarrow{EtOH, HCl} HCl \cdot NH_2CH_2CO-NHCH_2COOC_2H_5 \quad \text{XXXVIII}$$

$$\xrightarrow{aq.\ HCl} HCl \cdot NH_2CH_2CO-NHCH_2COOH \xrightarrow{LiOH} NH_2CH_2CO-NHCH_2COOH$$
$$\text{XXXIX} \qquad\qquad \text{XL}$$

The procedure for the preparation of 2:5-diketopiperazine, given below, is the authors' modification of the method of Fischer (157).

Illustrative procedure 10–3. 2:5-Diketopiperazine (XXXVII). To 279 g. of glycine ethyl ester hydrochloride (XXXIV) in a 1-l. beaker is added 210 ml. of water. The mixture is chilled to about 0–5° and 279 ml. of ice-cold triethylamine added thereto with stirring at a rate such that the temperature remains below 5°. After all the triethylamine has been added, the solution is allowed to stand at room temperature for 36–48 hr., after which time it is chilled at 4° for 4 hr. and then filtered over suction. The white, crystalline precipitate is washed successively with 300 ml. of cold water and 300 ml. of cold ethanol, and then dried *in vacuo*. Yield; 56–62 g. (49–54%). Purification of the compound may be effected by crystallization from hot water.

Glycylglycine hydrochloride monohydrate (XXXIX) (103, 179). A mixture, prepared by adding 20.5 g. (0.18 mole) of finely powdered diketopiperazine to 110 ml. of hot concentrated hydrochloric acid, is rapidly heated to boiling, boiled for 90–100 sec., and then rapidly cooled in an ice-water bath. After 1 hour, the crystalline mass is filtered on an acid-resistant paper or a sintered glass funnel and the crystals are washed with three 20-ml. portions of 95% ethanol and finally dried at 50°. The yield of glycylglycine hydrochloride monohydrate is about 30 g. (89%). The product may be purified by recrystallization from water-ethanol.

Glycylglycine (XL). Twenty-five grams of glycylglycine hydrochloride monohydrate (XXXIX) is dissolved in the minimal amount of warm water. The solution is cooled to room temperature and neutralized to *p*H 6.0 by the dropwise addition of conc. lithium hydroxide solution. If necessary, the mixture is warmed to bring any precipitated material into solution. A ten-fold volume of absolute alcohol is added thereto and the mixture allowed to stand at 4° overnight. Recrystallization of the white crystalline precipitate is effected from water-alcohol. The material so obtained should show a negative silver chloride test and an over-all yield of about 80% of theory.

Glycylglycine ethyl ester hydrochloride (XXXVIII) (103). Twenty grams of finely powdered 2:5-diketopiperazine is suspended in 540 ml. of absolute alcohol. The mixture is rapidly saturated with dry hydrogen chloride gas, with cooling in an ice bath, and solution becomes virtually complete as the reaction mixture subsequently is rapidly heated to boiling over the steam bath with shaking. Prolonged heating of the solution should be avoided in order to obviate the formation of excessive amounts of contaminating glycine ethyl ester hydrochloride, and undissolved material should be removed by rapid filtration through a hot funnel. The solution is then cooled to 0°, and after several hours the crystalline mass of glycylglycine ethyl ester hydrochloride (XXXVIII) is filtered over suction and washed with cold alcohol, and then with ether. The yield, after drying over sodalime, is about 80% of theory. M.p. = 182° d. (corr.). Recrystallization may be accomplished from hot alcohol.

6. Acylamino Acid Chlorides and Azides in Peptide Synthesis. *Principle.*

Although the ester condensation and diketopiperazine methods described above have proved useful for the synthesis of peptides in certain restricted instances, they nevertheless provided no general scheme whereby a desired amino acid could be placed in any position in the peptide chain. The early studies of both Curtius and Fischer are worthy of elaboration in this connection, for, although they did not provide the means whereby free peptides as such could be secured, the methods developed were later extensively employed for "inserting" the requisite amino acids into any position in a given peptide combination. Such methods involved the conversion of an acylamino acid (I) to the corresponding azide (II; $X = N_3$) or acid chloride (II; $X = Cl$) and subsequently condensing these reactive forms with the pertinent amino acid or peptide, or the corresponding ester derivative thereof. Reconstitution of the reactive acid chloride or azide group in the peptide derivative (III), so secured, then provided the basis for further elongation of the peptide chain in a comparable manner.

$$\text{RCO—NHCHR'CO}_2\text{H} \longrightarrow \text{RCO—NHCHR'COX} \xrightarrow{\text{NH}_2\text{CHR''CO—}} \text{RCO—NHCHR'CO—NHCHR''CO—}$$
$$\text{I} \qquad\qquad\qquad \text{II} \qquad\qquad\qquad\qquad\qquad\qquad \text{III}$$

Azide Method. The report of Fischer and Forneau (103) on the synthesis of glycylglycine from diketopiperazine was followed, one year later, by an announcement of Curtius (115) of a new method for combining amino acids in peptide linkage. This method, utilized for the preparation of the benzoyl derivatives of di-, tri-, and tetraglycine, was concerned with a stepwise synthesis of the pertinent acylated peptide from benzoylglycine (IV). Such a process involved a conversion of the latter compound to the corresponding hydrazide (VI) by the action of hydrazine on its ethyl ester derivative (V). Treatment of the hydrazide (VI) with nitrous acid then transformed it into the reactive azide (VII) which, in aqueous solution under the usual Schotten-Baumann (201) conditions, coupled readily with glycine or glycylglycine.

$$\text{C}_6\text{H}_5\text{CO—NHCH}_2\text{CO}_2\text{H} \xrightarrow[\text{Ag salt}]{\text{C}_2\text{H}_5\text{I}} \text{C}_6\text{H}_5\text{CO—NHCH}_2\text{CO}_2\text{Et} \xrightarrow{\text{NH}_2\text{NH}_2} \text{C}_6\text{H}_5\text{CO—NHCH}_2\text{CONHNH}_2$$
$$\text{IV} \qquad\qquad\qquad\qquad\qquad \text{V} \qquad\qquad\qquad\qquad\qquad \text{VI}$$

$$\xrightarrow{\text{HNO}_2} \text{C}_6\text{H}_5\text{CO—NHCH}_2\text{CON}_3 \xrightarrow[\text{H}_2\text{O, NaOH}]{\text{NH}_2\text{CH}_2\text{CO}_2\text{H}} \text{C}_6\text{H}_5\text{CO—NHCH}_2\text{CO—NHCH}_2\text{CO}_2\text{H}$$
$$\qquad\qquad\qquad \text{VII} \qquad\qquad\qquad\qquad\qquad\qquad \text{VIII}$$

Further elongation of the peptide chain was subsequently accomplished by a repetition of the entire process with the benzoyl dipeptide (VIII) so derived. Table 10–6 identifies the several peptide derivatives of glycine described by Curtius in this and later reports.

TABLE 10–6

Some Benzoylated Glycine Derivatives of the Curtius Group
(115, 117, 202)

Melting Point of Derivative, °C.

Compound	Free Acid	Ethyl Ester	Hydrazide	Azide
Benzoylglycine	187.5	60.5	162.5	98
Benzoyldiglycine	206.5	117	227–229	109–110
Benzoyltriglycine	215–216	173	245–250	162
Benzoyltetraglycine	235	213		
Benzoylpentaglycine	246–252		268–269	254–255
Benzoylhexaglycine	268	258–263		
Benzoylheptaglycine	274–277			

Some two years after his initial report, Curtius (203) completely described his syntheses of benzoylated peptide derivatives in a series of nine publications under the running title of "Verkettung von Amidosäuren." The syntheses, which utilized the coupling of azide derivatives with either amino acids or peptides in alkaline aqueous solution as previously, or with amino acid or peptide esters in chloroform solution, were extended to benzoylated peptides of alanine (116, 204), aspartic acid (118), isoserine (119), β-butyrine (119), γ-butyrine (205), phenylalanine (205), and urea (206). Of especial interest in this connection are the peptides of aspartic acid (118), since amide linkages implicating both the α- and its β-carboxyl groups were here involved. Such a synthesis, which resulted in the formation of a polycarboxylic acid (XV), is typified by

$$RN_3 + \underset{\underset{X}{CH_2CO_2H}}{\overset{}{NH_2CHCO_2H}} \xrightarrow[NaOH]{aqueous} \underset{\underset{XI}{CH_2CO_2H}}{\overset{}{RNHCHCO_2H}} \xrightarrow[Ag\ salt]{C_2H_5I\ on} \underset{\underset{XII}{CH_2CO_2Et}}{\overset{}{RNHCHCO_2Et}} \xrightarrow{NHNH_2}$$

$$\underset{\underset{XIII}{CH_2CONHNH_2}}{\overset{}{RNHCHCONHNH_2}} \xrightarrow{HNO_2} \underset{\underset{XIV}{CH_2CON_3}}{\overset{}{RNHCHCON_3}} \xrightarrow[aqueous\ NaOH]{aspartic\ acid} \underset{\underset{XV}{\underset{CH_2CO_2H}{\overset{}{CH_2CO—NHCHCO_2H}}}}{\overset{CH_2CO_2H}{RNHCHCO—NHCHCO_2H}}$$

where R equals $C_6H_5CO—NHCH_2CO—$.

Acid Chloride Method. One year after Curtius' first report (115) on the use of azides in peptide bond synthesis, Fischer and Otto (120, 121, 207) succeeded for the first time in preparing and using acid chlorides of acylated amino acids and peptides for the same purpose. The procedure employed may be exemplified with carboethoxyglycine (XVI) which, upon treatment with thionyl chloride at 35–40°, yielded an analytically impure acid chloride (XVII). Condensation of the latter compound with ethyl glycinate in chloroform or ether solution subsequently yielded the expected ethyl carboethoxyglycylglycinate (XVIII). Saponification of the ester with normal alkali at room temperature resulted in the corresponding free acid (XIX).

$$C_2H_5O_2C-NHCH_2CO_2H \xrightarrow{SOCl_2} C_2H_5O_2C-NHCH_2COCl \xrightarrow{NH_2CH_2CO_2C_2H_5}$$
$$\text{XVI} \qquad\qquad \text{XVII}$$

$$C_2H_5O_2C-NHCH_2CO-NHCH_2CO_2C_2H_5 \xrightarrow{NaOH} C_2H_5O_2C-NHCH_2CO-NHCH_2CO_2H$$
$$\text{XVIII} \qquad\qquad\qquad\qquad\qquad \text{XIX}$$

This method was used by the Fischer school for the preparation of a number of other carboethoxylated peptides, several of which are listed in Table 10–7.

TABLE 10–7

Some Carboethoxy Derivatives Prepared by the Fischer Group

Melting Point[a] of Derivative, °C.

Compound	Free Acid	Ethyl Ester	Amide	Ref.
Carboethoxy-DL-alanine	84	25	120–121	208
Carboethoxy-DL-alanylglycine	122	67.5	119	208
Carboethoxyglycine	75	27–28	101–103.5	121
Carboethoxyglycylglycine	140	87	183	103, 171
Carboethoxytriglycine	212–214	163–164	235	120
Carboethoxytetraglycine	–	235–236	275	120
Carboethoxyglycyl-DL-alanine	187.5–188.5	65.5–66.5	136.5–137.5	121

[a] Corrected values.

The striking resemblance of the carboethoxy group to an ethyl ester group of an aliphatic carboxylic acid led Fischer (120) to assume mistakenly that, like the latter, the former substituent would undergo simple saponification, in the presence of alkali, to the N-carboxyl group:

$$C_2H_5O_2C-NHCH_2CO-NHCH_2CO_2C_2H_5 \rightarrow HO_2C-NHCH_2CO-NHCH_2CO_2H + C_2H_5OH$$
$$\text{XX} \qquad\qquad\qquad\qquad \text{XXI}$$

That such an assumption had validity was confirmed in Fischer's mind by the finding that ethyl carboethoxyglycylglycinate (XX) and related compounds, when subjected to the action of alkali for several hours at 80°, yielded products whose elemental analyses were in complete agreement with N-carboxy peptides of the type (XXI) indicated above. Attempts to secure the free peptide from such compounds by removal of the N-carboxyl group as carbon dioxide were without success however, a factor which eventually compelled Fischer to abandon the method as a potential route to synthetic peptides. Discussion of this process by Fischer (209) was accompanied by a revealing statement that touched upon the brisk rivalry which prevailed between Curtius and himself: "Diese und ähnliche Verbindungen standen den freien Polypeptiden schon näher, als die Benzoylderivate von Curtius, da sie nur das eine Carboxyl als fremden Bestandteil enthielten. Aber die Hoffnung dieses als Kohlensäure abspalten zu können, wie man es nach dem Verhalten der Carbaminsäure und ähnlicher Substanzen erwarten musste, einen anderen Weg eingeschlagen, um die freien Polypeptide zu gewinnen."[43]

In view of the above, it is somewhat ironical that Wessely and Kemm (210), some twenty years later, presented unequivocal evidence that the "glycylglycine carbamino acid" of Fischer was in actuality carbonyl-bis-glycine (XXII). The latter compound, secured upon saponification of the ethyl carbonyl-bis-glycinate (XXIII) derived in turn from the action of phosgene on glycine ethyl ester, was shown to be identical with the product of alkali-treated ethyl carboethoxyglycylglycinate (XXIV). Carbonyl-bis-glycine (XXII) also resulted from the alkaline cleavage of hydantoin-3-acetic acid (XXV), while the action of ammonia on the latter compound produced carbonyl-bis-glycinamide (XXVI). As a consequence of these

$$\begin{array}{c}\text{NHCH}_2\text{CO}_2\text{H}\\ \text{CO}\\ \text{NHCH}_2\text{CO}_2\text{H}\end{array} \underset{\text{saponification}}{\overset{\text{esterification}}{\rightleftarrows}} \begin{array}{c}\text{NHCH}_2\text{CO}_2\text{C}_2\text{H}_5\\ \text{CO}\\ \text{NHCH}_2\text{CO}_2\text{C}_2\text{H}_5\end{array}$$

XXII XXIII

$$\text{C}_2\text{H}_5\text{O}_2\text{C—NHCH}_2\text{CO—NHCH}_2\text{CO}_2\text{C}_2\text{H}_5$$
XXIV

$$\begin{array}{c}\text{NH—CO}\\ | \diagdown\text{NCH}_2\text{CO}_2\text{H}\\ \text{CH}_2\text{—CO}\end{array} \xrightarrow{\text{ammonia}} \begin{array}{c}\text{NHCH}_2\text{CONH}_2\\ \text{CO}\\ \text{NHCH}_2\text{CONH}_2\end{array}$$

XXV XXVI

findings, Wessely and Kemm offered the suggestion that the alkaline cleavage of ethyl carboethoxyglycylglycinate (XXIV) proceeded through the hydantoin (XXV) as a transitory intermediate. A later report by Wessely, Kemm, and Mayer (211) extended these studies to several carbomethoxylated dipeptides.

Evaluation of the Method. Early utilization of the azide and acid chloride procedures for the synthesis of peptides suffered by virtue of the unavailability of acyl substituents which could be removed without accompanying breakdown of the labile peptide molecule. A lapse of some twenty years followed the introduction of these procedures before the development of suitable blocking substituents, as the toluenesulfonyl (127) and carbobenzoxy (128) groups, permitted their general use in peptide chemistry. In fact, during the highly productive period of 1932 to 1950, when large numbers of synthetic peptides were prepared for enzyme specificity studies (129–133), the azide and acid chloride methods were utilized almost exclusively in synthetic peptide procedures involving removable acyl substituents. The innovation of a host of auxiliary condensation procedures after 1949, however, has resulted in a markedly decreased employment of the relatively tedious acid chloride procedure. Certain inherent advantages of azides, on the other hand, resulted in their continued and widespread use for coupling purposes. The relative merits and disadvantages of the various condensation procedures will be discussed more fully below (Sections 10–26 to 10–38).

7. The α-Haloacyl Halide and Related Methods. *Principle.* A classical preparation of α-amino acids (II) involves the reaction of the requisite α-chloro (I; X = Cl) or α-bromo acid (I; X = Br) with an excess of alcoholic or aqueous ammonia, as in the following (Chapters 8 and 42):

$$X-CHRCO_2H \xrightarrow{NH_3} NH_2-CHRCO_2H$$
$$\text{I} \qquad\qquad\qquad \text{II}$$

Treatment of the same α-halo acid (III) with phosphorus pentachloride or thionyl chloride converts it to the corresponding acid chloride (IV). The latter compound may then be coupled with a free amino acid or peptide in alkaline aqueous solution, or with their respective ester derivatives in chloroform or ether solution. The α-haloacylamino acid (VII) or peptide is obtained upon neutralization of the alkali salt (V), where the former solvent system is employed, or in the case of the latter, upon saponification of the ester derivative (VI). Subsequent ammonolysis of the α-haloacyl compound (VII) results in the formation of the desired peptide (VIII).

$$X-CHRCO_2H \xrightarrow{PCl_5} X-CHRCOCl \xrightarrow[\text{aq. NaOH}]{NH_2CHR'CO_2H} X-CHRCO-NHCHR'CO_2Na$$
$$\text{III} \qquad\qquad \text{IV} \qquad\qquad\qquad\qquad \text{V}$$

$$\Big\downarrow {NH_2CHR'CO_2Et \atop CHCl_3 \text{ or } (C_2H_5)_2O} \qquad\qquad \Big\downarrow HCl$$

$$X-CHRCO-NHCHR'CO_2Et \xrightarrow{NaOH} X-CHRCO-NHCHR'CO_2H \xrightarrow{NH_3} NH_2-CHRCO-NHCHR'CO_2H$$
$$\text{VI} \qquad\qquad\qquad\qquad \text{VII} \qquad\qquad\qquad\qquad \text{VIII}$$

If higher polypeptides are desired, the α-haloacylamino acid (IX) derived above may be converted to the corresponding acid chloride (X) by treatment with phosphorus pentachloride in acetyl chloride solution, and the coupling with another amino acid, peptide, or ester derivative thereof, effected as above. Alternatively, the peptide (XII) secured upon amination of (IX) might be converted to its respective α-haloacyl derivative (XIII) by reaction with an α-haloacyl halide in alkaline solution. Ammonolysis of (XI) and (XIII) then yields the next higher peptide:

$$\text{X—CHRCO—NHCHR}^1\text{CO}_2\text{H} \xrightarrow[\text{CH}_3\text{COCl}]{\text{PCl}_5} \text{X—CHRCO—NHCHR}^1\text{COCl}$$
$$\text{IX} \qquad\qquad\qquad\qquad\qquad\qquad \text{X}$$

$$\downarrow \text{NH}_2\text{CHR}^2\text{CO}_2\text{H}, \text{aq. NaOH}$$

$$\text{X—CHRCO—NHCHR}^1\text{CO—NHCHR}^2\text{CO}_2\text{H} \xrightarrow{\text{NH}_3}$$
$$\text{XI}$$

$$\text{TRIPEPTIDE}$$

$$\text{NH}_3 \downarrow \qquad\qquad\qquad\qquad\qquad \uparrow \text{NH}_3$$

$$\text{NH}_2\text{—CHRCO—NHCHR}^1\text{CO}_2\text{H} \xrightarrow[\text{aq. NaOH}]{\text{X—CHR}^2\text{COCl}}$$
$$\text{XII}$$

$$\text{X—CHR}^2\text{CO—NHCHRCO—NHCHR}^1\text{CO}_2\text{H}$$
$$\text{XIII}$$

Use of this scheme permits the stepwise construction of a peptide by the addition of residues to either the N-terminal end of an amino acid or peptide or the C-terminal end of their pertinent α-haloacyl derivatives.

Development of the α-Haloacyl Method. This ingenious scheme, developed as a result of the efforts of Emil Fischer and his school, was the basis of the preparation of most of the peptides studied during the first three decades of the present century and may, without reservation, be considered the most noteworthy of Fischer's numerous achievements in the field of protein chemistry. Development of the method as a general route to synthetic peptides was prompted by the lack of success experienced with the aforementioned carboethoxy method (Section 10-6). The method as initially approached by Fischer, in collaboration with Otto (121), employed the device of starting with the α-haloacyl substituent as a precursor to the N-terminal amino acid of the peptide chain rather than with the corresponding α-amino acid *per se*. Thus treatment of glycylglycine ethyl ester (XV) with chloroacetyl chloride (XIV) in chloroform solution yielded the acylated dipeptide ester (XVI) which, upon saponification with aklali followed by warming the chloroacetylglycylglycine (XVII) so derived with a ten-fold volume of 25% ammonia for 1 hour at 100°, proceeded with the formation of diglycylglycine (XVIII).

$$\text{Cl—CH}_2\text{COCl} + \text{NH}_2\text{CH}_2\text{CO—NHCH}_2\text{CO}_2\text{Et} \rightarrow \text{Cl—CH}_2\text{CO—NHCH}_2\text{CO—NHCH}_2\text{CO}_2\text{Et} \rightarrow$$
$$\text{XIV} \qquad\qquad \text{XV} \qquad\qquad\qquad\qquad\qquad \text{XVI}$$

$$\text{Cl—CH}_2\text{CO—NHCH}_2\text{CO—NHCH}_2\text{CO}_2\text{H} \rightarrow \text{NH}_2\text{CH}_2\text{CO—NHCH}_2\text{CO—NHCH}_2\text{CO}_2\text{H}$$
$$\text{XVII} \qquad\qquad\qquad\qquad\qquad \text{XVIII}$$

Extension of the above studies by Fischer (212), shortly thereafter, to the use of α-bromopropionyl bromide and α-bromoisocaproyl chloride in lieu of (XIV), resulted in the production of DL-alanylglycylglycine and DL-leucylglycylglycine, respectively. The various halogenated acyl halides which Fischer utilized for the synthesis of α-haloacylamino acids, together with the N-terminal amino acid residues to which they were subsequently transformed upon treatment with ammonia, are listed below:

Bromoacetyl bromide	Glycyl-
Chloroacetyl chloride	Glycyl-
α-Bromopropionyl bromide (or chloride)	Alanyl-
α-Bromobutyryl chloride	α-Aminobutyryl-
α-Bromoisovaleryl chloride	Valyl-
α-Bromoisocaproyl chloride	Leucyl-
α-Bromo-β-phenylpropionyl chloride	Phenylalanyl-
α,δ-Dibromovaleryl chloride	Prolyl-

An impressive array of well-defined peptides were synthesized by the Fischer group through the intermediate α-halo acids, most of which are listed in Table 10–8.

TABLE 10–8

Some Peptides of the Fischer School Obtained upon Ammonolysis of α-Halogen Acid Intermediates

α-Halo Acid Precursor		Product of Ammonolysis (Peptide)[a]			
Compound	M.P. (corr.), °C.	$[α]_D$, deg.	Temp., °C.	Concn.	Ref.
Chloroacetyl-		Glycyl-			
DL-ala·OH	125–127	–	–	–	213
L-ala·OH	93.5–94.5	–50	20	8.7%, H_2O	214
L-ala·gly·OH	178	–64.3	20	4.4%, H_2O	215
L-ala·gly·L-tyr·OH	206–207	+4.0	20	10%, H_2O	215
L-ala·L-tyr·OH	236	–4.8	20	4.3%, H_2O	216
DL-aminostearic acid	103–107	–	–	–	217
L-(asp-NH$_2$)·OH	148–149	–6.4	20	7%, H_2O	143
L-asp·OH	142–143	+11.1	20	10%, H_2O	218
L-(asp-NH$_2$)·L-leu·OH	167	–46.8	20	4.8%, H_2O	144
DL-(asp-gly)·gly·OH	142–143	–	–	–	218
L-cystine (mono)	185–190	–	–	–	219
3:5-diiodo-L-tyr·OH	218–221	+51.2	20	4%, 25%. NH$_4$OH	220
L-glu·OH	143	–6.3	20	10%, H_2O	221
DL-glu·OH	120–123	–	–	–	221
L-(glu-gly)·gly·OH	173	<+1	20	10%, 20% HCl	221
gly·gly·OH	178–180	–	–	–	213; 121
gly·gly·gly·OH	224	–	–	–	213

TABLE 10-8 (*continued*)

α-Halo Acid Precursor		Product of Ammonolysis (Peptide)[a]			
Compound	M.P. (corr.), °C.	$[\alpha]_D$, deg.	Temp., °C.	Concn.	Ref.
Chloroacetyl-		Glycyl-			
gly·gly·gly·gly·OH	256	–	–	–	213
gly·DL-phe·OH	151–152	–	–	–	222
DL-leu·OH	142	–	–	–	187
L-leu·OH	136	–35.1	20	4.2%, H_2O	223
DL-phe·OH	130–131	–	–	–	222
L-phe·OH	123–126	+42.0	20	1.8%, H_2O	224
DL-ser·OH	122–123	–	–	–	225
L-try·OH	159	+21.6	20	10%, N HCl	226
L-tyr·OH	155–156	–	–	–	213
L-tyr·gly·OH	188–190	0	20	2.5%, H_2O	227
L-val·OH	113–115	–19.7	20	10%, H_2O	185
L-cystine (di)	134.5–136.5	–	–	–	228
DL-α-Bromopropionyl-		DL-Alanyl-			
gly·OH	104	–	–	–	187
gly·gly·OH	166–167	–	–	–	212
gly·gly·gly·OH	180	–	–	–	215
DL-leu·OH (A)	147–150	–	–	–	187
DL-leu·OH (B)	113–118	–	–	–	187
D-α-Bromopropionyl-		L-Alanyl-			
L-ala·OH	175	–	–	–	214
D-ala·OH	170	+68.7	20	8%, H_2O	196
gly·OH	122–123	+50.3	18	10%, H_2O	215
gly·gly·OH	172	+31.4	20	10%, H_2O	215
gly·gly·gly·OH	189.5	+27.0	20	3.2%, H_2O	216
3:5-diiodo-L-tyr·OH	217.3	+62.9	20	8%, 25% NH_4OH	216
gly·L-tyr·OH	157	+41.9	20	4.5%, H_2O	229
L-leu·OH	50–51	–17.2	20	8.8%, H_2O	230
L-tyr·OH	65–72	+18.7	20	6.2%, H_2O	226
L-tyr·OH	165.2	+43.1	20	2%, H_2O	216
L-val·OH	180	–5.9	20	10%, H_2O	185
L-α-Bromopropionyl-		D-Alanyl-			
L-ala·OH	165	–68.5	20	8.7%, H_2O	196
DL-α-Bromoisocaproyl-		DL-Leucyl-			
DL-ala·gly·OH (A)	157	–	–	–	187
DL-ala·gly·OH (B)	oil	–	–	–	187

TABLE 10–8 (continued)

α-Halo Acid Precursor		Product of Ammonolysis (Peptide)[a]			
Compound	M.P. (corr.), °C.	$[\alpha]_D$, deg.	Temp., °C.	Concn.	Ref.
DL-α-Bromoisocaproyl-		DL-Leucyl-			
gly·OH	135	–	–	–	187
gly·gly·OH	144–145	–	–	–	212
(gly)$_2$·gly·OH	168	–	–	–	194
(gly)$_3$·gly·OH	218	–	–	–	156
(gly)$_4$·gly·OH	237	–	–	–	156
(gly)$_5$·gly·OH	250	–	–	–	156
(gly)$_6$·gly·OH	256–259	–	–	–	157
(gly)$_8$·gly·OH	288	–	–	–	157
(gly)$_{10}$·gly·OH	293	–	–	–	157
D-α-Bromoisocaproyl-		L-Leucyl-			
L-ala·OH	101–103	+23.5	20	4.8%, MeOH	157
L-(asp-NH$_2$)·OH	146–148	+17.8	20	5.4%, H$_2$O	144
L-asp·OH	150	+27.1	18	6.2%, H$_2$O	218
L-cystine (mono)	194	–	–	–	219
gly·OH	85–86	+86.0	20	8.6%, H$_2$O	157
L-glu·OH	108–109	+10.5	20	8.2%, N HCl	229
gly·L-ala·OH	118	+20.3	20	10%, H$_2$O	223
gly·L-asp·OH	119–120	+55.3	20	5.2%, H$_2$O	218
(gly)$_2$·gly·OH	168–169	+45.9	20	9.6%, H$_2$O	157
(gly)$_6$·gly·OH	>246	+6.3	20	6%, H$_2$O + 1 eq. NaOH	230
(gly)$_8$·gly·OH	300	–	–	–	230
(gly)$_3$·L-leu·OH	182	+21.3	20	2.5%, H$_2$O	223
(gly)$_3$·L-leu·(gly)$_8$·gly·OH	305	–	–	–	230
(gly)$_3$·L-leu·(gly)$_3$·L-leu·(gly)$_8$·gly·OH	310	–	–	–	230
gly·L-try·OH	90–98	+32.3	20	8.1%, N HCl	226
(gly)$_3$·L-tyr·OH	220	+36.5	20	5%, H$_2$O	229
L-his·OH	118	+32.1	18	5%, H$_2$O	231
D-leu·OH	128	+53.0	20	10%, 0.5N NaOH	232
L-leu·OH	149	–13.4	20	4.3%, N NaOH	157
L-try·OH	118	+4.5	20	7.2%, N HCl	226
L-tyr·OH	oil	+10.4	20	2%, H$_2$O	216
L-val·OH	150–151	+18.0	20	10.4%, H$_2$O	185
Di-D-α-bromoisocaproyl-		Di-L-leucyl-			
L-cystine	121–123	–136.6	20	2.5%, N HCl	219

TABLE 10-8 (continued)

α-Halo Acid Precursor		Product of Ammonolysis (Peptide)[a]			
Compound	M.P. (corr.), °C.	$[\alpha]_D$, deg.	Temp., °C.	Concn.	Ref.
L-α-Bromoisocaproyl-		D-Leucyl-			
L-(asp-NH₂)·OH	178	−53.8	20	5%, H₂O	143, 144
D-leu·OH	149	+13.2	20	9%, N NaOH	232
L-leu·OH	128	−68.0	20	9.4%, N HCl	232
DL-α-Bromobutyryl-		DL-α-Aminobutyryl-			
DL-butyrine (A)	133	−	−	−	187
DL-butyrine (B)	95	−	−	−	187
gly·OH	101–105	−	−	−	187
DL-Phenylbromoacetyl-		DL-Phenylglycyl-			
DL-ala·OH (A)	170–171	−	−	−	187
DL-ala·OH (B)	148–151	−	−	−	187
gly·OH	106–109	−	−	−	187
DL-α-Bromo-β-phenylpropionyl-		DL-Phenylalanyl-			
gly·gly·OH	157–158	−	−	−	233
DL-leu·OH (A)	166.5	−	−	−	234
DL-leu·OH (B)	148	−	−	−	234
D-α-Bromo-β-phenylpropionyl-		L-Phenylalanyl-			
gly·OH	145–146	+54.2	20	2.4%, H₂O	224
DL-α-Bromoisovaleryl-		DL-Valyl-			
DL-ala·OH (A)	165–168	−	−	−	235
DL-ala·OH (B)	129–132	−	−	−	235
gly·OH	139–141	−	−	−	235
D-α-Bromoisovaleryl-		L-Valyl-			
gly·OH	119–120	+93.6	20	10.3%, H₂O	185, 236
L-α-Bromoisovaleryl-		D-Valyl-			
L-val·OH	163–165	−74.0	20	10%, H₂O	185

[a] Ammonolysis in these cases does not affect the nature of the remainder of the peptide as given in the first column. Exceptions to this rule, e.g., the ammonolysis of α-bromoisocaproylproline, are described in the text.

Diastereomeric mixtures of peptides unless separated (i.e., A and B) have been omitted from this table.

Perhaps no more vivid illustration of the combination of the α-haloacyl method with the earlier ester condensation (Section 10–4) and diketopiperazine (Section 10–5) methods can be offered than by Fischer's remarkable synthesis (230), in 1907, of the octadecapeptide, L-leucyl-triglycyl-L-leucyl-triglycyl-L-leucyl-octaglycylglycine (XXI). Thus the hydrolysis of glycine anhydride resulted in glycylglycine (diketopiperazine method) which, when coupled in alkaline solution with chloroacetyl chloride (α-haloacyl method) followed by treatment with ammonia, yielded the tripeptide diglycylglycine. Condensation of the ester of the tripeptide by heating at 100° (ester condensation method), succeeded by saponification of the hexapeptide ester isolated from the polymeric mixture, gave rise to the hexapeptide pentaglycylglycine. α-Bromoisocaproyl chloride was then coupled with diglycylglycine, yielding α-bromoisocaproyldiglycylglycine. The acid chloride of the latter compound was condensed with the hexapeptide of glycine in alkaline solution to yield a coupling product which was, in turn, converted to leucyl-octaglycylglycine (XIX) upon amination in liquid ammonia.

$$NH_2-CH(C_4H_9)CO-(NHCH_2CO)_8-NHCH_2CO_2H$$
$$\text{XIX}$$

In like manner, the decapeptide was condensed with α-bromoisocaproyldiglycylglycine and the product converted upon ammonolysis to the tetradecapeptide leucyltriglycylleucyloctaglycylglycine (XX). Repetition of the

$$NH_2-CH(C_4H_9)CO-(NHCH_2CO)_3-NHCH(C_4H_9)CO-(NHCH_2CO)_8-NHCH_2CO_2H$$
$$\text{XX}$$

reaction sequence subsequent to the interaction of (XX) with α-bromoisocaproyldiglycylglycine ultimately led to the desired octadecapeptide (XXI). The eighteen-membered polypeptide so secured resembled a

$$\begin{array}{ccc}
H_3C\diagdown\!\!\diagup CH_3 & H_3C\diagdown\!\!\diagup CH_3 & H_3C\diagdown\!\!\diagup CH_3 \\
CH & CH & CH \\
| & | & | \\
CH_2 & CH_2 & CH_2 \\
| & | & | \\
\end{array}$$
$$NH_2CHCO-(NHCH_2CO)_3-NHCHCO-(NHCH_2CO)_3-NHCHCO-(NHCH_2CO)_8-NHCH_2CO_2H$$
$$\text{XXI}$$

protein in that it exhibited a positive biuret reaction and was readily "salted out" of solution. Some nine years after this notable achievement, Abderhalden and Fodor (158) utilized these same general procedures to effect the synthesis of a nonadecapeptide, the longest synthetic polypeptide recorded to date.

The synthesis of prolyl peptides from the corresponding α,δ-dibromovaleryl intermediates deserves special attention. Ammonolysis of the latter compounds does not give rise to the respective ornithyl derivatives, as would be anticipated from the interaction of both halogen atoms with ammonia, but proceeds instead with the amination of only one halogen atom followed by an intramolecular cyclization to the pyrrolidine ring. Such a reaction

CHEMICAL PROCEDURES FOR SYNTHESIS OF PEPTIDES

might be considered akin to that involved in the preparation of proline by ammonolysis of the intermediate α,δ-dihalo-, α-amino-δ-halo-, or α-halo-δ-aminovaleric acids by Willstätter (237), Fischer (238), and later workers (Chapter 35). Its more specific application to the synthesis of prolylalanine (XXVI), via the transitory intermediates (XXV) and (XXVII), is depicted in the following (239):

$$\text{Br—CH}_2\text{CH}_2\text{CH}_2\text{CH(Br)COCl} + \text{NH}_2\text{CH(CH}_3\text{)CO}_2\text{H} \xrightarrow[\text{NaOH}]{\text{aq.}} \text{Br—CH}_2\text{CH}_2\text{CH}_2\text{CH(Br)CO—NHCH(CH}_3\text{)CO}_2\text{H}$$

XXII   XXIII   XXIV

$$\begin{bmatrix}\text{Br} & \text{NH}_2 & \text{CH}_3 \\ \text{CH}_2\text{CH}_2\text{CH}_2\text{CHCO—NHCHCO}_2\text{H}\end{bmatrix} \rightarrow \begin{bmatrix}\text{—NH} & \text{CH}_3 \\ \text{CH}_2\text{CH}_2\text{CH}_2\text{CHCO—NHCHCO}_2\text{H}\end{bmatrix} \leftarrow \begin{bmatrix}\text{NH}_2 & \text{Br} & \text{CH}_3 \\ \text{CH}_2\text{CH}_2\text{CH}_2\text{CHCO—NHCHCO}_2\text{H}\end{bmatrix}$$

XXV   XXVI   XXVII

Essentially the same procedure has since been employed for the preparation of several prolyl peptides (168, 240–242).

That the ammonolysis of an α-haloacyl acid does not invariably yield the expected peptide was strikingly demonstrated in the attempt by Fischer and Reif (64) to prepare leucylproline by the action of ammonia on α-bromoisocaproylproline (XXXI). Although an earlier study (243) had presumably indicated that such reaction produced the desired dipeptide, closer scrutiny of the reaction product (XXVIII) revealed that it readily lost half of its nitrogen in the form of ammonia (XXIX) at the melting point, a property

$$\underset{\text{XXVIII}}{\text{C}_{11}\text{H}_{20}\text{O}_3\text{N}_2} \rightarrow \underset{\text{XXIX}}{\text{NH}_3} + \underset{\text{XXX}}{\text{C}_{11}\text{H}_{17}\text{O}_3\text{N}}$$

which was not characteristic of peptides previously studied. Further study suggested that the decomposition product (XXX) was the lactone of α-hydroxyisocaproylproline (XXXIII), which could be alternatively obtained by the successive treatment of (XXVIII) first with alkali, then with dilute acid. These observations pointed to the constitution of (XXVIII) as that of an α-hydroxyisocaproylproline amide (XXXII). The above sequence of events is given in the following:

$$\begin{array}{c}\text{CH}_3 \quad \text{Br} \qquad \text{CH}_2\text{—CH}_2 \\ \text{CHCH}_2\text{CHCO—NH} \qquad | \\ \text{CH}_3 \qquad \text{HO}_2\text{C—CH—CH}_2\end{array} \xrightarrow{\text{NH}_3} \begin{array}{c}\text{CH}_3 \quad \text{OH} \qquad \text{CH}_2\text{—CH}_2 \\ \text{CHCH}_2\text{CHCO—NH} \qquad | \\ \text{CH}_3 \qquad \text{H}_2\text{NOC—CH—CH}_2\end{array} \rightarrow \begin{array}{c}\text{CH}_3 \qquad\qquad \text{CH}_2\text{—CH}_2 \\ \text{CHCH}_2\text{CHCO—NH} \qquad | \\ \text{CH}_3 \quad \text{O—OC—CH—CH}_2\end{array}$$

XXXI   XXXII   XXXIII

A comparable situation was later found to obtain upon the treatment of α-bromoisocaproyl-N-phenylglycine with ammonia (244).

Another instance in which the desired product could not be successfully isolated after the ammonolysis stage involved the α-halosuccinylamino acids. When subjected to the action of ammonia, these compounds eliminated hydrogen halide with concomitant formation of the corresponding fumaryl derivatives. In this manner, for example, fumaryl-dialanine (XXXV) was derived from chlorosuccinyldialanine (XXXIV). However, since fumaryl derivatives readily add ammonia across the double bond, heating of the former derivative with concentrated aqueous ammonia subsequently yielded the corresponding aspartyl peptide (XXXVI) (143).

$$\underset{\underset{\text{XXXIV}}{CH_2CO-NHCH(CH_3)CO_2H}}{Cl-CHCO-NHCH(CH_3)CO_2H} \xrightarrow{NH_3} \underset{\underset{\text{XXXV}}{CHCO-NHCH(CH_3)CO_2H}}{\overset{NH_3}{\underset{\|}{CHCO-NHCH(CH_3)CO_2H}}} \xrightarrow[\Delta]{NH_3} \underset{\underset{\text{XXXVI}}{CH_2CO-NHCH(CH_3)CO_2H}}{NH_2-CHCO-NHCH(CH_3)CO_2H}$$

Although extension of this reaction to fumaryl-monoglycine (XXXVII) gave the anticipated aspartyl derivative (XXXVIII or XXXIX), uncertainty existed with regard to the α or β position of the glycine residue. Recent reinvestigation of the constitution of this product by Liwschitz and Zilkha (245) established its identity as β-DL-aspartylglycine (XXXIX). As in the

$$\underset{\underset{\text{XXXVII}}{CHCO_2H}}{\overset{NH_3}{\underset{\|}{CHCO-NHCH_2CO_2H}}} \xrightarrow{} \underset{\underset{\text{XXXVIII}}{CH_2CO_2H}}{NH_2CHCO-NHCH_2CO_2H} \quad \text{or} \quad \underset{\underset{\text{XXXIX}}{NH_2CHCO_2H}}{CH_2CO-NHCH_2CO_2H}$$

case of α-halosuccinylamino acids, the ammonolysis of α-bromo-β-phenyl-propionylglycine (XL) proceeds, to large extent, with the elimination of hydrogen halide to give cinnamoylglycine (XLI) in addition to the desired dipeptide (XLII) (234).

$$\underset{\text{XL}}{C_6H_5CH_2CH(Br)CO-NHCH_2CO_2H} \rightarrow$$

$$\underset{\text{XLI}}{C_6H_5CH=CHCO-NHCH_2CO_2H} + \underset{\text{XLII}}{C_6H_5CH_2CH(NH_2)CO-NHCH_2CO_2H}$$

α-Azidoacyl Method. As an alternative method to the use of ammonia for the substitution of the α-halogen group with an amino moiety, the technique involving reduction of α-azidoacyl intermediates deserves brief mention. This method, as devised by Bertho and Maier (246), involved the initial replacement of the α-halogen moiety with an azido group by treatment of the halogenated peptide ester (XLIII) with sodium azide. Conversion of the azidoacyl intermediate (XLIV) to the corresponding amino compound (XLV) was effected via a catalytic reduction of the azido group. Subsequent saponification of the peptide ester (XLV) so derived then led to the free peptide (XLVI):

$$\underset{\text{XLIII}}{Br-CHRCO-NHCHR'CO_2Et} \xrightarrow{NaN_3} \underset{\text{XLIV}}{N_3-CHRCO-NHCHR'CO_2Et} \xrightarrow{H_2}$$

$$\underset{\text{XLV}}{NH_2-CHRCO-NHCHR'CO_2Et} \xrightarrow{NaOH} \underset{\text{XLVI}}{NH_2-CHRCO-NHCHR'CO_2H}$$

Alternatively, the requisite α-azidoacyl intermediate (L) could be formed by the reaction of an α-azidoacyl halide (XLIX) with an amino acid in alkaline solution, according to the following scheme of Freudenberg, Eichel, and Leutert (247):

$$\underset{\text{XLVII}}{\text{Cl—CHRCO}_2\text{H}} \xrightarrow{\text{NaN}_3} \underset{\text{XLVIII}}{\text{N}_3\text{—CHRCO}_2\text{H}} \longrightarrow \underset{\text{XLIX}}{\text{N}_3\text{—CHRCOCl}} \xrightarrow[\text{aq. NaOH}]{\text{NH}_2\text{CHR'CO}_2\text{H}}$$

$$\underset{\text{L}}{\text{N}_3\text{—CHRCO—NHCHR'CO}_2\text{H}} \xrightarrow{\text{reduction}} \underset{\text{LI}}{\text{NH}_2\text{—CHRCO—NHCHR'CO}_2\text{H}}$$

This method has proved of some value in those instances where the use of aqueous ammonia on the halogenated molecule failed to effect the formation of the free peptide. However, reliance upon α-halo intermediates as precursors for the corresponding α-azido derivatives has made the method of limited general applicability.

Stereoisomerism. The synthesis of optically active peptides with N-terminal glycine residues, e.g., glycyl-L-tyrosine, afforded Fischer no stereochemical difficulties since the α-haloacetyl substituent of the coupling product, secured via the reaction of chloroacetyl chloride with an optically active amino acid, was converted to the non-asymmetric glycine residue upon amination. Details for the preparation of glycyl-L-serine by way of this route are given in procedure 10-4. However, the preparation of stereochemically defined peptides from intermediates wherein the α-halo substituent has an α-center of asymmetry, such as the α-bromopropionyl or α-bromoisocaproyl radicals, was exceedingly more complex. Thus the halogenation of a fatty acid through substitution of one of the α-hydrogen atoms leads to a racemic compound the separation of whose isomers is quite tedious. Inasmuch as the α-haloacyl substituent of the α-haloacylamino acid intermediates was derived from such racemic compounds, the ammonolysis step yielded peptides which were diastereomeric mixtures by virtue of the formation of an N-terminal DL-amino acid residue. Fischer initially attacked the problem by coupling the racemic α-haloacyl radical with an optically active amino acid. Fractionation of the epimeric coupling product, followed by ammonolysis of each of the optically active α-haloacylamino acids so derived, then resulted in the corresponding optically active peptides. The L- and D-leucyl-L-asparagines could be so secured (144). However, such method was fraught with difficulty since the solubilities of most diastereomers were generally so similar as to make facile separation infeasible. The degree of homogeneity of many of the earlier peptides described by Fischer, e.g., leucyl-L-tyrosine (213), is consequently open to question.

The lack of promise shown by fractionation procedures for isolating optically homogeneous peptides from their epimeric mixtures led to a search for alternative methods. The more successful of these methods involved the initial employment of optically active halogenated acids, procured via the action of nitrosyl halide on optically active amino acids. As only the optical forms of the naturally occurring amino acids were then available, Fischer (157) soon made the disappointing discovery that the N-terminal amino acid residue of the peptide ultimately derived from such α-halo acids is of a configuration opposite to that of the parent amino acid (see Section 2-23). Thus, owing to the occurrence of a Walden inversion during some stage of the procedure, peptides which incorporated the antipodes of naturally occurring amino acids as the N-terminal residues could be prepared. This state of affairs was hardly satisfactory, however, and it compelled Fischer to prepare the optical antipodes of these natural forms through resolution of the racemic amino acids (Chapter 9).

The above scheme may be readily illustrated by the preparation of L-alanyl-L-valine (LVI) (185). This scheme involves the initial conversion of unnatural D-alanine (LII) to D-α-bromopropionic acid (LIII) by the action of nitrosyl bromide. Subsequent conversion of the active α-halo acid to the corresponding acid chloride (LIV), followed by condensation of the latter with L-valine, then yields D-α-bromopropionyl-L-valine (LV). Ammonolysis of this compound proceeds with Walden inversion and thereby leads to a peptide (LVI) whose N-terminal amino acid residue is of a configuration opposite to that of the precursor α-haloacyl substituent. The sequence of events for this specific case is

$$NH_2CH(CH_3)CO_2H \xrightarrow{NOBr} BrCH(CH_3)CO_2H \xrightarrow{PCl_5} BrCH(CH_3)COCl$$

D-alanine   D-Bromopropionic acid   D-Bromopropionyl chloride

LII   LIII   LIV

↓ L-valine, alkaline solution

$$BrCH(CH_3)CO-NHCH(C_3H_7)CO_2H \xrightarrow{NH_3} NH_2CH(CH_3)CO-NHCH(C_3H_7)CO_2H$$

D-Bromopropionyl-L-valine   L-Alanyl-L-valine

LV   LVI

In connection with the above, it is of interest to note that Fischer (157, 208) assumed that the final amination step proceeded with retention of configuration, whereas the inversion presumably occurred during the nitrosyl bromide treatment. Freudenberg and Märkert (248) subsequently indicated the essential fallacy of this assumption in their demonstration that the transformation of L-alanine to the corresponding α-bromopropionic acid analog proceeds with retention of configuration, a conclusion which was later reinforced by kinetic studies (249) (see Chapter 2-26). Whether the inversion occurred during the initial or the final step of the reaction sequence did not, however, alter the fact that the synthesis of peptides of the L-series required for the most part α-halo acids derived from D-amino acids. Table 10-8 includes the correct configurational designation of most of the optically active α-haloacylamino acids synthesized by Fischer and his co-workers as well as the peptides derived therefrom.

The condensation of racemic α-haloacyl halides with racemic amino acids or peptides leads to even greater complications than condensations which involve optically active reactants solely, in that the former results in the formation of a mixture of diastereoisomeric racemates, the total number of stereoisomers in such mixture being equal to 2^n, where n refers to the number of asymmetric centers. Thus α-haloacylamino acids which contain two centers of asymmetry may exist as four stereomers or two racemic diastereoisomeric pairs. These are the L-D, D-L, and the L-L, D-D racemates, as illustrated by the α-bromoisovalerylvalines below:

D-α-Bromoisovaleryl-D-valine	D-α-Bromosiovaleryl-L-valine
L-α-Bromoisovaleryl-L-valine	L-α-Bromoisovaleryl-D-valine
Racemate A	Racemate B

Owing to a Walden inversion, the peptides prepared by amination of the corresponding α-halo intermediates assume the constitution

L-Valyl-D-valine	L-Valyl-L-valine
D-Valyl-L-valine	D-Valyl-D-valine
Racemate A	Racemate B

Advantage may sometimes be taken of the differences in solubility properties either of the racemic diastereomeric peptides so secured, or of the precursor α-haloacyl intermediates, to accomplish their separation. Such an approach was successfully employed by Fischer and his associates for the fractionation of the racemic leucylphenylalanines (222), alanylleucines (187), leucylisoserines (187) and valylalanines (235), among others (Table 10–8). Fischer termed the individual racemates of each diastereoisomeric mixture as the A or the B forms, dependent upon their relative solubilities. However, it should be noted that the solubility differences in numerous other instances were not sufficiently divergent to permit a similar separation. Added to this difficulty was the fact that, even in the event of successful separation, the stereochemical identification of each diastereomeric pair was unknown in the absence of other data. Although such identification may be made through the tedious process of total synthesis of the peptide using optically active starting materials and unequivocal techniques, the employment of this means is, of course, impracticable. In this connection, it is worthy of note that Hinman, Caron, and Christensen (250) were able to identify the racemic L-D, D-L form of valylvaline as its benzoyl derivative via an initial synthesis of the component L-D and D-L isomers.

α-Aminoacyl Halide Method. In the quest for methods which would lead to optically active peptides, Fischer (194) explored the use of amino acid chloride hydrochlorides (LVIII) as acylating agents. These compounds, which deposited as crystalline materials upon shaking the free amino acid

(LVII) with phosphorus pentachloride in acetyl chloride solution for several hours at room temperature, reacted readily with amino acid esters in ether or chloroform solution to yield the corresponding peptide ester derivative (LIX). The free peptide (LX) could be obtained by saponification of the latter compound. Although apparently more direct than the α-haloacyl method in that the amination step is obviated, a serious limitation is none the less imposed on this procedure by the appreciable amount of diketopiperazine (LXI) formation which accompanies syntheses directed toward dipeptide esters (LIX) as the reaction products.

$$NH_2CHRCO_2H \xrightarrow[CH_3COCl]{PCl_5} HCl \cdot NH_2CHRCOCl \xrightarrow{NH_2CHR'CO_2Et} NH_2CHRCO-NHCHR'CO_2Et$$
$$\text{LVII} \qquad\qquad \text{LVIII} \qquad\qquad\qquad \text{LIX}$$

$$\downarrow \text{saponification} \downarrow$$

$$NH_2CHRCO-NHCHR'CO_2H$$
$$\text{LX}$$

$$\begin{array}{c} CO-NH \\ RHC \qquad CHR' \\ NH-CO \\ \text{LXI} \end{array}$$

The above procedure was later extended to the acid chloride hydrochlorides of peptides. However, owing to the appreciable amount of racemization which may attend the conversion of an amino acid to its acid chloride derivative, the hope of Fischer that this method would serve as a route to optically active peptides could never be fully realized. For example, analysis of L-alanine regenerated by decomposition of its corresponding acid chloride hydrochloride in water showed it to contain some 30% racemic material (251). Aside from this disadvantage, the generally unsatisfactory yields secured via this method have markedly limited its general use. Most of the peptides produced by Fischer and his co-workers through the application of this procedure are given in Table 10-9.

Evaluation of the Method. That the α-haloacyl method has been of inestimable value in the early synthesis of a multitude of peptides which could not otherwise be secured is open to little question. However, several severe limitations inherent in the method have culminated in its gradual disuse. Chief among these is the apparent restriction of the method to simple monoamino acids, and thus even Fischer's octadecapeptide may be considered merely an elongated dipeptide with but one amino and one carboxyl group. The α-haloacyl method cannot be utilized for the introduction of the hexone bases into peptides, and yet it is just such complex amino acids which form the reactive groups of proteins. Again, the treatment of the halogen peptide with excess ammonia results, in certain instances, not in a substitution of amino for halogen but in hydrolysis, e.g., α-bromoisocaproylproline → α-hydroxyisocaproylproline amide, or in an elimination of hydrogen halide, e.g., α-chlorosuccinyldialanine → fumaryldialanine. Even

TABLE 10-9
Peptides Derived from Acid Chloride Hydrochlorides of Amino Acids and Peptides

Parent Acid Chloride	Compound	$[\alpha]_D$	Temp., °C.	Concn.	Ref.
Hydrochloride of					
L-Alanyl chloride	L-Alanylglycine	+50.2°	20	10%, H_2O	251
	L-Alanyl-L-alanine	−21.6°	20	5%, H_2O	156
DL-Leucylglycyl chloride	DL-Leucyldiglycine	−	−	−	251
DL-Leucyldiglycyl chloride	DL-Leucyltriglycine	−	−	−	251
DL-Phenylalanyl chloride	DL-Phenylalanylglycine	−	−	−	251
L-Prolyl chloride	L-Prolyl-L-phenylalanine	−40.9°	20	5%, 20% HCl	252
	L-Prolyl-D-phenylalanine	−52.0°	20	4%, H_2O	252
L-Tryptophyl chloride	L-Tryptophylglycine	+78.7°	20	4·4%, H_2O	226

in those instances where amination is effected, it is probable that the yield of peptide is often diminished by the concomitant occurrence of these reactions. Furthermore, the final purification of the peptide is frequently rendered difficult because of contamination with greater or lesser amounts of ammonium halide. Many crystallizations are usually required before the last traces of salt can be separated from the crystalline peptide. Another serious source of concern with the α-haloacyl method is the difficulty in securing optically active peptides. Despite Fischer's ingenious device for preparing optically active α-haloacyl moieties via a nitrosyl halide step, it is doubtful if a certain amount of racemization did not occur. Partial racemization can conceivably take place during the step concerned with the amination of the position occupied by the halogen moiety which, for certain peptides, is carried out at relatively high temperatures. From a practical point of view, therefore, the procedure should not be generally employed for optically active peptides other than those wherein the α-haloacyl substituent converted to an N-terminal glycine residue.

Illustrative Peptide Synthesis. The preparation and ammonolysis of chloroacetyl-L-serine (LXIV) should adequately serve to illustrate the α-haloacyl method. With slight modification in certain instances, the procedure is generally applicable to the synthesis of all the chloroacetyl- and glycyl-L-amino acids listed in Table 10–10, as well as their respective D-antipodes (253–255). The particular reaction sequence employed here is

$$\text{Cl—CH}_2\text{COCl} + \text{NH}_2\text{CH(CH}_2\text{OH)CO}_2\text{H} \xrightarrow[\text{2. HCl}]{\text{1. NaOH}}$$
$$\text{LXII} \qquad\qquad \text{LXIII}$$

$$\text{Cl—CH}_2\text{CO—NHCH(CH}_2\text{OH)CO}_2\text{H} \xrightarrow{\text{NH}_3} \text{NH}_2\text{CH}_2\text{CO—NHCH(CH}_2\text{OH)CO}_2\text{H}$$
$$\text{LXIV} \qquad\qquad\qquad\qquad \text{LXV}$$

TABLE 10-10
Physical Constants of Chloroacetyl- and Glycyl-L-amino Acids (253)

Amino Acid	Chloroacetyl-L-amino Acids M.P.,[a] °C.	$[\alpha]_D^{25}$, deg.	Concn. and Solvent	Glycyl-L-amino Acids $[\alpha]_D^{25}$, deg.	Concn. and Solvent
Alanine	93	−45.4	2%, H_2O	−51.0	2%, H_2O
α-Amino-n-butyric	118	−31.5	2%, H_2O	−31.0	2%, H_2O
Valine	114	+15.0	2%, EtOH	−19.9	2%, H_2O
Norvaline	104	−25.8	2%, H_2O	−27.5	2%, H_2O
Leucine	133	−15.8	2%, EtOH	−36.3	2%, H_2O
Norleucine	76	−17.0	2%, H_2O	−16.0	2%, H_2O
Isoleucine	74	+24.0	2%, EtOH	−14.1	2%, H_2O
Alloisoleucine	106	+25.0	2%, EtOH	−5.2	2%, H_2O
Methionine	98	−19.7	2%, H_2O	−10.2	2%, H_2O
Serine	58	+5.5[b]	5%, H_2O	−7.2	2%, H_2O
Threonine	111	+7.5	5%, H_2O	−16.2	2%, H_2O
Phenylalanine	125	+50.4	2%, EtOH	+41.5	2%, H_2O
Tyrosine	155	+59.0	2%, EtOH	+44.0	1%, H_2O
Tryptophan	158	+32.0	2%, EtOH	+34.3	2%, 5N HCl
Glutamic acid	142	−14.4	2%, H_2O	−6.8	5%, H_2O
Aspartic acid	144	+4.0	5%, H_2O	+12.5	2%, H_2O
Asparagine	165	−2.5	5%, H_2O	−7.0	5%, H_2O
Lysine (α)	–	–	–	−10.0[c]	5%, H_2O
Glycine	100	–	–	–	–

[a] All melting points are corrected.
[b] As the monohydrate.
[c] As the sulfate. This compound was prepared by the ammonolysis of α-chloroacetyl-ε-carbobenzoxy-L-lysine (oil), followed by a palladium-catalyzed hydrogenolysis (Section 10-44) of the α-glycyl-ε-carbobenzoxy-L-lysine so secured.

Illustrative procedure 10-4. Chloroacetyl-L-serine monohydrate (LXIV) (253). One-tenth mole of L-serine (LXIII) is dissolved in 25 ml. of ice-cold 4N NaOH in a 100-ml. Erlenmeyer flask. Treatment with 0.15 mole of chloroacetyl chloride (LXII) and 38 ml. of 4N NaOH is effected by the portionwise and alternate addition of each reagent over a period of about 30–45 min., with intermittent vigorous shaking and cooling in an ice bath. It is essential that the reaction mixture be kept on the alkaline side and cold (<5°) at all times. After the addition of reagents is complete, the mixture is allowed to stand for 10 min. in the cold with periodic shaking. It is then acidified (pH 1.7) by the careful addition of conc. HCl and extracted several times with ethyl acetate. The combined ethyl acetate extracts are dried over anhydrous sodium sulfate, and the filtrate evaporated to dryness at about 40° under reduced pressure. The residual syrup is washed several times with petroleum ether and then taken up in a minimal amount of hot ethyl acetate. On chilling to $-15°$, chloroacetyl-L-serine appears as large prismatic crystals. These are transferred to a filter with dry ether, washed with ether, and recrystallized from a little warm ethyl acetate. The yield of pure white, air-dried crystals is about 40% of theory. The compound is secured as the monohydrate. $[\alpha]_D$ for a 5% solution in water at 25° is $+5.5°$; m.p. $= 58°$. Loss of the water of crystallization by drying *in vacuo* leaves the anhydrous compound as a glassy residue.

Glycyl-L-serine (LXV) (253). A quantity of chloroacetyl-L-serine monohydrate is dissolved in 20 times its weight of 25% ammonia water, and, after standing for 72 hr. at room temperature, the solution is evaporated to dryness under reduced pressure. The residue is taken up in a small amount of water and the evaporation repeated. The latter operation is performed twice more. The residue is washed with ethanol several times, dissolved in a small amount of water, and crystallized by the addition of a ten-fold volume of methanol. Such crystallization from water-methanol is repeated until the crystals show a negative Nessler's test for ammonia. The yield is approximately 80% of theory. $[\alpha]_D$ for a 2% solution in water at 25° is $-7.2°$.

8. The Azlactone Method in the Synthesis of Saturated and Unsaturated Peptides. *Principle.* Azlactones may be regarded as five-membered inner anhydrides which arise from α-acylamino (I) or α-acyldehydroamino (II) acids in consequence of the loss of the elements of water. Being dependent upon their derivation from the former or latter compounds, azlactones may be categorized either as *saturated* (III) or *unsaturated* (IV) types:

$$\underset{I}{RCO-NH\overset{\overset{R^1}{|}}{C}R^2CO_2H} \qquad \underset{II}{RCO-NH\overset{\overset{CR^1R^2}{\|}}{C}CO_2H}$$

$-H_2O \updownarrow +H_2O \qquad -H_2O \updownarrow +H_2O$

III   IV

Owing to the presence of a double bond at the C_4-position of *unsaturated* azlactones, these compounds may exist as stereoisomeric *cis* and *trans* forms (IV). In the present section, azlactones are named as their corresponding amino acid or oxazolone derivatives. Thus, for example, (V) may be referred to as benzoyl-α-aminocinnamic azlactone or 2-phenyl-4-benzal-5-oxazolone, while (VI) may be designated as benzoylphenylalanine azlactone or 2-phenyl-4-benzyl-5-oxazolone.

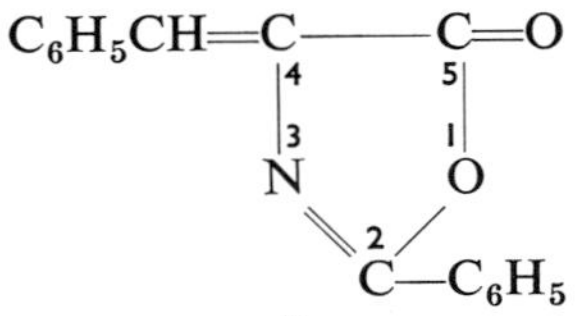

$$C_6H_5CH=C\underset{\underset{\underset{C-C_6H_5}{\overset{\|}{2}}}{\overset{|}{N}}}{\overset{|}{4}}\underset{O}{\overset{\|}{5}}C=O$$

V

$$C_6H_5CH_2CH\underset{\underset{\underset{C-C_6H_5}{\overset{\|}{2}}}{\overset{|}{N}}}{\overset{|}{4}}\underset{O}{\overset{\|}{5}}C=O$$

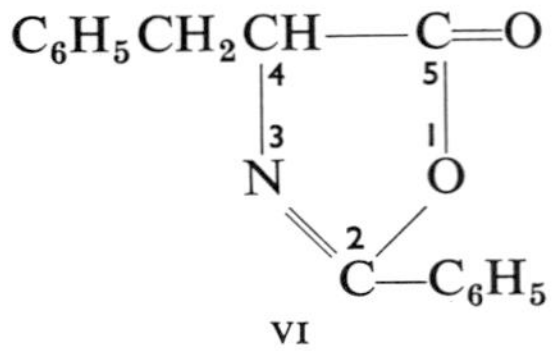

VI

The partial hydrolysis of *saturated* azlactones with water or alcohol results in a slow ring cleavage, with concomitant regeneration of the parent acylamino acid where the former solvent is employed, or with the formation of the acylamino acid ester in the presence of the latter solvent. Analogous reactions with amines proceeds with markedly greater facility, with the production of the corresponding amide derivative. Thus reaction of a saturated azlactone (VII) with the ester or sodium salt of an amino acid leads to the formation of the respective acyldipeptide derivative (VIII and IX). The latter reaction was that employed by Mohr and Stroschein (256), in 1908, for the synthesis of the first peptide derivative obtained via azlactone intermediates. Conversion of (VIII) and (IX) to the free peptide (X), after saponification of the ester group of the former intermediate or neutralization of the sodium salt of the latter, may be accomplished by selective hydrolysis of the acyl substituent.

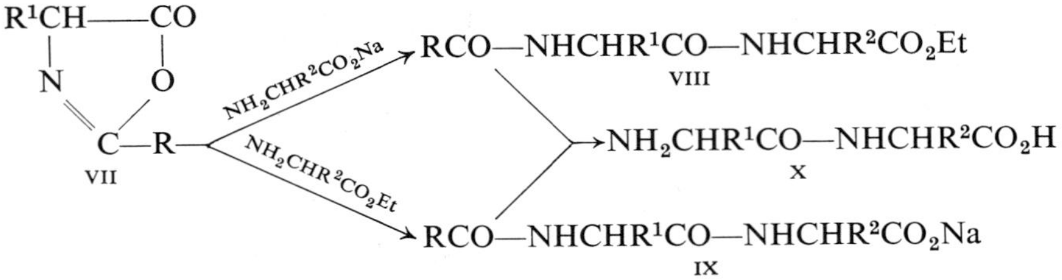

$$R^1CH\text{———}CO$$
VII → RCO—NHCHR¹CO—NHCHR²CO₂Et (VIII)
→ NH₂CHR¹CO—NHCHR²CO₂H (X)
→ RCO—NHCHR¹CO—NHCHR²CO₂Na (IX)

Unlike their saturated counterparts, the *unsaturated* azlactones remain unaltered upon prolonged contact with water and may, in fact, be recrystallized from hot ethanol. Strong acids and alkalis hydrolyze these compounds to the corresponding acyldehydroamino acids, whereas cleavage by alcohol proceeds in the presence of sodium alkoxide with the formation of the acyldehydroamino acid ester. Although condensation occurs with amines, such reaction takes place with much less facility and requires longer periods of time at room temperature than the comparable reaction implicating saturated azlactones. Marked acceleration of the reaction rate is induced by an increase in temperature, however, with a period of warming at 50–100°

sometimes being employed. Thus reaction of unsaturated azlactones (XI) with the sodium salt or ester derivatives of an amino acid, e.g., $NH_2CHR^2CO_2Na$, yields products which contain a dehydroamino acid residue adjacent to the acyl substituent. Such *dehydropeptide* derivatives (XII) may, upon suitable reduction, be transformed into the corresponding saturated peptide derivatives (XIII) to yield an obviously racemic residue.

$$R_2C=C-CO \atop \underset{\underset{XI}{C-R^1}}{N\diagup O} \xrightarrow{NH_2CHR^2CO_2Na} \underset{XII}{R^1CO-NHCCO-NHCHR^2CO_2Na \atop \| \atop CR_2} \xrightarrow[2.\,H_2]{1.\,HCl}$$

$$\underset{XIII}{R^1CO-NHCHCO-NHCHR^2CO_2H \atop | \atop CHR_2}$$

When subjected to the action of hot, dilute mineral acids, a dehydropeptide (represented in XIV and XV by its tautomeric forms) is converted to the corresponding α-keto acid (XVI), the corresponding acid (XVII) from the acyl residue, and ammonia:

$$\underset{XIV}{RCH_2CONHC(=CHR^1)CO_2H} \rightleftarrows \underset{XV}{RCH_2CON=C(CH_2R^1)CO_2H} \xrightarrow[\Delta]{HCl} \underset{XVI}{R^1CH_2COCO_2H} + \underset{XVII}{RCH_2CO_2H} + \underset{XVIII}{NH_3}$$

It should be noted that these same products are formed from dehydropeptides, with suitable R and R^1 substituents, upon incubation with a wide variety of plant and animal tissues under mild physiologic conditions. In fact, under such conditions, certain dehydropeptides are enzymatically hydrolyzed at the peptide bond with great rapidity by suitable preparations of all plant and animal tissues which have hitherto been studied (cf. 257). The enzyme responsible is referred to under the designation *dehydropeptidase*.

Preparation of Unsaturated Azlactones. The preparation of the first unsaturated azlactone (XXI) was reported in 1883 by Plöchl (258), who condensed benzaldehyde (XIX) with hippuric acid (XX) in the presence of acetic anhydride:

$$\underset{XIX}{C_6H_5CHO} + \underset{XX}{C_6H_5CONHCH_2CO_2H} \xrightarrow{Ac_2O} \underset{XXI}{C_6H_5CH=C-CO \atop \underset{C-C_6H_5}{N\diagup O}}$$

Although it was initially postulated (259) that the structure of the azlactone so derived incorporated a three-membered cyclic structure, as represented by

(XXII), the investigations of Erlenmeyer (260) in 1900 led to the assignment of the five-membered arrangement (XXIII) which is now generally accepted

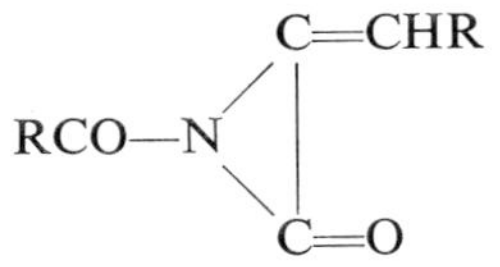

$$\begin{array}{cc} \text{RCO—N}\diagup\!\!\!\begin{array}{c}\text{C}=\text{CHR}\\|\\\text{C}=\text{O}\end{array} & \begin{array}{c}\text{RCH}=\text{C}\text{———}\text{CO}\\|\quad\quad\quad|\\\text{N}\quad\quad\text{O}\\\diagdown\diagup\\\text{C—R}\end{array}\\ \text{XXII} & \text{XXIII} \end{array}$$

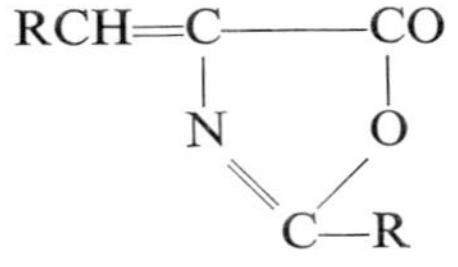

as valid. The designation *azlactone* was applied to such compounds by Erlenmeyer (260), who extended the procedure to include other aldehydes and, in addition, established the usefulness of azlactones as intermediates in the synthesis of α-keto and α-amino acids. Various synthetic routes have since been employed for the preparation of a variety of unsaturated azlactones. These have been detailed in a noteworthy review by Carter (261) and are reiterated briefly below:

(*a*) Condensation of an aromatic or aliphatic aldehyde (XXIV) with an acylglycine (XXV) in the presence of acetic anhydride and, sometimes, with added sodium acetate (260, 262–266), cupric acetate (267), lead acetate (268, 269), potassium carbonate (271), or potassium bicarbonate (271) as catalyst.

Illustrative procedure 10–5 (270). 2-Methyl-4-benzal-5-oxazolone (XXVIII; R = C_6H_5, R′ = CH_3). A mixture of 58.5 g. (0.5 mole) of acetylglycine (XXV; R′ = CH_3), 30 g. (0.37 mole) of anhydrous sodium acetate, 79 g. (0.74 mole) of freshly distilled benzaldehyde (XXIV; R = C_6H_5), and 134 g. (1.25 moles) of 95% acetic anhydride in a loosely corked 1-l. Erlenmeyer flask is warmed on the steam bath with occasional stirring until solution is complete (10–20 min.). The resulting solution is boiled for 1 hr. under reflux, cooled, and placed in a refrigerator overnight. The solid mass of crystals is treated with 125 ml. of cold water, broken up with a stirring rod, filtered over suction, and washed thoroughly with cold water. After being dried *in vacuo* over phosphorus pentoxide and potassium hydroxide, the crude azlactone weighs 69–72 g. (74–77% of theory). The product, which melts at 148–150° and is sufficiently pure for preparative purposes, may be recrystallized from ethyl acetate or carbon tetrachloride by the addition of petroleum ether; m.p. 151–152°.

(*b*) Action of an excess of acetic anhydride on an acyldehydroamino acid (XXIX) or, in the presence of pyridine, on an α-haloacylamino acid (XXX) (272–277).

(*c*) Reaction of an aqueous solution of the acyldehydroamino acid (XXVII) with acetic anhydride in the presence of sodium acetate (273).

(*d*) Action of acetic anhydride or an acid chloride on an α-acylamino-β-hydroxy(alkoxy or acyloxy) acid (XXVI), either under anhydrous conditions or in water in the presence of sodium acetate (265, 273, 274, 278–281).

CHEMICAL PROCEDURES FOR SYNTHESIS OF PEPTIDES

The afore-mentioned procedures, of which method *a* is the most commonly employed, are depicted in the following:

$$\text{RCHO} + \text{R'CONHCH}_2\text{CO}_2\text{H} \qquad\qquad \text{RCH(OR'')CH(NHCOR')CO}_2\text{H}$$
XXIV   XXV   XXVI

$$\text{RCH}=\text{C}-\text{CO}$$
$$|\qquad\qquad|$$
$$\text{N}\qquad\text{O}$$
$$\diagdown\;\;\diagup$$
$$\text{C}-\text{R'}$$

(with Ac₂O from XXV, and NaOAc / R''COCl or Ac₂O from XXVI)

$$\text{R'CONHC}(=\text{CHR})\text{CO}_2\text{H} \xrightarrow[\text{NaOAc}]{\text{Ac}_2\text{O, H}_2\text{O}} \text{XXVIII} \xleftarrow[\Delta]{\text{Ac}_2\text{O}} \text{R'CONHC}(=\text{CHR})\text{CO}_2\text{H}$$
XXVII   XXIX

Also,

$$\text{XCHR'CO}-\text{NHCH}(\text{CH}_2\text{R})\text{CO}_2\text{H} \xrightarrow[\text{(C}_5\text{H}_5\text{N)}]{\text{Ac}_2\text{O}}$$
XXX

$$\text{RCH}=\text{C}-\text{CO}$$
$$|\qquad\qquad|$$
$$\text{N}\qquad\text{O}$$
$$\diagdown\;\;\diagup$$
$$\text{C}-\text{CH}_2\text{R'}$$
XXXI

A convenient procedure, which utilizes free glycine in lieu of the acylated amino acid, has been employed as an alternative route to 2-methyl-5-oxazolones (272, 282). The procedure, in essence, involves the interaction of glycine and acetic anhydride to yield the corresponding acetyl derivative. The latter compound is not isolated, however, but its solution is treated *in situ* with the requisite aldehyde, sodium acetate, and additional acetic anhydride. The preliminary isolation of acetylglycine is thereby rendered unnecessary.

Illustrative procedure 10-6 (272). 2-Methyl-4-benzal-5-oxazolone (XXVIII; R = C₆H₅, R' = CH₃). A mixture of 20 g. of glycine, 33 ml. of benzaldehyde, 100 ml. of acetic anhydride, and 12 g. of anhydrous sodium acetate is gradually heated to 100° with shaking until solution occurs, and then maintained at a gentle boil for 45 min. After cooling to 20°, the excess acetic anhydride is decomposed by the addition of 150 ml. of water, with shaking. This is soon followed by the appearance of the crystalline azlactone, which is filtered and washed cautiously with a small amount of ether (the compound is somewhat soluble in this solvent). A yield of 22–25 g. (44–50% of theory) is secured. Recrystallization is effected from carbon tetrachloride or ethyl acetate by the addition of petroleum ether; m.p. 151–152°.

The synthetic work related to penicillin, and the early postulation of a thiazolidine-oxazolone structure for this molecule, stimulated considerable interest in the general preparation and chemistry of oxazolones during the early 1940's. An appreciable portion of the experimental and theoretical studies on oxazolones carried out during this fruitful period was admirably summarized by Cornforth (283) in a comprehensive volume entitled *The Chemistry of Penicillin*, edited by Clarke, Johnson, and Robinson. Preparation of the many new unsaturated azlactones recorded therein was effected, in the main, either via the general procedures listed above or through suitable modifications thereof. Aside from their practical significance, however, many interesting theoretical sidelights arose in consequence of such preparations. Thus, for example, a partial illumination of the mechanism of the Erlenmeyer azlactone synthesis was attributed to the discovery that 2-phenyl-5-oxazolone (XXXIII), derived from hippuric acid (XXXII) and acetic anhydride in acetone solution, subsequently reacted with acetone in the absence of acetic anhydride but in the presence of sodium acetate to yield 2-phenyl-4-isopropylidene-5-oxazolone (XXXIV; $R = R' = CH_3$). Similarly, condensation of cold alcoholic solutions of (XXXIII) with benzaldehyde (RCOR'; $R = C_6H_5$, $R' = H$) or other aldehydes was shown to occur readily in the presence of a basic catalyst such as pyridine or N-ethylpiperidine with the production of 2-phenyl-4-benzylidene-5-oxazolone (XXXIV; $R = C_6H_5$, $R' = H$). These findings were strongly suggestive of the formation of 2-phenyl-5-oxazolone-type intermediates prior to substitution at the C_4-position of the azlactone ring.

$$\begin{array}{ccc}
C_6H_5 & CH_2\!-\!\!-\!\!-C\!=\!O & RR'C\!=\!C\!-\!\!-\!\!-C\!=\!O \\
| & |\quad\quad\quad | & |\quad\quad\quad\quad | \\
CO & N\quad\quad\; O & N\quad\quad\quad\; O \\
| & \diagdown\!\diagup & \diagdown\!\diagup \\
NHCH_2CO_2H & C\!-\!C_6H_5 & C\!-\!C_6H_5 \\
\text{XXXII} & \text{XXXIII} & \text{XXXIV}
\end{array}$$

with arrows: XXXII $\xrightarrow[(CH_3)_2CO]{Ac_2O}$ XXXIII $\xrightarrow[\text{basic catalyst}]{RCOR'}$ XXXIV

Of considerable theoretical interest, in the present connection, is the possible existence of unsaturated azlactones as their geometrical *cis* and *trans* isomers. This isomerism was experimentally established in a notable series of investigations with the benzoylaminocrotonic and the benzoylaminocinnamic azlactones by Carter, in collaboration with Stevens (273) and Risser (274). Such investigations (273) initially involved the conversion of N-benzoyl-O-methyl-DL-allothreonine to benzoyl-α-aminocrotonic azlactone II by method *d* above. The latter compound was shown to be isomeric with the lower-melting azlactone I (XXXVII), which had been previously secured (279) by the treatment of the N-benzoyl derivative of DL-threonine or allothreonine (XXXV) with acetic anhydride or benzoyl chloride in pyridine solution. The reaction presumably proceeded through preliminary formation of the azlactone ring, succeeded by the spontaneous elimination of a molecule of water:

$$\begin{array}{ccc}
CH_3 & CH_3CH\!-\!CH\!-\!\!-\!\!-CO & CH_3CH\!=\!C\!-\!\!-\!\!-CO \\
| & |\quad\;\; |\quad\quad\; | & |\quad\quad\quad\; | \\
CHOH & OH\;\; N\quad\; O & N\quad\quad\; O \\
| & \diagdown\!\diagup & \diagdown\!\diagup \\
C_6H_5CO\!-\!NHCHCO_2H & C\!-\!C_6H_5 & C\!-\!C_6H_5 \\
\text{XXXV} & \text{XXXVI} & \text{XXXVII}
\end{array}$$

with arrows: XXXV $\xrightarrow[C_5H_5N]{C_6H_5COCl}$ XXXVI $\xrightarrow{-H_2O}$ XXXVII

Azlactone II could be readily converted to azlactone I in almost quantitative yield when subjected to the action of pyridine for several minutes at room temperature (273). In like manner, benzoyl-α-aminocinnamic azlactone II (XXXIX) could be derived (274) from benzoyl-O-methylphenyl-DL-serine B (XXXVIII) by the action of acetic anhydride. The geometric form so secured was isomeric to the higher-melting azlactone I earlier studied by Erlenmeyer (260, 264) and could in fact be converted into it by the action of pyridine.

$$\underset{\text{XXXVIII}}{\overset{\overset{\text{OCH}_3}{|}\quad\overset{\text{NHCOC}_6\text{H}_5}{|}}{\text{C}_6\text{H}_5\text{CH}\text{---}\text{CHCO}_2\text{H}}} \xrightarrow{\text{Ac}_2\text{O}} \underset{\text{XXXIX}}{\overset{\text{C}_6\text{H}_5\text{CH}=\text{C}\text{---}\text{CO}}{\underset{\diagdown\text{C}\text{---}\text{C}_6\text{H}_5\diagup}{\text{N}\qquad\text{O}}}} \xrightarrow{\text{C}_5\text{H}_5\text{N}} \text{Azlactone I}$$

Preparation of Saturated Azlactones. The relative ease with which saturated azlactones undergo hydrolysis was presumably responsible for the failure experienced in the earlier attempts to isolate these compounds (266). It remained for Mohr and Geis (284) in 1908, some fifteen years after the synthesis of the first unsaturated azlactone, to announce the preparation of 2-phenyl-4,4-dimethyl-5-oxazolone (XLI; R = R′ = CH₃), the first saturated azlactone. Preparation of this compound was achieved by heating 1 mole of benzoyl-α-aminoisobutyric acid (XL; R = R′ = CH₃) with 1.2 moles of acetic anhydride for 1 hour at 100°. In like manner, synthesis of the saturated azlactones of benzoyl-DL-alanine (XLI; R = H, R′ = CH₃) and benzoyl-DL-phenylalanine (XLI; R = H, R′ = CH₂C₆H₅) was accomplished by Mohr and Stroschein (256) one year later.

$$\underset{\text{XL}}{\overset{\overset{\text{R}\text{---}\text{C}\text{---}\text{CO}_2\text{H}}{\diagup\ |}}{\underset{\diagdown\text{C}\text{---}\text{C}_6\text{H}_5\diagup}{\text{R}'\ \text{NH}\quad\text{O}}}} \xrightarrow{\text{Ac}_2\text{O},100°} \underset{\text{XLI}}{\overset{\overset{\text{R}\text{---}\text{C}\text{---}\text{CO}}{\diagup\ |}}{\underset{\diagdown\text{C}\text{---}\text{C}_6\text{H}_5\diagup}{\text{R}'\ \text{N}\quad\text{O}}}}$$

Illustrative procedure 10-7 (283). 2-Phenyl-5-oxazolone (XLI; R = R′ = H). A mixture of 100 g. of hippuric acid (XL; R = R′ = H) and 300 ml. of acetic anhydride is heated on the steam bath with stirring until a clear solution results. The solvent is then removed at water-pump pressure while the reaction mixture is still being heated. After the addition of 200 ml. of light petroleum (60–70°) to the hot residue, the mixture is stirred and then allowed to cool. The pinkish solid which separates is removed by filtration, washed with light petroleum, and dried overnight in a vacuum desiccator. By crystallization from absolute ethyl alcohol there is obtained some 44 g. of 2-phenyl-5-oxazolone (49% of theory); m.p. 91–92°. Further recrystallizations raise the melting point to 94–95°.

Despite the later development of alternative synthetic routes to saturated azlactones, the earlier acetic anhydride method has remained the most generally applied technique. As in the early procedures, later syntheses were effected primarily through the initial use of acylamino acids, although the free amino acids *per se* have been frequently employed. Methods which employ these starting materials are enumerated in the following (cf. 261, 283):

(*a*) Reaction of an amino acid (XLIII), or its acyl derivative (XLII), with acetic anhydride either alone or employing acetic acid as solvent (123, 256, 273, 274, 283–290).

(*b*) Action of an acid anhydride or acid chloride on the sodium salt of either an amino acid (XLVI) or acylamino acid (XLV) (273, 278, 283).

(*c*) Action of an acid anhydride or acid chloride on an acylamino acid (XLIV) in pyridine solution (279, 283, 291).

(*d*) Action of silver salts, e.g., silver benzenesulfonate or silver oxide, on phenylthioacetyl (XLVIII; R = C$_6$H$_5$CH$_2$) or thiobenzoyl (XLVIII; R = C$_6$H$_5$) derivatives of amino acids (283).

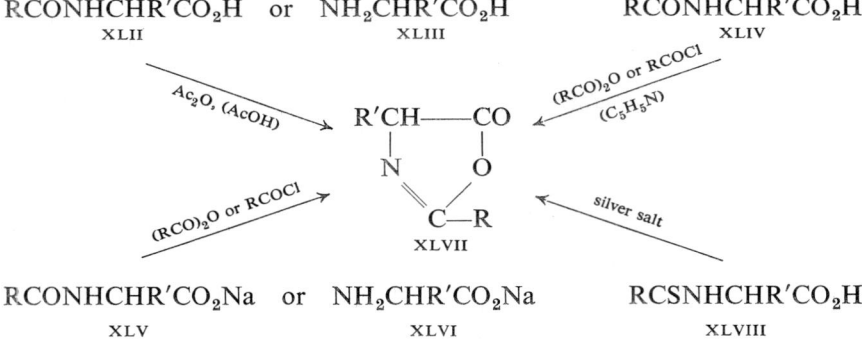

In connection with the above, the acyl derivatives of glutamic and aspartic acids deserve added consideration. Thus Nicolet (292) demonstrated that acylated glutamic acids (L; $x = 2$), upon treatment with acetic anhydride, are transformed exclusively into the six-membered cyclic anhydride (XLIX; $x = 2$) in preference to the azlactone. That acylaspartic acids (L; $x = 1$) behave in a comparable manner was later established by Harington and Overhoff (293), who showed that the treatment of acetyl-L-aspartic acid in acetic anhydride at 95° resulted in the production of acetyl-L-aspartic anhydride without the occurrence of appreciable racemization. However, when the reaction temperature was increased to the reflux point, a different product was isolated which was assumed to be the azlactone but which, upon later reinvestigation independently by Barker and by Swan (293a), was identified as acetyl-DL-aspartic anhydride. Racemization was presumed to arise from enolization of the anhydride, as represented by structure (LI), rather than through the formation of an azlactone intermediate as is usually the case with other acetylamino acids (see below).

In 1925, Karrer and Widmer (294) anticipated a new route to azlactone synthesis when they prepared a substance by the action of diazomethane on hippuryl chloride which, some sixteen years later, was assigned (295) the structure of 2-phenyl-5-oxazolone. In this later work, the statement was made that "Die Einwirkung von Diazomethan auf Hippursäurechlorid nimmt einen anderen Verlauf als die Reactionen des Diazomethans mit den meisten anderen Säurechloriden. Diazomethan wirkt hier Chlorwasserstoff-entziehend."[44] Such peculiar behavior of "hippuryl chloride" was subsequently explained on the basis of the startling suggestion that "halides" of α-acylamino acids are in actuality oxazolone hydrohalides (283). If such view was indeed correct, then any reagent which was capable of transforming an acylamino acid into its corresponding acid chloride might, similarly, be expected to transform this same compound into its oxazolone hydrohalide. Evidence in support of this assumption initially arose with the observation that the action of water or sodium acetate on "hippuryl halide" resulted in its hydrolysis to hippuric acid via the intermediate 2-phenyl-5-oxazolone. Thus the reaction of hippuric acid (LII) with phosphorus tribromide yielded a crystalline salt which, in the presence of either diazomethane or sodium acetate under an organic solvent, subsequently gave 2-phenyl-5-oxazolone (LIV). 2:4-Diphenyl-5-oxazolone and 2-benzyl-4:4-dimethyl-5-oxazolone were prepared from the pertinent starting materials in comparable manner, while 2-phenyl-4-benzyl-5-oxazolone was secured by the action of phosphorus tribromide on benzoylphenylalanine in the presence of pyridine.

$$\underset{\text{LII}}{\begin{array}{c}C_6H_5\\|\\CO\\|\\NHCH_2CO_2H\end{array}} \xrightarrow{PBr_3} \underset{\text{LIII}}{\text{"Crystalline salt"}} \xrightarrow[\text{or } CH_2N_2]{NaOAc} \underset{\text{LIV}}{\begin{array}{c}CH_2-CO\\|\quad\quad|\\N\quad\quad O\\\diagdown\diagup\\C-C_6H_5\end{array}}$$

Although the formulation of α-acylamino acid halides as oxazolone hydrohalides receives strong support from the fact that these substances usually exhibit "the appearance and solubilities of salts, they are in some cases convertible to the oxazolones by very mild reagents (e.g., water), and their reactions with alcohols and bases in general give the same products as the oxazolones provided" (283), certain other evidence seemed, nevertheless, directed toward a contrary view. Illustrative of such counter-evidence is the finding, for example, that, whereas an ether-insoluble precipitate arises from the treatment of 2-phenyl-5-oxazolone with hydrogen chloride, hippuryl chloride shows free solubility in ether. In addition, certain "acylamino acid halides" reveal an absorption spectrum characteristic of the parent oxazolone whereas others do not. As yet, the evidence in favor of one or the other view appears too scant to be decisive. However, an opinion most in accord with the presently available facts is that which assumes the existence of an α-acylamino acid halide structure (LV) in equilibrium with the oxazolone hydrohalide structure (LVI), the position of such equilibrium being dependent upon individual circumstances.

$$\begin{array}{cc} \text{RCH——CO—Br} & \text{RCH——CO Br}^- \\ | \quad\quad\quad\quad & | \quad\quad\quad\quad \\ \text{NH} \quad \text{O} \quad \rightleftarrows \text{H}^\oplus \text{N} \quad \text{O} \\ \diagdown \diagup & \diagdown \diagup \\ \text{C—R}' & \text{C—R}' \\ \text{LV} & \text{LVI} \end{array}$$

In addition to the afore-mentioned methods, saturated azlactones have been prepared by catalytic reduction of the corresponding unsaturated azlactones (283). Thus hydrogenation of 2-phenyl-4-benzylidene-5-oxazolone (V) over palladized charcoal gave rise to 2-phenyl-4-benzyl-5-oxazolone (VI). Comparable reduction of 2-phenyl-4-isopropylidene-5-oxazolone could be accomplished to yield the corresponding saturated analog, which was not isolated as such but rather converted directly to benzoylvaline anilide upon treatment with aniline.

Racemization of Acylamino Acids via Saturated Azlactone Intermediates. Inasmuch as the C_4-atom of saturated azlactones is asymmetric in nature, these compounds should be expected to exist theoretically as the enantiomorphic D- and L-forms. However, isolation of these optical forms has been achieved only in rare instances, a phenomenon which may be primarily attributed to the extreme ease with which the C_4-center of asymmetry of the azlactone ring undergoes spontaneous racemization. The first demonstration of such ready racemization of azlactones was made in 1926 by Bergmann and Köster (296), who noted the apparent facility with which L-arginine was optically inactivated upon its conversion to the α-monoacetyl derivative by the action of cold excess acetic anhydride. The two alternative mechanisms suggested for such optical inactivation involved (*a*) a keto-enol shift between the α-asymmetric carbon and the carboxyl carbon atoms, i.e., LVII $\rightleftarrows$ LVIII:

$$\begin{array}{cc} \text{—CH—C}{=}\text{O} \rightleftarrows \text{—C}{=}\text{C—OH} \\ |\quad\quad | \quad\quad\quad |\quad\quad | \\ \text{—NH} \quad \text{OH} \quad\quad \text{—NH} \quad \text{OH} \\ \text{LVII} \quad\quad\quad\quad \text{LVIII} \end{array}$$

and (*b*) a tautomeric shift which involved the presumed formation of a transitory azlactone intermediate during the acetylation. Further elaboration of the latter mechanism was presented some two years later by Bergmann and Zervas (297) in a notable report which demonstrated that an acetyl amino acid (LX), derived by the action of exactly one equivalent of acetic anhydride on one equivalent of an optically active amino acid (LIX) in glacial acetic acid solution at 100°, suffered no loss in optical activity. However, in the presence of two or more moles of acetic anhydride, an isolable azlactone (LXI) was formed which gave rise in turn to a racemic acetylated derivative. Although no azlactone could be isolated when only between one and two moles of acetic anhydride was employed, *catalytic racemization* of the derivative none the less occurred, a phenomenon which was attributed to the generation of a transitory azlactone intermediate (LXI) which existed in equilibrium with its tautomeric enol form (LXII). An alternative racemization route via a cyclic keto-enol rearrangement intermediate (LXIII and LXIV), formed prior to the dehydration to the azlactone (LXI), was also postulated.

That an azlactone intermediate was involved in the above racemization process received strong support from the fact that, although α-acetyl-L-arginine, for example, exhibited no apparent racemization upon treatment for several hours with boiling glacial acetic acid solution, the addition of a little acetic anhydride thereto was accompanied by a rapid and complete loss in optical activity. In addition, the involvement of a keto-enol rearrangement as the responsible racemization mechanism was made more tenable by the further demonstration that L-isovaline (LXV), which contains no α-hydrogen atom, exhibited no apparent change in optical activity subsequent to treatment with hot acetic anhydride. Although azlactone

(LXVII) formation with this amino acid is feasible, the absence of a removable proton makes enolization impossible here:

$$\underset{\text{LXV}}{\underset{\mid}{\text{CH}_3\text{CH}_2\overset{\overset{\text{CH}_3}{\mid}}{\text{C}}\text{CO}_2\text{H}}} \xrightarrow{\text{Ac}_2\text{O}} \underset{\text{LXVI}}{\underset{\mid}{\text{CH}_3\text{CH}_2\overset{\overset{\text{CH}_3}{\mid}}{\text{C}}\text{CO}_2\text{H}}} \xrightarrow{\text{Ac}_2\text{O}} \underset{\text{LXVII}}{\text{(LXVII structure)}}$$

However, racemization proved successful with the optical forms of histidine, arginine, glutamic acid, and tyrosine, all of which incorporate an α-hydrogen atom.

The method described above, with minor modifications, has been successfully employed in the authors' laboratory for the preparation of several racemic amino acids from their corresponding active forms. In brief, the method involves the interaction of the pertinent optical isomer in hot glacial acetic acid solution with an excess of acetic anhydride. The formation of the corresponding racemic acetyl derivative generally proceeds with facility over a period of several minutes. Of especial interest in this connection is the fact that the racemization of an optical stereomer of a diasymmetric amino acid, such as isoleucine, proceeds with the formation of an epimeric mixture wherein the α-asymmetric center is totally racemized while the optical configuration of the β-asymmetric center remains essentially unaltered. Thus L-isoleucine is readily converted to an epimeric mixture composed of the acetyl derivatives of L-isoleucine and D-alloisoleucine (298). It might be added that the method, in its present form, cannot be utilized for such amino acids as serine or threonine, which presumably suffer marked dehydration under the drastic conditions employed. However, conditions with the glacial acetic acid–acetic anhydride system have recently been found which permit the racemization of the highly labile L-cystine without the danger of extensive desulfuration (299). The method, as ordinarily employed, is detailed below for the racemization of L-leucine.

Illustrative procedure 10–8. Conversion of L-leucine to DL-leucine. One mole (131 g.) of L-leucine is dissolved in 10 volumes of hot, glacial acetic acid, the solution heated to the boiling point, and 2.2 moles (207 ml.) of acetic anhydride is *cautiously* added thereto. The reaction mixture is allowed to boil gently for 5 min. and then permitted to stand at room temperature for 2 hr. After evaporation *in vacuo* to dryness, a small amount of water is added to the residue and the evaporation repeated. The residue is taken up in boiling acetone, charcoal is added, and the solution is filtered while hot. After concentration of the filtrate to a small volume, the crystalline precipitate of acetyl-DL-leucine is filtered off and washed first with a small amount of cold acetone, then with ether, and finally dried *in vacuo*; m.p. 159°; yield, 85–95% of theory.

A solution of 100 g. of acetyl-DL-leucine in 1 l. of 2N hydrochloric acid is refluxed for 2–3 hr. and the reaction mixture then concentrated to dryness *in vacuo*. The residue is taken up in 100–200 ml. of water and the evaporation repeated. The residual DL-leucine hydrochloride is then dissolved in the minimal amount of water, the pH of the solution adjusted to 5.5 with lithium hydroxide solution, and 10 volumes of ethanol added thereto. After some 6 hr. at 4°, the precipitate is filtered off, washed with alcohol and finally recrystallized from water-alcohol. The yield of DL-leucine so obtained is 80–90% of theory.

The mechanism of the *catalytic racemization* of α-acylamino acids in glacial acetic acid (297), discussed above, was further elucidated by Carter and Stevens (273), who observed that benzoyl-*p*-methoxy-L-phenylalanine (LXIX; $R^2 = C_6H_5$, $R^3 = p\text{-}CH_3OC_6H_4CH_2$) was racemized at an appreciably more rapid rate in the presence of catalytic amounts of other azlactones, e.g., benzoyl-DL-alanine azlactone (LXVIII; $R = C_6H_5$, $R^1 = CH_3$), than in the presence of an equivalent amount of acetic anhydride. Such occurrence was attributed to a chemical reaction between the azlactone and the α-acylamino acid, as in the following:

$$\underset{\text{LXVIII}}{\begin{array}{c}R^1CH\!\!-\!\!CO\\|\quad\quad\;|\\N\quad\;\;O\\\diagdown\!\!\diagup\\C\!\!-\!\!R\end{array}} + \underset{\text{LXIX}}{\begin{array}{c}R^3CHCO_2H\\|\\NH\\|\\COR^2\end{array}} \rightleftharpoons \underset{\text{LXX}}{\begin{array}{c}R^1CHCO_2H\\|\\NH\\|\\COR\end{array}} + \underset{\text{LXXI}}{\begin{array}{c}R^3CH\!\!-\!\!CO\\|\quad\quad\;|\\N\quad\;\;O\\\diagdown\!\!\diagup\\C\!\!-\!\!R^2\end{array}}$$

The correctness of this assumption was later confirmed by the finding that benzoylphenylalanine (LXIX; $R^2 = C_6H_5$, $R^3 = C_6H_5CH_2$), when warmed with one equivalent of 2-benzyl-4-methyl-5-oxazolone (LXVIII; $R = C_6H_5CH_2$, $R^1 = CH_3$), was converted to 2-phenyl-4-benzyl-5-oxazolone (LXXI; $R^2 = C_6H_5$, $R^3 = C_6H_5CH_2$) which could in turn be isolated in good yield (283).

That the action of acetic anhydride on an aqueous solution of an optically active acylamino acid, either as its sodium salt or in the presence of sodium acetate, may also induce racemization was observed by du Vigneaud in collaboration with Sealock (300) and Meyer (301). Optical inactivation of tryptophan, methionine, glutamic acid, phenylalanine, arginine, and tyrosine was so effected. Similar attempts to racemize acetyl-L-proline, which cannot form an azlactone, were unsuccessful. In the light of these findings, the following mechanism for the racemization in aqueous solution was proposed (302):

$$\underset{\text{LXXII}}{CH_3CO\!\!-\!\!NHCHRCO_2H}$$
$$\Updownarrow$$

$$\underset{\text{LXXIII}}{\begin{array}{c}RC\!\!=\!\!=\!\!C\!\!-\!\!OH\\|\quad\quad\;|\\N\quad\;\;O\\\diagdown\!\!\diagup\\C\!\!-\!\!CH_3\end{array}} \leftrightharpoons \underset{\text{LXXIV}}{\begin{array}{c}RCH\!\!-\!\!C\!\!=\!\!O\\|\quad\quad\;|\\N\quad\;\;O\\\diagdown\!\!\diagup\\C\!\!-\!\!CH_3\end{array}} \leftrightharpoons \underset{\text{LXXV}}{\begin{array}{c}RC\!\!-\!\!-\!\!C\!\!=\!\!O\\\|\quad\quad\;|\\N\quad\;\;O\\\diagdown\!\!\diagup\\H\!\!-\!\!C\!\!-\!\!CH_3\end{array}}$$

The suggestion of a transitory azlactone intermediate (LXXIV), in equilibrium with its tautomeric enol form (LXXIII), was identical with the mechanism previously offered by Bergmann and Zervas (297) for non-aqueous systems. The implication of an alternative form (LXXV) which arises from the migration of a hydrogen atom to the C_2-position of the azlactone ring, although somewhat less tenable, cannot be entirely precluded. In this connection, it is worthy of note that compounds of comparable structure (LXXVI) have, in fact, been prepared by Bergmann, Ensslin, and Zervas (303). However, these were susceptible to easy hydrolytic cleavage with the concomitant formation of an aldehyde (LXXVIII) and an acylated amino acid (LXXVII).

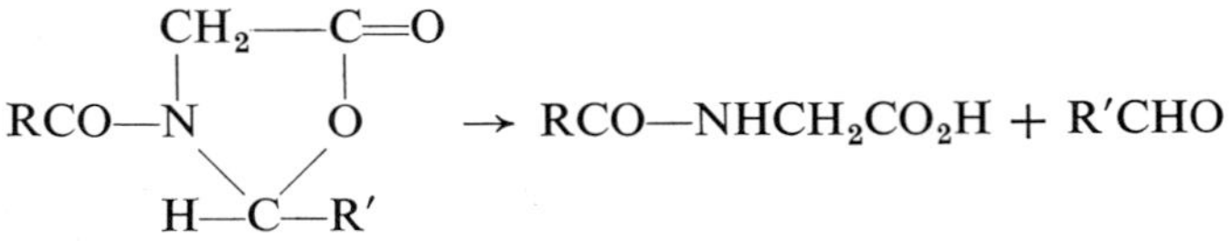

$$\text{RCO—N} \underset{\substack{| \\ H-C-R'}}{\overset{\substack{CH_2-C=O \\ |}}{\diagdown_O\diagup}} \rightarrow \text{RCO—NHCH}_2\text{CO}_2\text{H} + \text{R'CHO}$$

LXXVI LXXVII LXXVIII

The inability of acylated proline derivatives to form azlactones, as well as their failure to undergo racemization in aqueous solutions, afforded considerable support for the contention that racemizations induced by acetic anhydride were mediated exclusively by azlactone intermediates (302). Later evidence demonstrated, however, that the racemization of the optical forms of both proline (273, 304) and hydroxyproline (305) could be accomplished under the somewhat more severe conditions imposed by a mixture of acetic anhydride in hot glacial acetic acid. Since structural considerations obviate the possibility of azlactone formation with either of these compounds, the postulation of alternative intermediates is required. Consideration of the enol-keto shifts of acylated amino acids proposed earlier (296, 297), as depicted for acetylproline (LXXX) below, thereby becomes somewhat more likely here, although the implication of still other intermediates cannot as yet be precluded.

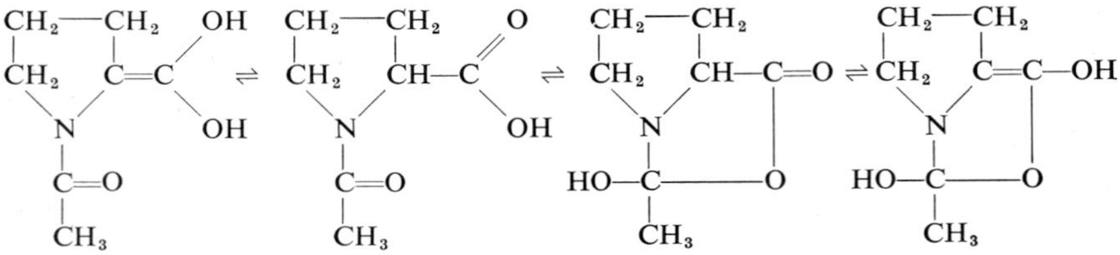

LXXIX LXXX LXXXI LXXXII

Optically Active Azlactones. Despite the rapid rate at which racemization occurs at the α-asymmetric center of optically active acylamino acids upon their transformation into azlactones, the existence of optically active azlactones is none the less theoretically possible. Thus Johnson and

Scott (306) in 1913 reported that 1-acyl-2-thiohydantoins (LXXXVI) are obtained upon treatment of an α-acylamino acid (LXXXIV) with acetic anhydride and ammonium thiocyanate. That an azlactone intermediate (LXXXV) might be involved was indicated by the finding that, although 2-thiohydantoins may be secured from azlactones in the absence of acetic anhydride, the presence of the latter reagent was essential for their production from α-acylamino acids. On the basis of these conclusions, the actual existence of optically active azlactones was suggested some twenty years later by Csonka and Nicolet (307), who isolated optically active 1-acetyl-2-thio-5-methylhydantoin (LXXXVI; R = R' = CH$_3$) from the reaction of L-alanine (LXXXIII; R = CH$_3$) with a five-fold excess of acetic anhydride containing somewhat more than one equivalent of ammonium thiocyanate. If the addition of thiocyanate was withheld for some thirty minutes after the initiation of the reaction, however, a racemic product was isolated. Such occurrence was presumably due to catalytic racemization (297) via an azlactone intermediate. The rationale for invoking an intermediate optically active azlactone (LXXXV; R = R' = CH$_3$) was presented as follows: "(a) In the presence of a large excess of acetic anhydride, azlactone formation can take place so rapidly that little racemization occurs. (b) An *active azlactone* is thus formed. This can react with ammonium thiocyanate with sufficient rapidity to stabilize the product as the thiohydantoin with little racemization. (c) In the absence of thiocyanate, the *active azlactone*, which must have formed at approximately the same rate in both cases, is completely racemized in half an hour, and perhaps in less time, under the conditions used" (307). Active 1-benzoyl-2-thio-5-isobutylhydantoin (LXXVI; R = CH$_3$CH(CH$_3$)CH$_2$, R' = C$_6$H$_5$) could later be similarly obtained from benzoyl-L-leucine (283).

$$\underset{\text{LXXXIII}}{\overset{NH_2}{\underset{|}{RCHCO_2H}}} \xrightarrow{Ac_2O} \underset{\text{LXXXIV}}{\overset{NHCOR'}{\underset{|}{RCHCO_2H}}} \xrightarrow{Ac_2O} \underset{\text{LXXXV}}{\begin{array}{c} RCH\text{---}CO \\ | \quad \quad | \\ N \quad \quad O \\ \diagdown \;\; \diagup \\ C\text{---}R' \end{array}} \xrightarrow{NH_4CNS} \underset{\text{LXXXVI}}{\begin{array}{c} RCH\text{---}CO \\ | \quad \quad | \\ R'CON \quad NH \\ \diagdown \;\; \diagup \\ CS \end{array}}$$

If the afore-mentioned assumptions of Csonka and Nicolet (307) possessed validity, then one means whereby the existence of optically active azlactones might be demonstrated involved the actual "trapping" of the azlactone prior to the occurrence of appreciable racemization. Subsequent experiments toward this end included the combined use of absorption spectra and polarimetry for following the rate of azlactone formation (283). Thus the point of quantitative conversion of benzoyl-L-leucine to its oxazolone, as mediated by acetic anhydride at room temperature, could be detected on the basis of the intensity of the absorption band characteristically exhibited by the oxazolone at 243 mμ. A similar experiment in dioxane, followed polarimetrically, revealed that the initial dextrorotation of the solution passed to a maximal levorotation at the point where the ultraviolet absorption indicated oxazolone formation as essentially complete. A steady decline in rotation due to racemization then ensued, the rotation eventually becoming constant at a slight dextrorotation, presumably because of the presence of some impurity in the starting material. With such data on hand, the isolation of several crystalline optically active azlactones, e.g., 2-phenyl-4-isobutyl-5-oxazolone, could be successfully achieved. The problem concerning the involvement of optically active azlactones as intermediates in thiohydantoin formation was thereby satisfactorily resolved.

Utilization of optically active azlactones in the preparation of ester or amide derivatives has invariably proceeded with the formation of racemic products (283). Such a phenomenon could be directly ascribed to the rate of the reaction which, for both methanolysis and aminolysis, was shown to occur at a markedly slower pace than that of racemization. However, the reaction of oxazolones with thiocyanates is a remarkably facile one, a factor to which the successful isolation of optically active thiohydantoins is presumably attributable.

Peptide and Dehydropeptide Formation via Azlactone Intermediates. The quite vigorous reaction which saturated azlactones undergo with amines was first demonstrated in 1908 by Mohr and Geis (284), who obtained benzoyl-α-aminoisobutyric acid amide (XCI; R = R′ = CH$_3$) by treatment of 2-phenyl-4:4-dimethyl-5-oxazolone (LXXXVIII; R = R′ = CH$_3$) with an alcoholic solution of ammonia. One year later, Mohr and Stroschein (256) extended these studies to include the reaction of 2-phenyl-4-methyl-5-oxazolone (LXXXVIII; R = H, R′ = CH$_3$) and 2-phenyl-4-benzyl-5-oxazolone (LXXXVIII; R = H, R′ = CH$_2$C$_6$H$_5$) with alcoholic ammonia, aniline, and aqueous alkaline solutions of glycine, alanine, and α-aminoisobutyric acid. The corresponding amide or peptide derivatives of benzoyl-DL-alanine and benzoyl-DL-phenylalanine were thereby secured. These are depicted in the accompanying scheme. Where benzoyldipeptides were

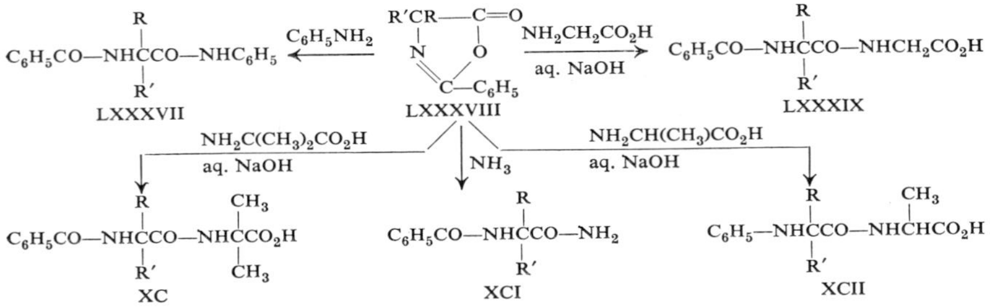

obtained, these were racemic or, if they contained two centers of asymmetry, were mixtures of the epimeric racemates. Further reaction of the benzoyldipeptides so secured could be effected upon their conversion to the corresponding azlactone, followed by condensation with an amine or an amino acid, as previously. These preliminary investigations were more fully described in a later series of five papers by Mohr (285, 288, 289) entitled, "Mitteilung über lactonähnliche Anhydride acylierter Aminosaüren."[45] Although several studies which implicated saturated azlactones as intermediates in the synthesis of peptides have since appeared, these have for the most part been of limited general application (123, 273, 283, 286). In these later syntheses it was reported that the treatment of the azlactone with a free amino acid in boiling aqueous alcohol, and in the absence of alkali, may be employed as an alternative route to the desired peptide.

Illustrative procedure 10-9 (283). Hippurylglycine (LXXXIX; R = R′ = H). To a solution of 0.9 g. glycine in 50 ml. of 60% alcohol is added 2 g. of 2-phenyl-5-oxazolone (LXXXVIII; R = R′ = H) (procedure 10-7). The reactants are heated under reflux for 12 hr., and the alcohol is then distilled. The crystalline precipitate which separates from the residual solution is collected and extracted with benzene, which dissolves 0.2 g. of the unchanged azlactone. The benzene-insoluble portion is crystallized several times from hot water and ultimately yields 2 g. of hippurylglycine; m.p. 206°.

In an endeavor to extend the scope of then available peptide syntheses, Bergmann and his collaborators intelligently exploited the properties of azlactones to permit the incorporation into peptides of some of the more complex amino acids. Unlike the work of earlier investigators which relied solely upon the use of saturated azlactones, these studies employed unsaturated azlactones of the type previously investigated by Erlenmeyer and Früstück (265). These were utilized in a series of ingeniously conceived procedures which ultimately led to the production of a variety of phenylalanyl and tyrosyl peptides, in addition to a host of dehydropeptides. Such studies were launched in 1926 by Bergmann, Stern, and Witte (123), who observed that, although unsaturated azlactones were relatively stable in cold water, their reaction with amines was quite facile. As with the saturated azlactones, treatment of an unsaturated azlactone with the alkali salt of an amino acid proceeded with the opening of the azlactone ring and the attendant formation of a peptide bond. This reaction scheme was subsequently employed for the synthesis of a notable series of dehydrogenated peptides containing C-terminal glycine, leucine, glutamic acid, tyrosine, arginine, serine, phenylalanine, phenylserine, and cystine residues (123–125, 308–314). The resulting N-acylated dehydropeptide could be converted to the corresponding saturated peptide derivative upon catalytic reduction. In several instances, selective hydrolytic removal of the acyl substituent could be mediated with acid, and the free peptide thereby obtained. The synthesis of phenylalanylglutamic acid (XCVII), as given below, is illustrative of the use of the method (123).

$$\underset{\underset{\text{XCIII}}{\text{2-Methyl-4-benzal-5-oxazolone}}}{\overset{\text{C}_6\text{H}_5\text{CH}=\text{C}-\text{C}=\text{O}}{\underset{\text{N}\diagdown\diagup\text{O}}{\underset{\text{C}-\text{CH}_3}{|}}}} + \underset{\underset{\text{XCIV}}{\text{L-Glutamic acid}}}{\overset{\text{NH}_2\text{CHCO}_2\text{H}}{\underset{\text{CH}_2\text{CO}_2\text{H}}{\underset{|}{\text{CH}_2}}}} \xrightarrow[(\text{CH}_3)_2\text{CO-H}_2\text{O}]{\text{NaOH}} \underset{\underset{\text{XCV}}{\alpha\text{-Acetamidocinnamyl-L-glutamic acid}}}{\overset{\text{CHC}_6\text{H}_5\ \ \text{CO}_2\text{H}}{\underset{\text{CH}_3\text{CO}-\text{NHCCO}-\text{NHCHCH}_2\text{CH}_2\text{CO}_2\text{H}}{||\qquad\qquad\ \ |}}} \xrightarrow[\text{catalyst}]{\text{H}_2}$$

$$\underset{\underset{\text{XCVI}}{\substack{\text{Acetyl-L-phenylalanyl-L-glutamic acid}\\ \text{Acetyl-D-phenylalanyl-L-glutamic acid}}}}{\overset{\text{CH}_2\text{C}_6\text{H}_5\ \ \text{CO}_2\text{H}}{\underset{\text{CH}_3\text{CO}-\text{NHCHCO}-\text{NHCHCH}_2\text{CH}_2\text{CO}_2\text{H}}{|\qquad\qquad\qquad\ |}}} \xrightarrow[\text{hydrolysis}]{\text{selective}} \underset{\underset{\text{XCVII}}{\substack{\text{L-Phenylalanyl-L-glutamic acid}\\ \text{D-Phenylalanyl-L-glutamic acid}}}}{\overset{\text{CH}_2\text{C}_6\text{H}_5\ \ \text{CO}_2\text{H}}{\underset{\text{NH}_2\text{CHCO}-\text{NHCHCH}_2\text{CH}_2\text{CO}_2\text{H}}{|\qquad\qquad\ |}}}$$

Inasmuch as the reduction of a dehydropeptide to the corresponding saturated peptide derivative proceeds with the generation of an asymmetric carbon atom, the problem of separation of diastereomers becomes of some concern here. In the synthesis cited above, the conversion of the non-asymmetric dehydrophenylalanine to the racemic phenylalanine residue in a molecule which already incorporated an L-glutamic acid residue gave rise to an acyldipeptide (XCVI) constituted of an epimeric mixture of the D-L and L-L stereomers. In this instance, the separation of the diastereomeric forms could be achieved through fractional crystallization procedures and each of the pure optically active stereomers subsequently secured. Unfortunately, isolations of comparable type were not invariably successful. Thus the preparation of D-phenylalanyl-L-arginine (124) and D-tyrosyl-L-arginine (125) from the corresponding dehydropeptide intermediates did not, for example, lead to the isolation of the respective L-L stereomers. Whether hydrogenation proceeded asymmetrically with the production of a single stereomeric form or whether the L-L form was lost during the isolation procedure could not be ascertained. Despite this apparent shortcoming, however, the method possessed the virtue of permitting the synthesis of such peptides as DL-histidylglycine (290), which were hitherto unavailable through other synthetic routes.

Doherty, Tietzman, and Bergmann (308) demonstrated that peptides with a C-terminal glycine residue, when treated with an aromatic aldehyde at 40° in the presence of acetic anhydride and sodium acetate, gave rise to the azlactones of unsaturated peptides. Thus the interaction of acetyl-dehydrophenylalanylglycine (XCVIII) and benzaldehyde yielded an azlactone (XCIX) which, upon alkaline hydrolysis, was converted to the doubly unsaturated peptide acetyldehydrophenylalanyldehydrophenylalanine (C). Use of *p*-hydroxybenzaldehyde in lieu of benzaldehyde permitted access to peptides which incorporated a dehydrogenated tyrosine residue. The azlactone (XCIX) could be alternatively obtained by the condensation of 2-methyl-4-benzal-5-oxazolone (CI) with *trans*-phenylserine (CII), succeeded

CHEMICAL PROCEDURES FOR SYNTHESIS OF PEPTIDES

by treatment of the resulting peptide (CIII) with an acetic anhydride–sodium acetate mixture at room temperature. The suggestion was offered that the transformation of the peptide into the azlactone proceeded, not by the simple elimination of two molecules of water, but rather through an intermediary stage whereby the β-hydroxyl group of the phenylserine residue was first acetylated and one equivalent of acetic acid subsequently eliminated from the molecule.

$$\underset{\text{XCVIII}}{\underset{\|}{\text{CH}_3\text{CO—NHCCO—NHCH}_2\text{CO}_2\text{H}}^{\text{CHC}_6\text{H}_5}} \xrightarrow[\text{Ac}_2\text{O}]{\text{C}_6\text{H}_5\text{CHO}} \underset{\underset{\text{CH}_3\text{CONHC=CHC}_6\text{H}_5}{\text{XCIX}}}{\text{C}_6\text{H}_5\text{CH=C}\underset{\text{N}\diagdown\diagup\text{O}}{\overset{\text{C}=\text{O}}{|}}} \xrightarrow[\text{alkali}]{\text{H}_2\text{O}} \underset{\text{C}}{\underset{\|}{\text{CH}_3\text{CO—NHCCO—NHCCO}_2\text{H}}^{\text{CHC}_6\text{H}_5}_{\overset{\|}{\text{CHC}_6\text{H}_5}}}$$

$$\underset{\text{CI}}{\text{C}_6\text{H}_5\text{CH=C}\underset{\text{N}\diagdown\diagup\text{O}}{\overset{\text{C}=\text{O}}{|}}\atop\text{C—CH}_3} + \underset{\text{CII}}{\text{C}_6\text{H}_5\text{CH—CHCO}_2\text{H}}^{\text{OH NH}_2} \longrightarrow \underset{\text{CIII}}{\underset{\|}{\text{CH}_3\text{CO—NHCCO—NHCHCO}_2\text{H}}^{\text{CHC}_6\text{H}_5\ \ \ \text{CH(OH)C}_6\text{H}_5}}$$

Illustrative procedure 10–10 (308). Acetyldehydrophenylalanylglycine (XCVIII). To a suspension of 30 g. of glycine in 400 ml. of acetone is added with stirring 400 ml. of N NaOH and, after several minutes, 75 g. of 2-methyl-4-benzal-5-oxazolone (procedures 10–5 and 10–6). After several hours, 410 ml. of N HCl is added to the clear solution, with the acetyldehydrophenylalanylglycine (95 g.) crystallizing out at 0°. The precipitate is recrystallized from aqueous potassium bicarbonate by the addition of hydrochloric acid; m.p., 194–195° (corr.). Preparation of the acetyldehydrophenylalanyl derivative of L-alanine, L-arginine, L-glutamic acid, L-leucine, L-phenylalanine, L-proline, DL-serine, or L-tyrosine may be achieved through an essentially similar procedure upon substitution of the requisite amino acid for glycine (Table 10–11).

Acetyldehydrophenylalanyldehydrophenylalanine azlactone (XCIX). Sixty-five grams of acetyldehydrophenylalanylglycine is thoroughly mixed with 75 ml. of acetic anhydride, 30 ml. of benzaldehyde, and 17 g. of anhydrous sodium acetate, and the reaction mixture kept for 2 days at room temperature. The excess acetic anhydride is then decomposed with 75 ml. of water at 0°. On filtration, 60 g. of the desired azlactone is obtained, and this compound recrystallized from water-acetone; m.p. 184–186° (corr.).

Acetyldehydrophenylalanyldehydrophenylalanine (C). Thirty grams of the azlactone (XCIX) is dissolved in a mixture of 300 ml. of acetone and 125 ml. of N NaOH. After some 2 hr., 130 ml. of N HCl is added. Needles of a bright buff color precipitate, and these are dissolved in a boiling mixture of 500 ml. of ethanol and 230 ml. of water; precipitation is effected by the addition of more water at 0°; yield, 28.0. g; m.p. 204–205° d. (corr.).

The intermediate azlactone (XCIX) has also been utilized for elongation of the dehydropeptide chain by reaction with an amino acid in aqueous alkali-acetone solution. Preparation of doubly unsaturated tripeptide derivatives could be thereby accomplished. The latter compounds have in turn been involved in the production of tri-, tetra-, and pentapeptides incorporating from two to four double bonds subsequent to their conversion to the corresponding azlactone intermediates, as above. Through the employment of such procedures, Bergmann and his collaborators were able to synthesize an impressive number of dehydropeptides of diverse composition, many of which are listed in Table 10–11. Note should be taken that, since the possibility of *cis-trans* isomerism exists in peptides and azlactones which incorporate one or more double bonds, these compounds may be expected to exist as several different stereoisomeric forms.

Illustrative procedure 10–11 (308). Acetyl-bis-(dehydrophenylalanyl)glycine. This acylated tripeptide is prepared by stirring 4.7 g. of glycine with 100 ml. of acetone, 62.5 ml. of N NaOH, and 20.7 g. of the pertinent azlactone (XCIX) (procedure 10–10). After 3–4 hr., the clear solution is acidified with 65 ml. of N HCl, some 24.5 g. of the tripeptide crystallizing as heavy plates at 0°. This is dissolved in a mixture of 600 ml. of water and 250 ml. of methanol with the aid of 12 g. of sodium bicarbonate. Upon acidification with hydrochloric acid followed by the addition of some ether, the peptide crystallizes. Recrystallization is effected by dissolving the material in 1 l. of hot methanol containing 100 ml. of water, and subsequently adding 1 l. of water thereto; yield, 21.7 g.; m.p. 216° d. (corr.). The acetyl-bis-(dehydrophenylalanyl) derivative of L-alanine, L-glutamic acid, L-leucine, L-phenylalanine, DL-phenylserine, L-proline, or L-tyrosine may be prepared by essentially the same procedure upon substitution of the requisite amino acid for glycine (Table 10–11).

Bergmann and Stern (272) demonstrated that the use of aldehydes in the preparation of unsaturated azlactones could be avoided through the utilization of haloacylamino acids. Thus the chloroacetyl derivatives of phenylalanine (272) and leucine (308), for example, when warmed with acetic anhydride, readily form the requisite unsaturated azlactone by the elimination of one molecule each of water and hydrogen chloride. However, if chloroacetylphenylserine (CIV) is dehydrated under carefully controlled conditions by the action of acetic anhydride, the corresponding azlactone (CV) may be formed with the chloroacetyl moiety left intact (281). Upon hydrolysis with dilute alkali, scission of the ring occurs and chloroacetyldehydrophenylalanine (CVI) is formed. Glycyldehydrophenylalanine (CVII) is produced upon amination of the latter with aqueous ammonia.

Glycyldehydrophenylalanine may be considered the first member of the class of unsaturated peptides which possessed both a free α-amino group and a free α-carboxyl group. Availability of this material facilitated and encouraged the use of substances of this type in studies on tissue metabolism. Peptides wherein the dehydrophenylalanine residue occupied a position in the middle of the peptide chain could be prepared (281) by permitting the pertinent azlactone (CV) to open in the presence of sodium glycinate; the chloroacetyldehydrophenylalanylglycine (CVIII) thereby obtained could, in turn, be converted to glycyldehydrophenylalanylglycine (CIX) upon treatment with ammonia. Alternative methods for the preparation of analogous dehydropeptides involved the condensation of amides or nitriles with α-keto acids (Section 10–9).

Evaluation of the Method. Although the azlactone procedure has permitted the synthesis of a number of complex peptides which were hitherto unavailable through employment of the earlier methods of Fischer and his contemporaries, the results were on the whole far from satisfactory. Removal of the N-acetyl group with hot acid entailed a certain breakdown of the peptide molecule, but, even more serious, the formation of a racemic residue at the N-terminal position of the peptide chain necessarily led to either a racemic or an epimeric mixture. In a few exceptional instances, fractional separation of diastereomers could be achieved via a series of tedious manipulations which were reminiscent of the earlier procedures of Fischer. In other instances, only the undesirable stereomer could be isolated. Such was the case with the arginine peptides alluded to above, wherein isolation of only the unnatural D-L stereomer was achieved from a synthesis potentially directed toward the preparation of DL-phenylalanyl-L-arginine (or DL-tyrosyl-L-arginine). The azlactone method has, however, currently assumed importance as a source of dehydropeptides, which have been extensively employed in enzyme specificity studies.

9. Properties of Dehydropeptides and Their Preparation via the Condensation of Amides or Nitriles with α-Keto Acids. *Principle.* An alternative to the azlactone procedure for the preparation of the shorter-chain dehydropeptides (I) is offered by the direct condensation, through heating, of an α-keto acid (III) with one equivalent of a fatty acid amide (II), or by treatment of an α-keto acid (III) with a nitrile (II) in the presence of dry hydrogen chloride gas. If the former reaction proceeds with the condensation of two molecules of amide per molecule of α-keto acid, the corresponding α,α-di(acylamino)aliphatic acid (IV) is formed. This compound (IV) may also arise from the treatment of the α-keto acid with an excess of the nitrile in sulfuric acid solution (Böttinger reaction). Warming of (IV) under certain circumstances with glacial acetic acid results in partial deacylation with the concomitant formation of the corresponding dehydropeptide (I). Controlled

TABLE 10-11
Some Dehydropeptides Prepared via Azlactone Intermediates by Bergmann and Co-workers

Dehydropeptide	M.P., °C.	$[\alpha]_D$, deg.	Temp., °C.	Solvent	Ref.
Dipeptides with one double bond					
Acetyldehydroleucylglycine	185–187	—	—	—	308
Acetyldehydrophenylalanyl-L-alanine	195–196	+69.4	32	2%, pyridine	124
Acetyldehydrophenylalanyl-L-arginine	192–193	−18.0	23	9.4%, H_2O	124
Acetyldehydrophenylalanyl-L-glutamic acid	170	−4.6	22	8.9%, pyridine	123
Acetyldehydrophenylalanylglycine	194–195	—	—	—	314
Acetyldehydrophenylalanyl-L-leucine	218–219	+37.2	31	2.5%, pyridine	313
Acetyldehydrophenylalanyl-L-phenylalanine	213–215	+37.6	28	5%, pyridine	308
Acetyldehydrophenylalanyl-DL-phenylserine	226–228	—	—	—	308
Acetyldehydrophenylalanyl-L-proline	140–142	+80.5	32	2%, pyridine	313
Acetyldehydrophenylalanyl-DL-serine	179	—	—	—	311
Acetyldehydrophenylalanyl-L-tyrosine	217–218	+47.1	20	2.3%, pyridine	123
Acetyl-DL-phenylalanyldehydrophenylalanine	206–207	—	—	—	308
Benzoyldehydrophenylalanylglycine	200–201	—	—	—	308
Benzoyldehydrophenylalanyl-DL-phenylserine	180	—	—	—	308
Carbobenzoxyglycyldehydrophenylalanine	141–142	—	—	—	308
Chloroacetyldehydrophenylalanyl-L-glutamic acid	91–92	—	—	—	281
Chloroacetyldehydrophenylalanylglycine	>200	—	—	—	281
Glycyldehydrophenylalanine	277	—	—	—	281
Glycyldehydrophenylalanyl-L-glutamic acid	174	—	—	—	281
Glycyldehydrophenylalanylglycine	224	—	—	—	281

Dipeptides with two double bonds				
Acetyldehydroleucyldehydrophenylalanine	215–216	—	—	—	308
Acetyldehydrophenylalanyldehydrophenylalanine	204–205	—	—	—	308
Acetyldehydrophenylalanyldehydrotyrosine	218	—	—	—	308
Benzoyldehydrophenylalanyldehydrophenylalanine	180–181	—	—	—	308
Benzoyldehydrophenylalanyldehydrotyrosine	164–166	—	—	—	308
Tripeptides with one double bond				
Carbobenzoxyglycyldehydrophenylalanyl-L-glutamic acid	177–179	−29.6	28	4.8%, pyridine	308
Carbobenzoxyglycyldehydrophenylalanyl-DL-phenylserine	168–170	—	—	—	308
Tripeptides with two double bonds				
Acetylbis(dehydrophenylalanyl)-L-alanine	215–216	−268.4	29	2.3%, pyridine	308
Acetylbis(dehydrophenylalanyl)-L-glutamic acid	209–210	−182.6	30	pyridine[a]	308
Acetylbis(dehydrophenylalanyl)glycine	216	—	—	—	308
Acetylbis(dehydrophenylalanyl)-L-leucine	235–236	−245.6	32	2%, pyridine	308
Acetylbis(dehydrophenylalanyl)-L-phenylalanine	229–230	−172.2	28	5%, pyridine	308
Acetylbis(dehydrophenylalanyl)-DL-phenylserine	223–225	—	—	—	308
Acetylbis(dehydrophenylalanyl)-L-proline	203–204	+50.6	29	2%, pyridine	308
Acetylbis(dehydrophenylalanyl)-L-tyrosine	172–173.5	−137.1	30	2.1%, pyridine	308
Bis(acetyldehydrophenylalanyl)-L-cystine	212–213	−19.5	30.5	2%, pyridine	308
Tetrapeptides with three double bonds				
Acetyltris(dehydrophenylalanyl)-L-phenylalanine	201–202	−36.3	30	2.3%, pyridine	308
Acetyltris(dehydrophenylalanyl)-DL-phenylserine	199	—	—	—	308
Pentapeptide with four double bonds				
Bis(acetyldehydrophenylalanyldehydrophenylalanyl)-L-cystine	209–211	−82.3	30	2%, pyridine	308

[a] No concentration given.

hydrolysis of C-terminal peptides of (IV) with hydrochloric acid, on the other hand, leads to a keto acid peptide.

$$\begin{array}{c} \text{RCO—NHC}(=\text{CHR}')\text{CO}_2\text{H} \\ \updownarrow \\ \text{RCO—N}=\text{C}(\text{CH}_2\text{R}')\text{CO}_2\text{H} \\ \text{I} \end{array} \quad \begin{array}{c} \text{RCO—NH}_2 \\ \text{or} \\ \text{RCN} \\ \text{II} \end{array} \xrightarrow{\text{warm glacial acetic acid}} \begin{array}{c} + \text{R}'\text{CH}_2\text{COCO}_2\text{H} \rightarrow \\ \text{III} \end{array} \quad \begin{array}{c} \text{RCO—NH} \quad \text{CH}_2\text{R}' \\ \diagdown \diagup \\ \text{C} \\ \diagup \diagdown \\ \text{RCO—NH} \quad \text{CO}_2\text{H} \\ \text{IV} \end{array}$$

Condensation of Amides with α-Keto Acids. In 1930, Bergmann and Grafe (315) observed that a mixture of acetamide (II; $R = CH_3$) and pyruvic acid (III; $R' = H$), when heated under reduced pressure, reacted with the formation of a mixture of α,α-di(acetamino)propionic acid (IV; $R = CH_3$, $R' = H$) and α-acetaminoacrylic acid (I; $R = CH_3$, $R' = H$). Formation of the former or the latter product was contingent upon whether the condensation proceeded with the reaction of one or two molecules of amide per molecule of pyruvic acid. Separation of these compounds could be readily achieved by fractional crystallization from ethyl acetate. The dehydropeptide (VI) could, in addition, be prepared from pure di(acetamino)propionic acid (V) by treatment with warm glacial acetic acid.

$$(CH_3CONH)_2C(CH_3)CO_2H \underset{CH_3CONH_2}{\rightleftarrows} CH_3CO—NHC(=CH_2)CO_2H$$
$$\text{V} \hspace{5cm} \text{VI}$$

$$CH_3COCO_2H + 3CH_3CONH_2 \rightarrow \left[\begin{array}{c} \text{OH} \\ | \\ CH_3-C-CO_2H \\ | \\ NHCOCH_3 \end{array} \right] \cdot 2CH_3CONH_2$$
$$\text{VII}$$

That the latter reaction was reversible was later demonstrated by Shemin and Herbst (316), who secured diacetaminopropionic acid (V) upon heating a mixture of acetylaminoacrylic acid (VI) and acetamide. A subsequent study of the interaction of acetamide with pyruvic acid by Herbst (317) indicated that the first step of the condensation probably resulted in the formation of a complex (VII) derived from one molecule of α-hydroxy-α-acetaminopropionic acid and two molecules of acetamide. Upon heating *in vacuo*, decomposition of such complex to the products (V and VI) noted then occurred.

That other acid amides would likewise condense with pyruvic acid when mixtures of the two reactants are simply heated was subsequently shown by Bergmann and Grafe (315), who obtained a mixture of chloroacetoaminacrylic acid (I; $R = ClCH_2$, $R' = H$) and α,α-di(chloroacetamino)propionic acid (IV; $R = ClCH_2$, $R' = H$) from chloroacetamide (II; $R = ClCH_2$)

and pyruvic acid; by Nicolet (318), who secured a mixture of α,α-di(benzoyl-amino)propionic acid (IV; R = C₆H₅, R' = H) and α-benzoylaminoacrylic acid (I; R = C₆H₅, R' = H) from benzamide (II; R = C₆H₅) and pyruvic acid; and by Martell and Herbst (319), who prepared a number of benzyl carbonyl derivatives through the interaction of benzyl carbamate (II; R = C₆H₅CH₂O) with a variety of carbonyl compounds. The analogous condensation of pyruvic acid with formamide (IX), by Shive and Shive (320), resulted in the formation of α-hydroxy-α-formaminopropionic acid (X), which upon decomposition yielded α-formiminopropionic acid (XI).

$$CH_3COCO_2H + HCONH_2 \rightarrow CH_3\underset{\underset{VIII}{}}{C}(OH)CO_2H \rightarrow CH_3\underset{\underset{XI}{}}{C}CO_2H$$
$$\underset{VIII}{} \quad \underset{IX}{} \quad \overset{\underset{|}{NHCHO}}{\underset{X}{}} \quad \overset{\underset{\|}{NCHO}}{\underset{XI}{}}$$

According to Martell and Herbst (319), the interaction between an amide and a keto acid proceeds through the primary addition of the amide to the carbonyl group, followed either (*a*) by the direct replacement of the hydroxyl group with another residue (see VII) to form the di(acylamino)propionic acid, or (*b*) by the elimination of water with the formation of unsaturated intermediates (acylated α-aminoacrylic acids) to which a second molecule of amide might add under the proper conditions. Although Shemin and Herbst (316) were able to demonstrate the reversibility of such reaction when pyruvic acid was the keto acid employed, comparable demonstration could not be achieved when the keto acid was phenylpyruvic acid (III; R' = C₆H₅), for acetamide would not condense with acetaminocinnamic acid (I; R = CH₃, R' = C₆H₅). This seeming discrepancy was ascribed (319) to the pronounced tendency of the phenyl group in the aminocinnamic acid derivatives to hold the side-chain double bond in a position conjugated with the aromatic ring, and thereby effectively prevent the tautomeric shift of the double bond to the carbon-nitrogen position. Thus, although di(acyl-amino)phenylpropionic acids (IV; R' = C₆H₅) may be readily prepared by heating two molecules of amide (II) with one of phenylpyruvic acid (III; R' = C₆H₅) (319), and acetaminocinnamic acid (I; R' = C₆H₅) prepared by heating one molecule of acetamide (II) with one of phenylpyruvic acid (III; R' = C₆H₅) (316), it is apparently much more difficult to prepare the di(acylamino)phenylpropionic acids by condensing acylaminocinnamic acids with amides. It therefore appears feasible that, for this class of compounds, mechanism (*a*) above would prevail, whereas the alternative mechanism (*b*) might in turn hold for pyruvic acid derivatives.

The ready preparation of acylaminoacrylic acids (dehydropeptides) from the corresponding di(acylamino)propionic acids strongly suggests that one of the amide residues of these latter compounds is relatively labile. In other words, it might appear that the di(acylamino)propionic acids are probably acylaminoacrylic acids to which an amide residue is more or less loosely attached at the double bond, as in

$$\begin{bmatrix} RCH_2CON=C \diagup^{CH_3}_{\diagdown CO_2H} \\ RCH_2CONH_2 \end{bmatrix} \rightleftharpoons \begin{array}{c} RCH_2CONH \diagdown \diagup CH_3 \\ C \\ RCH_2CONH \diagup \diagdown CO_2H \end{array}$$
$$\text{XII} \qquad\qquad\qquad\qquad \text{XIII}$$

Although these compounds are quite stable in aqueous solution under ordinary circumstances, removal of one of the acyl groups with the concomitant liberation of a free amino group, as exemplified by α-acetamino-α-aminopropionic acid (XIV) (321), then causes the compound to become exceedingly unstable in aqueous solution and to undergo spontaneous decomposition into one mole each of ammonia, pyruvic acid, and acetamide (Figure 10-2). In the presence of aqueous rat kidney extract, such decomposition is markedly accelerated (322).

$$\begin{array}{c} CH_3CONH \diagdown \diagup CH_3 \\ C \\ NH_2 \diagup \diagdown CO_2H \end{array} \xrightarrow{H_2O} NH_3 + CH_3COCO_2H + CH_3CONH_2$$
$$\text{XIV} \qquad\qquad\qquad \text{XV} \qquad \text{XVI} \qquad\qquad \text{XVII}$$

The Böttinger Synthesis. The preparation of large quantities of pure di(acylamino)propionic acids, uncontaminated with the corresponding acylaminoacrylic acids, may be effected (322) by a reaction first described by Böttinger (323) in 1881. This reaction involves the addition of an excess of a nitrile to a solution of pyruvic acid in chilled concentrated sulfuric acid which, when poured onto cracked ice, results in the appearance of the desired di(acylamino)propionic acid in good yield. In this manner, considerable amounts of crystalline di(acetamino)propionic acid (326), di(chloroacetamino)propionic acid (322), and several other α,α-di(acylamino)aliphatic acids (324, 325) could be obtained (Table 10-12).

The Böttinger synthesis may be considered to proceed primarily via two steps, the first a condensation of nitrile (XVIII) with keto acid (XIX) to form the corresponding dehydropeptide (XX), the second a fixation of a second molecule of nitrile, in the presence of water (whereby the nascent amide is formed), on the double bond of the dehydropeptide, thereby giving rise to the α,α-di(acylamino)aliphatic acid (XXI). This is exemplified by the preparation of α,α-di(chloroacetamino)propionic acid (XXI) below (procedure 10-12):

$$ClCH_2CN + CH_3COCO_2H \xrightarrow{H_2SO_4} ClCH_2CON=C(CH_3)CO_2H \xrightarrow[ClCH_2CN]{H_2O}$$
$$\text{XVIII} \qquad \text{XIX} \qquad\qquad\qquad \text{XX}$$

$$(ClCH_2CONH)_2C(CH_3)CO_2H \xrightarrow{NH_3} HCl \cdot (NH_2CH_2CONH)_2C(CH_3)CO_2H$$
$$\text{XXI} \qquad\qquad\qquad\qquad\qquad \text{XXII}$$

On treatment with aqueous ammonia, (XXI) is converted to α,α-di(glycylamino)propionic acid hydrochloride (XXII) which, in aqueous solution, is both stable and neutral in reaction. Analogous reactions involving the action of α-chloroacetonitrile on a variety of α-keto acids (325, 327), and of DL-α-chloropropionitrile on pyruvic acid (324), are also known (Table 10–12).

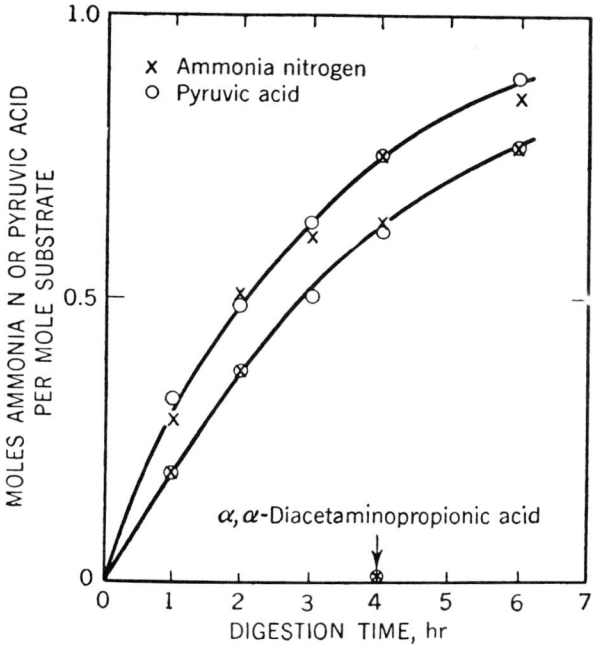

Figure 10–2. Spontaneous hydrolysis of α-acetamino-α-aminopropionic acid to equivalent amounts of ammonia and pyruvic acid at 37°: upper curve with rat kidney extract; lower curve, in water. Gonçalves, J. M., and Greenstein, J. P., *Arch. Biochem.*, **16**, 1 (1948).

Illustrative procedure 10–12 (322). α,α-Di(chloroacetamino)propionic acid (XXI). Sixty grams of freshly distilled pyruvic acid is dissolved in 500 ml. of chilled, concentrated sulfuric acid, the solution placed in an ice-salt bath, and 100 g. of redistilled chloroacetonitrile added slowly thereto with stirring; the temperature is never allowed to rise above 15°. The addition requires about 2 hr. to complete, at the end of which time the solution is highly viscous. This is poured in a thin stream over 4 l. of ice shavings with vigorous stirring. A white precipitate appears almost immediately. After the ice has melted, the precipitate is filtered by suction, washed several times with ice water, and crystallized twice from hot water. The product appears as large, glistening prisms in 33% yield (based on the amount of chloroacetonitrile employed); m.p. 201°. Through initial employment of the pertinent reactants, a variety of other α,α-di(acylamino)aliphatic acids (Table 10–12) may be prepared by essentially the same procedure.

TABLE 10–12
α,α-Di(acylamino)aliphatic Acids Secured via the Böttinger Synthesis and Aminolysis Products Thereof

α,α-Di(acylamino)aliphatic Acid	M.P., °C.	Product of Aminolysis	M.P., °C.	Ref.
Di(acetamino)propionic	—	—	—	326
Di(acrylamino)propionic	154–5	—	—	325
Di(β-bromopropionylamino)propionic	136–7	—	—	325
α-Chloroacetamino-α-acetaminopropionic	176	α-Glycylamino-α-acetaminopropionic	—	325
Di(chloroacetamino)butyric	169–70	Di(glycylamino)butyric[a]	206d.	325
Di(chloroacetamino)-n-caproic	140–1	Di(glycylamino)-n-caproic[a]	206–7d.	325
Di(chloroacetamino)isocaproic	134	Di(glycylamino)isocaproic[a]	237d.	325
Di(chloroacetamino)propionic	201	Di(glycylamino)propionic[a]	199d.	322
		Di(N-methylglycylamino)propionic[a]	215d.	327
		Di(N-dimethylglycylamino)propionic[a]	219d.	327
Di(chloroacetamino)-n-valeric	140	Di(glycylamino)-n-valeric[a]	234d.	325
Di(chloroacetylglycylamino)propionic	98	Di(glycylglycylamino)propionic[a]	164d.	327
Di(γ-chlorobutyrylamino)propionic	112–5	—	—	325
Di(DL-chloropropionylamino)propionic	185	α-DL-Alanylamino-α-DL-chloropropionyl-aminopropionic	207d.	324
		Di(DL-alanylamino)propionic[a]	196d.	324
Di(β-chloropropionylamino)propionic	126–7	—	—	325

[a] As the monohydrochloride.

α,α-Di(glycylamino)propionic acid monohydrochloride (XXII). Twenty grams of di(chloroacetamino)propionic acid is dissolved in 200 ml. of 28% ammonia water and the reaction mixture kept at 37° for 36 hr. The solution is then evaporated *in vacuo* at 35° to a colorless syrup, the residue dissolved in 50 ml. of water, and the resulting solution treated with 200 ml. of absolute alcohol. The peptide precipitates as an oil which rapidly hardens. Three repetitions of this procedure ultimately yield a white precipitate of the peptide hydrochloride, which is filtered, washed successively with alcohol and ether, and finally dried over P_2O_5. The yield is 60 g. (80% of theory); m.p. 199° (d.).

Some attention has been paid to the enzymic behavior of α,α-di(acylamino)aliphatic acids because of their close relation to the dehydropeptides. Since several of these compounds, such as di(glycylamino)propionic acid, have been found to be highly susceptible to the enzymic hydrolytic activity of animal tissues, the mechanism of such breakdown may well involve intermediate dehydropeptide formation.

Condensation of Nitriles with α-Keto Acids. A relatively simple method of synthesis for certain dehydropeptides is based upon the reaction of a nitrile (XXIII) with an α-keto acid (328, 329). This mixture, when saturated with dry hydrogen chloride gas, leads to the nearly quantitative formation of the desired dehydropeptide (XXV) in a high degree of purity and in only a relatively brief space of time. So far as has been observed, the reaction is limited to the use of nitriles with a halogen substituent on the α-carbon atom; acetonitrile fails to react with pyruvic acid under identical conditions. The reaction may, in essence, be interpreted as due to the primary formation of the imino chloride of the amide (XXIV), which subsequently reacts with the enolic form of the keto acid. In this fashion, considerable quantities of α-haloacyldehydroamino acids have been prepared (procedure 10–13) from which the corresponding α-aminoacyldehydroamino acid may be secured by amination in aqueous ammonia (328–331) (Table 10–13).

$$\text{Cl—CHRCN} \xrightarrow{\text{HCl}} \text{Cl—CHRC} \begin{array}{c} \text{NH} \\ \diagup \\ \diagdown \\ \text{Cl} \end{array} \xrightarrow{\text{OHC(=CHR')CO}_2\text{H}} \begin{array}{c} \text{Cl—CHRCONHC(=CHR')CO}_2\text{H} \\ \updownarrow \\ \text{Cl—CHRCON=C(CH}_2\text{R')CO}_2\text{H} \end{array}$$

XXIII   XXIV   XXV

Illustrative procedure 10–13 (329). Chloroacetyldehydroalanine (XXV; R = R' = H). Seven and six-tenths grams of redistilled chloroacetonitrile is mixed with 10.6 g. of redistilled pyruvic acid, the reaction mixture chilled and saturated with dry hydrogen chloride gas. After standing for 1 hr. at 5°, the mixture turns to a solid mass of crystals of nearly pure chloroacetyldehydroalanine. The mixture is allowed to stand in ice for another 12 hr. and is then washed on a suction filter with dry ether; yield, 14 g. (86% of theory); m.p. 156°. A single recrystallization from acetone raises the melting point to 162°. This general procedure may be employed for the synthesis of all the α-haloacyldehydroamino acids listed in

TABLE 10–13
Dehydropeptides Secured via the Hydrogen Chloride-Catalyzed Condensation of Nitriles with α-Keto Acids and Aminolysis Products Thereof

Reactants α-Keto Acid	Nitrile	Condensation Product	Product upon[e] Amination	Ref.
α-Ketobutyric	Chloroacetonitrile	Chloroacetyldehydrobutyrine	Glycyldehydrobutyrine	332
α-Keto-n-caproic	Chloroacetonitrile	Chloroacetyldehydronorleucine	Glycyldehydronorleucine	332
α-Ketoisocaproic	Chloroacetonitrile	Chloroacetyldehydroleucine	Glycyldehydroleucine	331
α-Ketoisovaleric	Chloroacetonitrile	Chloroacetyldehydrovaline	Glycyldehydrovaline	331
α-Keto-β-methylvaleric	Chloroacetonitrile	Chloroacetyldehydroisoleucine	Glycyldehydroisoleucine	331
α-Keto-n-valeric	Chloroacetonitrile	Chloroacetyldehydronorvaline	Glycyldehydronorvaline	332
Pyruvic	Chloroacetonitrile	Chloroacetyldehydroalanine	Glycyldehydroalanine Sarcosyldehydroalanine[d]	328, 329 329
		Chloroacetylglycyldehydroalanine[a]	Glycylglycyldehydroalanine	329, 333
		Chloroacetylsarcosyldehydroalanine[b]	Glycylsarcosyldehydroalanine	329, 330
Pyruvic	α-Chloropropionitrile	DL-α-Chloropropionyldehydroalanine	DL-Alanyldehydroalanine	329

[a] Prepared by chloroacetylation of glycyldehydroalanine.
[b] Prepared by chloroacetylation of sarcosyldehydroalanine.
[c] These compounds are pure. The precursor condensation products are contaminated with chloroacetamide, and hence their melting points are not given; on aminolysis this contaminant is converted to the alcohol-soluble glycine amide, which is easily separated from the alcohol-insoluble peptides.
[d] From the treatment of chloroacetyldehydroalanine with methylamine.

Table 10–13. Amination with aqueous ammonia, as described in procedure 10–12, yields the respective α-aminoacyldehydroamino acid.

The reaction indicated by (XXIII) to (XXV) is analogous to the Böttinger synthesis (XVIII–XXI), which yields the di(acylamino)propionic acids. In the former synthesis, the keto acid is in excess and moisture is carefully excluded. In the latter synthesis, however, the nitrile is in excess, and the presence of water is required to permit the addition of the second amide residue to the dehydropeptide molecule.

Pyruvoylpeptides. Dipeptides of α-aminoacrylic acid (XXVI), on complete hydrolysis by acids or by enzymic action, yield, among other products, ammonia and pyruvic acid:

$$CH_3C(=NCOR)CO_2H \xrightarrow[\text{or HCl}]{\text{dehydropeptidase}} CH_3COCO_2H + NH_3 + RCO_2H$$
   XXVI   XXVII   XXVIII   XXIX

In comparable manner, tripeptides wherein the dehydroalanyl residue is in the middle of the chain give rise to pyruvoylpeptides upon controlled hydrolysis of the acyl residue. Thus Bergmann and Grafe (287) noted that α,α-di(acetamino)propionylglycine (XXXIV), which was synthesized via the action of glycine on the azlactone of α,α-di(acetamino)propionic acid (XXXIII), was converted to pyruvoylglycine (XXXV), acetic acid, and ammonia upon treatment with warm hydrochloric acid (procedure 10–14). Fruton and Bergmann (334) comparably observed the formation of phenylpyruvoylglycine from α-acetaminocinnamoylglycine and demonstrated, in addition, that α-keto peptides of the latter type exhibit a ready susceptibility to the action of crystalline carboxypeptidase.

$$CH_3CN + CH_3COCO_2H \xrightarrow{H_2SO_4} \underset{CH_3CONH}{\overset{CH_3CONH}{>}}C\underset{CO_2H}{\overset{CH_3}{<}} \xrightarrow{Ac_2O} \underset{CH_3}{\overset{CH_3CONH-C-C=O}{>}}N\underset{C-CH_3}{\overset{}{<}}O$$
   XXX   XXXI   XXXII   XXXIII

$$\xrightarrow{NH_2CH_2CO_2H,\ aq.\ NaOH}$$

$$(CH_3CONH)_2C(CH_3)CO-NHCH_2CO_2H \xrightarrow[HCl]{H_2O} CH_3COCO-NHCH_2CO_2H + 2CH_3CO_2H + NH_3$$
   XXXIV   XXXV   XXXVI   XXXVII

Illustrative procedure 10–14. α,α-Di(acetamino)propionic acid (XXXII) (323, 326). Four hundred milliliters of concentrated sulfuric acid is chilled to 10° with stirring and 77 g. of pyruvic acid (XXXI) added thereto. With good stirring, 100 g. of acetonitrile (XXX) is slowly added, care being taken that the temperature does not rise above 50°. The reaction requires about 1 hr, after which time the mixture is cooled to 10° and poured onto 4 l. of shaved ice. Intense chilling occurs and the reaction product crystallizes out. After the ice has melted, the precipitate is filtered off and washed thoroughly with cold water. A single crystallization from alcohol gives a 70–80% yield of pure di(acetamino)propionic acid (XXXII); m.p. 189–190° d. (corr.).

α,α-Di(acetamino)propionic acid azlactone (XXXIII) (287). A mixture of 38 g. of α,α-di(acetamino)propionic acid and 250 ml. of acetic anhydride is heated over a steam bath until complete solution is accomplished (about 2.5 hr.). The solution is then evaporated to dryness under reduced pressure, with the exclusion of moisture, and the slightly yellowish crystalline residue recrystallized from dry ethyl acetate. The yield, upon reworking of the mother liquors, is 85–90% of theory; m.p., 152° (corr.).

α,α-Di(acetamino)propionylglycine (XXXIV) (287). A suspension of 8.6 g. (0.05 mole) of di(acetamino)propionic acid azlactone (XXXIII) in 75 ml. of acetone is added, with cooling under tap water, to a solution of 3.8 g. (0.05 mole) of glycine in 50 ml. of N NaOH. After 10 min., 50 ml. of N sulfuric acid is added to the clear solution and the resulting mixture concentrated to dryness under reduced pressure without prior separation of any precipitated material. The residue is extracted four times, each with 50 ml. of boiling ethanol. Upon cooling, 12.5 g. of di(acetamino)propionylglycine (XXXIV) precipitates from the combined extracts and another 1.2 g. can be secured from the mother liquor; yield 95% of theory. The material contains 1 molecule of ethanol of crystallization. Recrystallization may be effected from ethanol; m.p. 215° d. (corr.).

Pyruvoylglycine (XXXV) (287). A solution of 10 g. of di(acetamino)propionylglycine (XXXIV) in 125 ml. of N hydrochloric acid is gently refluxed for 30 min. in an oil bath maintained at 115°. The solution is concentrated to dryness at 40–50° *in vacuo*, water added, and the evaporation repeated. After thorough extraction of the residue with ether, the combined ethereal extract is dried and concentrated. The resulting residue of pyruvoylglycine (XXXV) is taken up in warm dry ether and carefully precipitated by the slow addition of petroleum ether. Yield, 2.5 g. (50% of theory); m.p. 90%. If this final hydrolytic step is not carefully carried out, further cleavage of the desired compound (XXXV) may result with the consequent formation of pyruvic acid.

Another procedure whereby keto acid peptides have been obtained utilized compounds of the type represented by 3-methylene-2:5-diketopiperazine (XXXIX), which is in effect a cyclic anhydride of α-aminoacrylic acid and glycine. Preparation of (XXXIX) was effected by the successive treatment of glycylserine methyl ester (XXXVIII), first with thionyl chloride and subsequently with aqueous ammonia (309). Upon mild hydrolysis with mineral acid, the diketopiperazine ring was opened, with the concomitant production of pyruvoylglycine (XL) (310). A similar reaction was achieved with the corresponding "anhydroalanylserine anhydride"

$$NH_2CH_2CO-NHCH(CH_2OH)CO_2CH_3 \xrightarrow[\text{2. NH}_3]{\text{1. SOCl}_2} \begin{matrix} CO-NH-C=CH_2 \\ | \quad\quad\quad\quad | \\ CH_2-NH-CO \end{matrix} \xrightarrow[\text{acid}]{H_2O} CH_3COCO-NHCH_2CO_2H$$

XXXVIII　　　　　　　　　　　XXXIX　　　　　　　　XL

(3-methylene-6-methyl-2:5-diketopiperazine) (310). It is of interest to note the demonstration of Herbst (335) that pyruvoylpeptides could be converted to the corresponding saturated peptides on catalytic reduction in the presence of ammonia, pyruvoylglycine (XLI; R = H) thus yielding DL-alanylglycine

(XLIII; R = H). An alternative procedure (316) involved the initial conversion of the pyruvoylamino acid to the corresponding oxime (XLII), followed by platinum oxide-catalyzed hydrogenolysis of the latter to the pertinent dipeptide (XLIII). This procedure permitted the conversion of

$$\underset{\text{XLI}}{CH_3COCO-NHCHRCO_2H} \xrightarrow{NH_2OH} \underset{\text{XLII}}{CH_3C(=NOH)CO-NHCHRCO_2H} \xrightarrow{H_2} \underset{\text{XLIII}}{CH_3CH(NH_2)CO-NHCHRCO_2H}$$

pyruvoylglycine (XLI; R = H) and pyruvoyl-DL-alanine (XLI; R = CH$_3$) to DL-alanylglycine (XLIII; R = H) and DL-alanyl-DL-alanine (XLIII; R = CH$_3$), respectively. Similar reaction with pyruvoyl-DL-phenylalanine (XLI; R = C$_6$H$_5$CH$_2$) was accompanied by reduction of the aromatic ring with the ultimate formation of DL-alanyl-DL-cyclohexylalanine (XLIII; R = C$_6$H$_{11}$CH$_2$). A related procedure described by Hartung and co-workers (336, 337) involved the catalytic reduction of various N-benzyl- or N-alkyloximinoacylamino acids (XLV) or their esters in alkaline medium to the requisite peptide (XLIV); use of an acidic medium during the reduction

$$\underset{\text{XLIV}}{\overset{NH_2}{\underset{|}{R}CHCO-NHCHR'CO_2H}} \xleftarrow{H_2}{OH^-} \underset{\text{XLV}}{\overset{NOCH_2C_6H_5}{\underset{\|}{R}CCO-NHCHR'CO_2H}} \xrightarrow{H_2}{H^+} \underset{\text{XLVI}}{\overset{RCH-NH-CO}{\underset{CO-NH-CHR'}{|\qquad\qquad|}}}$$

proceeded with the predominant formation of the corresponding diketopiperazine (XLVI).

Certain differences in chemical behavior that exist between pyruvoyl and phenylpyruvoyl peptides should be elaborated here. It has been shown (338) that pyruvoylglycine possessed a pK' of 3.3 at 25°, readily formed a crystalline dinitrophenylhydrazone, underwent ready quantitative cleavage by hot hydrochloric acid into pyruvic acid and glycine, and yielded a characteristic ultraviolet absorption spectrum at pH < 10, with maxima at 240 mμ and 340 mμ, respectively. However, at pH > 10, the aqueous solution no longer yielded a dinitrophenylhydrazone, no pyruvic acid or glycine was recoverable after treatment with hot hydrochloric acid, the absorption maxima in the ultraviolet disappeared, and the original properties of the pyruvoylglycine could not be restored upon acidification. Nevertheless, the pK' value at 25° and the nitrogen content of the isolated material were identical with those of pyruvoylglycine. Subsequent studies (339) on the ultraviolet absorption spectra of aqueous solutions of phenylpyruvic acid and phenylpyruvoylglycine, at pH 7.8, indicated absorption bands of 285 mμ and 250 mμ for the former and latter compounds, respectively. Adjustment of the pH of these solutions to 11.5 was followed by immediate alteration of the spectra, with a well-defined maximum appearing at 325 mμ for both compounds. On readjustment of the pH to 7.0, the original spectra of both compounds was restored. Thus, although the effect of alkalinization of pyruvic acid, of phenylpyruvic acid, and of phenylpyruvoylglycine was reversible (339), that of pyruvoylglycine was irreversible (338, 340).

Extension of the afore-mentioned studies to the pyruvoyl derivatives of α-aminoisobutyric acid, DL-alanine, and DL-phenylalanine revealed that all possessed the same type of absorption in aqueous solution, with maxima at 243–245 mμ and 310–337 mμ (341). On alkalinization of the solution, the characteristic absorption of the latter two compounds disappeared and was not restored on acidification; this behavior is reminiscent of that exhibited by pyruvoylglycine (338, 340). The characteristic absorption of pyruvoyl-α-aminoisobutyric acid revealed only slight change on like alkalinization of the solution, on the other hand, such change being wholly reversed upon acidification (341). That the pyruvoyl derivatives of glycine, alanine, and phenylalanine underwent irreversible ring closure to the pertinent γ-hydroxypyrrolidonecarboxylic acid derivative in alkaline solution by virtue of their possession of an α-hydrogen atom on the amino acid residue, while the lack of a like α-hydrogen atom in pyruvoyl-α-aminoisobutyric acid did not permit comparable cyclization of this reactant, was suggested early as the basis of such differences. More recent studies in the writers' Laboratory necessitate revision of such interpretation, however.

The treatment of pyruvoylglycine with alkali at 25°, followed by acidification of the solution, led to the ultimate isolation of a crystalline material which revealed the same empirical composition as pyruvoylglycine but was not structurally identical with this compound (340). Chromatographic and infrared absorption comparison of such material with the two stereomeric racemates of γ-hydroxypyrrolidone-α-carboxylic acid, prepared by cyclization of the pertinent racemate of γ-hydroxyglutamic acid, also revealed that it was not identical with either of these compounds. The reaction involved, and the products formed, are discussed in detail in Chapter 43 of Volume 3.

Ultraviolet Absorption Spectra of Dehydropeptides. Inasmuch as the dehydropeptides in aqueous solution might be expected to exist as several forms in tautomeric equilibrium, it would be anticipated that certain characteristic properties might be revealed by their absorption spectra in the ultraviolet region, and such was actually shown to be the case. Thus a characteristic absorption with a maximum at 240 mμ was demonstrated (342) for aliphatic dehydropeptides (Fig. 10-3), while the shape of the absorption curve for the acylated peptides of α-aminoacrylic acid was shown to be practically independent of the nature of the acyl residue (343). In contrast to the characteristic absorption exhibited by acetyldehydroalanine, that of acetyldehydroaminobutyric acid, acetyldehydrovaline, and acetyldehydroleucine is only general (344, 345). On the other hand, the saturated analogs of the dehydropeptides revealed only very little uncharacteristic absorption in the ultraviolet region.

The shape of the absorption curves for the acylated peptides of α-aminophenylacrylic acid showed considerable differences as compared to those of

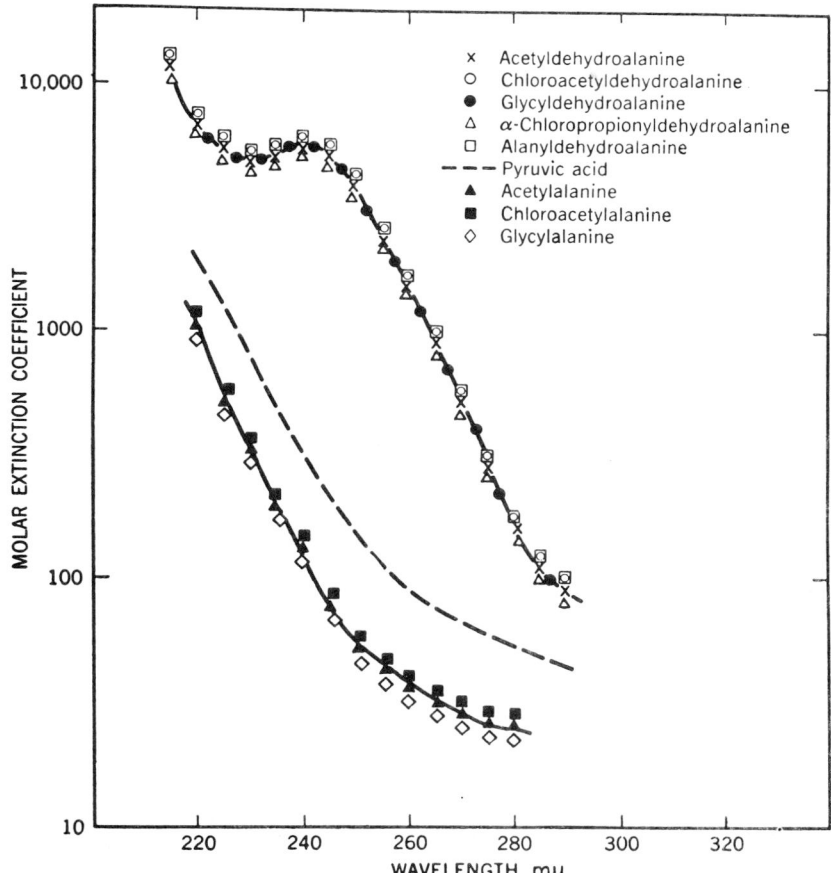

Figure 10–3. Absorption curves in the ultraviolet of peptides of dehydroalanine and of alanine at pH 7.0. Price, V. E., and Greenstein, J. P., *J. Biol. Chem.*, **171**, 477 (1947).

aliphatic dehydropeptides (Fig. 10–4). Thus the curves for the aromatic dehydropeptides possessed a minimum and a maximum at 240 mμ and 275 mμ, respectively. In general, these curves resembled those of the saturated analogs of the phenylated amino acids (Fig. 10–4), but the amount of absorption of the dehydropeptides was considerably greater, and the maximum was shifted from 260 mμ to 275 mμ. The presence of the resonating double bond adjacent to the phenyl group might be viewed as enormously enhancing the absorption of ultraviolet light by the entire molecular system. As for the aliphatic dehydropeptides, the shape shown by the absorption curves of the aromatic dehydropeptides was largely independent of the nature of the acyl residue (329). The absorption curves in the ultraviolet for acetyldehydrotyrosine were determined at two pH values by Fruton, Simmonds, and Smith (344) (Fig. 10–5).

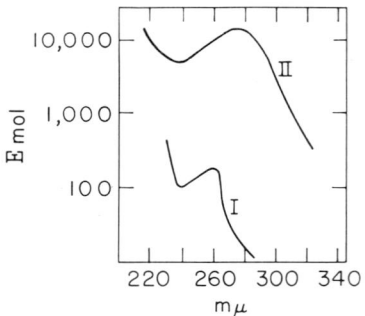

Figure 10–4. Absorption curves in the ultraviolet of peptides of phenylalanine (curve I) and of dehydrophenylalanine (curve II) at pH 7.0. Price, V. E., and Greenstein, J. P., *J. Biol. Chem.*, **171**, 477 (1947).

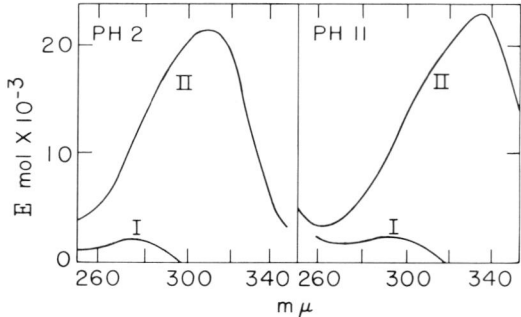

Figure 10–5. Absorption curves in the ultraviolet of acyltyrosine (curve I) and of acyldehydrotyrosine (curve II) in acid (pH 2) and alkaline (pH 11) solution. Fruton, J. S., Simmonds, S., and Smith, V. A., *J. Biol. Chem.*, **169**, 267 (1947).

Unsaturated Character of Dehydropeptides. The unsaturated character of dehydropeptides is strikingly revealed in part by several types of addition reactions, such as the decolorization of bromine and permanganate (272, 346), and the addition of catalytic hydrogen (272), mercaptans (347), amides (316), and amines (329, 346, 348). The ease and mode of addition of these reagents may vary, however. Thus, although catalytic hydrogen and

CHEMICAL PROCEDURES FOR SYNTHESIS OF PEPTIDES

mercaptans add equally well to peptides of dehydroalanine and dehydrophenylalanine, acetamide adds to acetyldehydroalanine but not to acetyldehydrophenylalanine (316). Whereas acetyldehydroalanine readily reacts quantitatively with bromine (346) and with amines (329, 346), acetyldehydrovaline reacts only partially, and acetyldehydrophenylalanine not at all, with bromine, while neither of the latter compounds reacts with amines (346). Furthermore, although mercaptans (346, 349) and amines (329) add to acetyldehydroalanine to form, respectively, α-acylamino-β-alkylmercaptopropionic acids and α-acylamino-β-alkylaminopropionic acids, acetamide adds in such a way as to form chiefly α,α-di(acetamino)propionic acid (316). One of the principal criteria employed in following the addition or lack of addition of reagents is the change or absence of change of the characteristic absorption in the ultraviolet of the original dehydropeptide (322, 329, 335, 345). This is illustrated in Table 10–14.

The reactions exhibited by chloroacetyldehydroalanine (XLIX) with various amines deserve added mention. Treatment of this compound with aqueous ammonia at 0° or 25° invariably yields the corresponding glycyldehydroalanine (XLVII). However, although this same compound (XLIX), when treated with aqueous methylamine at 0°, results in the corresponding sarcosyldehydroalanine (XLVIII), increasing the temperature to 25° leads to the formation of sarcosyl-α-amino-β-methylaminopropionic acid (L) (329). When treated with aqueous dimethylamine at either 0° or 25°,

TABLE 10–14
Molar Extinction Coefficient (ϵ) of Some Addition Products in 80% Ethanol (346)

Dehydropeptide[c]	Added Reagent	Wavelength, mμ	ϵ
Acetyldehydroalanine	–	240[a]	6,050
Acetyldehydroalanine	Benzyl mercaptan	240	1,160[b]
Acetyldehydroalanine	Phenyl mercaptan	240	850[b]
Acetyldehydroalanine	Benzylamine	250[a]	245
Acetyldehydroalanine	Dimethylamine	240	20
Acetyldehydroalanine	Methylamine	240	20[b]
Acetyldehydrophenylalanine	–	280[a]	18,000
Acetyldehydrophenylalanine	Benzyl mercaptan	280	4,400
Acetyldehydrophenylalanine	Phenyl mercaptan	260[a]	4,420

[a] Maximum absorption.
[b] No peak of absorption.
[c] The molar extinction coefficient of chloroacetyldehydroalanine at the absorption maximum of 240 mμ is 6550. The coefficients for the addition (and replacement) products with methylamine and with dimethylamine, namely, N-methylglycyl-α-amino-β-methylaminopropionic acid·HCl and N,N-dimethylglycyl-α-amino-β-dimethylaminopropionic acid·HCl, are, respectively, 44 and 48.

chloroacetyldehydroalanine yields N,N-dimethylglycyl-α-amino-β-dimethylaminopropionic acid (LI). Thus methylamine and dimethylamine may,

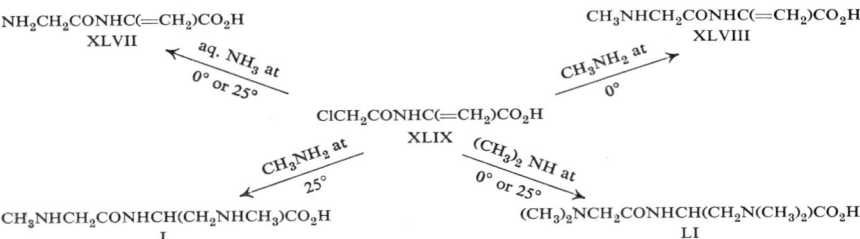

under relatively mild conditions, substitute not only at the α-carbon but also at the double bond of chloroacetyldehydroalanine, thereby producing the corresponding saturated peptides.

Evaluation of the Method. Use of condensation reactions of amides or nitriles with α-keto acids affords an alternative to, and often provides a more convenient method than, the azlactone procedure for the preparation of dehydropeptides. However, the former methods have, at present, been confined to the preparation of the simpler dehydropeptides which embody only a single unsaturated linkage. Although the utilization of the hydrogen chloride-catalyzed condensation of nitriles with α-keto acids has provided a simple and direct route for securing several such peptides in high yield, the reaction appears restricted to the use of those nitriles which contain an α-halo substituent. Where this reaction cannot be effected, preparation of the corresponding di(acylamino)aliphatic acid via the Böttinger synthesis, followed by selective cleavage of the latter compound to the desired dehydropeptide by the action of warm glacial acetic acid (315, 350), is best employed (procedure 10–15). Di(acylamino)aliphatic acids may also be obtained by the condensation of amides with α-keto acids, but this procedure has proved generally less satisfactory than the Böttinger synthesis.

Illustrative procedure 10–15. Conversion of α,α-di(acetamino)propionic acid to acetaminoacrylic acid (315). α,α-Di(acetamino)propionic acid (prepared as in procedure 10–14) is boiled with 4 volumes of acetic acid for 8 min., the solution quickly cooled, and, after standing for 1 hour at 0°, the precipitate of α-acetaminoacrylic acid is filtered off and crystallized from methanol. Yield, 50–60% of theory; m.p. 198–200° d. (corr.) (cf. illustrative procedure for the synthesis of cystine in Chapter 24).

10. The N-Carboxy-α-amino Acid Anhydride Method. *Principle.* The 2:5-oxazolidinediones (I) may be viewed as intramolecular anhydrides of the hypothetical carbamic acid HO₂C—NH·CHR·CO₂H. Such compounds are more commonly referred to as N-carboxy-α-amino acid anhydrides, amino acid carbonic anhydrides, or anhydro-N-carboxyamino acids, although the term Leuchs' anhydride (for its discoverer) is also employed. As Leuchs (102) realized in 1906, N-carboxy-α-amino acid anhydrides undergo rapid decomposition in the presence of a large excess of water with the evolution of carbon dioxide and the generation of the parent amino acid. If only a little water is employed, however, a polymeric material is secured in lieu of the free amino acid. Such observations were extended by Curtius and Sieber (351), Wessely (104, 352), and later investigators, who studied not only the water-induced polymerization of N-carboxy-α-amino acid anhydrides but polymer formation induced by amines as well. It is at present generally assumed that the first step in such a polymerization reaction involves the interaction of the N-carboxy-anhydride (I) with a suitable initiator, e.g., water, an amine, or an amino acid ester (II), with the concomitant formation of a transitory carbamate intermediate (III). Decomposition of the latter compound proceeds with the liberation of a free amino group (IV) which serves as the focal point for attack by another molecule of N-carboxy-anhydride (I). Thus polypeptides (VI) of considerable size may result from such spontaneous build-up, and this method has indeed been extensively utilized for the production of a wide variety of amino acid polymers. However, the method has only occasionally been employed for the controlled, stepwise synthesis of smaller peptides of more defined composition and size. In the latter connection, Bailey (353) demonstrated that careful regulation of the reaction conditions can so suppress the polymerization tendencies of N-carboxy-anhydrides as to make practicable their condensation with the esters or sodium salts of amino acids (II; $R'' =$ alkyl or Na) for the production of small peptides (IV) of well-defined character.

$$\underset{I}{\underset{\diagdown CO \diagup}{\overset{NH \text{———} CO}{\underset{|}{RCH} \quad O}}} + \underset{II}{\underset{CO_2R''}{\overset{NH_2}{\underset{|}{CHR'}}}} \rightarrow \underset{III}{\underset{CO \text{—} NHCHR'CO_2R''}{\overset{NHCO_2H}{\underset{|}{CHR}}}} \xrightarrow{\underset{\downarrow}{\overset{NH_2CHRCO \text{—} NHCHR'CO_2R'' + CO_2}{IV \quad\quad\quad V}}} \underset{VI}{NH_2CHRCO(\text{—}NHCHRCO\text{—})_x NHCHR'CO_2R''}$$

Preparation of N-Carboxy-α-Amino Acid Anhydrides. The N-carboxy-α-amino acid anhydrides are colorless crystalline compounds which possess sharp melting points when pure. As traces of contaminants such as moisture may cause these substances to undergo ready polymerization, only reactants and solvents which are carefully dried and which possess a high degree of chemical purity should be employed in their preparation; the rigid exclusion of moisture during this operation is essential, and the glassware employed must apparently be carefully dried by heating at 120 to 150° for 2 hours. If the α-amino acid involved in such preparation has a reactive group on its side chain, e.g., the hydroxyl function of serine, threonine, and tyrosine, the ω-basic substituent of ornithine, lysine, and arginine, or the ω-carboxyl moiety of glutamic and aspartic acids, it must be masked with a suitable protecting substituent prior to the formation of the N-carboxy-anhydride.

For such purposes, it has been common practice to mask the hydroxyl functions with an acetyl or a carbobenzoxy group, the ω-basic substituents with a carbobenzoxy group, and the ω-carboxyl moieties with a methyl, ethyl, or benzyl ester group, although the use of yet other masking substituents is not precluded. Methods whereby such masking may be achieved are considered in subsequent sections of this chapter, and the several different routes whereby suitably constituted α-amino acids may be converted to the corresponding N-carboxy-anhydrides are described directly below. Because these compounds tend to polymerize upon storage in the solid state, even in a vacuum desiccator, their preparation should be performed no more than a few hours before use.

(a) *The carboalkoxy procedure.* That the action of heat on a carboalkoxylated amino acid chloride (X) induces it to undergo intramolecular cyclization, with the concomitant formation of the corresponding N-carboxy-anhydride (XI) and the elimination of alkyl halide (XII), was first demonstrated by Leuchs (102) in collaboration with Manasse (354) and Geiger (355). These studies involved a variety of carbomethoxy (IX; $R' = CH_3$) and carboethoxy (IX; $R' = C_2H_5$) amino acids prepared by the acylation of the pertinent amino acid (VII) with methyl chloroformate (VIII; $R' = CH_3$) or ethyl chloroformate (VIII; $R' = C_2H_5$) under alkaline conditions. Treatment of (IX) with thionyl chloride resulted in the production of the acid chloride (X; X = Cl) which, upon being warmed at 60–70° *in vacuo*, was converted to the desired N-carboxy-anhydride (XI) (procedure 10–18). It was noted that the initial employment of a carbomethoxy amino acid (IX; $R' = CH_3$) not only led to a higher over-all yield than was secured with the corresponding carboethoxy derivative, but also permitted the cyclization reaction to be carried out at a lower temperature. The afore-mentioned

$$\underset{\text{VII}}{\begin{array}{c} NH_2 \\ | \\ CHR \\ | \\ CO_2H \end{array}} + \underset{\text{VIII}}{\begin{array}{c} Cl \\ | \\ CO \\ | \\ OR' \end{array}} \xrightarrow{OH^-} \underset{\text{IX}}{\begin{array}{c} NHCO_2R' \\ | \\ CHR \\ | \\ CO_2H \end{array}} \xrightarrow[\text{or PBr}_3]{SOCl_2,\ PCl_5,} \underset{\text{X}}{\begin{array}{c} NHCO_2R' \\ | \\ CHR \\ | \\ COX \end{array}} \xrightarrow{\Delta} \underset{\text{XI}}{\begin{array}{c} NH\text{———}CO \\ | \qquad\quad | \\ RCH \quad\ O \\ \diagdown\diagup \\ CO \end{array}} + \underset{\text{XII}}{R'X}$$

method of Leuchs has with minor modifications served as one of the principal routes for the preparation of a host of N-carboxy-α-amino acid anhydrides. Thus it has often been found more advantageous to employ phosphorus pentachloride and an inert solvent, e.g., ether, instead of thionyl chloride for the preparation of the intermediate acid chloride (procedure 10–17). Especially noteworthy was the extensive utilization of carbobenzoxyamino acids in lieu of the corresponding carbomethoxy or carboethoxy derivatives. In addition to the fact that carbobenzoxyamino acids may be conveniently prepared both in excellent yield and with a high degree of chemical purity (see Section 10–14), cleavage of the carbobenzoxy group during the intramolecular cyclization process has been found by Katchalski and Ben-Ishai (356) to occur with greater facility than does cleavage of the carbomethoxy or carboethoxy groups. The same investigators (357) subsequently observed that the acid bromides (X; X = Br) formed by the treatment of an ethereal solution of a carboalkoxy-α-amino acid (IX) with phosphorus tribromide at room temperature undergo more ready cyclization to the N-carboxy-anhydrides (XI) than do the corresponding acid chlorides (procedure 10–16).

Illustrative procedure 10–16 (357). To a suspension or solution of 0.05 mole of a carbobenzoxyamino acid (procedures 10–28 to 10–30) in 50 ml. of anhydrous ether is slowly added 0.02 mole of phosphorus tribromide. The reaction mixture is kept at room temperature for 12 hr., 100 ml. of petroleum ether added thereto, and crystallization of the anhydride promoted by keeping the reaction mixture at 4° for several hours. The anhydride is then filtered, washed thoroughly with dry petroleum ether, and recrystallized from a dry mixture of ethyl acetate and petroleum ether. This procedure is generally applicable to N-carboalkoxylated amino acids.

Illustrative procedure 10–17 (358). A fine suspension or solution of 0.05 mole of a carbobenzoxyamino acid (procedures 10–28 to 10–30) in about 75 ml. of dry ether, benzene, or chloroform is cooled to 0° to 5° and 0.05 mole of finely powdered phosphorus pentachloride added slowly thereto with intermittent cooling and shaking. After nearly all the phosphorus pentachloride has dissolved, the reaction mixture is filtered and the solution permitted to stand at room temperature for 1 hr. If separation of a product occurs at this point, it is filtered off; if no separation occurs, the solution is concentrated to dryness *in vacuo* at 40–50° and the concentration repeated several times after the addition each time of fresh, dry solvent. The residue is thoroughly washed with dry petroleum ether and then recrystallized from a suitable solvent system. All these operations must be carried out with the careful exclusion of moisture.

Illustrative procedure 10–18 (102). A mixture of 5 g. of the pertinent carbo-alkoxyamino acid in 25 ml. of purified thionyl chloride is warmed at 60° for 30 min., the reaction mixture being guarded from moisture with a calcium chloride drying tube. After removal of the excess thionyl chloride under reduced pressure, the residual material is triturated with petroleum ether until it solidifies. Recrystallization of the resulting N-carboxy-anhydride may be accomplished from dry ethyl acetate-petroleum ether or some other suitable solvent system.

Several of the N-carboxy-α-amino acid anhydrides which have been secured via the afore-mentioned three procedures are listed in Table 10–15.

(*b*) The azide rearrangement procedure. In 1922, Curtius and Sieber (351) described a preparation of N-carboxy-α-amino acid anhydrides which involved the classical azide rearrangement discovered by the former investigator (cf. 383) many years earlier. Such preparation employed an appropriately substituted malonic ester derivative (XIII) which, after partial hydrolysis to the half ester (XIV), was converted to the half hydrazide (XV)

TABLE 10-15
N-Carboxy-α-amino Acid Anhydrides Prepared via the Leuchs Procedure

N-Carboxyanhydride of	M.P., °C.	N-Carboalkoxy-α-amino Acid[a] Precursor	M.P., °C.	Method of Preparation	Ref.
DL-Alanine	44–45	N-Cetho-DL-alanine (208)	84	PBr$_3$ in ether[b]	357
D-Alanine	89	Cbzo-D-alanine (359)	87	PCl$_5$ in ether	359
L-Alanine	92 d.	N-Cmetho-L-alanine (360)	oil	SOCl$_2$	360
N-Benzyl-DL-alanine	60–61	N-Cmetho-N-benzyl-DL-alanine (361)	oil	SOCl$_2$	361
N-Methyl-DL-alanine	75–76	N-Cmetho-N-methyl-DL-alanine (361)	oil	SOCl$_2$	361
N$^\omega$-p-NO$_2$-Cbzo-L-arginine	150–151	N$^\alpha$,N$^\omega$-di-p-NO$_2$-Cbzo-L-arginine (362)	180.5–181.5	SOCl$_2$	363
β-Benzyl L-aspartate	121 d.	β-Benzyl N-Cbzo-L-aspartate (364)	108	PCl$_5$ in benzene	364
α-Aminoisobutyric acid	100	N-Cmetho-α-aminoisobutyric acid (361)	158–160	SOCl$_2$	361
S-Cbzo-L-cysteine	75 d.	N,S-Dicbzo-L-cysteine (365)	97–98	PCl$_5$ in benzene	365
L-Cystine	128 d.	N,N'-Dicbzo-L-cystine[c]	123	PCl$_5$ in dioxane	353
β-Cbzo-α,β-diaminopropionic acid	139–140 d.	N$^\alpha$,N$^\beta$-Dicbzo-α,β-diaminopropionic acid (366)	150–151	PCl$_5$ in chloroform	366
γ-Benzyl L-glutamate	96–97 d.	γ-Benzyl N-Cbzo-L-glutamate (367)	76–78	PCl$_5$ in ether	367
γ-Ethyl L-glutamate	71–72 d.	γ-Ethyl N-Cbzo-L-glutamate (367)	87	PCl$_5$ in ether[d]	367
γ-Methyl L-glutamate	99–100 d.	γ-Methyl N-Cbzo-L-glutamate (367)	72–73	PCl$_5$ in ether	367
Glycine	100 d.	N-Cmetho-glycine (102)	95–96	SOCl$_2$	102

Glycine	100 d.	N-Cbzo-glycine (128)	120	PCl$_5$ in ether[e]	368
N-Phenylglycine	139–140 d.	N-Cetho-N-phenylglycine (354)	oil	SOCl$_2$[f]	354
1'-Benzyl-L-histidine·HCl	187–189 d.	N-Cbzo-1'-benzyl-L-histidine (369)	216 d.	PCl$_5$ in dioxane	370
DL-Isoleucine	70–72	N-Cmetho-DL-isoleucine (361)	oil	SOCl$_2$	361
DL-Leucine	48–50	N-Cmetho-DL-leucine (355)	oil	SOCl$_2$	355
L-Leucine	76–77.5	N-Cbzo-L-leucine	oil	PCl$_5$ in ether[g]	368
L-Leucine	77	N-Cbzo-L-leucine	oil	SOCl$_2$	360
DL-tert-leucine	123	N-Cbzo-DL-tert-leucine (371)	88	PCl$_5$	371
DL-Norleucine	84–86 d.	N-Cmetho-DL-norleucine (361)	64	PCl$_5$ in benzene	361
ε-Cbzo-L-lysine	100 d.	α,ε-Dicbzo-L-lysine (358)	150	PCl$_5$ in ether[h]	358
δ-Cbzo-DL-ornithine	110 d.	α,δ-Dicbzo-DL-ornithine (372)	110–112	PCl$_5$ in benzene	372
δ-Cbzo-L-ornithine	86–88°	α,δ-Dicbzo-L-ornithine (373)	112–114	PCl$_5$ in ether	373
DL-Phenylalanine	125–126 d.	N-Cetho-DL-phenylalanine (357)	76	PBr$_3$ in ether[i]	357
p-Cbzo-amino-DL-phenylalanine	145 d.	N,N'-Dicbzo-p-amino-DL-phenylalanine (374)	168	PBr$_3$ in dioxane	374
p-Nitro-DL-phenylalanine	178 d.	N-Cbzo-p-nitro-DL-phenylalanine (374)	152	PBr$_3$ in dioxane	374
N-Methyl-DL-phenylalanine	104–105	N-Cmetho-N-methyl-DL-phenylalanine (361)	oil	SOCl$_2$	361
DL-α-Phenylglycine	99–100 d.	N-Cmetho-DL-α-phenylglycine (355)	87–88	SOCl$_2$	355
L-Proline	45	N-Cbzo-L-proline (375)	76–77	PCl$_5$ in benzene	375
Sarcosine	99–100 d.	N-Cmetho-sarcosine (376)	oil	SOCl$_2$	376
Sarcosine	99 d.	N-Cbzo-sarcosine (357)	53–54	PBr$_3$ in ether	357

TABLE 10-15 (continued)
N-Carboalkoxy-α-amino Acid[a]

N-Carboxyanhydride of	M.P., °C.	Precursor	M.P., °C.	Method of Preparation	Ref.
O-Acetyl-DL-serine	—	O-Acetyl-N-Cbzo-DL-serine (377)	116–118	PCl$_5$ in ether	377
O-Cbzo-DL-serine	95 d.	O-N,-Dicbzo-DL-serine (377)	94	PCl$_5$ in ether	377
O-Acetyl-D-tyrosine	120	O-Acetyl-N-Cbzo-L-tyrosine (378)	120–121	PCl$_5$ in dioxane[j]	353
O-Cbzo-L-tyrosine	101 d.	O,N-Dicbzo-L-tyrosine (379)	117	PCl$_5$ in benzene	379
DL-Valine	77–79	N-Cetho-DL-valine (357)	56	PBr$_3$ in ether[k]	357
DL-Valine	78–79	N-Cmetho-DL-valine (361)	88–89	SOCl$_2$	361
DL-Valine	80	N-Cbzo-DL-valine	72–73	SOCl$_2$ in chloroform	380

[a] Cmetho = carbomethoxy, cetho = carboethoxy, cbzo = carbobenzyloxy, and callo = carboallyloxy.

[b] Cbzo-DL-alanine, m.p. 114–115° (128), was similarly employed (357).

[c] Treatment of the N,N′-dicetho-L-cystine with SOCl$_2$ gave an N-carboxyanhydride melting at 115–150° d. (381).

[d] γ-Ethyl N-callo-L-glutamate was similarly employed (382).

[e] Cetho-glycine was similarly employed (368).

[f] Like treatment of N-cmetho-N-phenylglycine gave an N-carboxyanhydride melting at 142° d. (104).

[g] The N-carboxyanhydride was also prepared from the N-cmetho and N-callo derivatives (368).

[h] Use of PBr$_3$ in ether gave an N-carboxyanhydride melting at 99° d. (357).

[i] The cbzo-derivative was similarly used (356), whereas use of the cbzo or callo derivatives with PCl$_5$ in ether gave an N-carboxyanhydride melting at 126–128° d. (368).

[j] Use of SOCl$_2$ plus Ac$_2$O also gave the N-carboxyanhydride, m.p. 119–121° (369).

[k] Cbzo-DL-valine, m.p. 71°, was similarly employed (357).

by the action of hydrazine. The action of nitrous acid on (XV) yielded the corresponding azide (XVI) which, upon standing for several days at room temperature or refluxing for several hours in dry chloroform or ether, was transformed to the desired N-carboxy-anhydride (XVIII), presumably via a transitory isocyanate intermediate (XVII):

$$\underset{\text{XIII}}{\overset{\text{CO}_2\text{Et}}{\underset{\text{CO}_2\text{Et}}{\text{CHR}}}} \xrightarrow{\text{KOH}} \underset{\text{XIV}}{\overset{\text{CO}_2\text{H}}{\underset{\text{CO}_2\text{Et}}{\text{CHR}}}} \xrightarrow{\text{NH}_2\text{NH}_2} \underset{\text{XV}}{\overset{\text{CO}_2\text{H}}{\underset{\text{CONHNH}_2}{\text{CHR}}}} \xrightarrow{\text{HNO}_2} \underset{\text{XVI}}{\overset{\text{CO}_2\text{H}}{\underset{\text{CON}_3}{\text{CHR}}}} \xrightarrow{\Delta} \underset{\text{XVII}}{\left[\overset{\text{CO}_2\text{H}}{\underset{\text{NCO}}{\text{CHR}}}\right]} \rightarrow \underset{\text{XVIII}}{\text{RCH}\overset{\text{CO—O}}{\underset{\text{NH—CO}}{\diagdown}}}$$

The method was employed by Curtius and his collaborators for the preparation of the racemic N-carboxy-α-amino acid anhydrides with melting points corresponding to: α-aminobutyric acid, 113° (dec.); α-aminoisoamylacetic acid, 68° (dec.); glycine, 100° (dec.); leucine, 48–50° (dec.); phenylalanine, 127–8°; *m*-tolylalanine, 135°; and valine, 79° (dec.). However, its use as a routine procedure possesses several severe limitations, not the least of which is the large number of steps and tedious manipulations involved, as well as the difficulty encountered in obtaining pure intermediates at the earlier stages of the reaction sequence. It is therefore of little practical value in the present connection.

(*c*) *The phosgenation procedure.* In 1922, Fuchs (384) developed a synthesis of the N-carboxy-anhydrides of N-phenylglycine (XXII) and N-*p*-tolylglycine which precipitated as fine white needles during the introduction of phosgene gas (XX) into a cold alkaline aqueous solution of the pertinent amino acid (XIX):

$$\underset{\text{XIX}}{\text{C}_6\text{H}_5\text{NHCH}_2\text{CO}_2\text{H}} + \underset{\text{XX}}{\text{COCl}_2} \xrightarrow{\text{aq. NaOH}} \underset{\text{XXI}}{\left[\overset{\text{C}_6\text{H}_5\text{NCH}_2\text{CO}_2\text{H}}{\underset{\text{COCl}}{|}}\right]} \rightarrow \underset{\text{XXII}}{\overset{\text{C}_6\text{H}_5\text{NCH}_2\text{CO}}{\underset{\text{CO—O}}{|\qquad\qquad|}}}$$

Modification of the afore-mentioned procedure has permitted the simple and facile synthesis of a host of N-carboxy-α-amino acid anhydrides. The modified procedure involves the direct treatment with a slow stream of phosgene (XXIV) of a suspension of the free amino acid (XXIII) in dry dioxane, tetrahydrofuran, toluene, or some other suitable organic solvent, generally with warming at 40–50° for several hours (385–387) (procedure 10–19). That an intermediate carbamyl chloride (XXV) is formed during such reaction could be demonstrated by its reaction with aniline to yield an anilide (XXVII) (387). Ring closure of (XXV) then yields the desired N-carboxy-anhydride (XXVI). Formation of the latter is nearly quantitative under the proper conditions, the sole possible contaminants arising from the intermediate carbamyl chloride (XXV) and the isocyanate (XXVIII) derived therefrom. However, both are generally liquids and can be readily removed by the recrystallization procedure. It should be emphasized that the use of highly pure amino acids is deemed essential here, as the purity of the N-carboxy-anhydrides are difficult to establish by virtue of their extreme lability.

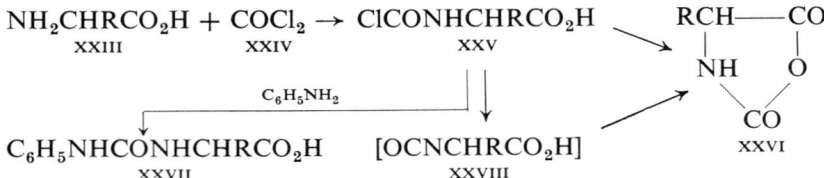

Illustrative procedure 10–19 (387). N-Carboxyglycine anhydride. A suspension of 8 g. of finely ground glycine is stirred with 375 ml. of *dry* dioxane in a *dry* 2-l. 3-necked flask fitted with a gas lead, water reflux condenser, and liquid sealed stirrer, and immersed in a water bath at 40°. Carbonyl chloride is slowly introduced through the gas lead for 4–5 hr., the glycine slowly dissolving during this time. The reaction mixture is then treated with a stream of dry air for 12 hr. at room temperature to sweep out the dissolved gases. The stirrer and gas lead are removed, the condenser changed to the downward position, and the dioxane removed under reduced pressure at 40°. A liquid remains which solidifies on further heating at 40° *in vacuo*; if no solidification occurs after 1 hr., crystallization may be induced by the addition of a little dry ether. The material is filtered with the aid of a little dry ether and dried over phosphorus pentoxide and flaked paraffin *in vacuo*. Yield 9.2 g. (85%); m.p. 100° (dec.).

The above reaction is quite general and may be accomplished with a large variety of amino acids. However, the time of phosgene introduction depends upon the time required to achieve complete solution of the reactant amino acid. Thus, for example, the time of solution of DL-methionine in dioxane at 40° is 10 minutes on phosgenation, whereas the solution of α-aminoisobutyric acid requires some 9 hours at 50°. Several of the N-carboxyanhydrides secured essentially by this procedure are listed in Table 10–16.

Behavior of N-Carboxy-Anhydrides in Aqueous Media. That aqueous solutions of N-carboxyglycine anhydride exhibit peculiar differences in behavior at 0° and 15° was noted by Leuchs (102) in his first publication on this subject: "Bemerkenswerth ist das Verhalten des Anhydrids der Glycincarbonsäure gegen Wasser. Bei 0° löst es sich darin ohne merkbare Veränderung; erst beim Erwärmen auf etwa 15° erfolgt Entwicklung von Kohlensäure, während in der Lösung sich reines Glycin befindent."[46] Such behavior was attributed to the transformation of the N-carboxy-anhydride (XXX) to the heat-labile substituted carbamic acid (XXXI) at the lower temperature. Elevation of the temperature to 15° induced the decomposition of (XXXI) accompanied by the simultaneous evolution of carbon dioxide and generation of glycine (XXXII). That the carbamic acid structure (XXXI) he postulated was indeed a valid one was shown by Leuchs (102)

TABLE 10–16
N-Carboxy-α-amino Acid Anhydrides Prepared via the Phosgenation Procedure

N-Carboxy-α-amino Acid Anhydride	M.P., °C.	Ref.
DL-Alanine	45–46	353
L-Alanine	90	353
DL-C-Allylglycine	92–94	388
α-Aminoisobutyric acid	95–97	387
β-Methyl DL-aspartate	84	389
S-Benzyl-D-cysteine	104	390
S-Benzyl-L-cysteine	104	390
S-Carbobenzoxy-L-cysteine	75 d.	365
γ-Ethyl L-glutamate	71	389
γ-Methyl L-glutamate	99	389
Glycine	100	387
O-Acetyl-L-hydroxyproline	120 d.[a]	390a
O-Tosyl-L-hydroxyproline	115 d.	390a
DL-Isoleucine	76–77	391
DL-Leucine	47–50	391, 392
L-Leucine	76–77	353, 386, 391
ε-Tosyl-L-lysine	101–103	393
DL-Methionine	oil	387
DL-Norleucine	84–86	394
DL-Phenylalanine	127	385, 391
p-Nitro-DL-phenylalanine	183–184 d.	395
L-Proline	45 d.	390a
O-Acetyl-DL-serine	53–56	396, 397
O-Benzyl-DL-serine	76–77 d.	398
DL-Tryptophan	142 d.	399
L-Tryptophan	135	399
O-Acetyl-L-tyrosine	118–120	400
DL-Valine	81	391, 394

[a] $[\alpha]_D^{25} = -75°$ (1% in ethyl acetate).

when the insoluble barium salt (XXIX), which rapidly formed upon the addition of one equivalent of an ice-cold solution of barium hydroxide to N-carboxyglycine anhydride (XXX), was found to be identical with that previously prepared by Siegfried (401) via the passage of a stream of carbon dioxide through a cold solution of glycine in aqueous baryta.

$$\underset{\text{XXIX}}{\begin{array}{c}\text{COO}\\|\\ \text{CH}_2\quad\text{Ba}\\|\\ \text{NHCOO}\end{array}}\xleftarrow[0°]{\text{Ba(OH)}_2}\underset{\text{XXX}}{\begin{array}{c}\text{CO—O}\\|\\ \text{CH}_2\\|\\ \text{NH—CO}\end{array}}\xrightarrow[0°]{\text{H}_2\text{O}}\underset{\text{XXXI}}{\begin{array}{c}\text{CO}_2\text{H}\\|\\ \text{CH}_2\\|\\ \text{NHCO}_2\text{H}\end{array}}\xrightarrow[15°]{\text{H}_2\text{O}}\underset{\text{XXXII}}{\begin{array}{c}\text{CO}_2\text{H}\\|\\ \text{CH}_2\\|\\ \text{NH}_2\end{array}}+\underset{\text{XXXIII}}{\text{CO}_2}$$

aq. Ba(OH)$_2$ at 0° + CO$_2$

Salts of the type described above are commonly referred to as Siegfried salts (see Chapter 6), and they have provided the subject of innumerable studies. Noteworthy in this regard are the series of basic salts prepared by Neuberg and Kerb (402) and the interesting amino acid ester salts of Frankel and Katchalski (403). Exhaustive study by Faurholt (404) of the physical chemistry of the carbamino reaction revealed that only the more basic form of the amines, e.g., NH_3, CH_3NH_2, $(CH_3)_2NH$, and $NH_2CHRCO_2^-$, possess the ability to combine with carbon dioxide. Later work by Meldrum and Roughton (405) and Stadie and O'Brien (406) conclusively confirmed the fact that the reactive species of an amino acid is the anionic form ($NH_2CHRCO_2^-$) and not the dipolar form ($^+NH_3CHRCO_2^-$). Pertinent in this connection is the demonstration by Farthing (387) of the formation of N-carboxyamino acids in sodium carbonate solutions of amino acids. The equilibria here postulated are

$$NH_2CHRCO_2H + Na_2CO_3 \rightleftharpoons NH_2CHRCO_2^- + 2Na^+ + HCO_3^- \rightleftharpoons {^-O_2C-NHCHRCO_2^-} + 2Na^+$$

Actual isolation of the disodium salt of the N-carboxy-α-amino acid (NaO_2C—$NHCHRCO_2Na$) can be achieved upon the addition of methanol to a solution containing equimolar amounts of sodium carbonate and the free amino acid. Treatment of such disodium salt with baryta converts it to the corresponding Siegfried salt (XXIX), while treatment with thionyl chloride or phosgene leads to the formation of the N-carboxy-anhydride.

Leuchs (102) observed that the decomposition of N-carboxy-α-amino acid anhydrides with only a small amount of water proceeds with the generation of polymeric material in lieu of the free amino acid. Thus, when N-carboxyglycine anhydride was rubbed with only twice the amount of water at room temperature, carbon dioxide evolved and a water-insoluble substance formed which was biuret-positive and revealed analytical values in agreement with those of 2:5-diketopiperazine, but which possessed neither the definite crystalline form nor the properties characteristic of this substance. It was typical of the remarkable chemical intuition with which he was endowed that Leuchs quickly recognized the polymeric nature of his insoluble substance and suggested that it might possibly be identical with the glycine polymer previously prepared by Balbiano and Trasciatti (101) upon heat treatment of glycine in glycerol solution, or else closely related to the "biuret base" of Curtius (96, 97) (Section 10–4). Some two decades later, Wessely (104) carried out a systematic study of the degree of polymerization which N-carboxyglycine anhydride undergoes in the presence of varying amounts of water and clearly demonstrated that the extent of polymerization shows an inverse though not proportionate increase with the concentration of water employed. Thus mere exposure of N-carboxyglycine anhydride to water vapor for several days resulted in its conversion to a highly insoluble polymeric product with relatively few free amino groups, while the use of larger amounts of water led to the formation of water-soluble products of lower molecular weight and containing a higher proportion of free amino groups. It was noted too that a several hundredfold excess of water over N-carboxy-anhydride was required to yield a product composed almost exclusively of glycine, an indication of the comparatively slower reactivity of N-carboxy-α-amino acid anhydrides with water than with amino groups. In any event, where the water-initiated decomposition of N-carboxy-anhydrides (XXXIV) yields polymers (XXXVI) as products, these contain detectable terminal free α-amino and α-carboxyl groups (104, 360), as in

$$x\begin{bmatrix} \text{RCH·CO·O} \\ | \quad\quad | \\ \text{NH——CO} \end{bmatrix} + H_2O \rightarrow NH_2\cdot CHR\cdot CO(-NH\cdot CHR\cdot CO-)_{x-2}NH\cdot CHR\cdot CO_2H + xCO_2$$

XXXIV XXXV XXXVI XXXVII

Stepwise Synthesis of Peptides. The reaction of N-carboxy-α-amino acid anhydrides with a suitably constituted amine such as ammonia, an alkyl or dialkyl amine, an amino acid or peptide ester, or even the free amino acid or peptide *per se*, proceeds with the formation of the corresponding amide or peptide derivative under the appropriate conditions. Such a reaction was first described in 1907 by Leuchs and Manasse (354), who prepared N-phenylglycinamide (XXXVIII) by treatment of N-carboxy-N-phenylglycine anhydride (XL) with an excess of ethanolic ammonia. The reaction was later extended to the preparation of the corresponding anilide

C₆H₅NHCH₂CO—NH₂   C₆H₅NHCH₂CO—NHCHRCO₂Et
XXXVIII   XXXIX

$$\begin{array}{c} H_2C\text{——}CO \\ | \quad\quad | \\ C_6H_5N \quad O \\ \diagdown \diagup \\ CO \end{array}$$
XL

↑ NH₃   ↑ NH₂CHRCO₂Et

↓ NH₂R   ↓ NH₂CH₂CO₂H

C₆H₅NHCH₂CO—NHR   C₆H₅NHCH₂CO—NHCH₂CO₂H
XLI   XLII

(XLI; R = C₆H₅) by Fuchs (384) in 1922 and of the ethylamide (XLI; R = C₂H₅) by Wessely (104) some three years later. When the latter investigator treated (XL) with a hot aqueous solution of glycine, carbon dioxide was evolved and N-phenylglycylglycine (XLII) deposited upon the cooling of the clear solution. In addition, the treatment of a chloroform solution of L-tyrosine ethyl ester with one equivalent of (XL) led to the production of the expected dipeptide ester (XXXIX; R = *p*-OHC₆H₄CH₂). These studies were extended during the following year by Sigmund and Wessely (376), who synthesized DL-phenylalanylglycine (XLIII; R¹ = R² = H) and DL-phenylalanylglycylglycine by the interaction, at room temperature, of a solution of N-carboxy-DL-phenylalanine anhydride (XLIV) in ethyl acetate with aqueous solutions of glycine and glycylglycine, respectively. However, when a comparable condensation was attempted by heating a mixture of (XLIV) and tyrosine ethyl ester in chloroform solution, the reaction yielded phenylalanyltyrosyl anhydride (XLVI) by virtue of the initial formation and subsequent cyclization of the intermediate dipeptide ester (XLIII; $R^1 = p\text{-OHC}_6H_4CH_2$, $R^2 = C_2H_5$). That reaction of N-carboxy-anhydrides with amines may sometimes lead to polymerization

$$NH_2CH(C_6H_5CH_2)CO\text{—}NHCHR^1CO_2R^2$$
XLIII

$$C_6H_5CH_2CH\text{——}CO$$
$$\underset{\text{NH}}{|}\quad\underset{\text{O}}{|}\quad\xrightarrow[\text{NH}_2C_6H_5]{NH_2CHR^1CO_2R^2}\quad\xrightarrow{\Delta}\quad C_6H_5CH_2CH\underset{NH\text{—}CO}{\overset{CO\text{—}NH}{\diagup\diagdown}}CHCH_2C_6H_4OH$$
$$\diagdown\diagup$$
$$CO$$
XLIV   XLVI

$$NH_2CH(C_6H_5CH_2)CO\text{—}NHCH(C_6H_5CH_2)CO\text{—}NHC_6H_5$$
XLV

was indicated, for example, by the isolation of phenylalanylphenylalanine anilide (XLV) as the principal product in lieu of the anticipated phenylalanine anilide upon treatment of (XLIV) with aniline. Formation of (XLV) is explicable on the basis of a two-step reaction which involves the initial production of phenylalanine anilide followed by the action of another molecule of N-carboxy-anhydride (XLIV) on the latter intermediate; further recurrence of this two-step reaction was attested to by the isolation of a polyphenylalanine anilide of unidentified chain length as a side product. In accord with the latter behavior, it should be noted that only a polymeric product was formed when N-methylaniline was employed instead of aniline as the reactant amine. Such was the history of early attempts to utilize N-carboxy-anhydrides in the stepwise synthesis of peptides.

Despite the paucity of satisfactory methods for the preparation of well-defined peptides which prevailed for some years after the studies of Sigmund and Wessely (376), the utilization of N-carboxy-anhydrides for such purposes was only rarely exploited. It was not until 1938 that Hunt and du Vigneaud (359) employed these compounds to prepare D-alanyl-L-histidine ($[\alpha]_D^{25} = +7.0°$, 1% in water). The latter compound was secured via a condensation of N-carboxy-D-alanine anhydride with histidine methyl ester in chloroform solution at room temperature, followed by saponification of the D-alanyl-L-histidine methyl ester so derived. Comparison of the specific rotation of this dipeptide with an authentic sample obtained via an alternative procedure indicated that the synthesis proceeded without the occurrence of detectable racemization. However, it remained for Bailey (353) over a decade later to carry out the first systematic study on the use of N-carboxy-anhydrides for the preparation of simple di- and tripeptides containing N-terminal alanine, cystine, glycine, leucine, and tyrosine residues. The basis for this procedure rested upon the fact that, whereas an N-carboxy-α-amino acid anhydride generally undergoes rapid polymerization in the presence of a tertiary amine, e.g., triethylamine, at room temperature, the rate of polymerization is markedly decreased at $-40°$ and is slower at $-70°$. The procedure employed therefore involved the interaction of a solution of the pertinent N-carboxyanhydride (XLVII) in ethyl acetate, chloroform, or tetrahydrofuran, at temperatures ranging between $-40°$ and $-65°$, with an equivalent quantity of an α-amino acid ester in the presence of a tertiary base such as triethylamine or methyldioctylamine. Inasmuch as the condensation proceeds at these low temperatures with the intermediate formation of a carbamate (XLVIII), it follows that the further condensation of (XLVIII) with another molecule of N-carboxy-anhydride is effectively blocked. By virtue of its instability at higher temperatures, the carbamate decomposes with the formation of the peptide ester (XLIX) and with the evolution of carbon dioxide upon warming the reaction mixture to room temperature. The dipeptide ester (XLIX) may then either be converted to the free dipeptide (LIV) by saponification or, after again cooling the reaction mixture to $-40°$ to $-65°$, condensed *in situ* with another molecule of N-carboxyanhydride to form the tripeptide ester (LII). As observed earlier (359), no detectable racemization appears to accompany the procedure. In the wake of the simultaneous development of more facile procedures for the stepwise synthesis of peptides, the afore-mentioned method has not been extensively applied.

$$\begin{array}{c}
\text{RCH—CO} \\
| \quad \diagdown \\
\quad \quad \text{O} \\
| \quad \diagup \\
\text{NH—CO} \\
\text{XLVII}
\end{array} \xrightarrow[-40° \text{ to } -65°]{\text{NH}_2\text{CHR'CO}_2\text{Et, NEt}_3} \begin{array}{c} \text{RCHCO—NHCHR'CO}_2\text{Et} \\ | \\ \text{NH·CO}_2\text{H,NEt}_3 \\ \text{XLVIII} \end{array} \xrightarrow{25°} \begin{array}{c} \text{RCHCO—NHCHR'CO}_2\text{Et} + \text{CO}_2 + \text{NEt}_3 \\ | \\ \text{NH}_2 \\ \text{XLIX} \quad \quad \text{L} \quad \text{LI} \end{array}$$

$$\xrightarrow{\overline{\text{NHCHRCO·O·CO}} \text{ at } -40° \text{ to } -65°} \quad \quad \downarrow \text{OH}^-$$

$$\begin{array}{c} \text{RCHCO—NHCHR'CO}_2\text{Et} \\ | \\ \text{NH—COCHRNH·CO}_2\text{H,NEt}_3 \\ \text{LII} \end{array} \xrightarrow{25°} \begin{array}{c} \text{RCHCO—NHCHR'CO}_2\text{Et} \\ | \\ \text{NH—COCHRNH}_2 \\ \text{LIII} \end{array} \quad \begin{array}{c} \text{RCHCO—NHCHR'CO}_2\text{H} \\ | \\ \text{NH}_2 \\ \text{LIV} \end{array}$$

Illustrative procedure 10–20 (353). L-Alanyl-L-alanylglycine. To 1.2 ml. of a 2% solution of ammonia in chloroform is added 0.28 g. of glycine ethyl ester hydrochloride with stirring, and the precipitated ammonium chloride then removed by filtration. Removal of the slight excess of ammonia is effected by concentration of the residue to dryness *in vacuo* at a temperature not exceeding 35°. The residue is taken up in 2 ml. of chloroform, and the solution is cooled to $-65°$ in a solid carbon dioxide-acetone bath. After the addition of 0.40 ml. of methyldioctylamine, a solution of 0.23 g. of N-carboxy-L-alanine anhydride (procedures 10–16 to 10–19) in 1.5 ml. of tetrahydrofuran is precooled to $-65°$ and run slowly into the mixture. After some 3 hr., the reaction mixture is allowed to warm to room temperature and a vacuum is applied. The solution, which now contains a mixture of L-alanylglycine ethyl ester and methyldioctylamine, is again cooled to $-65°$ and treated with a second equivalent of N-carboxy-L-alanine anhydride as before. After 3 hr., the solution is permitted to warm to room temperature and then concentrated to dryness *in vacuo*. The residue is saponified with 1.2 equivalents of a $0.3N$ baryta solution at room temperature for 15 min. and the solution then neutralized with $0.3N$ sulfuric acid, filtered, and the filtrate concentrated *in vacuo*. The residue is dissolved in a few drops of water and the L-alanyl-L-alanylglycine precipitated by the addition of acetone. Yield, 85%; $[\alpha]_D^{22} = -48.1°$ (2% in water).

In connection with this procedure, it is of interest to note that the reaction of N-carboxy-DL-alanine anhydride (LV) with two equivalents of glycine ethyl ester (LVI) in ethyl acetate solution at $-10°$ leads to the crystallization of the glycine ethyl ester salt of N-carboxy-DL-alanylglycine ethyl ester (LVII) (353). Although (LVII) when in solution in chloroform evolves carbon dioxide slowly at room temperature and more rapidly at 40°, it may be stored without appreciable decomposition in the dry state at room temperature under an atmosphere of carbon dioxide. The general properties of (LVII) resemble those of the carbamates (LX) previously prepared by Frankel and Katchalski (403) by the passage of carbon dioxide into α-amino acid ester (LIX) solutions at 0°. Thus, for example, the reaction of both types of carbamate (LVII and LX) with diazomethane proceeds with the formation of the corresponding carbomethoxy derivatives (LVIII and LXI):

$$\underset{\text{LV}}{\begin{array}{c}CH_3CH\cdot CO\\|\diagdown\\ O\\|\diagup\\ NH\cdot CO\end{array}} + 2NH_2CH_2CO_2Et \xrightarrow[\text{EtOAc}]{-10°} \underset{\text{LVII}}{\begin{array}{c}CH_3CHCO-NHCH_2CO_2Et\\|\\NHCO_2H,NH_2CH_2CO_2Et\end{array}} \xrightarrow{CH_2N_2} \underset{\text{LVIII}}{\begin{array}{c}CH_3CHCO-NHCH_2CO_2E\\|\\NHCO_2CH_3\end{array}}$$

$$\underset{\text{LIX}}{2NH_2CH_2CO_2Et} \xrightarrow[0°]{CO_2} \underset{\text{LX}}{\begin{array}{c}RCHCO_2Et\\|\\NHCO_2H,NH_2CH_2CO_2Et\end{array}} \xrightarrow{CH_2N_2} \underset{\text{LXI}}{\begin{array}{c}RCHCO_2Et\\|\\NHCO_2CH_3\end{array}}$$

Polymerization of N-Carboxy-α-Amino Acid Anhydrides. All known N-carboxy-α-amino acid anhydrides undergo polymerization with the concomitant liberation of carbon dioxide under the appropriate conditions. In contradistinction to the previously discussed polymerization of peptide esters (Section 10–4) wherein chain elongation presumably could be achieved by a condensation of two polymer molecules, propagation in the present instance occurs exclusively via the repeated addition of the N-carboxyanhydride monomer to the polymer molecule. Such polymerization may be accomplished in the solid state, in the liquid state, or in solution, as described below.

(*a*) Solid state. The use of water vapor as a catalyst for the polymerization of N-carboxy-anhydrides has been alluded to above. Polyamino acids so derived incorporate terminal free α-amino and α-carboxyl groups and are presumably formed according to the general scheme given by formulas (XXXIV) to (XXXVII). Crystalline N-carboxy-anhydrides also undergo extensive polycondensation upon prolonged storage at room temperature for several months, although the aging process may be appreciably accelerated by heating the monomer at temperatures below its melting point. Thus Bergmann, Zervas, and Ross (358) observed that the decomposition point of 100° revealed by freshly prepared N-carboxy-ε-carbobenzoxy-L-lysine anhydride rises to over 250° after storage at room temperature for several months. This finding was reaffirmed by Miller, Fankuchen, and Mark (407) who, in addition, demonstrated via changes in X-ray diagrams that the polycondensation of the crystalline monomer is essentially complete upon heat treatment at 85° for 24 hours. In the main, however, studies on the polymerization of N-carboxy-anhydrides in the solid state have not been extensively pursued.

(b) *Liquid state.* When heated above their melting points, N-carboxy-α-amino acids decompose with the evolution of carbon dioxide and the formation of a polymeric material. During the course of the propagation the liquified mass undergoes a gradual solidification to a glass-like polymer whose average chain length varies with the side-chain structure of the amino acid involved. Although polypeptides of an average size of close to 100 amino acid residues may be secured by such procedure, products of smaller size are generally more common. The presence of traces of water in the monomer leads to a marked acceleration in the rate of polymerization. Thus, in a carefully conceived study by Katchalski, Grossfeld, and Frankel (408), a well-dried sample of N-carboxy-ε-carbobenzoxy-L-lysine anhydride was converted to a polymeric material containing 32 amino acid units upon heating *in vacuo* at 102–105° for 1 hour; the presence of traces of moisture in the monomer sufficed to reduce to about 20% the time required for the near completion of such polymerization. Measurement of the optical rotation of the L-lysine hydrochloride recovered from an acid hydrolysate of the polymer revealed the absence of detectable racemization during the polycondensation process (112). Such retention of optical configuration is a generally observed characteristic of polymerizations involving optically active N-carboxy-α-amino acid anhydrides (409).

(c) *Solutions.* N-Carboxy-anhydrides are most frequently polymerized as solutes in highly purified inert organic solvents, e.g., benzene, chloroform, dioxane, ethyl acetate, or nitrobenzene. The reaction is generally catalyzed by the addition of a suitable initiator such as a trace of water or of a primary or secondary amine, while tertiary amines, free amino acids, amino acid esters, preformed polymer, alkali metal salts, and alkali metal hydroxides are less commonly employed. Where a primary or secondary amine (LXIII) is implicated as the initiator, the over-all process may be represented by

$$x\begin{bmatrix} R^1CH\cdot CO\cdot O \\ | \quad\quad | \\ N \longrightarrow CO \end{bmatrix} + HN\begin{matrix}R^2\\ \diagdown \\ R^3\end{matrix} \rightarrow NH_2\cdot CHR^1\cdot CO(-NH\cdot CHR^1\cdot CO-)_{x-2}NH\cdot CHR^1\cdot CO-N\begin{matrix}R^2\\ \diagdown \\ R^3\end{matrix} + xCO_2$$

LXII　　　　LXIII　　　　　　　　　　　　LXIV　　　　　　　　　　　　　　LXV

It should be noted that, inasmuch as the initial step of the propagation involves the condensation of the amine catalyst with one equivalent of N-carboxy-anhydride, it follows that the polymer which ultimately arises contains a free α-amino moiety and a blocked carboxyl substituent. The average size of the polymer which forms is governed by such factors as its own solubility, as well as by the ratio of N-carboxy-anhydride to initiator concentration and the nature of the solvent employed. Under suitable conditions, polymers which incorporate an average of 1000 or more amino acid residues may be readily prepared by this method. The method has been applied to the preparation of polyamino acids containing a single type of amino acid residue in addition to polymers which incorporate two or more different kinds of residues (copolymers). As mixed polymers of the latter type are generally prepared via the random polycondensation of a mixture of two or more different N-carboxy-α-amino acid anhydrides, they reveal a known over-all composition but an unknown residue sequence and distribution. In reactions of the afore-mentioned type, termination of the polymerization reaction may sometimes arise in consequence of cyclic peptide formation; for example, the polymerizations of N-carboxyglycine anhydride in dimethylformamide solution containing lithium chloride yielded *cyclo*-hexaglycyl in appreciable amount (409a).

Unfortunately, space permits discussion neither of the vast array of polymers and copolymers which have been prepared by the methods outlined above, nor of the extensive physical, chemical, or biological studies to which these interesting compounds have been subjected. Authoritative and comprehensive coverage of these aspects has been presented by Katchalski (112) and by Bamford, Elliott, and Hanby (113).

Evaluation of the Method. The generally marked lability of N-carboxy-amino acid anhydrides in the presence of traces of moisture, as well as the special precautions required during their controlled condensation with a suitably constituted amine, has discouraged the widespread use of these reactants in the stepwise synthesis of small peptides. However, N-carboxy-anhydrides have proved of inestimable value as the monomeric reactants in the preparation of amino acid polymers and, indeed, presently provide the most convenient and most generally utilized source of these materials. Although the polymerization of N-carboxy-anhydrides may be effected in the solid state, in the liquid state, or in solution, the latter procedure appears to provide the only currently available means whereby high molecular weight polypeptides with a predetermined degree of polymerization may be prepared. Indeed, most of the amino acid polymers described to date have been synthesized by this procedure.

11. The Thio-thiazolidone Method. *Principle.* The 2-thio-5-thiazolidones are sulfur analogs of the N-carboxy-α-amino acid anhydrides (Section

10–10) and may, in essence, be considered intramolecular anhydrides of the dithiocarbamic acid $HS_2C \cdot NH \cdot CHR \cdot CO_2H$. Treatment of a 2-thio-5-thiazolidone (V) with alcoholic hydrogen chloride yields the corresponding amino acid ester hydrochloride (I), while its condensation with an amino acid ester in an organic medium, or with the sodium salt of an amino acid in aqueous solution, proceeds with the formation of the corresponding peptide derivative (III and VI) and the concomitant liberation of carbon disulfide (IV). The 2-thio-5-thiazolidones are generally stable crystalline compounds which show a markedly lesser inclination to undergo polymerization than their corresponding N-carboxy-α-amino acid anhydride analogs. Polymerization (II) of these compounds may sometimes be induced, however, upon heating in a suitable organic solvent.

$$\begin{array}{c}
\text{HCl·NH}_2\text{CHRCO}_2\text{Et} \xleftarrow{\text{EtOH—HCl}} \text{RCH—CO} \xrightarrow{\Delta} \text{NH}_2\text{CHRCO—(NHCHRCO)}_x\text{—NHCHRCO}_2\text{H} \\
\text{I} \quad\quad \text{NH}_2\text{CHR'CO}_2\text{Et} \quad\quad\quad \text{HN} \quad \text{S} \quad \text{1. NH}_2\text{CHR'CO}_2\text{Na} \quad\quad \text{II} \\
\downarrow \quad\quad\quad\quad\quad\quad\quad\quad\quad\quad\quad \text{CS} \quad \text{2. HCl} \quad\quad\quad\quad \downarrow \\
\text{NH}_2\text{CHRCO—NHCHR'CO}_2\text{Et} + \text{CS}_2 \quad\quad\quad\quad\quad\quad\quad \text{NH}_2\text{CHRCO—NHCHR'CO}_2\text{H} + \text{CS}_2 \\
\text{III} \quad\quad\quad\quad\quad\quad \text{IV} \quad\quad \text{V} \quad\quad\quad\quad\quad\quad\quad\quad\quad\quad\quad\quad \text{VI} \quad\quad\quad\quad \text{IV}a
\end{array}$$

Preparation of 2-Thio-5-thiazolidones. A synthesis of 2-thio-5-thiazolidone (XIII; $R = R' = H$) was described in 1948 by Cook, Heilbron, and Levy (410); it involved the sodium ethoxide-catalyzed condensation of aminoacetonitrile (VII; $R = R' = H$) and acetone (VIII) to give 5-imino-2:2-dimethyloxazolidine (IX) which, in turn, underwent ready ring fission in the presence of carbon disulfide with the formation of carbamylmethylammonium carbamylmethyldithiocarbamate (X). Treatment of the latter intermediate with cold dilute aqueous mineral acid then yielded the desired product (XIII) (procedure 10–21). Although 2-thio-5-thiazolidone could be obtained more directly via the action of carbon disulfide on aminoacetonitrile, followed by treatment of the intermediate (XII; $R = R' = H$) so derived with aqueous mineral acid, such a procedure was not so satisfactory as the above route from the standpoint of yield and purity of product.

$$\begin{array}{c}
\text{NH}_2 \quad \text{CH}_3 \quad\quad\quad \text{RCR'—C}=\text{NH} \quad\quad \text{CRR'CONH}_2 \quad\quad\quad\quad\quad \text{CONH}_2 \\
\text{CRR'} + \text{CO} \xrightarrow{\text{NaOEt}} \text{NH} \quad \text{O} \xrightarrow{\text{CS}_2} \text{NH} \quad\quad\quad \xleftarrow{\text{CS}_2} \text{CRR'} \\
\text{CN} \quad\quad \text{CH}_3 \quad\quad\quad\quad\quad \text{C(CH}_3)_2 \quad\quad \text{CS}_2\text{H·NH}_2\text{CRR'CONH}_2 \quad \text{NH}_2 \\
\text{VII} \quad\quad \text{VIII} \quad\quad\quad\quad\quad\quad \text{IX} \quad\quad\quad\quad\quad \text{X} \quad\quad\quad\quad\quad\quad\quad \text{XI} \\
\quad\quad\quad\quad\quad\quad\quad\quad\quad\quad\quad\quad\quad\quad\quad\quad\quad\quad\quad\quad \downarrow \text{aq. HCl} \\
\quad\quad\quad\quad\quad\quad\quad\quad \text{RCR'—C}=\text{NH} \quad\quad\quad\quad \text{RCR'—CO} \\
\xrightarrow{\text{CS}_2} \quad\quad\quad\quad \text{NH} \quad \text{S} \xrightarrow{\text{aq. HCl}} \text{NH} \quad \text{S} \\
\quad\quad\quad\quad\quad\quad\quad\quad\quad\quad \text{CS} \quad\quad\quad\quad\quad\quad\quad\quad \text{CS} \\
\quad\quad\quad\quad\quad\quad\quad\quad\quad\quad \text{XII} \quad\quad\quad\quad\quad\quad\quad\quad \text{XIII}
\end{array}$$

Use of α-aminopropionitrile (VII; R = H, R' = CH$_3$) in lieu of aminoacetonitrile permitted Cook and Levy (411) to prepare 2-thio-4-methyl-5-thiazolidone (XIII; R = H, R' = CH$_3$) by the former procedure, while the 2-thio-5-thiazolidone derivatives of α-aminoisobutyric acid, glutamine, leucine, methionine, norleucine, tyrosine, and valine were subsequently prepared in comparable manner by Davis and Levy (412), who secured the requisite dithiocarbamic acid derivative (X) by the action of carbon disulfide on the pertinent amino acid amide (XI) in potassium carbonate solution. It is worthy of note that the tyrosine and leucine amides employed were both of the L-configuration. Although the thiothiazolidone derived from L-tyrosine was optically active, it underwent racemization rapidly in the presence of base or during 2 to 3 hours standing in methanol solution; however, considerably greater stability was shown in the presence of 0.1 equivalent of hydrogen chloride or in ethanol solution, whereas no noticeable racemization occurred in ethyl acetate. Crude leucine thiothiazolidone similarly revealed optical activity in the freshly prepared state, although attempts to purify the material by crystallization led to the recovery of racemic material only. In any event, the ease of racemization of optically active thiothiazolidones was amply demonstrated. The action of carbon disulfide on an alkaline solution of the pertinent amino acid amide has also been employed by Hofmann, Lindenmann, Magee, and Khan (413) to secure the thiothiazolidone derivatives of alanine, leucine, tyrosine, and aspartic acid (procedure 10–22).

Illustrative procedure 10–21 (410). 2-Thio-5-thiazolidone (XIII). Five hundred milliliters of conc. sulfuric acid is added during 30 min. to 2.5 l. of ethanol in a 5-l. flask with stirring and moderate cooling, and 700 g. of methylene aminoacetonitrile is then added rapidly thereto at 45°. After some 5–10 min., crystals separate which are filtered off after several hours of stirring and washed with 1 l. of ethanol. The product is dissolved in 1 l. of water and the solution run into 3 l. of ethanol, with stirring. After storage overnight, the deposited neutral aminoacetonitrile sulfate is recovered by filtration; yield, 725 g.; m.p. 177° d.

A solution of 4.9 g. of sodium in 120 ml. of ethanol is added during 2 hr. to a fine, stirred suspension of 26 g. of aminoacetonitrile sulfate in 105 ml. of acetone until neutral to phenolphthalein. Sodium sulfate is removed by filtration and 15 ml. of carbon disulfide added to the filtrate. The crystalline precipitate is filtered off and another crop of material obtained upon dilution of the mother liquor with ether and storage at 0° overnight; combined yield, 9.5 g. Crystallization of the combined precipitate upon the addition of ethanol or acetone to its aqueous solution in the minimum amount of water gives 6.8 g. of carbamylmethylammonium carbamylmethyldithiocarbamate (X); m.p. 139° d. When a 2.0 g. of this compound in 5 ml. of conc. HCl is cooled to 0° and diluted with 10 ml. of water, 1 g. of 2-thio-5-thiazolidone (XIII) separates. Recrystallization may be effected from benzene. The compound melts above 300° with decomposition.

Illustrative procedure 10–22 (413). DL-2-Thio-4-methyl-5-thiazolidone. To a solution of 16.2 g. of potassium carbonate in 65 ml. of water is added 7.2 ml. of of carbon disulfide and 9.0 g. of DL-alanine amide (Section 10–43) and the mixture shaken for 9 hr. at room temperature. The resulting suspension is extracted with three 40-ml. portions of ether and the aqueous phase cooled at $-2°$ and acidified to Congo red with conc. hydrochloric acid. The mixture is stored at 4° for 30 min., and the yellow crystals collected and washed repeatedly with ice-water, then dried *in vacuo* at room temperature. Recrystallization is effected from aqueous methanol; yield, 6.2 g. (41%); m.p. 124–126°.

An alternative route to 4-substituted 2-thio-5-thiazolidones was devised by Billimoria and Cook (414) in 1949. This involved the initial formation of either the 4-alkylidene- or the 4-arylidenethiazolidone (XVI) from the condensation of an aliphatic or an aromatic aldehyde or ketone (XIV) with 2-thio-5-thiazolidone (XV) in boiling glacial acetic acid containing a trace of either piperidine or some other primary, secondary, or tertiary amine as catalyst. Reduction of the intermediate (XVI) so procured with zinc and hot acetic acid then led to the desired product (XVII) (procedure 10–23).

$$\begin{array}{c}\text{R}\\|\\\text{CO} + \text{NH}\\|\\\text{R}'\\\text{XIV}\end{array}\quad\begin{array}{c}\text{CH}_2\text{—CO}\\\diagup\quad\diagdown\\\text{S}\\\diagdown\quad\diagup\\\text{CS}\\\text{XV}\end{array}\xrightarrow[\Delta]{\text{AcOH}}\begin{array}{c}\text{R—C=C—CO}\\|\qquad\diagdown\\\text{R}'\quad\text{NH}\qquad\text{S}\\\diagdown\qquad\diagup\\\text{CS}\\\text{XVI}\end{array}\xrightarrow{\text{Zn—HOAc}}\begin{array}{c}\text{R—CHCH—CO}\\\diagup\quad|\qquad|\\\text{R}'\quad\text{NH}\quad\text{S}\\\diagdown\qquad\diagup\\\text{CS}\\\text{XVII}\end{array}$$

In this manner, reactions involving the condensation of acetaldehyde (XIV; $R = CH_3$, $R' = H$), methyl 2,2-diethoxyethyl sulfide (CH_3SCH_2CH-$(OC_2H_5)_2$), *n*-butyraldehyde (XIV; $R = CH_3CH_2CH_2$, $R' = H$), isobutyraldehyde (XIV; $R = CH(CH_3)_2$, $R' = H$), acetone (XIV; $R = R' = CH_3$), benzaldehyde (XIV; $R = C_6H_5$, $R' = H$), and *p*-hydroxybenzaldehyde (XIV; $R = p\text{-HOC}_6H_4$, $R' = H$) with 2-thio-5-thiazolidone (XV) proceeded with the ultimate formation of the thiothiazolidone derivative (XVII) of α-amino-*n*-butyric acid, methionine, norleucine, leucine, valine, phenylalanine, and tyrosine, respectively. As an asymmetric center is generated during the course of such synthesis, it follows that the products obtained are invariably racemic.

Illustrative procedure 10–23 (414). 2-Thio-4-benzyl-5-thiazolidone. Twenty grams of 2-thio-5-thiazolidone (XV) (procedure 10–21) is dissolved in 200 ml. of boiling glacial acetic acid, 21 g. of benzaldehyde (XIV; $R = C_6H_5$, $R' = H$) is added thereto, and the solution treated with 3 drops of piperidine. After some 15 min. at room temperature, the solution sets to a solid mass of yellow crystals. These are filtered off after 12 hr. and a second crop of crystals secured by concentration of the mother liquor. The combined yield of 2-thio-4-benzylidene-5-thiazolidone (XVI; $R = C_6H_5$, $R' = H$) is *zoftig*, 31 g. (98% of theory). The melting point, 212–214°, remains unchanged upon recrystallization from glacial acetic acid.

Twenty-five grams of 2-thio-4-benzylidene-5-thiazolidone is dissolved in 1 l. of glacial acetic and 0.5 ml. of conc. HCl added. Addition of 40 g. of zinc dust in 10-g. portions is followed after 0.5 hr. by decolorization of the solution, removal of the excess of zinc dust by filtration, and concentration to dryness *in vacuo*. The solid is digested with 6N hydrochloric acid and filtered, the filtrate containing the last traces of zinc being rejected. The residue (23.5 g.), m.p. 152–153°, is

TABLE 10-17
4-Substituted 2-Thio-4-thiazolidone Derivatives of Some α-Amino Acids

2-Thio-4-thiazolidone Derivative	M.P., °C.	Ref.[b]
DL-Alanine	128.5	*411*, 413
DL-α-Amino-n-butyric acid	79–80	414
α-Aminoisobutyric acid	132	412
DL-Aspartic acid	161–163	413
DL-Cyclohexylglycine	185–186	414
DL-Glutamine	143–145	412
Glycine	>300 d.	410
DL-Leucine	96–97	412, *413*
DL-Methionine	97	412
DL-Norleucine	73–74	412
DL-Phenylalanine	159–160	414
DL-Tyrosine	166–169	*413*, 414
L-Tyrosine[a]	154	412
DL-Valine	88	412

[a] $[\alpha]_D^{22} = +174°$ (2.4% in methanol).
[b] Where two references are given, the melting point data were selected from the one in italics.

purified by rapid dissolution in cold 2N sodium hydroxide, followed by acidification and cooling. Filtration yields a mat of needles melting at 157–160°. Although recrystallization from benzene-petroleum ether leads to the slow separation of a product melting at 159–160°, this process may be effected only with great losses.

Several of the 4-substituted 2-thio-5-thiazolidones which have been prepared by the procedures described above are listed in Table 10–17.

Stepwise Synthesis of Peptides. The employment of 2-thio-5-thiazolidone for the synthesis of N-terminal glycine peptides was initially described by Cook and Levy (415) in 1950. Condensation of this crucial intermediate with a suitably constituted amine to yield a peptide derivative proceeds in a manner analogous to that observed with the N-carboxy-α-amino acid anhydrides (Chapter 10–10). Thus the reaction of one equivalent of 2-thio-5-thiazolidone (XVIII) with two equivalents of an amino acid or peptide ester, in an organic solvent such as ethanol or chloroform, proceeds with the

CHEMICAL PROCEDURES FOR SYNTHESIS OF PEPTIDES

formation of a dithiocarbamate intermediate (XIX) which, in turn, undergoes facile decomposition to one molecule each of the N-terminal glycine derivative (XX), carbon disulfide, and glycine ester hydrochloride upon the addition of cold aqueous mineral acid; the reaction is generally accomplished at or below room temperature, although higher temperatures are occasionally employed. A somewhat more practicable modification involves either the substitution of one equivalent of triethylamine for one equivalent of the amino acid ester, or the use of one equivalent of the hydrochloride salt of the amino acid ester plus two equivalents of triethylamine in lieu of the two

$$\underset{\text{XVIII}}{\begin{array}{c} CH_2{-\!\!\!-}CO \\ | \quad\quad | \\ NH \quad S \\ \diagdown / \\ CS \end{array}} \xrightarrow{2NH_2CHRCO_2Et} \underset{\text{XIX}}{\begin{array}{c} CH_2CO{-\!\!\!-}NHCHRCO_2Et \\ | \\ NH \\ | \\ CS_2H \cdot NH_2CHRCO_2Et \end{array}} \xrightarrow{\text{aq. HCl}} \underset{\text{XX}}{\underbrace{\begin{array}{c} CH_2CO{-\!\!\!-}NHCHRCO_2Et \\ | \\ NH_2 \cdot HCl \\ \\ + \;CS_2 \;+\; HCl \cdot NH_2CHRCO_2Et \end{array}}}$$

equivalents of the amino acid ester (procedure 10–24); the possibility of contamination with the excess amino acid ester is thereby appreciably diminished. Such a procedure has been employed to obtain the crystalline hydrochloride salts of the following peptide esters: H·Gly·Gly·OEt, H·(Gly)$_3$·OEt, H·(Gly)$_4$·OEt, H·(Gly)$_5$·OEt, H·Gly·DL-Phe·OEt, and H·Gly·L-Tyr·OMe (415). An alternative approach, which involved the preparation of the free peptide from the treatment of an amino acid with 2-thio-5-thiazolidone in alkaline aqueous solution followed by neutralization of the reaction mixture, was implicated in the synthesis of glycyl-DL-phenylalanine.

Illustrative procedure 10–24 (415). Triglycine ethyl ester hydrochloride. To a mixture of 15 g. (1 eq.) of glycylglycine ethyl ester hydrochloride (procedure 10-3) and 15 g. (2 eq.) of triethylamine in 150 ml. of ethanol is added 10 g. of 2-thio-5-thiazolidone (procedure 10-21) and, after standing for some 15 min. at room temperature, the clear solution is acidified with 30 ml. of 5N hydrochloric acid. Scratching or seeding the solution leads to the separation of triglycine ethyl ester hydrochloride as a mass of plates; yield, 16.7 g. (86%); m.p. 216–217°.

Although the unsubstituted 2-thio-5-thiazolidone undergoes facile condensation with a suitably constituted amine to form the corresponding N-terminal glycine derivative, the comparable reaction with 4-substituted 2-thio-5-thiazolidones to yield derivatives which incorporate other N-terminal amino acid residues is sometimes not so satisfactorily accomplished. Thus, for example, an attempt by Cook and Levy (416) to condense 2-thio-4-methyl-5-thiazolidone (V; R = CH$_3$) with an amino acid ester, in a manner analogous to that described above with the unsubstituted thiothiazolidone, led generally to low yields of the desired N-terminal alanine peptide ester (III; R = CH$_3$). However, the condensation of 2-thio-4-methyl-5-thiazolidone with a free amino acid, either in alkaline solution or in hot glacial acetic acid, yielded the desired peptide in more satisfactory amount, although this product was invariably highly contaminated with the component amino acids; purification of the free peptide from its amino acid contaminants necessitated separation on a column of cation exchange resin. Although a later attempt by Davis and Levy (412) to condense the optically active 2-thio-5-thiazolidone derivative of L-tyrosine (V; R = p-OHC$_6$H$_4$CH$_2$) with glycylglycine ethyl ester in ethanol solution led to the isolation of a high yield of tyrosylglycylglycine ethyl ester hydrochloride, the product was wholly racemic. The apparent ease with which optically active thiothiazolidones undergo racemization in the presence of base has been alluded to above. Aside from the studies mentioned, thiothiazolidones have been only occasionally employed for the stepwise synthesis of peptides.

By virtue of their greater stability, 2-thio-5-thiazolidones are somewhat less prone to undergo polymerization reactions than their corresponding N-carboxy-α-amino acid anhydride analogs (Section 10-10). Although extensive data are lacking, it appears that not only do the thiothiazolidones require somewhat more drastic thermal conditions for intermolecular condensation, but that also the polymer ultimately secured is of smaller average chain length than that which arises from the analogous N-carboxy-anhydride. Thus Cook and Levy (417) described the preparation of a polyglycine polymer (II; $x = 7$, R = H) with an average length of about nine residues from the treatment of 2-thio-5-thiazolidone (V; R = H) with boiling pyridine, ethanol, or methanol for a few minutes. In this connection, it is worthy of note that the mono-sulfur analog of N-carboxyglycine anhydride, namely thiazolid-2:5-dione, possesses a stability which is apparently intermediate between those of N-carboxyglycine anhydride and 2-thio-5-thiazolidone. This material, although fairly stable toward moist air, was shown by Aubert, Jeffreys, and Knott (418) to undergo ready polymerization to a glycine polymer upon brief heating in the presence of water. Preparation of crystalline thiazolid-2:5-dione (XXIV), m.p. 110°, may be accomplished by heating the potassium salt of glycine (XXII) with ethyl ethoxydithioformate (XXI) in aqueous solution for some 18 hours, followed by the action of phosphorus trichloride on the N-thioncarbethoxyglycine (XXIII) so derived (418, 419). A comparable attempt to effect the

$$\underset{\text{XXI}}{\text{CH}_3\text{CH}_2\text{O}\overset{\text{S}}{\overset{\|}{\text{C}}}\text{SEt}} + \underset{\text{XXII}}{\text{NH}_2\text{CH}_2\text{CO}_2\text{K}} \xrightarrow{\Delta} \underset{\text{XXIII}}{\underset{\text{COCH}_2\text{CH}_3}{\overset{\text{CH}_2-\text{CO}_2\text{H}}{\text{NH}\diagdown\diagup\text{S}}}} \xrightarrow{\text{PCl}_3} \underset{\text{XXIV}}{\underset{\text{CO}}{\overset{\text{CH}_2-\text{CO}}{\text{NH}\diagdown\diagup\text{S}}}}$$

cyclodealkylation of N-thioncarbethoxysarcosine and N-thioncarbethoxy-DL-alanine led to the formation of non-crystallizable oils (418).

Evaluation of the Method. 2-Thio-5-thiazolidones have been only occasionally employed in the stepwise synthesis of small peptides, and such application has, in the main, been confined to peptides that incorporate an N-terminal glycine residue. The few attempts to employ 4-substituted-2-thio-5-thiazolidones have not been invariably successful, and, indeed, use of the 4-methyl derivative led to the formation of N-terminal alanine peptides which were both low in yield and highly contaminated with the component amino acids. An additional shortcoming of the method rests in the remarkable facility with which optically active 4-substituted-2-thio-5-thiazolidones undergo racemization in the presence of base, and such racemization has been encountered in the few attempts to prepare optically active peptides via this route. Utilization of 2-thio-5-thiazolidone derivatives as monomeric reactants for the synthesis of amino acid polymers has been too infrequent to occasion comment at the present time.

SYNTHETIC PEPTIDE METHODS INVOLVING SELECTIVELY REMOVABLE ACYL BLOCKING GROUPS

12. General Considerations. In any consideration of methods that may be employed for the union of two amino acids via a peptide linkage, the direct condensation of the α-amino group of one amino acid and the α-carboxyl group of the other, with the elimination of a single molecule of water, is most readily and simply visualized. Such an idealized synthesis may be represented by

$$NH_2CHRCO_2H + NH_2CHR'CO_2H \rightarrow NH_2CHRCO-NHCHR'CO_2H + H_2O$$
$$\text{I} \qquad\qquad \text{II} \qquad\qquad\qquad \text{III} \qquad\qquad\qquad \text{IV}$$

Achievement of peptide bond synthesis through direct condensation, as formulated above, is made difficult, however, not only by virtue of the dipolar nature of the amino acids involved, but by energy considerations as well. Since such condensation implicates the carboxyl function of one amino acid (I) and the amino function of the other (II), it becomes essential to suppress the reactive character of the amino group of the first and of the carboxyl group of the second. In practice, therefore, appropriate substitution of these functional groups becomes a necessary prelude to condensation. The masking substituents must be of such nature as to permit their ready removal, subsequent to condensation, by procedures which will not induce breakdown of the labile peptide molecule. With the foregoing in mind, the sequence of events for the coupling of amino acids via peptide linkages may be enumerated as follows.

(*a*) *Masking of the amino function.* Implicit in the choice of a suitable blocking substituent for the amino group of an amino acid are the conditions that not only should the derivative which incorporates such substituent be easily prepared, but also that subsequent removal of this substituent should proceed under conditions that would lead to no appreciable destruction of the remainder of the molecule. Among the various substituents which have been found to satisfy these criteria are the carbobenzoxy ($C_6H_5CH_2OCO-$), p-nitrocarbobenzoxy ($NO_2C_6H_4CH_2OCO-$), carboallyloxy [$CH_2=CHCH_2OCO-$), p-toluenesulfonyl ($CH_3C_6H_4SO_2-$), phthalyl ($C_6H_4(CO)_2=$), trityl [$(C_6H_5)_3C-$], benzyl ($C_6H_5CH_2-$), dibenzyl (($C_6H_5CH_2)_2=$], benzylsulfonyl ($C_6H_5CH_2SO_2-$), trifluoroacetyl (CF_3CO-), chloroacetyl ($ClCH_2CO-$), formyl ($HCO-$), and o-nitrophenoxyacetyl ($NO_2C_6H_4OCH_2CO-$) groups. Selective methods employed for their ultimate removal include, among others, fission by acid in aqueous and non-aqueous media, cleavage with dilute alkali, hydrogenolysis, and hydrazinolysis.

(b) *Masking of the carboxyl function.* Appropriate substitution of the carboxyl group of an amino acid presents little difficulty and is conveniently achieved through the formation of the alkali salt, NH_2CHRCO_2Na, if the peptide synthesis is to be effected in aqueous media, or the ester derivative (methyl, ethyl, or benzyl), if non-aqueous media are to be employed. Regeneration of the carboxyl group is readily accomplished by neutralization with acid in the former instance, whereas saponification with alkali or selective cleavage with dilute acid is commonly utilized in the case of the methyl or ethyl ester derivatives. For the selective cleavage of benzyl esters, hydrogenolysis is generally employed.

(c) *Coupling.* Subsequent to adequate masking of the two reactant amino acids, as given in *a* and *b*, there arises the problem of how condensation of the resulting derivatives should be achieved. This problem has been satisfactorily met by conversion of the unsubstituted carboxyl function of the acylated amino acid, e.g., $C_6H_5CH_2OCO-NHCHRCO_2H$, to the corresponding azide, acid chloride, mixed anhydride, "activated ester," "carbodiimide" derivative, or other active intermediate, followed by reaction of the group so activated with the unprotected amino group of the other reactant, e.g., $NH_2CHR'CO_2Et$. The method may be illustrated by

$$C_6H_5CH_2OCO-NHCHRCON_3 + NH_2CHR'CO_2Et \rightarrow C_6H_5CH_2OCO-NHCHRCO-NHCHR'CO_2Et + HN_3$$
V　　　　　　　　　　　VI　　　　　　　　　　　VII　　　　　　　　　　　VIII

Formation of a peptide bond may be alternatively attained through activation of the amino group of an amino acid ester (IX) by reaction with such agents as phosgene, phosphorus trichloride, or tetraethyl pyrophosphite, succeeded by treatment of the "activated amine" (X) with an acylamino acid, e.g.,

$$NH_2CHR'CO_2Et \xrightarrow{COCl_2} OCN \cdot CHR'CO_2Et \xrightarrow{C_6H_5CH_2OCO-NHCHRCO_2H}$$
IX　　　　　　　　　　　　　X

$$C_6H_5CH_2OCO-NHCHRCO-NHCHR'CO_2Et$$
XI

(d) *Elongation of the peptide chain.* Additional amino acid residues may be affixed to an acyldipeptide or derivative thereof, in a manner comparable to that given in c above, subsequent to pertinent activation either of the C-terminal carbonyl function (XII), e.g.,

$$-CO_2Et \xrightarrow{NH_2NH_2} -CONHNH_2 \xrightarrow{HNO_2} -CON_3 \xrightarrow{NH_2CHRCO_2Et} -CONHCHRCO_2Et$$
$$\text{XII} \qquad\qquad \text{XIII} \qquad\qquad \text{XIV} \qquad\qquad \text{XV}$$

or of the amino moiety (XVII) which results from selective removal of the acyl blocking group, e.g.,

$$C_6H_5CH_2OCO-NHCHRCO- \xrightarrow{H_2} NH_2CHRCO- \xrightarrow{COCl_2} OCN\cdot CHRCO- \xrightarrow{RCO_2H} RCONHCHRCO-$$
$$\text{XVI} \qquad\qquad \text{XVII} \qquad\qquad \text{XVIII} \qquad\qquad \text{XIX}$$

(e) *Removal of masking substituents.* After the desired acylated peptide derivative has been secured, final removal of the protecting groups on both ends of the peptide chain (XX) is accomplished with liberation of the free peptide (XXII), e.g.,

$$C_6H_5CH_2OCO-NHCHRCO-NHCHR'CO_2Et \xrightarrow{NaOH}$$
$$\text{XX}$$

$$C_6H_5CH_2OCO-NHCHRCO-NHCHR'CO_2H \xrightarrow{H_2} NH_2CHRCO-NHCHR'CO_2H$$
$$\text{XXI} \qquad\qquad\qquad\qquad\qquad \text{XXII}$$

The foregoing discussion presents a rather simplified picture of the procedures currently employed in the synthesis of peptides involving a variety of amino acids. In actuality, such picture becomes somewhat more complicated in syntheses wherein the possibility of racemization of optically active components must be considered, as well as in syntheses in which reactive basic or acidic radicals as occur in lysine, histidine, and arginine, or glutamic and aspartic acids, respectively, are involved. Still further complications are imposed by the presence of the hydroxyl groups of threonine, serine, hydroxyproline, and hydroxylysine, and by the sulfur atoms of cystine and methionine. Recent methods of peptide synthesis applicable to each of these amino acids, together with the limitations implicit in their use, will be discussed in greater detail below.

Masking of the Amino Function

In order that a blocking substituent may be satisfactorily utilized for masking the amino function of an amino acid employed in peptide synthesis, it should conform to the following criteria: (a) the pertinent acylated amino acid derivative should be conveniently available through the use of simple organic chemical techniques; (b) the acylation should proceed in high yield; (c) the conditions employed for acylation should not lead to racemization where optically active amino acids are used; (d) the acylated amino acids so derived should be easily crystallizable in order to permit their ready characterization and purification; (e) the acyl blocking group should be stable under the conditions utilized for coupling with other amino acid residues; (*f*) during the terminal stages of the synthesis, the acyl blocking group should be selectively removable under conditions that would not lead to racemization or destruction of the labile peptide molecule; and (*g*) the removal of the acyl blocking group should not be accompanied by the formation of side products which would make purification of the desired product difficult. During the period from 1926 to 1949, only the *p*-toluenesulfonyl (127) and the carbobenzoxy (128) groups exhibited the properties necessary to meet these rigid criteria. Since 1949, however, some dozen other acyl blocking substituents have been introduced into synthetic peptide procedures with varying degrees of success. Several of the acylated amino acids which incorporate the more successful of these groups, together with methods for their preparation, are described more fully below.

13. *p*-Toluenesulfonyl Group. This acyl blocking substituent, more commonly referred to as the "tosyl" group, was the first selectively removable acyl radical successfully applied to synthetic peptide procedures. Introduction of the tosyl group by Schoenheimer (127) in 1926 was based upon the selective fission which it undergoes when its amide linkage with an amino acid residue is subjected to the action of a warm phosphonium iodide–hydriodic acid mixture. Preparation of the tosylamino acids (III) employed in peptide synthesis is generally effected by the action of toluenesulfonyl chloride (I) on the pertinent amino acid (II) in alkaline solution, according to the general procedure of Fischer and Lipschitz (420) (procedure 10–25). Reaction presumably occurs in the absence of appreciable racemization (420). Table 10–18 lists several of the tosylamino acids which have thus far been described.

$$CH_3C_6H_4SO_2Cl + NH_2CHRCO_2H \xrightarrow[\text{2. HCl}]{\text{1. aq. NaOH}} CH_3C_6H_4SO_2-NHCHRCO_2H$$

I   II   III

Illustrative procedure 10–25 (421). Tosyl-L-valine (III; R = (CH$_3$)$_2$CH). To a solution of 5 g. of L-valine in 55 ml. of *N* NaOH is added 11 g. of solid *p*-toluenesulfonyl chloride; the mixture is stirred vigorously at room temperature for 3 hr., the excess acid chloride removed by filtration, and the filtrate acidified to Congo red with dilute HCl. Tosyl-L-valine, which separates as a white crystalline precipitate, is collected, washed with water, and dried. Crystallization from a mixture of ethyl acetate–light petroleum ether yields rectangular plates. Yield, 6.8 g.; m.p. 144°.

An alternative procedure, more recently described by Theodoropoulos and Craig (439), obviates the use of strong alkali (procedure 10–26).

Illustrative procedure 10–26 (439). Tosyl-L-leucine. A mixture of 8 ml. of water, 4 ml. of tetrahydrofuran, 1.6 g. of triethylamine, and 0.65 g. of L-leucine is treated with 1.45 g. of tosyl chloride, added in small portions, with stirring over a half-hour period. After some 45 min., during which time all the amino acid dissolves, the tetrahydrofuran is removed by concentration *in vacuo* and 10 ml. of water added to the residual solution. The solution is washed twice with ether and the tosyl-L-leucine precipitated upon strong acidification with hydrochloric acid. Recrystallization is effected from aqueous ethanol; yield, 1 g.; m.p. 120–122°.

The procedures described above, with minor modifications, such as the quantities of reagents employed or the solvent required for crystallization or purification of the final product, may for the most part be utilized for the preparation of all the tosylamino acids listed in Table 10–18 with certain exceptions, e.g., the glutamine derivative, ε-tosyllysine, δ-tosylornithine, and O-tosyltyrosine. It must be remembered that the quantities of reagents required in these preparations will depend upon the nature of the amino acid involved, as well as upon the derivative desired. Thus such amino acids as aspartic acid will need an additional equivalent of alkali to compensate for the extra acidic function, while formation of the ditosyl derivative of tyrosine will necessitate additional toluenesulfonyl chloride to provide for both the phenolic-hydroxyl and the amino functions, with a corresponding increase in the required amount of alkali; in the acidification step of the α-tosylarginine synthesis, acetic acid is employed in lieu of hydrochloric acid (422). Although δ-tosylornithine and ε-tosyllysine may be synthesized essentially by the procedure described above, the synthesis must be effected with the copper complex of the pertinent amino acid to prevent acylation of the α-amino group, while the copper ions are subsequently removed with hydrogen sulfide prior to isolation of the desired compound (393, 423). Preparation of O-tosyltyrosine is achieved through preferential cleavage of the N-tosyl group of O,N-ditosyltyrosine by the action of a mixture of phosphonium iodide and hydriodic acid at 100° (126).

14. The Carbobenzoxy and Related Groups. Bergmann and Zervas (128), impressed by the ready scission which O- and N-bound benzyl groups underwent upon catalytic hydrogenation (449–451), studied the benzyl analog of the carboethoxy group (unfruitfully employed by Fischer) as a selectively removable acyl blocking substituent. Thus was conceived the extraordinary acyl blocking group which has proved more versatile, and has been more universally utilized, than any other in the preparation of synthetic peptides. The acylating agent (VI) employed by Bergmann and Zervas (128) for the carbobenzoxylation of amino acids was prepared by the action of benzyl alcohol (IV) upon a cold solution of phosgene (V) in toluene, followed by removal of the toluene under reduced pressure. The benzyl chlorocarbonate (benzyl chloroformate) so derived has been more commonly referred to as carbobenzoxy chloride. Its synthesis via the direct interaction of phosgene and benzyl alcohol under conditions of low

TABLE 10-18
Toluenesulfonyl Derivatives of Amino Acids

Toluenesulfonyl(Tosyl)amino Acid	M.P., °C.	$[\alpha]_D$, deg	Temp., °C.	Concn. and Solvent	Ref.[a]
Tosyl-DL-alanine	138–139	—	—	—	424, 425
Tosyl-L-alanine	134–135	−6.8	20	3.1%, ethanol	420, 424, 425
Tosyl-β-alanine	119.5–121	—	—	—	426
Tosyl-DL-α-amino-n-butyric acid	152–153	—	—	—	427
Tosyl-α-aminoisobutyric acid	149–150	—	—	—	427, 428
α-Tosyl-DL-arginine	>330	—	—	—	429
α-Tosyl-L-arginine	256–257 d.	—	—	—	422, 429
α-Tosyl-L-arginine·HBr	197–199 d.	—	—	—	429
Tosyl-L-aspartic acid	139–140	—	—	—	430, 431
Tosyl-S-benzyl-L-cysteine	125–126	+11.3	21	2%, 95% ethanol	400, 432, 432a
bis-Tosyl-L-cystine	204–205	—	—	—	425, 430
α-Tosyl-γ-cbzo-L-α,γ-diaminobutyric acid	149.5–150.5	—	—	—	429
Tosyl-DL-glutamic acid	172	—	—	—	433, 434
Tosyl-D-glutamic acid	142–145	—	—	—	433
Tosyl-L-glutamic acid	131[a]	+22.0	—	1%, ethanol	434
Tosyl-D-glutamine	166	—	—	—	433
Tosyl-L-glutamine	165–166	+8.7	21	2.4%, 0.5N KHCO₃	435, 436
Tosylglycine	149–150	—	—	—	425, 430, 437
Tosyl-L-histidine	202–204	—	—	—	425
N-Tosyl-L-hydroxyproline	153	—	—	—	425
O-Tosyl-L-hydroxyproline	163–165	—	—	—	390a
Tosyl-DL-isoleucine	141	—	—	—	146, 425
Tosyl-L-isoleucine	135–136	−12.3	21	2%, 0.5N KHCO₃	425, 438
Tosyl-L-leucine	124	+4.5	20	9%, ethanol	420, 425, 439

Compound	mp (°C)	$[\alpha]_D$		Solvent	Ref.
α-Tosyl-L-lysine	263–264	—	—	—	439a, 439b
ε-Tosyl-L-lysine	237–238 d.	+13.6	21	3.2%, N HCl	393
α-Tosyl-L-lysine·HCl	187–188	—	—	—	439b
α-Tosyl-ε-cbzo-L-lysine	123–124	—	—	—	429, 439a
Tosyl-DL-methionine	104–105	—	—	—	425
Tosyl-DL-norleucine	124	—	—	—	425
α-Tosyl-DL-ornithine	212.5–213.5 d.	—	—	—	429
α-Tosyl-L-ornithine·½H₂O	212–213 d.	—	—	—	439b
δ-Tosyl-L-ornithine	212 d.	+20.8	23	2%, 6N HCl	423
α-Tosyl-δ-cbzo-DL-ornithine	134–135	—	—	—	429
α-Tosyl-δ-cbzo-L-ornithine	120.5–121.5	—	—	—	429
Tosyl-DL-phenylalanine	134–135	—	—	—	425
Tosyl-D-phenylalanine	164–165	+2.4	19	7.6%, acetone	420, 425, 440
Tosyl-L-phenylalanine	164–165	−2.1	20	7.5%, acetone	420
Tosyl-DL-proline	130–133	—	—	—	441, 442
Tosyl-L-proline·H₂O	58–60	−163.0	24	2.3%, H₂O + 2 eq. NaOH	442, 443
Tosyl-DL-serine	212–213 d.	—	—	—	425
Tosyl-L-serine	235–236	−32.3	25	2.0%, pyridine	444
Tosyl-DL-threonine	181–182	—	—	—	445
Tosyl-D-threonine	136–137	−14.7	18	2%, methanol	445
Tosyl-L-threonine	136–137	+14.8	18	2%, methanol	445
Tosyl-L-tryptophan	176	—	—	—	430
N-Tosyl-L-tyrosine	187–188	−8.6	20	6.7%, 0.5N NaOH	420
O-Tosyl-L-tyrosine	218 d.	−11.7	17	6.2%, N NaOH[b]	126, 446
O,N-Ditosyl-L-tyrosine	117–119	—	—	—	126, 430
Tosyl-DL-valine	166–167	—	—	—	427
Tosyl-L-valine	147	+25.0	20	—,[c] ethanol	421, 425, 430

[a] Melting points of 115–117° (447), 135° (448), and 145–146° (436) have also been reported for this compound.
[b] $[\alpha]_D^{22} = +9.0°$ (3% in N HCl) (446).
[c] No concentration given.
[d] Where more than one reference is given, the one in italics is that from which the physical constants were selected.

temperature has been more recently described by Farthing (387) (procedure 10–27). Use of the latter synthesis in the writers' Laboratory has permitted the convenient preparation of 20-kg. batches of the acid chloride.

$$\underset{\text{IV}}{C_6H_5CH_2OH} + \underset{\text{V}}{COCl_2} \rightarrow \underset{\text{VI}}{C_6H_5CH_2OCOCl} + \underset{\text{VII}}{HCl}$$

Illustrative procedure 10–27. Carbobenzoxy chloride (VI). The Farthing procedure (387), as generally carried out in the authors' Laboratory, is given as follows. *All operations must be conducted in the hood.* Into an *open*, tared, 5-l. 3-necked round-bottomed flask, equipped with a gas inlet tube, thermometer, and mechanical stirrer, is placed 2 kg. of benzyl alcohol. The internal temperature is then lowered to about −10° by means of an ethanol–dry ice bath (*caution:* pure benzyl alcohol freezes at −15 to −16°), and a stream of phosgene is introduced with vigorous stirring. After the initial introduction of phosgene, the rate of gas entry should be so regulated as to maintain the internal temperature of the reaction mixture between −10° and −30°. After about 2 kg. of phosgene has been introduced, as measured by periodic weighings of flask plus contents, the thermometer and the dry ice bath are removed, and the reaction mixture allowed to attain room temperature *slowly*, with vigorous stirring. Evolution of hydrogen chloride and excess phosgene accompanies this step. A stream of dry, compressed air is then passed through the gas inlet lead with stirring for 24 hr. The stirrer and gas lead are removed, and the flask is evacuated for 5 minutes at the water pump. The colorless (or sometimes faintly straw-colored) liquid is dried over sodium sulfate, filtered, and then stored in glass-stoppered bottles over sodium sulfate. A 95–99% yield of nearly pure carbobenzoxy chloride is generally secured. Traces of the acid chloride on glassware, apparatus, etc., may be destroyed by careful treatment with aqueous or ethanolic ammonia.

Carbobenzoxy chloride secured in the above manner may be further purified by distillation from an 85° oil bath under high vacuum. Despite numerous statements to the contrary, carbobenzoxy chloride is not appreciably more unstable than the average fatty acid chloride. Although prolonged storage may be accompanied by slight decomposition, with the concomitant formation of carbon dioxide and hydrogen chloride, these gases may be readily removed by flushing the reagent with a stream of dry air for several hours, filtering, and re-storing over fresh sodium sulfate. Despite such apparent decomposition, however, the reagent has been stored at room temperature in the writers' Laboratory for periods of nearly a year without any appreciable decrease in total reactivity.

Condensation of carbobenzoxy chloride (VIII) with an amino acid (IX) to give the desired carbobenzoxy amino acid (X) is generally carried out by the usual Schotten-Baumann procedure (procedures 10–28 and 10–29). In contradistinction to the racemization sometimes observed with other acylating agents, such as acetic anhydride (297, 452), benzoic anhydride (297), or ketene (453), the use of carbobenzoxy chloride induces no detectable racemization when optically active amino acids are employed. The derivatives are usually obtained in excellent yield (about 70–95% of theory) and, with only the noteworthy exceptions to date of the isoleucines and the optical forms of leucine, are readily obtained in crystalline form. Physical constants for several of these are shown in Table 10–19.

$$C_6H_5CH_2OCOCl + NH_2CHRCO_2H \xrightarrow[NaHCO_3]{NaOH \text{ or }} C_6H_5CH_2OCO-NHCHRCO_2H$$
$\quad\quad\quad$ VIII $\quad\quad\quad\quad\quad$ IX $\quad\quad\quad\quad\quad\quad\quad\quad\quad\quad\quad\quad$ X

Illustrative procedure 10–28 (128). Carbobenzoxyglycine (X; R = H). A solution of 7.5 g. (0.1 mole) of glycine in 25 ml. of $4N$ NaOH (0.1 mole) is chilled to about 5° and a total of 30 ml. of $4N$ NaOH (0.12 mole) and 18.7 g. (0.11 mole) of carbobenzoxy chloride (see procedure 10–27) added alternately thereto in about 5 equal portions over a period of 20–30 min., with vigorous shaking and cooling in an ice bath. *The reaction mixture should be kept on the slightly alkaline side at all times, additional alkali being used if necessary.* Upon completion of the reaction, the solution is extracted once with about 20 ml. of ether to remove excess acid chloride, and the aqueous fraction acidified slowly to Congo red with $5N$ HCl, with cooling in an ice bath. After further cooling for about 15 min. in the ice bath, the crystalline carbobenzoxyglycine is filtered off and dried. Recrystallization is achieved from chloroform. Yield, 70–80% of theory; m.p. 120° (corr.).

Illustrative procedure 10–29 (454). Carbobenzoxy-L-alloisoleucine. The carbobenzoxylation of 13.1 g. (0.1 mole) of L-alloisoleucine is achieved in the same manner as given for glycine above (procedure 10–28). After acidification with $5N$ HCl, an oil is secured. This is extracted into ethyl acetate and the ethyl acetate fraction dried over anhydrous sodium sulfate and subsequently concentrated at 40° *in vacuo* to an oily residue. Crystallization can be accomplished from ethyl acetate by the addition of petroleum ether. Yield, 76%; m.p. 65°; $[\alpha]_D^{27} = +16°$ (2% in acetone). The carbobenzoxy derivatives of the L- and D-antipodes of leucine (455) and of isoleucine (454, 465) may be obtained in like manner. However, since the latter compounds have thus far been isolated only as non-crystallizable oils, they are dried and stored as such *in vacuo* over phosphorus pentoxide.

A simplified version of the conventional Schotten-Baumann procedure has been successfully utilized in the writers' Laboratory for the preparation of a large variety of carbobenzoxyamino acids. The procedure consists, in the main, in treating a sodium bicarbonate solution of the requisite amino acid (IX) with the acid chloride (VIII) *at room temperature* (procedure 10–30). Maintenance of the pH of the solution in a slightly alkaline range by the sodium bicarbonate renders needless the tedious manipulation of alternate addition of acid chloride and alkali customarily employed in the Schotten-Baumann method. The yields, melting points, and optical rotations of the products so secured are comparable to those obtained by the conventional procedure.

TABLE 10-19
Carbobenzoxy Derivatives of Amino Acids

Carbobenzoxy(Cbzo)amino Acid	M.P., °C.	$[\alpha]_D$, deg.	Temp., °C.	Concn. and Solvent	Ref.[c]
Cbzo-DL-alanine	114–115	—	—	—	128
Cbzo-D-alanine	87	+14.0	27	2%, acetic acid	359, 466–469
Cbzo-L-alanine	87	−13.9	27	2%, acetic acid	128, 359
Cbzo-L-α-amino-n-butyric acid	78–79	−32	16	2.8%, ethanol	58
Cbzo-α-aminoisobutyric acid	78	—	—	—	466
Cbzo-DL-aminotricarballylic acid	134	—	—	—	470
Cbzo-DL-alloaminotricarballylic acid	178	—	—	—	470
α-Cbzo-L-arginine	175	−9.2	20	5.5%, 0.2N HCl	128, 459
ω-Cbzo-L-arginine	190	+9.5	25	6.1%, H₂O + 1 eq. HCl	459
α,ω-Dicbzo-L-arginine	150	−10.0	25	1%, pyridine	458, 459
ω,ω-Dicbzo-L-arginine	160	—	—	—	459
α,ω,ω-Tricbzo-L-arginine	138–139	+15.5	25	1%, chloroform	458, 459
α-Cbzo-L-arginine·HBr	177–179.5	−6.9	24	2%, H₂O	471, 471a
Cbzo-L-asparagine	165	+7.6	18	1.6%, acetic acid	128, 364, 472
Cbzo-L-aspartic acid	116	+9.6	18	7.1%, acetic acid	128
Cbzo-S-benzyl-D-cysteine	—	+45.1	26	2%, acetone	473
Cbzo-S-benzyl-L-cysteine	99	—	—	—	365, 390, 474, 475
S-Cbzo-L-cysteine	177	−50.0	20	1%, acetic acid	365
N,S-Dicbzo-L-cysteine	97–98	−32.4	20	8.5%, acetic acid	128, 476, 477
Bis-Cbzo-L-cystine	123	−91.7	20	6.7%, acetic acid	299
Mono-Cbzo-L-cystine	235–236 d.	−126	23	1%, 5N HCl	429
γ-Cbzo-L-α,γ-diaminobutyric acid	123–125	—	—	—	478
Dicbzo-meso-α,ε-diaminopimelic acid	164–165	—	—	—	478
Dicbzo-DL-α,ε-diaminopimelic acid	150–151	—	—	—	366
Dicbzo-DL-α,β-diaminopropionic acid	120	—	—	—	479, 480
Cbzo-DL-glutamic acid	120–121	−7.1	19	8%, acetic acid	128, 475
Cbzo-L-glutamic acid	135	+5.8	20	2%, ethanol	128, 472, 480–482a
Cbzo-L-glutamine	120	—	—	—	128
Cbzoglycine					

Compound	mp (°C)	[α]	conc/temp	solvent	Ref.
Cbzo-DL-histidine	209–210 d.	—	—	—	128, 483
Cbzo-L-histidine	166–167 d.	−25.0	22	6%, 6N HCl	483
Cbzo-L-1-benzylhistidine	216 d.	—	—	—	369, 484
im,N-Dicbzo-L-histidine·1MeOH	105–107 d.	+15.3	20	6.3%, acetone-methanol (4:1)	483
im,N-Dicbzo-L-histidine·H₂O	103–105 d.	+34.0	14	2.9%, ethyl acetate	841
Cbzo-γ-hydroxy-DL-glutamic acid	132–133	—	—	—	485
Cbzo-5-hydroxy-L-pipecolic acid	150–152	−17.9	20	1%, acetone	487
Cbzo-L-hydroxyproline	106–107	−72.0	20	1%, chloroform	486, 487
Cbzo-D-allohydroxyproline	110.5–111.5	+26.3	20	1%, chloroform	487
Cbzo-L-allohydroxyproline	110–111	−23.7	20	1%, chloroform	487
N-Cbzo-O-tosyl-L-allohydroxyproline	100–101.5	−20.0	—	1%, methanol	487
Cbzo-D-alloisoleucine	65	−15.8	27	2%, acetone	454
Cbzo-L-alloisoleucine	65	+16.0	27	2%, acetone	454
Cbzo-DL-leucine	52–55	—	—	—	486, 488
Cbzo-DL-tert-leucine	88	+14.4	—	1·6%, 2 eq. HCl	371
ε-Cbzo-L-lysine	255	—	—	—	358, 457
α, ε-Dicbzo-L-lysine	150[a]	—	—	—	358, 471a
α-Cbzo-ε-tosyl-L-lysine	85–88	−13.3	21	1%, 5% NaHCO₃	393
Cbzo-DL-methionine	112	—	—	—	489
Cbzo-D-methionine	69–70	—	—	—	489
Cbzo-L-methionine	68–69	−31.6	21	1%, methanol	444, 490
Cbzo-nitro-L-arginine	134–136	−3.5	27	1%, methanol	491, 492
α-Cbzo-L-ornithine·HCl	187–189	−11.5	25	1%, H₂O	904
δ-Cbzo-DL-ornithine	256	—	—	—	421, 429
δ-Cbzo-L-ornithine	254	+17.0	16	2.9% acetone +2 eq. HCl	373, 421, 613
		+5.0	25	2%, N NaOH	372
α, δ-Dicbzo-DL-ornithine	110–112	—	—	—	373, 421
α, δ-Dicbzo-L-ornithine	112–114	−4.0	20	3%, ethanol	299
Cbzo-S-benzyl-DL-penicillamine	81	—	—	—	299
Cbzo-S-methyl-DL-penicillamine	89	—	—	—	128
Cbzo-DL-phenylalanine	103	—	—	—	469
Cbzo-D-phenylalanine	88–89[b]	−4.6	24	4%, acetic acid	486, 493, 494, 495
Cbzo-L-phenylalanine	88–89[b]	+5.1	20	2%, ethanol	375, 393, 486, 487
Cbzo-L-proline	76–77	−61.7	20	5.3%, acetic acid	496
Cbzo-4-keto-D-proline	99–100	−19.4	20	1%, chloroform	487
Cbzo-4-keto-L-proline	101–102	+18.5	20	1%, chloroform	487

TABLE 10-19 (continued)

Carbobenzoxy(Cbzo)amino Acid	M.P., °C.	$[\alpha]_D$, deg.	Temp., °C.	Concn. and Solvent	Ref.[c]
Cbzo-sarcosine	53–54	—	—	—	357
Cbzo-DL-serine	125	—	—	—	128, 377, 497, 498
Cbzo-D-serine	119	−5.6	—	7%, acetic acid	499, 500
Cbzo-L-serine	121	+5.6	32	6%, acetic acid	471a, 480, 499, 501, 502
O-Cbzo-DL-serine	132	—	—	—	377
O, N-Dicbzo-DL-serine	94	—	—	—	377, 503
N-Cbzo-O-acetyl-DL-serine	116–118	—	—	—	377
N-Cbzo-O-benzyl-DL-serine	99–100	—	—	—	398, 504, 829
Cbzo-DL-threonine	74–75	—	—	—	498
Cbzo-L-threonine	103–104	−5.5	28	4%, acetic acid	504a
Cbzo-DL-tryptophan	169–170	—	—	—	505
Cbzo-L-tryptophan	126	—	—	—	505
N-Cbzo-DL-tyrosine	124	—	—	—	379
N-Cbzo-L-tyrosine	101	+11.1	20	3%, acetic acid	128
O-Cbzo-L-tyrosine	215 d.	—	—	—	369
O, N-Dicbzo-DL-tyrosine	106	—	—	—	379
O, N-Dicbzo-L-tyrosine	117	−5.0	20	10%, acetic acid	379
N-Cbzo-O-acetyl-L-tyrosine	120–121	—	—	—	378
N-Cbzo-O-tosyl-L-tyrosine	124–126	−27	25	1%, dimethylformamide	446
Cbzo-DL-valine	76–78	—	—	—	357, 380, 488, 506
Cbzo-L-valine	66–67	+0.1	20	2.0%, ethanol	373, 486, 507, 508

[a] $[\alpha]_D^{21} = -7.8°$ (2.0 % in pyridine), m.p. 80° (471a).

[b] Holley and Holley (494) suggested that the crystalline carbobenzoxy D- and L-phenylalanine of m.p. 126–128° (469, 493) was, in actuality, an impure product, the purified product being an oil. Such suggestion was based upon the finding that the neutralization equivalent of the former was approximately 370 as opposed to a calculated value of 299. Purification of this material by copiously washing its ethereal solution with N HCl and then water eventually yielded an oil with a neutralization equivalent of 310. However, Clayton, Farrington, Kenner, and Turner (495) observed that purification of the L-form by countercurrent distribution led to the isolation of a material with a m.p. of 87° and a neutralization equivalent of 298. A still later report by Grassmann and Wünsch (486) revealed that the contamination was due to the sodium salt of the carbobenzoxyamino acid and that such contamination could be avoided upon *strong acidification* of the Schotten-Baumann reaction mixture followed by extraction of the carbobenzoxy-L-amino acid into ethyl acetate; a melting point of 88–89° and $[\alpha]_D^{20} = +5.1°$ (2% in alcohol) was reported for the pure compound.

[c] Where more than one reference appears, the ones in italics are those from which the physical data were selected.

Illustrative procedure 10–30. Carbobenzoxy-L-threonine. To a suspension of 42 g. (0.5 mole) of sodium bicarbonate in 250 ml. of water in a 1-l. beaker is added 23.8 g. (0.2 mole) of L-threonine and the mixture *stirred vigorously with* a mechanical stirrer. To the mixture is added 37.4 g. (0.22 mole) of carbobenzoxy chloride in about 5 portions over a period of 30 min. The stirring is continued 1 hr. longer and the reaction mixture then extracted once with 50 ml. of ether. The aqueous fraction is *carefully acidified* to Congo red by the dropwise addition of 5N HCl with cooling and stirring, and the resulting oil extracted into ethyl acetate. After the ethyl acetate layer is dried over anhydrous sodium sulfate, it is taken to dryness *in vacuo* at 40° and the residual oil extracted into absolute ether and brought to crystallization by the addition of petroleum ether (storage in the cold, with occasional scratching, may be necessary to effect crystallization). Recrystallization from ether–petroleum ether results in a 75–85% yield of carbobenzoxy-L-threonine; m.p. 105–106°.

With the notable exceptions of δ-carbobenzoxyornithine, ε-carbobenzoxylysine, O-carbobenzoxytyrosine, monocarbobenzoxycystine, and the ω-mono-, α,ω-di-, and α,ω,ω-tricarbobenzoxy derivatives of arginine, most of the compounds listed in Table 10–19 may be prepared either according to procedure 10–28, 10–29, or 10–30, or through minor variations thereof. In addition, the first three compounds listed above may be produced essentially by procedure 10–28, provided that the carbobenzoxylation involves the copper complex of the respective amino acid to prevent acylation of the α-amino group (369, 373, 421, 457). The monocarbobenzoxylation of cystine can be achieved under Schotten-Baumann conditions, in like manner, if a large excess of the amino acid is present (299). Finally, synthesis of α,ω,ω-tricarbobenzoxyarginine can be accomplished by treatment of arginine with the acid chloride in highly alkaline solution, while the α,ω-dicarbobenzoxy derivative is formed upon selective hydrolysis of this compound (458). Conversion of α,ω-dicarbobenzoxyarginine into ω-carbobenzoxyarginine N-carboxyanhydride, succeeded by decomposition of the latter in water, then leads to ω-monocarbobenzoxyarginine (459).

Since 1950, several acyl blocking groups related to the carbobenzoxy group have been introduced into synthetic peptide procedures. The justification advanced for the investigation of such groups has been (*a*) the *presumed* instability of the carbobenzoxy chloride reagent upon prolonged storage, and (*b*) the existence of a few carbobenzoxyamino acids as noncrystallizable oils. Among the first of these was the structurally analogous carboallyloxy group which, although shown by Stevens and Watanabe (460) to respond to some of the methods employed for the selective removal of the carbobenzoxy group, nevertheless lacked the greater versatility exhibited by the carbobenzoxy moiety in its response to all cleavage methods studied as well as in its ability to provide crystalline derivatives. One year later, a preliminary note by Channing, Turner, and Young (461) reported studies on the carbo-α-naphthylmethoxy, carbo-*p*-tolyloxy, and carbo-*p*-bromobenzyloxy groups as acyl masking substituents. Although the suggestion was made that the last group might possess certain advantages in view of the facility with which its compounds may be secured in crystalline form, reports with regard to its further application to synthetic peptide procedures have since been lacking. Of more successful application was the *p*-nitrocarbobenzoxy group (*p*-NO$_2$C$_6$H$_4$CH$_2$OCO$^-$) introduced by Carpenter and Gish (462) in 1952. The chief virtue of this group rested in its ability to yield crystalline derivatives with certain amino acids whose corresponding carbobenzoxy derivatives have hitherto been shown to give only noncrystallizable oils. However, it possessed, according to the authors' own statement, at least two severe limitations not encountered with the carbobenzoxy group, namely, (*a*) its possession of a nitro group which precluded the use of an "unmodified Kjeldahl method" for nitrogen determination, and (*b*) its conversion, in part, to nonvolatile *p*-toluidine upon reductive cleavage, with the resulting danger of contamination of the final product. The group has none the less been successfully utilized in one of the first syntheses of N-terminal arginine peptides (463), and has since proved invaluable in the preparation of a variety of other peptides. Details for the preparation of the *p*-nitrocarbobenzoxy chloride reagent (procedure 10–31), as well as for the utilization of this reagent for the synthesis of *p*-nitrocarbobenzoxyamino acids (procedure 10–32), are given immediately below.

Illustrative procedure 10–31 (462). *p*-Nitrocarbobenzoxy chloride (*p*-nitrobenzyl chloroformate). A stream of dry phosgene is bubbled into 180 ml. of cold, purified dioxane until 174 g. of the gas is absorbed. To this solution is added a solution of 60 g. of *p*-nitrobenzyl alcohol in 75 ml. of dioxane. The reaction vessel is stoppered with a cork and the mixture permitted to stand overnight at room temperature, after which time it is concentrated *in vacuo* at a bath temperature not exceeding 50°. The concentration is repeated after the addition of fresh dioxane and the latter operation again repeated several times. *All the manipulations should be cautiously effected in a well-ventilated hood*! The oily residue ultimately secured is dissolved in 120 ml. of toluene, the solution cooled to about 0°, petroleum ether (about 150 ml.) added to opalescence, and crystallization induced by scratching the walls of the vessel. An additional 400 ml. of petroleum ether is then added, the mixture cooled to −50°, and the crop of crystals collected, washed successively with toluene-petroleum ether and petroleum ether, and finally dried *in vacuo* over phosphorus pentoxide; yield, 80 g. (95%); m.p. 33.5–34°.

Illustrative procedure 10–32 (462). *p*-Nitrocarbobenzoxyglycine. To an ice-cold solution of 3.78 g. of glycine in 15.6 ml. of 4*N* sodium hydroxide are added, in approximately five equal and alternate portions, a cold solution of 13.5 g. of *p*-nitrocarbobenzoxy chloride (procedure 10–31) in 32 ml. of dioxane and 15.6 ml. of cold 4*N* sodium hydroxide. An interval of at least 5 min. is allowed between additions, during which time the reaction mixture is mechanically shaken or vigorously stirred in an apparatus designed to permit simultaneous cooling in an ice bath; the mixture is agitated for 1 hr. after the final addition. A crystalline by-product of di-*p*-nitrobenzyl carbonate forms during the reaction, and this is removed by filtration. The filtrate is acidified with concentrated hydrochloric acid, and the oil which separates is extracted into three 35-ml. portions of ethyl acetate. After the combined ethyl acetate extracts are washed with *N* hydrochloric acid, the product is extracted into *N* sodium bicarbonate. The alkaline solution is washed several times with fresh ethyl acetate, treated with decolorizing carbon, and the ice-cold solution finally acidified with concentrated hydrochloric acid in an ice bath. A crystalline product (9.93 g.) is secured which, upon recrystallization from water (1.8 g. per 100 ml. of solvent), melts at 122.5–124°. A similar procedure, with suitable modification, may generally be employed for the preparation of other *p*-nitrocarbobenzoxyamino acids.

In the above connection, it may be noted that McKay and Albertson (464) in 1957 introduced a series of carboalkoxy protecting groups related to the carbobenzoxy group, i.e., carbo-*t*-butyloxy, carbo*cyclo*pentyloxy, α,ε-dicarbo*cyclo*pentyloxy, carbo*cyclo*hexyloxy, carbo-*p*-methoxybenzyloxy, and carbo-(diisopropyl)-methoxy. The carbo-*t*-butyloxy substituent was introduced independently by Anderson and McGregor (465) during the same year. Although a number of acylated amino acids which incorporate the afore-mentioned blocking groups have been prepared, and although a few of these have been implicated in the synthesis of peptides, application of these blocking groups has as yet been too scant to permit a proper evaluation of their relative merits and deficiencies as compared to other available masking substituents. Table 10–20 lists the physical properties of several acylated amino acids which incorporate these groups, as well as the structurally related carboallyloxy, *p*-nitrocarbobenzoxy, and *p*-chlorocarbobenzoxy moieties.

The relatively recent introduction of the *p*-phenylazobenzyloxycarbonyl $\left(\bigcirc\!\!-N\!=\!N\!-\!\bigcirc\!\!-CH_2OCO-\right)$ and the *p*-(*p'*-methoxyphenylazo)-benzyloxycarbonyl $\left(CH_3O\!-\!\bigcirc\!\!-N\!=\!N\!-\!\bigcirc\!\!-CH_2OCO-\right)$ groups by Schwyzer, Sieber, and Zatsko (514a) is of particular interest in that not only do they form stable crystalline derivatives when combined with the amino function of amino acids and peptides, but also impart to these derivatives an orange-yellow color. Hence, such masking substituents provide a means whereby the course and the purity of the products of a peptide synthesis may be followed with the aid of highly sensitive chromatographic or colorimetric techniques. Preparation of the pertinent N-acylated amino acids is achieved by interaction of the corresponding acyl chloride with the amino acid in an aqueous medium under alkaline conditions, whilst the ultimate removal of the protecting group is effected by the same procedures

TABLE 10-20
Carboallyloxy- and p-Nitrocarbobenzoxyamino Acids and Related Derivatives

Acylated Amino Acid	M.p., °C.	[α]_D, deg.	Temp., °C.	Concn. and Solvent	Ref.[a]
Carboallyloxy (Callo) derivatives					
Callo-DL-alanine	60–61	—	—	—	460
Callo-DL-leucine	41–42	—	—	—	460
Callo-DL-lysine	237	—	—	—	460
ε-Callo-DL-lysine	225–230	—	—	—	460
ε-Callo-L-lysine	44–45	—	—	—	460
Callo-DL-methionine	83–84	—	—	—	460
Callo-DL-phenylalanine	115–116	—	—	—	460
Callo-DL-tryptophan	105–106	—	—	—	460
O,N-Dicallo-L-tyrosine		—	—	—	460
p-Nitrocarbobenzoxy (p-NO$_2$-Cbzo) derivatives					
p-NO$_2$-Cbzo-DL-alanine	132.5–134	—	—	—	362
αp-NO$_2$-Cbzo-L-arginine·½H$_2$O	193–193.5	+11.8	25	0.5%, dioxane + H$_2$O (1:1)	463
ωp-NO$_2$-Cbzo-L-arginine	140.5–142	+16.8	24	1.0%, 6N HCl	463
α,ω-Di-p-NO$_2$-Cbzo-L-arginine	180.5–181.5	+6.3	25	1.0%, 0.6N HCl + dioxane (1:4)	362
p-NO$_2$-Cbzo-DL-asparagine	159–160	—	—	—	509
p-NO$_2$-Cbzo-DL-aspartic acid	150–151	—	—	—	362
p-NO$_2$-Cbzo-S-benzyl-L-cysteine	132.5–133	–47.0	22	1.0%, 95% ethanol	510, 511
Mono-p-NO$_2$-Cbzo-L-cystine	203.5–204.5	–125.2	24	1.0%, N NaOH	362
Bis-p-NO$_2$-Cbzo-L-cystine	99–115	–129.8	24	1.0%, 95% ethanol	362, 512
p-NO$_2$-Cbzo-L-glutamic acid	159–161	–8.2	25	2.0%, 95% ethanol	362
p-NO$_2$-Cbzo-glycine	122.5–124	—	—	—	462
p-NO$_2$-Cbzo-DL-histidine	206.5–208.5	—	—	—	362

p-Nitrocarbobenzoxy (*p*-NO₂-Cbzo) derivatives—*continued*					
p-NO₂-Cbzo-L-hydroxyproline	136.5–139	−41.6	26	1.0%, *N* NaOH	462
p-NO₂-Cbzo-DL-isoleucine	114.5–116.5	—	—	—	462
p-NO₂-Cbzo-L-isoleucine	77.5–80	−12.6	23	1.0%, *N* NaOH	462
p-NO₂-Cbzo-L-leucine·H₂O	60–61	−15.8	27	1.0%, *N* NaOH	462
α,ε-Di-*p*-NO₂-Cbzo-L-lysine·H₂O	56–72	−5.4	23	1.0%, pyridine	362
p-NO₂-Cbzo-DL-methionine	117–119	—	—	—	362
p-NO₂-Cbzo-nitro-L-arginine	145–146	−8.0	22	1.1% acetone	513
p-NO₂-Cbzo-DL-phenylalanine	134.5–136.5	—	—	—	362
p-NO₂-Cbzo-L-proline·H₂O	50–56	−38.9	25	1.0%, *N* NaOH	462
p-NO₂-Cbzo-DL-serine	140.5–142.5	—	—	—	362
p-NO₂-Cbzo-DL-threonine	141.5–143	—	—	—	362
p-NO₂-Cbzo-DL-tryptophan	151–152.5	—	—	—	362
O,N-Di-*p*-NO₂-Cbzo-DL-tyrosine	154–162	—	—	—	362
p-NO₂-Cbzo-DL-valine	125.5–127.5	—	—	—	362
p-Chlorocarbobenzoxy (*p*-Cl-Cbzo) derivatives					
p-Cl-Cbzo-DL-alanine	133.5	—	—	—	514
p-Cl-Cbzo-glycine	130	—	—	—	514
p-Cl-Cbzo-DL-leucine	75.5	—	—	—	514
p-Cl-Cbzo-DL-phenylalanine	136	—	—	—	514
tert-Butyloxycarbonyl (C-*t*-buo) derivatives					
C-*t*-buo-DL-alanine	110.5–111.5	—	—	—	464, 465
C-*t*-buo-L-alanine	83–84	−22.4	25	2.1% acetic acid	465
C-*t*-buo-S-benzyl-L-cysteine	63–65	−41.0	25	1.0% acetic acid	465
C-*t*-buo-glycine	88.5–89	—	—	—	464, 465
C-*t*-buo-L-isoleucine·½H₂O	49–57	+3.0	25	2.0% acetic acid	465
C-*t*-buo-L-leucine·H₂O	74–80	−24.0	25	2.0% acetic acid	464, 465
C-*t*-buo-DL-methionine	93.5–94.5	—	—	—	464, 465
C-*t*-buo-DL-phenylalanine	144.5–145	—	—	—	465

TABLE 10-20 (continued)

Acylated Amino Acid	M.p., °C.	[α]_D, deg.	Temp., °C.	Concn. and Solvent	Ref.[a]
tert-Butyloxycarbonyl (C-*t*-buo) derivatives—*continued*					
C-*t*-buo-L-phenylalanine	79–80	−0.8	25	5.0%, acetic acid	465
C-*t*-buo-L-proline	136–137	−60.2	25	2.0%, acetic acid	465
C-*t*-buo-L-tryptophan	136.5–140.5 d.	−18.2	25	2.0%, acetic acid	465
C-*t*-buo-L-tyrosine	136–138	+3.9	25	2.0%, acetic acid	465
C-*t*-buo-L-valine	77–79	−5.8	25	1.2%, acetic acid	465
*Cyclo*pentyloxycarbonyl (C-*cy*-peo) derivatives					
C-*cy*-peo-DL-alanine	120–123	—	—	—	464
C-*cy*-peo-β-alanine	54–58	—	—	—	464
C-*cy*-peo-L-asparagine	177–179	—	—	—	464
C-*cy*-peo-glycine	77–80	—	—	—	464
C-*cy*-peo-DL-isoleucine	95–99	—	—	—	464
α,ε-Di-C-*cy*-peo-L-lysine	93–100	—	—	—	464
C-*cy*-peo-DL-methionine	111–113	—	—	—	464
C-*cy*-peo-DL-norleucine	98–102	—	—	—	464
C-*cy*-peo-L-phenylalanine	123–127	—	—	—	464
C-*cy*-peo-DL-α-phenylglycine	93–95	—	—	—	464
C-*cy*-peo-DL-serine	118–119	—	—	—	464
C-*cy*-peo-DL-valine	100–102	—	—	—	464
*Cyclo*hexyloxycarbonyl (C-*cy*-hexo) derivatives					
C-*cy*-hexo-DL-alanine	125–126	—	—	—	464
C-*cy*-hexo-glycine	97–99	—	—	—	464
C-*cy*-hexo-DL-methionine	97–100	—	—	—	464
C-*cy*-hexo-DL-phenylalanine	105–108	—	—	—	464

[a] Where more than one reference appears, the one in italics is the one from which the physical data were taken.

used to remove the carbobenzoxy substituent. The melting points of the p-phenylazobenzyloxycarbonyl derivatives of several amino acids have been reported (514a) as follows: L-alanine 158–159°, glycine 179–182°, L-leucine 109–113°, L-phenylalanine 164–167°, L-proline 129–132°, L-serine 177–179°, L-tryptophan 157–159°, and L-valine 124–127°; the melting points of the various p-(p'-methoxyphenylazo)benzyloxycarbonylamino acids are: L-alanine 162–164°, L-arginine(N$^\alpha$) 225°, β-methyl L-aspartate 104–106°, γ-methyl L-glutamate 123–125°, glycine 176–177°, N^{im}-benzyl-L-histidine 225°, L-methionine 130–132°, L-phenylalanine 157–158°, L-proline 165–167°, L-serine 166–168°, L-tryptophan 137–139°, and L-valine 134–136°.

15. Phthalyl Group. Radenhausen (515) in 1895, and Ing and Manske (516) in 1926, reported that the action of hydrazine could mediate a ready cleavage of a phthalyl group bound in imide linkage with an amino acid or derivative thereof. Successful application of this scheme to synthetic peptide procedures was announced by Kidd and King (517) in 1948, and independently by Sheehan and Frank (518) one year later. Preparation of the phthalylamino acids (XIII) employed in such procedures was generally achieved through the direct fusion of a mixture of phthalic anhydride (XI) and the free amino acid (XII) at temperatures of about 145–150°, according to the method of Reese (519):

$$\text{(XI)} \quad \underset{CO}{\overset{CO}{\diagup}}\!\!\!\diagdown\!O \;+\; NH_2CHRCO_2H \;\xrightarrow{\Delta}\; \underset{CO}{\overset{CO}{\diagup}}\!\!\!\diagdown\!NCHRCO_2H \;+\; H_2O$$

XI   XII   XIII   XIV

Use of these reaction conditions with the D- and L-antipodes of leucine and valine was later described by Fling, Minard, and Fox (520), who indicated that the optical rotation values of the enantiomorphic phthalylated derivatives were equal and opposite within the limits of experimental error. In a further extension of this reaction by Billman and Harting (521), a variety of phthalylated amino acids were prepared by allowing the fusion to proceed at 180–185°. The statement was made, without experimental substantiation, that optically active amino acids under these conditions yielded optically active products without the apparent occurrence of racemization.

As a consequence of the elevated temperatures to which optically active amino acids were subjected by the above procedures, the question whether any racemization had occurred during the synthesis became of primary concern. Among the first to shed light upon this question were Kidd and King (517), who unequivocally demonstrated that the attempted preparation of phthalyl-L-glutamic acid, according to the directions of Billman and Harting (521), led instead to the production of the racemic material as the only isolable product. Further support for the occurrence of extensive racemization at high fusion temperatures was subsequently reported by Sheehan, Chapman, and Roth (522), who observed that when phthalic anhydride and L-phenylalanine were fused at 180° a racemic product resulted. However, when the fusion was carried out at 145–150°, according to the general method of Fling, Minard, and Fox (520), an optically active material was secured (procedure 10–33). That no appreciable racemization occurred during the fusion was demonstrated when the regenerated free amino acid, obtained by dephthalylation with alcoholic hydrazine, possessed the same optical rotation properties as the starting material.

Illustrative procedure 10–33 (522). Phthalyl-L-phenylalanine (XIII; R = CH$_2$C$_6$H$_5$). An intimate mixture of 9.90 g. (0.06 mole) of L-phenylalanine and 8.95 g. (0.06 mole) of finely ground phthalic anhydride is heated for 30 min. with stirring in an oil bath at 145–150°. After cooling, the solid material is dissolved in 40 ml. of hot methanol, the filtered solution diluted with 40 ml. of water, and the product allowed to crystallize slowly. The yield is 15.5 g. (88%) of fine colorless needles; m.p. 183–185°; $[\alpha]_D = -212°$ (1.9% in ethanol).

A large measure of caution should be exercised if this procedure is to be utilized generally for the preparation of optically active phthalylamino acids. The absence of noticeable racemization when L-phenylalanine was employed does not necessarily imply that amino acids with other side chains would exhibit a comparable retention of configuration under relatively drastic thermal conditions. In this connection, it should be pointed out that the preparation of phthalyl-L-glutamic acid, under these same conditions, proceeded with the formation of a material which contained some 16% of the racemic form (523). After employment of this procedure, therefore, regeneration of the reactant amino acid, followed by a determination of its optical characteristics, should be carried out with all optically active phthalylamino acids not previously tested in this manner. Such precaution is of course unnecessary when racemic amino acids with only a single center of asymmetry are the starting materials. When a racemic amino acid with more than one asymmetric center, such as DL-isoleucine, is employed, however, then the situation becomes exceedingly more complex. Thus, for example, DL-isoleucine could upon racemization lead to an epimeric mixture of the racemic phthalylated isoleucine and alloisoleucine derivatives. With such compounds, therefore, either the stereochemical identity of the regenerated amino acid should be ascertained, or the phthalylated amino acid should be prepared by a less equivocal alternative route (see procedure 10–35).

With the exceptions of the phthalyl derivatives of L-aspartic acid,

L-glutamic acid, the glutamines, O-acetyl-L-serine and L-threonine, all the compounds listed in Table 10-21 have been prepared either by procedure 10-33 or by slight modifications thereof. Since the synthesis of phthalylhydroxyamino acids could not be readily achieved under the conditions of fusion (524), a suitable solvent system had to be employed where L-threonine and L-serine were implicated (procedure 10-34). On the other hand, the L-aspartic acid and L-glutamic acid derivatives were secured by less direct methods (procedure 10-35) under conditions that would avoid racemization (517, 527, 528).

A variation of the above-described procedure for the preparation of phthalylamino acids involves the reaction of phthalic anhydride with the amino acid in the presence of a solvent, either as a heterogeneous mixture or in solution. Such a procedure has been described by Wanag and Veinbergs (525) for the preparation of some phthalylamino acids in refluxing acetic acid. More recently, O'Neill, Veitch, and Wagner-Jauregg (526) have used p-cymene as the reaction solvent for the preparation of phthalylglycine, whereas King and Kidd (527) obtained phthalyl-DL-glutamic acid from the interaction of phthalic anhydride and L-glutamic acid in boiling pyridine, followed by treatment with acetic anhydride. Racemization in the latter instance could be presumably attributed to intermediate azlactone formation (Section 10-8). However, utilization of a suspension of an optically active amino acid and phthalic anhydride in hot dioxane has resulted in an optically active product (procedure 10-34). In this manner, the phthalylated derivatives of L-threonine and O-acetyl-L-serine were prepared by Sheehan, Goodman, and Hess (524).

Illustrative procedure 10-34 (524). Phthalyl-L-threonine. To a solution of 4.54 g. (0.03 mole) of phthalic anhydride in 25 ml. of dry dioxane is added 3.04 g. (0.025 mole) of L-threonine. The heterogeneous mixture is submerged in an oil bath at 105° and stirred vigorously for 5 hr. After evaporation of the solvent under reduced pressure, the residual phthalyl-L-threonine crystallizes from acetone–water. Yield, 6.0 g. (95%); m.p. 135–140°. Two recrystallizations from ethanol–water suffice to raise the melting point to 143–144°; $[\alpha]_D^{26} = -36.7°$ (3.2% in ethanol).

Finally, consideration should be given to a method introduced by Kidd and King (517, 527) and a related method later developed by Balenović, Gaspert, and Stimac (528) which, although less direct and somewhat more tedious than the afore-mentioned procedures, leads to optically active phthalylamino acids wherein no apparent racemization is observed. The Kidd and King procedure, as described for phthalyl-L-glutamic acid (XIX), involves successively (*a*) the condensation of phthalic anhydride (XV) with the amino acid ester (XVI), (*b*) ring closure of the intermediate phthalamic acid (XVII) by the action of ethanolic hydrogen chloride or thionyl chloride,

TABLE 10-21
Phthalyl Derivatives of Amino Acids

Phthalyl(Phth)amino Acid	M.p., °C.	$[\alpha]_D$, deg.	Temp., °C.	Concn. and Solvent	Ref.[b]
Phth-DL-alanine	160–161	—	—	—	521, 529
Phth-L-alanine	150–151	−17.8	20	9.8%, ethanol	530
Phth-DL-α-amino-n-butyric acid	95.5–96.5	—	—	—	521, 532
Phth-α-aminoisobutyric acid	152–153	—	—	—	521, 529
Phth-DL-α-aminophenylacetic acid	167–168	—	—	—	521, 531
Phth-L-aspartic acid	197	−58	20	0.4%, methanol	528
Phth-S-benzyl-L-cysteine	128–129	−150.1	20	1.1%, methanol	533
γ-Phth-DL-α,γ-diaminobutyric acid	197 d.	—	—	—	534
Phth-DL-glutamic acid	189–190	—	—	—	527
Phth-L-glutamic acid	158–159	−42.6	21	1.0%, 95% ethanol	517, 523, 527, 533, 535
Phth-DL-glutamine	194–195	—	—	—	481, 527
Phth-L-glutamine	162	−16.9	18	−, 0.33N Na$_2$CO$_3$	527
Phth-glycine	192–194	—	—	—	519, 521, 526, 536
Phth-L-histidine	294–296	—	—	—	537, 538

Compound	mp (°C)	[α]	T (°C)	Solvent	Ref.
Phth-DL-isoleucine	120–121	–	–	–	521
Phth-DL-isovaline	139–140	–	–	–	*521*, 539
Phth-DL-leucine	140–141	–	–	–	*521*, 540
Phth-D-leucine	118–119	+22.8	27	–, ethanol	520
Phth-L-leucine	118.5–119.5	−24.0	27	2.9%, ethanol	520, *521*, 522, 536
Phth-L-methionine	124	−75.5	23	4.7%, dimethylformamide	471a
Phth-nitro-L-arginine	209–210.5	–	–	–	541
Phth-DL-norleucine	111.5–112.5	–	–	–	521
Phth-DL-norvaline	103–104	–	–	–	521
Phth-DL-phenylalanine	177.5–179	–	–	–	*518*, 521
Phth-D-phenylalanine	180–180.5	+207.0	–	2.9%, ethanol	522
Phth-L-phenylalanine	183–185	−212.0	–	1.9%, ethanol	522
Phth-O-acetyl-L-serine	152–153	−63.1	27	2.4%, ethanol	524
N-Phth-O-methyl-D-serine	101–102.5	+46.9	20	1.8%, ethanol	542
N-Phth-O-methyl-L-serine	101–102	−48.1	20	2%, ethanol	542
Phth-DL-threonine	102–103	–	–	–	521
Phth-L-threonine	143–144	−36.7	26	1.6%, ethanol	524
Phth-DL-valine	101.5–102[a]	–	–	–	*521*, 543
Phth-DL-valine·H₂O	80–81.5	–	–	–	543
Phth-D-valine	113–114	+69.0	27	–, ethanol	520, *543a*
Phth-L-valine	114–115	−68.5	27	–, ethanol	520, *543a*, 544

[a] A melting point of 165–167° has also been reported (380) for this compound.
[b] Where more than one reference appears, the one in italics is the one from which the physical constants were taken.

and (*c*) selective acid hydrolysis of the ester groups of the phthalylamino acid ester (XVIII) so derived (procedure 10–35):

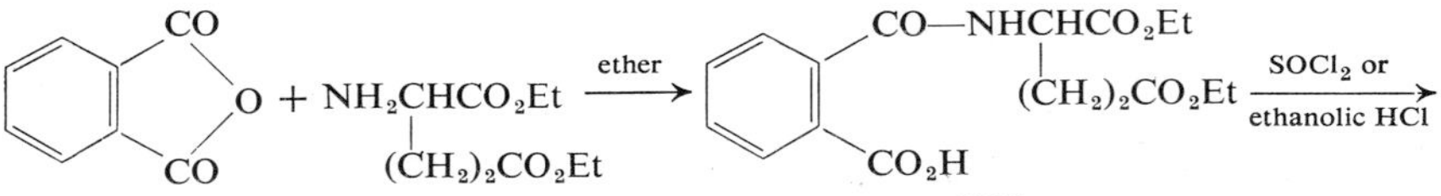

XV XVI XVII

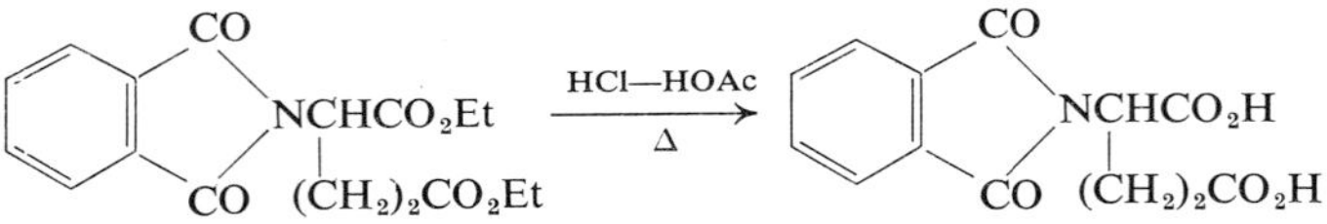

XVIII XIX

The procedure of Balenović, Gaspert, and Stimac (528) as employed for phthalyl-L-aspartic acid (XXIV), on the other hand, involves (*a*) the interaction of diethyl L-aspartate hydrochloride (XXI) with the sodium salt of *o*-carboethoxythiobenzoic acid (XX) in dimethylformamide solution, (*b*) cyclization of the diethyl N-(*o*-carboethoxybenzoyl)-L-aspartate (XXII) so derived to diethyl N-phthalyl-L-aspartate (XXIII) upon treatment with ethanolic HCl, and (*c*) hydrolysis of (XXIII) to N-phthalyl-L-aspartic acid with a refluxing mixture of concentrated hydrochloric acid and acetic acid:

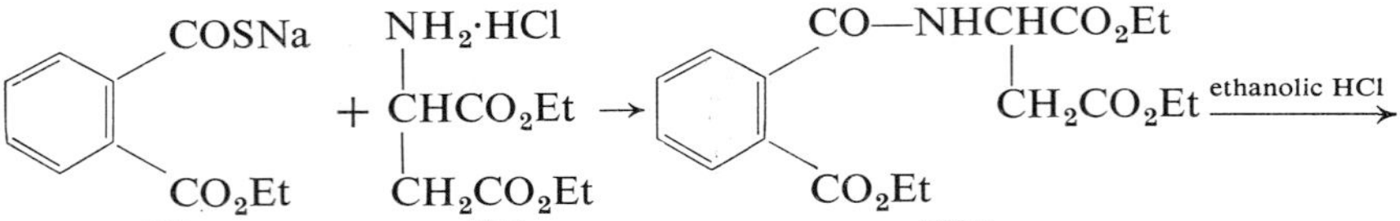

XX XXI XXII

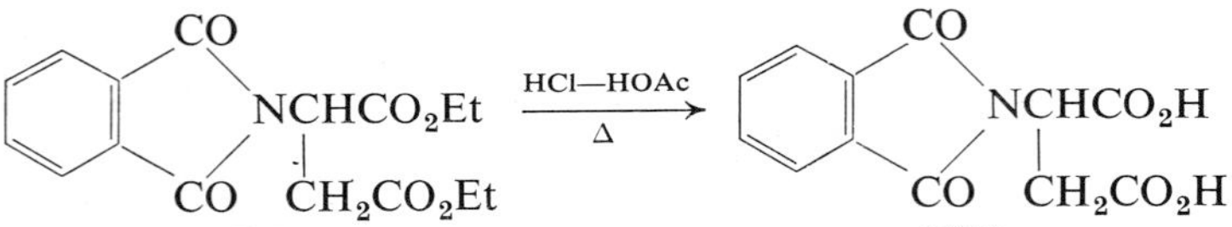

XXIII XXIV

Illustrative procedure 10–35 (527). Phthalyl-L-glutamic acid (XIX). Crystalline diethyl L-glutamate hydrochloride, obtained from 28.5 g. of L-glutamic acid and 400 ml. of boiling 4% ethanolic hydrogen chloride (procedure 10–49), is treated under benzene with 24.4 ml. of diethylamine added in portions with cooling. After thorough mixing, diethylamine hydrochloride is precipitated with anhydrous ether and removed by filtration; 32.2 g. of diethyl L-glutamate is obtained upon evaporation of the solvents. To an ethereal solution of the latter ester is added 23.5 g. of phthalic anhydride in small portions, which when shaken dissolves with the evolution of heat. Scratching causes the separation of 46.2 g. of diethyl *o*-carboxybenzoyl-L-glutamate (XVII) as a solid mass which is collected after some 24 hr. and washed with ether. Recrystallization is effected from benzene–light petroleum; m.p. 94°. The product so secured is heated in 15 volumes of refluxing

4% ethanolic hydrogen chloride for 2 hr. The residual material that remains on evaporation is shaken with water and chloroform, the chloroform layer washed successively with aqueous sodium bicarbonate and water, dried, and finally evaporated. There remains a residue of diethyl phthalyl-L-glutamate which may be distilled (bath temperature, 190–200°) at 0.05 mm. as a colorless viscous syrup; $[\alpha]_D^{19} = -33.5°$ (in ethanol). Fifty and one-half grams of the undistilled diethyl phthalyl-L-glutamate (XVIII) is dissolved in a mixture of 450 ml. of acetic acid and 110 ml. of concentrated hydrochloric acid, and the solution heated under reflux for 2 hr. Evaporation to 100 ml. at reduced pressure and storage for several hours in the refrigerator causes phthalyl-L-glutamic acid to separate. Recrystallization is carried out from water. Yield, 28.2 g. (65%); m.p. 158–159°; $[\alpha]_D^{18} = -27.4°$ (in 0.33N sodium carbonate).

16. Trityl Group. In 1925, Helferich, Moog, and Jünger (545) described the use of the triphenylmethyl (trityl) substituent as a protective group for the primary hydroxyl functions of carbohydrates, and as a masking substituent for the amino moiety of amino acids and peptides as well. Despite the fact that the trityl group in such linkages was heretofore known to undergo ready cleavage in the presence of mineral acids under very mild conditions, some thirty years elapsed before this substituent was applied to synthetic peptide procedures (546–548). Early preparation of tritylamino acids (XXVIII) was effected by the action of trityl chloride (XXV) on the amino acid ester hydrochloride (XXVI) in hot pyridine solution, followed by saponification of the tritylamino acid ester (XXVII) so derived (545). A later refinement of the coupling step involved triethylamine in chloroform solution at room temperature, in lieu of hot pyridine, as the solvent system (546–548) (procedure 10–36).

$$(C_6H_5)_3CCl + HCl \cdot NH_2CHRCO_2R' \xrightarrow[\text{(C}_2\text{H}_5\text{)}_3\text{N}]{C_5H_5N \text{ or}} (C_6H_5)_3CNHCHRCO_2R' \xrightarrow{OH^-} (C_6H_5)_3CNHCHRCO_2H$$
$$\text{XXV} \qquad \text{XXVI} \qquad\qquad\qquad\qquad \text{XXVII} \qquad\qquad\qquad \text{XXVIII}$$

Illustrative procedure 10–36 (548). Tritylglycine ethyl ester (XXVII; R = H, R' = C_2H_5). To a suspension of 1.39 g. (0.01 mole) of glycine ethyl ester hydrochloride (XXVI; R = H, R' = C_2H_5) in 15 ml. of dry chloroform is added 2.2 g. (0.022 mole) of triethylamine followed by 2.8 g. (0.01 mole) of triphenylchloromethane (XXV), and the mixture is allowed to react for 6 hr. at room temperature. The solution is washed twice with water, dried with sodium sulfate, and the solvent evaporated *in vacuo*. Complete removal of the chloroform is ensured by the addition of a few milliliters of ethanol and reconcentration *in vacuo*. The residue, after recrystallization from ethanol, leads to an 86% yield of tritylglycine ethyl ester; m.p. 114°. A comparable procedure may be utilized for the synthesis of each of the tritylamino acid esters listed in Table 10–22.

Tritylglycine (XXVIII; R = H). Tritylglycine ethyl ester (3.45 g., 0.01 mole) is dissolved on warming in 11 ml. (10% excess) of N alcoholic potassium hydroxide and 6 ml. of alcohol. After the solution has stood at room temperature for 1 hr., it is diluted to three times its volume with water, cooled, and then acidified with acetic acid. The precipitated tritylglycine is washed several times with water and recrystallized from alcohol; yield, 92%; m.p. 178–179°.

In connection with the general applicability of this procedure, it becomes important to consider the relative rates of saponification exhibited by various tritylamino acid esters. That the side chain of the amino acid residue exerts a very marked influence on the facility with which such esters are saponified was initially noted by Hillmann-Elies, Hillmann, and Jatzkewitz (546), who reported that the tritylated esters of glycine and alanine were cleaved by a refluxing 30% sodium hydroxide-propylene glycol (1 : 4) mixture with lesser difficulty than were the corresponding derivatives of leucine, methionine, and phenylalanine. A subsequent report by Zervas and Theodoropoulos (548) demonstrated that the relative rates of saponification of the tritylated methyl esters of several different amino acids in a N methanolic potassium hydroxide-dioxane (1 : 1) mixture at 50° were as follows: glycine > alanine > phenylalanine > cystine. Apparently, amino acids with larger side chains further augment the steric hindrance imposed by the trityl group toward the saponification of ester groups. From a preparative point of view, such differences become of serious concern since tritylated amino acid esters, with the possible exceptions of those of glycine (548), alanine (548), and serine (547), generally have been found to require high temperatures and excess alkali for saponification (546–548), conditions which are conducive to both racemization and partial destruction of the tritylated amino acids. The above general procedure has none the less been utilized for the preparation of nearly all the tritylamino acids listed in Table 10–22.

In order to circumvent the limitations imposed by the afore-mentioned procedure, Zervas and Theodoropoulos (548) prepared several tritylamino acids (XXXI) directly from trityl chloride (XXIX) and the amino acid (XXX) in aqueous isopropanol containing diethylamine (procedure 10–37). Triphenylcarbinol and a small amount of trityldiethylamine, derived from the reaction of trityl chloride with water and diethylamine, respectively, formed the major side products. Despite the extreme instability of trityl chloride in hydroylzing media, glycine, alanine, asparagine, leucine, and phenylalanine could nevertheless be successfully tritylated in modest yields of 35% and above. Although these over-all yields are generally somewhat smaller than those secured by the less direct method (procedure 10–36) described above, the less drastic conditions employed removes the danger of racemization where optically active amino acids are involved. Note should be made that the use of a tertiary base, such as pyridine or triethylamine in lieu of diethylamine, results in an inferior yield of the tritylamino acid, virtually all the trityl chloride being converted to triphenylcarbinol (548).

$$(C_6H_5)_3CCl + NH_2CHRCO_2H \xrightarrow[(C_2H_5)_2NH,\ 20-25°]{\text{aq. isopropanol}} (C_6H_5)_3CNHCHRCO_2H$$

XXIX XXX XXXI

TABLE 10-22
Triphenylmethyl Derivatives of Amino Acids

Triphenylmethyl(Trityl)amino Acid	Free Acid	Methyl Ester	Ethyl Ester	Ref.[h]
Trityl-DL-alanine	170	101	101–102	545, *547*, 548
Trityl-L-alanine	200–205 d.	–	–	548
Trityl-L-arginine	>250°	–	–	471a
Trityl-L-asparagine	173–174[a]	–	–	548
S-Trityl-L-cysteine	203–205[b]	–	–	549
S,N-Ditrityl-L-cysteine	–[c]	90–92	–	548, *549*
Bistrityl-L-cystine	150	146	–	*546*, 548
Trityl-L-glutamic acid	–[d]	–	–	549
Tritylglycine	178–179	106–107	114	545, 547, *548*
α-Trityl-L-histidine	202[e]	–	–	548a
Ditrityl-L-histidine	184–185[f]	–	–	547, *548a*
Trityl-DL-leucine	203–204	–	–	546
Trityl-L-leucine	160–165 d.	–	–	548
ε-Trityl-DL-lysine	225–230	–	–	550
ε-Trityl-L-lysine	230 d.[g]	–	–	550
Trityl-DL-methionine	190–192 d.	124–125	–	546, *547*
Trityl-DL-phenylalanine	194 d.	–	–	546
Trityl-L-phenylalanine	185–188 d.	95	–	548
Trityl-DL-serine	180	–	111–112	547
Trityl-DL-tryptophan	245	171–172	–	547
Trityl-DL-valine	183	–	–	546

[a] $[\alpha]_D^{20} = -6.1°$ (3.5% in methanol).
[b] $[\alpha]_D^{20} = +19°$ (2% in 0.1N NaOH).
[c] $[\alpha]_D^{20} = +71°$ (2% in chloroform).
[d] The triethylamine salt melts at 100°, $[\alpha]_D^{20} = -32°$ (2% in chloroform).
[e] $[\alpha]_D = +23.7°$ (3.3% in pyridine).
[f] $[\alpha]_D^{20} = +9.6°$ (1% in chlorofororm) (547); m.p. = 198–200°, $[\alpha]_D = +3.7°$ (5% in pyridine) (548a).
[g] $[\alpha]_D^{20} = +9°$ (2% in N HCl).
[h] Where more than one reference is given, the one in italics is that from which the physical data were taken.

Illustrative procedure 10–37 (548). Tritylglycine (XXXI; R = H). To a solution of 0.75 g. (0.01 mole) of glycine in a mixture of 4 ml. of water, 3 ml. (0.03 mole) of diethylamine and 8 ml. of isopropyl alcohol is added 3.6 g. (0.013 mole) of trityl chloride with continuous shaking; the addition is accomplished in twelve portions within 1 hr. at room temperature. When the reaction is complete, 25 ml. of water is added and the mixture of triphenylcarbinol and trityldiethylamine that precipitates is filtered and washed thoroughly with water. Acidification of the combined filtrate and washings with acetic acid brings about the precipitation of tritylglycine, which is recrystallized from ethanol; yield, 47%; m.p. 178–179°.

Inasmuch as some tritylamino acids do not possess a well-defined melting point, it is sometimes advantageous to prepare the diethylammonium salts which have more desirable physical properties. Preparation of the latter may be achieved by the addition of diethylamine to a solution of the pertinent tritylamino acid in ether or acetone, followed by recrystallization of the precipitate from hot acetone. An alternative procedure is to prepare the diethylammonium salt of the tritylamino acid directly from the free amino acid according to procedure 10–37a. The physical properties of various of these diethylammonium salts have been reported for the different amino acid residues as follows (548, 548a): DL-alanine, m.p. 151–152°; L-alanine, m.p. 157°, $[\alpha]_D = -18.9°$; L-asparagine, m.p. 150–151°; L-glutamine, m.p. 142–144°, $[\alpha]_D = +21.9°$; glycine, m.p. 132°; L-leucine, m.p. 154–155°, $[\alpha]_D = +3.0°$; L-methionine, m.p. 152–153°, $[\alpha]_D = +21.7°$; L-phenylalanine, m.p. 150°, $[\alpha]_D = +12.5°$; L-proline, m.p. 163–165°, $[\alpha]_D = -57.7°$; L-tryptophan, m.p. 150–152°, $[\alpha]_D = +4.5°$; L-valine, m.p. 160°, $[\alpha]_D = +6.7°$, where all optical rotations were taken in the temperature range 22–25° and all concentrations were 5% in methanol, except for the proline derivative, which was 5% in chloroform. The diethylammonium salts of α,ε-ditrityl-DL-lysine (m.p. 130°) and of α,ε-ditrityl-L-lysine (m.p. 150°, $[\alpha]_D^{20} = +23°$ in chloroform) have also been prepared (550).

Illustrative procedure 10–37a (548a). Diethylammonium trityl-L-leucinate. A mixture containing 1.3 g. (0.01 mole) of L-leucine, 4 ml. of water, 3 ml. (0.03 mole) of diethylamine, and 8 ml. of isopropyl alcohol is treated with 3.6 g. (0.013 mole) of trityl chloride in the manner described for the preparation of tritylglycine (procedure 10–37). Upon completion of the reaction, 30 ml. of water is added and the mixture is extracted twice with chloroform. The combined chloroform extracts are washed with a small amount of water, dried over sodium sulfate, and concentrated to dryness *in vacuo*. Complete removal of the chloroform is ensured by the addition of a few milliliters of ethanol followed by reconcentration *in vacuo*. The residual material is dissolved in anhydrous ether and the ethereal solution treated with a few drops of diethylamine. After cooling at 4°, the precipitated diethylammonium salt of trityl-L-leucine is recovered by filtration, washed repeatedly with anhydrous ether, and dried *in vacuo*; yield, 28%; m.p. 154°; $[\alpha]_D = +3.0°$ (5% in methanol).

Transformation of the diethylammonium salts of tritylamino acids to the corresponding free acids may be achieved by dissolving the former in exactly one molecular equivalent of 0.2N aqueous sodium hydroxide, storing the solution under reduced pressure at 20–25° for several minutes in order to remove most of the liberated diethylamine, and then acidifying the solution with acetic acid in the cold. The resulting precipitate is filtered off, washed copiously with cold water, and dried first on a porous plate and then *in vacuo* over phosphorus pentoxide.

Finally, it should be mentioned that, although tritylamino acids behave as weak acids that give salts with such bases as diethylamine, blocking of the amino function of amino acids or their ester derivatives with the trityl group does not entirely mask its basic properties. The trityl derivatives are in essence secondary amines, and as such they are capable of undergoing hydrochloride formation in non-aqueous media (548) (procedure 10–38). These hydrochloride derivatives are extremely unstable, however, and undergo complete hydrolysis in the presence of cold water.

$$(C_6H_5)_3CNHCHRCO_2R' \underset{H_2O \text{ or } OH^-, 0°}{\overset{HCl \text{ (gas), chloroform}}{\rightleftarrows}} ((C_6H_5)_3CNH_2CHRCO_2R')^+Cl^-$$
XXXII XXXIII

Illustrative procedure 10–38 (548). Tritylglycine ethyl ester hydrochloride (XXXIII; R = H, R' = C_2H_5). To 3.45 g. (0.01 mole) of tritylglycine ethyl ester (procedure 10–36) (XXXII) dissolved in a few milliliters of dry chloroform is added anhydrous ethyl ether saturated with dry hydrogen chloride. The salt precipitates at once and is redissolved in chloroform and precipitated with anhydrous ethyl ether; yield, 3 g. (78%); m.p. 95–96°.

This salt is hydrolyzed rapidly and almost quantitatively either with cold water (1–2°) or with a dilute solution of sodium bicarbonate to give tritylglycine ethyl ester, m.p. 114°.

In this connection, it is of interest to point out that the N-benzyl ($C_6H_5CH_2NHCHRCO_2H$) and the N,N-dibenzyl (($C_6H_5CH_2)_2NCHRCO_2H$) derivatives of amino acids, which are in effect secondary and tertiary amines, respectively, have also been applied to synthetic peptide procedures (551–555). Like the carbobenzoxy group, their ultimate removal in such procedures has generally been achieved through catalytic hydrogenolysis. Since the N-benzyl substituent possesses no apparent advantages over existing masking groups, its employment in preparative peptide chemistry has been somewhat restricted. The group has nevertheless been recently utilized for the synthesis of O-peptides of serine and threonine (565), compounds that may serve as intermediates in the preparation of the anticarcinogenic agent azaserine (500, 502) and its analogs. Table 10–23 lists several of the N-benzylated amino acids which have hitherto been used in synthetic peptide procedures.

17. Trifluoroacetyl Group. That a trifluoroacetyl (TFA) group which is bound in chemical linkage with a nitrogen atom may undergo a ready cleavage in dilute base was initially noted by Swarts (566), who in 1922 described the alkali-induced conversion of trifluoroacetonitrile to trifluoroacetic acid. Some thirty years later, Weygand and Csendes (567) comparably demonstrated that dilute alkali, under mild conditions, would also induce the hydrolysis of TFA-amino acids, a finding that ushered in the subsequent use of the TFA-substituent as an acyl masking group in peptide syntheses

TABLE 10-23
N-Benzyl (N-Bz) and N,N-Dibenzyl (N,N-diBz) Derivatives of Amino Acids

Benzylated Amino Acid	M.P., °C	[α]$_D$, deg.	Concn. and Solvent	Ref.
N-Bz-DL-alanine	250	–	–	551
N,N-diBz-DL-alanine	97–98[a]	–	–	553, *554*
N,N-diBz-L-alanine	64–65	–45.0	2%, methanol	553
N,N-diBz-DL-α-amino-*n*-butyric acid	128–129[b]	–	–	554
N-Bz-DL-asparagine	216[c]	–	–	*556*, 557
N-Bz-DL-aspartic acid	194 d.	–	–	556
N-Bz-DL-aspartic acid·HCl	87	–	–	558
N,N-diBz-DL-glutamic acid	211–212	–	–	559
N-Bz-glycine	198–200	–	–	*551*, 560–563
N,N-diBz-glycine	200	–	–	*551*, 564
N-Bz-DL-leucine	225 d.	–	–	551
N-Bz-L-leucine	225 d.	+12.0	2%, 20% HCl	551
N,N-diBz-DL-leucine	99	–	–	554
N,N-diBz-L-leucine	104–106	–68	2%, methanol	553
N,N-diBz-DL-norvaline	122–124[d]	–	–	554
N,N-diBz-L-norvaline	118–119	–71.5	1%, methanol	553
N-Bz-D-phenylalanine	234	–	–	559
N-Bz-L-phenylalanine	234	–	–	559
N-Bz-DL-serine	235–236	–	–	551
N,N-diBz-DL-serine	145–146	–	–	553
N,N-diBz-L-serine	142–143	–79	2%, methanol	553
N,N-diBz-DL-threonine	142–143	–	–	553
N,N-diBz-L-threonine	94–96	–111.0	2%, methanol	553
N-Bz-DL-tryptophan	250	–	–	551
N-Bz-L-tyrosine	244	–	–	559
O,N,N-triBz-L-tyrosine	118–119	–15.0	2%, methanol	553
N,N-diBz-DL-valine	114–115	–	–	554
N,N-diBz-L-valine	75	–119.5	2%, methanol	553

[a] An isomorphous form of this compound melts at 78–80°.
[b] Two other isomorphous forms of this compound melt at 98° and 84–85°, respectively.
[c] A melting point of 265° has also been reported (557) for this compound.
[d] An isomorphous form of this compound melts at 83–85°.

CHEMICAL PROCEDURES FOR SYNTHESIS OF PEPTIDES

(568, 569). Despite their marked instability toward alkali, however, the TFA-amino acids are stable, crystalline compounds which show no detectable evidence of decomposition after several years of storage (569). Titration with aqueous alkali has revealed a striking lability of the TFA-nitrogen bond at pH values greater than 10.

The TFA-amino acids (XXXVI) employed in peptide syntheses were initially prepared by the direct action of trifluoroacetic anhydride (XXXIV) upon the free amino acid (XXXV), as in the following (567):

$$(CF_3CO)_2O + NH_2CHRCO_2H \rightarrow CF_3CO\text{---}NHCHRCO_2H + CF_3CO_2H$$
$$\text{XXXIV} \qquad \text{XXXV} \qquad \text{XXXVI} \qquad \text{XXXVII}$$

Although such a procedure sufficed for the preparation of a few racemic derivatives, the method was of limited applicability (*a*) owing to incomplete or retarded reaction in consequence of the generally limited solubility of amino acids in one equivalent of trifluoroacetic anhydride, and (*b*) because of the danger of racemization to which optically active aminu acids were exposed, presumably via azlactone formation (Section 10-8), when an excess of the anhydride was employed (570, 571). Finally, the procedure did not permit the successful isolation of characterizable derivatives of several amino acids, e.g., arginine and cystine (570). Despite these shortcomings, the method was none the less profitably applied to the preparation of the optically active derivatives of aspartic (XL; $x = 1$) and glutamic (XL; $x = 2$) acids, both of which, in the presence of excess trifluoroacetic anhydride, undergo intramolecular anhydride (XXXIX) rather than azlactone formation (568) (procedure 10-39). Decomposition of the anhydride (XXXIX) with water proceeded with generation of the desired acylated amino acid (XL). By the use of carefully controlled conditions, the optical derivatives of alanine and valine could also be secured through the direct interaction of amino acid and trifluoroacetic anhydride (572, 573).

$$\underset{\text{XXXVIII}}{\underset{|}{\overset{NH_2CHCO_2H}{\underset{(CH_2)_xCO_2H}{}}}} \xrightarrow{(CF_3CO)_2O} \underset{\text{XXXIX}}{\underset{|}{\overset{CF_3CO\text{---}NHCHCO\text{---}O}{\underset{(CH_2)_x\text{---}CO}{|}}}} \xrightarrow{H_2O} \underset{\text{XL}}{\underset{|}{\overset{CF_3CO\text{---}NHCHCO_2H}{\underset{(CH_2)_xCO_2H}{}}}}$$

Illustrative procedure 10-39 (568). Trifluoroacetyl-L-glutamic acid (XL; $x = 2$). Two grams of L-glutamic acid is mixed with 6 ml. of trifluoroacetic anhydride, at which point a vigorous reaction ensues. After all the material has gone into solution, 50 ml. of cold water is added to the reaction mixture and the mixture placed in the cold overnight. The resulting crystals are filtered and recrystallized from the minimal amount of hot water; yield, 76% of theory; m.p. 192°; $[\alpha]_D^{20} = -23.8°$ (2.5% in H_2O).

In the attempt to circumvent the possibility of racemization during the synthesis of TFA-amino acids, Fones and Lee (574) treated a variety of optically pure amino acids as suspensions in petroleum ether at 60° with slightly less than the theoretical quantity of trifluoroacetic anhydride. An impressive array of optically active TFA-D- and L-amino acids was so obtained, although often in quite modest yield. That no racemization had indeed occurred during such synthesis was demonstrated (574) when several of the free D-amino acids, regenerated by acid hydrolysis of the corresponding acylated D-forms, revealed no detectable amount of their respective L-antipodes in optical purity determinations (Chapter 19) with L-amino acid oxidase. An invaluable series of reference compounds, free from any measurable optical contamination, was thereby made available.

A more recent procedure by Weygand and Geiger (570), which took advantage of the ready solubility of free amino acids in trifluoroacetic acid, has also been utilized for the preparation of optically active TFA-amino acids. Addition of trifluoroacetic anhydride to such solutions, which were maintained at temperatures between $-10°$ and $+10°$, proceeded with the rapid formation of the acyl derivative in good yield without the concomitant occurrence of any detectable racemization (procedure 10–40). In view of the rapid racemization which optically active amino acids undergo in the presence of glacial acetic acid–acetic anhydride mixtures (Section 10–8), it is somewhat surprising that no optical inactivation was noted even in the presence of excess trifluoroacetic anhydride. Such a phenomenon has been ascribed to the lack of dissociation of the carboxyl group of TFA-amino acids in anhydrous trifluoroacetic acid, which obviates the occurrence of potential azlactone formation through the interaction of a TFA cation, $CF_3 \cdot \overset{\oplus}{C}O$, with an anion of the dissociated acid (570). It is of additional interest to note that this procedure, when applied to the trifluoroacetylation of the basic amino acids, namely, ornithine, arginine, and lysine (procedure 10–41), gave rise exclusively to the corresponding α-monoacylated derivative in good yield (70%). No acylation of the more basic ω-groups occurred, presumably because of their existence in trifluoroacetic acid solution as the ammonium form.

Illustrative procedure 10–40 (570). Trifluoroacetyl-L-valine. A solution of 1.17 g. (0.01 mole) of thoroughly dried L-valine is dissolved in 6 ml. of anhydrous trifluoroacetic acid; solution may be effected, if necessary, by warming under reflux in an atmosphere from which moisture is excluded. After the solution is cooled to $-10°$ in a salt-ice bath, 1.76 ml. (0.012 mole) of trifluoroacetic anhydride is added dropwise over a period of several minutes, with shaking. The ice bath is either removed entirely or replaced by a $+10°$ water bath. After about one-half hour, the excess anhydride and trifluoroacetic acid are distilled under reduced pressure at a bath temperature not exceeding 30° into a receiver cooled in a dry ice–acetone mixture. The residue is extracted with 20 parts of dry ether, and the ethereal extract filtered and concentrated. Crystallization is achieved from toluene; yield, 1.71 g. (80% of theory); m.p. 86–87°; $[\alpha]_D^{19} = -15.1°$ (1.7% in H_2O).

Illustrative procedure 10–41 (570). α-Trifluoroacetyl-DL-lysine. To a chilled solution of 0.458 g. of DL-lysine (free base) in 4 ml. of trifluoroacetic acid is added 0.6 ml. of trifluoroacetic anhydride, and the reaction mixture is permitted to stand at 0° to 15° for 15 min. After evaporation of the excess trifluoroacetic acid, as in procedure 10–40, the residue is dissolved in water, neutralized with dilute ammonium hydroxide, and the solution again evaporated to dryness *in vacuo*. The residue is extracted twice with absolute alcohol to remove ammonium trifluoroacetate and then crystallized from water–acetone; yield, 0.615 g. (81% of theory); m.p. 233°.

Utilization of trifluoroacetic anhydride in acylation reactions of the Schotten-Baumann type was largely handicapped by virtue of the extreme reactivity of the reagent in water. Introduction of the less chemically labile ethyl thioltrifluoroacetate (XLI) (procedure 10–42) as an acylating agent by Schallenberg and Calvin (569) has, however, permitted the ready acquisition of TFA-amino acids (XLIII) in aqueous media without the danger of concomitant racemization (procedure 10–43). That this reagent would undergo a ready acyl transfer reaction from the ethyl mercaptide radical to an amino nitrogen atom was strongly suggested by the marked electrophilic nature of the TFA group, together with the known striking aminophilicity exhibited by the sulfur atom in a thiol group. Inasmuch as a hydrolytic cleavage of the TFA substituent results at a pH greater than 10, the acylation was performed at pH 8–9 under mild conditions. The desired product (XLIII), which formed simultaneously with the low-boiling ethyl mercaptan (XLIV), could generally be precipitated upon acidification of the reaction mixture. It is of especial interest to note that, while both lysine and ornithine yield mono-TFA derivatives in the ω-terminal position by this procedure (procedure 10–44), use of the trifluoroacetic anhydride-trifluoroacetic acid system (570), alluded to previously, results in the exclusive formation of the corresponding mono-α-acylated derivatives.

$$CF_3CO-SC_2H_5 + NH_2CHRCO_2H \xrightarrow[pH\ 8-9]{H_2O} CF_3CO-NHCHRCO_2H + C_2H_5SH$$

XLI XLII XLIII XLIV

Illustrative procedure 10–42 (575). Ethyl thioltrifluoroacetate. Thirty-one grams of ethyl mercaptan is chilled in an ice bath and 130 g. of trifluoroacetic anhydride added dropwise thereto over a period of 1 hr. with intermittent chilling and shaking (*Hood!*). The reaction vessel is then fitted with a reflux condenser protected from atmospheric moisture with a calcium chloride drying tube, permitted to stand at room temperature for 1 hr, and heated at 100° for 3 hr., during which time the solution turns a reddish color. Excess anhydride and trifluoroacetic acid are removed by washing twice with 500-ml. portions of a cold, 5% potassium hydroxide solution and twice with water. After drying over anhydrous magnesium sulfate, the product is fractionally distilled; b.p. 90.5° at 760 mm; yield, 60% of theory (based on ethyl mercaptan).

Illustrative procedure 10–43 (569). Trifluoroacetylation with ethyl thioltrifluoroacetate. The amino acid (XLII) is dissolved in 1.00 equivalent of N sodium hydroxide in a flask possessing a ground glass joint and stopper fitted with a stopcock open to the atmosphere. Such arrangement is necessary to permit ethyl mercaptan, the by-product of the acylation, to escape from the system; the reaction is performed in a well-ventilated hood. A quantity of ethyl thioltrifluoroacetate (XLI) (procedure 10–42), equal to 0.2 ml. per mmole of amino acid employed, i.e., 1.6 : 1 molar ratio, is added and the heterogeneous reaction mixture shaken mechanically for 24 hr. The mixture is cooled in an ice bath, acidified with concentrated hydrochloric acid, and the precipitated product is collected by filtration.

The TFA-amino acids which have been prepared in this manner, together with their yields and recrystallization solvents, are: L-arginine dihydrate, 62.9%, water; L-asparagine, 64.5%, methanol–water; DL-methionine, 70.2%, benzene–pet. ether (2 : 1); DL-phenylalanine, 80.4%, benzene–hexane (1 : 1); L-phenylalanine, 76.2%, benzene–hexane (1 : 1); and tryptophan hydrate, 48.4%, water. In addition, the glycine and DL-norleucine derivatives were prepared by a comparable procedure, but these were extracted into ether and ethyl acetate, respectively, subsequent to the acidification step. After concentration of the respective extracts, the residues were recrystallized from benzene. Melting points of these derivatives are given in Table 10–24.

Illustrative procedure 10–44 (569). ε-Trifluoroacetyl-DL-lysine. To a solution of 1.83 g. (10.0 mmoles) of DL-lysine monohydrochloride in 10 ml. of N sodium hydroxide is added 2.0 ml. of ethyl thioltrifluoroacetate (procedure 10–42). The heterogeneous mixture is shaken for 6 hr., during which time the precipitate slowly separates and finally fills the solution. The reaction mixture is cooled in ice water, the solid collected by filtration, the crude material dissolved in 10 ml. of hot water, and the resulting solution diluted with 15 ml. of hot ethanol. White, rectangular crystals separate on cooling; yield, 1.25 g.; m.p. 226–231° d.

Table 10–24 (pp. 918–919) lists the various TFA-amino acids which have been prepared by the afore-mentioned procedures or modifications thereof.

18. The Phenylthiocarbonyl and Related Groups. In 1947, Ehrensvärd (578) proposed the use of the phenylthiocarbonyl group (PhTC—) in synthetic peptide procedures because of its ready cleavage from peptide derivatives when subjected to the action of lead acetate in 70% ethanol or lead hydroxide (or carbonate) in dilute alkali. Reinvestigation of this procedure, by Lindenmann, Khan and Hofmann (579), demonstrated that such cleavage proceeds, in reality, with the generation of hydantoins rather than the desired peptides. A subsequent report by Kollonitsch, Gabor, and Hajos (580) indicated, however, that the free peptides may be readily secured from their respective PhTC derivatives through oxidative scission with perbenzoic acid. Like susceptibility of the methylthiocarbonyl (MeTC-) and benzylthiocarbonyl (BzTC-) groups to such cleavage was also demonstrated (580).

No extensive use of any of these interesting groups for the preparation of peptides has as yet been reported.

Attempts to prepare PhTC-amino acids (XLVII) by acylation of the free amino acid (XLVI) with PhTC-chloride (XLV) (581), under Schotten-Baumann conditions, have proved unsuccessful (578, 582). Study of this reaction with L-phenylanine (XLVI; $R = C_6H_5CH_2$), by Schuller and Niemann (582), led to the isolation of diphenyl dithiocarbonate (LII) and N,N'-carbonyl-bis-L-phenylalanine (XLIX; $R = C_6H_5CH_2$) in lieu of the desired PhTC-L-phenylalanine (XLVII; $R = C_6H_5CH_2$). It was inferred that the transitory appearance of the latter compound (XLVII) had indeed occurred, and the suggestion was offered that the products isolated arose as a consequence of subsequent reactions, as in

$$C_6H_5SCOCl + NH_2CHRCO_2^- + OH^- \rightarrow C_6H_5SCO-NHCHRCO_2^- + Cl^- + H_2O$$
$$\text{XLV} \quad\quad \text{XLVI} \quad\quad\quad\quad\quad \text{XLVII}$$

$$C_6H_5SCO-NHCHRCO_2^- + NH_2CHRCO_2^- + OH^- \rightarrow O=C(NHCHRCO_2^-)_2 + C_6H_5S^- + H_2O$$
$$\text{XLVII} \quad\quad\quad\quad \text{XLVIII} \quad\quad\quad\quad\quad\quad \text{XLIX} \quad\quad\quad\quad \text{L}$$

$$C_6H_5S^- + C_6H_5SCOCl \rightarrow C_6H_5SCOSC_6H_5 + Cl^-$$
$$\text{L} \quad\quad \text{LI} \quad\quad\quad\quad \text{LII}$$

Exploitation of this reaction scheme has permitted the synthesis of a number of mono- and disubstituted ureas (583).

As a consequence of the above, preparation of PhTC-amino acids (LVI) is generally carried out by the action of PhTC-chloride (LIII) on the pertinent amino acid ester (LIV) in chloroform solution, followed by selective acid hydrolysis of the acylamino acid ester (LV) so derived (578, 579):

$$C_6H_5SCOCl + NH_2CHRCO_2Et \xrightarrow[(C_2H_5)_2NH]{CHCl_3}$$
$$\text{LIII} \quad\quad\quad \text{LIV}$$

$$C_6H_5SCO-NHCHRCO_2Et \xrightarrow{HCl-HOAc} C_6H_5SCO-NHCHRCO_2H$$
$$\text{LV} \quad\quad\quad\quad\quad\quad\quad\quad\quad\quad\quad \text{LVI}$$

Since such a procedure for securing the appropriately masked amino acid is relatively tedious, it constitutes a severe handicap to the use of the PhTC group. It is therefore of interest to note that the structurally related MeTC- and BzTC-amino acids (LIX; $R = CH_3$ or $C_6H_5CH_2$), which are utilizable in synthetic peptide procedures in the same manner as their PhTC analogs, may be prepared by the action of MeTC-chloride (LVII; $R = CH_3$) and BzTC-chloride (LVII; $R = C_6H_5CH_2$), respectively, on aqueous solutions of the amino acid (LVIII) in the presence of sodium bicarbonate, sodium carbonate, or magnesium oxide (580).

$$RSCOCl + NH_2CHR'CO_2H \xrightarrow[\text{or MgO}]{NaHCO_3, Na_2CO_3} RSCO-NHCHR'CO_2H$$
$$\text{LVII} \quad\quad\quad \text{LVIII} \quad\quad\quad\quad\quad\quad\quad\quad\quad \text{LIX}$$

TABLE 10-24
Trifluoroacetyl Derivatives of Amino Acids

Trifluoroacetyl(TFA)amino Acid	M.P., °C.	$[\alpha]_D$, deg.	Temp., °C.	Concn. and Solvent	Ref.[a]
TFA-DL-alanine	120.5	—	—	—	567, 568, 570
TFA-D-alanine	66–68	+60.6	25	2%, H_2O	572
TFA-L-alanine	66–68	−60.7	18	2%, H_2O	568, 570, 572
TFA-D-α-amino-n-butyric acid	55–57	+41.8	25	2%, H_2O	574
TFA-L-α-amino-n-butyric acid	55–57	−42.1	25	2%, H_2O	574
TFA-D-α-aminodecylic acid	75–77	+5.0	25	2%, ethanol	574
TFA-L-α-aminodecylic acid	75–77	−5.0	25	2%, ethanol	574
α-TFA-L-arginine	130–132	−3.5	18	2%, H_2O	570
α-TFA-L-arginine·2H_2O	140–142	—	—	—	569
TFA-DL-aspartic acid	160–162	—	—	—	574
TFA-L-asparagine	164–165	—	—	—	569
TFA-S-benzyl-DL-cysteine	129–130	—	—	—	570
TFA-S-benzyl-L-cysteine	84–85	−84.5	12	1.5%, 99% ethanol	570
bis-TFA-L-cystine	165–166	−247.5	14	1.3%, 99% ethanol	570
TFA-L-glutamic acid	192	−23.8	20	2.5%, H_2O	568
TFA-glycine	117–119	—	—	—	567–569, 574
TFA-D-leucine	72–75	+40.0	25	2%, ethanol	574
TFA-L-leucine	72–75	−39.5	25	2%, ethanol	570, 574

CHEMICAL PROCEDURES FOR SYNTHESIS OF PEPTIDES

Compound	mp (°C)	[α]	T (°C)	Solvent	Refs.
α-TFA-DL-lysine	233.0	—	—	—	570
ε-TFA-DL-lysine	226–231 d.	—	—	—	569
α,ε-di-TFA-DL-lysine	122–123	—	—	—	570
TFA-DL-methionine	95–96	—	—	—	569, *570*, 574
TFA-D-methionine	69–71	+22.0	25	2%, H$_2$O	574
TFA-L-methionine	69–71	−22.7	25	2%, H$_2$O	574
TFA-DL-norleucine	79–82.5	—	—	—	569
TFA-D-norleucine	70–72	+13.5	25	2%, ethanol	574
TFA-L-norleucine	71–73	−13.0	25	2%, ethanol	574
TFA-D-norvaline	65–68	+32.0	25	2%, H$_2$O	574
TFA-L-norvaline	64–67	−31.5	25	2%, H$_2$O	574
α-TFA-L-ornithine	232–233	−9.5	20	0.7%, 5% ethanol	570
δ-TFA-DL-ornithine	228–232	—	—	—	569
δ-TFA-L-ornithine	250–251	+12.9	20	0.5%, H$_2$O	570
TFA-DL-phenylalanine	127–128	—	—	—	569, *572*
TFA-D-phenylalanine	120–122	−17.2	25	2%, ethanol	574
TFA-L-phenylalanine	120–122	+17.4	25	2%, ethanol	569, *574*
TFA-DL-proline	81–83	—	—	—	572
TFA-L-proline	46–48	−60.3	14	1.0%, benzene	576
TFA-L-tryptophan	162–163	—	—	—	570
TFA-L-tryptophan·H$_2$O	95	—	—	—	569
N-TFA-L-tyrosine	192.5–193.5	+45.0	25	2%, H$_2$O + 1 eq. NaOH	570, *577*
TFA-DL-valine	121–121.5	—	—	—	567, 569, *570*
TFA-D-valine	86–88	+15.0	25	2%, H$_2$O	574
TFA-L-valine	86–88	−15.2	25	2%, H$_2$O	570, *573*, 574

[a] Where more than one reference is given, the one in italics is that from which the physical constants were taken.

Table 10-25 lists several of the BzTC-, MeTC-, and PhTC- amino acids which have been thus far described.

TABLE 10–25
Some Benzyl (BzTC)-, Methyl (MeTC)-, and Phenyl (PhTC)- thiocarbonyl Derivatives of Amino Acids

Acylamino Acid	M.P., °C.	Ref.
BzTC-DL-alanine	177–178	580
BzTC-L-alanine	128–129	580
BzTC-L-glutamic acid	118–120	580
BzTC-glycine	151–152	580
BzTC-DL-phenylalanine	110	580
BzTC-*threo*-β-phenyl-DL-serine	153	580
BzTC-DL-serine	146–147	580
MeTC-glycine	118–119	580
MeTC-*threo*-β-phenyl-DL-serine	129–130	580
PhTC-DL-alanine	136–138	579
PhTC-L-glutamic acid[a]	111–113	579
PhTC-glycine	153–154	578, 579
PhTC-L-valine	114	421

[a] $[\alpha]_D^{26} = -22°$ (1%, MeOH).

19. *o*-Nitrophenoxyacetyl and Chloroacetyl Groups. In 1952, Holley and Holley (494) reported that *o*-nitrophenoxyacetyl ($NO_2C_6H_4OCH_2CO-$) derivatives of peptides, upon catalytic reduction to the corresponding *o*-aminophenoxyacetyl ($NH_2C_6H_4OCH_2CO-$) peptide followed by treatment with hot water, undergo cleavage to the lactam of *o*-aminophenoxyacetic acid ($\overline{NHC_6H_4OCH_2CO}$) and the free peptide. The same investigators also demonstrated that *o*-amino-N-phenylglycyl ($NH_2C_6H_4NHCH_2CO-$) peptides may be induced to undergo analogous reactions, this time with the formation of the lactam of *o*-aminophenylglycine ($\overline{NHC_6H_4NHCH_2CO}$) and the free peptide. Inasmuch as chloroacetylated peptides are readily converted to the corresponding *o*-amino-N-phenylglycyl peptides upon treatment with *o*-phenylenediamine in hot aqueous solution, a procedure was thereby available which enabled utilization of the chloroacetyl group as a masking substituent in synthetic peptide procedures. Unfortunately, no further exploitation of either of these two promising blocking groups has appeared in the literature to the present time.

20. Formyl Group. In consequence of the extreme lability of formamides to the action of ethanolic hydrogen chloride, removal of formyl (HCO-) groups from their peptide derivatives may be achieved without rupture of the sensitive peptide linkages. Although utilization of this procedure in synthetic peptide techniques was initially described by Waley (584, 584a) in 1953, further application of this method has since received only scant attention (585, 586). Despite the rather late introduction of the formyl masking substituent into such peptide procedures, methods for the preparation of formylamino acids have long been known. Thus Zehra (584) as early as 1890 prepared formyl-*p*-aminobenzoic acid via the action of warm concentrated formic acid on *p*-aminobenzoic acid. More extensive application of this method was made by Emil Fischer (cf. 593), who employed the reaction with α-amino acids but, ironically, he overlooked the worth of the highly acid-labile formyl radical as a selectively removable blocking group in peptide synthesis. The preparation of formylamino acids (LXII), as employed by Fischer and Warburg (593), involved the prolonged heating of a solution of the pertinent amino acid (LXI) in concentrated formic acid (LX) solution, followed by evaporation of the solvent, addition of fresh formic acid, and repetition of the entire procedure (procedure 10–45). A less time consuming procedure was described by du Vigneaud, Dorfmann, and Loring (590), who treated the requisite amino acid with a mixture of formic acid (LXIV) and acetic anhydride at 50–60°; the active acylating agent was presumably formic anhydride (LXIII), which could arise as a result of disproportionation of the latter mixture. A modification of this procedure by Sheehan and Yang (586) involved the use of lower temperatures (procedure 10–46) in order to minimize the danger of racemization where optically active amino acids are implicated.

$$\underset{\text{LX}}{\text{HCOOH}} + \underset{\text{LXI}}{\text{NH}_2\text{CHRCO}_2\text{H}} \xrightarrow{\Delta} \underset{\text{LXII}}{\text{HCO—NHCHRCO}_2\text{H}} \xleftarrow{\text{NH}_2\text{CHRCO}_2\text{H}} \underset{\text{LXIII}}{(\text{HCO})_2\text{O}} \xleftarrow{\text{Ac}_2\text{O}} \underset{\text{LXIV}}{\text{HCOOH}}$$

Illustrative procedure 10–45 (593). Formylglycine. A mixture of 5 g. of glycine in 7.5 g. of 98.5% formic acid is heated at 100° for 3 hr. and the reaction mixture then concentrated to dryness under reduced pressure. The entire procedure is repeated two more times. The residual crystalline mass ultimately obtained is treated with a little cold water to remove the unchanged amino acid and then recrystallized from 3 volumes of hot water. Further recrystallization may be effected from 80 volumes of ethyl acetate; m.p. 153–154° d.

Illustrative procedure 10–46 (586, 590). Formylamino acids. To a mixture of approximately 0.10 mole of the pertinent amino acid in 210 ml. of 98% formic acid is added 70 ml. of acetic anhydride, in dropwise fashion, with the temperature of the reaction mixture maintained between 5° and 15° by means of an ice bath. The reaction mixture is stirred for 1 hr. at room temperature after the addition is complete, 80 ml. of ice water added thereto, and the solution concentrated to dryness under reduced pressure. Recrystallization of the residual material is achieved from water, aqueous ethanol, or some other suitable solvent. Yields generally are greater than 80% of theory.

Table 10-26 lists several of the formylamino acids that have been prepared according to essentially the afore-mentioned procedures. It should be noted that the formyl-L-cysteine listed here was obtained by Fruton and Clarke (590) via a zinc-hydrochloric acid mediated reduction of the disulfide linkage of bis-formyl-L-cystine.

TABLE 10-26
Formyl Derivatives of Amino Acids

Formylamino Acid	M.P., °C.	$[\alpha]_D$, deg.	Temp., °C.	Concn. and Solvent	Ref.
Formyl-DL-alanine	150	–	–	–	587
α-Formyl-L-arginine	269–270	–	–	–	588
Formyl-L-asparagine·H$_2$O	168–169 d.	–	–	–	589
Formyl-L-cysteine	87–89	–	–	–	590
Formyl-S-benzyl-L-cysteine	126	−8.6	18	5%, ethanol	432a
bis-Formyl-DL-cystine	194–196	–	–	–	590
bis-Formyl-L-cystine	187–188	−162.1	25	1.0%, N NaOH	590
Formyl-L-glutamic acid	112–113	−7.3	20	2%, water	591, 592
Formyl-L-glutamine	118–120 d.	−2.5	28	2%, N HCl	591
Formylglycine	153–154 d.	–	–	–	593
Formyl-DL-histidine	207–208	–	–	–	594
Formyl-L-histidine	202 d.	+56.7	20	2.2%, water	594
Formyl-DL-isoleucine	121–122	–	–	–	595
Formyl-D-isoleucine	156–157	−27.8	20	10.1%, ethanol	595
Formyl-L-isoleucine	157	+27.0	25	3%, ethanol	298, 595
Formyl-L-alloisoleucine	123	+27.9	25	3%, ethanol	298
Formyl-DL-leucine	115–116	–	–	–	593
Formyl-D-leucine	–	+18.8	20	10.0%, ethanol	593
Formyl-L-leucine	–	−18.5	20	10.0%, ethanol	593
α-Formyl-L-lysine	193–193.5	–	–	–	42
Formyl-DL-methionine	99–100	–	–	–	596
Formyl-D-methionine	99–100	+10.6	25	0.8%, water	596
Formyl-L-methionine	99–100	−10.0	25	0.8%, water	596
Formyl-DL-phenylalanine	169–170	–	–	–	224
Formyl-D-phenylalanine	167	−75.4	20	4%, ethanol	224
Formyl-L-phenylalanine	167	+75.2	20	4%, ethanol	224
Formyl-DL-tryptophan	167–168 d.	–	–	–	597
Formyl-DL-tyrosine·H$_2$O	182 d.	–	–	–	598
Formyl-L-tyrosine	170–171	+89.4	10	1.7%, ethanol	584a, 599
N-Formyl-O-acetyl-L-tyrosine	164–165	+73.5	19	1.9%, ethanol	584a
Formyl-DL-valine	140–145	–	–	–	600
Formyl-D-valine	156	+13.1	20	9.0%, ethanol	600
Formyl-L-valine	156	−13.0	20	9.0%, ethanol	600

21. Benzylsulfonyl Group. A comparison of the benzylsulfonyl substituent (LXVI) with the tosyl (LXVII) and the carbobenzoxy (LXV) groups reveals that the former substituent may be considered a hybrid of the latter two:

C₆H₅CH₂—OCO—   C₆H₅CH₂—SO₂—   CH₃C₆H₄—SO₂—
      LXV   LXVI   LXVII

Application of this group to synthetic peptide techniques was reported by Milne and Peng (601), who demonstrated its selective cleavage from amide linkages with an amino acid residue through the catalytic action of Raney nickel or, like the tosyl and carbobenzoxy groups, via the reductive action of sodium and liquid ammonia. The benzylsulfonylamino acids (LXX) may also be prepared through the action of the pertinent acid chloride, i.e., benzylsulfonyl chloride (LXVIII), on the amino acid (LXIX) under Schotten-Baumann conditions (procedure 10–47). Table 10–27 reveals the method of preparation, yield, recrystallization solvent, and physical characteristics of a variety of benzylsulfonylamino acids.

C₆H₅CH₂SO₂Cl + NH₂CHRCO₂H → C₆H₅CH₂SO₂—NHCHRCO₂H
   LXVIII   LXIX   LXX

Illustrative procedure 10–47 (601). Benzylsulfonylamino acids. Method A. The chosen amino acid (usually 0.01–0.03 mole) is dissolved in 1.2 equivalents of N sodium hydroxide solution, and the solution cooled in an ice bath. To the mixture are added 1.2 equivalents of pulverized benzylsulfonyl chloride and 1.4 equivalents of N sodium hydroxide solution in five approximately equal portions. The reaction mixture is cooled and shaken vigorously for 15–20 min. between successive additions (except in the case of L-proline, when 30 min. is allowed). Finally the mixture is shaken for an additional hour at room temperature and made basic to litmus paper with N sodium hydroxide solution. Unchanged material is separated by filtration, and the filtrate is washed in a separatory funnel with two 20-ml. portions of ether, and the dissolved ether removed from the aqueous layer under reduced pressure. The solution is acidified (Congo red) slowly with concentrated hydrochloric acid and the derivative which separates recrystallized from an appropriate solvent as indicated in Table 10–27.

Method B. To a solution consisting of 0.03 equivalent of the amino acid, 30 ml. of N sodium hydroxide solution, and 30 ml. of dioxane are simultaneously added, in ten approximately equal portions, 50 ml. of N sodium hydroxide solution and 0.045 equivalent of benzylsulfonyl chloride in 50 ml. of dioxane. Between the additions of reagents, the mixture is shaken vigorously for 15 to 20 min. (mechanically) first in an ice bath, then, after all reagents have been added, for one to two additional hours at room temperature. After the solution has been made basic to litmus paper it is filtered, and the filtrate washed with two 40-ml. portions of ether. The aqueous solution is acidified (Congo red) with concentrated hydrochloric acid, saturated with sodium chloride and extracted with three 50-ml. portions of ethyl acetate. The ethyl acetate solution is washed with 30 ml. of water, and 100 ml. of petroleum ether (b.p. 30–60°) added thereto. The derivative is extracted with three 50-ml. portions of N sodium bicarbonate solution, the aqueous extract evaporated

TABLE 10-27
Benzylsulfonyl Derivatives of Amino Acids (601)

Benzylsulfonyl Derivative of	M.P., °C.	Specific Rotation (1% in N NaOH) $[\alpha]_D$ deg.	Temp., °C	Yield, % Method A	Yield, % Method B	Solvent for Recrystallization
DL-Alanine	164–165	–	–	41	40	Hot water
D-Alanine	128	+38.7	26		36	Hot water
L-Alanine	127–128	−38.5	26		29	Hot water
β-Alanine	149–150	–	–	38		EtOH–water
L-Arginine (α,ω-di-)[a]	84–86	−8.7	26	27		Acetone–ether
DL-Aspartic acid	106–107	–	–	26		EtOAc–CHCl$_3$
L-Cystine (α,α'-di-)	172–173	+72.2	26	61		Water–acetone
DL-Ethionine	95	–	–		65	Ether–pet. ether
DL-Glutamic acid	131–132	–	–		40	EtOAc–CHCl$_3$
Glycine	151–152	–	–	44		Hot water
L-Histidine (α-)	182–185	−22.2	25	38		Water–acetone
L-Hydroxyproline	143–144	−40.6	24	32		Ether–hexane
DL-Isoleucine[b]	113	–	–	30		EtOH–water
L-Isoleucine	146–147	−39.9	24	39		EtOH–water
DL-Leucine	113–114	–	–	52	58	EtOH–water
D-Leucine	133–134	+23.7	26	41	55	EtOH–water
L-Leucine	133–134	−23.1	26	63	72	EtOH–water
L-Lysine (α,ε-di-)	144–145	−9.9	26	27	50	EtOH–water
DL-Methionine	110–111	–	–	42	47	EtOH–water
D-Methionine	90–91	+13.6	26		49	Ether–hexane
L-Methionine	90–91	−13.5	26	58	70	Ether–hexane
DL-Norleucine	103–104	–	–	40		EtOH–water
DL-Norvaline[c]	84–85	–	–	41		EtOH–water
DL-Ornithine (α,δ-di-)	54–55	–	–	48		EtOH–water
DL-Phenylalanine	151–152	–	–	47		EtOH–water
L-Phenylalanine	156–157	−12.6	25	28	58	EtOH–water
L-Proline[d]	107–108	−72.3	25	22		Ether
DL-Serine	123–124	–	–	47		EtOAc–pet. ether
DL-Threonine	143–144	–	–	51		EtOAc–pet. ether
DL-Tryptophan·H$_2$O	95–96	–	–	65	52	EtOH–water
DL-Tyrosine (O,N-di-)	195–196	–	–	43		Acetone–water
L-Tyrosine (O,N-di-)	191–192	−9.2	24	40		Acetone–water
DL-Valine[e]	123–124	–	–	53	58	Ethanol–water

[a] The derivative precipitated from acetone–ether as an oil; when it was dried under reduced pressure, it was converted to a glass-like solid.

[b] The derivative was recrystallized from ethanol–water as a hydrate, m.p. 74–75°, which loses water of hydration at about 90°.

[c] The derivative was recrystallized from ethanol–water in the cold as a needle-like crystalline hydrate, m.p. 50–51°, which may be dried to constant weight at 100°.

[d] The derivative was dissolved in a small amount of ether, and crystallization was induced by slow evaporation of the solvent.

[e] The derivative was recrystallized from ethanol–water as a hydrate, m.p. 65.5–66.5°, and the water of hydration removed *in vacuo* over phosphorus pentoxide.

in vacuo until the odor of ethyl acetate no longer persists and then acidified (Congo red) slowly with concentrated hydrochloric acid with vigorous stirring. The derivative that separates is recrystallized from an appropriate solvent as indicated in Table 10–27.

Masking of the Carboxyl Function

In the chemical union of two amino acids via peptide bonds, the condensation of an appropriately activated acylamino acid with another amino acid requires that the reactivity of the carboxyl group of the latter reactant be adequately suppressed. If the condensation is effected in an alkaline, aqueous medium, then the problem of masking the reactive carboxyl function of the free amino acid may be simply disposed of through alkali salt formation. However, if a non-aqueous solvent, such as chloroform, dioxane, or ethyl acetate is employed for such reaction, then the carboxyl group of the pertinent amino acid is generally masked by its conversion to an ester derivative prior to the condensation step. Before such ester derivatives may be considered satisfactorily applicable to synthetic peptide techniques, they should conform essentially to the same criteria that obtained for blocking groups of the amino function, as enumerated above. These are reiterated here: (a) the pertinent amino acid ester should be conveniently available through the use of simple organic chemical techniques; (b) the esterification should proceed in high yield; (c) the conditions employed for esterification should not lead to racemization where optically active amino acids are used; (d) the amino acids esters so derived should be easily crystallizable to permit their ready characterization and purification; (e) the ester group should be stable under the conditions utilized for coupling with other amino acid residues; (f) during the terminal stages of the synthesis, the ester group should be selectively removable under conditions that would not lead to racemization or destruction of the labile peptide molecule; and (g) the removal of the ester group should not result in the formation of side products that would make purification of the desired product difficult.

Aside from the alkali salts, the groups employed as C-terminal blocking substituents for amino acids in synthetic peptide procedures have been confined largely to methyl, ethyl, and benzyl ester derivatives. The former two groups, because of their ready susceptibility to cleavage by alkali, were extensively employed in peptide condensation procedures by both Fischer and Curtius during the first decade of the present century (Section 10-4). Later introduction of benzyl ester derivatives by Bergmann, Zervas, and Salzmann (602) was based on the hitherto known susceptibility of this group to undergo scission upon catalytic hydrogenolysis. Methods generally utilized for the preparation of methyl, ethyl, and benzyl ester derivatives of amino acids are detailed below.

22. Amino Acid Methyl and Ethyl Esters. Despite the numerous methods provided by preparative organic chemistry for the synthesis of amino acid esters, the methods which are employed routinely for securing these compounds have been relatively few. Chief among these is the method utilized in 1888, by Curtius and Goebel (603), for the preparation of glycine ethyl ester hydrochloride via the action of absolute alcohol and hydrogen chloride on glycine. In practice, a suspension of the free amino acid (I) in absolute methanol or ethanol (II) is treated to saturation with a stream of dry hydrogen chloride gas. The amino acid ester hydrochloride (III) so derived is isolated either by filtration, if an insoluble product is formed, i.e., glycine ethyl ester hydrochloride and lysine methyl ester dihydrochloride, or by evaporation of the alcoholic mother liquors, if soluble products are encountered (procedure 10–48). In general, the ester hydrochlorides are secured in excellent yield and, in the case of optically active amino acids, are apparently devoid of any measurable racemization.

$$\underset{\text{I}}{NH_2CHRCO_2H} + \underset{\text{II}}{R'OH} \xrightarrow{HCl} \underset{\text{III}}{HCl \cdot NH_2CHRCO_2R'} + \underset{\text{IV}}{H_2O}$$

Illustrative procedure 10–48. Esterification of amino acids (Method I). A stream of dry hydrogen chloride gas is passed rapidly through a suspension of 10 g. of the pertinent amino acid in 150 ml. of absolute methanol or ethanol, without external cooling. After all the amino acid has gone into solution, the hot reaction mixture is cooled in an ice bath and the introduction of gas continued to saturation at 0–5°. The reaction mixture, protected from atmospheric moisture with a calcium chloride drying tube, is then permitted to stand at room temperature for about 3–4 hr. Dependent upon whether an insoluble or a soluble product is formed, the remainder of the procedure is as follows: (*a*) If the product is insoluble, the mixture is allowed to stand in the cold overnight, filtered, washed with cold methanol (ethanol in the case of ethyl esters), then ether, and dried *in vacuo* over sodium hydroxide pellets; recrystallization is effected from the parent alcohol. (*b*) Where soluble products are encountered, the reaction mixture is concentrated to dryness *in vacuo* below 50°, 50 ml. of the parent alcohol is added, and the concentration to dryness repeated. The dry residue, which may be secured as crystals or a syrup, is rubbed with anhydrous ether, and the resulting crystalline suspension filtered and washed with dry ether. After drying *in vacuo* over sodium hydroxide pellets to remove the excess hydrogen chloride, the ester hydrochloride is recrystallized from the parent alcohol by the addition of anhydrous ether.

Since the rate of esterification varies with the degree of steric hindrance imposed by the amino acid side chain, more drastic conditions than those given above are sometimes required for certain of the more highly hindered amino acids. Thus, for example, a suspension of DL-*tert*-leucine in methanol, upon saturation with dry hydrogen chloride gas, yielded solely the unesterified amino acid hydrochloride; the same reaction mixture, after having stood at room temperature for some 18 hours and thereafter being refluxed under anhydrous conditions for 6 hours, led to the desired product in excellent yield (371). Note too should be made that in order to ensure the complete conversion of the dicarboxylic acids, i.e., glutamic and aspartic acids, to their respective di-ester hydrochlorides, it is desirable to carry out the esterification under conditions of reflux (procedure 10–49). Similar procedure should be employed with such amino acids as lysine, which are sluggishly soluble in alcoholic hydrogen chloride solutions unless heated.

Illustrative procedure 10–49. Esterification of amino acids (Method II). To a round-bottomed flask equipped with a reflux condenser and gas inlet tube are added 20 g. of the pertinent amino acid and 300 ml. of absolute methanol or ethanol. A stream of dry hydrogen chloride is passed through the gas inlet tube and the reaction mixture maintained at a gentle reflux by the application of heat for 1–3 hr. After an additional hour at room temperature, the reaction mixture is worked up as in procedure 10–48.

In addition to the above, the selective esterification of the α- or ω-carboxyl groups of the dicarboxylic acids, i.e., glutamic and aspartic acids, deserves added consideration. A convenient preparation of the γ-ethyl ester of glutamic acid, virtually free from any contaminating α-ester, was described by Bergmann and Zervas (604). The method, in essence, involved the addition of glutamic acid to a solution of approximately two equivalents of hydrogen chloride in absolute ethanol. Upon shaking at room temperature, the amino acid went into solution, forming γ-ethyl glutamate, which was isolated as its hydrochloride derivative after the addition of ether to the condensed reaction mixture. Later modification of this procedure by various investigators (367, 391, 482, 605–608), permitted the preparation of the γ-methyl and ethyl ester derivatives of glutamic acid as both the free base and the hydrochloride salt (procedure 10–50). Worthy of note is the utilization of thionyl chloride (472) and acetyl chloride (367) as catalysts in lieu of hydrogen chloride (procedure 10–51).

Illustrative procedure 10–50 (482). γ-Ethyl L-glutamate. A suspension of 35 g. (0.24 mole) of L-glutamic acid in 350 ml. of absolute ethanol containing 23 g. (0.63 mole) of dry hydrogen chloride is shaken until complete solution occurs (20 min.). The solution is diluted to 1 l. with absolute ethanol, triethylamine being added dropwise until the solution just becomes alkaline. After standing at 0–5° for 16 hr., the product is filtered, washed with cold absolute ethanol and ether, and air-dried on the filter. Drying is completed *in vacuo*; yield, 29 g. (70%). The product, after recrystallization from water–alcohol, melts at 194°.

Illustrative procedure 10–51 (472). γ-Methyl L-glutamate·HCl. Thirty grams of L-glutamic acid is added to a chilled solution of 20 ml. of thionyl chloride in 140 ml. of methanol and the mixture shaken vigorously for a few minutes until most of the solid has dissolved. The reaction mixture is then permitted to stand for 25 min. at 20° and 400 ml. of ether added thereto. The precipitated γ-methyl L-glutamate·HCl is filtered, washed with ether, and dried *in vacuo* over sodium hydroxide pellets; yield, 24 g. (60% of theory); m.p. 154°.

Although the ω-esters of the dicarboxylic amino acids may be prepared with facility, no convenient method has as yet been described which permits the selective esterification of the α-carboxyl groups of these amino acids. The α-ethyl esters of both aspartic acid and glutamic acid have, nevertheless, been secured by Le Quesne and Young (609, 610) via a circuitous route. The procedure involved the initial preparation of the carbobenzoxyamino acid (VI; $x = 1$ or 2) which, after conversion to the anhydride (VII) by treatment with acetic anhydride, was reacted with ethanol to give a mixture of the carbobenzoxylated α- and ω-ethyl ester derivatives (VIII). Successful fractionation of the latter mixture was achieved in aqueous sodium carbonate, and the uncontaminated carbobenzoxylated α-ethyl ester (IX), so isolated, was converted to the desired amino acid α-ethyl ester (X) by catalytic hydrogenolysis.

$$\underset{V}{\underset{(CH_2)_xCO_2H}{NH_2CHCO_2H}} \xrightarrow[\text{aq. NaOH}]{Cbzo—Cl} \underset{VI}{\underset{(CH_2)_xCO_2H}{Cbzo—NHCHCO_2H}} \xrightarrow{Ac_2O} \underset{VII}{\underset{(CH_2)_x—CO}{Cbzo—NHCHCO—O}} \xrightarrow{EtOH}$$

$$\underbrace{\underset{(CH_2)_xCO_2H}{Cbzo—NHCHCO_2Et} + \underset{(CH_2)_xCO_2Et}{Cbzo—NHCHCO_2H}}_{VIII} \xrightarrow{\text{aq. Na}_2CO_3} \underset{IX}{\underset{(CH_2)_xCO_2H}{Cbzo—NHCHCO_2Et}} \xrightarrow{H_2, Pd} \underset{X}{\underset{(CH_2)_xCO_2H}{NH_2CHCO_2Et}}$$

Tables 10–28 and 10–29 list several of the more common amino acid methyl and ethyl esters, most of which may be obtained by the above procedures or slight modifications thereof. As several of the ester hydrochlorides tend to be somewhat hygroscopic, they are best stored *in vacuo* over phosphorus pentoxide.

23. Amino Acid Benzyl Esters. The utilization of benzyl esters in synthetic peptide procedures sometimes offers certain advantages over the corresponding methyl or ethyl ester derivatives. Whereas the latter groups must be saponified during the terminal stages of a peptide synthesis, the benzyl esters, in consequence of their simultaneous removal with the carbobenzoxy group upon catalytic hydrogenation, obviate the need for an additional de-esterification step where this acyl blocking group is employed. Additionally, the benzyl group is of value in procedures wherein the use of alkali must be avoided, namely those which implicate such alkali-labile acyl masking substituents as the phthalyl and trifluoroacetyl groups. Despite these apparent advantages, however, the practicable use of benzyl esters has until recently been markedly limited because of the paucity of convenient methods for preparing these derivatives readily and in high yield.

The initial preparation of glycine benzyl ester hydrochloride (XIII), by the action of hydrogen chloride on a suspension of glycine (XI; R = H) in benzyl alcohol (XII), was described by Abderhalden and Suzuki (181) in 1928. Unlike the analogous reaction in methanol or ethanol, the esterification in benzyl alcohol proceeded with difficulty and led to low yields of the desired compound. This may be attributed, in part, to the higher degree of steric hindrance imposed by the bulky benzyl group, the unfavorable equilibrium which resulted because of inadequate removal of water from the reaction mixture, and the difficulties encountered in evaporating the high-boiling benzyl alcohol solutions at temperatures that would not lead to extensive decomposition of the product. Later modification

TABLE 10-28
Amino Acid Methyl Ester Hydrochlorides

Methyl Ester Hydrochloride	M.P., °C.	$[\alpha]_D$, deg.	Temp., °C.	Concn. and Solvent	Ref.[f]
DL-Alanine	158–158.5	—	—	—	351, 611
L-Alanine	154–155[a]	—	—	—	432a, 611a
DL-α-Amino-n-butyric acid	150–151	—	—	—	612
D-Arginine (di-HCl)	—	−17.0	25	5%, water	613
L-Arginine (di-HCl)	195 d.	+17.2	25	5%, water	141, 471a, 613
DL-Aspartic acid (diester)	111–114	—	—	—	509
L-Aspartic acid (diester)	116–117	—	—	—	613a
DL-Aspartic acid (β-ester)	190	—	—	—	389
L-Aspartic acid (β-ester)	191–193	+21.4	25	1.0%, ethanol–water (1:3)	389, 508, 614
L-Cysteine	140	−2.9	20	10%, methanol	548, 615
S-Benzyl-DL-cysteine	112	—	—	—	616
S-Benzyl-L-cysteine	150	−13.9	21	2.9%, water	432a, 472
mono-Cbzo-L-cystine (diester)	159–160	−82.5	25	1.0%, methanol	876
L-Cystine (diester, di-HCl)	173	−38.4	20	4%, methanol	145, 617
3:4-Dihydroxyphenyl-DL-alanine	180–181	—	—	—	526
DL-Glutamic acid (diester)	149	—	—	—	618
L-Glutamic acid (γ-ester)	167[b]	—	—	—	389, 472
L-Glutamine	145–147	—	—	—	619
Glycine	175	—	—	—	603
DL-Histidine (di-HCl)	191–193	—	—	—	509
L-Histidine (di-HCl)	200–201	—	—	—	231, 620, 621
im-Benzyl-L-histidine (di-HCl)	111–115	—	—	—	484
L-Hydroxyproline	162–164 d.	—	—	—	169

TABLE 10-28 (continued)

Specific Rotation

Methyl Ester Hydrochloride	M.P., °C.	$[\alpha]_D$, deg.	Temp., °C.	Concn. and Solvent	Ref.[f]
D-Isoleucine	98–100	−26.6	21	2%, water	622
L-Isoleucine	100.5–101	+26.6	23	2%, water	622, 623
DL-Leucine	113–114	—	—	—	624
D-Leucine	149–150	—	—	—	469
L-Leucine	150–151	−13.4	26	5%, water	179, 624, 625
DL-Lysine (di-HCl)	218 d.	—	—	—	141, 149
L-Lysine (di-HCl)	212	—	—	—	626
ε-Cbzo-L-lysine	117	+16.7	21	2.0%, methanol	358, 471a
ε-Tosyl-L-lysine	135	—	—	—	626a
DL-Methionine	109–111	—	—	—	509, 627
D-Methionine	149–150	−26.3	21	5%, water	490, 627
L-Methionine	150	+26.8	19	5%, water	490, 627
Nitro-L-arginine	159–161	+17.5	25	3.2%, methanol	491, 541
DL-Norleucine	122–123	—	—	—	612
DL-Norvaline	116–117	—	—	—	612
δ-Cbzo-L-ornithine	140–141	+15.6	19	3%, methanol	372, 373, 421
DL-Phenylalanine	158	—	—	—	509, 628
D-Phenylalanine	—	+3.9	25	2.7%, water	423
L-Phenylalanine	159–161	−4.6	25	5%, water	508, 629
L-Proline	—	−40.1	24	0.5%, water	423
DL-Serine	133–134[c]	—	—	—	141, 509, 630
L-Serine	165–166	+0.9	24	6%, water	183, 471a, 631
O-Bz-L-serine	169	−2.7	13	3%, water	828

β-2-Thienyl-DL-alanine	160	—	—	—	632
DL-Threonine	125 d.	—	—	—	633
DL-Allothreonine	150 d.	—	—	—	633
DL-Tryptophan	225 d.	—	—	—	399, 509, *634, 635*
L-Tryptophan	214 d.	—	—	—	*471a, 636*
L-Tyrosine	190	+74.3	23	3%, pyridine	472, *637, 830*
O-Acetyl-L-tyrosine	201 d.	—	—	—	637
O-Benzyl-L-tyrosine	181	+11.5	25	4%, methanol	830
DL-Valine	120–122^a	—	—	—	509, *622, 638*
D-Valine	167.5–168	−15.6	21	2%, water	*543a, 622*
L-Valine	167.5–168^e	+15.5	21	2%, water	373, 421, *471a, 543a*
					605, *622, 629, 638a*

^{a} A melting point of 109–110° has also been reported (611a).
^{b} The free base, m.p. 182° d., has also been prepared (367).
^{c} Melting points of 112–114° (630) and 114° (141) have also been reported.
^{d} Other reported melting points are 90–97° (638) and 112–113° (509).
^{e} Melting points of 146–149° (373), 161–162° (605), 170° (421, 629), and 175° (471a) have also been reported.
^{f} Where more than one reference is given, the ones in italics are those from which the physical constants were taken.

TABLE 10-29
Amino Acid Ethyl Ester Hydrochlorides

Ethyl Ester Hydrochloride	M.P., °C.	[α]$_D$ deg.	Temp., °C	Concn. and Solvent	Ref.[d]
DL-Alanine	86.5–87	–	–	–	509, *639*
L-Alanine	76	−11.4	25	2%, 5N HCl	468, *605*
L-α-Amino-*n*-butyric acid	–	+6.1	25	2%, 5N HCl	468
DL-Aspartic acid (α-ester)[a,b]	165	–	–	–	640
DL-Aspartic acid (β-ester)[a]	200 d.	–	–	–	*640*, 641
L-Aspartic acid (diester)	109–110	+8.1	24	1%, water	528, *642*
L-Aspartic acid (β-ester)[c]	199–200	–	–	–	*643*, 644
L-Cysteine	115	–	–	–	645
S-Benzyl-D-cysteine	163	+28.1	26	2%, ethanol	473
S-Benzyl-L-cysteine	155	−25.4	–	2.3%, water	*390*, 646
S-*p*-Nitrobenzyl-L-cysteine	172–173	+27.3	25	1.1%, 95% ethanol	512
S-Thiophenyl-L-cysteine	130–131.5	−43.6	19	0.9%, ethanol	647
L-Cystine (diester, di-HCl)	188	−48.0	20	3.7%, water	617
DL-Glutamic acid (γ-ester)	105–107	–	–	–	608
L-Glutamic acid (diester)	113–114	+22.4	–	4%, water	448, *648–651*
L-Glutamic acid (α-ester)[a]	116–118	–	–	–	610
L-Glutamic acid (γ-ester)	134–135	–	–	–	389, *604–606*
L-Glutamic acid (γ-ester)[a]	194	+14	–	1%, water	367, 482, *604*, *606*
Glycine	144	–	–	–	509, *603*, 652
L-Hydroxyproline	147–148	–	–	–	182
L-Allohydroxyproline	148–151	–	–	–	657
DL-Leucine	112	–	–	–	509, *653*
L-Leucine	134	+18.4	–	5%, ethanol	653
ε-Tosyl-L-lysine	129–131	+8.5	23.5	1%, water	393
L-Methionine	81–82	+18.7	21	2.2%, ethanol	654
L-Norvaline	–	+9.5	25	2%, 5N HCl	468
L-Lysine	143.5–144.5	+11.7	17	2.5%, ethanol	*655*, 656
ε-Cbzo-L-lysine	115.5–116.5	+12.2	17	2.1%, 0.1N HCl	584a
DL-Phenylalanine	127	–	–	–	628
L-Phenylalanine	–	−7.6	20	3%, water	224
4-Methoxy-L-proline	150–152	–	–	–	657
L-Serine	130–131	−4.8	–	2.1%, water	498
O-Bz-DL-serine	118	–	–	–	*828*, 829
DL-Threonine	116–117	–	–	–	498
L-Tryptophan	225–226	–	–	–	*658*, 659
DL-Tyrosine	105–106	–	–	–	509
L-Tyrosine	166	–	–	–	492
O-Benzoyl-L-tyrosine	225 d.	–	–	–	646
O-Methyl-L-tyrosine	202	−4.9	22	2%, water	660
L-Valine	102–104	+6.7	24	2%, water	*507*, 610

[a] As the free base.
[b] α-Ethyl L-aspartate as the free base, m.p. 181–183°, has also been described (609).
[c] A melting point of 200° has been reported (661) for the free base.
[d] Where more than one reference is given, the one in italics is that from which the physical constants were taken.

of this procedure has none the less permitted its successful application to the preparation of the benzyl ester hydrochloride derivatives of L-proline (642) and L-hydroxyproline (169), as well as dibenzyl L-glutamate hydrochloride (662) (procedure 10–52). However, the tedious manipulations involved have discouraged further exploitation of the method.

$$\text{NH}_2\text{CHRCO}_2\text{H} + \text{C}_6\text{H}_5\text{CH}_2\text{OH} \xrightarrow{\text{HCl}} \text{HCl}\cdot\text{NH}_2\text{CHRCO}_2\text{CH}_2\text{C}_6\text{H}_5 + \text{H}_2\text{O}$$
$$\text{XI} \qquad\qquad \text{XII} \qquad\qquad\qquad \text{XIII} \qquad\qquad\qquad \text{XIV}$$

Illustrative procedure 10–52 (662). Dibenzyl L-glutamate hydrochloride. A suspension of 10 g. (0.068 mole) of L-glutamic acid in 150 ml. of benzyl alcohol is warmed to 55°, agitated with a magnetic stirrer while dry HCl is passed in for 1 hr., and the temperature permitted to rise. The mixture is transferred to a vacuum still, 75 ml. of benzene added, and the solution concentrated at a bath temperature of about 40°. The mixture is now left *in vacuo* (approximately 10 mm.) for 1 hr. at a bath temperature of 85°, and dry HCl again passed in for 1 hr., as described above. Unchanged glutamic acid hydrochloride (about 2 g.) is filtered off, benzene added, and the process as described above repeated. Dry HCl is passed in for a third time; after removal of about one-half of the benzyl alcohol *in vacuo* (steam bath), the diester hydrochloride is precipitated with ether (5–7 volumes), and recrystallized from methanol–ether. The yield of pure compound is 15 g. (61%); m.p. 100–102°; $[\alpha]_D^{22} = +9.4°$ (1.5% in 0.1 N HCl). Comparable procedures may be applied to the preparation of the benzyl ester hydrochlorides of glycine (181), L-proline (642) and hydroxy-L-proline (169) (Table 10–30).

Inasmuch as the direct esterification of amino acids in benzyl alcohol did not initially provide a generally satisfactory route to amino acid benzyl esters, resort was made to less direct methods which involved various amino acid derivatives as the starting materials. Thus, Ruggli, Ratti, and Henzi (663) were enabled to secure improved yields of glycine benzyl ester hydrochloride by the action of glycyl chloride hydrochloride (251) on benzyl alcohol. Harington and Mead (474), on the other hand, prepared L-cysteine benzyl ester hydroiodide by the action of bis(carbobenzoxy)-L-cystinyl chloride on benzyl alcohol, followed by decarbobenzoxylation and cleavage of the bis(carbobenzoxy)-L-cystine benzyl ester so derived with phosphonium iodide in glacial acetic acid. Through an analogous, though greatly simplified procedure, Ben-Ishai and Berger (664, 665) prepared the benzyl ester hydrobromide derivatives (XVII) of a variety of amino acids via the *p*-toluenesulfonic acid-catalyzed condensation of the pertinent carbobenzoxyamino acid (XV) with benzyl alcohol, followed by selective hydrolysis

$$\text{C}_6\text{H}_5\text{CH}_2\text{OCO-NHCHRCO}_2\text{H} \xrightarrow[\text{CH}_3\text{C}_6\text{H}_4\text{SO}_3\text{H}]{\text{C}_6\text{H}_5\text{CH}_2\text{OH}}$$
$$\text{XV}$$

$$\text{C}_6\text{H}_5\text{CH}_2\text{OCO-NHCHRCO}_2\text{CH}_2\text{C}_6\text{H}_5 \xrightarrow[\text{gl. HOAC}]{\text{HBr}} \text{HBr}\cdot\text{NH}_2\text{CHRCO}_2\text{CH}_2\text{C}_6\text{H}_5$$
$$\text{XVI} \qquad\qquad\qquad\qquad\qquad\qquad\qquad \text{XVII}$$

TABLE 10-30
Salts of Benzyl Esters of Amino Acids

Benzyl Ester	M.P., °C.	$[\alpha]_D$, deg.	Temp., °C.	Concn. and Solvent	Ref.[a]
Benzenesulfonic acid salts					
S-Benzyl-L-cysteine	134–135	—	—	—	482a
L-Glutamic acid (diester)	109–113	+8.4	21	1.9%, 96% ethanol	677
Glycine	135.5–137	—	—	—	670
DL-Serine	115–116	—	—	—	498
Hydrobromide salts					
DL-Alanine	107	—	—	—	664
β-Alanine	57	—	—	—	664
L-Aspartic acid (diester)	117	−3.9	23	9.6%, water	664
S-Benzyl-L-cysteine	127	−21.7	23	1.7%, 96% ethanol	664
Glycine	147	—	—	—	664
L-Glutamic acid (diester)	100–102[a]	+9.3	21	1.9%, 96% ethanol	677
DL-Phenylalanine	200	—	—	—	664
L-Phenylalanine	209	+5.4	25	2.3%, ethanol	665
DL-Valine	109	—	—	—	664
Hydrochloride salts					
D-Alanine	139–140	+10.5	25	2%, 0.1N HCl	666
L-Alanine	140	−10.9	25	2%, 0.1N HCl	666, 668
L-Arginine (mono HCl)	152 d.	−9.2	25	1.9%, 40% ethanol	678
DL-Aspartic acid (diester)	108–109	—	—	—	674

L-Aspartic acid (diester)	123–124	−2.0	20	2%, chloroform	672, 673
L-Aspartic acid (α-benzyl-β-methyl ester)	115–120	−23.0	20	4%, water	673
S-Benzyl-DL-cysteine	154–154.5	—	—	—	432a
S-Benzyl-D-cysteine	126	+29.0	22	1%, water	390
S-Benzyl-L-cysteine	129–130[b]	−18.9	22	1.2%, ethanol	390, 432a, 482a
L-Cystine (diester)	—	+32.8	25	0.7%, 0.1N HCl	668
L-Cysteine	106	−26.6	25	1%, 0.1N HCl	668
DL-Glutamic acid (diester)	119–123	—	—	—	677
D-Glutamic acid (diester)	100–102	−9.0	25	2.0%, 0.1N HCl	662, 679
L-Glutamic acid (diester)	100–102	+9.4	22	1.5%, 0.1N HCl	662, 677, 679
Glycine	139	—	—	—	474, 663, 666 669, 670
L-Hydroxyproline	147–150	—	—	—	169
L-Leucine	129	−8.0	30	2%, 0.1N HCl	668, 669
ε-Cbzo-D-lysine	139	+9.5	25	0.5%, 0.1N HCl	667
ε-Cbzo-L-lysine	139	−9.9	22	0.5%, 0.1N HCl	667
DL-Phenylalanine	196	—	—	—	668, 669
L-Phenylalanine	203	−22.5	25	1%, 0.25N HCl	668
L-Proline	148–148.5	—	—	—	169, 642
DL-Serine	154	—	—	—	498
D-Tyrosine	200	+20.8	25	0.5%, 0.1N HCl	679a
L-Tyrosine	205	−23.3	25	1%, 0.1N HCl	668
Hydroiodate salt					
L-Cysteine	139 d.	—	—	—	474
Nitrate salt					
L-Glutamic acid (diester)	134–137	+10.9	20	1.1%, 96% ethanol	677

TABLE 10-30 (continued)

Benzyl Ester	M.P., °C.	$[\alpha]_D$, deg.	Temp., °C.	Concn. and Solvent	Ref.[a]
p-Toluenesulfonic acid salts					
D-Alanine	113–114	+6.9	27	2%, water	454, 680
L-Alanine	114	−6.8	13	2%, water	680
β-Alanine	138–139	—	—	—	680
L-α-Amino-n-butyric acid	117	−6.3	13	2%, ethanol	680
α-Aminoisobutyric acid	154	—	—	—	680
L-Aspartic acid (diester)	158–160	+1.0	25	2%, methanol	459, 673, 680
S-Benzyl-L-cysteine	162–163	−20.9	25	2%, methanol	390, 432a, 459
mono-Cbzo-L-cystine (diester)	133–134	−37.0	25	1%, acetone	876
L-Glutamic acid (diester)	144–145	+7.6	25	2%, methanol	459, 680
Glycine	132–134	—	—	—	459, 680
L-Hydroxyproline	107–109	−21.8	13	2%, water	680
L-Isoleucine	153–154	−0.1	25	2%, methanol	459
D-Alloisoleucine	162–164	−0.2	25	2%, methanol	459
L-Leucine	158.5–160	−1.7	25	2%, methanol	459, 680
L-Lysine (ditosylate)	147–149	−2.8	13	2%, water	680
L-Norleucine	127	−9.0	13	2%, ethanol	680
L-Phenylalanine	170.5–171.5	−7.2	25	2%, methanol	459
L-Tyrosine	179–180.5	−12.2	25	2%, methanol	459
L-Valine	158–160	+1.2	25	2%, methanol	459
Free base					
ω-Cbzo-L-arginine	129–130	—	—	—	904
L-Aspartic acid (β-ester)	154	+11.4	23	7.7%, water	664

mono-α-Cbzo-L-cystine (α-ester)	—	−191.2	25	0.5%, methanol + 1 eq. HCl	876
D-Glutamic acid (α-ester)	147–148	−11.9	25	2.0%, 0.1N HCl	662
L-Glutamic acid (α-ester)	147–148	+12.2	25	2.9%, 0.1N HCl	662
D-Glutamic acid (γ-ester)	—	−19.1	25	4.7%, acetic acid	367
L-Glutamic acid (γ-ester)	169–170[c]	+18.7	25	7%, acetic acid	*367, 471a*, 676
L-Tyrosine	120	−12.5	25	2%, methanol	675

[a] An isomorphous form melts at 81–83°.
[b] A melting point of 148–151° has also been reported for this compound (674).
[c] A melting point of 189° and $[\alpha]_D^{23} = +27.7$ (2.5% in N HCl) has also been reported (471a).
[d] Where more than one reference is given, the one in italics is that from which the physical constants were taken.

of the carbobenzoxyamino acid benzyl ester (XVI) so formed with a solution of dry hydrogen bromide in glacial acetic acid (procedure 10–53).

Illustrative procedure 10–53 (664). Carbobenzoxyamino acid benzyl esters. A solution of 0.05 mole of the pertinent carbobenzoxyamino acid (procedures 10–28 to 10–30) in 75 ml. of benzene is refluxed with 8 g. of benzyl alcohol and 0.75 g. of *p*-toluenesulfonic acid, the water being removed azeotropically through the use of a Dean and Stark distilling receiver. Refluxing is continued until the theoretical quantity of water has distilled off (1–3 hr.). The benzene solution is washed with two portions (25 ml. each) of aqueous 5% potassium bicarbonate solution, dried over anhydrous sodium sulfate, and concentrated. After crystallization of the residue from petroleum ether, the desired compound is obtained in about 90% yield. The melting points of the various carbobenzoxyamino acid benzyl esters thus derived are: DL-alanine, 59°; β-alanine, 22°; S-benzyl-DL-cysteine, 66°; glycine, 72°; DL-phenylalanine, 84°; and DL-valine, 45°.

Decarbobenzoxylation of carbobenzoxyamino acid benzyl esters. Ten grams of a saturated solution of dry hydrogen bromide in glacial acetic acid (36%) is added to 0.01 mole of the carbobenzoxyamino acid benzyl ester in a reaction flask protected with a calcium chloride drying tube. Immediately after the addition of the reagent, carbon dioxide begins to evolve. After the evolution of carbon dioxide has ceased (about 15 min.), 100 ml. of dry ether is added to precipitate the benzyl ester hydrobromide formed. The ethereal solution is permitted to stand in the refrigerator for a few hours and the hydrobromide salt filtered off, washed with several portions of anhydrous ether, and dried *in vacuo* over sulfuric acid and sodium hydroxide pellets. Table 10–30 includes the melting points of the amino acid benzyl ester hydrobromides so secured.

Utilization of N-carboxy amino acid anhydrides as intermediates in the synthesis of amino acid benzyl esters was first reported by Bergmann, Zervas, and Ross (358). Preparation of these intermediates may be generally achieved from either the free amino acid or its carbobenzoxy derivative (XVIII) according to procedures 10–16 to 10–19. Reaction of the N-carboxy-anhydride (XIX) with benzyl alcohol in an ethereal-HCl solution then leads to the desired benzyl ester (XX) as its hydrochloride derivative (procedure 10–54). The method has been employed for the benzyl ester hydrochlorides of glycine (666), D- and L-alanine (666), ε-carbobenzoxy-D- and L-lysine (667) and S-benzyl-L-cysteine (390).

$$\underset{\text{XVIII}}{C_6H_5CH_2OCO-NHCHRCO_2H} \longrightarrow \underset{\text{XIX}}{\overline{CO-NHCHRCOO}} \xrightarrow[\text{Et}_2\text{O}-\text{HCl}]{C_6H_5CH_2OH} \underset{\text{XX}}{HCl \cdot NH_2CHRCO_2CH_2C_6H_5}$$

Illustrative procedure 10–54 (666). Glycine benzyl ester hydrochloride. The N-carboxy-anhydride of glycine is obtained from 0.06 mole of glycine or carbobenzoxyglycine (see procedures 10–16 to 10–19). The anhydride is transferred with the aid of 30 ml. of benzyl alcohol to a 500-ml. flask containing 200 ml. of ether previously saturated with HCl gas at 0°. On warming to 25° while stirring magnetically, CO_2 evolution begins and the benzyl ester hydrochloride starts to crystallize as long needles as the anhydride dissolves. After further stirring overnight at 25°, the hydrochloride is filtered off and washed with ether. Recrystallization from anhydrous methanol–ether yields 8.8 g. (70% based on carbobenzoxyglycine); m.p. 140°.

The ready availability of a number of benzyl esters by the afore-mentioned methods led to their increased use in peptide syntheses. However, the indirect nature of the methods employed in their preparation encouraged a search for more convenient synthetic routes to these valuable substances. One interesting procedure which arose in consequence of such a search was described by Erlanger and Hall (668) and consisted, in essence, of the direct interaction of the free amino acid and benzyl alcohol in the presence of polyphosphoric acid as a dehydrating agent (procedure 10-55). Application of this reaction to a variety of amino acids led to the formation of the benzyl esters, which were isolated in good yield as their respective hydrochloride salts. Upon oxidation of L-cysteine benzyl ester thus obtained with iodine in ethanolic solution the corresponding L-cystine derivative was secured. Esters derived from optically active amino acids exhibited no appreciable racemization, as indicated by the optical rotation values of the free amino acids regenerated therefrom by catalytic hydrogenolysis.

Illustrative procedure 10-55. Polyphosphoric acid. This reagent is readily prepared by *carefully* adding 34.5 ml. of 85% phosphoric acid to 41 g. of phosphorus pentoxide with stirring.

L-Phenylalanine benzyl ester hydrochloride (668). Two grams (0.012 mole) of L-phenylalanine is added to a large test tube containing a homogenous solution of 25 ml. of benzyl alcohol and 5 g. of polyphosphoric acid. The mixture is stirred in an oil bath at 90–95° for 4 hr. (The amino acid dissolves within a few minutes.) The solution is then poured into 200 ml. of water containing about 10 ml. of concentrated HCl, ether is added and the water layer collected. The ether layer is washed three times with 2% HCl. All aqueous fractions are collected, brought to a pH of about 10 with solid sodium carbonate and shaken with three 100-ml. portions of ether. The ether layer is dried over magnesium sulfate and nearly saturated with HCl gas. The L-phenylalanine benzyl ester hydrochloride which precipitates is secured in about 65% yield. Recrystallization is carried out from methanol–ether; m.p. 203°; $[\alpha]_D^{25} = -22.5°$ (1% in 0.25N HCl). Essentially this procedure or slight modifications thereof have also been applied to the preparation of the benzyl ester hydrochloride derivatives of L-alanine, L-cysteine, L-cystine, L-leucine, DL-phenylalanine, and L-tyrosine (Table 10-30).

The most convenient of currently available methods for the synthesis of amino acid benzyl esters arose from the finding of Miller and Waelsch (669) that benzenesulfonic acid may serve as a catalyst in lieu of hydrogen chloride for the direct esterification of amino acids in benzyl alcohol. Use of the former catalyst rendered the amino acid soluble in excess benzyl alcohol as its benzenesulfonic acid salt, the distillation of such solutions at

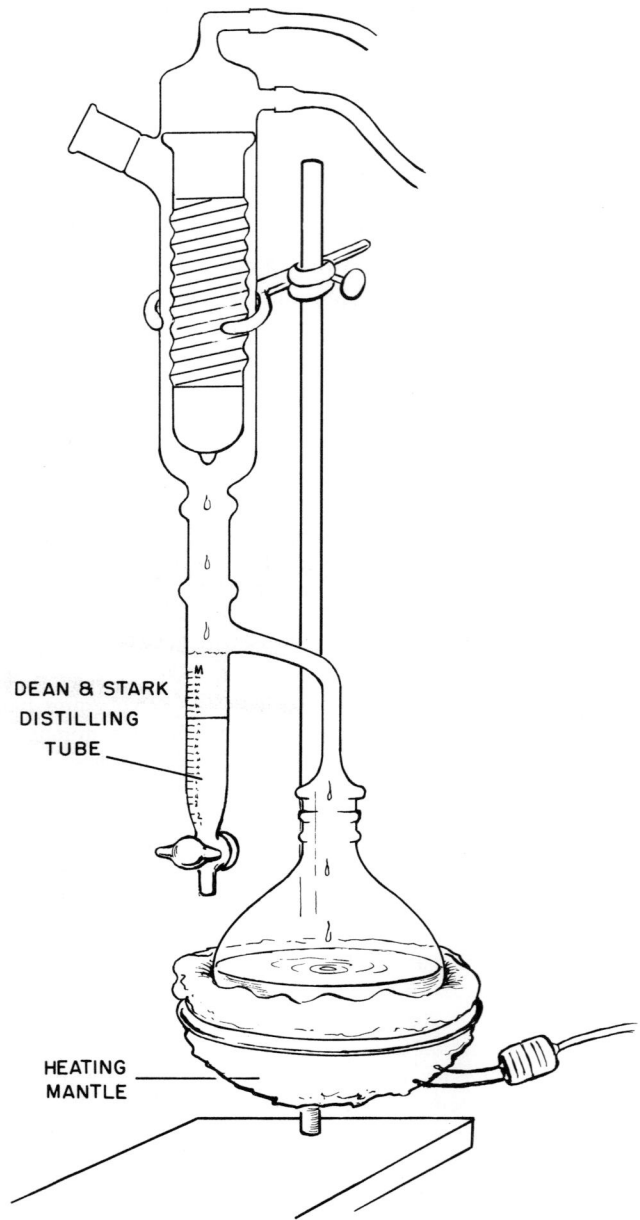

Figure 10-6. Dean and Stark distillation tube in azeotropic distillation.

temperatures not exceeding 130° subsequently leading to the isolation of the amino acid benzyl ester benzenesulfonate in good yields. Marked improvement of this procedure by Cipera and Nicholls (670) resulted from the incorporation of an azeotropic distillation technique to remove the water liberated as a result of the esterification reaction. The need for both large excesses of benzyl alcohol and high temperatures to remove the water of reaction, in order to achieve a favorable equilibrium, was thereby avoided. A further modification of the method, reported by Kollonitsch and Vita (671), utilized the great reactivity of boric acid esters with water to shift the equilibrium of the reaction in the direction of the desired benzyl ester without any involvement of distillation techniques. The afore-mentioned method of Miller and Waelsch and its subsequent modifications have led to the synthesis of the benzyl ester derivatives of L-aspartic acid (di-ester) (672, 673), DL-aspartic acid (diester) (674), S-benzyl-L-cysteine (390, 674), glycine (669, 670), L-leucine, (669), DL-phenylalanine (669), and L-tyrosine (675) (Table 10–30). Recent application of essentially this method by Izumiya and Makisumi (680) led to the preparation of the benzyl ester *p*-toluenesulfonates of D- and L-alanine, β-alanine, L-α-amino-*n*-butyric acid, α-aminoisobutyric acid, L-aspartic acid, L-glutamic acid, glycine, L-hydroxyproline, L-leucine, L-lysine, and L-norleucine.

For the routine preparation of amino acid benzyl esters in the writers' Laboratory (459), it has been found most expedient to employ a variation of the Cipera and Nicholls (670) azeotropic distillation procedure wherein liberated water from the esterification reaction is trapped and measured by means of a Dean and Stark distilling receiver (Figure 10–6). The synthesis, in essence, involves the azeotropic distillation of a mixture of the pertinent amino acid (XXI), *p*-toluenesulfonic acid (XXIII), benzyl alcohol (XXII), and benzene (procedure 10–56). After the theoretical quantity of water has been liberated, the addition of benzene or ether to the reaction mixture leads to the precipitation of the desired benzyl ester as its *p*-toluenesulfonic acid salt (XXIV) in yields that generally range from 70–95% of theory. Since the internal temperature of the reaction mixture never exceeds 80°, the danger of racemization is minimized where optically active amino acids are concerned, and the occurrence of appreciable decomposition of the desired

$$NH_2CHRCO_2H + C_6H_5CH_2OH + CH_3C_6H_4SO_3H \xrightarrow[\Delta]{C_6H_6} CH_3C_6H_4SO_3H \cdot NH_2CHRCO_2CH_2C_6H_5$$

XXI   XXII   XXIII   XXIV

product avoided. This method has been successfully applied to the synthesis of the benzyl ester *p*-toluenesulfonates of L-aspartic acid, S-benzyl-L-cysteine, L-glutamic acid, glycine, L-isoleucine, D-alloisoleucine, L-leucine, L-phenylalanine, L-tyrosine, and L-valine (Table 10–30). Conversion of the *p*-toluenesulfonic acid salt to the hydrochloride salt of the benzyl ester could be accomplished by its initial transformation to the free base, followed by treatment of an ethereal solution thereof with dry hydrogen chloride (669) (procedure 10–57).

Illustrative procedure 10–56. Glycine benzyl ester *p*-toluenesulfonate (459). Into a 500-ml. round-bottom flask are placed 18.8 g. (0.25 mole) of glycine, 48.5 g. (0.255 mole) of *p*-toluenesulfonic acid monohydrate, 100 ml. of benzyl alcohol, and 50 ml. of benzene. The mixture is heated under reflux, the liberated water being removed azeotropically by means of a Dean and Stark distilling receiver (Fig. 10–6). A clear solution is obtained soon after reflux begins. When water (about 9 ml.) is no longer distilled off, the reaction mixture is permitted to cool to room temperature and 500 ml. of ether added thereto. After standing for about 2 hr. in the refrigerator, the crystalline benzyl glycinate *p*-toluenesulfonate is filtered, washed with anhydrous ether, and recrystallized from methanol–ether. Yield, 90% of theory; m.p. 132–134°.

Illustrative procedure 10–57 (669). Glycine benzyl ester hydrochloride. To a suspension of 67.4 g. (0.2 mole) of glycine benzyl ester *p*-toluenesulfonate (procedure 10–56) in 300 ml. of chloroform at 0–5°, 20 g. (0.2 mole) of triethylamine is added with stirring over a period of 10 min. After the addition of 1 l. of absolute ether, the mixture is allowed to stand for 10 min., after which time the precipitated triethylammonium *p*-toluenesulfonate is filtered off and the ethereal solution concentrated *in vacuo* with the rigid exclusion of moisture. The residual oil is taken up in anhydrous ether and treated with dry hydrogen chloride until no further precipitation of the hydrochloride occurs. The hydrochloride, which precipitates in about 70% yield, may be recrystallized from ethylene glycol monomethyl ether acetate (methyl Cellosolve acetate); m.p. 131–132°.

In addition to the above, mention should be given to the preparation of the α- and ω-half benzyl esters of glutamic and aspartic acids. The β-benzyl ester of L-aspartic acid was prepared by the selective saponification of carbobenzoxy-L-aspartic acid dibenzyl ester to the corresponding β-benzyl ester (364), followed by decarbobenzoxylation with dry hydrogen bromide in glacial acetic acid (664) (procedure 10–53). Preparation of the α-benzyl ester of D- and L-glutamic acid was effected by Sachs and Brand (662) by the selective cleavage of dibenzyl glutamate with hydriodic acid in glacial acetic acid solution (procedure 10–58). Synthesis of the γ-benzyl ester of glutamic acid, on the other hand, is more directly achieved either by the action of benzyl alcohol on glutamic acid in the presence of either hydriodic acid (367) or *p*-toluenesulfonic acid (676) or by the action of benzyl chloride on the copper complex of glutamic acid in slightly alkaline, aqueous medium (367). A convenient preparation, employed in the writers' Laboratory, involves the direct interaction of glutamic acid and benzyl alcohol in the presence of concentrated hydrochloric acid (procedure 10–59).

Illustrative procedure 10–58 (662). α-Benzyl L-glutamate. Ten grams of dibenzyl L-glutamate hydrochloride (procedure 10–52 or 10–56) is dissolved in 100 ml. of glacial acetic acid. Ten milliliters (0.12 mole) of constant-boiling HI (sp. gr.

1.7) is added and the solution kept at 50° for 5.5 hr. The reaction mixture is concentrated *in vacuo* and the resulting oil repeatedly (at least twice) treated with 50 ml. of benzene, which each time is distilled off *in vacuo*. The brown syrup is then taken up in 60 ml. of cold ($-10°$) 95% ethanol containing 7 ml. (0.029 mole) of tri-*n*-butylamine. Additional tri-*n*-butylamine (3–4 ml.) is added to bring the *p*H to approximately 7, whereupon the product begins to crystallize. After being stored in the ice box overnight, the product is filtered off and washed copiously with absolute ethanol and ether to give 5.7 g. of crystalline material. The crystals are dissolved at room temperature in 11 ml. of water containing 0.034 mole of HCl, decolorized with charcoal, and an equal volume of absolute alcohol is added. Upon neutralization with tri-*n*-butylamine, crystallization takes place; the mixture is then cooled at 0° for several hours and filtered. Yield 4.3 g. (67%); m.p. 147–148°; $[\alpha]_D^{25} = +12.2°$ (2.9% in 0.1*N* HCl).

Illustrative procedure 10–59. γ-Benzyl L-glutamate. A mixture of 147 g. of L-glutamic acid, 250 ml. of concentrated hydrochloric acid, and 1 l. of benzyl alcohol, in a round-bottomed flask, is heated over the steam bath, with constant shaking, until complete solution is effected (40–60 min. generally required). After an additional 10 min., the reaction mixture is cooled in an ice bath, 8 l. of ether added thereto and, after an additional 30 min. in the cold, is filtered. The precipitate is taken up in 1200 ml. of cold water, the *p*H adjusted to 6.0–6.5 with lithium hydroxide, and, after cooling for 2 hr. in an ice bath, the mixture is filtered. The precipitate is washed with ethanol until chloride-free (test with silver nitrate), and then with ether. After recrystallization from about 800 ml. of boiling water, a 30–40% yield of pure γ-benzyl L-glutamate is obtained.

Procedures for Coupling Acylamino Acids with Amino Acids, Peptides, or Ester Derivatives Thereof

24. Types of Coupling Procedures. The condensation of an acylamino acid with an amino acid (or ester derivative thereof), with the formation of a peptide bond between the two, may be considered generally to proceed via the following two steps: (*a*) suitable activation of either the carboxyl function of the former reactant or the amino function of the latter; and (*b*) condensation of the reactant so activated with the other component. Until about 1950, this procedure was confined almost exclusively to the conversion of the carboxyl group of the acylamino acid (I) to either its corresponding azide (II; $X = N_3$) or acid chloride (II; $X = Cl$) derivative. Either of these derivatives was, in turn, condensed with an amino acid in alkaline aqueous medium, or with an amino acid ester in some non-reactive organic solvent, such as chloroform, ether or ethyl acetate, to produce the desired peptide derivative (III). These procedures, whose development can be traced to the classical efforts of Fischer and Curtius (Section 10-6), are generalized here:

$$\text{RCO—NHCHR}^1\text{CO}_2\text{H} \longrightarrow \text{RCO—NHCHR}^1\text{COX} \xrightarrow{\text{NH}_2\text{R}^2} \text{RCO—NHCHR}^1\text{CO—NHR}^2 + \text{HX}$$
$$\text{I} \qquad\qquad\qquad \text{II} \qquad\qquad\qquad \text{III} \qquad\qquad \text{IV}$$

With the advent of the 1950's, an almost dazzling variety of new "carboxyl activating" groups were ushered into synthetic peptide chemistry which, while providing an important supplement to the versatile azide group, cast the less advantageous acid chloride group into near-obsolescence. Probably the most extensively investigated among these were the intermolecular mixed anhydrides of acylamino acids with aliphatic and aromatic organic acids (II; X = —O$_2$CR), aliphatic alkoxy acids (II; X = —O$_2$COR), polybasic inorganic acid esters (II; X = —OP(OR)$_2$, —OAs(OR)$_2$, or —OPO(OR)$_2$) and polybasic inorganic acids or esters which retain an ionizable hydrogen atom subsequent to anhydride formation (II; X = —OPO(OR)OH or —OSO$_3^-$). Note should be made that, in anhydrides of this type, an oxy-acid replaces the classical HX acids, i.e., hydrochloric and hydrazoic acids. Of somewhat similar principle were procedures which employed the still more recently introduced acylamino acid esters (II; X = —OCH$_2$CN, C$_6$H$_5$O—, C$_6$H$_5$S—, p-NO$_2$C$_6$H$_4$S—, or NO$_2$C$_6$H$_4$O—), the favorable reactivity of which could be attributed to a highly electronegative ester moiety. Peptide bond syntheses which implicate reactants of the latter type are, in actuality, aminolysis reactions wherein the pertinent alcohol (IV) is liberated upon interaction of the compound with an amine.

The ability of amino acid esters (or other amines) to react with a variety of substituted phosphorus acid chlorides, with the formation of the corresponding phosphite amides, has provided an alternative route to those indicated above for the peptide union of an acylamino acid with an amino acid ester. Amides of this type (VII), which were initially prepared by the action of diethyl chlorophosphite (V) or tetraethyl pyrosphosphite on an amino acid ester (VI), may react with the free carboxyl group of an acylamino acid with the generation of a peptide derivative (X). Amide intermediates of related type and reactivity have been secured through the action of amines on o-phenylene chlorophosphite, diethyl chloroarsenite, and phenyl or ethyl dichlorophosphite, among others. Other "activated amines" which have been comparably employed in synthetic peptide procedures include phosphazo- (IX) and α-cyanato-ester derivatives (XI), formed by the action of phosphorus trichloride and phosgene, respectively, on an amino acid ester.

$$\underset{V}{(C_2H_5O)_2PCl} + \underset{VI}{NH_2CHR^1CO_2Et} \longrightarrow \underset{VII}{(C_2H_5O)_2PNHCHR^1CO_2Et} + \underset{VIII}{HCl}$$

$$\underset{IX}{EtO_2CCHR^1N{=}P{-}NHCHR^1CO_2Et} \xrightarrow{RCO_2H} \underset{X}{RCO{-}NHCHR^1CO_2Et} \xleftarrow{RCO_2H} \underset{XI}{OCNCHR^1CO_2Et}$$

In addition to the above, special mention should be made of those methods which permit the direct condensation of the amino and the carboxyl group in a single operation. Such a method was first effected by adding tetraethyl pyrophosphite to a solution of the acylamino acid and the amino acid ester in diethyl phosphite. The reaction presumably occurs either by way of the mixed anhydride with the free carboxyl group of the former reactant, i.e., RCO—NHCHR^{1}CO—O—OP(OEt)$_2$, or through the amide derived from the free amino group of the latter reactant, i.e., (EtO)$_2$PNHCHR^{2}CO$_2$Et, as described previously. Analogous procedures may be carried out in aqueous tetrahydrofuran in the presence of di*cyclo*hexylcarbodiimide, or other substituted carbodiimides, in lieu of tetraethyl pyrophosphite. These coupling procedures, as well as those alluded to above, will be more fully elaborated in the sections that follow.

Despite the impressive array of procedures which are available for uniting two amino acid residues in peptide linkage, the choice of any given coupling procedure should by no means be considered indiscriminate, but rather as dictated by a variety of factors. Among several of the factors to be considered are (*a*) the nature of the blocking group of the reactant acylamino acid, (*b*) the nature of the side chains of the amino acid residues involved in the condensation, (*c*) the possibility of racemization where optically active amino acid residues are employed, (*d*) the nature of the side products that might arise in consequence of a given condensation procedure, and (*e*) the ultimate yield of desired product that may be secured in a high degree of purity. Thus, for example, the use of the azide procedure with syntheses involving phthalylamino acids is handicapped by virtue of the ready cleavage which the phthalyl group undergoes during the preparation of the intermediate hydrazides required by this procedure. Again, the steric hindrance imposed by the bulky trityl group prevents the condensation of trityl amino acids (except for the relatively unhindered glycine and alanine derivatives) with other amino acid residues via the mixed anhydride procedure, while the implication of di*cyclo*hexylcarbodiimide as the condensing agent obviates this difficulty. That the nature of the amino acid side chains must also be considered is demonstrated by the extreme reactivity of the hydroxyl groups of serine, threonine, and hydroxyproline toward acid chlorides and mixed anhydrides, whereas no such problem arises in condensation procedures that utilize azides or carbodiimides. Additional precautions must be taken where yet other functional groups, such as the ω-carboxyl groups of glutamic and aspartic acids, the sulfur atoms of cystine and cysteine, the imidazole nucleus of histidine, the guanidino group of arginine, and the ε-amino moiety of lysine, are concerned. These problems, as well as others relating to the relative yields and possible contaminants which might result from the different condensation procedures, will be discussed more fully below.

25. Considerations of Optical Purity. Before embarking upon a fuller discussion of the individual coupling procedures, it would bode well to consider the stereochemical nature of the products that might arise from condensations involving two or more optically active amino acid residues. As the acquisition of final products which are optically as well as chemically homogenous is of major concern, attention must be critically focused upon the optical purity of the amino acids employed as the starting materials. The probability that a peptide composed of n amino acid residues will consist entirely of L-amino acids, if the starting material is a mixture of the L-amino acid and a proportion p of D-amino acid, may be given by $(1 - p)^n$. Table 10-31 presents calculations, based on this equation, for peptides of n residues derived from amino acids in various states of optical purity. Implied in these calculations is the assumption that, although different types of amino acid residues may be combined in the peptide, the degree of contamination of each type of amino acid by its respective enantiomorph is the same. From such data, it becomes clear that amino acids which reveal an optical purity of less than 99% are poor risks for peptide syntheses, and that not until an optical purity of 99.9% is approached for the amino acids can some measure of confidence be reposed in their use for the synthesis of the larger peptides. That such a degree of optical purity can readily be attained is

TABLE 10-31

Probability that all Amino Acid Residues in a Peptide Are of a Single Optical Configuration when the Starting Material is of Various Degrees of Optical Purity[a,b] (257)

	\multicolumn{4}{c}{p (Proportion of Optical Enantiomorph in the Starting Material)}
n	0.1	0.01	0.001	0.0001
3	0.73	0.97	0.997	0.9998
10	0.35	0.90	0.99	0.999
100	0[c]	0.37	0.91	0.99
1000	0	0[d]	0.37	0.91

[a] The treatment of the problem of optical homogeneity in synthetic peptides was suggested by Dr. John T. Edsall and was further developed after consultation with Mr. Jerome Cornfield of the National Institutes of Health.

[b] Based on the formula, probability = $(1 - p)^n$, in which n is the number of amino acid residues in the peptide, and p is the proportion of the optical enantiomorph in the amino acid used for the peptide synthesis.

[c] 0.3×10^{-4}.

[d] 0.4×10^{-4}.

shown by the experience in the writers' Laboratory with optically specific hydrolytic enzyme resolution procedures (Chapter 9); indeed, in the preparation of L-alanine and of L-serine by these methods, an optical purity for these isomers of greater than 99.99% was determined. The calculations revealed in Table 10-31 cannot emphasize too strongly the need for ascertaining the optical purity of amino acids employed in peptide syntheses. Methods for this type of assay which utilize optically specific L- and D-amino acid oxidases are described in Chapter 19, and there appears little reason why, by suitable enlargement and redesign of the Warburg vessels, this procedure could not be extended to larger quantities of amino acids, and their possible contamination studied at levels of 0.01 % or less.

In the afore-mentioned calculations, the influence of experimental synthetic conditions on the optical homogeneity of the peptides is not considered. These may include racemization during the synthetic reactions, favored as well as hindered syntheses between isomeric reactants, and separation of diastereoisomeric forms by fractional crystallization procedures. Although it is valid to assume that the two latter factors may, in certain instances, operate in favor of the formation of products of high optical homogeneity, it is also valid, by the same token, to assume that the same factors might lead to highly inhomogeneous products through concentration of the undesirable isomers. However, as the degree to which each of these factors enters into most synthetic peptide procedures is not yet adequately understood, it would be well-advised to assume, in the absence of other data, that the calculated data in Table 10–31 are reasonably representative of what would actually occur.

Despite the limited availability of knowledge regarding the degree of optical contamination which might arise during the course of a synthetic procedure, certain precautions may none the less be taken which would minimize the danger of obtaining inhomogeneous products. The need for amino acids of high optical purity as starting materials has already been discussed. The same requirement should, of course, be extended to the reactant acylamino acids and amino acid esters, the optical integrity of which may be readily determined by suitable degradation to their component amino acids, followed by optical purity determinations with L- and D-amino acid oxidases, as mentioned above. Unfortunately, the sensitive and accurate measurements permitted by such measurements have, to the present time, been employed but rarely in synthetic peptide chemistry. It has been common practice, on the other hand, to calculate the degree of racemization of the reconstituted amino acids from their optical rotatory values. Since the limits of error of such polarimetric measurements are ordinarily of the order of about ±2–3%, this less stringent technique can hardly be employed where levels of optical purity of 99.9% or greater are required for the synthesis of the larger peptides.

Measurement of the optical purity of the peptide derivatives that result from the condensation of the above reactants presents additional difficulties. That extensive racemization may occur under certain conditions of peptide bond synthesis has been demonstrated unequivocally through comparison of the optical rotation values of a given peptide derivative secured via different coupling procedures. While the proper control of experimental conditions can apparently minimize the extent of this racemization, the absence up to now of a general method whereby the optical purity of such peptides and peptide derivatives may be satisfactorily determined has left their degree of optical contamination open to some doubt. In this connection, acid hydrolysis of the peptide derivatives to the free amino acids, followed by optical purity measurements, would probably prove unfruitful because certain amino acids tend to undergo racemization, as well as decomposition, when subjected to such treatment. At the present time, a *limited* procedure for determining the optical purity of peptides has been developed in this Laboratory (Section 10–49) which depends on the hydrolysis of these compounds under mild conditions by renal aminopeptidase to the constituent amino acids followed by the use of L- and D-amino acid oxidases. This procedure is obviously limited to the determination of the optical purity of peptides (*a*) which are susceptible to the action of the aminopeptidase, and (*b*) which contain amino acids which when liberated by hydrolysis are susceptible to L- or D-amino acid oxidase.

In the absence of a *general* method for adequately determining the degree of optical purity of peptides and peptide derivatives, it becomes virtually essential to employ synthetic techniques which are known to lead to products with a minimum of optical contamination. Although knowledge of such techniques is quite limited at present, it is nevertheless known that peptide derivatives which incorporate certain acyl blocking groups, or which have been secured through the use of particular coupling procedures demonstrate, for the most part, little sign of racemization. Experience has shown, for example, that optically active amino acid residues adjacent to a carbobenzoxy group invariably couple with another amino acid residue by means of practically all the conventional coupling procedures without the occurrence of appreciable racemization, whereas these same residues may, in many instances, undergo extensive optical inactivation when adjacent to other acyl blocking groups, e.g., acetyl or benzoyl (681). The resistance toward racemization imparted by the carbobenzoxy group might presumably be ascribed to the retarded ability of amino acid residues associated with this group to undergo azlactone formation with attendant racemization (Section 10–8). A comparable resistance to racemization is associated with the use of certain coupling procedures, such as the azide procedure, which, irrespective of the nature of the acyl blocking group employed, leads to optically pure products under conditions which induce considerable inactivation with other coupling procedures, e.g., mixed anhydride or acid chloride (681). The solvent used in the coupling step has also been shown to assume an important role with respect to the extent to which racemization occurs (682). Discussion of the above will be more fully detailed in the appropriate sections.

The magnitude of the optical rotation of analytically pure peptides or peptide derivatives which contain a single center of asymmetry bears an inverse relationship to the amount of optical contamination by its enantiomorph, i.e., the higher the optical rotation value, the greater the degree of optical purity. Polarimetric measurements thereby provide a means whereby the relative degree of optical purity of a given mono-asymmetric compound, secured through different synthetic procedures, may be roughly estimated. In sharp contrast, however, the magnitude of the rotation of derivatives with two or more asymmetric centers may be expected to provide practically no information with respect to the degree of contamination by the various possible stereoisomers. This may be vividly demonstrated with the stereoisomers of alanylalanine, the D-D and L-D diastereomeric forms of which possess specific rotation values in water of $+21.3°$ and $+72.2°$, respectively. Thus an increasing degree of contamination by L-alanyl-D-alanine in D-alanyl-D-alanine will lead to an increase in the magnitude of the observed rotation, with a 20% contamination, for example, leading to a specific rotation of $+31.4°$, a value some 50% higher than that possessed by the pure D-D form. No reliable information with regard to the amount of racemization which has occurred during a particular synthesis should therefore be expected from a comparison of the relative magnitudes of rotation of a given compound, with more than one center of asymmetry, which has been obtained via two or more different procedures.

26. Azide Method. *Principle.* The acylamino acid ester (II), obtained either by the esterification of an acylamino acid (I) or upon acylation of an amino acid ester (III) with an acid chloride, is converted to the corresponding hydrazide (IV) by interaction with hydrazine in methanolic or ethanolic solution. Treatment of the hydrazide (IV) with nitrous acid results in the production of the acylamino acid azide (V) which, in turn, readily couples with an amino acid or peptide as its alkali metal salt in aqueous medium or as its methyl, ethyl, or benzyl ester derivative in an inert organic solvent to yield the corresponding acyl-dipeptide derivative (VI). The chain length of the latter product may be further elongated by its initial conversion to the hydrazide, as before, succeeded by a repetition of the coupling procedure.

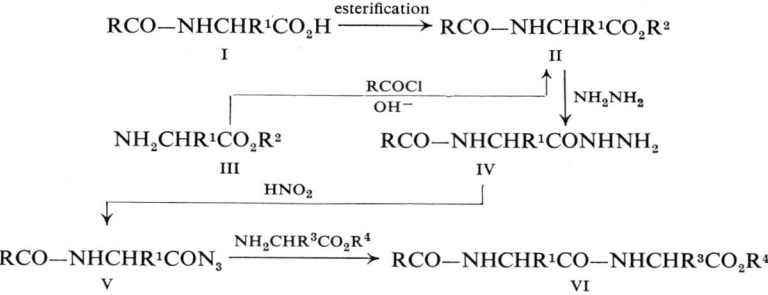

General Considerations. The announcement of the azide method by

Curtius (115) in 1902 introduced into synthetic peptide chemistry what was ultimately to become one of the most versatile and most universally used of all coupling procedures. Although the method was extensively employed by Curtius for the preparation of a number of benzoylated peptide derivatives (Section 10–6), its further exploitation for the preparation of free peptides was prohibited for some two decades by virtue of the early absence of selectively removable acyl blocking groups. With the introduction of the tosyl group in 1926, and especially the carbobenzoxy group in 1932, however, the method was elevated into prominence and was, together with the acid chloride method, utilized almost exclusively in synthetic peptide procedures involving removable acyl substituents during the period from 1932 to 1950. Despite the later development of less tedious coupling procedures, certain inherent advantages possessed by the azide method have been responsible for its widespread use to the present time.

Experimental Conditions. Preparation of acylamino acid azides may be accomplished through the interaction of acylamino acid chlorides and sodium azide or by the action of nitrous acid upon the acylamino acid hydrazide. As the former method utilizes an intermediate, i.e., the acid chloride, which may itself be employed in synthetic peptide procedures in lieu of the azide, such method of preparation is, of course, impractical. In practice, therefore, acylamino acid azides are generally prepared by treatment of an acidic aqueous solution of the parent hydrazide with sodium nitrite. Preparation of these crucial acylamino acid hydrazide (IV) intermediates is ordinarily achieved through treatment of a concentrated ethanolic or methanolic solution of the precursor acylamino acid ester (II) with a several-fold excess of hydrazine. The hydrazide is generally deposited from solution as a white crystalline material during the course of 12 to 48 hours at room temperature or, if it is soluble, is recovered by concentration of the solution to dryness *in vacuo.* Crystallization proceeds quite readily and is usually achieved from such solvents as water, ethyl acetate, ethanol, methanol, or ethanol-ether. The acylamino acid methyl or ethyl esters from which the hydrazides are derived may be secured by treatment of the respective acylamino acid either with diazomethane or with excess alcohol in the presence of mineral acid, or by the acylation of the pertinent amino acid ester (III) in the presence of a suitable base. Table 10–32 lists several of the acylamino acid methyl and ethyl esters which have been prepared in this manner. However, although it has been frequently the custom to isolate and characterize the crystalline acylamino acid esters prior to the hydrazinolysis step, it is somewhat more practicable, in terms of time and yield, to proceed to the desired hydrazide without isolation of the intermediate ester (procedure 10–60). Several of the acylamino acid hydrazides which have heretofore been described are listed in Table 10–33.

Illustrative procedure 10–60 (666). Carbobenzoxy-L-alanine hydrazide. Into a 500-ml. 3-necked flask equipped with a stirrer and immersed in an ice–salt bath are placed 15.4 g. (0.1 mole) of L-alanine ethyl ester hydrochloride (procedure 10–48), 75 ml. of water, and 180 ml. of chloroform. With vigorous stirring, 5.2 g. (0.13 mole) of MgO is added in three portions over a period of 30 min., while 22.2 g. (0.13 mole) of carbobenzoxy chloride (procedure 10–27) is added dropwise. Stirring is continued for another 30 min., when 5 ml. of pyridine is added, followed in 5 min. by acidification to Congo red with $5N$ HCl. The chloroform layer is separated, washed first with $0.5N$ HCl, then successively with water, 5% sodium bicarbonate solution, and water, dried over anhydrous sodium sulfate, and concentrated *in vacuo*. The resulting oil is repeatedly (three times) treated with 50 ml. of anhydrous ethanol, which each time is distilled off *in vacuo*. The residue (carbobenzoxy-L-alanine ethyl ester) is then dissolved in 100 ml. of anhydrous ethanol, 7 g. of hydrazine hydrate added, and the mixture allowed to stand overnight at room temperature. Most of the hydrazide crystallizes; it is filtered off, washed with cold anhydrous ethanol and dried; a second crop is recovered from the mother liquors. The material is recrystallized from ethyl acetate. Yield, 79%, of theory; m.p., 138.5°; $[\alpha]_D^{25} = -28.6°$ (2% in $0.5N$ HCl).

Experience has shown that aqueous solution of these acylamino acid hydrazides may be most expeditiously accomplished through the action of a mixture of hydrochloric and acetic acids (626). Since the solubility of certain of the hydrazides appears to be highly dependent upon the ratio of hydrochloric acid to acetic acid employed, and since this ratio might vary quite considerably for each individual hydrazide, the proper proportion of each acid required for solution of a new hydrazide is essentially found through trial and error. In practice, one or more equivalents of hydrochloric acid is added to an aqueous suspension of the hydrazide (IV), and glacial acetic acid is subsequently added dropwise thereto, with shaking, until solution is achieved. The addition of sodium nitrite to such solutions in the cold leads to the formation of the corresponding acid azide (V) derivatives. Although the latter compounds are in many instances crystalline, they are generally not isolated as such in consequence of their marked instability in the dry state but are, rather, extracted into some organic solvent as ethyl acetate, chloroform, or ether. As azide derivatives tend to lose nitrogen gas readily and undergo the well-known Curtius rearrangement to the isocyanate upon warming, it is essential to carry out the above operations in the cold to minimize these effects. Production of the desired peptide derivative (VI) is ultimately achieved through interaction of such azide solutions with the pertinent amino acid ester in an organic medium, or with the free amino acid in alkaline aqueous medium. These operations are described below for the preparation of carbobenzoxy-L-alanyl-L-alanine benzyl ester (procedure 10–61), but they may be generally extended to the preparation of a host of other acylated peptide esters.

TABLE 10-32
Benzyl, Ethyl, and Methyl Ester Derivatives of Acylamino Acids

Compound	M.P., °C.	$[\alpha]_D$, deg.	Temp., °C.	Concn. and Solvent	Ref.[c]
Cbzo-DL-alanine benzyl ester	59	—	—	—	664
Cbzo-β-alanine benzyl ester	22	—	—	—	664
Cbzo-nitro-L-arginine methyl ester	125	—	—	—	492
Cbzo-L-asparagine benzyl ester	132	—	—	—	604
Cbzo-L-asparagine methyl ester	150	−2.0	20	—, acetic acid	128
Cbzo-L-aspartic acid α-benzyl ester	84–85	—	—	—	602
Cbzo-L-aspartic acid β-benzyl ester	108	+12.1	25	10%, acetic acid	364
Cbzo-L-aspartic acid dibenzyl ester	66.5	−2.5	25	10%, acetic acid	364
Cbzo-L-aspartic acid α-ethyl ester	80–82	—	—	—	609
Cbzo-L-aspartic acid β-methyl ester	98	−17.4	25	2.5%, pyridine	508
Cbzo-S-benzyl-L-cysteine benzyl ester	66	−42.1	23	9.5%, acetic acid	664
Cbzo-S-benzyl-L-cysteine ethyl ester	52–53	—	—	—	390, 646
Cbzo-S-benzyl-L-cysteine methyl ester	66–67	—	—	—	606
α-Cbzo-α′-trityl-L-cystine bis-methyl ester	66–67	+103	25	1.0%, chloroform	876
Cbzo-L-glutamic acid α-benzyl ester	78–81	—	—	—	610
Cbzo-D-glutamic acid γ-benzyl ester	—	+24	25	5.8%, N KHCO$_3$	367
Cbzo-L-glutamic acid γ-benzyl ester	76–78	−23	22	6.3%, N KHCO$_3$	367
Cbzo-L-glutamic acid dibenzyl ester	95–96	−10.4	24	1.7%, acetic acid	367, 662, 677
Cbzo-DL-glutamic acid α-ethyl ester	99–101	—	—	—	610
Cbzo-L-glutamic acid α-ethyl ester	46–48	−21.4	16	7.7%, ethanol	475, 610, 682a
Cbzo-L-glutamic acid γ-ethyl ester	87	—	—	—	367, 606, 610
Cbzo-L-glutamic acid γ-methyl ester	72–73	−15.3	21	7.5%, 1.4N KHCO$_3$	367
Cbzo-L-glutamine benzyl ester	123	—	—	—	602
Cbzo-L-glutamine methyl ester	140–141	−19.4	23	1%, methanol	683

Cbzo-glycine benzyl ester	72	—	—	—	664
Cbzo-glycine ethyl ester	35.5–36.5	—	—	—	637
N,N′-Dicbzo-L-histidine methyl ester	45–46	—	—	—	483
1,N-Dicbzo-L-histidine methyl ester·HCl	117–118 d.	—	—	—	483
N-Cbzo-O-tosyl-L-hydroxyproline methyl ester	76–78	−32.4	20	1%, methanol	487
N-Cbzo-O-tosyl-L-allohydroxyproline methyl ester	138–139	−25.4	20	1%, chloroform	487
Cbzo-DL-leucine ethyl ester	18.5–19	—	—	—	684
Cbzo-DL-phenylalanine benzyl ester	84	—	—	—	664
Cbzo-DL-serine benzyl ester	74–75	—	—	—	497–499
Cbzo-D-serine benzyl ester	83.5–84.5	−5.5	—	4%, chloroform	499
Cbzo-L-serine benzyl ester	84–85	+5.7	—	4%, chloroform	499
Cbzo-L-threonine methyl ester	89–91	—	—	—	627
Cbzo-L-tyrosine ethyl ester	78	−4.7	25	1.9%, ethanol	128
N-Cbzo-O-acetyl-L-tyrosine methyl ester	73–74.5	—	—	—	637
N-Cbzo-O-benzoyl-L-tyrosine ethyl ester	92	—	—	—	646
Cbzo-DL-valine benzyl ester	45	—	—	—	664
Cbzo-DL-valine ethyl ester	32–33	—	—	—	684
Cbzo-L-valine methyl ester	56–57	−16.0	17	3.1%, ethanol	373, 625
p-NO$_2$-Cbzo-L-glutamic acid dibenzyl ester	81	−11.2	22	0.9%, 96% ethanol	677
p-NO$_2$-Cbzo-3:5-diiodo-L-tyrosine ethyl ester	151–152	−40.5	22	1%, pyridine	362
MeTC-glycine ethyl ester[a]	55	—	—	—	580
PhTC-DL-alanine methyl ester[a]	55–56	—	—	—	579
bis-PhTC-L-cystine dimethyl ester[a]	108	—	—	—	578
PhTC-glycine ethyl ester[a]	104–106	—	—	—	578, 579
o-NO$_2$PhOA-glycine ethyl ester[a]	92–93	—	—	—	494
o-NO$_2$PhOA-L-phenylalanine ethyl ester[a]	86.5–90	−12.0	25	1.2%, 95% ethanol	494
Phth-DL-asparagine methyl ester	170	—	—	—	685
Phth-DL-aspartic acid α-methyl ester	182	—	—	—	685
Phth-DL-aspartic acid γ-methyl ester	147–148	—	—	—	685
Phth-L-aspartic acid diethyl ester	oil	−40	17	0.5%, ethanol	528
Phth-DL-glutamic acid γ-benzyl ester	85–86	—	—	—	607

TABLE 10-32 (continued)

Compound	M.P., °C.	$[\alpha]_D$, deg.	Temp., °C.	Concn. and Solvent	Ref.[c]
Phth-L-glutamic acid γ-benzyl ester	66–67	−30.4	20	3%, chloroform	533
Phth-L-glutamic acid diethyl ester	oil	−33.5	19	–, ethanol	527
Phth-DL-glutamic acid α-methyl ester	149–151	–	–	–	523
Phth-L-glutamic acid α-methyl ester	138	−55.9	26	3.2%, ethyl acetate	523, 533
Phth-DL-glutamic acid γ-methyl ester	114	–	–	–	607
Phth-L-glutamic acid γ-methyl ester	136–137[b]	−40.5	20	2.7%, chloroform	523, 533
Phth-L-histidine ethyl ester	195	–	–	–	538
Phth-L-histidine methyl ester	187	–	–	–	537, 538
Phth-L-histidine methyl ester·HCl	238–240	–	–	–	537, 538
α-Phth-δ-cbzo-DL-ornithine methyl ester	176.5–177.5	–	–	–	429
Tos-DL-alanine ethyl ester	68	–	–	–	127
Tos-S-benzyl-L-cysteine methyl ester	73–73.5	+21.4	18	5%, methanol	432a
Tos-L-glutamic acid diethyl ester	76–76.5	–	–	–	686
Tos-L-glutamic acid γ-methyl ester	113–114	–	–	–	436
Tos-DL-leucine ethyl ester	83.5	–	–	–	127
α-Tos-L-lysine benzyl ester·HCl	170	–	–	–	439a
α-Tos-L-lysine ethyl ester·HCl	180.5	–	–	–	439a
α-Tos-L-lysine methyl ester·HCl	146–147	–	–	–	439b
α-Tos-ε-cbzo-L-lysine methyl ester	80–81	–	–	–	439b
α-Tos-DL-ornithine methyl ester·HCl	184.5–185.5	–	–	–	439b
α-Tos-L-ornithine methyl ester·HCl	152–153	–	–	–	439b
α-Tos-δ-cbzo-DL-ornithine methyl ester	93.5–94.5	–	–	–	439b
α-Tos-δ-cbzo-L-ornithine methyl ester	97–98	–	–	–	439b
Tos-DL-threonine methyl ester	80–89	–	–	–	687
Tos-D-threonine methyl ester	100–101	+8.0	16	2%, methanol	687
Tos-L-threonine methyl ester	100–101	−8.0	16	2%, methanol	687

Compound	m.p. (°C)	[α]D	t (°C)	Solvent	Ref.
Tos-L-valine ethyl ester	59	+4.0	20	–, ethanol	688
TFA-L-asparagine ethyl ester	122	−37.4	23	0.9%, methanol	576
TFA-L-aspartic acid diethyl ester	45	−11.6	23	1.1%, tetrahydrofuran	576
TFA-L-aspartic acid α-ethyl ester	96–97	−10.2	12	0.5%, tetrahydrofuran	576
TFA-L-glutamic acid α-ethyl ester	76–77	−42.9	20	2%, ethanol	477
TFA-glycine ethyl ester	51.5	–	–	–	568
TFA-DL-thyroxine methyl ester	203–206	–	–	–	689
TFA-DL-tyrosine ethyl ester	175–176	–	–	–	569
TFA-L-tyrosine ethyl ester	175–176	–	–	–	689
TFA-3:5-diiodo-L-tyrosine ethyl ester	172–173	–	–	–	689
TFA-3:5-diiodo-L-tyrosine methyl ester	166–169	–	–	–	689
Trityl-DL-alanine ethyl ester	100	–	–	–	545
Trityl-DL-alanine methyl ester	101	–	–	–	548
Trityl-L-alanine methyl ester	oil	–	–	–	548
α-Trityl-L-arginine methyl ester	120–125	+56.0	21	5%, methanol	471a
Trityl-L-aspartic acid dibenzyl ester	104–105	+7.5	20	2%, chloroform	673
bis-Trityl-L-cystine dimethyl ester	146	–	–	–	548
N,S-Ditrityl-L-cysteine methyl ester	90–92	–	–	–	548
Trityl-L-glutamic acid dibenzyl ester	87–89	+35.5	–	2%, chloroform	675
Trityl-L-glutamic acid α-benzyl-γ-methyl ester	91–92	+36	–	2%, chloroform	675
Trityl-L-glutamic acid α-methyl ester	140–141	+45.0	–	2%, methanol	675
Trityl-L-glutamic acid γ-methyl ester	116–117	+48.0	–	2%, methanol	675
Trityl-glycine ethyl ester	114	–	–	–	545, 548
Trityl-glycine ethyl ester·HCl	95–96	–	–	–	548
Trityl-glycine methyl ester	106–107	–	–	–	548
α-Trityl-L-histidine methyl ester·HCl	147	+27.7	–	5%, methanol	548a
α,ε-Ditrityl-DL-lysine methyl ester	149–150	–	–	–	550
Trityl-L-phenylalanine methyl ester	95	–	–	–	548

[a] o-NO₂-PhOA = o-nitrophenoxyacetyl, MeTC = methylthiocarbonyl, PhTC = phenylthiocarbonyl.
[b] A melting point of 118–120° ([α]D²¹ = −45.1° in methanol) has also been reported for this compound (523).
[c] Where more than one reference is given, the one in italics is that from which the physical data were taken.

TABLE 10-33
Hydrazide Derivatives of Acylamino Acids

Hydrazide of	M.P., °C.	$[\alpha]_D$, deg.	Temp., °C.	Concn. and Solvent	Ref.[c]
Callo-L-methionine	108–110	−19.7	19	1%, methanol	490
Cbzo-D-alanine	138.5	+28.7	25	2%, 0.5N HCl	666
Cbzo-L-alanine	138.5	−28.6	25	2%, 0.5N HCl	631, 666
Cbzo-β-alanine	143	—	—	—	690
Cbzo-S-benzyl-D-cysteine	135	—	—	—	473
Cbzo-S-benzyl-L-cysteine	133–135	−14.3	—	1%, ethanol	390, 606, 646
Bis-Cbzo-L-cystine (bis-hydrazide)	175–176	—	—	—	876
Cbzo-L-glutamic acid (α-hydrazide)	168–170	—	—	—	691
Cbzo-L-glutamic acid (γ-hydrazide)	178–179	−4	—	1%, H$_2$O + 1 eq. NaOH	606, 691, 692, 693
Cbzo-L-glutamine	174–176	—	—	—	619
Cbzo-glycine	116–117	—	—	—	666, 694
Cbzo-L-histidine	171–173	—	—	—	695
Dicbzo-DL-hydroxyllysine	145	—	—	—	830a
Dicbzo-DL-allohydroxyllysine	163	—	—	—	830a
Cbzo-L-hydroxyproline	149–149.5	—	—	—	169
Cbzo-D-leucine	121	—	—	—	469, 696
Cbzo-L-leucine	121	−20.8	25	4.1%, ethanol	466, 179, 625
Dicbzo-L-lysine	159	—	—	—	626, 697
Cbzo-DL-methionine	107–108	—	—	—	627
Cbzo-D-methionine	110–112	—	—	—	627
Cbzo-L-methionine	121–122[a]	−18.5	19	2%, methanol	490, 627

Dicbzo-L-ornithine	126–128	—	—	—	421
Cbzo-D-phenylalanine	169–170	—	—	—	698
Cbzo-L-phenylalanine	168	—	—	—	697, 698
Cbzo-DL-serine	162–163	—	—	—	498, 537
Cbzo-L-serine	181	—	—	—	498, *501*, 699
Cbzo-DL-threonine	171–172	—	—	—	498
Cbzo-L-tyrosine	220–221	—	—	—	*646*, 700
Cbzo-L-valine	178	−22.8	27	2.5%, N HCl	421, 625
C-t-Buo-L-methionine[b]	74	−12.4	23	2.5%, methanol	*471a*
Formyl-glycine	130	—	—	—	585
o-NO₂-PhOA-glycine[b]	182–184.5	—	—	—	494
o-NO₂-PhOA-L-phenylalanine[b]	176.5–179.5	—	—	—	494
Phth-glycine (hydrazide·HCl)	300 d.	—	—	—	413
Tos-DL-alanine	171	—	—	—	127
Tos-S-benzyl-DL-cysteine	162	—	—	—	*432a*
Tos-S-benzyl-L-cysteine	127.5	−9.3	19	0.6%, acetic acid	*432a*
Tos-L-glutamic acid (γ-hydrazide)	203–204 d.	+15.8	21	0.7%, 0.5N HCl	436, *701*
Tos-glycine	155.5	—	—	—	127
Tos-glycine (hydrazide·HCl)	174–177	—	—	—	413
Tos-DL-leucine	146	—	—	—	127
Tos-DL-serine	155	—	—	—	702
Tos-L-serine	179–181	—	—	—	444
Tos-D-threonine	195–197	+19.4	16	0.7%, methanol	687
Tos-L-threonine	195–197	−19.8	16	1%, methanol	687
Trityl-glycine	164–165	—	—	—	548

[a] A melting point of 110–112° was also reported for this compound (627).
[b] o-NO₂-PhOAc = o-nitrophenoxyacetyl and C-t-Buo = carbo-t-butyloxy.
[c] Where more than one reference is given, the ones in italics are those from which the physical data were taken.

Illustrative procedure 10–61 (666). Carbobenzoxy-L-alanyl-L-alanine benzyl ester. In a mixture of 60 ml. of glacial acetic acid, 24 ml. of 5N HCl, and 250 ml. of water is dissolved 11.9 g. (0.05 mole) of carbobenzoxy-L-alanine hydrazide (procedure 10–60) and the solution cooled to −5°. On adding in one portion, with shaking, a cold, concentrated aqueous solution of 3.7 g. (0.053 mole) of sodium nitrite, the azide precipitates as a syrup and is taken up in 300 ml. of cold ether. The ether layer is kept cold while washing successively with ice-cold water, 3% sodium bicarbonate solution, and again with water. After brief drying over sodium sulfate, the azide solution is added in one portion to a dry, cold, ethereal solution of L-alanine benzyl ester (previously prepared by shaking for 10 min. a suspension of 24.4 g. (0.07 mole) of L-alanine benzyl ester *p*-toluenesulfonate (procedure 10–57) in 100 ml. of chloroform containing 9.7 ml. (0.07 mole) of triethylamine, adding 350 ml. of absolute ether thereto, filtering off the precipitated triethylammonium *p*-toluenesulfonate after some 10 min., concentrating the filtrate to dryness *in vacuo*, and taking up the residue in dry ether). After standing for about 20 hr. at room temperature, the reaction mixture is washed successively with 0.5N HCl, water, 3% sodium bicarbonate solution, and water; after drying over sodium sulfate and removing the ether *in vacuo*, a crystalline product is obtained which is recrystallized from ethyl acetate-petroleum ether. The yield of pure product is 65–70% (based on the hydrazide used); m.p. 138°.

Treatment of an alcoholic solution of the methyl or ethyl ester derivative of an acyl-dipeptide (VI*a*) or a higher peptide with hydrazine proceeds with the formation of the corresponding hydrazide (VII) (procedure 10–62). Conversion of the latter compound to the azide (VIII) via the mediation of nitrous acid, followed by the coupling of (VIII) with a suitable amino acid or peptide derivative essentially according to procedure 10–61, results in an elongation of the peptide chain (IX); for example,

$$\text{RCO—NHCHR}^1\text{CO—NHCHR}^2\text{CO}_2\text{Et} \xrightarrow{\text{NH}_2\text{NH}_2} \text{RCO—NHCHR}^1\text{CO—NHCHR}^2\text{CO—NHNH}_2$$
$$\text{VI}a \hspace{4cm} \text{VII}$$

$$\text{HNO}_2 \downarrow$$

$$\text{RCO—NHCHR}^1\text{CO—NHCHR}^2\text{CON}_3 \xrightarrow{\text{NH}_2\text{CHR}^3\text{CO}_2\text{Et}} \text{RCO—NHCHR}^1\text{CO—NHCHR}^2\text{CO—NHCHR}^3\text{CO}_2\text{Et}$$
$$\text{VIII} \hspace{6cm} \text{IX}$$

Table 10–34 lists several of the higher acylated peptide hydrazides which have been previously prepared.

Illustrative procedure 10–62 (666). Carbobenzoxy-L-alanyl-L-alanine hydrazide. To a solution of 0.05 mole of carbobenzoxy-L-alanyl-L-alanine ethyl ester in 80–100 ml. of hot absolute ethanol is added 0.10–0.13 mole of hydrazine hydrate and the solution refluxed for 1 hr. After about 20 hr. of standing at room temperature most of the hydrazide has crystallized. After filtration, a small amount of second crop material may be obtained by the addition of ether to the mother liquors. The combined crystalline precipitate is recrystallized from ethanol-ether; yield 80–90% of theory; m.p. 209°.

Scope and Limitations. Practicable employment of the azide method in

TABLE 10-34
Hydrazide Derivatives of Acylated Peptides

Compound	Config.	M.P., °C.	Ref.
Cbzo·Ala·Ala·NHNH$_2$	D-D	208	666
Cbzo·Ala·Ala·NHNH$_2$	D-L	193	666
Cbzo·Ala·Ala·NHNH$_2$	L-D	193	666
Cbzo·Ala·Ala·NHNH$_2$	L-L	209	666
Cbzo·Ala·Ala·Ala·NHNH$_2$	L-L-D	205	703
Cbzo·Ala·Ala·Ala·NHNH$_2$	L-D-L	194	703
Cbzo·Ala·Ala·Ala·NHNH$_2$	L-L-L	235	703
Cbzo·Ala·Gly·NHNH$_2$	DL	156–157	704
Cbzo·Ala·Gly·NHNH$_2$	D	147–148	705
Cbzo·Ala·Gly·NHNH$_2$	L	157	*169*, 705, 875c
Cbzo·β-Ala·His·NHNH$_2$	L	188–189	621
Cbzo·Ala·(N$^\varepsilon$-Cbzo-Lys)·NHNH$_2$	L-D	190–191	667
Cbzo·Ala·(N$^\varepsilon$-Cbzo-Lys)·NHNH$_2$	L-L	165	667
Cbzo·Ala·(N$^\varepsilon$-Cbzo-Lys)·Ala·NHNH$_2$	L-L-L	208	706
Cbzo·Ala·Ser·NHNH$_2$	L-L	223–224	432a
Cbzo·CySBz·Ala·NHNH$_2$	L-L	181	432a
Cbzo·CySBz·Ala·Ser·NHNH$_2$	L-L-L	208–209	432a
Cbzo·CySBz·CySBz·NHNH$_2$	L-L	167	432a
Cbzo·CySBz·Gly·NHNH$_2$	L	142[a]	*390*, *432a*, 472
Cbzo·CySBz·Gly·Gly·NHNH$_2$	L	164	390
Cbzo·CySBz·Gly·Gly·Gly·NHNH$_2$	L	196	390
Cbzo·CySBz·Tyr·NHNH$_2$	L-L	208–209	707
Cbzo·CySBz·Tyr·Ileu·NHNH$_2$	L-L-L	238	472
Cbzo·CySBz·Tyr·Leu·NHNH$_2$	L-L-L	240	629
Cbzo·CySBz·Tyr·Phe·NHNH$_2$	L-L-L	243	629
Cbzo·CySBz·Tyr·Val·NHNH$_2$	L-L-L	241	*629*, 708
Cbzo·Glu-NH$_2$·Asp-NH$_2$·CySBz·NHNH$_2$	L-L-L	258	472
Cbzo·Glu-NH$_2$·CySBz·NHNH$_2$	L-L	233–234 d.	432a
Cbzo·Glu-NH$_2$·CySBz·CySBz·NHNH$_2$	L-L-L	227	432a
Cbzo·Glu-NH$_2$·Glu-NH$_2$·CySBz·NHNH$_2$	L-L-L	260	629
Cbzo·Glu·Tyr·NHNH$_2$	L-L	194	709
Cbzo·Gly·Ala·NHNH$_2$	DL	174–176	704
Cbzo·Gly·Ala·NHNH$_2$	L	158–160	*494*, 710
Cbzo·Gly·Ala·Leu·NHNH$_2$	L-L	186	710
Cbzo·Gly·Gly·Gly·NHNH$_2$	—	225 d.	*413*, 711
Cbzo·Gly·His·NHNH$_2$	L	200–202	537
Cbzo·Gly·His·Gly·NHNH$_2$	L	199–201	537
Cbzo·Gly·Leu·NHNH$_2$	L	134	413, 694
Cbzo·Gly·(N$^\varepsilon$-Cbzo-Lys)·NHNH$_2$	L	167	*358*, 667
Cbzo·Gly·Phe·NHNH$_2$	L	143–145	712
Cbzo·Gly·(O-Bz-Ser)·NHNH$_2$	DL	188–189	828
Cbzo·Gly·Tyr·NHNH$_2$	L	205–206	413
Cbzo·His·Ala·NHNH$_2$	L-L	203–204	695
Cbzo·His·Gly·NHNH$_2$	L	180–181	695
Cbzo·His·Leu·NHNH$_2$	L-L	175–177	695
Cbzo·His·Phe·NHNH$_2$	L-L	201–202	713
Cbzo·Ileu·His·NHNH$_2$	L-L	186–187[b]	714
Cbzo·Leu·Phe·NHNH$_2$	L-D	166	*423*, 698
Cbzo·Leu·Tyr·NHNH$_2$	L-D	208–209[c]	679a
Cbzo·(N$^\varepsilon$-Cbzo-Lys)·(N$^\varepsilon$-Cbzo-Lys)·NHNH$_2$	L-D	176	667
Cbzo·(N$^\varepsilon$-Cbzo-Lys)·(N$^\varepsilon$-Cbzo-Lys)·NHNH$_2$	L-L	190–191	667, *715*
Cbzo·(N$^\varepsilon$-Cbzo-Lys)·Tyr·NHNH$_2$	L-L	220–221	584a

TABLE 10-34 (*continued*)

Compound	Config.	M.P., °C.	Ref.
Cbzo·Phe·Gly·Gly·NHNH₂	DL	170–171	716
Cbzo·Phe·(N^(im)-Bz-His)·NHNH₂	L-L	183–186	484
Cbzo·Pro·Gly·Gly·NHNH₂	L	117–118	170
Cbzo·Pro·Leu·NHNH₂	L-L	133–135	717
Cbzo·Ser·Ala·NHNH₂	L-L	222–223	631
Cbzo·Ser·Gly·NHNH₂	DL	187–189	*537*, 704
Cbzo·Ser·Gly·NHNH₂	L	188	*631*, 699
Cbzo·Ser·Gly·Ala·NHNH₂	D-L	222–223[d]	717a
Cbzo·Ser·Gly·Ala·NHNH₂	L-L	221–222[e]	717a
Cbzo·Ser·His·NHNH₂	D-L	195–196[f]	718
Cbzo·Ser·His·NHNH₂	L-L	178–179[g]	718
Cbzo·Ser·Met·NHNH₂	L-L	215–216	444
Cbzo·Ser·Tyr·NHNH₂	L-L	213–214	*444*, 471a
Cbzo·Ser·Tyr·Ser·NHNH₂	L-L-L	210–213	*444*, 471a
Cbzo·Thr·His·NHNH₂	L-L	179–180	504a
Cbzo·Tyr·Tyr·NHNH₂·H₂O	L-L	246 d.	637
Cbzo·Val·His·NHNH₂	L-L	194–195	718a
Cbzo·Val·(N^δ-Tosyl-Orn)·NHNH₂	L-L	213	*423*, 719
Cbzo·Val·(N^δ-Tosyl-Orn)·Leu·Phe·Pro·NHNH₂	L-L-L-D-L	145–160[h]	423
Cbzo·Val·(N^δ-Tosyl-Orn)·Leu·Tyr·NHNH₂	L-L-L-D	236–239[i]	679a
Cbzo·Val·Tyr·NHNH₂	L-L	239–241[j]	508
p-NO₂-Cbzo·CySBz·Pro·NHNH₂	L-L	150–151[k]	511
Tosyl·CySBz·Tyr·NHNH₂	L-L	201	400
Tosyl·CySBz·Tyr·Gly·NHNH₂	L-L	217–218	400
Tosyl·CySBz·Tyr·Ileu·NHNH₂	L-L-L	242–243	400
Tosyl·CySBz·Tyr·Leu·NHNH₂	L-L-L	227	400
Tosyl·CySBz·Tyr·Phe·NHNH₂	L-L-L	242–243[l]	482a
Tosyl·Gly·Tyr·NHNH₂	L	204–207	413
Tosyl·Glu-NH₂·Asp-NH₂·CySBz·NHNH₂	L-L-L	224–225[m]	482a
Tosyl·Ser·Gly·NHNH₂	DL	215–216	702
Tosyl·Ser·Tyr·NHNH₂	L-L	200–202	444
Tosyl·Val·(N^δ-Cbzo-Orn)·NHNH₂	L-L	226–227	421
Trityl·Gly·CyS·NHNH₂	L	138–140	548
Trityl·Gly·CyS·NHNH₂	L		
Trityl·Gly·Gly·NHNH₂	–	147–148	546

[a] $[\alpha]_D^{23} = -38.5°$ (0.9% in ethanol) (472); $[\alpha]_D^{19} = -14.8°$ (1% in ethanol) (432a).
[b] $[\alpha]_D^{22} = -51°$ (1.3% in *N* HCl).
[c] $[\alpha]_D^{25} = +11.4°$ (0.5% in methanol).
[d] $[\alpha]_D^{25} = -4.8°$ (1% in acetic acid).
[e] $[\alpha]_D^{26} = -24°$ (1% in acetic acid).
[f] $[\alpha]_D^{27} = +5.0°$ (2% in methanol).
[g] $[\alpha]_D^{27} = -18.0°$ (2% in methanol).
[h] $[\alpha]_D^{25} = -75.1°$ (0.4% in methanol).
[i] $[\alpha]_D^{25} = -27.6°$ (1%, MeOH : 0.1*N* HCl : HOAc (3 : 1 : 1)).
[j] $[\alpha]_D^{25} = -13.7°$ (3.6% in dimethylformamide).
[k] $[\alpha]_D^{24} = -51.6°$ (1% in dimethylformamide).
[l] $[\alpha]_D^{24} = +6.8°$ (1% in dimethylformamide).
[m] $[\alpha]_D^{24} = -32.6$ (1% in dimethylformamide).

synthetic peptide procedures requires that acylamino acid hydrazides be readily available from the interaction of hydrazine and acylamino acid esters. However, since certain acyl blocking substituents, such as the phthalyl and trifluoroacetyl groups, undergo facile cleavage through the action of hydrazine, it follows that use of the afore-mentioned method for the preparation of hydrazide intermediates which incorporate these substituents would be accompanied by extensive deacylation. Although acylamino acid azides which embody these substituents have been prepared via the treatment of a phthalylamino acid chloride with sodium azide (720), or through the action of dicyclohexylamine azide upon a trifluoroacetylamino acid chloride (573), the preliminary need for an acid chloride intermediate tends to make the additional step to the azide somewhat superfluous. In consequence, the phthalyl and the trifluoroacetyl groups have been rarely utilized in conjunction with the azide procedure. Difficulty is encountered, too, where the trityl substituent is involved; the steric hindrance imposed by this bulky group has permitted only tritylglycine ester to undergo hydrazide formation (548), with the esters of higher tritylamino acids exhibiting a marked resistance to the action of hydrazine (546). In actual practice, therefore, use of the azide procedure for the preparation of acyl-dipeptides and acyl-dipeptide esters has been generally restricted to those syntheses which employ the more compatible carbobenzoxy or tosyl groups.

When compared with several of the more recently introduced coupling procedures, not only is the azide method somewhat more tedious, but also the yields of products secured are frequently less satisfactory, handicaps which at first glance would seem to spell the certain demise of the method for the practicable production of peptides. However, certain inherent virtues are possessed by the method which not only compensate for these deficiencies, but which also even make its continued use desirable. Thus, not only is the azide method applicable to the synthesis of peptides which incorporate virtually all varieties of the protein-bound amino acids, but also its implication in syntheses involving asymmetric residues invariably leads to the production of derivatives wherein the optical activity at each asymmetric center is fully retained. Striking demonstration of the latter attribute was reported by North and Young (681), who coupled acetyl-L-leucine with glycine ethyl ester via the classical azide and acid chloride routes, as well as through the later mixed anhydride (using isobutylchloroformate) (721), phosphoramide (employing tetraethylpyrophosphate) (722), and "phosphazo" (723) techniques. Only in that instance where the azide route was utilized could an optically active coupling product be secured, all other methods yielding the wholly racemic acetyl-DL-leucylglycine ethyl ester. The fact that the latter methods proceed with the formation of an optically inactive product should not necessarily be construed to imply that racemic materials will also be formed when an acyl substituent other than the acetyl group is employed, but should rather caution that such a danger does admittedly exist, a danger that is seemingly avoided by the azide method. This feature of the azide method speaks well for its utilization in syntheses leading to the larger polypeptides, where considerations of optical purity become of increasing importance (Section 10–25).

Since the hydroxyl groups of neither serine nor threonine exhibit any tendency to undergo reaction with acid azides under the ordinary conditions of peptide synthesis, the azide method has proved of especial value for the synthesis of peptides which incorporate these amino acids (501, 687). However, as acid azides will couple with the ω-functional groups of arginine and lysine, the basic character of these groups must be repressed prior to the condensation reaction. This is generally achieved through the conversion of the guanidino function of the former amino acid to either the nitro (491, 492) or the carbobenzoxy (458) derivative, while the ε-amino group of the latter is usually masked with an appropriate acyl substituent, e.g., carbobenzoxy (457), tosyl (393), or trifluoroacetyl (569). On the other hand, peptides which embody the histidine residue may be conveniently prepared without prior substitution of the basic imidazole nucleus (621, 626, 695).

In connection with the above, it is of interest to note that a number of γ-glutamyl derivatives have been reported (605, 606, 691) via the action of an amino acid ester upon carbobenzoxy-γ-glutamyl azide (X), where the α-carboxyl function of the latter reactant was free. That such a procedure did not provide an unequivocal synthetic pathway to γ-glutamyl peptides was shown by Sachs and Brand (724), who demonstrated that the condensation leads in effect to a mixture composed of the α- and γ-glutamyl derivatives (XIII and XIV, respectively), the nature of the isolable product being highly dependent upon reaction conditions, purification procedures, and the solubilities of both the isomeric intermediates and the free peptides. This unanticipated phenomenon was attributed to the preliminary transformation of the carbobenzoxy-γ-azide (X) into the intramolecular cyclic carbobenzoxyglutamic anhydride (XI) or a pseudo-anhydride intermediate

(XII) which could undergo reaction with an amino acid ester in either the α- or γ-position. No comparable studies have as yet been reported with the corresponding acyl-α-glutamyl azides or with the α- or β-azides of the acylaspartic acids, although these would prove of both theoretical and practical interest.

That acid azides may undergo yet other unpredictable transformations during peptide synthesis was shown by Prelog and Wieland (649), who isolated a considerable quantity of dicarbobenzoxy-L-lysine amide as a side product upon the conversion of the dicarbobenzoxyamino acid hydrazide into the azide. Additional examples of this curious behavior during azide couplings have been subsequently recorded (393, 606, 707), but the exact mechanism of the process remains obscure. Also worthy of note is the report of Fruton (501) that carbobenzoxy-L-serine azide (XV) undergoes ready rearrangement into 4-carbobenzoxyamino-oxazolidone-2 (XVI) upon brief warming of its ethyl acetate solution at 40°. However, the formation of appreciable quantities of this undesirable side product during the coupling of carbobenzoxyserine azide with an amino acid ester may be avoided, and the synthesis of the desired peptide derivative satisfactorily achieved, if such procedure is carried out in the cold (501, 631).

$$C_6H_5CH_2OCO-NHCH(CH_2OH)CON_3 \xrightarrow[40°]{\text{ethyl acetate}} C_6H_5CH_2OCO-NHCH(CH_2O-CO)NH$$

XV   XVI

Related Methods. An interesting variation of the hydrazide procedure was introduced by Hofmann, Lindenmann, Magee, and Khan (413, 725) which, in essence, involved the employment of α-amino acid carbobenzoxy hydrazides (XX) in lieu of amino acid esters in peptide syntheses. Preparation of these novel compounds is effected either via the interaction of 4-substituted 2-thio-5-thiazolidone derivatives (XVII) with carbobenzoxyhydrazine, or by the condensation of a phthalylamino acid chloride (XIX) with carbobenzoxyhydrazine, followed by dephthalylation of the coupling product (XVIII) with hydrazine; as the former procedure results in the production of racemic products only, its general use is severely limited. Alternatively, decarbobenzoxylation of (XVIII) may be achieved with the formation of the corresponding phthalylamino acid hydrazide, phthalylglycine hydrazide being prepared in this manner. Inasmuch as α-amino acid carbobenzoxyhydrazides (XX) possess a free amino group, they may, like amino acid esters, be readily combined in peptide linkage through the implication of conventional coupling techniques. Subsequent removal of the carbobenzoxy function from the condensation product (XXI) so derived,

TABLE 10-35

Carbobenzoxyhydrazide Derivatives of Amino Acid Hydrochlorides,
Acylamino Acids, and Acylpeptides (413, 725)

Compound[a]	Config.	M.P., °C.	$[\alpha]_D$, deg.	Temp., °C.	Concn. and Solvent
Amino acid derivatives					
H·Ala·NHNH·Cbzo·HCl	DL	192–193	–	–	–
H·Gly·NHNH·Cbzo·HCl	–	176–178	–	–	–
H·Leu·NHNH·Cbzo·HCl	DL	171–174	–	–	–
H·Phe·NHNH·Cbzo·HCl	DL	196–198	–	–	–
Acylamino acid derivatives					
Cbzo·Glu·NHNH·Cbzo	L	131–132	−26	26	1%, ethanol
Phth·Gly·NHNH·Cbzo	–	194–195	–	–	–
Phth·Phe·NHNH·Cbzo	DL	155–157	–	–	–
Tos·Gly·NHNH·Cbzo	–	132–134	–	–	–
Acylpeptide derivatives					
Cbzo·Glu·Gly·Gly·NHNH·Cbzo	L	162–164	−7	26	1%, methanol
Cbzo·Glu·Tyr·Gly·NHNH·Cbzo	L-L	200–202 d.	−6.5	27	2%, gl. acetic acid
Cbzo·Gly·Gly·Gly·NHNH·Cbzo	–	212–215	–	–	–
Cbzo·Gly·Gly·Leu·NHNH·Cbzo	DL	196–199	–	–	–
Cbzo·Gly·Leu·Gly·NHNH·Cbzo	L	142–144	−18	26	1%, methanol
Cbzo·Gly·Phe·Gly·NHNH·Cbzo	DL	162–163	–	–	–
Cbzo·Gly·Tyr·Gly·NHNH·Cbzo	L	175–177	−3	26	1%, methanol
Tos·Gly·Tyr·Gly·NHNH·Cbzo	L	185–187	−3	26	1%, methanol

[a] ·NHNH·Cbzo = carbobenzoxyhydrazide.

through hydrogenolysis, then yields an acyl-peptide hydrazide (XXII) which, after its conversion to the azide, may be further coupled with other amino acids, peptides, or their derivatives. Unfortunately, the large number of steps required for the preparation of amino acid carbobenzoxyhydrazides has restricted the use of these valuable intermediates in the routine synthesis of peptides.

Table 10–35 lists several of the amino acid carbobenzoxyhydrazides which have been described, in addition to some acyl derivatives thereof.

The use of azides for the formation of amino acid polymers was reported by Hofmann and Magee (725a), who showed that the selective diazotization (without appreciable deamination) of triglycine hydrazide (XXIII) to the corresponding azide (XXIV) could be accomplished in acidic media. Basification of a concentrated solution of the azide hydrochloride (XXIV) proceeded with the formation of a polyglycine. In an earlier discussion of the ester condensation method (Section 10-4), note was made that the use of highly dilute solutions favors ring formation rather than polymerization. It was with this concept in mind that Sheehan and Richardson (919) neutralized an aqueous solution of triglycine azide hydrochloride with sodium bicarbonate under conditions of relatively high dilution. A cyclic peptide was isolated which was subsequently identified (725b) as *cyclo*-hexaglycyl (XXVI). Reaction presumably occurred with an initial inter-

$$NH_2CH_2CO—NHCH_2CO—NHCH_2CO—NHNH_2 \xrightarrow[\text{aq. HCl}]{\text{NaNO}_2} HCl \cdot NH_2CH_2CO—NHCH_2CO—NHCH_2CON_3$$
XXIII XXIV

$$\downarrow \text{NaHCO}_3$$

$$NH_2CH_2CO(—NHCH_2CO—)_4NHCH_2CON_3 \longrightarrow cyclo\text{-}(NHCH_2CO)_6$$
XXV XXVI

molecular condensation of two molecules of triglycine azide followed by intramolecular cyclization of the hexapeptide azide (XXV) so derived; doubling reactions of this latter type have since been observed as a common occurrence in cyclization reactions involving the "active" ester derivatives of tri- and pentapeptides (Section 10-38).

27. Acid Chloride Method. *Principle.* Treatment of an acylamino acid (I) with thionyl chloride, phosphorus trichloride, or phosphorus pentachloride in an inert solvent converts it to the corresponding acid chloride (II). Interaction of the latter intermediate with a suitably constituted amine, e.g., an amino acid or ester thereof, proceeds with the formation of the peptide derivative (III) and the concomitant liberation of hydrogen chloride. The coupling may be effected in either aqueous or organic media in the presence of an appropriate base to neutralize the liberated acid.

$$RCO—NHCHR^1CO_2H \xrightarrow[\text{or PCl}_5]{\text{SOCl}_2} RCO—NHCHR^1COCl \xrightarrow{NH_2R^2} RCO—NHCHR^1CO—NHR^2 + HCl$$
I II III IV

General Considerations. One year after the introduction of acid azides into peptide chemistry by Curtius (115), Fischer and Otto (121) announced that acid chlorides of acylamino acids may be employed in a comparable manner. Although the latter compounds were initially utilized by Fischer and his collaborators for the preparation of a number of carboalkoxy- and α-haloacyl-peptide intermediates (Sections 10-6 and 10-7), their more general employment in synthetic peptide procedures had to await, as in the case of the acid azides, the future development of selectively removable acyl masking substituents. Although not so versatile as their contemporary acid azide analogs, acid chlorides none the less proved invaluable during the period from 1932 to 1950, not only for the preparation of peptides via the carbobenzoxy and tosyl intermediates, but also for the synthesis of an impressive variety of other acylated peptide derivatives, e.g., acetyl and benzoyl, which were employed as substrates in protease specificity studies. However, unlike the acid azides, which were able to survive in the wake of a tide of new coupling procedures introduced after 1950, the acid chloride intermediates possessed no singular attributes which would permit their like survival.

Experimental Conditions. The preparation of acylamino acid chlorides (II) is generally achieved through the interaction of a solution or a suspension of the pertinent acylamino acid (I) either with thionyl chloride (procedure 10–63) or with phosphorus pentachloride (procedure 10–64) in ether, benzene, or some other inert solvent. Owing to their reactivity, the hydroxyl functions of serine, threonine, hydroxyproline, and tyrosine, the sulfhydryl group of cysteine, and the ω-basic moieties of ornithine, lysine, and arginine must be appropriately masked prior to the formation of acylamino acid chlorides incorporating these groups. Such masking has led, for example, to the successful production of the acid chlorides of N-carbobenzoxy-O-acetyl-L-tyrosine (378), α,δ-dicarbobenzoxy-L-ornithine (373) and tosyl-S-benzyl-L-cysteine (400). In the case of the initially ω-unsubstituted α-p-nitrocarbobenzoxy-L-arginine, conversion to the acid chloride derivative via the action of thionyl chloride resulted in the protection of the reactive guanidino group as its hydrochloride salt in the wake of the hydrogen chloride liberated during the reaction (463). While acylamino acid chlorides which embodied the tosyl, trityl, phthalyl, and trifluoroacetyl groups have been employed in peptide syntheses to a limited extent, utilization of the carbobenzoxy group has been more extensive. Table 10–36 lists a number of such acylamino acid chlorides which have been secured in the crystalline state, whereas others, such as carbobenzoxy-L-alanyl chloride (128) and phthalyl-L-leucyl chloride (522), have been isolated only as non-crystallizable oils. Since these compounds undergo decomposition to the free acylamino acid upon prolonged contact with moisture, they should be routinely stored under anhydrous conditions. The propensity of carbobenzoxyamino acid chlorides to undergo facile decomposition to the corresponding N-carboxy-α-amino acid anhydrides has already been noted (Section 10–10). In view of the afore-mentioned, it is generally good practice to avoid continued storage by preparing acid chloride intermediates just before their use in the coupling reaction.

Illustrative procedure 10–63 (569). Trifluoroacetyl-L-phenylalanyl chloride. To a suspension of 261 mg. (1.00 mmole) of trifluoroacetyl-L-phenylalanine (procedures 10–39 to 10–43) in 5 ml. of dry benzene is added 0.20 ml. (0.32 g., 2.7

TABLE 10-36
Acid Chloride Derivatives of Acylamino Acids

Acid Chloride	M.P., °C.	Ref.
BzSO$_2$-L-leucyl chloride	67	601
Cbzo-L-aspartyl dichloride	46	726
Cbzo-L-β-aspartyl chloride α-benzyl ester	85	602, 727
bis-Cbzo-L-cystyl dichloride	67–68	128, 476
Cbzo-glycyl chloride	43	128
1,N-Dicbzo-L-histidyl chloride	98–100 d.	483
α,δ-Dicbzo-L-ornithyl chloride	54–56	373
Cbzo-L-phenylalanyl chloride	42	493
Cbzo-L-tryptophyl chloride	75 d.	505
N-Cbzo-O-acetyl-L-tyrosyl chloride	54	378
PhTC-DL-alanyl chloride	81–85	579
PhTC-glycyl chloride	83–85	579
Phth-L-alanyl chloride	156–159	808b
Phth-glycyl chloride	85–86	518, 536, 728, 808b
Phth-L-leucyl chloride	153.5–155.5	808b
Phth-DL-phenylalanyl chloride	124–126	518
Phth-L-phenylalanyl chloride	83–84	522
Tosyl-DL-alanyl chloride	93–94	427
Tosyl-β-alanyl chloride	82–84	427
Tosyl-DL-α-amino-n-butyryl chloride	56–57	427
Tosyl-α-aminoisobutyryl chloride	115–116	427
Tosyl-S-benzyl-L-cysteinyl chloride	112–114	400
Tosyl-L-glutamyl dichloride	71–74 d.	686
Tosyl-glycyl chloride	82–84	427
Tosyl-L-leucyl chloride	83–85	427
Tosyl-DL-norleucyl chloride	70–72	427
Tosyl-L-phenylalanyl chloride	128–129	440
Tosyl-L-prolyl chloride	56–57.5	427
Tosyl-DL-valyl chloride	76–78	427
TFA-L-β-aspartyl chloride α-ethyl ester	117–118[a]	576
TFA-L-γ-glutamyl chloride α-ethyl ester	89–90[b]	477
TFA-L-phenylalanyl chloride	109.5–111.5	569
Trityl-glycyl chloride hydrochloride	114–115	548
Trityl-L-phenylalanyl chloride hydrochloride	190 d.	548

[a] $[\alpha]_D^{23} = -26.9°$ (1.1% in tetrahydrofuran).
[b] $[\alpha]_D^{20} = -15.2°$ (1.4% in acetic acid).

mmoles) of purified thionyl chloride. The mixture is heated under reflux for 2.5 hr. in a system protected from atmospheric moisture by a calcium chloride tube. Solvent and excess thionyl chloride are removed under reduced pressure (in a system protected from moisture). The crude product is taken up in 5 ml. of dry benzene, again taken to dryness and the residue dissolved in 15 ml. of dry benzene; the hot solution is filtered and upon cooling is diluted with 10 ml. of petroleum ether (b.p. 30–60°). After storage of the solution in a refrigerator overnight, the crystalline solid is collected on a sintered glass filter and washed with several portions of petroleum ether. The fine, colorless, silky needles are stored in a vacuum desiccator; yield 172 mg. (60.3%), m.p. 105–107°. Two recrystallizations from benzene–petroleum ether (2 : 1) yield crystals, m.p. 109.5–111.5°; $[\alpha]_D^{28} = +15.5°$ (0.2% in glacial acetic acid).

Illustrative procedure 10–64 (518). Phthalylglycyl chloride. A suspension of 20.5 g. (0.1 mole) of phthalylglycine (procedure 10–33) and 20.8 g. (0.1 mole) of phosphorus pentachloride in 200 ml. of benzene is heated in a water bath at 60°. The mixture is shaken occasionally until a clear solution is obtained (about 30 min.). After heating for a total of 2 hr., the solution is concentrated under reduced pressure and the dry residue crystallized from benzene and petroleum ether (30–60°). The yield is 18.1 g. (81%); m.p. 83–85°.

Acylamino acid chlorides (II) may be generally coupled with free amino acids in an alkaline aqueous system (procedure 10–65) or with amino acid esters (or other amines) in some non-reactive organic medium (procedure 10–66). In either instance, sufficient base must be employed to neutralize the hydrogen chloride (IV) liberated during the coupling reaction, as well as to form a salt with the carboxyl group, where free amino acids are implicated. Since the amide bond associated with a trifluoroacetyl substituent is extremely sensitive to alkali, the use of highly alkaline coupling conditions must be avoided with acylamino acid chlorides which incorporate this group. Note should also be made that, with the exception of tritylglycyl chloride (and possibly tritylalanyl chloride), coupling reactions which employ tritylamino acid chlorides have proved unsuccessful because of the steric hindrance considerations alluded to previously (548) (Section 10–26). Procedures 10–65 and 10–66 may be considered illustrative of only two of the variety of conditions that have been utilized in coupling reactions involving acylamino acid chlorides.

Illustrative procedure 10–65 (518). Phthalylglycylglycine. A solution of 4.47 g. (0.02 mole) of phthalylglycyl chloride (procedure 10–64) in 25 ml. of dioxane is added dropwise over a period of 30 min. to a stirred, cooled (5°) suspension of 1.50 g. (0.02 mole) of glycine and 1.21 g. (0.03 mole) of magnesium oxide in 75 ml. of water. The mixture is stirred for an additional 10 min. at room temperature, then acidified with hydrochloric acid. A portion of the product precipitates and is removed by filtration; the remainder is obtained by evaporation of the filtrate under reduced pressure. The crude material is recrystallized from alcohol, and it gives a total yield of 89.5% in two crops; m.p. 229–231°.

Illustrative procedure 10–66 (569). Trifluoroacetyl-L-phenylalaninanilide. The acid chloride of trifluoroacetyl-L-phenylalanine (procedure 10–63) is prepared from 264.6 mg. (0.946 mmole) of the acylated amino acid and the crude acid chloride taken up in 5 ml. of dry benzene. To the cold solution is slowly added a solution of 0.21 ml. (0.20 g., 2.4 mmoles) of aniline in 5 ml. of dry benzene, during which time a heavy white precipitate separates. After the reaction mixture has been heated under reflux for 1 hr. and the solvent removed under reduced pressure, the solid residue is extracted with three 4-ml. portions of water and the crude product crystallized from 10 ml. of 70% aqueous ethanol. The white, fine, silky needles are filtered from the cold ethanolic solution, washed with two 5-ml. portions of water, and dried *in vacuo*; yield, 275.6 mg. (80.8%); m.p. 195.5–198.5°; $[\alpha]_D^{27} = +54.3°$ (3.9% in 95% ethanol).

Scope and Limitations. That acylamino acids which incorporate a free hydroxyl or thiol group in their respective side chains may be safely converted to the acid azide, but not to the acid chloride derivatives, has already been noted. An additional citation was concerned with the resistance to racemization exhibited by certain optically active acylamino acids when coupled with an amino acid ester via the azide procedure, as well as to the ready optical inactivation which may occur when the acid chloride procedure is employed. The facile racemization experienced by some acylamino acid chlorides may be presumably attributed to the fact that these compounds either actually exist as hydrohalides of azlactones, or may be readily converted thereto (Section 10–8). In any event, the degree to which these compounds are susceptible to racemization appears to be considerably dependent, at least in part, upon the nature of their respective acyl blocking substituents. This is emphasized by the marked optical inactivation which optically active acetylamino acids suffer upon conversion to their acid chloride derivatives (681), as opposed to the complete resistance to racemization revealed by the corresponding carbobenzoxyamino acids (128) upon like treatment. Comparably, no appreciable loss in optical activity apparently occurs upon the conversion of either phthalyl- (522) or trifluoroacetyl-L-phenylalanine (569) to its respective acid chloride. Regeneration of the parent acylamino acids from the latter compounds reveals that no significant changes in the magnitude of their optical rotation values had occurred as a result of the chemical treatment. With reference to the trifluoroacetyl group, studies in the writers' Laboratory have indicated that bis(trifluoroacetyl)-L-cystine exhibited a complete resistance to the racemizing action of a mixture of glacial acetic acid and acetic anhydride under conditions which induced bis(acetyl)-L-cystine to suffer complete loss of optical activity (299). Presumably, the ability of acylamino acids to undergo racemization (via azlactone formation) depends upon, among other factors, the acidity of the acyl group as well as upon steric considerations. Further studies are needed before any definite correlations can, however, be drawn.

28. Mixed Carboxylic Acid Anhydride Procedure.

Principle. A solution of an acylamino acid or acylated peptide (I) in an inert solvent containing one equivalent of a tertiary base, e.g., triethylamine (II), is converted to the mixed carboxylic acid anhydride (IV) upon the addition of a suitably constituted aliphatic or aromatic acid chloride (III). The anhydride (IV) is then coupled *in situ* with the alkali metal salt or ester derivative of an amino acid or peptide with the concomitant formation of a carboxylic acid (VI) and the desired peptide derivative (VII). Elongation of the peptide chain may be achieved upon conversion of the latter to the corresponding free acid (VIII) by a suitable procedure followed by a repetition of the entire process.

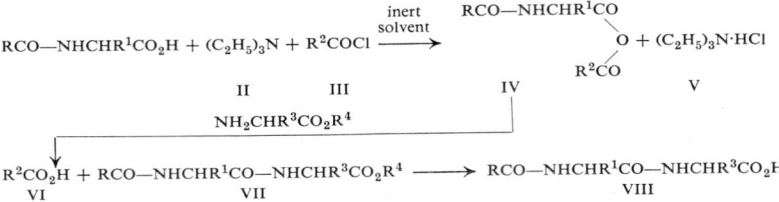

General Considerations. Description of the first mixed carboxylic acid anhydride of an acylamino acid may be attributed to Kraut and Hartmann (729) who, in 1865, isolated the hippuryl benzoate (XI) formed by the action of benzoyl chloride (X) upon a suspension of silver hippurate (IX) in boiling ether. Inadvertent use of this product (XI) for peptide bond synthesis

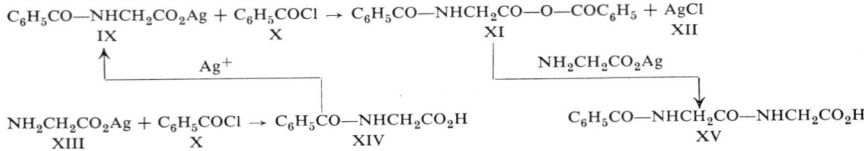

was made by Curtius (114, 730) some fifteen years later when the treatment of a suspension of silver glycinate (XIII) in boiling benzene with benzoyl chloride yielded hippuric acid (XIV) in addition to an unanticipated acyl-dipeptide identified as hippurylglycine (XV). Although he was fully aware of the earlier study of Kraut and Hartmann, Curtius did not recognize the possibility that his acyl-dipeptide might have been formed through the intermediacy of a mixed carboxylic acid anhydride (XI) but assumed, rather, that it arose from the acylation of silver glycinate by hippuryl chloride: "Der Prozess aus welchem die Hippuryl-amidoessigsäure hervorgeht, verläuft demnach in der Weise, dass sich zunächst durch Einwirkung von Benzoylchlorid auf Glycocollsilber Hippursäure und Chlorsilber bilden. Auf der erstere wirkt Benzoylchlorid weiter derart ein, dass Benzoesäure und Hippurylchlorid entstehen, von welchem das letztere endlich mit dem zweiter Molekül Glycocollsilber in Reaktion tritt, Hippurylglycocoll und

Chlorsilber erzeugend."[47] That the process is in all likelihood preceded by the intermediate formation of hippuryl benzoate (XI) was indeed demonstrated by Wieland and Sehring (731) some seventy-five years later.

The potential applicability of mixed carboxylic acid anhydrides in synthetic peptide procedures was not generally realized until about 1950 when Wieland, Kern, and Sehring (732) announced the isolation, characterization, and reactivity toward amines of mixed anhydrides of N-acylated amino acids with acetic or benzoic acid. Preparation of carbobenzoxyglycine acetate (m.p. 44°), carbobenzoxy-DL-alanine benzoate (m.p. 64°), and phthalylglycine benzoate (m.p. 125°) in the crystalline state was achieved via a modification of the Kraut and Hartmann (729) procedure; rapid and appreciable disproportionation of these compounds (IVa) to the corresponding symmetrical anhydrides (XVI and XVII) occurred upon mild heat treatment either in the solid state or in solution. A concurrent communication (731) by this same

$$\begin{array}{c} RCO-NHCHR^1CO \\ \diagdown \\ O \\ \diagup \\ R^2CO \\ IVa \end{array} \xrightarrow{\Delta} \begin{array}{c} RCO-NHCHR^1CO \\ \diagdown \\ O \\ \diagup \\ RCO-NHCHR^1CO \\ XVI \end{array} + \begin{array}{c} R^2CO \\ \diagdown \\ O \\ \diagup \\ R^2CO \\ XVII \end{array}$$

group described a more facile preparation of such mixed carboxylic acid anhydrides of benzoic acid (IV; $R^2 = C_6H_5$) by the interaction at 0° to 5° of equivalent quantities of an acylamino acid (I), benzoyl chloride (III; $R^2 = C_6H_5$), and a tertiary base in some inert organic solvent, such as benzene or benzonitrile. The anhydride (IV) so procured was not isolated as such, but rather permitted to undergo coupling *in situ* with aqueous solutions of an alkali metal salt or ester derivative of an amino acid to form the corresponding peptide derivative (VII). In this way, there was evolved the basis for a simplified coupling procedure which was destined to replace the classical azide method in part, and the acid chloride method virtually *in toto*, for the routine synthesis of peptide derivatives.

In contradistinction to the single coupling path available in the reaction between an acid azide or acid chloride and an amine, a mixed carboxylic acid anhydride (IVb) may theoretically couple with an amine (XVIII) at one or the other of its two carbonyl groups:

$$\begin{array}{c} RCO-NHCHR^1CO \\ \diagdown \\ O \\ \diagup \\ R^2CO \\ IVb \end{array} + NH_2R^3 \begin{array}{c} \nearrow RCO-NHCHR^1CO-NHR^3 + R^2COOH \\ \quad XIX XX \\ \searrow R^2CO-NHR^3 + RCO-NHCHR^1CO_2H \\ \quad XXI XXII \end{array}$$

The worth of mixed anhydrides (IVb) as intermediates for the preparation of peptides is of course contingent upon the extent to which the coupling reaction takes the desired course. Although the afore-mentioned method of Wieland and Sehring (731) apparently did not lead to the formation of detectable quantities of the unwanted side product (XXI), it none the less became essential to ascertain whether or not this would prove to be an invariable rule. It is pertinent at this point to recall the studies of Emery and Gold (733) which were concerned with the effect of steric hindrance, charge distribution, and solvent polarity on the ratio of chloroacetanilide (XXV) to acetanilide (XXVI) obtained from the reaction of acetic-chloroacetic anhydride (XXIII) with aniline (XXIV):

$$ClCH_2CO—O—COCH_3 + NH_2C_6H_5 \rightarrow ClCH_2CO—NHC_6H_5 + CH_3CO—NHC_6H_5$$
$$\text{XXIII} \qquad\qquad \text{XXIV} \qquad\qquad \text{XXV} \qquad\qquad \text{XXVI}$$

According to these investigators, the carbonyl carbon atom of the mixed anhydride most susceptible to nucleophilic attack by the amine was that which had the lowest electron density and, other things being equal, which was the least sterically hindered. It should be emphasized, however, that, although these conclusions were valid for coupling reactions accomplished under anhydrous conditions, they none the less proved inapplicable under aqueous conditions where marked deviations or even reversals of the expected acylation ratio were observed. In any event, the inference may be logically drawn that for the preparation of peptides via mixed carboxylic acid anhydrides under anhydrous conditions, the portion of the anhydride whose acylating properties are to be suppressed should possess steric and electronic characteristics that would decrease its susceptibility to nucleophilic attack and thereby permit substitution at the less hindered but more electrophilic carbonyl carbon atom to be favored.

With the above concepts in mind, Vaughan and Osato (734) employed *anhydrous conditions* to determine the yields of carbobenzoxyglycinanilide (XXX) obtained from the action of aniline on the mixed carboxylic acid anhydrides (XXIX) derived from the interaction of carbobenzoxyglycine (XXVII) and a series of aliphatic and aromatic acid chlorides (XXVIII) (see procedure 10–67):

$$Cbzo—NHCH_2CO_2H + RCOCl \xrightarrow[\text{toluene}]{(C_2H_5)_3N} Cbzo—NHCH_2CO—O—COR \xrightarrow{NH_2C_6H_5}$$
$$\text{XXVII} \qquad\qquad \text{XXVIII} \qquad\qquad\qquad\qquad \text{XXIX}$$

$$Cbzo—NHCH_2CO—NHC_6H_5$$
$$\text{XXX}$$

The percent yield of carbobenzoxyglycinanilide ultimately isolated in each instance was taken as a measure of the acylation ratio (Table 10–37). Inasmuch as the alkyl substituents of the α- and β-branched aliphatic acids, e.g., trimethylacetic, diethylacetic, and isovaleric acids, provide both marked steric and positive inductive effects, it followed that the mixed carboxylic acid anhydrides which incorporate these acids should theoretically exhibit an acylation ratio predominantly in favor of the acylamino acid portion of the molecule. On the other hand, the negative inductive and electronic effects exerted on the carbonyl carbon atom of the mixed anhydride by aromatic acids should lead to less satisfactory yields of the desired product. That such was indeed the case is revealed in Table 10–37.

TABLE 10–37
Preparation of Carbobenzoxyglycine Anilide by the Mixed Carboxylic Acid Anhydride Procedure (734)

Acid Chloride	Yield, %	Acid Chloride	Yield, %
Acetyl	36	Furoyl	46
Dimethylacetyl	65	2-Methoxybenzoyl	18
Diethylacetyl	85	4-Methoxybenzoyl	59
Trimethylacetyl	72	2:4-Dimethoxybenzoyl	38
Isovaleryl	83	3:4:5-Trimethoxybenzoyl	15
Isocaproyl	36	2-Methylbenzoyl	38
Heptanoyl	31	2-Chlorobenzoyl	34
Lauroyl	49	4-Chlorobenzoyl	63
Hexahydrobenzoyl	37	2:4-Dichlorobenzoyl	49
Phenylacetyl	40	3:4-Dichlorobenzoyl	62
Hexahydrophenylacetyl	35	3-Bromobenzoyl	48
Trichloroacetyl	48	2-Iodobenzoyl	45
Benzoyl	62		

Illustrative procedure 10–67 (734). Carbobenzoxyglycinanilide. A solution of 5.23 g. (0.025 mole) of carbobenzoxyglycine (procedure 10–28) and 2.55 g. (0.025 mole) of triethylamine in 50 ml. of toluene is cooled to 0° and 3.01 g. (0.025 mole) of isovaleryl chloride added thereto. After 2 hr. at this temperature, during which time some triethylamine hydrochloride deposits, 2.34 g. (0.025 mole) of aniline is added. The reaction mixture is then stored at 8° overnight. The carbobenzoxyglycinanilide crystallizes from the reaction mixture and is filtered off together with deposited triethylamine hydrochloride, washed successively with water, dilute sodium hydroxide solution, and dilute hydrochloric acid, and then dried; yield, 5.7 g. (83%); m.p. 146–147°. The same reaction conditions were followed with the other acid chlorides listed in Table 10–37.

Experimental Conditions. The observation that mixed carboxylic acid anhydrides which incorporated isovaleric acid were among the more satisfactory of those tested (Table 10–37) has resulted in the routine use of isovaleryl chloride as a reagent of choice for peptide bond synthesis. Preparation of the peptide derivative (VII) is generally achieved by the treatment of a solution of an amino acid ester in an inert organic medium, or the free amino acid in alkaline aqueous medium, with a solution of the pertinent mixed carboxylic acid anhydride (IV; $R^2 = (CH_3)_2CHCH_2$) below 10°

for about 12 hours. The latter intermediate (IV) is procured by the interaction of an acylamino acid (I) and isovaleryl chloride (III; $R^2 =$ $(CH_3)_2CHCH_2$) in an inert solvent containing one equivalent of a tertiary amine, e.g., triethyl, trimethyl, or tri-*n*-butyl amine. In order to minimize the danger of disproportionation, formation of the mixed anhydride is effected at temperatures of $-5°$ to $+5°$ for a period of less than 2 hours. These conditions suffice to give optimal yields of the desired intermediate but do not, at the same time, permit the participation of side reactions to an extent that would lead to serious contamination of the final product. As the presence of moisture during anhydride formation results in decreased over-all yields, the use of thoroughly dried solvents and anhydrous conditions should be rigidly adhered to for most satisfactory results. Solvents which prove eminently suitable for such purposes include toluene, chloroform, methylene chloride, ethyl acetate, ether, and dioxane. The use of such solvents as alcohol, which react with the mixed anhydrides, should be avoided. The experimental procedure, as detailed below for carbobenzoxy-L-leucylglycine ethyl ester (procedure 10–68), may be generally applied to the preparation of acylated peptide derivatives containing two or more amino acid residues.

Illustrative procedure 10–68 (734). Carbobenzoxy-L-leucylglycine ethyl ester. A solution of 5.30 g. (0.02 mole) of carbobenzoxy-L-leucine (see procedure 10–29) and 2.04 g. (0.02 mole) of triethylamine in a mixture of 25 ml. of toluene and 25 ml. of chloroform is cooled to $-5°$ and 2.41 g. (0.02 mole) of isovaleryl chloride added thereto. After 1.5 hr., a second precooled solution of 2.79 g. (0.02 mole) of ethyl glycinate hydrochloride (see procedure 10–48) and 2.04 g. (0.02 mole) of triethylamine in 50 ml. of chloroform is added and the reaction mixture stored overnight at 8°. The organic solution is washed successively with water and 3% sodium bicarbonate solution, then diluted with petroleum ether until cloudy. On cooling, the product separates as colorless crystals; yield 2.17 g. (31%); m.p. 103–104°. Concentration of the mother liquors almost to dryness in a stream of air, followed by redilution with petroleum ether, yields a second crop of crystalline product; yield 2.98 g. (43%); m.p. 102–103°. The combined crops yield 4.90 g. (70%) of pure crystalline product upon recrystallization from aqueous ethanol; m.p. 105–106°.

Note should be made that in the above procedure the amino acid ester is liberated from its hydrochloride salt by the addition of one equivalent of triethylamine. When the free amino acid ester is employed, the need for this extra equivalent of tertiary amine is removed. The solvents used may be varied in accordance with the solubilities of the reactants. Because of the heady fragrance of the isovaleric acid liberated during the course of the coupling reaction, the procedure is best carried out under a hood or in a well-ventilated room.

Scope and Limitations. Although the mixed carboxylic acid anhydride procedure proves quite satisfactory where phthalyl-, carbobenzoxy-, or most other acylamino acids are employed as the initial reactants, comparable use of trifluoroacetylamino acids is to be discouraged by virtue of the negligible yields of desired product obtained (573). As in the acid chloride procedure, the implication of tritylamino acids is restricted to the relatively unhindered glycine and alanine derivatives (548). As in the latter method, too, care must be exercised in properly masking reactive side-chain functions, i.e., hydroxyl, sulfhydryl, ω-amino, and ω-carboxyl groups. As considerable steric hindrance is afforded by acylamino acids which incorporate β-branched chain residues, e.g., valine and isoleucine, necessarily low yields of product result from the use of these reactants. However, when steric factors are negligible and reactive side-chain functions properly masked, the method can be expected to give generally satisfactory over-all yields of product.

The marked propensity revealed by certain mixed anhydrides which incorporate optically active amino acid residues to undergo racemization has been alluded to previously. According to current concepts, such optical inactivation presumably arises from the conversion of the mixed anhydride (XXXI) to an azlactone intermediate (XXXIV) (see Section 10–8). The series of electronic changes involved in this transition have been formulated by Baker, Ollis, and Poole (735). It is worthy of re-emphasis here that the

nature of the substituent adjacent to an optically active residue exerts a very marked influence upon the extent, if any, to which optical inactivation occurs. Thus, while acetylamino acids are highly susceptible to racemization upon conversion to their mixed anhydrides, like treatment of the corresponding carbobenzoxyamino acids is accompanied by virtually no optical inactivation. Optically active residues attached to the phthalyl substituent exhibit a similar resistance to racemization by virtue of their inability to undergo azlactone formation because of the lack of a proton on the nitrogen atom.

In connection with the above, it is of interest to note that the replacement of the proton on the α-amide linkage of an acylamino acid with a methyl group is accompanied by a markedly increased but not complete resistance of these compounds to racemization (302, 736). Existence of an alternative inactivation process to azlactone formation is thereby strongly implied. That this process, in the case of mixed anhydrides, might be attributed to the activating effect of the anhydride group on the hydrogen atom attached to the asymmetric carbon atom was suggested by Steiger (737) and by Carter and Stevens (738). This concept was more fully elucidated by Neuberger (739), who suggested that the steric arrangement provided by the anhydride molecule could be such as to enable the electron-donating oxygen atom to assume a position conducive to hydrogen bond formation and thereby promote the ionization of the proton on the α-asymmetric carbon atom; this is depicted by formula (XXXV). Additional explanation was offered on the basis of resonance considerations (239). Thus the resonance of the

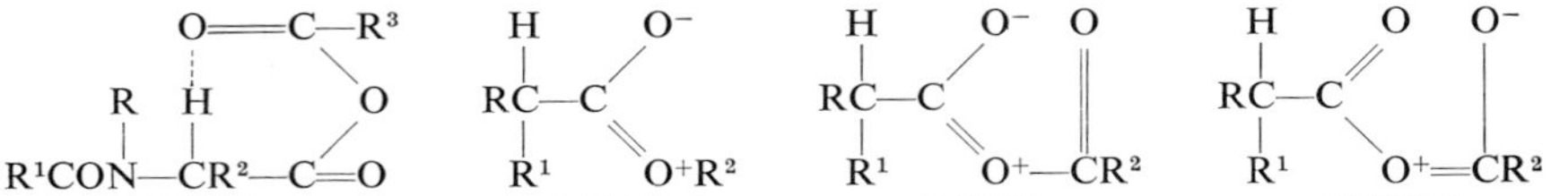

$$
\begin{array}{cccc}
\text{XXXV} & \text{XXXVI} & \text{XXXVII} & \text{XXXVIII}
\end{array}
$$

carboxyalkyl group in an optically active ester (XXXVI) would not be expected to promote racemization since the electropositive and electronegative charges within the molecule are about equidistant from the asymmetric center. A somewhat different situation is presented by the mixed anhydride molecule, which presumably reveals ester resonance (XXXVII), plus an additional structure (XXXVIII) which can activate the amide bond by an electrostatic mechanism and hence promote racemization by means of a greatly facilitated ionization at the asymmetric center. In any event, it appears that considerations concerned with optical inactivation in mixed anhydrides must, apart from azlactone formation, take into account the effects of electrostatic activation within the molecule itself.

Related Methods. The marked propensity of mixed carboxylic acid anhydrides to undergo disproportionation to a mixture of the two symmetrical acid anhydrides has been alluded to above. Reaction of a symmetrical acylamino acid anhydride (XVI*a*) with an amino group generally proceeds with the formation of one molecule each of the corresponding amide (XIX*a*) and the acylamino acid (XXII*a*):

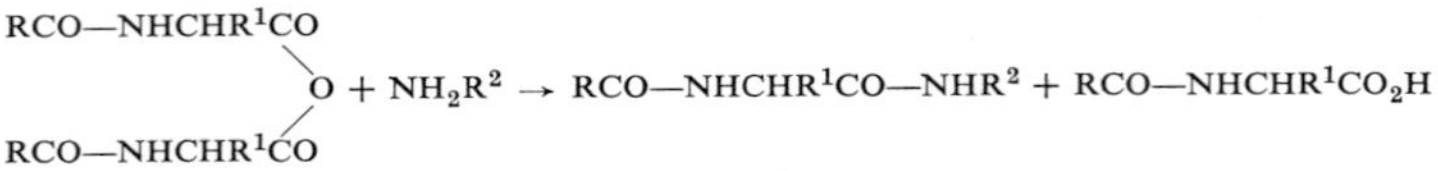

RCO—NHCHR¹CO
$\diagdown$
      O + NH₂R² → RCO—NHCHR¹CO—NHR² + RCO—NHCHR¹CO₂H
$\diagup$
RCO—NHCHR¹CO

    XVI*a*   XVIII*a*   XIX*a*   XXII*a*

Thus, for example, the interaction of *symm.* carbobenzoxyglycine anhydride, m.p. 118°, and aniline yields carbobenzoxyglycine anilide and carbobenzoxyglycine as products (732). Since a maximal over-all yield of only 50% is possible here (when based on the initial quantity of acylamino acid employed), the use of symmetrical acylamino acid anhydrides as acylation intermediates for the routine preparation of peptides should prove of little practical value.

CHEMICAL PROCEDURES FOR SYNTHESIS OF PEPTIDES

In this connection, it becomes of interest to cite the peculiar behavior revealed by symmetrical acylamino acid anhydrides which incorporate a trifluoroacetyl substituent. Thus the preparation of *symm.* trifluoroacetylglycine anhydride (XXXIX), m.p. 158°, may be readily achieved in nearly quantitative yield upon warming glycine with an excess of trifluoroacetic anhydride (568, 573). Subsequent treatment of (XXXIX) with one equivalent of dicyclohexylamine (XL) in ethanol at room temperature does not yield the anticipated trifluoroacetylglycine dicyclohexylamide, but rather results in the rapid deposition of the dicyclohexylamine salt of trifluoroacetylglycylglycine (XLI) and the concomitant formation of ethyl trifluoroacetate (XLII) (procedure 10–69):

$$(CF_3CO{-}NHCH_2CO)_2O + NH(C_6H_{11})_2 \xrightarrow{EtOH}$$
$$\text{XXXIX} \qquad\qquad \text{XL}$$

$$CF_3CO{-}NHCH_2CO{-}NHCH_2CO_2^-, NH_2^+(C_6H_{11})_2 + CF_3CO_2Et$$
$$\text{XLI} \qquad\qquad\qquad\qquad \text{XLII}$$

On the basis of the 85% yield of (XLI) so obtained, the occurrence of an intramolecular rearrangement is presumed here (573). Such rearrangement becomes understandable on the assumption that the inductive effect of the highly electronegative CF_3 group causes a marked activation of the imide hydrogen atoms of (XXXIXa) and thereby permits salt formation with the added amine. Nucleophilic attack by one of the imide nitrogen atoms on the C-terminal carbonyl group of the other half of the molecule should then lead to the dicyclohexylamine salt of the N,N-diacylamino acid (XLIII) which, in turn, should be readily cleaved by alcohol to the observed products (XLIa, XLIIa). The electronic changes involved in such transition may be formulated as follows:

[Scheme showing conversion of XXXIXa → XLIII → XLIa, XLIIa via $NH(C_6H_{11})_2$ and EtOH]

Comparable rearrangement is also observed with *symm.* trifluoroacetyl-DL-alanine anhydride (571).

Illustrative procedure 10–69 (573). N-Trifluoroacetylglycylglycine. One gram of glycine is added to 4.2 ml. of trifluoroacetic anhydride and solution effected upon brief warming under reflux (bath temperature at 50°). The reaction mixture is concentrated to dryness *in vacuo* and the residue crystallized from tetrahydrofuran-benzene (1 : 1). A nearly quantitative yield of *symm.* trifluoroacetylglycine anhydride, m.p. 158°, is so obtained. Upon the addition of a solution of 0.43 ml. of dicyclohexylamine in 10 ml. of absolute ethanol to 0.64 g. of the latter compound, a clear solution results which is rapidly followed by the deposition of the dicyclohexylamine salt of trifluoroacetylglycylglycine. This material is secured in some 85% yield upon filtration over suction and washing with a little absolute ethanol;

m.p. 242° d. Conversion of this compound to the free acid is achieved by dissolving 2.7 g. of the salt in 40 ml. of water and shaking the solution with 10 g. of Dowex-50 for 5 min. After removal of the ion exchange resin by filtration, it is washed with 10 ml. of water and the combined filtrate and washings concentrated to dryness under reduced pressure at 25°. The crystalline residue is dissolved in acetone, the solution treated with a little decolorizing carbon, and the desired trifluoroacetylglycylglycine deposited in 74% yield upon the addition of benzene; m.p. 185°.

29. Mixed Carboxylic-Carbonic Acid Anhydride Method. *Principle.* Treatment of a solution of an acylamino acid (I) or acylated peptide with one equivalent each of an alkylchlorocarbonate (II) and a tertiary amine, e.g., triethylamine, under anhydrous conditions proceeds with the formation of the mixed carboxylic-carbonic acid anhydride (IV). Condensation of the anhydride (IV) *in situ* with the alkali metal salt or ester derivative of an amino acid or peptide leads to the production of the desired peptide derivative (VIII) in addition to an alcohol (VI) and carbon dioxide (VII). Conversion of (VIII) to the corresponding free acid (IX) then permits its further condensation with another equivalent of amine by a similar procedure.

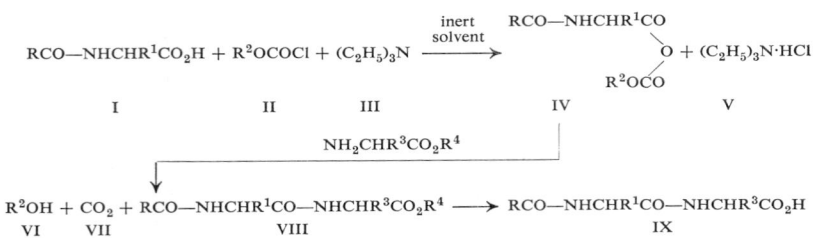

General Considerations. During 1951–1952, Vaughan and Osato (721), Boissonas (740), and Wieland and Bernhard (741) independently reported that mixed anhydrides of acylamino acids and alkylcarbonic acids may serve as excellent acylating agents for the synthesis of peptides. A particular virtue possessed by such mixed carboxylic-carbonic acid anhydrides (IV) lies in their ability to couple with an amino function in a manner such that the desired peptide derivative (VIII) is obtained almost exclusively, the sole by-products being a readily removable alcohol (VI) and carbon dioxide (VII). Derivatives are thereby secured in a high degree of chemical purity, and the need for repeated recrystallizations arising from the presence of contaminants considerably reduced. Studies by Vaughan and Osato (721), on the relative yields of carbobenzoxyglycinanilide (XII) formed by the action of aniline (XI) on various mixed carbonic-carboxylic acid anhydrides (X) which incorporate carbobenzoxyglycine, revealed that the steric and inductive effects of a given alkyl group on the acylation ratio are of much lesser importance here than was previously observed with mixed carboxylic acid anhydrides (Section 10–28). These results, as given in Table 10–38, are compatible with the later observations of Wieland and Stimming (742) that the action of aqueous hydroxylamine solutions on benzene solutions

$$\begin{array}{c} \text{Cbzo—NHCH}_2\text{CO} \\ \diagdown \\ \text{O} \\ \diagup \\ \text{R}^1\text{OCO} \end{array} + \text{NH}_2\text{C}_6\text{H}_5 \rightarrow \text{Cbzo—NHCH}_2\text{CO—NHC}_6\text{H}_5 + \text{R}^1\text{OH} + \text{CO}_2$$

X   XI   XII   VIa   VIIa

of various mixed anhydrides proceeds with the coupling of hydroxylamine to the more cationoid carbonyl component, and the concomitant liberation of the weaker acid.

TABLE 10–38
Preparation of Carbobenzoxyglycine Anilide by the Mixed Carbonic-Carboxylic Acid Anhydride Procedure (721)

Alkylchlorocarbonate	Yield, %
Ethyl	58
Isopropyl	49
Isobutyl	68
s-Butyl	70
2-Ethylbutyl	55
1:3-Dimethylbutyl	64
1-Ethylamyl	67
1-(2-Methylpropyl)-3-methylbutyl	65
Cyclohexyl	61
3:3:5-Trimethylcyclohexyl	61
Benzyl	44

Experimental Conditions. Formation of mixed carboxylic-carbonic acid anhydrides (IV) is generally achieved through the interaction of equivalent quantities of an alkylchlorocarbonate (II) and an acylamino acid (I), under anhydrous conditions, in the presence of one equivalent of a tertiary amine. The alkylchlorocarbonates most commonly employed are the ethyl, s-butyl, and isobutyl derivatives. Although the amount of solvent customarily employed varies between 25 and 50 ml. per 0.01 mole of reactant, the yield of product ultimately obtained is not appreciably affected either by the relative amount of solvent involved or by the presence of slight excesses of acylamino acid, alkylchlorocarbonate, or tertiary base (721). On the other hand, an extremely critical role is played by temperature during the anhydride formation, as the reaction is essentially inoperative at temperatures greater than $+15°$, while a marked decrease in over-all yield is associated with temperatures below $-20°$. Extensive disproportionation of the anhydride presumably attends the use of the higher temperatures (741).

In consequence, the anhydride-forming reaction is generally permitted to proceed at −5° for 25–30 minutes, after which time it is essentially complete (721). Reaction of the anhydride (IV) with an amino acid ester in an organic medium (procedure 10–70), or with a free amino acid in an alkaline aqueous medium (procedure 10–71) leads to the desired peptide derivative (VIII), the formation of an alcohol (VI), and the rapid evolution of carbon dioxide (VII).

Illustrative procedure 10–70 (473).   Carbobenzoxy-S-benzyl-L-cysteinyl-S-benzyl-L-cysteine ethyl ester.   A solution of 346 g. (1 mole) of carbobenzoxy-S-benzyl-L-cysteine (procedure 10–28) and 139 ml. (1 mole) of triethylamine in 3 l. of toluene is chilled to −5° and treated with 131 ml. (1 mole) of isobutylchlorocarbonate. After some 25 min. of standing, a cold solution of 276 g. (1 mole) of S-benzyl-L-cysteine ethyl ester hydrochloride (procedure 10–48) and 139 ml. of triethylamine in 2 l. of chloroform is added and the mixture allowed to stand overnight at 25°. One additional liter of chloroform is added, and the mixture washed successively with water, 3% bicarbonate solution, and water, and finally dried over anhydrous sodium sulfate. The filtrate is condensed *in vacuo* to low bulk and the residual solution treated with petroleum ether. The carbobenzoxy-S-benzyl-L-cysteinyl-S-benzyl-L-cysteine ethyl ester which precipitates is filtered over suction and recrystallized from ethanol.   The yield is 382 g. (67%); m.p. 105° (corr); $[\alpha]_D^{26} = -55.3°$ (2% in acetone).

Illustrative procedure 10–71 (721).   Carbobenzoxyglycyl-DL-phenylalanine.   A solution of 4.18 g. (0.02 mole) of carbobenzoxyglycine (procedures 10–28 and 10–30) and 2.04 g. (0.02 mole) of triethylamine in 50 ml. of toluene is cooled to −5° and 2.73 g. (0.02 mole) of isobutylchlorocarbonate added thereto. After 25 min. a solution of 3.28 g. (0.02 mole) of DL-phenylalanine in 20 ml. of N sodium hydroxide is added and the mixture stirred vigorously for 2–3 hr. during which time it is permitted to warm to room temperature. Carbon dioxide is evolved during this interval. The aqueous phase is isolated, extracted with ether, and acidified with hydrochloric acid to precipitate the product as a colorless oil which crystallizes rapidly upon cooling. After two recrystallizations from ethanol–water, 4.50 g. (63%) of pure product is obtained; m.p. 160–162°.

Scope and Limitations.   Where applicable, the use of the mixed carboxylic-carbonic acid procedure may be expected to give generally satisfactory yields of products which possess a high degree of analytical purity. The method may be applied to coupling reactions involving most acylamino acids with the notable exceptions of trifluoroacetyl- and tritylamino acids; reaction in the latter instance is restricted to the trityl derivatives of glycine and alanine. As with the mixed carboxylic acid anhydride procedure discussed earlier (Section 10–28), the present method requires that proper masking of reactive side-chain functions, i.e., hydroxyl, sulfhydryl, ω-carboxyl, be rigidly adhered to before anhydride formation. Unlike the former procedure, however, steric hindrance imposed by β-branched chain amino acid residues, e.g., valine and isoleucine, is of little significance, and acylamino acids which incorporate such residues should, on the whole, be expected to undergo facile coupling with little complication. This is strikingly demonstrated by the utilization of the method to secure carbobenzoxy-L-valyl-L-valine benzyl ester in some 82% yield from the coupling of carbobenzoxy-L-valine and L-valine benzyl ester, as accomplished by Dr. W. K. Paik in the authors' Laboratory.

The conditions under which mixed carboxylic-carbonic acid anhydrides which incorporate optically active residues suffer racemization, as well as the mechanism involved in such process, are not unlike those encountered with mixed carboxylic anhydrides and need not be fully reiterated here. However, it is of interest to note that, while little tendency toward racemization is revealed in the preparation of peptide derivatives wherein an optically active carbobenzoxy- or phthalylamino acid is employed as one of the reactants, like implication of an acylated dipeptide (or higher peptide) in mixed anhydride formation may be accompanied by extensive optical inactivation. In this connection, Vaughan (682) observed that the mixed anhydride derived from carbobenzoxyglycyl-L-phenylalanine and isobutyl chlorocarbonate, when coupled with ethyl glycinate in chloroform solution, yielded a tripeptide derivative which was virtually completely racemic. When a dioxane–toluene mixture was employed as the solvent system only a slight amount of racemization ensued, whereas no detectable loss of optical activity attended the use of tetrahydrofuran. That the nature of the solvent involved may play an important role in determining the stereochemical composition of the product is thus clearly revealed. However, to what extent the role of solvent participates with reactants of different composition has not yet been ascertained. In the absence of additional data, therefore, the use of mixed anhydrides in coupling reactions involving acylated peptides containing optically active residues should best be avoided if products of high optical purity are desired.

Related Methods. When a solution of an acylamino acid (Ia) in benzene containing one equivalent of a tertiary base is treated with a solution of carbonyl chloride (XIII) in toluene at 0°, reaction is accompanied by the generation of the symmetrical carboxylic acid anhydride (XV) and the evolution of carbon dioxide (741):

$$\begin{array}{cccccc}
\text{RCO—NHCHR}^1\text{CO}_2\text{H} & \text{Cl} & & \text{RCO—NHCHR}^1\text{COO} & & \text{RCO—NHCHR}^1\text{CO} \\
& \diagdown & \textit{tert.} & \diagdown & & \diagdown \\
& \text{C=O} & \xrightarrow{\text{base}} & \text{C=O} & \longrightarrow & \text{O} + \text{CO}_2 \\
& \diagup & \text{C}_6\text{H}_6 & \diagup & & \diagup \\
\text{RCO—NHCHR}^1\text{CO}_2\text{H} & \text{Cl} & & \text{RCO—NHCHR}^1\text{COO} & & \text{RCO—NHCHR}^1\text{CO} \\
\text{Ia} & \text{XIII} & & \text{XIV} & & \text{XV} \quad\quad \text{VII}b
\end{array}$$

Production of (XV) may be attributed to the initial formation of the mixed double carboxylic-carbonic acid anhydride (XIV) which undergoes rapid disproportionation. Analogous reaction occurs if thionyl chloride (XVI) is employed in lieu of carbonyl chloride (741):

$$\begin{matrix} \text{RCO—NHCHR}^1\text{CO}_2\text{H} & \text{Cl} \\ & \diagdown \\ & \text{S=O} \\ & \diagup \\ \text{RCO—NHCHR}^1\text{CO}_2\text{H} & \text{Cl} \\ \text{I}b & \text{XVI} \end{matrix} \xrightarrow[\text{base}]{tert.} \begin{matrix} \text{RCO—NHCHR}^1\text{COO} \\ \diagdown \\ \text{S=O} \\ \diagup \\ \text{RCO—NHCHR}^1\text{COO} \\ \text{XVII} \end{matrix} \rightarrow \begin{matrix} \text{RCO—NHCHR}^1\text{CO} \\ \diagdown \\ \text{O} + \text{SO}_2 \\ \diagup \\ \text{RCO—NHCHR}^1\text{CO} \\ \text{XV}a \quad\quad \text{XVIII} \end{matrix}$$

Although either of the above methods may be utilized for the smooth preparation of symmetrical carboxylic acid anhydrides which are virtually free of contaminating side products, such intermediates are of little value in the practicable synthesis of peptides for reasons given earlier.

That the ethyl chlorocarbonate-mediated condensation of carbobenzoxy-glycine with glycine ethyl ester, in toluene-chloroform solution at $-5°$, proceeds with the formation of appreciable amounts of an N-acylamide side product was reported by Kopple and Renick (742a) in 1958. This side product (m.p. 131.5–132°) could be assigned the composition given by structure (XIX) partly on the basis of its conversion to the linear tripeptide diglycylglycine ethyl ester hydrobromide (XX) upon decarbobenzoxylation with a solution of dry hydrogen bromide in glacial acetic acid (Section 10–46). Such finding is reminiscent of the N-acylamide formation observed

$$\begin{matrix} \text{C}_6\text{H}_5\text{CH}_2\text{OCO—NHCH}_2\text{CO—NCH}_2\text{CO—NHCH}_2\text{CO}_2\text{Et} \\ | \\ \text{C}_6\text{H}_5\text{CH}_2\text{OCO} \\ \text{XIX} \end{matrix} \xrightarrow[\text{HOAc}]{\text{HBr}} \begin{matrix} \text{HBr·NH}_2\text{CH}_2\text{CO—NHCH}_2\text{CO—NHCH}_2\text{CO}_2\text{Et} \\ \\ \text{XX} \end{matrix}$$

two years earlier by Wieland and Heinke (769) when a solution of carbobenz-oxyglycine in tetrahydrofuran was treated with a tertiary base and phosphorus oxychloride at $-15°$ (Section 10–34). However, since N-acylamide formation is probably hindered by the steric effect of amino acid side chains, it should not ordinarily be expected to occur in similar reactions which involve amino acid residues other than glycine.

30. Phosphate Anhydrides of Amino Acids and Acylamino Acids. *Principle.*
The interaction of an acylamino acid chloride (I) with silver dibenzyl phosphate (II) in an inert organic solvent proceeds with the formation of the

$$\begin{matrix} & \text{O} & & \text{OCH}_2\text{C}_6\text{H}_5 & & & \text{O} & \text{OCH}_2\text{C}_6\text{H}_5 \\ & \| & & \diagup & & & \| & \diagup \\ \text{RCO—NHCHR}^1\text{C—Cl} & + & \text{AgO—P=O} & & \rightarrow & \text{RCO—NHCHR}^1\text{C—O—P=O} & + \text{AgCl} \\ & & & \diagdown & & & & \diagdown \\ & & & \text{OCH}_2\text{C}_6\text{H}_5 & & & & \text{OCH}_2\text{C}_6\text{H}_5 \\ \text{I} & & \text{II} & & & \text{III} & & \text{IV} \end{matrix}$$

$$\downarrow \text{NH}_2\text{R}^2$$

$$\begin{matrix} & \text{O} & & \text{OCH}_2\text{C}_6\text{H}_5 & & & & \text{OCH}_2\text{C}_6\text{H}_5 \\ & \| & & \diagup & & & & \diagup \\ \text{RCO—NHCHR}^1\text{C—OAg} & + & \text{Cl—P=O} & & & \text{RCO—NHCHR}^1\text{CO—NHR}^2 + \text{HO—P=O} \\ & & & \diagdown & & & & \diagdown \\ & & & \text{OCH}_2\text{C}_6\text{H}_5 & & & & \text{OCH}_2\text{C}_6\text{H}_5 \\ \text{V} & & \text{VI} & & & \text{VII} & & \text{VIII} \end{matrix}$$

corresponding acylamino acid dibenzyl phosphate (III) and the deposition of silver chloride (IV). Similar products are obtained by the action of dibenzyl chlorophosphate (VI) on the silver salt of an acylamino acid (V). Treatment of (III) with an amino acid in slightly alkaline aqueous solution, or with a suitably constituted amine in an organic solvent, then yields the requisite amide derivative (VII) plus dibenzyl phosphate (VIII).

General Considerations. The past two decades have witnessed an intensive search for reactive intermediates which would condense to form polypeptides and proteins under the conditions found in the living cell. As was pointed out by Borsook and Dubnoff (743) in 1940, thermodynamic considerations require that the biosynthesis of the peptide bond be coupled with some energy-yielding process (Chapter 5). In a later discussion of the role of energetic coupling reactions in biological syntheses, Lipmann (744) speculated that *in vivo* peptide bond formation might conceivably be ascribed to the intermediate implication of energy-rich acyl phosphates of amino acids:

It [should be] remembered that the formation of a mixed acyl phosphate anhydride can be effected through phosphorylation from adenyl pyrophosphate [745]. [A large] part of the constituents of protoplasma are compounds which contain the ... peptide linkage. In the routine procedure or organic chemistry for the synthesis of compounds of this type the acyl chloride of the acid part is first prepared and then brought into reaction with the ... amino group of the other part. In an analogous procedure the cell might first prepare the acyl phosphate with adenyl pyrophosphate as the source of energy-rich phosphate groups. The acyl phosphates of amino acids might then condense with the amino groups of the other amino acids to form proteins.

$$\ldots R\cdot C\overset{O}{\overset{\|}{\cdot}}O\cdot PO_3H_2 + H_2N\cdot R'\cdot C\overset{O}{\overset{\|}{\cdot}}O\cdot PO_3H_2 + H_2N\cdot R''\cdot C\overset{O}{\overset{\|}{\cdot}}O\cdot PO_3H_2 + H_2N\cdot R''' \ldots \rightarrow$$

$$\ldots R\cdot C\overset{O}{\overset{\|}{-}}NH\cdot R'\underset{+}{-}C\overset{O}{\overset{\|}{-}}NH\cdot R''\underset{+}{-}C\overset{O}{\overset{\|}{-}}NH\cdot R''' \ldots$$
$$\quad\quad\quad H_3PO_4 \quad\quad H_3PO_4 \quad\quad H_3PO_4$$

The phosphoryl groups, continuously generated in metabolizing cells, might thus find application for protoplasmic synthesis.

Such postulated participation of adenosinetriphosphate in a transphosphorylation reaction with free amino acids has since received considerable support from studies concerned with the biosynthesis of *p*-aminohippuric acid (746), glutamine (747, 748), and glutathione (749), among others. The isolation and characterization of phosphorylated amino acids from such biosynthetic systems would, of course, provide overwhelming evidence in favor of their mediation in the biogenesis of proteins. However, efforts in this direction have hitherto been thwarted because of the marked chemical reactivity as well as the extreme instability of these compounds.

In connection with the above, several studies have been directed toward the chemical synthesis of compounds which might serve as adequate models for the postulated biosynthetic "energy-rich" phosphates. Thus Chantrenne (750, 751) demonstrated that acylphosphate or acylamino acid phosphate, the phosphoric acid groups of which are bound in ester linkage, undergo ready reaction with the amino moiety of a free amino acid to form the corresponding acylated amino acid or peptide under conditions of physiological pH and temperature. The system studied may be exemplified by the following (751):

$$\underset{\text{IX}}{\text{Cbzo—NHCH}_2\text{COCl}} + \underset{\text{X}}{\text{AgO—P(OC}_6\text{H}_5\text{)(OAg)=O}} \rightarrow \underset{\text{XI}}{\text{Cbzo—NHCH}_2\text{COO—P(OC}_6\text{H}_5\text{)(OAg)=O}} \xrightarrow[p\text{H 7.4, 37°}]{\text{NH}_2\text{CHRCO}_2\text{H}}$$

$$\underset{\text{XII}}{\text{Cbzo—NHCH}_2\text{CO—NHCHRCO}_2\text{H}}$$

where the reaction of carbobenzoxyglycyl chloride (IX) with disilver phenylphosphate (X) yielded the "energy-rich" silver salt of carbobenzoxyglycine phenylphosphate (XI) which, in turn, underwent facile reaction with aqueous solutions of an amino acid at 37° and a pH of 7.4 to form the corresponding carbobenzoxy dipeptide (XII). The carbobenzoxy derivatives of glycylglycine, glycyltyrosine, and glycylglycyltyrosine were so prepared.

Shortly after the appearance of the pioneer studies of Chantrenne (750, 751), Sheehan and Frank (752) described the synthesis of glycine dibenzyl phosphate as its N-phthalyl (XIV) and N-carbobenzoxy derivatives (III; R = C$_6$H$_5$CH$_2$O—; R^1 = H). Preparation of the former intermediate was effected via the action of a suspension of the silver salt of dibenzyl phosphate (IIa) on phthalylglycyl chloride (XIII) in benzene solution at room temperature. A comparable reaction was employed wherein carbobenzoxyglycyl chloride was used in lieu of (XIII). The very marked instability of the acylamino acid dibenzyl phosphates so derived was strikingly revealed when attempts to recrystallize the phthalylglycyl dibenzyl phosphate (XIV) from benzene was accompanied by ready disproportionation with the concomitant formation of *symm*. phthalylglycine anhydride (XVI), m.p. 240–241°, and tetrabenzyl pyrophosphate (XVII). A similar decomposition of (XIV) was induced by the presence of a small amount of triethylamine, or upon prolonged standing. Reaction of (XIV) with water–dioxane resulted in its hydrolysis to the acylamino acid (XVIII), while its interaction with aniline or benzylamine in dioxane–benzene, or with glycine or DL-phenylalanine in aqueous solution at pH 7.4, proceeded with the formation of the pertinent amide or dipeptide derivative (XV).

A procedure analogous to that described by Sheehan and Frank was employed by Bentler and Netter (753) for the preparation of the free dibenzyl phosphate anhydrides (XXI) of glycine (m.p. 62°), of DL-alanine (oil), and of DL-phenylalanine (m.p. 104–106°). Thus reaction of the pertinent α-azido acid chloride (XIX) with silver dibenzyl phosphate (II*b*) led to the corresponding coupling product (XX) which, upon hydrogenolysis in the presence of Raney nickel catalyst, was reduced to the amino acid dibenzyl phosphate (XXI). Although debenzylation of the latter to the free phosphate anhydrides (XXII) was achieved via a palladium-catalyzed reduction, no properties were described for these materials.

An alternative method for the synthesis of free phosphate anhydrides of amino acids was described by Katchalsky and Paecht (754, 755). Thus the silver salt of a carbobenzoxyamino acid (V; R = $C_6H_5CH_2O$—) was condensed with dibenzyl chlorophosphate (VI) in dry carbon tetrachloride at room temperature to yield the carbobenzoxyamino acid dibenzyl phosphate (III). Treatment of the product (IIIa) with a stream of dry hydrogen bromide in carbon tetrachloride resulted in a cleavage of the carbobenzoxy and benzyl groups with the concomitant formation of the desired amino acid phosphate (XXIIa), benzyl bromide (XXIII), and carbon dioxide (XXIV):

$$C_6H_5CH_2OCO\text{—}NHCHRC(\text{=}O)\text{—}O\text{—}P(\text{=}O)(OCH_2C_6H_5)_2 \xrightarrow{\text{HBr in } CCl_4} NH_2CHRC(\text{=}O)\text{—}O\text{—}P(\text{=}O)(OH)_2 + 3C_6H_5CH_2Br + CO_2$$

$$\text{IIIa} \qquad\qquad \text{XXIIa} \qquad \text{XXIII} \qquad \text{XXIV}$$

Essentially the same procedure was employed to synthesize the free phosphate anhydrides of glycine, alanine, and leucine. In addition, the β- and γ-phosphate anhydrides of L-aspartic acid and L-glutamic acid, respectively, were prepared in a comparable manner from the requisite carbobenzoxyamino acid α-benzyl ester ω-dibenzyl phosphate (XXV), i.e.,

$$C_6H_5CH_2OCO\text{—}NHCH(COOCH_2C_6H_5)(CH_2)_xC(\text{=}O)\text{—}O\text{—}P(OCH_2C_6H_5)_2$$

XXV

where x equals 1 or 2. The free phosphate anhydrides were obtained as clear, heavy, and highly hygroscopic oils of about 70–90% purity. As a consequence of the extreme lability of these substances, attempts to effect further purification resulted in their extensive decomposition.

From the viewpoint of the postulated biological role of amino acid phosphates (744), the properties of these compounds as described by Katchalsky and Paecht (755) become of extreme interest. Thus these substances react spontaneously with alcohols to yield esters (XXVI), with amines to yield amides (XXVII), and with hydroxylamine to yield hydroxamic acids (XXVIII):

$$NH_2CHRCO_2R^1 \xleftarrow{R^1OH} NH_2CHRC(\text{=}O)\text{—}O\text{—}P(\text{=}O)(OH)_2 \begin{array}{c} \xrightarrow{NH_2R^2} NH_2CHRCO\text{—}NHR^2 \quad \text{XXVII} \\ \xrightarrow{NH_2OH} NH_2CHRCO\text{—}NHOH \quad \text{XXVIII} \end{array}$$

XXVI XXIIb

The β- and γ-phosphates of aspartic acid and glutamic acid, respectively, react with aqueous ammonia, asparagine and glutamine being formed. By virtue of the strong acidity of the phosphate group, it has been suggested that amino acid phosphates exist as dipolar ions (XXIX), i.e.,

$$\overset{+}{N}H_3-CHRC(=O)-O-P(=O)(O^-)(OH)$$

XXIX

These substances phosphorylate adenylic acid in aqueous solution to adenosine diphosphate. Although the phosphate anhydrides of the dibasic amino acids fail to exhibit ready polymerization, those of the neutral amino acids are not only hydrolyzed but, in addition, undergo facile condensation with the formation of polypeptides in aqueous solution at room temperature and a neutral pH. In any event, it is clear that the extreme lability and reactivity of amino acid phosphates would not be likely to permit their ready isolation from biological sources if these substances were, indeed, the reactive intermediates involved in *in vivo* polypeptide synthesis.

In view of the availability of more convenient methods, the phosphate anhydrides of acylamino acids are not commonly utilized for the routine synthesis of peptides. These intermediates are important, however, for the preparation of model "high energy" amino acid phosphates. The method given immediately below for the preparation of leucine phosphate (procedure 10–72) may, with suitable modifications, be extended to the synthesis of other amino acid phosphates.

Illustrative procedure 10–72 (756). Dibenzyl chlorophosphate. A solution of 216 g. (2 moles) of benzyl alcohol in 242 g. (2 moles) of dimethylaniline is added dropwise over a period of 2 hr. to an ice-cold solution of 137.5 g. (1 mole) of phosphorus trichloride in 750 ml. of dry benzene with continuous agitation. Stirring is continued 0.5 hr. longer, 108 g. (1 mole) of benzyl alcohol added slowly over 20 min., and the reaction mixture permitted to stand at room temperature overnight. The precipitated dimethylaniline hydrochloride is dissolved by the addition of 500 ml. of water, and the benzene layer separated, washed in turn with two 500-ml. portions of water, two 500-ml. portions of 5N ammonia, and two 500-ml. portions of water, and dried over anhydrous sodium sulfate. Evaporation of the benzene under reduced pressure leaves 190 g. of a pale yellow oil which is subjected, in portions of 40–50 g., to slow distillation under 10^{-3} mm. from a short path alembic type of still. The colorless dibenzyl phosphite is collected at 110–120°; n_D^{25} 1.5521; yield 149 g. A solution of 8.6 g. of dibenzyl phosphite in 44 ml. of dry carbon tetrachloride is cooled to −15° and 48.4 ml. of a 1.4N solution of chlorine in carbon tetrachloride added dropwise with stirring, the temperature being kept below −10°. Dry nitrogen is now passed through the liquid for about 30 min. to sweep out the excess chlorine and hydrogen chloride. The carbon tetrachloride solution of dibenzyl chlorophosphate so obtained is used directly below without prior isolation of the ester.

L-Leucine phosphate (755). To a 2M aqueous solution of the sodium salt of carbobenzoxy-L-leucine (procedure 10–29), containing no excess sodium hydroxide, an equivalent amount of silver nitrate solution is slowly added. The precipitated silver salt of carbobenzoxyleucine is washed with distilled water, extracted with ether, and then dried to constant weight in the dark. Twelve grams of this silver salt is added to the carbon tetrachloride solution of dibenzyl chlorophosphate prepared above, and the reaction mixture agitated for 2 hr. at room temperature by a stream of dry nitrogen. After standing overnight, the silver chloride and the excess silver salt of carbobenzoxyleucine are removed by filtration, and the carbon tetrachloride removed by distillation under reduced pressure. The carbobenzoxyleucine dibenzyl phosphate remains as a viscous oil. To prepare the free leucine phosphate, a stream of dry hydrogen bromide is passed through a 10% solution of carbobenzoxyleucine dibenzyl phosphate in water-free carbon tetrachloride. The temperature of the solution rises during this reaction. After the solution becomes saturated with gas (about 20 min.), the leucine phosphate separates as a heavy oil and the oil is washed copiously with ether; traces of solvent are removed *in vacuo* with a diffusion pump at room temperature. Although this procedure does not remove all traces of the entrapped side product (benzyl bromide), more drastic procedures result in decomposition of the leucine phosphate. Essentially the same method has, in addition, been employed to prepare glycine phosphate and alanine phosphate (754) in addition to the β- and γ-phosphates of L-aspartic acid and L-glutamic acid (755), respectively.

31. Methods Involving Substituted Phosphite Ester Intermediates. *Principle.* An appropriately substituted chlorophosphite (II; $X = Cl$) or pyrophosphite (II; $X = (RO)_2P$—O—) may react in an inert solvent containing a tertiary base, e.g., triethylamine, either with an acylamino acid (I) to yield the corresponding mixed carboxylic acid-phosphite anhydride (III), or with an

$$R^1CO-NHCHR^2CO_2H + X-P(OR)_2 \xrightarrow{(C_2H_5)_3N} R^1CO-NHCHR^2COOP(OR)_2 + (C_2H_5)_3N \cdot HX$$
$$\text{I} \qquad \text{II} \qquad \text{III} \qquad \text{IV}$$

$$\Big| NH_2CHR^3CO_2Et$$

$$R^1CO-NHCHR^2CO_2H + NH_2CHR^3CO_2Et + X-P(OR)_2 \rightarrow R^1CO-NHCHR^2CO-NHCHR^3CO_2Et$$
$$\text{I}a \qquad \text{V} \qquad \text{II}a \qquad \text{VI} \qquad + (RO)_2POH$$
$$\text{VII}$$

$$R^1CO-NHCHR^2CO_2H \Big\uparrow$$

$$(RO)_2P-X + NH_2CHR^3CO_2Et \xrightarrow{(C_2H_5)_3N} (RO)_2P-NHCHR^3CO_2Et + (C_2H_5)_3N \cdot HX$$
$$\text{II}b \qquad \text{V}a \qquad \text{VIII} \qquad \text{IV}a$$

amino acid ester (V*a*) to yield the corresponding phosphite amide (VIII). Reaction of the former intermediate (III) with an amino acid ester, or of the latter intermediate (VIII) with an acylamino acid, proceeds with the generation of the requisite acyl-dipeptide ester (VI). By virtue of the fact that the chlorophosphite or pyrophosphite reactant may activate either an amino or

CHEMICAL PROCEDURES FOR SYNTHESIS OF PEPTIDES

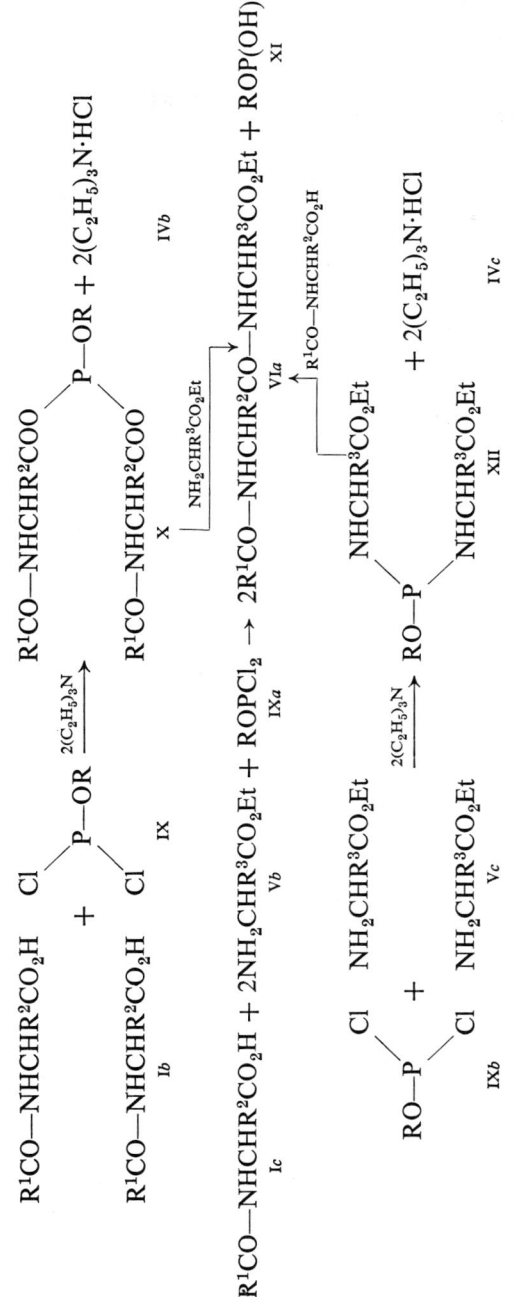

a carboxyl function for coupling purposes, it is possible to achieve the same results as above by adding this reagent (IIa) directly to a mixture of the acylamino acid (Ia) and the amino acid ester (V) in a suitable solvent containing the tertiary base.

Dichlorophosphite esters may be employed in exactly the same manner as the afore-mentioned monochlorophosphites for coupling purposes. As both halogens of the former (IX) are reactive, 1 mole of (IX) may react either with 2 moles of an acylamino acid (Ib) to form the mixed anhydride (X), or with 2 moles of an amino acid ester (Vc) to form the phosphite amide (XII). Reaction of the former intermediate (X) with an amino acid ester or of the latter intermediate (XII) with an acylamino acid then yields the pertinent acyl-dipeptide ester (VIa). As with the monochlorophosphite esters, the desired peptide derivative (VIa) may be prepared by adding the dichlorophosphite ester (IXa) directly to a solution of the acylamino acid (Ic), amino acid ester (Vb), and tertiary base in an inert solvent. (See p. 989.) If the procedure above is modified by using a 1:1 ratio of dichlorophosphite ester (IXc) to amino acid ester (Vd), the reaction presumably proceeds with the formation of the "phosphite imide" (XIII) which, in turn, undergoes coupling with an acylamino acid as before:

$$ROPCl_2 + NH_2CHR^3CO_2Et \rightarrow [ROP{=}NCHR^3CO_2Et] \xrightarrow{R^1CO-NHCHR^2CO_2H}$$
$$\text{IXc} \qquad \text{Vd} \qquad\qquad \text{XIII}$$

$$R^1CO-NHCHR^2CO-NHCHR^3CO_2Et$$
$$\text{VIb}$$

General Considerations. In a series of papers by Anderson (697, 722, 757, 758) and his collaborators, it was revealed that tetraethyl pyrophosphite (XIV), diester chlorophosphites such as diethyl chlorophosphite (XV), *o*-phenylene chlorophosphite (XVI), or ethylene chlorophosphite (XVII), or monoester dichlorophosphites such as ethyl dichlorophosphite (XVIII) may be employed as reagents for forming a peptide link. Thus reaction of

such reagents with either an amino function or a carboxyl function proceeds with the formation of a reactive phosphite amide or mixed carboxylic acid–phosphite anhydride which, in turn, undergoes a smooth reaction with the other function. Similar utilization of ethyl dichlorophosphite (XVIII) and phenyl dichlorophosphite (XIX) was independently demonstrated by Goldschmidt and Obermeier (759). Use of reagents of this type for coupling purposes is particularly convenient in that they may be added directly to a mixture of the reactant carboxylic acid and amine in a suitable solvent without prior formation of either the phosphite amide or the mixed anhydride. That mixed carboxylic acid–phosphite anhydrides may undergo disproportionation reactions was indicated when the mixed anhydride (XX) between o-phenylene chlorophosphite and phthalylglycine deposited some 20% of the symmetrical anhydride of phthalylglycine (XXI) upon standing for some 2 days at 30° in benzene solution (697):

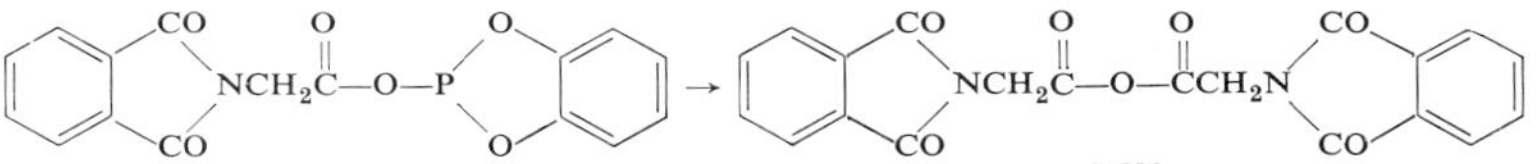

In contrast, the phosphite amides are stable albeit non-crystalline compounds which may be stored for several months in the cold without any seeming alteration in appearance or reactivity (757). Moisture must be excluded, however, as the compounds are readily decomposed by water.

Experimental Conditions. Tetraethyl pyrophosphite (XIV) has emerged as a reagent of choice for coupling procedures involving substituted phosphite ester intermediates as a result of the fact that it can be obtained initially in a pure form by distillation and its purity can be periodically checked by refractive index measurements, virtues not generally possessed by the chlorophosphite esters (722). Preparation of the desired peptide derivative is most conveniently achieved by the addition of one equivalent of the pertinent phosphite ester reagent to a solution of one equivalent each of the acylamino acid (or peptide), the amino acid ester (or peptide ester), and triethylamine in a dry inert solvent (procedure 10–74). Usually only some 15 to 30 minutes of heating on a steam bath is adequate to complete the reaction, although longer periods of heating may be desirable in some instances. In alternative procedures, the mixed carboxylic acid–phosphite anhydride may be first prepared by the interaction of the acylamino acid, triethylamine, and the phosphite reagent in an inert solvent below 25° (procedure 10–75), or the phosphite amide prepared by the addition of the phosphite reagent to a solution of the amine reactant in a suitable solvent containing sufficient triethylamine to neutralize all the hydrogen chloride present or formed in the reaction (temperature sometimes kept below 25° by external cooling) (procedure 10–73). Addition of the pertinent amine reactant to the former reactive intermediate or the carboxylic reactant to the latter, followed by heating over the steam bath as above, then yields the desired peptide derivative. By virtue of the facile decomposition which the reactive intermediates undergo in the presence of water, anhydrous conditions should be observed, and thoroughly dried solvents employed. Solvents which have proved most suitable include benzene and toluene, while the utilization of yet other solvents, e.g., dioxane or chloroform, have led to less satisfactory over-all yields (722); especially high yields have been noted (759a) when anhydrous pyridine was employed. The use of diethyl phosphite as the solvent in the peptide-forming reaction affords a particular advantage not only in that it is frequently effective with the higher, less-soluble peptide derivatives, but also because its miscibility with both water and ordinary organic solvents permits the ready precipitation of the product by the addition of one or the other of these solvents (722). Trialkyl phosphites such as trimethyl, triethyl, and triallyl phosphite have also been employed (758). As these solvents (XXII) react with hydrogen halides (XXIII) to form inert alkyl halides (XXV) and dialkyl phosphites (XXIV),

$$(RO)_3P + HX \rightarrow (RO)_2POH + RX$$
$$XXII XXIII XXIV XXV$$

it follows that the use of organic bases to neutralize the hydrogen halide generated during the peptide-forming reaction may be avoided here.

Illustrative procedure 10–73 (760). Diethyl chlorophosphite. A solution of 87 ml. (1 mole) of phosphorus trichloride in 200 ml. of dry ether contained in a 1-l. 3-necked flask fitted with rubber-sealed stirrer, dropping funnel, thermometer, and exit tube containing calcium chloride is cooled in an ice bath. A solution of 117 ml. (2 mole) of dry ethanol and 253 ml. (2 mole) of dimethylaniline in 200 ml. of dry ether is added dropwise over a period of 1hr., the temperature being kept below 25°. Stirring is continued at room temperature for 30 min. and the reaction mixture then filtered and the granular precipitate of dimethylaniline hydrochloride washed thrice with 100 ml. dry ether each time. The solvent is removed from the combined filtrate and washings by distillation from a water bath through a short column; yield 131.5 g. Fractionation is achieved under an atmosphere of nitrogen with the fraction coming over at 40–50° at 11 mm. collected. A yield of 80.9 g. (52%) of diethyl chlorophosphite is so secured which, although not pure, is suitable for use below. The percentage of purity for such purposes is calculated from the chlorine content on the assumption that all chlorine arises from the diethyl chlorophosphite.

Carbobenzoxy-L-asparaginylglycine benzyl ester (482). A suspension of 10.1 g. (0.05 mole) of glycine benzyl ester hydrochloride (procedures 10–52, 10–54, and 10–57) in 300 ml. of absolute ether is shaken with 10.1 g. (0.10 mole) of triethylamine in 50 ml. of absolute ether for 1 hr.; 7.83 g. (0.05 mole) of diethyl chlorophosphite dissolved in 50 ml. of absolute ether is then added, and the mixture shaken from time to time for another hour. The mixture is held at 0–5° for 18 hr., filtered, concentrated *in vacuo*, the resulting oil dissolved in 250 ml. of dry toluene, and 13.3 g. (0.05 mole) of carbobenzoxy-L-asparagine (procedure 10–30) added thereto. The mixture is refluxed until solution is complete (1 hr.). Upon cooling, a copious gelatinous precipitate is obtained. This is washed with small amounts of toluene and ether and recrystallized from large volumes of boiling water; yield, 10 g. (50%); m.p. 181–183°.

Illustrative procedure 10–74 (722). Tetraethyl pyrophosphite. To a solution of 138 g. (1 mole) of diethyl phosphite and 101 g. (1 mole) of triethylamine (redistilled) in 200 ml. of benzene at 0° is added rapidly (10 min.) with stirring 1 mole of diethyl chlorophosphite (procedure 10–73) dissolved in 200 ml. of benzene. The mixture is cooled for an additional 15 min. and then filtered under nitrogen to remove the triethylamine hydrochloride. After the latter is washed with 200 ml. of benzene, the combined filtrate and washings are distilled under vacuum and the fraction boiling at 79–81° at 0.15 mm. collected; yield 41%; n_D^{26} 1.4313, d^{20} 1.053. The n_D^{26} of 1.4313 is taken as a measure of 100% pure tetraethyl pyrophosphite for the present purposes. Inasmuch as water reacts with this reagent to produce diethyl phosphite, the following refractive indices of mixtures of diethyl phosphite and tetraethyl pyrophosphite may be employed to estimate roughly the composition of the reagent at any given time: N (mole fraction of the pyrophosphite) 0.00, n_D^{26} 1.4050; N 0.21, n_D^{26} 1.4128; N 0.35, n_D^{26} 1.4160; N 0.52, n_D^{26} 1.4220; N 0.62, n_D^{26} 1.4235; N 0.68, n_D^{26} 1.4258; N 1.00, n_D^{26} 1.4314. A curve plotted from these figures indicates that n_D^{26} 1.4300 would correspond to 93% of the pyrophosphite by weight. Consequently the use of a 10% excess of the pyrophosphite by weight in peptide coupling procedures assures an adequate amount of this reagent if the n_D^{26} is 1.4300 or higher.

Carbobenzoxy-L-leucyl-L-tyrosine ethyl ester (722). To 7 ml. (0.050 mole) of diethyl phosphite are added 2.65 g. (0.01 mole) of carbobenzoxy-L-leucine (procedure 10–29), 1.11 g. (0.011 mole) of triethylamine, and 2.44 g. (0.01 mole) of tyrosine ethyl ester hydrochloride (procedure 10–48). Then 2.84 g. (0.011 mole) of tetraethyl pyrophosphite is added and the mixture heated over a steam bath for 30 min. After this time some 25–50 ml. of water is added, the reaction mixture is cooled in ice water, and the precipitated product separated and washed first with 10–20 ml. of 5% sodium bicarbonate solution, then with water. The crude product is dried and finally recrystallized from ethyl acetate–petroleum ether; yield 40%; m.p. 112–114°; $[\alpha]_D^{24} = -14°$ (5% in ethanol).

Illustrative procedure 10–75 (758). Ethyl dichlorophosphite. To 360 ml. (3.99 moles) of phosphorus trichloride is added 167 g. (3.63 moles) of absolute alcohol through a dropping funnel over a period of 1 hr. with mechanical stirring and cooling in an ice–water bath. Fumes of hydrogen chloride are evolved during the addition (*Use hood!*). Within a few minutes after the addition is complete the mixture clears of fumes, and the dropping funnel and fume outlet are replaced by Drierite drying tubes. The mixture is stirred at room temperature for 16 hr. and then distilled *in vacuo* at 40–50° to obtain one large fraction. Redistillation at atmospheric pressure in a Vigreaux column yields ethyl dichlorophosphite in about 42% of theory. The refractive index at 25° ranges from 1.4643 (second fraction, b.p. 115–116°) to 1.4622 (third fraction, b.p. 117–118°).

Phthalylglycyl-L-leucine ethyl ester (758). To a solution of 2.05 g. (0.01 mole) of phthalylglycine (procedure 10–33) in 30 ml. of benzene containing 1.01 g. (0.01 mole) of triethylamine is added 0.74 g. (0.005 mole) of ethyl dichlorophosphite in 10 ml. of benzene. After removal of the deposited amine hydrochloride by filtration, a suspension of 1.94 g. (0.01 mole) of L-leucine ethyl ester hydrochloride (procedure 10–48) in 25 ml. of benzene containing 1.11 g. (0.011 mole) of triethylamine is added and the reaction mixture either held at reflux for 15 min. or permitted to stand at room temperature overnight. After completion of the reaction, the reaction mixture is washed with 10 ml. of water and 15 ml. of saturated sodium bicarbonate solution. The benzene solution is dried over sodium sulfate, concentrated to dryness *in vacuo*, and the residue is crystallized from 50% ethanol; yield 91%; m.p. 143–144°; $[\alpha]_D^{25} = -29.0°$ (2% in ethanol).

In connection with the afore-mentioned studies, it was shown that the formation of at least some peptide derivatives (VIc) may occur by simply heating an acylamino acid (Id) with an amino acid ester (Ve) in an inert solvent such as toluene (757):

$$R^1CO-NHCHR^2CO_2H + NH_2CHR^3CO_2Et \xrightarrow[\Delta]{\text{toluene}} R^1CO-NHCHR^2CO-NHCHR^3CO_2Et + H_2O$$
$$\text{Id} \qquad\qquad \text{Ve} \qquad\qquad\qquad\qquad \text{VIc}$$

Such reaction is of course slower than those wherein the activating phosphite reagent is employed, and is accompanied by diketopiperazine formation resulting from the interaction of two molecules of reactant amino acid ester (procedure 10–76). The procedure should not be considered generally applicable to the preparation of dipeptide derivatives.

Illustrative procedure 10–76 (757). Carbobenzoxyglycyl-DL-phenylalanine ethyl ester. A solution of 4.18 g. (0.02 mole) of carbobenzoxyglycine (procedures 10–28 and 10–30) and 3.87 g. (0.02 mole) of ethyl DL-phenylalaninate in 50 ml. of toluene is refluxed for 1 hr. After cooling, 0.30 g. of DL-phenylalanine anhydride crystallizes out and is separated by filtration. The filtrate is washed first with 25 ml. of 10% sodium bicarbonate, then 10 ml. of water, and finally concentrated under reduced pressure to an oily residue which crystallizes from 40 ml. of 50% alcohol. Yield of carbobenzoxyglycyl-DL-phenylalanine ethyl ester is 2.92 g. (38%); m.p. 87–89°. A similar experiment in which a 2-hr. reflux is employed leads to a 55% yield of the peptide derivative.

Scope and Limitations. Although chlorophosphite and pyrophosphite ester reagents may be utilized to form reactive phosphite amide derivatives for coupling purposes with a carboxyl function, generally more satisfactory yields of product are secured where activation proceeds either with the prior formation of the mixed carboxylic acid–phosphite anhydride or with the addition of the reagent to a solution containing both the amino and carboxylic components. Appropriate masking of reactive ω-amino, ω-carboxyl, hydroxyl, or sulfhydryl substituents in the side-chain functions of implicated residues must be effected preliminary to activation with the phosphite reagent. In this connection, it should be noted that masking of the reactivity of the guanidino group of carbobenzoxy-L-arginine with one equivalent of hydrogen bromide sufficed to permit the successful coupling of this compound with methyl-L-leucinate in diethyl phosphite solution upon the addition of tetraethyl pyrophosphite (471). Phosphite reagents have also been involved in the synthesis of peptides of asparagine and glutamine (482, 672, 674). In contradistinction to the mixed carboxylic acid anhydride procedure (Section 10–28), the steric hindrance presented by the β-alkyl amino acids presumably plays only a minor role in coupling reactions mediated by phosphite ester intermediates, as indicated by the 82% yield of carbobenzoxy-DL-valylglycine ethyl ester obtained from the condensation of carbobenzoxy-DL-valine and glycine ethyl ester (697). The use of phosphite ester intermediates in peptide-forming reactions is convenient and proceeds in generally good yield, and may, to all intents and purposes, be interchanged with the mixed carboxylic acid anhydride and the mixed carboxylic-carbonic acid anhydride procedures.

The formation of peptide intermediates via the implication of reactive phosphite ester intermediates proceeds with little tendency toward racemization when an optically active carbobenzoxy- or phthalylamino acid is employed as one of the reactants (722). However, appreciable racemization may prevail in similar reactions which involve optically active acetylamino acids (681). As was experienced with the mixed carboxylic-carbonic acid anhydride method (Section 10–29), the nature of the reaction solvent may here play an important role in governing to what extent, if any, optical inactivation ensues. Thus, for example, little loss in optical activity is encountered in the formation of the carbobenzoxy-tripeptide ester from the interaction of carbobenzoxyglycyl-L-phenylalanine and glycine ethyl ester in benzene or toluene solution (697). However, when the same reaction is performed in diethylphosphite or trimethylphosphite as the reaction solvent in the presence of hydrogen chloride, either free or bound as the hydrochloride, various degrees of racemization dependent upon the conditions employed are induced (758). Such racemization is presumed to occur via the formation of an oxazolidine salt which effectively destroys the asymmetry about the α-carbon atom. (See the reaction at the top of page 996.) No racemization occurs with these solvent systems in the absence of hydrogen chloride. In this connection, it should be noted that no loss in optical activity is occasioned in those instances where a hydrogen halide is present in inert reaction solvents, such as benzene or toluene, to which a tertiary amine, e.g., triethylamine, has been added to remove the inorganic acid from solution effectively.

Related Methods. A preliminary communication by Vaughan (761) reported that diethyl chloroarsenite (XXVI) may be utilized *in lieu* of the corresponding phosphite analog for the preparation of reactive anhydrides

$$\text{Cbzo—NHCH}_2\overset{\underset{\|}{O}}{C}\text{—NHCHC—O—P}\overset{OR}{\underset{OR}{\diagdown}} \overset{+H^\oplus}{\rightleftharpoons}$$
(with CH₂C₆H₅ side chain; P=O)

$$\text{Cbzo—NHCH}_2\overset{\underset{\|}{O}}{C}\text{—NHCHC—O—P}\overset{OR}{\underset{OR}{\diagdown}} \text{ (OH)} \rightleftharpoons$$

$$\begin{array}{c} \text{HO—C—O—P(OR)}_2 \\ \oplus O \diagup \diagdown \text{CHCH}_2\text{C}_6\text{H}_5 \\ \text{Cbzo—NHCH}_2\text{C}\!=\!\!=\!\!\text{NH} \end{array}$$

$$\begin{array}{c} \text{HO—C—O—P(OR)}_2 \\ O\diagup \diagdown \text{CHCH}_2\text{C}_6\text{H}_5 \\ [\text{Cbzo—NHCH}_2\text{C}\!=\!\!=\!\!\text{N}] + H^\oplus \end{array} \rightleftharpoons \begin{array}{c} \text{HO—C—O—P(OR)}_2 \\ O\diagup \diagdown \text{CCH}_2\text{C}_6\text{H}_5 \\ \text{Cbzo—NHCH}_2\text{CH—N} + H^\oplus \end{array}$$

$$\updownarrow$$

$$\begin{array}{c} \text{C—O—P(OR)}_2 \\ O\diagup \diagdown \text{CCH}_2\text{C}_6\text{H}_5 \\ \text{Cbzo—NHCH}_2\text{C}\!=\!\!=\!\!\text{N} + H_3O^\oplus \end{array}$$

(XXVII) and amides (XXVIII) which, in turn, form useful intermediates in the peptide-forming reaction:

$$\underset{Ie}{R^1CO\text{—NHCHR}^2CO_2H} + \underset{XXVI}{Cl\text{—As(OC}_2H_5)_2} \xrightarrow{(C_2H_5)_3N} \underset{XXVII}{R^1CO\text{—NHCHR}^2CO_2As(OC_2H_5)_2} + \underset{IVd}{(C_2H_5)_3N\cdot HCl}$$

$$\downarrow NH_2CHR^3CO_2Et$$

$$\underset{VId}{R^1CO\text{—NHCHR}^2CO\text{—NHCHR}^3CO_2Et} + (C_2H_5O)_2AsOH$$

$$\uparrow R^1CO\text{—NHCHR}^2CO_2H$$

$$\underset{XXVIa}{(C_2H_5O)_2As\text{—Cl}} + \underset{Vf}{NH_2CHR^3CO_2Et} \xrightarrow{(C_2H_5)_3N} \underset{XXVIII}{(C_2H_5O)_2As\text{—NHCHR}^3CO_2Et} + \underset{IVe}{(C_2H_5)_3N\cdot HCl}$$

The reaction conditions are generally the same as those employed with the phosphite reagent, and comparable yields of product (VI*d*) are obtained with either reagent.

32. Sulfuric Acid Anhydride Method. *Principle.* The mixed anhydride (III) of an acylamino acid (or peptide) and sulfuric acid is formed upon the addition of one equivalent of sulfur trioxide (II) in dimethylformamide solution to a solution of the alkali metal or quaternary ammonium salt of the acylated acid (I). Treatment of (III) with the alkali metal salt of an amino acid or peptide in aqueous solution, or with the ester of an amino acid or peptide in an inert organic solvent containing a tertiary amine, then leads to the desired peptide derivative (IV) with the simultaneous formation of bisulfate ion (V).

$$\underset{\text{I}}{\text{RC(=O)—NHCHR}^1\text{C(=O)—O}^-} + \text{SO}_3 \underset{\text{II}}{\longrightarrow} \underset{\text{III}}{\text{RC(=O)—NHCHR}^1\text{C(=O)—O—SO}_3^-} \xrightarrow{\text{NH}_2\text{R}^2} \underset{\text{IV}}{\text{RC(=O)—NHCHR}^1\text{C(=O)—NHR}^2} + \underset{\text{V}}{\text{HSO}_4^-}$$

General Considerations. In 1952, Kenner and Stedman (712) reported that mixed anhydrides of an acylamino acid (or an acylated peptide) and sulfuric acid, i.e., acyl sulfates, may serve as satisfactory acylating agents for the synthesis of peptide bonds; this study was subsequently extended by Clayton, Farrington, Kenner, and Turner (495). Like the situation previously encountered with mixed carboxylic acid anhydrides (Section 10–28), acyl sulfates (VII) are theoretically subject to attack by amines (VIII) at two competitive sites, i.e.,

$$\underset{\text{VI}}{\text{RCO—NHR}^1} \leftarrow \underset{\text{VII}}{\text{RCO—O—SO}_3^-} + \underset{\text{VIII}}{\text{NH}_2\text{R}^1} \rightarrow \underset{\text{IX}}{{}^-\text{SO}_3\text{—NHR}^1}$$

the reaction that leads to the desired peptide derivative (VI) largely predominating over that which yields the sulfamate (IX). Unlike mixed carboxylic acid anhydrides, however, acyl sulfates reveal little inclination to undergo disproportionation. A somewhat unusual feature of the acyl sulfates rests on their solubility in water as well as on their stability to hydrolysis by the same solvent; a markedly lesser resistance to the hydrolytic action of hydroxyl ions is revealed. This is strikingly depicted by the estimated half-life periods of the lithium salt of carbobenzoxyglycyl sulfate at various pH values (762):

pH	6	7	8	9	10
Half-life (hr.)	10.5	9.6	5.3	1.0	0.1

Experimental Conditions. Formation of the requisite reactive acyl sulfate intermediate is generally achieved via the interaction of the lithium or potassium salt of an acylamino acid with an equimolar amount of sulfur trioxide at 0° under anhydrous conditions. The sulfur trioxide is employed here as its dimethylformamide coordination complex which, in turn, is conveniently prepared by the distillation of sulfur trioxide from oleum directly into anhydrous dimethylformamide at −15° (procedure 10–77); a solution of such a complex is stable upon storage at −40° for several months, but it undergoes slow decomposition at 0°. The reagent is easily standardized by titration with alkali. Dimethylformamide serves as a suitable anhydrous solvent system for the anhydride-forming reaction by virtue of the fact that acylated amino acids and peptides dissolve freely in it and may then be directly transformed into their anhydrous alkali metal salts upon neutralization with methanolic alkali and subsequent fractional distillation of a portion of the solvent *in vacuo* at 50°. Condensation of the mixed anhydride with a suitably constituted amine may be effected in either an aqueous medium or under anhydrous conditions. A generally satisfactory technique with the former medium involves the addition of the dimethylformamide solution of the anhydride to a cold aqueous solution of the amino acid or peptide buffered to about *p*H 6.8 with powdered magnesium carbonate; where anhydrous conditions are used, the acyl sulfate solution is added to a dimethylformamide solution of the ester hydrochloride salt of the amino acid or peptide in the presence of adequate amounts of triethylamine (procedure 10–77).

Illustrative procedure 10–77 (495). Sulfur trioxide–dimethylformamide complex. One-hundred milliliters of oleum (60%) is heated at 110° under a 6 in. by 1 in. column packed with Fenske glass helices through which nitrogen is bubbled. The receiver is cooled in ice and guarded from atmospheric moisture with a phosphoric oxide drying tube. After about 30 g. of sulfur trioxide has collected, the distillation is terminated and most of the distillate redistilled upon gentle warming into a bulb fitted with a tail-joint. The bulb is then immediately attached to a 3-necked flask fitted with a stirrer and drying tube and containing 85 ml. of *anhydrous* dimethylformamide (dried by azeotropic distillation with benzene). The flask is cooled to −15° and the bulb warmed gently so that sulfur trioxide distills over the surface of the dimethylformamide. This process is interrupted when oily droplets appear in the residue; about 21 g. of sulfur trioxide is so added. The reaction mixture is then stored for 2 hr. at −40° to −60° and the yellow mother liquor sucked off with the aid of a sintered glass filter stick. The residual colorless crystals are washed with 10 ml. of precooled dimethylformamide and then dissolved in 200 ml. of the same solvent. Determination of the molar strength of the solution is achieved by titration with alkali. Storage of the solution at −40° for 1 month in a flask protected with a phosphoric oxide drying tube leads to no marked deterioration of the reagent, while approximately a 3% drop in activity occurs upon similar storage at −5°.

Carbobenzoxy-L-phenylalanylglycine ethyl ester. A solution of 2 millimoles of carbobenzoxy-L-phenylalanine (procedures 10–28 and 10–30) in 50 ml. of dimethylformamide is neutralized with methanolic potassium hydroxide and the mixture then concentrated to about one-half the volume by distillation at 50° and 50 mm. through a 6 in. by 1 in. column packed with steel gauze. To the concentrate is added a dimethylformamide solution containing 2 millimoles of the sulfur trioxide-dimethylformamide complex (see above) at 0°. The mixed anhydride so derived is chilled in an ice bath, a solution of 2 millimoles of glycine ethyl ester hydrochloride and 4 millimoles of triethylamine in dimethylformamide added thereto, and the reaction mixture permitted to stand at 20° for 1 hr. A little water is then added and the *p*H brought to 5 with *N* sulfuric acid. The solution is concentrated to dryness under reduced pressure, the residue shaken with a mixture of 30 ml. of ethyl acetate and 10 ml. of 3*N* sulfuric acid, the ethyl acetate layer separated, and the aqueous fraction extracted five additional times with ethyl acetate. The combined ethyl acetate extracts are washed thrice each with water and then half-saturated sodium bicarbonate, dried over anhydrous sodium sulfate, then concentrated to dryness *in vacuo*. The residual dipeptide derivative is crystallized from ethyl acetate–petroleum ether; yield, 83%; m.p. 107.5–108.5°; $[\alpha]_D^{16} = -19.2°$ (4.1% in ethanol).

Scope and Limitations. Where applicable, the use of the sulfuric acid anhydride method provides an efficient means for acylating a suitably constituted amine under either aqueous or anhydrous conditions. By virtue of the fact that the by-product of such reaction is an easily extractable sulfamic acid, the desired product is generally obtained in a high degree of analytical purity. As in previously discussed methods of the mixed-anhydride type, the sulfuric acid anhydride method requires that the reactivity of ω-amino, ω-carboxyl, hydroxyl, or sulfhydryl substituents in the side-chain functions of the implicated amino acid residues be suitably masked before the anhydride-forming step. Since the reactivity of triethylamine toward sulfur trioxide obviates its use in the preparation of the reactive acyl sulfate intermediates, the alkali metal salt of the acylated amino acid or peptide must be employed. Such requirement constitutes a drawback to the use of the method as compared to the use of the mixed-anhydride methods discussed earlier inasmuch as the preparation of these alkali metal salts is somewhat more tedious than that of the corresponding triethylamine salts.

A particular virtue possessed by the sulfuric acid anhydride method rests on the apparently complete retention of optical integrity exhibited by peptide derivatives prepared in anhydrous dimethylformamide. In such an instance, for example, the condensation of the sulfuric anhydrides of carbobenzoxyglycyl-L-phenylalanine and carbobenzoxyglycyl-L-alanine with the ethyl esters of glycine and L-phenylalanylglycine, respectively, yields a tri- and a tetrapeptide derivative wherein no racemic material can be detected (495). With this in mind, it should be noted that the same coupling reactions, when effected in aqueous solution at *p*H 8, proceed with the occurrence of appreciable racemization. However, if the *p*H of such reactions is kept below 6.8 through the use of powdered magnesium carbonate, the extent to which racemization occurs appears to be negligible. Thus, although the latter method may prove useful for acylating amino acids and peptides in aqueous media with relatively little risk of racemization, such risk is nevertheless necessarily greater than where anhydrous dimethylformamide is employed.

33. Phosphazo Method. *Principle.* When phosphorus trichloride (I) is added to a solution of a suitably constituted amine, e.g., an amino acid ester (II) or peptide ester (IX), and triethylamine in a non-polar solvent such as toluene, reaction proceeds with the formation of the pertinent phosphazo compound (III or X) and triethylamine hydrochloride (IV). If dry pyridine is employed as the solvent, the requirement for the tertiary amine is obviated.

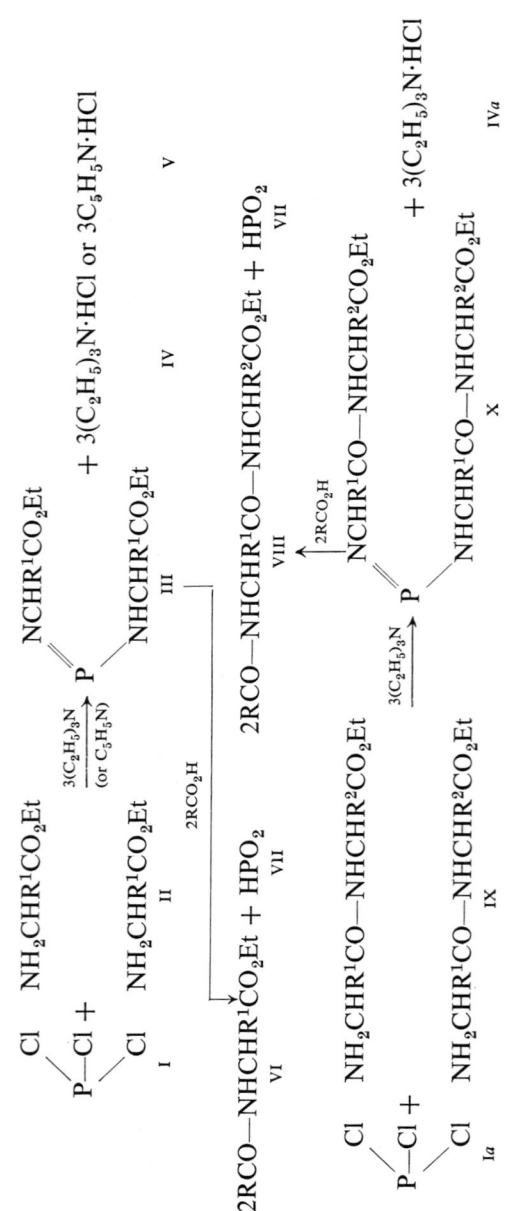

Treatment of the phosphazo intermediate (III or X) with a carboxylic acid, e.g., an acylamino acid or acyl peptide, thereupon leads to the requisite peptide derivative (VI or VIII) with the concomitant liberation of metaphosphorous acid (VII).

General Considerations. Aromatic phosphazo compounds were first described in 1894 by Michaelis and Schroeter (763) who prepared phenylphosphazopiperidide (XIII) by the action of phosphorus trichloride (Ib) on aniline hydrochloride (XI), followed by treatment of the phenylphosphazo chloride (XII) so derived with piperidine:

$$\underset{Ib}{PCl_3} + \underset{XI}{C_6H_5NH_2 \cdot HCl} \rightarrow \underset{XII}{C_6H_5N{=}P{-}Cl} \xrightarrow{C_5H_{11}N} \underset{XIII}{C_6H_5N{=}P{-}NC_5H_{10}}$$

Comparable treatment of (XII) with aniline resulted in the production of phenylphosphazoanilide, $C_6H_5N{=}P{-}NHC_6H_5$. However, efforts to confirm the synthesis by analysis were precluded by the difficulties encountered upon attempted purification of these highly labile products by recrystallization. Some fifty years later, Grimmel, Guenther, and Morgan (764) showed that such phosphazo compounds could be conveniently prepared by the interaction of five moles of a primary aliphatic or aromatic amine (XIV) with one mole of phosphorus trichloride (Ic) in toluene solution. Treatment of one mole of the resultant phosphazo-amide (XV) with two moles of an aromatic or aliphatic carboxylic acid in refluxing toluene then yielded the corresponding substituted acid amide (XVII):

$$\underset{Ic}{PCl_3} + \underset{XIV}{5RNH_2} \longrightarrow \underset{XV}{RN{=}P{-}NHR} + \underset{XVI}{3RNH_2 \cdot HCl} \xrightarrow{2R^1CO_2H} \underset{XVII}{2R^1CO{-}NHR} + \underset{VIIa}{HPO_2}$$

The method does not appear to be similarly applicable to the preparation of N- substituted sulfonamides.

Brief mention should be made here of some of the more general properties of phosphazo-amides. Thus, although these substances undergo slow decomposition upon prolonged exposure to light or heat (100° or above), they are quite stable upon storage for several months at room temperature in the dark. In the presence of moisture, a phosphazo-amide (XVa) is transformed into the so-called "hydrate" which, in essence, corresponds in its reactivity to an N-substituted diamidophosphorous acid (XVIII). While phosphazo compounds are subject to slow hydrolysis by water or dilute alkalis, such a reaction is rapid in warm dilute mineral acids (764):

$$\underset{XVIII}{(RNH)_2P{-}OH} \xleftarrow{H_2O} \underset{XVa}{RN{=}P{-}NHR} \xrightarrow{aq.\ HCl} \underset{XVIa}{RNH_2 \cdot HCl} + \underset{XIX}{H_3PO_3}$$

The exact structural nature of phosphazo compounds has not yet been fully elucidated. Although these substances resemble the diazoamides formula-wise, further structural analogy necessitates the assumption of a true double bond between the phosphorus and the nitrogen atoms. In this connection, the study of Goldschmidt and Krauss (765) on trivalent phosphorus compounds formed from the interaction of phosphorus trichloride with various aromatic amines becomes of interest. This study established the reaction sequence

$$PCl_3 + RNH_2 \cdot HCl \xrightarrow{-HCl} R-N\begin{matrix}PCl_2\\PCl_2\end{matrix} \xrightarrow{>T} R-N\begin{matrix}P=N-R\\P=N-R\end{matrix} \xleftarrow[-RNH_2]{>T} R-N\begin{matrix}RHN-P-NHR\\P=NR\end{matrix}$$

Id   XVIb   XX   XXI   XXII

where each of the compounds formed possessed a markedly different thermal stability. Thus, although compounds of the type represented by (XX) generally revealed melting points in the range of 40°, those represented by (XXI) and (XXII) decomposed at temperatures above 300° and 200°, respectively. The latter two compounds are of especial interest since they may conceivably exist as ring structures (XXIa and XXIIa), in addition to the afore-mentioned open-chain structures (XXI and XXII). Choice between structures (XXI) and (XXIa) is permitted by dipole moment

$$\begin{matrix}&P&\\R-N&N&N-R\\&P&R\end{matrix} \qquad \begin{matrix}&P-NHR&\\R-N&&N-R\\&RHN-P&\end{matrix}$$

XXIa   XXIIa

measurements inasmuch as the former open-chain molecule should be expected to show an appreciable dipole moment while the latter cage-like molecule should be virtually dipole-free. Such measurements indeed revealed a value of 2.03 Debye units for the dipole of (XXI), where R = $CH_3OC_6H_4$, and thereby established its occurrence as the open-chain form. Since (XXI) is readily derived from (XXII) by thermal decomposition, an open-chain structure for this phosphazo compound becomes highly probable (765). Formula (XXII) is also supported by molecular weight determinations on phosphazo compounds which revealed values twice as great as those indicated by their respective empirical formulas, RN=P—NHR[1] (764).

In contrast with the highly crystalline nature of phosphazo compounds which incorporate aromatic amines such as aniline, those which are derived from amino acid or peptide esters are generally secured as highly viscous syrups which show little inclination to crystallize. The ease with which phosphazo compounds of the latter type suffer decomposition does not permit their ready purification. That this is of little consequence in so far as the employment of these reactive compounds for peptide synthesis is concerned was demonstrated by Goldschmidt (766) in collaboration with

Lautenschlager (723) and Jutz (475, 767), who did not isolate such phosphazo intermediates but rather effected their reaction *in situ* with acylamino acids and acylated peptides for the synthesis of peptide derivatives. Good over-all yields of the desired product were obtained under conditions which ensured interaction between the amino acid ester (II) or peptide ester (IX) with phosphorus trichloride (I) in the mole ratio of 2 : 1. In this connection, it should be noted that phosphazo intermediates may sometimes prove useful in the synthesis of acylamino acids. Thus, for example, the acylation of S-benzyl-L-cysteine with phenacetyl chloride in alkaline medium to yield N-phenacetyl-S-benzylcysteine is accompanied by partial racemization (476). However, the reaction of phenylacetic acid with the phosphazo derivative of S-benzyl-L-cysteine methyl ester results in a nearly quantitative yield of optically pure N-phenacetyl-S-benzyl-L-cysteine methyl ester which, upon saponification, may be converted to the corresponding free acid (723).

That phosphazo derivatives of amino acid esters and peptide esters may probably possess the open-chain structure represented by formula (XXII) has been indicated above. However, the suggestion has been made that, when the ester derivative of lysine (XXIII) is involved, an intramolecular ring-type phosphazo intermediate (XXIV) is formed (723). Interaction of this intermediate with an acylamino acid thereupon leads to the corresponding α,ε-disubstituted lysine derivative (XXV):

$$\underset{\text{XXIII}}{\underset{|}{\text{CH}_2\cdot(\text{CH}_2)_3\cdot\overset{|}{\text{CHCO}_2\text{CH}_3}}{\overset{\text{NH}_2\quad\quad\text{NH}_2}{|}}} \xrightarrow[\text{pyridine}]{\text{PCl}_3} \underset{\text{XXIV}}{\underset{|}{\text{CH}_2\cdot(\text{CH}_2)_3\cdot\overset{|}{\text{CHCO}_2\text{CH}_3}}{\overset{\text{N}\quad\quad\quad\text{P}=\text{N}}{|}}} \xrightarrow{\text{R}^1\text{CO}_2\text{H}} \underset{\text{XXV}}{\underset{|}{\text{CH}_2\cdot(\text{CH}_2)_3\cdot\overset{|}{\text{CHCO}_2\text{CH}_3}}{\overset{\text{R}^1\text{CO}-\text{NH}\quad\quad\text{NH}-\text{COR}^1}{|}}}$$

Experimental Conditions. The preparation of reactive phosphazo intermediates (III and X) may be achieved by the interaction of two moles of an amino acid ester (II) or peptide ester (IX) with one mole of phosphorus trichloride (I) in an inert solvent, such as toluene, which contains three moles of a tertiary base in order to neutralize the liberated hydrogen chloride. However, it is generally more expedient to utilize pyridine as the reaction solvent since not only does the reaction proceed smoothly in this medium but also the need for added tertiary amine may here be rendered unnecessary and the ester hydrochloride of the amino acid or peptide directly employed. Anhydrous conditions must be observed and the solvents thoroughly dried. Addition of the phosphorus trichloride to the solution of the amine is accomplished at 0°, the reaction mixture then being permitted to stand at room temperature for some 15 minutes, after which time the formation of the phosphazo intermediate has reached a maximal yield. This reactive intermediate is not isolated as such but rather treated *in situ* with an acylated amino acid or peptide to secure the desired peptide derivative (VI and VIII). Such a reaction is essentially complete after the mixture has been either heated for some 3 hours over a steam bath (procedure 10–78) or stored for several days at room temperature.

Illustrative procedure 10–78 (723). Carbobenzoxyglycylglycine ethyl ester. Five grams of finely divided glycine ethyl ester hydrochloride is dissolved in 100 ml. of dry pyridine with brief warming and the solution cooled to 0°. To the solidified mass is slowly added a solution of 1.6 ml. of phosphorus trichloride in 20 ml. of dry pyridine with thorough mixing. The reaction mixture is permitted to stand at room temperature for 30 min. and 7.5 g. of carbobenzoxyglycine (procedures 10–28 and 10–30) then added thereto. After the mixture has been heated for 3 hr. over a boiling water bath or permitted to stand at room temperature for about 60 hr., it is evaporated *in vacuo* to a residual mass which, after the addition of a little water, is extracted several times with ethyl acetate. The combined ethyl acetate extracts are washed successively with dilute hydrochloric acid, water, 10% sodium bicarbonate and water, then dried with anhydrous sodium sulfate, decolorized with activated charcoal, and finally concentrated to a small volume. After the addition of petroleum ether thereto, followed by storage in the cold, a 9.1-g. yield of carbobenzoxyglycylglycine ethyl ester is recovered by filtration; m.p. 82°.

Scope and Limitations. Reactions which involve phosphazo intermediates for the preparation of peptide derivatives generally proceed smoothly and in high yield when carried out in anhydrous pyridine solution (765). Use of this solvent is particularly advantageous in that the addition of a tertiary base to neutralize hydrogen chloride generated during the phosphazo-forming reaction is avoided; in addition, the ester hydrochloride salts of amino acids and peptides may be employed without prior neutralization. Reactive substituents, e.g., amino or carboxyl moieties on the side-chain functions of the implicated amino-ester reactant, should be suitably masked preliminary to the phosphorus trichloride treatment. In the latter connection, it should be noted that the method may be employed to acylate simultaneously both amino groups of a diamino acid such as lysine (723). Since phosphazo intermediates combine with the carboxyl group of the other reactant in the peptide-forming step, appropriate masking of one or the other carboxyl groups is required when such dicarboxylic acids as aspartic or glutamic acids are implicated; such selective masking has indeed been utilized in the synthesis of a large series of both α- and γ-glutamyl peptides (475, 767). The claim has been made that no racemization is suffered during the synthesis of optically active peptide derivatives via the phosphazo method (765–767). That the tendency toward racemization is not completely absent, however, is indicated by the fact that the acetylleucylglycine ethyl ester which arises from the interaction of acetyl-L-leucine with the phosphazo derivative of glycine ethyl ester is wholly racemic (681). Although more recent use of the method has permitted the synthesis (486) of a variety of optically active carbobenzoxy-dipeptide esters without the occurrence of detectable racemization, similar synthesis of carbobenzoxy polypeptide esters from the condensation of an optically active carbobenzoxy-peptide with an amino acid ester led to partial racemization, except in those instances wherein a glycine or a proline residue was on the C-terminal end of the carbobenzoxy-dipeptide reactant.

Related Methods. An earlier discussion was concerned with the synthesis of peptide derivatives via the mediation of reactive phosphite amide derivatives which were derived from the interaction of a dichlorophosphite ester with a suitably constituted amine (Section 10–31). That such reaction does not invariably proceed as stated, but may alternatively proceed by way of the phosphazo compound which arises from the decomposition of the corresponding phosphite amide, has been pointed out by Goldschmidt and Obermeier (759). Thus, for example, it was noted that the action of aniline on phenyl dichlorophosphite (XXVI) sometimes yields phenylphosphazoanilide (XXXI) in lieu of the phosphite amide (XXVII) as the reactive intermediate. The occurrence of this phenomenon could be demonstrated (*a*) when careful treatment of the oily intermediate (XXXI) with water yielded a crystalline material which was shown to be identical with the phenylphosphazoanilide "hydrate" (XXXII) of Michaelis and Schroeter (763), and (*b*) when the end products of the reaction of either the reactive intermediate (XXXI) or the "hydrate" (XXXII) with benzoic acid were phenol (XXX) and phosphorous acid (XIX*a*) in addition to the expected benzanilide (XXVIII*a*). If the reaction had actually proceeded through the phosphite

$$C_6H_5O-P\begin{subarray}{l}Cl\\ \\Cl\end{subarray} \xrightarrow{NH_2C_6H_5} C_6H_5O-P\begin{subarray}{l}NHC_6H_5\\ \\NHC_6H_5\end{subarray} \xrightarrow{C_6H_5CO_2H} C_6H_5CO-NHC_6H_5 + C_6H_5O-P\begin{subarray}{l}OH\\ \\OH\end{subarray}$$

XXVI XXVII XXVIII XXIX

$$C_6H_5OH + P\begin{subarray}{l}NC_6H_5\\ \\NHC_6H_5\end{subarray} \xrightarrow{H_2O} HO-P\begin{subarray}{l}NHC_6H_5\\ \\NHC_6H_5\end{subarray} \xrightarrow{C_6H_5CO_2H} C_6H_5CO-NHC_6H_5 + H_3PO_3$$

XXX XXXI XXXII XXVIII*a* XIX*a*

amide intermediate (XXVII), then phenyl phosphite (XXIX) should have been produced instead of the former two products. It therefore appears that intermediates of the type represented by (XXVII) may, under certain circumstances, split off alcohol and hence become transformed into phosphazo compounds which can react with carboxylic acids in the usual way.

A study by Süs (768) in 1951 demonstrated that acylated peptide derivatives (VIII*a*) could be secured upon heating a solution containing an acylamino acid (XXXIII) and an amino acid ester (II*a*) in dioxane or benzene to which phosphorus trichloride had been added. A similar reaction was subsequently effected in toluene (757) (procedure 10–79) and in pyridine (723) solution. However, it is not clear at present whether such reactions involve the intermediate formation of a phosphazo compound or an energy-rich intermediate of some other type.

$$\text{RCO—NHCHR}^1\text{CO}_2\text{H} + \text{NH}_2\text{CHR}^2\text{CO}_2\text{Et} \xrightarrow{\text{PCl}_3} \text{RCO—NHCHR}^1\text{CO—NHCHR}^2\text{CO}_2\text{Et}$$
XXXIII　　　　　　　IIa　　　　　　　　　　　　VIIIa

Illustrative procedure 10–79 (757). Carbobenzoxyglycyl-DL-phenylalanine ethyl ester. To a solution of 0.03 mole of ethyl DL-phenylalaninate hydrochloride (procedure 10–48), 0.03 mole of carbobenzoxyglycine (procedures 10–28 and 10–30), and 0.09 mole of triethylamine in 100 ml. of toluene is added 0.01 mole of phosphorus trichloride. The reaction mixture is allowed to stand at room temperature for 20 min., refluxed for 30 min., and then washed successively with water, 10% sodium bicarbonate solution, water, dilute hydrochloric acid, and finally water. Removal of the toluene *in vacuo*, followed by crystallization of the residue from alcohol–water, then yields the desired product; yield 5.98 g. (52%); m.p. 85–87°.

34. Phosphorus Oxychloride Method. *Principle.* Treatment of a chilled solution of equimolar amounts of an acylated amino acid or peptide, an amino acid or peptide ester, and phosphorus oxychloride in dry tetrahydrofuran with two molar equivalents of triethylamine results in the formation of a peptide derivative (VI). This reaction presumably occurs via the initial interaction of the carboxylic acid reactant (I) with the acid chloride (II) to form the corresponding mixed carboxylic-dichlorophosphoric acid anhydride (IV). The action of the latter intermediate on the amine reactant then leads to the desired product (VI).

$$\text{RCO—NHCHR}^1\text{CO}_2\text{H} + \text{POCl}_3 + (\text{C}_2\text{H}_5)_3\text{N} \rightarrow \text{RCO—NHCHR}^1\text{CO—O—POCl}_2 + (\text{C}_2\text{H}_5)_3\text{N·HCl}$$
I　　　　　　　　II　　　III　　　　　　　　　IV　　　　　　　　　　V

$$\text{NH}_2\text{CHR}^2\text{CO}_2\text{Et} + (\text{C}_2\text{H}_5)_3\text{N}$$

$$\downarrow$$

$$\text{RCO—NHCHR}^1\text{CO—NHCHR}^2\text{CO}_2\text{Et} + [(\text{C}_2\text{H}_5)_3\text{N·HO—POCl}_2]$$
　　　　　　　　VI　　　　　　　　　　　　　　　　　VII

General Considerations. In 1951, Wieland and Bernhard (741) attempted to develop a practicable peptide-forming procedure which involved mixed anhydrides derived from the interaction of an acylamino acid with thionyl chloride, sulfuryl chloride, or phosphorus oxychloride in an inert organic medium containing a tertiary base. Although such mixed anhydrides formed readily in anhydrous tetrahydrofuran as the solvent, and these in turn could be successfully coupled *in situ* with sodium glycinate in aqueous solution to yield the desired peptide derivative, the amount of product ultimately isolated was invariably less than 50% of theory. The low yields of the product were ascribed to extensive decomposition of the mixed anhydride as a result of disproportionation and hydrolytic reactions. In a reinvestigation of this work by Wieland and Heinke (769), attempts were made to circumvent these earlier difficulties by combining the anhydride- and the peptide-forming steps into a single operation, and by employing low temperatures and anhydrous conditions throughout the reaction period. Thus the desired peptide derivative could be produced upon treatment of a solution of the acylamino acid, amino acid ester, and triethylamine in anhydrous tetrahydrofuran at $-15°$ with the pertinent acid chloride. Although the yields of product ultimately isolated were only 50% at best when thionyl chloride was employed as the acid chloride, a similar implication of phosphorus oxychloride led to over-all yields which ranged between 70 and 80% of theory for most of the reactants tested. Only in the specific instance where carbobenzoxyglycine was coupled with methyl or ethyl glycinate were the yields of product substantially lower than these values; modification of the reaction conditions permitted the isolation of good yields of the desired product. However, as a study of the original reaction conditions revealed some interesting phenomena, these will be briefly discussed.

Treatment of a tetrahydrofuran solution of carbobenzoxyglycine (VIII) and triethylamine with phosphorus oxychloride at $-15°$, in the absence of an added amine reactant, leads to the formation of an acid of peptide nature in some 30% yield which, upon recrystallization from methanol–water, is recovered as a crystalline compound, m.p. 136–137°, with the empirical formula $C_{20}H_{20}N_2O_7$. This compound (IX) is quantitatively converted to glycylglycine (X) upon catalytic hydrogenolysis, while its treatment with hydroxylamine transforms it to a mixture of carbobenzoxyglycine hydroxamic acid (XI) and carbobenzoxyglycine (XII); the use of ammonia in lieu of hydroxylamine leads to a mixture of carbobenzoxyglycine amide (XIII) and carbobenzoxyglycine (XII):

$$\text{Cbzo—NHCH}_2\text{CO}_2\text{H} \xrightarrow[\text{(C}_2\text{H}_5\text{)}_3\text{N}]{\text{POCl}_3} C_{20}H_{20}N_2O_7 \xrightarrow{\text{H}_2,\text{Pd}} \text{NH}_2\text{CH}_2\text{CO—NHCH}_2\text{CO}_2\text{H}$$

VIII　　　　　　　　　　　　　　IX　　　　　　　　　　　　X

NH₂OH ↓　　　　　　　　　　　　　　　　　　　　　　　　↓ NH₃

Cbzo—NHCH₂CO—NHOH　　Cbzo—NHCH₂CO₂H　　Cbzo—NHCH₂CO—NH₂
　　　XI　　　　　　　　　　　　XII　　　　　　　　　　　XIII

On the basis of these reactions, the structure of N,N'-dicarbobenzoxyglycylglycine (XIV) could be assigned to the unknown material (IX). Treatment of this material (XIV) with a solution of hydrogen bromide in glacial acetic acid results in the cleavage of the N-terminal carbobenzoxy moiety and the concomitant formation of the hydrobromide salt of N'-carbobenzoxyglycylglycine (XV), m.p. 151–152° d. It thus appears that the carbobenzoxy moiety attached to the imido nitrogen atom is more tightly bound than its N-terminal sister group. It is of interest to note also that catalytic hydrogenolysis of (XV) transforms it to glycylglycine (X*a*) while this same compound (XV), upon treatment with hydroxylamine, is converted to the monohydroxamic acid of carbonylbisglycine (XVIII), presumably via an intra-molecular cyclization to the corresponding hydantoin intermediate (XVI) which is formed with the concomitant loss of a molecule of benzyl alcohol (XVII):

$$\begin{array}{cccccc}
\text{Cbzo—NHCH}_2\text{CO} & \xrightarrow{\text{HBr in}} & \text{HBr·NH}_2\text{CH}_2\text{CO} & \xrightarrow{\text{NH}_2\text{OH}} & \text{HN}\diagup\!\!\!\diagdown\text{C=O} & + \text{C}_6\text{H}_5\text{CH}_2\text{OH} \\
| & \text{HOAc} & | & & | \quad\quad | & \\
\text{Cbzo—NCH}_2\text{CO}_2\text{H} & & \text{Cbzo—NCH}_2\text{CO}_2\text{H} & & \text{O=C—NCH}_2\text{CO}_2\text{H} & \\
\text{XIV} & & \text{XV} & & \text{XVI} & \text{XVII}
\end{array}$$

$$\downarrow \text{H}_2, \text{Pd} \quad\quad\quad\quad \downarrow \text{NH}_2\text{OH}$$

$$\text{NH}_2\text{CH}_2\text{CO—NHCH}_2\text{CO}_2\text{H} \quad\quad \text{HO}_2\text{CCH}_2\text{NH—CO—NHCH}_2\text{CO—NHOH}$$
$$\text{X}a \quad\quad\quad\quad\quad\quad\quad \text{XVIII}$$

That the afore-mentioned phosphorus oxychloride-mediated condensations proceed via the activation of the carboxylic acid reactant as the mixed anhydride, rather than via the activation of the amine reactant as the corresponding *tris*-amido derivative of phosphoric acid (XIX), is strongly suggested by the fact that the latter intermediate requires relatively drastic conditions both for its initial formation and for its subsequent participation in a coupling reaction. With this in mind, the question is presented whether a single (XX), double (XXI), or triple (XXII) mixed anhydride arises in consequence of the replacement of one, two, or three chlorine atoms, respectively, of the phosphorus oxychloride (IIa) reagent. In this connection, it should be noted that a 1 : 1 mole ratio of phosphorus oxychloride

$$\begin{array}{ccccccc}
\text{NHR} & & \text{Cl} & \text{1, 2, or 3} & \text{Cl} & \text{O—COR} & \text{O—COR} \\
\diagup & \xleftarrow{\text{NH}_2\text{R}} & \diagup & \xrightarrow{\text{RCO}_2\text{H}} & \diagup & | & | \\
\text{O=P—NHR} & & \text{O=P—Cl} & & \text{O=P—O—COR} \text{ or } \text{O=P—Cl} \text{ or } \text{O=P—O—COR} \\
\diagdown & & \diagdown & & \diagdown & | & | \\
\text{NHR} & & \text{Cl} & & \text{Cl} & \text{O—COR} & \text{O—COR} \\
\text{XIX} & & \text{IIa} & & \text{XX} & \text{XXI} & \text{XXII}
\end{array}$$

to acylamino acid is required to obtain maximal yields of the desired peptide derivative, while only about a 35% yield of the product is usually secured when these same reagents are present in the mole ratio 0.3 : 1. The preponderant involvement of a singly substituted mixed anhydride of the type represented by structure (XX) is thereby strongly implied.

Experimental Conditions. Preparation of peptide derivatives via the phosphorus oxychloride method may be generally achieved by one of the following three procedures: (*a*) a solution of equimolar amounts of the acylamino acid or acyl-peptide and the amino acid ester or peptide ester in tetrahydrofuran, which contains two equivalents of a tertiary amine, is treated with an equimolar amount of phosphorus oxychloride added slowly as its tetrahydrofuran solution in dropwise fashion; (*b*) the amine and carboxylic acid reactants in tetrahydrofuran solution are treated with the adduct formed from the addition of one molecular equivalent of phosphorus oxychloride and two molecular equivalents of the tertiary base; and (*c*) the amine and carboxylic acid components in tetrahydrofuran are treated first with an equimolar amount of the acid chloride and immediately thereafter with two equivalents of the tertiary base (procedure 10–80). Since modification *a* leads to the formation of a considerable amount of side products if an acylglycine is implicated as the carboxylic acid component, modifications *b* and *c* are generally favored; both of the latter methods as a rule give the same yield of product. When the ester hydrochloride salt of the amine reactant is involved, the addition of one equivalent of a tertiary amine is required to liberate the free base. The coupling reaction is usually carried out at −15° for a period of about 1 hour, after which time it is essentially complete; the use of dry solvents and the maintenance of anhydrous conditions must be rigidly observed. Triethylamine is most commonly employed as the tertiary base, although such bases as tributylamine, N-ethylpiperidine, or pyridine will also suffice.

Illustrative procedure 10–80 (769). Carbobenzoxyglycyl-L-tyrosine ethyl ester. A solution of 2.1 g. (0.01 mole) of carbobenzoxyglycine (procedures 10–28 and 10–30), 2.5 g. (0.01 mole) of L-tyrosine ethyl ester hydrochloride (procedure 10–48) and 1.4 ml. (0.01 mole) of triethylamine in 50 ml. of anhydrous tetrahydrofuran is cooled to −15° with shaking. The solution is then treated with 0.92 ml. (0.01 mole) of purified phosphorus oxychloride and immediately thereafter with 2.8 ml. (0.02 mole) of triethylamine. After the reaction mixture has stood for 1 hr. at −15°, 20 ml. of water is added and the mixture evaporated *in vacuo* at room temperature in order to remove the tetrahydrofuran. The residual material is treated with 20 ml. of water, extracted thrice with 20-ml. portions of ethyl acetate, and the combined ethyl acetate extracts are washed three times each with 5-ml. portions of water, with several portions of 5% sodium bicarbonate solution, and finally with water. After being dried with sodium sulfate, the ethyl acetate fraction is concentrated to dryness at room temperature. The residual carbobenzoxyglycyl-L-tyrosine ethyl ester is so obtained in some 90% yield with a melting point at 126–127° prior to recrystallization.

Scope and Limitations. The phosphorus oxychloride method leads to generally high yields of product when an acylamino acid or acyl-peptide is coupled with either an amino acid ester or peptide ester. This method must be carried out in anhydrous media for satisfactory results. Because the process proceeds with negligible side-product formation, the desired peptide derivative may be isolated in a high degree of analytical purity prior to crystallization (769). A particular advantage possessed by the method lies in its ability to be employed with amino acid residues which possess an unprotected hydroxyl function, e.g., threonine, hydroxyproline, or tyrosine, in either the carboxylic acid or the amine component. Thus, for example, the phosphorus oxychloride-induced coupling of carbobenzoxy-L-hydroxyproline with L-tryptophan methyl ester leads to the pertinent dipeptide ester derivative in some 75% over-all yield. However, if the unprotected sulfhydryl group of a cysteine residue is involved, the coupling reaction proceeds in the normal way but with the concomitant oxidation of the cysteine to a cystine residue. If ω-amino or ω-carboxyl groups are present in either of the reactants, their reactivity must be appropriately masked before condensation. The presence of a β-branched side chain in the reactants apparently does not result in a diminution of the over-all yield; thus an 88% yield of carbobenzoxy-DL-valylglycine ethyl ester is ultimately secured from the condensation of carbobenzoxy-DL-valine with glycine ethyl ester. Although no racemization is evident if the reactants concerned are an optically active carbobenzoxyamino acid and an optically active amino acid ester, the lack of adequate data does not yet permit like assurance to be made where acyl blocking substituents other than the carbobenzoxy group are utilized, or where optically active reactants of a peptide nature are involved.

Related Methods. The discussion above is concerned primarily with the role of phosphorus oxychloride as a carboxyl-activating reagent in the synthesis of peptide bonds. This reagent, or suitably substituted derivatives thereof, may also be employed to activate the amine component involved in the peptide-forming reaction. In the attempt to test the relative reactivities of such phosphate amide intermediates, Goldschmidt and Obermeier (759) synthesized several derivatives of the following general types:

$$\underset{\text{XIX}a}{\overset{\text{NHR}}{\underset{\text{NHR}}{\text{O}=\text{P}-\text{NHR}}}} \quad \underset{\text{XXIII}}{\overset{\text{NHR}}{\underset{\text{NHR}}{\text{O}=\text{P}-\text{OC}_6\text{H}_5}}} \quad \underset{\text{XXIV}}{\overset{\text{OC}_6\text{H}_5}{\underset{\text{OC}_6\text{H}_5}{\text{O}=\text{P}-\text{NHR}}}} \quad \underset{\text{XXV}}{\overset{\text{OH}}{\underset{\text{OC}_6\text{H}_5}{\text{O}=\text{P}-\text{NHR}}}} \quad \underset{\text{XXVI}}{\overset{\text{NHR}}{\underset{\text{NHR}}{\text{O}=\text{P}-\text{OH}}}}$$

Compounds (XIX*a*), (XXIII), and (XXIV) were prepared by the action of the pertinent amine on phosphorus oxychloride, phenyl dichlorophosphate, and diphenyl chlorophosphate respectively, while compounds (XXV) and (XXVI) were formed upon saponification of their precursor monochlorophosphate analogs (XXVIII and XXIX):

$$\underset{\text{XXVII}}{\overset{\text{Cl}}{\underset{\text{OC}_6\text{H}_5}{\text{O}=\text{P}-\text{Cl}}}} \xrightarrow{\text{NH}_2\text{R}} \underset{\text{XXVIII}}{\overset{\text{Cl}}{\underset{\text{OC}_6\text{H}_5}{\text{O}=\text{P}-\text{NHR}}}} \xrightarrow{\text{NaOH}} \text{XXV} \quad \quad \text{XXVI} \xleftarrow{\text{NaOH}} \underset{\text{XXIX}}{\overset{\text{NHR}}{\underset{\text{NHR}}{\text{O}=\text{P}-\text{Cl}}}} \xleftarrow{\text{NH}_2\text{R}} \underset{\text{II}b}{\overset{\text{Cl}}{\underset{\text{Cl}}{\text{O}=\text{P}-\text{Cl}}}}$$

Although the phosphate amides may react with carboxylic acids, forming amide derivatives, the reaction generally occurs with greater difficulty than in those instances where the analogous phosphite amides (Section 10–31) are implicated. Thus the neutral phosphate amides (XIX*a*, XXIII, and XXIV) require conditions of thermal fusion to undergo reaction with carboxylic acids, while the slightly more reactive acid phosphate amide intermediates (XXV and XXVI) will condense with carboxylic acids in boiling toluene solution. In any event, the relatively drastic conditions required in the coupling stage has discouraged the widespread use of phosphate amide intermediates for peptide bond synthesis.

Despite the afore-mentioned shortcomings, acid phosphate amide intermediates of the type represented by structure (XXV) have been utilized by Schramm and Wissmann (769a) for the preparation of a few simple acylated peptide ester derivatives. Thus the successive addition of a tertiary base and a suitably constituted amine hydrochloride, e.g. an amino acid or peptide ester hydrochloride, to a solution of phosphorus pentoxide in diethyl phosphite (XXX) at 100° was reported to lead to the corresponding phosphoric acid monoethyl ester monoamide (XXXII). The reaction presumably proceeds through the intermediate formation of ethyl metaphosphate (XXXI) which, in fact, may be used in boiling chloroform solution in lieu of the phosphorus pentoxide–diethyl phosphite reagent to obtain the pertinent acid phosphate amide (XXXII). Condensation of the carboxylic acid reactant with (XXXII), either *in situ* or after isolation, to yield the desired amide derivative (XXXIII) is effected upon refluxing in chloro-

$$C_2H_5O-P\underset{OC_2H_5}{\overset{OH}{\diagup}} \xrightarrow{P_2O_5} C_2H_5O-P\overset{O}{\diagdown} \xrightarrow[\Delta]{NH_2R} C_2H_5O-P\underset{O}{\overset{OH}{\diagup}}-NHR \xrightarrow{R'CO_2H} R'CO-NHR + C_2H_5O\underset{O}{\overset{HO\ OH}{\diagup}}P\diagdown$$
$$\text{XXX} \qquad \text{XXXI} \qquad \text{XXXII} \qquad \text{XXXIII} \qquad \text{XXXIV}$$

form or heating at 100° in diethyl phosphite for several hours, or after several days of storage at room temperature.

35. N-Carbonyl-α-amino Acid Ester Method. *Principle.* The action of phosgene (I) on an amino acid ester hydrochloride (II), in hot toluene solution, proceeds with the formation of the corresponding N-carbonyl-α-amino acid ester (III). Treatment of the latter compound (IIIa) with an acylamino acid, an acylated peptide, or some other carboxylic acid (V) in a suitable organic medium results in the production of the pertinent substituted acid amide derivative (VII) with the concomitant liberation of carbon dioxide. Such coupling reaction presumably occurs by way of an intermediate mixed carboxylic-carbamic acid anhydride (VI) which subsequently undergoes decomposition to the desired product (VII).

$$COCl_2 + HCl\cdot NH_2CHRCO_2Et \xrightarrow[\Delta]{\text{toluene}} O{=}C{=}NCHRCO_2Et + 3HCl$$
$$\text{I} \qquad \text{II} \qquad\qquad \text{III} \qquad \text{IV}$$
$$R'CO_2H + O{=}C{=}NCHRCO_2Et \rightarrow R'CO{-}O{-}CONHCHRCO_2Et \rightarrow R'CO{-}NHCHRCO_2Et + CO_2$$
$$\text{V} \qquad \text{IIIa} \qquad\qquad \text{VI} \qquad\qquad \text{VII} \qquad\qquad \text{VIII}$$

General Considerations. Although the properties of N-carbonylamino acid esters have long been known, the potential value of these reactive intermediates in synthetic peptide coupling procedures attracted virtually no attention until the turn of the 1950's. Wurtz (770) as early as 1850 demonstrated the formation of simple substituted acid amides (VII) from the interaction of isocyanic acid esters (IIIa) with carboxylic acids (V). That such reaction proceeds through the intermediacy of an isolable mixed carboxylic-carbamic acid anhydride (VI) was indicated by the studies of several investigators (771–773). However, despite the early intensive search for adequate peptide coupling procedures, the potential utility of this reaction was overlooked. Such seeming oversight might in part be attributed to the then-known fact that appreciable side reactions almost invariably characterize reactions wherein aromatic isocyanates, e.g., phenylisocyanate, are involved. Thus it was shown that the mixed anhydrides (X) derived from aromatic isocyanates undergo, in addition to the desired peptide-yielding reaction, an extensive disproportionation to the disubstituted urea (XI) as well as to two symmetrical acid anhydrides (XII and XIII). It

$$RCO_2H + O{=}C{=}NAr \rightarrow RCO{-}O{-}CONHAr \rightarrow (ArNH)_2CO + (RCO_2)_2CO \rightarrow (RCO)_2O + CO_2$$
$$Va \qquad\qquad IX \qquad\qquad X \qquad\qquad\qquad XI \qquad\quad XII \qquad\qquad XIII \quad\; VIIIa$$

remained for Goldschmidt and Wick (774) in 1950, some one hundred years after the studies of Wurtz, to extend such studies to the synthesis of peptide derivatives. Hence, when an acylamino acid (XIV) or an acylated peptide was employed as the source of carboxylic acid in a Wurtz-type reaction, the corresponding peptide derivative (XV) was obtained. Investigation of the mechanism of the reaction with C^{14}-carboxyl labeled acids by Fry (775)

$$RCO{-}NHCHR^1CO_2H + O{=}C{=}NCHR^2CO_2Et \rightarrow RCO{-}NHCHR^1CO{-}NHCHR^2CO_2Et + CO_2$$
$$XIV \qquad\qquad\qquad IIIb \qquad\qquad\qquad\qquad XV$$

indicated that the carbon dioxide evolved during the treatment of isocyanates with carboxylic acids originates in the former reactant.

Preparation of reactive N-carbonyl-α-amino acid esters may be achieved by (a) the interaction of α-halogen fatty acid esters with salts of cyanic acid (776), (b) Curtius degradation of the half-ester azides of C-substituted aminomalonic acids (777), and (c) the action of phosgene (I) on amino acid ester hydrochlorides (II) (774, 778–780). In actual practice, however, both methods a and b must be eliminated, the former because a substitution occurs at the α-carbon atom and hence can be accompanied by either Walden inversion or racemization where optically active α-halogen fatty acid esters are employed, and the latter because an α-center of asymmetry is formed during the course of synthesis and thereupon results in racemic material. Method c, on the other hand, may be routinely utilized for the preparation of optically active N-carbonylamino acid esters without the accompaniment of detectable racemization (774). Similar application of method c to peptide esters does not proceed with the formation of the N-carbonyl derivative, however. An attempt by Goldschmidt and Wick (774) to prepare N-carbonylglycylglycine ethyl ester from the treatment of glycylglycine ethyl ester hydrochloride (XVI) with phosgene (Ia) in hot toluene solution led instead to the nearly quantitative formation of hydantoin-3-acetic acid ester (XVIII), presumably by way of an intramolecular cyclization of the desired N-carbonyl-peptide ester (XVII):

$$COCl_2 + HCl \cdot NH_2CH_2CO-NHCH_2CO_2Et \rightarrow \begin{bmatrix} N-CH_2 \\ \parallel \quad \mid \\ OC \quad CO \\ \diagdown \diagup \\ NHCH_2CO_2Et \end{bmatrix} \rightarrow \begin{matrix} NH-CH_2 \\ \mid \quad \mid \\ OC \quad CO \\ \diagdown \diagup \\ NCH_2CO_2Et \end{matrix}$$
Ia   XVI   XVII   XVIII

N-Carbonylamino acid esters may be likened to the simple isocyanates in their chemical behavior and hence may be applied in an interesting variety of reactions. Thus the action of amines on these reactive derivatives (IIIc) lead to the corresponding carbamylamino acid esters (XIX) which, in turn, undergo ready transformation to hydantoins (XX) upon treatment with hydrochloric acid (774). Treatment of N-carbonylamino acid esters with alcohols, on the other hand, give excellent yields of the carboalkoxyamino acid ester (XXI) which are converted to the carboalkoxyamino acid (XXII) upon saponification. The latter procedure may, in fact, be employed to

$$O=C=NCHR'CO_2Et \xrightarrow{RNH_2} RNHCO-NHCHR'CO_2Et \xrightarrow{HCl} \begin{matrix} NH-CHR' \\ \mid \quad \mid \\ OC \quad CO \\ \diagdown \diagup \\ NR \end{matrix}$$
IIIc   XIX   XX

$$\Big\downarrow ROH$$

$$ROCO-NHCHR'CO_2Et \xrightarrow{OH^-} ROCO-NHCHR'CO_2H$$
XXI   XXII

secure the useful carbobenzoxy- (XXII; R = $C_6H_5CH_2$) and *t*-butyloxycarbonyl- (XXII; R = $(CH_3)_3C$) amino acids (procedure 10–81), among others (465, 774).

Illustrative procedure 10–81 (465). *t*-Butyloxycarbonylglycine. A mixture of 0.37 mole of N-carbonylglycine ethyl ester (carboethoxymethyl isocyanate), 1.0 mole of *t*-butyl alcohol, and 0.37 mole of triethylamine is refluxed for 2.5 hr. with the exclusion of moisture, and then permitted to stand at room temperature overnight. Excess volatile materials are removed *in vacuo* over a steam bath and the crude residue saponified by treatment for 2 hr. at room temperature with a mixture of 100 ml. of dioxane and 100 ml. of 15% sodium hydroxide. After acidification with concentrated hydrochloric acid, the crude product is extracted with three 100-ml. portions of ether, leaving, upon evaporation, 55 g. (85%) of a solid residue, m.p. 80–85°. Recrystallization from ethyl acetate–petroleum ether yields the desired product with a melting point of 85–90°.

Experimental Conditions. In practice, N-carbonylamino acid esters are generally prepared by the action of phosgene on the pertinent amino acid ester hydrochloride in toluene solution at 120° (procedure 10–82); no detectable racemization ensues where optically active reactants are employed (774). The phosgenation reaction, if properly conducted, usually proceeds with a yield which is in excess of 90% of theory; the rigid exclusion of moisture is essential here. A prerequisite to high yields is the condition that the esterification of the amino acid esters be complete, a condition that may be satisfied by repeated esterification of the amino acid with ethanolic hydrogen chloride. As perchloroformic acid methyl ester ($ClCO_2CCl_3$) decomposes to two molecules of phosgene upon warming, this reagent may be used in lieu of phosgene, although sometimes at considerable sacrifice in over-all yield. N-Carbonylamino acid esters are colorless oils which possess a piercing lachrymatory odor, can be distilled without appreciable decomposition, and are highly stable upon prolonged storage in the absence of moisture; the tendency toward polymerization which is characteristic of many isocyanates is not observed here. If traces of moisture are present, however, decomposition occurs with the formation of urea derivatives.

The coupling of an acylamino acid (XIV) or an acylated peptide with an N-carbonylamino acid ester (IIIb) to yield the desired peptide derivative (XV) is generally performed by heating a mixture of the two reactants in a dry inert solvent, e.g., toluene, xylene, or isoamyl ether, at 110° until the evolution of carbon dioxide subsides; if the melting point of the acylamino acid component does not exceed 150°, the two reactants may be heated at 110° in the absence of solvent (procedure 10–83) (774). Pyridine is of especial value as a solvent because its catalytic action permits the peptide-forming reaction to commence at room temperature and to be rapidly and smoothly brought to completion at 50–60°. The relative reactivities of the various N-carbonylamino acid esters apparently vary markedly with the degree of steric hindrance, the highly hindered α-aminoisobutyric acid derivative, for example, revealing a significantly slower rate of reaction than the unhindered glycine derivative; carbobenzoxyamino acids react with greater facility than the corresponding phthalylamino acids, a factor presumably associated with their relative solubilities. In any event, some 30–60 minutes are generally required for the termination of the reaction in pyridine solution, somewhat longer periods being required in other media or in the absence of solvent. Product yields generally range in the vicinity of 90% of theory.

Illustrative procedure 10–82 (774). N-Carbonyl-S-benzyl-L-cysteine ethyl ester. To 27.5 g. of S-benzyl-L-cysteine ethyl ester·HCl (procedure 10–48) (which had been dried at 50° *in vacuo*) in a 3-necked flask fitted with a sealed stirrer, gas inlet tube, and reflux condenser, is added 100 ml. of absolute toluene. The flask is placed over an oil bath maintained at 130–160°, and a strong stream of phosgene is introduced with vigorous stirring over a period of 1.5 hr., whereupon hydrogen chloride gas is evolved as the ester gradually goes into solution. When solution is complete, the toluene is distilled off at 45° with the aid of an efficient column, and the residue purified by distillation. The carbonyl-S-benzyl-L-cysteine ethyl ester, b.p. 201°/11 mm., is secured as a pungent, colorless liquid in a 24-g. yield (91%); $[\alpha]_D^{18} = -41.9°$ (homogeneous); it should be stored in the absence of moisture.

The N-carbonyl ethyl ester derivatives of other amino acids, prepared in comparable manner, show the following boiling points: DL-α-amino-*n*-butyric acid, 81°/13; DL-α-aminoisobutyric acid, 61.5°/12; DL-isoleucine, 94°/11; DL-leucine, 97°/11; L-leucine, 104.5°/15; DL-norleucine, 104°/14; DL-norvaline, 94°/14; DL-methionine, 155°/24; DL-phenylalanine, 152°/10; DL-phenylglycine, 152°/17; DL-valine, 87°/11. The N-carbonyl diethyl ester derivatives of L-aspartic acid (b.p. 130°/10) and L-glutamic acid (b.p. 151°/10) are prepared in xylene solution under slightly different conditions. A yield of 90% or better is achieved in most instances.

Illustrative procedure 10-83 (774). Carbobenzoxyglycyl-S-benzyl-L-cysteine ethyl ester. A mixture of 2.3 g. of *dry* carbobenzoxyglycine (procedure 10–28) and 2.6 g. of carbonyl-S-benzyl-L-cysteine ethyl ester (procedure 10–82) is heated over an oil bath at 110° until the evolution of carbon dioxide terminates (about 1.5 hr.). The reaction mixture is cooled and then treated with 2 ml. of a 10% sodium carbonate solution. Crystallization of the residual material from methanol yields the desired product in some 90% yield; m.p. 80°; $[\alpha]_D^{20} = -45.9°$ in methanol.

Scope and Limitations. Utilization of the N-carbonylamino acid ester method generally leads to high yields of the desired peptide derivative. Although the preparation of optically active carbobenzoxy- or phthalyl-dipeptide esters via this procedure occurs in the absence of racemization, little is known concerning the effect on optical activity where yet other N-acyl blocking substituents are employed or where one of the reactants is an acylated peptide which embodies an optically active amino acid as the C-terminal residue. If the N-acylated reactant contains a glutamic, aspartic, or other polycarboxylic acid residue, those carboxyl functions which are not to participate in the coupling reaction must be appropriately masked; similar precaution is required if additional acidic or basic moieties are present in the N-carbonylamino acid ester precursor. The action of traces of water on the reactive N-carbonyl esters readily leads to the formation of urea derivatives which are not always easily separable from the final product (cf. 781). Consequently, rigid anhydrous conditions must be maintained. In addition, acylated hydroxyamino acids (XXIII) yield urethanes (XXIV) whereas acylated glutamine (XXV; $x = 2$) and asparagine (XXV; $x = 1$) yield N-acylureas (XXVI) (cf. 781):

$$\begin{array}{ccc}
\text{CH}_2\text{OH} & & \text{CH}_2\text{O-CO-NHCHR}'\text{CO}_2\text{Et} \\
| & & | \\
\text{RCO-NHCHCO}_2\text{H} + \text{O=C=NCHR}'\text{CO}_2\text{Et} \rightarrow & \text{RCO-NHCHCO}_2\text{H} \\
\text{XXIII} & \text{IIId} & \text{XXIV}
\end{array}$$

$$\begin{array}{ccc}
\text{RCO-NHCHCO}_2\text{H} + \text{O=C=NCHR}'\text{CO}_2\text{Et} \rightarrow & \text{RCO-NHCHCO}_2\text{H} \\
| & & | \\
(\text{CH}_2)_x\text{CONH}_2 & & (\text{CH}_2)_x\text{CO-NH-CO-NHCHR}'\text{CO}_2\text{Et} \\
\text{XXV} & \text{IIIe} & \text{XXVI}
\end{array}$$

Finally, it should be noted that the carbonyl-bis-amino derivatives of the monoaminodicarboxylic acid esters may be isolated from reaction mixtures which involve the interaction of N-carbonylaspartic or -glutamic acid ester with an acylamino acid; a disproportionation reaction analogous to that which occurs with the aromatic isocyanates discussed earlier presumably is involved here.

36. Carbodiimide Method. *Principle.* Facile preparation of a peptide derivative (IV) may be achieved through the action of 1 equivalent of an N,N'-disubstituted carbodiimide (III) on a solution containing 1 equivalent each of an acylated amino acid (I) or peptide and an amino acid (II) or peptide ester; if the acid salt of the latter reactant is used, 1 equivalent of a tertiary base is also added. The formation of 1 equivalent of an N,N'-disubstituted urea derivative (V) accompanies the reaction. The latter derivative (V) may be obtained either as an insoluble precipitate or as a soluble one, dependent upon the constitution of the reactant N,N'-disubstituted carbodiimide (III) initially utilized as well as the nature of the solvent medium. The peptide-forming step is generally carried out at room temperature in an inert organic solvent, although water or aqueous mixtures may sometimes be advantageously employed.

$$RCO-NHCHR^1CO_2H + NH_2CHR^2CO_2Et + R^3N=C=NR^3 \rightarrow$$
$$\text{I} \qquad \text{II} \qquad \text{III}$$

$$RCO-NHCHR^1CO-NHCHR^2CO_2Et + R^3NH-CO-NHR^3$$
$$\text{IV} \qquad \text{V}$$

General Considerations. Synthesis of the first aliphatic carbodiimide, N,N'-diethylcarbodiimide (III; $R^3 = C_2H_5$), was described by Chancel (782) in 1893 and was succeeded, some forty-five years later, by an elaborate description of the N,N'-di-*n*-propyl-, N,N'-di-*n*-butyl-, N,N'-diisobutyl-, N,N'-diallyl-, N-*n*-propyl-N'-allyl-, N-*cyclo*hexyl-N'-allyl-, N-*cyclo*hexyl-, N'-crotyl-, N,N'-di*cyclo*hexyl-, and N-*β*-hydroxyethyl-N'-allylcarbodiimides by Schmidt, Hitzler, and Lahde (782). That this class of reagent was useful for promoting the condensation of the pertinent carboxylic acids and phosphate esters in the synthesis of monophosphate and polyphosphate esters of nucleosides and analogous compounds was demonstrated by the elegant studies of Khorana (783) and Zetzsche (784) and their associates. In a brief communication during 1955, Sheehan and Hess (785) announced that N,N'-disubstituted carbodiimides may be alternatively utilized to mediate the formation of a peptide bond between an amino and a carboxyl function. Hence the action of N,N'-di*cyclo*hexylcarbodiimide (III; $R^3 = cyclo\text{-}C_6H_{11}$) on a solution of the pertinent reactants (I and II) yielded as products the desired peptide derivative (IV) in addition to N,N'-di*cyclo*hexylurea (V; $R^3 = cyclo\text{-}C_6H_{11}$). By virtue of its general insolubility in most of the

CHEMICAL PROCEDURES FOR SYNTHESIS OF PEPTIDES 1017

solvents employed during the coupling step, the latter product was easily separable from the former, and thus the danger of contamination was avoided. A particular virtue associated with the use of N,N'-dicyclohexylcarbodiimide was convenience of manipulation, since the action of the reagent was effective on a solution which contained both the amine and the carboxylic acid reactants at room temperature in either the presence or the absence of water. Other attributes ascribed to the condensing reagent were its lack of sensitivity to moisture and the fact that it could be implicated in syntheses wherein the hydroxyl function of hydroxyamino acid residues was unprotected, an advantage hitherto possessed only by the classical azide method (Section 10–26). Preparation of the important N,N'-dicyclohexylcarbodiimide reagent may be generally achieved by the initial condensation of two molecules of cyclohexylamine (VI) with one of carbon disulfide (VII) in warm ethanolic solution which contains a trace of alkali, followed by desulfhydration of the N,N'-dicyclohexylthiourea (VIII) so derived with mercuric oxide (procedure 10–84):

$$\text{VI} \;\; -NH_2 + CS_2 \;\; \text{VII} \xrightarrow{KOH} \;\; -NH-CS-NH- \;\; \text{VIII} \xrightarrow{HgO} \;\; -N=C=N- \;\; \text{IX}$$

Illustrative procedure 10–84 (782). N,N'-Dicyclohexylcarbodiimide (IX). Sixty grams of cyclohexylamine, dissolved in 150 g. of ethanol, is treated with 60 g. of carbon disulfide and a small pellet of potassium hydroxide, and the mixture heated until the evolution of hydrogen sulfide subsides; evaporation of the solution, followed by crystallization of the residue from ethanol, yields pure N,N-dicyclohexylthiourea melting at 180–181° (786). Forty grams of the finely powdered product, 400 ml. of carbon disulfide, and 100 g. of mercuric oxide are placed in a dry, stoppered 1-l. flask and the mixture is shaken for 75 min. The solid material is filtered off, washed thrice with petroleum ether, and the combined filtrates again filtered. Concentration of the solution under reduced pressure leaves an oily residue of the crude product which is distilled at 11 mm. nearly to dryness (discard first 2–3 ml. of distillate); yield, 29.5 g. (86%). Redistillation gives pure N,N'-dicyclohexylcarbodiimide boiling at 154–156°/11 mm. (oil bath temperature maintained at 185°). The product crystallizes at room temperature and is quite stable upon prolonged storage.

Several months after the appearance of the report of Sheehan and Hess (785), Khorana (787) published a critical study which described the general mechanism of the peptide-forming reaction mediated by dicyclohexylcarbodiimide and which astutely assayed the problems that could arise from the use of this reagent. Thus Khorana considered the possibility that the coupling reaction to form the desired peptide derivative (XV) might occur as shown on p. 1018, where an initial interaction of the carbodiimide reagent (IIIa) with the carboxylic acid reactant (X) was presumed to give an O-acyllactimide (XI) which, in turn, could undergo either conversion to two activated forms (XII and XIII) of the original carboxylic acid or rearrangement via acyl transfer to an N-acylurea (XIV). If the above interpretation was correct, then it might be expected that the synthesis of peptide or amide derivatives (XV) would proceed through one or more

$$\underset{X}{\underset{\|}{\overset{O}{RC-OH}}} + \underset{IIIa}{\underset{NR'}{\overset{NR'}{\|}{C}}} \longrightarrow \underset{XI}{\underset{NHR'}{\overset{O}{\underset{\|}{RC-O-C}}}} \xrightarrow{H^+} \underset{XII}{\underset{NHR'}{\overset{\overset{+}{NHR'}}{\underset{\|}{RC-O-C}}}} \xrightarrow{RCO_2^-} \underset{Va}{\underset{NHR'}{\overset{NHR'}{C=O}}} + \underset{XIII}{\overset{RC=O}{\underset{RC=O}{\diagdown O}}}$$

$$\underset{XIV}{\underset{NHR'}{\overset{RC-NR'}{\underset{\|}{\overset{\|}{O}}\underset{\|}{C=O}}}} \xrightarrow{NH_2R''} \underset{XV}{RCO-NHR''} + \underset{Vb}{\underset{NHR'}{\overset{NHR'}{C=O}}} \qquad \underset{XV}{RCO-NHR''} + \underset{Xa}{\overset{O}{\underset{\|}{RC-OH}}}$$

of the following three routes: (a) (XII) + NH$_2$R'' → (XV), (b) (XIII) + NH$_2$R'' → (XV), and (c) (XIV) + NH$_2$R'' → (XV).

With this in mind, Khorana treated mixtures of glycine ethyl ester and various N-acylamino acids (X) with N,N'-di*cyclo*hexylcarbodiimide (IIIa; R' = *cyclo*-C$_6$H$_{11}$) in chloroform, dioxane, ether, and tetrahydrofuran solutions, removed the insoluble di*cyclo*hexylurea (Va,b; R' = *cyclo*-C$_6$H$_{11}$), and fractionally separated the neutral products. Such neutral products were identified as the desired peptide esters (XV) and as N-acylureas of the type represented by (XIV). The latter compounds (XIV) were apparently quite stable and exhibited little inclination to undergo condensation with an amino acid ester under mild conditions. That like stability should not be invariably associated with compounds of this type, however, was indicated by the fact that N-(N-carbobenzoxyglycyl)-N,N'-di-*p*-tolylurea (XIV; R = C$_6$H$_5$CH$_2$OCO—NHCH$_2$, R' = *p*-CH$_3$C$_6$H$_4$SO$_2$) underwent facile reaction with *cyclo*hexylamine to form carbobenzoxyglycine *cyclo*hexylamide and di-*p*-tolylurea. On the basis of these and other observations, it was concluded that (a) the relative proportions of (XIV) formed during the coupling reaction will depend largely upon the particular peptide derivative, carbodiimide, and solvent involved, (b) the presence of (XIV) in relatively small amount may complicate the isolation of desired products in satisfactory amount, and (c) the separation of di*cyclo*hexylurea may not always be readily achieved, especially in the synthesis of the higher peptide derivatives. Note was made too that, since the rearrangement of (XI) → (XIV) occurs via an intramolecular mechanism while the reactions (XI) → (XII) → (XIII) and (XII) → (XV) are bimolecular, the formation of the desired products should be favored by an increase in the concentration of the reactants. Hence the desired reaction is favored by keeping the amount of solvent employed to a minimum.

In 1946, Sheehan, Goodman, and Hess (524) elaborated more fully on their earlier communication concerned with the utility of N,N'-dicyclohexylcarbodiimide as a condensing agent for the synthesis of peptides which incorporate hydroxyamino acid residues, i.e., threonine, hydroxyproline, and serine. Such study revealed some interesting results on the effect of various solvents on the relative degree of N-acylurea formation, findings that were in accord with the previously expressed views of Khorana (787). Thus the condensation of phthalyl-L-threonine (X; R = Phth—NCH (CHOHCH$_3$)) with amino acid esters in either dioxane or tetrahydrofuran was accompanied by the formation of phthalyl-L-threonyl-N,N'-dicyclohexylurea (XIV; R = Phth—NCH(CHOHCH$_3$), R' = cyclo-C$_6$H$_{11}$) in addition to the desired peptide. However, when the similar reaction was effected in purified methylene chloride or acetonitrile, no evidence of side-product formation was observed. These results should not be construed to imply that a like situation would necessarily obtain where yet other reactants or other types of carbodiimides are involved.

As pointed out by Khorana (787), the insoluble co-product (1,3-dicyclohexylurea) which formed during the implication of 1,3-dicyclohexylcarbodiimide as a condensing agent in peptide syntheses could sometimes prove undesirable as, for example, in cases involving the synthesis of the less soluble higher polypeptides. In an effort to circumvent this difficulty, Sheehan and Hlavka (788) described the preparation of several new carbodiimides which incorporated tertiary or quaternary amine substituents and whose corresponding urea derivatives were soluble, respectively, in dilute acid and in pure water; fractional separation of the desired peptide product from its urea co-product could thereupon be accomplished with facility. Among the most promising of the pertinent carbodiimides investigated were 1-cyclohexyl-3-(2-morpholinyl-(4)-ethyl)carbodiimide (XIX) and its corresponding metho-p-toluenesulfonate derivative (XX), prepared by the interaction of cyclohexyl isothiocyanate (XVI) with N-(2-aminoethyl)morpholine (XVII), followed by the successive desulfhydration of the resulting thiourea (XVIII) to (XIX) and the conversion of (XIX) to (XX) upon treatment with methyl p-toluenesulfonate (procedure 10–85):

A comparable procedure was applied to the preparation of 1:3-di-(4-diethylamino*cyclo*hexyl)carbodiimide, 1-*cyclo*hexyl-3-(β-diethylaminoethyl)-carbodiimide, 1-*cyclo*hexyl-3-(4-diethylamino*cyclo*hexyl)carbodiimide, and the metho-*p*-toluenesulfonate derivative of the latter. In this connection, it might be noted that 1-*cyclo*hexyl-3-(morpholinyl-(4)-ethyl)carbodiimide in dimethylformamide solution has been successfully employed to condense Cbzo-L-Asp-NH$_2$·L-NO$_2$-Arg·L-Val·L-Tyr·OH with H·L-Ileu·L-His·L-Pro·L-Phe·OMe to yield Cbzo-L-Asp-NH$_2$·L-NO$_2$-Arg·L-Val·L-Tyr·L-Ileu·L-His·L-Pro·L-Phe·OMe, the precursor intermediate of hypertensin II (714); advantage was here taken of the extreme water solubility of the substituted urea co-product to permit its separation from the highly insoluble carbobenzoxy-octapeptide ester.

Illustrative procedure 10–85 (788). 1-*Cyclo*hexyl-3-(2-morpholinyl-(4)-ethyl)-carbodiimide metho-*p*-toluenesulfonate (XX). To a solution of 30 g. of *cyclo*hexylamine in absolute ether is added 11.4 g. of carbon disulfide, the ether evaporated off, and the residue treated with 40.5 g. of mercuric chloride and 600 ml. of water. Distillation of the mixture through a descending condenser by heating at atmospheric pressure, followed by extraction of the distillate with ether and subsequent evaporation of the ethereal extracts, yields 27 g. of *cyclo*hexyl isothiocyanate (XVI) with a boiling point of 219° at 746 mm. (786). The oil has an extremely penetrating odor reminiscent of mustard oil. A solution of 19.4 g. (0.138 mole) of *cyclo*hexyl isothiocyanate and 18.0 g. (0.138 mole) of N-(2-aminoethyl)morpholine (XVII) in 500 ml. of ether is heated under reflux for ten minutes. Upon cooling, the crystalline 1-*cyclo*hexyl-3-(2-morpholinyl-(4)-ethyl)thiourea (XVIII) separates; yield, 36 g. (96%); m.p. 128–129°. A mixture of 4.0 g. of the latter and 6.0 g of mercuric oxide in 50 ml. of acetone is refluxed for 6 hr., the reaction mixture filtered, a second 6.0-g. portion of mercuric oxide added to the filtrate, and the suspension refluxed for an additional 6 hr. After removal of the suspended material, the filtrate is concentrated *in vacuo* and flushed twice with benzene. The oily residue of crude 1-*cyclo*hexyl-3-(2-morpholinyl-(4)-ethyl)carbodiimide (XIX) is evaporatively distilled at 145°/0.2 mm.; yield, 2.4 g. (70%). A mixture of 0.5 g. (2.1 mmoles) of the latter compound and 0.39 g. (2.1 mmoles) of methyl *p*-toluenesulfonate is heated over a steam bath for 20 min. A solution of the reaction mixture in benzene deposits 0.6 g. (68%) of the desired crystalline quaternary metho-*p*-toluenesulfonate salt (XX); m.p. 113–115°.

Experimental Conditions. Of the variety of N,N'-disubstituted carbodiimides presently available as condensing agents, di*cyclo*hexylcarbodiimide and 1-*cyclo*hexyl-3-(morpholinyl-(4)-ethyl)carbodiimide (or its metho-*p*-toluenesulfonate derivative) have emerged as reagents of choice for the synthesis of small and large peptide derivatives, respectively. N,N'-Di*cyclo*hexylurea is formed as the co-product where the former reagent is employed, and, as this substance possesses an extremely low solubility in most organic and aqueous solvents, it is easily separable via filtration from most of the smaller acylated peptide esters which, by contrast, show a pronounced solubility in a number of organic solvents. However, as the larger acylated peptide derivatives are more often than not characterized by a marked insolubility in aqueous and most non-aqueous media, it becomes almost obligatory that the carbodiimides which mediate their synthesis be converted to readily soluble co-products during the coupling reaction; this requirement is met by carbodiimides which incorporate tertiary or quaternary amine substituents and which undergo conversion to water- or acid-soluble urea derivatives. Preparation of the pertinent carbodiimide reagents are given in procedures 10–84 and 10–85. Their involvement in the peptide coupling step is generally achieved by stirring a solution containing one equivalent each of the carbodiimide, acylamino acid or acylpeptide, and amino acid or peptide ester at room temperature; the time of reaction varies with the nature of the carbodiimide, ranging from 4 to 15 hours with di*cyclo*hexylcarbodiimide (procedure 10–86) and 1-*cyclo*hexyl-3-(morpholinyl-(4)-ethyl)carbodiimide to some 48 hours with the metho-*p*-toluenesulfonate derivative of the latter (procedure 10–87). Although coupling may be effected in such diverse organic media as dioxane, tetrahydrofuran, methylene chloride, acetonitrile, and dimethylformamide among others, aqueous mixtures and even pure water have been successfully employed; best results are most consistently obtained, however, in nonaqueous solvents.

Illustrative procedure 10–86 (454). Carbobenzoxy-L-threonyl-D-alanine benzyl ester. To a solution of 12.7 g. of carbobenzoxy-L-threonine (procedure 10–30), 17.6 g. of D-alanine benzyl ester *p*-toluenesulfonate (procedure 10–56) and 7.0 ml. of triethylamine in 200 ml. of dichloromethane is added 10.9 g. of N,N'-di*cyclo*hexylcarbodiimide (procedure 10–84). The mixture is allowed to stand for 4 hr. at 25° and 0.5 ml. of acetic acid then added thereto. The precipitated di*cyclo*hexylurea is removed by filtration and the filtrate washed successively with water, dilute hydrochloric acid, water, half-saturated sodium bicarbonate solution, and water, and finally dried over anhydrous sodium sulfate. Evaporation of the solution gives a residual mixture of crystals and oil. This is dissolved in a small amount of dichloromethane and the insoluble portion removed via filtration. The filtrate is evaporated and the residual oil converted to crystals upon drying *in vacuo* over phosphorus pentoxide. These are treated with *a small amount of ether* and filtered; although the material is quite soluble in ether and hence is lost in appreciable amount when this solvent is employed, such treatment is necessitated by virtue of the fact that attempted recrystallization of the crude, unwashed crystals from ether–petroleum ether or from acetone–petroleum ether gives a gelatinous mass which is filtered only with extreme difficulty. The white crystals are recrystallized from acetone–petroleum ether; yield 5.4 g.; m.p. 147°; $[\alpha]_D^{27} = -0.6°$ (2% in glacial acetic acid).

Phthalyl-L-threonyl-L-phenylalanine methyl ester (524). To a solution of 0.35 g. (0.0014 mole) of phthalyl-L-threonine (procedure 10–34) in 6 ml. of purified methylene chloride is added 0.50 g. (0.0028 mole) of freshly prepared L-phenylalanine methyl ester; the latter reactant is prepared by neutralizing a solution of L-phenylalanine methyl ester hydrochloride (procedure 10–48) to pH 9.0 with potassium carbonate and subsequent extraction into ether. Upon the addition of 0.29 g. (0.0014 mole) of N,N-di*cyclo*hexylcarbodiimide (procedure 10–84) to the reaction mixture a precipitate of N,N-di*cyclo*hexylurea forms immediately, but the reaction is allowed to proceed for 5 hr. at room temperature. The precipitate is then removed by filtration and the methylene chloride solution extracted successively with N hydrochloric acid, water, N potassium bicarbonate, and water. After the organic layer is dried over anhydrous sodium sulfate, the solvent is removed *in vacuo* at 40° and the resulting residual material crystallized from acetone–ether; yield, 0.52 g. (91%). The melting point is 153–154° after two recrystallizations from acetone–ether; $[\alpha]_D^{27} = +1.9°$ (6.6% in dimethylformamide).

Illustrative procedure 10–87 (788). Phthalyl-L-phenylalanyl-L-leucine ethyl ester. To 0.268 g. (1.36 millimoles) of L-leucine ethyl ester hydrochloride (procedure 10–48) in 4 ml. of acetonitrile is added 0.19 ml. (1.36 millimoles) of triethylamine followed by 0.40 g. (1.36 mmoles) of phthalyl-L-phenylalanine (procedure 10–33) and 0.58 g. (1.36 millimoles) of 1-*cyclo*hexyl-3-(2-morpholinyl-(4)-ethyl)carbodiimide metho-*p*-toluenesulfonate (procedure 10–85). The mixture is stirred for 2 days at room temperature, the solvent evaporated under reduced pressure, and the residue taken up in ether. After extraction with dilute hydrochloric acid, water, N potassium bicarbonate solution, and water, the ethereal layer is dried over anhydrous soldium sulfate and concentrated to dryness *in vacuo*. The residual material is recrystallized from ethyl acetate–ligroin; yield, 0.45 g. (80%); m.p. 108–109°; $[\alpha]_D^{26} = -115°$ (in ethanol).

Scope and Limitations. Although the use of N,N'-disubstituted carbodiimides as peptide condensing agents may ordinarily be expected to provide satisfactory yields of products which possess a high degree of analytical purity, the concomitant formation of N-acylureas as side products sometimes leads to the desired peptide derivative in markedly lesser yield (524, 678, 787). Despite the latter deficiency, however, methods involving the use of N,N'-disubstituted carbodiimides provide one of the simplest and most convenient of all hitherto available means for mediating the peptide coupling step. By virtue of the relatively high stability of these condensing agents in the presence of water, moisture is without effect on the course of the coupling process, and such process may, indeed, be effectively carried out in an aqueous medium (785, 788). In any event, the necessary precautions associated with the use of reagents which require anhydrous media are precluded. Added to this is the advantage that the reaction may be satisfactorily carried out at room temperature.

Although the carbodiimide method may be satisfactorily applied to reactions which involve most acylamino acids, its application to formyl- and tritylamino acids is noteworthy. Reaction in the latter instance is not confined to the trityl derivatives of glycine and alanine, as was the case with various coupling methods alluded to previously (cf. Sections 10–26 to

10–29), but may be applied with equal satisfaction to a variety of other tritylamino acids (cf. 675, 789, 790). That coupling reactions promoted by carbodiimides may sometimes be attended by appreciable racemization is indicated by the finding of Hofmann, Woolner, Spühler, and Schwartz (791) that the N,N'-di*cyclo*hexylcarbodiimide-induced condensation of carbobenzoxy-L-histidyl-L-phenylalanyl-nitro-L-arginine with the benzyl ester of L-tryptophylglycine gave a carbobenzoxypentapeptide benzyl ester which, after conversion to the free pentapeptide by catalytic hydrogenolysis, was shown to contain only some 40% of the desired all-L isomer through enzymic assay with trypsin and leucine aminopeptidase; such finding was promptly reaffirmed by Anderson and Callahan (791) who, after comparable condensation of carbobenzoxyglycyl-L-phenylalanine with ethyl glycinate, demonstrated that the product contained up to some 12% racemic material by fractional crystallization techniques. It is perhaps significant that the carbodiimide-mediated condensation of formyl-L-phenylalanine with glycine anilide yielded products that showed no sign of optical inactivation (586), while the same reaction, when performed via the mixed carboxylic-carbonic acid anhydride method (Section 10–29), led to a product that was appreciably racemic (586). Like the previously discussed coupling procedures, the present method requires that any reactive amino or carboxyl side-chain functions not involved in the condensation reaction be appropriately masked before treatment with the carbodiimide reagent. In this connection, it has been claimed that neither the hydroxyl function of serine, threonine, or hydroxyproline (524, 785), nor the basic imidazole nucleus of histidine (cf. 714) requires masking prior to condensation, advantages reminiscent of the classical azide procedure (Section 10–26). Subsequent studies have shown, however, that the presence of unmasked hydroxyl functions in serine residues may lead to considerable side-product formation (Section 10–39).

Related Methods. That the nitrogen analogs of ketenes, which are structurally related to the carbodiimides, may be employed as condensing agents for the formation of an amide bond between a carboxyl and an amino

$$\text{RCO—NHCHR}^1\text{CO}_2\text{H} + (\text{C}_6\text{H}_5)_2\text{C}=\text{C}=\text{NC}_6\text{H}_4\text{CH}_3 \longrightarrow$$
$$\text{I}a \qquad\qquad \text{XXI}$$

$$\text{RCO—NHCHR}^1\text{CO—N}\left(p\text{-H}_3\text{C—}\langle\bigcirc\rangle\right)\text{—COCH(C}_6\text{H}_5)_2 \xrightarrow{\text{NH}_2\text{CHR}^2\text{CO}_2\text{Et}}$$
$$\text{XXII}$$

$$\text{RCO—NHCHR}^1\text{CO—NHCHR}^2\text{CO}_2\text{Et} + \text{H}_3\text{C—}\langle\bigcirc\rangle\text{—NH—COCH(C}_6\text{H}_5)_2$$
$$\text{IV}a \qquad\qquad\qquad \text{XXIII}$$

function was reported by Stevens and Munk (791*a*). Thus, treatment of a solution of an acylamino acid (I*a*) with diphenylketene-N-*p*-tolylamine

(XXI) in benzene, 95% ethanol or aqueous dioxane yields a stable adduct (XXII) which may be isolated and purified by crystallization; the adducts of phthalylglycine, phthalyl-β-alanine, phthalyl-DL-methionine, and carbobenzoxyglycine were so secured, with melting points, respectively, of 179.5–180.5°, 121.5–122.5°, 135–136°, and 166–167°. Interaction of such adducts with a suitably constituted amine, e.g., amino acid ester, in refluxing benzene or methylene chloride solution then leads to the desired peptide derivative (IVa) in addition to diphenylacetic acid p-toluidide (XXIII) as an easily separable co-product.

37. N-Acyl-5-oxazolidone Method. *Principle.* N-Acyl-5-oxazolidones (IV) may be procured either (*a*) upon treatment of the pertinent precursor N-acylamino acid (I) in a glacial acetic acid–acetic anhydride mixture with formaldehyde (II) at 100° or (*b*) by the azeotropic removal of water from a mixture of the acylamino acid (I), formaldehyde (II), and p-toluenesulfonic acid in benzene solution. Such compounds are presumably formed by way of the corresponding intermediate N-hydroxymethyl derivative (III) which, in turn, undergoes intramolecular cyclization with the concomitant loss of a molecule of water. The action of a suitably constituted amine, e.g., an amino acid ester, on the N-acyl-5-oxazolidone, either in the presence or absence of solvent, then yields the desired peptide derivative (V); formaldehyde (IIa) liberation accompanies the condensation reaction.

$$\text{RCO—NHCHR}^1\text{CO}_2\text{H} + \text{HCHO} \xrightarrow[\substack{\text{CH}_3\text{C}_6\text{H}_4\text{SO}_3\text{H} \\ \text{C}_6\text{H}_6, \Delta}]{\text{HOAc—Ac}_2\text{O}} \left[\begin{array}{c} \text{CHR—CO}_2\text{H} \\ | \\ \text{RCO—N} \\ \phantom{\text{RCO—N}}\diagdown \\ \phantom{\text{RCO—N}\diagdown}\text{CH}_2\text{OH} \end{array} \right] \xrightarrow{-\text{H}_2\text{O}}$$

I　　　　　　　II　　　　　　　　　　　　　　　　III

$$\begin{array}{c} \phantom{\text{RCO—N}}\text{CHR—CO} \\ \phantom{\text{RCO—N}}|\phantom{\text{CHR}}| \\ \text{RCO—N}\phantom{\text{CHR}}\text{O} \\ \phantom{\text{RCO—N}}\diagdown\phantom{\text{CO}} \\ \phantom{\text{RCO—NN}}\text{CH}_2 \end{array} \xrightarrow{\text{NH}_2\text{CHR}^2\text{CO}_2\text{Et}} \text{RCO—NHCHR}^1\text{CO—NHCHR}^2\text{CO}_2\text{Et} + \text{HCHO}$$

IV　　　　　　　　　　　　　　　　V　　　　　　　　　　　　　　　IIa

General Considerations and Experimental Conditions. The action of formaldehyde (IIb) or paraformaldehyde on primary amides (VI) under acidic conditions proceeds with the formation of the corresponding methylenediamides (VII), whereas the presence within the reactant amide molecule of

$$2\text{RCONH}_2 + \text{HCHO} \xrightarrow{\text{H}^+} \text{RCONH—CH}_2\text{—NHCOR} + \text{H}_2\text{O}$$
　　VI　　　　　　IIb　　　　　　　　　　VII　　　　　　　　　VIII

other functional groups could lead to cyclic products by virtue of the formation of an intramolecular methylene bridge (cf. 792); as illustrative of the latter situation, the production of (X) and (XI) from the interaction of formaldehyde with asparagine (IX) and histidine (XII), respectively, might be noted. It was with reactions of the afore-mentioned type in mind that Ben-Ishai (793) in 1957 investigated the action of paraformaldehyde on various acylated amino acids. Thus, when a mixture of a carbobenzoxyamino acid (I; $R = C_6H_5CH_2O$) and paraformaldehyde was heated under reflux in benzene solution, which contained p-toluenesulfonic acid as a catalyst, a

```
CONH₂              CO—NH              CH₂
 |                /      \            /  \
CH₂   HCHO    H₂C        CH₂     N——C    NH      HCHO    N——CH    NH₂
 |    ——→      |          |      ‖   |    |      ←——      ‖   ‖    |
CHNH₂          CH—NH             HC  C   CHCO₂H          HC   C   CHCO₂H
 |              |                 \ / \                   \ / \
CO₂H           CO₂H                NH  CH₂                 NH  CH₂
 IX              X                   XI                      XII
```

crystalline neutral compound in addition to an acidic product was isolated. The former was identified as the N-carbobenzoxy-5-oxazolidone (IV; $R = C_6H_5CH_2O$) on the basis of analytical and infrared spectra data, whereas the latter was shown to be the methylenebiscarbobenzoxyamino acid (XV) in consequence of its independent synthesis from the appropriate carbobenzoxyamino acid ethyl ester (XIII):

```
                              C₆H₅CH₂OCO—NCHRCO₂Et           C₆H₅CH₂OCO—NCHRCO₂H
                   HCHO              |                OH⁻            |
2C₆H₅CH₂OCO—NHCHRCO₂Et  ——→         CH₂              ——→            CH₂
                   −H₂O              |                               |
                              C₆H₅CH₂OCO—NCHRCO₂Et           C₆H₅CH₂OCO—NCHRCO₂H
       XIII                          XIV                            XV
```

Oxazolidones which were derived from optically active carbobenzoxyamino acids possessed high optical rotations and, upon treatment with an excess of ethanolic ammonia, were converted to the corresponding carbobenzoxyamino acid amide in the absence of detectable racemization. Details both for the preparation of N-carbobenzoxy-5-oxazolidones (procedure 10–88) and for the use of these compounds in the synthesis of carbobenzoxyamino acid amides (procedure 10–89) are given below. In this connection, it is worthy of added note that, while the treatment of N-carbobenzoxy-5-oxazolidone (XVII; $R = H$) with an excess of benzylamine in ethanolic solution at room temperature provides the pertinent carbobenzoxyamino acid benzylamide (XVI; $R = H$, $R' = C_6H_5CH_2$) in goodly yield after several hours, comparable treatment of the former reactant (XVII) with only one equivalent of benzylamine gives rise to a crystalline intermediate which is readily converted to (XVI) upon further treatment with either ammonia or benzylamine; the assignment of an N-methylol-N-carbobenzoxyglycine benzylamide (XVIII; $R = H$, $R' = C_6H_5CH_2$) to such

```
         R'NH₂ |                           CHR—CO                      CH₂OH
               ↓              R'NH₂        |     |      R'NH₂           |
C₆H₅CH₂OCO—NHCHRCO—NHR'  ←——  C₆H₅CH₂OCO—N     O   ——→  C₆H₅CH₂OCO—NCHRCO—NHR¹
                              excess        \   /        1 eq.
                                              CH₂
           XVI                                XVII                      XVIII
```

intermediate was proposed on the basis of analytical data, infrared spectrum, and the fact that it is transformed to sarcosine benzylamide on catalytic hydrogenation.

Illustrative procedure 10–88 (793). N-Carbobenzoxy-5-oxazolidones. A mixture of 0.025 mole of the pertinent carbobenzoxyamino acid (Section 10–14), 1 g. of paraformaldehyde, and 250 mg. of *p*-toluenesulfonic acid in 200 ml. of benzene is refluxed for 0.5 hr., the liberated water being trapped in a Dean and Stark distilling receiver (see Figure 10–6). The benzene solution is washed with 5% aqueous potassium bicarbonate solution, dried over sodium sulfate, and the solvent removed *in vacuo*. Crystallization of the residual material from petroleum ether or benzene–petroleum ether then yields the pure N-carbobenzoxy-5-oxazolidone. The N-carbobenzoxy-5-oxazolidone derivatives of glycine (m.p. 84°), DL-alanine (m.p. 65°), L-leucine (m.p. 63°, $[\alpha]_D^{20} = +108°$ in chloroform), L-phenylalanine (m.p. 83°, $[\alpha]_D^{20} = +212°$ in chloroform), and L-valine (m.p. 54°, $[\alpha]_D^{20} = +95°$ in chloroform) have been so prepared, the yields ranging from 40 to 80% of theory.

Illustrative procedure 10–89 (793). Carbobenzoxy-L-phenylalanine amide. A solution of 3.11 g. of N-carbobenzoxy-L-4-benzyl-5-oxazolidone (procedure 10–88) in a mixture of 25 ml. of ethanol and 3 ml. of concentrated aqueous ammonia is permitted to stand at room temperature for 5 hr., the ethanol then removed *in vacuo*, and the residual material crystallized from ethyl acetate–petroleum ether; yield, 2.5 g. (83%); m.p. 167°; $[\alpha]_D^{20} = +12.0°$ (1% in chloroform).

At about the same time that Ben-Ishai (793) reported his studies on N-acyl-5-oxazolidones, Micheel and Thomas (794) independently described the synthesis of the same class of reactive intermediates via an alternative route. Thus, the action of formaldehyde on a solution of an N-tosylamino acid (XIX) in glacial acetic acid–acetic anhydride at 100° under pressure yields the corresponding N-tosyl-5-oxazolidone (XXI) (procedure 10–90), presumably via an N-hydroxymethyl intermediate (XX). Treatment of the latter derivative with a suitably constituted amine or an amino acid ester at an elevated temperature, in the absence of solvent, leads to the N-tosyl-amino acid amide derivative (XXII) (procedure 10–91). However, interaction of the oxazolidone with alcohol does not proceed in the expected manner. Thus, whereas the stability of the alanine derivative toward alcohol is sufficiently great to permit it to be safely recrystallized from ethanol or isopropanol, the corresponding glycine derivative (XXI; R = H) decomposes upon prolonged heating in ethanol, not to the anticipated tosylglycine ethyl ester but rather to the acylamino acid (XIX); cleavage occurs in the absence of water. Although the mechanism of such reaction is not yet understood, it presumably differs from that wherein ring cleavage is mediated by amines.

Illustrative procedure 10–90 (794). N-*p*-Tosyl-5-oxazolidone. Ten grams of N-tosylglycine (procedures 10–25 and 10–26) is dissolved in 50 ml. of glacial acetic acid with gentle warming, 39.0 ml. of acetic anhydride and 6.9 ml. of 35% formaldehyde solution are added thereto, and the reaction mixture is heated for 3 hr. at 100° in a sealed vessel. After cooling, 1.0 ml. of concentrated sulfuric acid is added, and the reaction mixture heated for an additional 30 min. at 95–100°. To the slightly yellowish solution is added 3.5 g. of anhydrous sodium acetate and the mixture concentrated to dryness *in vacuo*. The residual syrup is neutralized with concentrated sodium bicarbonate solution and the white precipitate filtered off, washed twice with bicarbonate solution and several times with water, and finally dried; yield, 5.4 g. (51%). Recrystallization is effected from benzene–petroleum ether; m.p. 119–120°. Preparation of N-*p*-tosyl-DL-4-methyl-5-oxazolidone, m.p. 104–105°, from tosyl-DL-alanine is achieved in essentially the same manner.

Illustrative procedure 10–91 (794). N-Tosylglycylglycine. A mixture of 1.5 g. of N-*p*-tosyl-5-oxazolidone and 1.24 ml. of glycine ethyl ester (prepared from the hydrochloride salt) is heated at 100° for 10 min., the reaction mixture cooled, the residue taken up in 6.8 ml. of methanol, and the latter solution treated with 6.8 ml. of 2N sodium hydroxide. After 1 hr., the *p*H is adjusted to 6 with hydrochloric acid and the solution then concentrated *in vacuo*. The partially crystalline residue is taken up in the minimal amount of water, hydrochloric acid added to a *p*H of 1–2, the resulting oil brought to crystallization by scratching the sides of the vessel, and the precipitate (yield, 1.62 g.) recrystallized several times from water; m.p. 178–179°.

Scope and Limitations. Utilization of N-acyl-5-oxazolidones in the synthesis of peptides has not yet been sufficiently widespread to warrant a proper assay of their practicable worth as reactive intermediates. However, from the scant data presently at hand, it appears that the general employment of these compounds should be fraught with difficulties, not the least of which is presented by the marked reactivity of formaldehyde toward a number of functional groups which are frequently found in the reactant molecules but which are not to be implicated in the coupling step. Added to this is the present requirement that the reactive intermediate be isolated before condensation with an amine, a manipulation often unnecessary with a number of other modern coupling methods.

38. Active Ester Method.

Principle. By virtue of their incorporation of electronegative substituents in the alcohol portion of the ester function, certain carboxylic acid esters may possess the reactive character of acylating agents and hence may serve as useful intermediates for the synthesis of peptides. Where the active ester in point is aliphatic in nature, the activating influence of negative substituents can be ascribed essentially to an inductive effect, e.g., cyanomethyl esters (I), while the reactive nature of aromatic esters which bear an electronegative substituent in the *ortho* or *para* positions is presumably attributable to an electromeric mechanism, e.g., *p*-cyanophenyl esters (II):

$$\underset{I}{R-\underset{\delta+}{\overset{O}{\overset{\|}{C}}}\rightarrow O \rightarrow CH_2 \rightarrow \underset{\delta-}{C \equiv N}}$$

$$\underset{II}{R-\underset{\delta+}{\overset{O}{\overset{\|}{C}}}-O-\underset{}{\bigcirc}-\underset{\delta-}{C \equiv N}}$$

In any event, alkyl esters which incorporate such moieties as cyanomethyl (III; $R^1 = CH_2CN$), carboethoxymethyl (III; $R^1 = CH_2CO_2C_2H_5$), or methoxymethyl (III; $R^1 = CH_2OCH_3$), as well as aromatic esters which possess *o*-nitrophenyl (IV; $R^1 = NO_2$, $R^2 = H$), *p*-nitrophenyl (IV; $R^1 = H, R^2 = NO_2$), *p*-carbomethoxyphenyl (IV; $R^1 = H, R^2 = CH_3OCO$), or analogous substituents, are highly susceptible to aminolysis by suitably constituted amines. Unsubstituted O-phenyl esters (IV; $R^1 = R^2 = H$),

$$\underset{III}{R\overset{O}{\overset{\|}{C}}-OR^1} \qquad \underset{IV}{R\overset{O}{\overset{\|}{C}}-O-\underset{}{\bigcirc}\overset{R^1}{\underset{R^2}{}}} \qquad \underset{V}{R\overset{O}{\overset{\|}{C}}-S-\underset{}{\bigcirc}\overset{R^1}{\underset{R^2}{}}}$$

S-phenyl esters (V; $R^1 = R^2 = H$), and especially *ortho* or *para* negatively substituted derivatives of the latter, are extremely sensitive to like reaction. The aminolysis of an active ester derivative of an acylamino acid (VIII and IX), as mediated by an amino acid, peptide, or ester derivative thereof, may be effected in either organic or aqueous medium at room temperature, although elevated temperatures are occasionally needed; formation of the desired peptide derivative (X and Xa) proceeds with the concomitant liberation of the alcohol portion (XI and XII) of the active ester moiety. Preparation of the pertinent reactive alkyl O-ester (VIII; R^3 = alkyl) intermediates may be achieved through the action of the pertinent alkyl halide (XR^3), e.g., $ClCH_2CN$, $BrCH_2CO_2Et$, or $ClCH_2OCH_3$, on the carboxylic acid reactant (VI) in the presence of a tertiary amine, either in solution in an inert organic medium or in the absence of solvent; O-aryl esters (VIII;

$$RCO-NHCHR^1CO_2H \longrightarrow RCO-NHCHR^1CO-Cl \text{ (or } -O_2COR^2) \xrightarrow[(C_2H_5)_3N]{ArOH \text{ or } R^3OH}$$

VI → VII

$\begin{array}{c} XR^3.P(OAr)_3 \\ \text{or } SO(OAr)_2 \end{array}\Bigg\downarrow \qquad \qquad P(SAr)_3 \qquad \qquad \Bigg\downarrow \begin{array}{c} R^3SH \text{ or } ArSH \end{array}$

$RCO-NHCHR^1CO-OAr$ (or $-OR^3$) $\qquad\qquad RCO-NHCHR^1CO-SAr$ (or $-SR^3$)
VIII $\qquad\qquad\qquad\qquad\qquad\qquad\qquad\qquad$ IX

$\Bigg\downarrow NH_2R^4 \qquad\qquad\qquad\qquad\qquad\qquad\qquad\qquad \Bigg\downarrow NH_2R^4$

$RCO-NHCHR^1CO-NHR^4 + ArOH$ (or R^3OH) $\qquad RCO-NHCHR^1CO-NHR^4 + ArSH$ (or R^3SH)
X $\qquad\qquad$ XI $\qquad\qquad\qquad\qquad\qquad\qquad$ Xa $\qquad\qquad\qquad$ XII

Ar = aryl) and S-aryl esters (IX; Ar = aryl), on the other hand, may be prepared via an initial conversion of the carboxylic acid reactant to its corresponding mixed carboxylic-carbonic acid anhydride (Section 10–29) or acid chloride (Section 10–27) derivative (VII), followed by treatment of the latter with the requisite alcohol or mercaptan. A somewhat more direct synthesis of O-aryl esters (VIII) is afforded by the action of a diaryl sulfite (SO(OAr)$_2$) or triaryl phosphite (P(OAr)$_3$) on a pyridine solution of the pertinent carboxylic acid reactant (VI); the alternative use of a triaryl phosphorotrithioite (P(SAr)$_3$) as the esterification agent yields the corresponding aryl thiolester (IX) in either pyridine or dimethylformamide solution.

General Considerations and Experimental Conditions. The early unfruitful attempts of Emil Fischer and his contemporaries to utilize the aminolysis of methyl and ethyl esters of acylated amino acids and peptides as a means for effecting the controlled stepwise synthesis of peptides has been alluded to previously (Section 10–4). That the more highly reactive thiophenyl esters of acylated amino acids (IX; Ar = C$_6$H$_5$) and peptides may successfully serve for such purpose was announced by Wieland, Schäfer, and Bokelmann (795) in 1951. Preparation of the pertinent thiophenyl ester intermediate (IX) was achieved via the action of an alkyl chlorocarbonate on a cooled solution containing the acylamino acid (VI) (or acylated peptide) and a tertiary amine, followed by treatment of the resulting mixed carboxylic-carbonic acid anhydride (VII) *in situ* with thiophenol (procedure 10–92); an inert anhydrous solvent medium, e.g., tetrahydrofuran, chloroform, or ethyl acetate, is generally employed, and the same precautions and limitations are applicable here as with other coupling reactions involving mixed anhydrides (Sections 10–28 and 10–29). Although such preparation requires the synthesis of a reactive intermediate, i.e., the mixed carboxylic-carbonic acid anhydride, which might itself be utilized in the peptide coupling step, the thiophenyl esters nevertheless possess certain virtues which sometimes make their alternative use highly desirable. Thus the thiophenyl esters of acylated amino acids and peptides may be obtained in crystalline form, possess well-defined melting points, undergo no detectable decomposition upon prolonged storage at room temperature, and are highly resistant to the solvolytic action of boiling water, alcohol, and dilute acids. Although the action of warm aqueous alkali promotes a slow saponification of the active ester group, the aminolysis reaction proceeds at a much more rapid rate when such medium contains a suitably constituted amine and thereupon permits a preferential occurrence of a coupling reaction rather than a hydrolytic reaction in aqueous alkaline medium (procedure 10–93); similar reaction may also be achieved with the alkali metal salt of an amino acid or peptide in alcoholic solution without the danger of accompanying esterification. Thus, for example, carbobenzoxyglycyl-DL-alanine is formed upon treatment under reflux of a mixture of carbobenzoxyglycine thiophenyl ester with DL-alanine, either as its sodium salt in methanolic solution or in aqueous alkali (795). Note should be made that, while aminolytic reactions which involve active esters of this type take place with facility, relatively longer reaction periods and more drastic thermal conditions are here necessitated than are required by reactions which employ the more reactive acid chloride, mixed anhydride, or azide intermediates.

Illustrative procedure 10–92 (170). Carbobenzoxyglycylglycine thiophenyl ester. A mixture of 5.32 g. of carbobenzoxyglycylglycine and 2.8 ml. of N-ethylpiperidine in 20 ml. of dry tetrahydrofuran is treated at 0° with 2 ml. of ethyl chlorocarbonate. After 15 min. at 0°, 2 ml. of thiophenol is added to the semisolid mass and the reaction mixture kept at room temperature for 4 hr. The solid material is filtered off, washed with a little tetrahydrofuran, and the combined filtrate and washings concentrated to dryness *in vacuo*. Recrystallization of the solid residue from 200 ml. of benzene yields 5.0 g. (70%) of the desired material; m.p. 117°. A similar procedure may be employed for the preparation of the thiophenyl ester derivatives of other acylated amino acids and peptides, the melting point constants for which are given in Table 10–40 (p. 1072).

Illustrative procedure 10–93 (170). Carbobenzoxyglycylglycyl-L-proline. A solution of 3.6 g. of carbobenzoxyglycylglycine thiophenyl ester (procedure 10–92) in 40 ml. of tetrahydrofuran is treated with a solution of 1.15 g. of L-proline in 10 ml. of N sodium hydroxide and the mixture heated under reflux to 65° for 4 hr. after homogenization with methanol. The reaction mixture is concentrated *in vacuo*, extracted with ether to remove the thiophenol, and acidified. Crystallization of the resulting oil can be effected upon scratching with a glass rod and cooling; yield, 3 g. (82%). A melting point of 137° is obtained after recrystallization from ethyl acetate.

In connection with the above, it should be noted that Wieland and Weidenmüller (481) prepared the α-thiophenyl ester (XV) and the γ-thiophenyl ester (XVI) of carbobenzoxy-L-glutamic acid by the action of thiophenol (XIV) on a mixture of carbobenzoxy-L-glutamic acid anhydride (XIII) and a tertiary base in an inert organic solvent medium. The reaction yielded a mixture of the α- and γ-thiolesters, the exact constitution of which varied markedly with the nature of both the solvent and the tertiary base employed. Thus the ratio of α- to γ-thiolester formed was 2 : 1 when reaction was carried out in tetrahydrofuran solution which contained pyridine, while a 1 : 4.5 ratio of the former to the latter product was secured in the presence of triethylamine as the base but under otherwise identical conditions; isolation of the pure α- or γ-thiolester could be effected from the appropriate

$$\begin{array}{c}
\text{Cbzo—NHCH—C=O} \\
\quad\quad\quad\quad\quad\backslash \\
\quad\quad\quad\quad\quad\quad\text{O} \; + \; \text{C}_6\text{H}_5\text{SH} \\
\quad\quad\quad\quad\quad/ \\
\text{(CH}_2\text{)}_2\text{C=O} \\
\quad\text{XIII} \quad\quad\quad \text{XIV}
\end{array}
\xrightarrow{\text{tertiary base}}
\begin{array}{c}
\text{Cbzo—NHCHCO—SC}_6\text{H}_5 \\
| \\
\text{(CH}_2\text{)}_2\text{CO}_2\text{H} \\
\text{XV}
\end{array}
\; + \;
\begin{array}{c}
\text{Cbzo—NHCHCO}_2\text{H} \\
| \\
\text{(CH}_2\text{)}_2\text{CO—SC}_6\text{H}_5 \\
\text{XVI}
\end{array}$$

reaction mixture upon suitable recrystallization of the impure product (procedures 10–94 and 10–95). Use of formamide in lieu of tetrahydrofuran as the solvent medium and triethylamine as the base led to the formation of a wholly racemic product composed almost exclusively of the γ-thiophenyl ester (XVI). Similar preparation of the pure γ-thiophenyl ester of phthalyl-L-glutamic acid was permitted by the interaction of phthalyl-L-glutamic acid anhydride and thiophenol in triethylamine-tetrahydrofuran. It is of interest to note that the afore-mentioned N-acylated half thiolesters of glutamic acid have not only proved of value in the synthesis of α- and γ-glutamyl peptide derivatives (procedure 10–96), but have also been successfully utilized in coupling reactions with such reactants as cysteinylglycine, wherein the reactivity of the sulfhydryl moiety was not masked by a blocking group.

Illustrative procedure 10–94 (481). Carbobenzoxy-L-glutamic acid α-thiophenyl ester. To a solution of 2.64 g. of carbobenzoxy-L-glutamic anhydride (procedure 10–132) in 20 ml. of tetrahydrofuran are added 1.0 ml. of thiophenol[1] and 1.6 ml. of pyridine. After some 2 days at room temperature, the reaction mixture is acidified with a solution of 0.9 g. of anhydrous oxalic acid in 10 ml. of tetrahydrofuran, the precipitated triethylamine salt filtered off, and the filtrate concentrated to dryness *in vacuo* at 20°. The residual material is taken up in 20 ml. of absolute ether, the solution filtered, and the filtrate treated with 10 ml. of petroleum ether and cooled at 0° for 3 hr. Upon filtration, 1.8 g. (48%) of the desired compound is obtained; m.p. 111–113°; $[\alpha]_D^{19} = -25.5°$ (2% in dioxane).

Illustrative procedure 10–95 (481). Carbobenzoxy-L-glutamic acid γ-thiophenyl ester. The reaction is carried out in the same manner and with the same reactants as given in procedure 10–94 with the single exception that 1.4 ml. of triethylamine is used in lieu of the pyridine. The residual material ultimately obtained upon concentration of the reaction mixture is taken up in 10 ml. of absolute ether, filtered, and the filtrate treated with 2 ml. of petroleum ether. After some 3 hr. in the cold, the product is filtered off and recrystallized from ethyl acetate–petroleum ether; yield, 0.5 g. (13.5%); m.p. 129–131°; $[\alpha]_D^{19} = +3.5°$ (8.5% in dioxane).

Illustrative procedure 10–96 (481). Carbobenzoxy-L-glutamine. A solution of 0.2 g. of carbobenzoxy-L-glutamic acid γ-thiophenyl ester (procedure 10–95) in 5 ml. of tetrahydrofuran is cooled to 0° and a stream of dry ammonia gas introduced. The oil that separates is washed with ether, dissolved in 1 ml. of water, and the aqueous solution treated with 0.5 ml. of 2N hydrochloric acid. An oil is deposited which quickly crystallizes upon chilling and rubbing with a glass rod; yield, 0.09 g. (65%); m.p. 134°.

In 1948, the studies of Gordon, Miller, and Day (796) denoted that the relative rates of aminolysis of various ester derivatives of a given fatty acid were of the following order: phenyl > vinyl > methyl > benzyl > ethyl. With the relatively high degree of reactivity of the phenyl esters in mind, Bodanszky (797) investigated the effect of *ortho*-, *meta*-, and *para*-nitro substitution on the rate of aminolysis of phthalylglycine phenyl ester by glycine ethyl ester in boiling benzene solution. After some 20 minutes, a 90% or greater formation of phthalylglycylglycine ethyl ester was indicated where the *o*-, *m*-, or *p*-nitrophenyl ester was employed, while only a 26.5% conversion to the desired product was shown with the unsubstituted phenyl ester; under like conditions, the thiophenyl ester of phthalylglycine underwent a 47.5% conversion to the peptide derivative. Such data clearly revealed that the thiophenyl ester possessed a reactivity which was greater than that of the corresponding unsubstituted O-phenyl ester, albeit less than that of the various nitrophenyl esters. In any event, the high degree of susceptibility to aminolysis exhibited by nitrophenyl esters suggested their potential utility as reactive intermediates in the synthesis of peptide derivatives and, indeed, permitted Bodanszky (797) and his co-workers (798) to synthesize a number of such compounds.

The phenyl and nitrophenyl ester derivatives employed by Bodanszky (797) were prepared by heating a mixture of phenol or nitrophenol either with the pertinent acylamino acid chloride in the absence of solvent or with the mixed anhydride of the acylamino acid in chloroform or tetrahydrofuran solution (procedure 10–97). A more direct synthetic route to these and other substituted phenyl ester derivatives was described by Iselin, Rittel, Sieber, and Schwyzer (799), who employed diaryl sulfites (XX) and triaryl phosphites (XXIII) as esterifying agents. Preparation of the latter reagents was effected by the dropwise addition of triethylamine (XIX) or pyridine to a mixture of the substituted phenol (XVIII and XVIIIa) and thionyl chloride (XVII) or phosphorus trichloride (XXII) in an inert solvent medium (procedure 10–98):

$$\underset{\text{XVII}}{SOCl_2} + \underset{\text{XVIII}}{2ArOH} + \underset{\text{XIX}}{2N(C_2H_5)_3} \rightarrow \underset{\text{XX}}{SO(OAr)_2} + \underset{\text{XXI}}{2(C_2H_5)_3N \cdot HCl}$$

$$\underset{\text{XXII}}{PCl_3} + \underset{\text{XVIIIa}}{2ArOH} + \underset{\text{XIXa}}{3N(C_2H_5)_3} \rightarrow \underset{\text{XXIII}}{P(OAr)_3} + \underset{\text{XXIa}}{3(C_2H_5)_3N \cdot HCl}$$

The various symmetrical diaryl sulfite and triaryl phosphite esters so secured are listed in Table 10–39. Reaction of these compounds with carboxylic acids to yield the desired active carboxylic acid ester was carried out in pyridine solution at room temperature (2–3 hours reaction time) or in an inert solvent, e.g., ethyl acetate, treated with pyridine (procedure 10–99). One equivalent of a symmetrical diaryl sulfite (XXa) or triaryl phosphite (XXIIIa) reacts with a carboxylic acid (XXIV and XXIVa) to yield one equivalent and two equivalents, respectively, of the desired product (XXV and XXVa):

$$\underset{\text{XXIV}}{RCO_2H} + \underset{\text{XXa}}{SO(OAr)_2} \xrightarrow{\text{pyridine}} \underset{\text{XXV}}{RCO_2Ar} + \underset{\text{XXVI}}{SO_2} + \underset{\text{XVIIIb}}{ArOH}$$

$$\underset{\text{XXIVa}}{2RCO_2H} + \underset{\text{XXIIIa}}{P(OAr)_3} \xrightarrow{\text{pyridine}} \underset{\text{XXVa}}{2RCO_2Ar} + \underset{\text{XXVII}}{ArO-PH(=O)OH}$$

TABLE 10-39
Some Diaryl Sulfite (SO(OAr)$_2$) and Triaryl Phosphite (P(OAr)$_3$) Esters (799)

Aryl Group	Diaryl Sulfite (MP or BP)	Triaryl Phosphite (MP or BP)
phenyl	172–174°/11 mm.	129–130°/0.01 mm.
1-naphthyl	90–92°	91°
2-naphthyl	78–79°	97°
2,6-dimethoxyphenyl (OCH$_3$ / OCH$_3$)	97–99°	–
2-(CO$_2$CH$_3$)phenyl	181–183°/0.07 mm.	–
4-(CO$_2$CH$_3$)phenyl	90°[a]	–
4-N(CH$_3$)$_2$phenyl	58°	71°
4-C≡N phenyl	97°[a]	129–130°
4-SO$_2$CH$_3$ phenyl	146–149°[a]	185–188°
4-NO$_2$ phenyl	98–100°	170–171°

[a] Data for crude material.

Aromatic O-esters of acylamino acids and peptides may be coupled with suitably constituted amines in aqueous or non-aqueous media by essentially the same procedure described above for the corresponding thiophenyl esters (procedure 10–100).

Illustrative procedure 10–97 (797). Carbobenzoxy-S-benzyl-L-cysteine *p*-nitrophenyl ester. A solution of 0.01 mole of carbobenzoxy-L-cysteine (see procedures 10–28 and 10–30) and 0.01 mole of triethylamine in 10 ml. of chloroform is cooled to 0° and 0.01 mole of ethyl chlorocarbonate then added thereto. After about 8 min., the reaction mixture is treated with 0.01 mole of *p*-nitrophenol and thereupon heated to boiling for 1–2 min. Finally, concentration of the solution *in vacuo* yields a residue which is crystallized from methanol; yield, 66.5%; m.p. 84–86°. Use of the appropriate reactants permits like synthesis of the phenyl, thiophenyl, *o*-, *m*-, and *p*-nitrophenyl, and 2:4-dinitrophenyl esters of phthalylglycine, the *p*-nitrophenyl esters of carbobenzoxyglycine, phthalyl-L-alanine, phthalyl-D-leucine, and phthalyl-L-leucine, and the *o*-, *m*-, and *p*-nitrophenyl esters of carbobenzoxy-S-benzyl-L-cysteine, among others. Table 10–40 lists the melting points of the pertinent compounds.

Illustrative procedure 10–98 (799). Di-*p*-nitrophenyl sulfite. To a mixture of 4.13 g. (0.029 mole) of *p*-nitrophenol and 1.06 ml. (0.0146 mole) of thionyl chloride in 25 ml. of absolute ether is slowly added a solution of 4.8 ml. (0.035 mole) of triethylamine in 15 ml. of absolute ether, with concurrent stirring and cooling in an ice bath. After about 1 hr., the reaction mixture is concentrated to dryness under a jet of dry air and the residue washed copiously with water, dried, and crystallized from acetone-ether; m.p. 98–100°.

Illustrative procedure 10–99 (799). Carbobenzoxyglycine *p*-nitrophenyl ester. A solution of 209 mg. (0.001 mole) of carbobenzoxyglycine (procedure 10–28) in a mixture of 2 ml. of ethyl acetate and 0.16 ml. (0.002 mole) of pyridine is treated with 324 mg. (0.001 mole) of di-*p*-nitrophenyl sulfite (procedure 10–98) and then warmed at 50° for 3 hr. The reaction mixture is cooled to 0°, washed successively with 2N hydrochloric acid, saturated sodium bicarbonate solution and water, and finally dried over sodium sulfate. Upon concentration to dryness, a crystalline residue is obtained which is recrystallized from ethanol; yield, 315 mg. (95%); m.p. 124–125°.

Illustrative procedure 10–100 (798). Phthalylglycyl-L-asparagine. A solution of 1.63 g. of phthalylglycine *p*-nitrophenyl ester (see procedure 10–97) in a mixture of 15 ml. of dioxane and 5 ml. of water is heated over a steam bath and 0.80 g. of L-asparagine monohydrate is added thereto, followed by the portionwise addition over a 5-min. period of 0.70 ml. of triethylamine; complete solution is achieved during the course of the reaction. Heating is continued for an additional 5 min. subsequent to treatment of the reaction mixture with 10 ml. of water. The solution is then cooled, 8 ml. of *N* hydrochloric acid and 60 ml. of water are added, and the resulting precipitate is filtered, washed thrice with 10 ml. portions of water, and dried; yield, 1.02 g. (63.5%); m.p. 206–208°. A melting point of 210° is obtained after a single recrystallization from water.

A novel study by Farrington, Hextall, Kenner, and Turner (800) described the facile esterification of acylated amino acids (XXIV*b*) and peptides as mediated by tri-*p*-nitrophenyl phosphorotrithioite (XXVIII) in either pyridine or dimethylformamide solution at room temperature. The corresponding

$$RCO_2H + P(S-C_6H_4-NO_2)_3 \rightarrow RCO-S-C_6H_4-NO_2 \xrightarrow{NH_2R'} RCO-NHR' + HS-C_6H_4-NO_2$$

XXIV*b*   XXVIII   XXIX   XXX   XXXI

thio-*p*-nitrophenyl esters (XXIX) were secured in excellent yield. That these compounds are more susceptible to aminolysis (XXIX → XXX) than are the unsubstituted thiophenyl esters was indicated by the fact that the former readily undergo such reaction at room temperature in contrast to the elevated temperatures generally required for the latter derivatives. Thus, for example, the relative rates of aminolysis of the *p*-nitrophenyl ester, thiophenyl ester, and thio-*p*-nitrophenyl ester of carbobenzoxyglycine by alanine in dioxane–water at 21° were in the ratio 16 : 1 : 140. It is worthy of emphasis that the reactivity of the thio-*p*-nitrophenyl ester was some nine times greater than that of the corresponding O-ester.

That the introduction of electron-attracting substituents into the alcoholic component of methyl hippurate leads to activated esters which may behave as characteristic acylating agents was shown by Schwyzer, Iselin, and Feuer (801) in 1955. A number of activated esters of hippuric acid were prepared according to the reaction

$$C_6H_5CO-NHCH_2CO_2H + RX \xrightarrow[\Delta, EtOAc]{(C_2H_5)_3N} C_6H_5CO-NHCH_2CO_2R + (C_2H_5)_3N \cdot HX$$

XXXII   XXXIII   XXXIV   XXXV

where RX may be $ClCH_2CN$, $BrCH_2CO_2Et$, $BrCH(CO_2Et)_2$, $ClCH_2OCH_3$, $ClCH_2-C_6H_4-NO_2$, $ClCH_2COCH_3$, or $ClCH_2CH_2N(Et)_2$. Reaction of the active aliphatic esters so secured with benzylamine in anhydrous ethyl acetate solution revealed the following order of reactivity: $-CH_2CN >$ $-CH(CO_2Et)_2 > -CH_2CO_2Et > -CH_2OCH_3 > -CH_2-C_6H_4-NO_2$ $> -CH_2COCH_3 > -CH_3$. That the role of the solvent was also of importance here was indicated by the fact that the use of dioxane, acetonitrile, ethanol-water (1 : 1), water-saturated ethyl acetate, benzene, chloroform, aqueous ethanol (1 : 1), or dimethylformamide-water (2 : 3) in lieu of anhydrous ethyl acetate led to a marked diminution in over-all yield. With these results at their disposal, Schwyzer and his co-workers (802–806) further investigated the practical worth of cyanomethyl esters of acylated amino acids and peptides as intermediates for the preparation of amides from amines and amino acid and peptide esters. Where ethyl acetate, acetonitrile, or tetrahydrofuran was implicated as the solvent medium, the desired reaction indeed proceeded with facility at room temperature, completion of the reaction being generally attained during 0.5 to 48 hours; small amounts of such acids as acetic and sulfuric, as well as tertiary bases, e.g. triethylamine, were shown to have a marked catalytic effect on the reaction rate (procedure 10–102), with the rate of aminolytic cleavage being favored too by a high concentration of reactants. Preparation of the desired reactive cyanomethyl ester intermediates is conveniently achieved by the direct interaction of the carboxylic acid reactant with an excess of chloroacetonitrile and triethylamine in the absence of solvent (procedure 10–101); these compounds are readily isolable in pure crystalline form (see Table 10–40) and show a high degree of stability to prolonged storage at room temperature.

Illustrative procedure 10–101 (806). Tritylglycine cyanomethyl ester. Fifty grams of tritylglycine (procedures 10–36 and 10–37) is treated with a mixture of 69 ml. of triethylamine and 43 ml. of chloroacetonitrile at 0° and the mixture stirred until solution is complete. The solution is carefully warmed to 40°, with intermittent cooling to prevent the exothermic reaction mixture from heating beyond 45°. Reaction is almost wholly complete after some 40 min., but the mixture is warmed at 45° for an additional 2 hr. The reaction mixture is taken up in ethyl acetate and the latter then washed successively with water, citric acid solution, dilute sodium bicarbonate solution, and saturated sodium chloride solution. After drying over anhydrous sodium sulfate, the ethyl acetate solution is concentrated *in vacuo* and the residue crystallized from 150 ml. of ether upon the addition of 150 ml. of petroleum ether; yield, 54.5 g. (98%).

Illustrative procedure 10–102 (806). Tritylglycylglycine ethyl ester. A mixture of 20 g. of tritylglycine cyanomethyl ester (procedure 10–101), 20 ml. of triethylamine, 6 drops of glacial acetic acid, and 20 g. of glycine ethyl ester hydrochloride in 80 ml. of tetrahydrofuran is warmed at 60° for 1 hr. The reaction mixture is poured into 500 ml. of water and the resultant precipitate filtered over suction, washed thoroughly with water, and dried *in vacuo* over sodium hydroxide pellets; yield, 22.3 g. (98%).

In an attempt to demonstrate the applicability of various esters in the peptide-forming reaction, Iselin and Schwyzer (807) studied the behavior of the tetrahydropyranyl-(2)-ester of carbobenzoxyglycine, m.p. 96–98°. This reactive intermediate (XXXVIII), derived via a facile addition reaction between the acylamino acid (XXXVI) and dihydropyran (XXXVII), was coupled with benzylamine to yield the expected benzylamide (XXXIX) in addition to a co-product, 5-hydroxypentanal (XLI). Rapid and spontaneous reaction of the latter co-product with another molecule of benzylamine led to the formation of a Schiff base. In view of the occurrence of such auxiliary reaction, the presence of at least two equivalents of the amine reactant formed a necessary condition for completion of the desired reaction. Such

$$C_6H_5CH_2OCO-NHCH_2CO_2H + \underset{XXXVII}{\bigcirc_O} \rightarrow \underset{XXXVIII}{C_6H_5CH_2OCO-NHCH_2CO_2-\bigcirc_O}$$

$$\downarrow C_6H_5CH_2NH_2$$

$$\underset{XXXIX}{C_6H_5CH_2OCO-NHCH_2CO-NHCH_2C_6H_5} + \underset{XL}{HO-\bigcirc_O} \rightleftharpoons \underset{XLI}{O=CH\ CH_2OH}$$

considerations make it clear that the practicable utilization of the tetrahydropyranyl residue should provide, at best, only a rather limited means for the activation of esters. Nevertheless, this residue is of potential value for temporarily masking the reactive hydroxyl function of such amino acids as serine and tyrosine by way of an ether linkage which is stable to the action of alkali but which undergoes ready cleavage in the presence of acid (807). Thus, for example, N-carbobenzoxy-O-(tetrahydropyranyl-(2)-)-L-tyrosine ethyl ester (XLII; b.p. = 215–217°/0.03 mm.; $[\alpha]_D^{24} = +40°$ (4.1% in chloroform), was formed by the interaction of carbobenzoxy-L-tyrosine

$$\underset{XLII}{C_6H_5CH_2OCO-NHCHCH_2-\langle\rangle-O-\bigcirc_O}\ \ \overset{CO_2C_2H_5}{|}$$

ethyl ester with 2:3-dihydropyran; such reaction proceeds with the introduction of a new center of asymmetry at the 2-position of the tetrahydropyran ring. Saponification of the ethyl ester moiety of (XLII) with dilute alkali yielded a diastereoisomeric mixture of the corresponding free acids which could be fractionally separated into two isomeric forms with $[\alpha]_D$ values in ethanol of $-47°$ and $+46°$, and with melting points of 135–137° and 80°, respectively. The action of chloroacetonitrile on the higher-melting acid in the presence of triethylamine gave the corresponding cyanomethyl ester (m.p. 89–91°; $[\alpha]_D^{22} = -65°$ (3.8% in chloroform)), which, in turn, was converted to N-carbobenzoxy-O-tetrahydropyranyl-L-tyrosyl-L-isoleucine ethyl ester (m.p. 101–102°; $[\alpha]_D^{21} = -35°$ (4.8% in chloroform)) upon treatment with L-isoleucine ethyl ester. Selective cleavage of the carbobenzoxy group of the peptide derivative yielded O-tetrahydropyranyl-L-tyrosyl-L-isoleucine ethyl ester which, in consequence of its protected hydroxyl function, is capable of undergoing further condensation with other acylated amino acids or peptides through the use of otherwise inapplicable coupling procedures. A comparable series of reactions was effected starting with carbobenzoxy-DL-serine methyl ester.

That methoxyacetylene (XLIII; $R^2 = CH_3$) may serve as a condensing agent which mediates the peptide-forming step between an acylamino acid (VIa) and an amino acid ester was shown by Arens (808) in 1955; the reaction is conveniently effected at 40–50° either as a solution of the reactants in an inert medium, e.g., nitromethane or methanol, or upon admixture of the reactants in the absence of solvent. Such a reaction presumably occurs via the addition of the carboxylic acid reactant (VIa) across the triple bond of the ethine (XLIII) with the formation of a transitory activated ester (XLIV) which, in turn, undergoes a coupling reaction with the amine to

$$\text{RCO—NHCHR}^1\text{CO}_2\text{H} + \text{HC≡C—OR}^2 \rightarrow (\text{RCO—NHCHR}^1\text{CO—O—C(=CH}_2)\text{OR}^2)$$
$$\text{VIa} \qquad\qquad \text{XLIII} \qquad\qquad\qquad \text{XLIV}$$

$$\downarrow \text{NH}_2\text{CHR}^3\text{CO}_2\text{Et}$$

$$\text{RCO—NHCHR}^1\text{CO—NHCHR}^3\text{CO}_2\text{Et} + (\text{HO—C(=CH}_2)\text{OR}^2) \rightarrow \text{CH}_3\text{CO}_2\text{R}^2$$
$$\text{XLV} \qquad\qquad\qquad \text{XLVI} \qquad\qquad \text{XLVII}$$

yield the desired peptide derivative (XLV) in addition to methyl acetate (XLVII; $R^2 = CH_3$); the latter co-product probably arises from rearrangement of the initially liberated half-acetal of ketene (XLVI). Evidence in support of this mechanism was subsequently reported by Sheehan and Hlavka (808a), who noted the deposition of 1-ethoxyvinyl phthalylglycinate (m.p. 108–110°) during the interaction of phthalylglycine, glycine ethyl ester and ethoxyacetylene (XLIII; $R^2 = C_2H_5$) in aqueous solution and showed that this deposit (XLIV) condensed with glycine ethyl ester in dioxane or methylene chloride to yield phthalylglycylglycine ethyl ester in good over-all yield. It is of interest to note also that α-chlorovinylethyl ether ($H_2C=C(OC_2H_5)Cl$) and α,α-dichlorodiethyl ether ($CH_3C(OC_2H_5)Cl_2$), obtained from ethoxyacetylene by the addition of 1 or 2 equivalents of hydrogen chloride, respectively, have been shown by Heslinga and Arens (808b) similarly to mediate peptide bond formation between an acylamino acid and an amino acid ester in warm ethyl acetate; the reaction presumably proceeds in these instances through the initial conversion of the acylamino acid reactant to its corresponding acid chloride derivative which, in turn, condenses with the amine reactant to give the desired peptide derivative.

Application of active esters to the formation of amino acid polymers was reported by Wieland and Schäfer (809) in 1952. Thus the glycine, leucine, methionine, and valine thiophenyl ester hydrochlorides (XLIX) were synthesized via admixture of the requisite amino acid chloride hydrochloride (XLVIII), prepared essentially according to the classical procedure of Fischer (Section 10–7), with thiophenol in the absence of solvent at 70°. The free base of the glycine derivative, formed upon neutralization of the corresponding hydrochloride salt (XLIX; R = H) with alkali, suffered polymerization upon standing in aqueous solution at room temperature, the

$$\text{HCl·NH}_2\text{CHRCOCl} \xrightarrow{\text{C}_6\text{H}_5\text{SH}} \text{HCl·NH}_2\text{CHRCO—SC}_6\text{H}_5 \xrightarrow[\text{H}_2\text{O}]{\text{OH}^-} \text{NH}_2\text{CHRCO(—NHCHRCO—)}_x\text{SC}_6\text{H}_5$$
$$\text{XLVIII} \qquad\qquad\qquad \text{XLIX} \qquad\qquad\qquad\qquad \text{L}$$

glycine polymer (L) ultimately secured possessing an average chain length of 6 to 7 residues. That comparable treatment of valyl thiophenyl ester (LI; R = CH(CH$_3$)$_2$) did not proceed with the production of a polymeric material was subsequently reported by Wieland and Bernhard (810), who isolated the 2:5-diketopiperazine (LIII) from an ethereal solution of the free base but detected no evidence of accompanying polymer formation; the product (LIII) presumably arose from an initial intermolecular condensation of two molecules of the thiophenyl ester reactant (LI), followed by an intramolecular cyclization of the dipeptide ester (LII) so derived. Evidence in

$$\text{NH}_2\text{CHRCO—SC}_6\text{H}_5 \rightarrow \text{NH}_2\text{CHRCO—NHCHRCO—SC}_6\text{H}_5 \rightarrow \begin{array}{c} \text{NH—CO} \\ \text{RCH} \qquad \text{RCH} \\ \text{CO—NH} \end{array}$$
$$\text{LI} \qquad\qquad\qquad \text{LII} \qquad\qquad\qquad\qquad \text{LIII}$$

favor of the operation of such a mechanism was supported by the fact that similar treatment of the thiophenyl esters of glycyl-DL-valine and glycyl-DL-leucine likewise resulted in diketopiperazine but not in polymer formation. Such a situation could be obviated through the use of tripeptide derivatives, however. Thus, when glycylvalylisoleucine thiophenyl ester was permitted to stand in acetone solution for several days at room temperature, a polymer was gradually deposited which contained an average of approximately nine monomeric units (27 residues). Such finding suggests that active esters are of potential value for the synthesis of amino acid polymers wherein a sequence of three or more residues found in the monomeric reactant is to recur regularly along the entire polypeptide chain.

Finally, it should be noted that the use of active esters has hitherto provided the most important means for obtaining a number of cyclic peptides. Thus the preparation of *cyclo*-Gly·L-Leu·Gly·L-Leu·Gly (LVI) was achieved by Kenner and Turner (811) in 1955 according to the following reaction scheme:

$$\text{Cbzo—Gly·Leu·Gly·Leu·Gly·S—}\langle\text{C}_6\text{H}_4\rangle\text{—NO}_2 \xrightarrow{\text{HOAC—HBr}}$$
$$\text{LIV}$$

$$\text{HBr·H·Gly·Leu·Gly·Leu·Gly·S—}\langle\text{C}_6\text{H}_4\rangle\text{—NO}_2 \xrightarrow[\text{H}_2\text{O}]{\text{MgO}} \text{Gly·Leu·Gly·Leu·Gly}$$
$$\text{LV} \qquad\qquad\qquad\qquad\qquad \text{LVI}$$

Cyclization (LV → LVI) was accomplished in a highly dilute solution in order to minimize the possibility of polymer formation; the L-D isomer of (LVI) as well as the *cyclo*-hexapeptide, *cyclo*-Gly·L-Leu·Gly·Gly·L-Leu·Gly, were subsequently prepared in like manner (812*a*). Application of a comparable technique to the synthesis of *cyclo*-tetraglycyl and *cyclo*-hexaglycyl was described in a praiseworthy study by Schwyzer, Iselin, Rittel, and Sieber (806) in 1956. Preparation of the former compound (LIX; $x = 2$) arose from the dropwise addition of a dimethylformamide solution of tetraglycine cyanomethyl ester hydrochloride (LVIII; $x = 4$) into hot pyridine, whilst the *cyclo*-hexapeptide (LIX; $x = 4$) was prepared in comparable manner from either triglycyl thioglycolic acid hydrobromide (LXI) or triglycine cyanomethyl ester hydrochloride (LVIII; $x = 3$); in the latter instance, a preliminary condensation of two molecules of tripeptide derivative (LXI → LXII) presumably preceded the intramolecular cyclization step. The pertinent hydrohalide intermediate (LVIII or LXI) was secured

$$\text{Trityl—(Gly)}_x\cdot\text{OCH}_2\text{CN} \xrightarrow{\text{HCl}} \text{HCl·H·(Gly)}_x\cdot\text{OCH}_2\text{CN} \xrightarrow{\text{C}_5\text{H}_5\text{N}} \text{Gly·(Gly)}_x\cdot\text{Gly}$$
$$\text{LVII} \qquad\qquad \text{LVIII} \qquad\qquad \text{LIX}$$

$$\text{Cbzo—(Gly)}_3\cdot\text{SCH}_2\text{CO}_2\text{H} \xrightarrow[\text{HOAc}]{\text{HBr}} \text{HBr·H·(Gly)}_3\cdot\text{SCH}_2\text{CO}_2\text{H} \xrightarrow{\text{C}_5\text{H}_5\text{N}} \text{H·(Gly)}_6\cdot\text{SCH}_2\text{CO}_2\text{H}$$
$$\text{LX} \qquad\qquad \text{LXI} \qquad\qquad \text{LXII}$$

via the hydrogen halide-mediated cleavage of the trityl (806) or the carbobenzoxy (812) moiety from the corresponding precursor acylated peptide ester (LVII and LX). Use of an essentially similar procedure permitted Schwyzer and Sieber to accomplish an elegant synthesis of gramicidin S (719) in 1957 and homogramicidin S (626*a*) in the following year. These compounds were prepared by the trifluoroacetic acid-induced removal of the trityl group from trityl·[L-Val·(N$^\delta$-tosyl-L-Orn)·L-Leu·D-Phe·L-Pro]$_2$·

O—⟨⟩—NO$_2$ and trityl·[L-Val·(N$^\varepsilon$-tosyl-L-Lys)·L-Leu·D-Phe·L-Pro]$_2$·

Gramicidin S ($x = 2$) or homogramicidin S ($x = 3$)

O—⟨C₆H₄⟩—NO₂, respectively, followed by successive cyclization of the de-tritylated intermediate in warm pyridine and removal of the tosyl group by the reductive action of sodium in liquid ammonia (Section 10–45). The same *cyclo*-decapeptides were subsequently obtained (814a) when trityl·L-Val·(N^δ-tosyl-L-Orn)·L-Leu·D-Phe·L-Pro·O—⟨C₆H₄⟩—NO₂ and trityl·L-Val·(N^ε-tosyl-L-Lys)·L-Leu·D-Phe·L-Pro·O—⟨C₆H₄⟩—NO₂ were used in lieu of the corresponding tritylated decapeptide ester derivatives; the cyclization step was presumably preceded by a preliminary condensation of two molecules of pentapeptide derivative, a situation analogous to the formation of *cyclo*-hexaglycyl described above. That such "doubling reaction" may indeed be quite common was further attested to by the fact that the attempted cyclizations of the *p*-nitrophenyl (812c) and thio-*p*-nitrophenyl (812a) esters of glycyl-L-leucylglycine, as well as of the *p*-methanesulfonylphenyl ester of glycylglycyl-DL-phenylalanine and the cyanomethyl ester of glycyl-DL-phenylalanylglycine (812b), proceeded in each instance with the formation of the *cyclo*-hexapeptide. Despite the success attained with the cyclization of tetraglycine cyanomethyl ester to the corresponding *cyclo*-tetrapeptide (806), similar attempts to cyclize L-leucylglycyl-L-leucylglycine thio-*p*-nitrophenyl ester (812a) proved unfruitful. Such a situation, in addition to the doubling reaction observed with certain tri- and pentapeptide derivatives, emphasizes the strong influence of optical configuration and steric factors in governing the course of cyclization reactions.

Table 10–40 presents the melting point data for several active esters which have been described.

Scope and Limitations. Experience has pointed to the cyanomethyl, thiophenyl, *p*-nitrophenyl, and *p*-nitrothiophenyl esters as among the most practicable of the impressive variety of active esters of acylated amino acids and peptides which are readily available via synthetic means. Although intermediates of this type are not nearly so reactive as the corresponding acid chloride, mixed anhydride, or azide derivatives, they none the less possess certain inherent characteristics which occasionally render their use as acylating agents most advantageous. Thus the fact that active esters may be prepared in large quantity and stored safely until needed arises from the remarkable stability, crystallinity, and well-defined physical properties of these compounds. The relatively high degree of resistance toward saponification displayed by these reactive intermediates permits their condensation with amino acids or peptides to be achieved in aqueous alkali in generally satisfactory yield. Since active esters are extremely stable as solutions in inert organic or aqueous media over prolonged periods and are not so readily

TABLE 10-40

Active Ester Derivatives

Active Ester	Melting Point, °C.	Ref.
Cbzo-DL-CySBz·OCH$_2$CN	102–103	804
Cbzo-L-CySBz·OCH$_2$CN	67–68[a]	804
Cbzo-L-CySBz·SC$_6$H$_5$	100	390
Cbzo-L-CySBz·O—C$_6$H$_4$-NO$_2$ (o-NO$_2$)	80	797
Cbzo-L-CySBz·O—C$_6$H$_4$-NO$_2$ (o-O$_2$N)	101–102	797
Cbzo-L-CySBz·O—C$_6$H$_4$—NO$_2$ (p-)	89–91	797, 799
Cbzo-L-CySBz·Gly·SC$_6$H$_5$	102[b]	390
Cbzo-L-CySBz·Gly·Gly·SC$_6$H$_5$	105–106[c]	390
Cbzo-L-CySBz·L-Tyr·OCH$_2$CN	114–115[d]	804
Cbzo-L-Glu·SC$_6$H$_5$	111–113[e]	481
Cbzo-DL-Glu·OH └—SC$_6$H$_5$	129–130	481
Cbzo-L-Glu·OH └—SC$_6$H$_5$	129–131[f]	481
Cbzo-L-Glu·OMe └—L-Glu-OMe·SC$_6$H$_5$	111–112[g]	679
Cbzo-Gly·OCH$_2$CN	70	802
Cbzo-Gly·OC$_6$H$_5$	68–70	799
Cbzo-Gly·O—C$_6$H$_4$—CN	94	799
Cbzo-Gly·O—C$_6$H$_4$ (o-CO$_2$CH$_3$)	70–72	799
Cbzo-Gly·O—C$_6$H$_4$—CO$_2$CH$_3$	121	799
Cbzo-Gly·O—C$_6$H$_4$—NO$_2$	128	797, 799, 800
Cbzo-Gly·O—C$_6$H$_4$—N(CH$_3$)$_2$	109	799
Cbzo-Gly·O—naphthyl	109–110	799

CHEMICAL PROCEDURES FOR SYNTHESIS OF PEPTIDES 1043

TABLE 10-40 (*continued*)

Active Ester	Melting Point, °C.	Ref.
Cbzo-Gly·O—(2-naphthyl)	87–89	799
Cbzo-Gly·SC$_6$H$_5$	72	795
Cbzo-Gly·S—C$_6$H$_4$—NO$_2$	112.5	800, 811
Cbzo-Gly·SCH$_2$CO$_2$H	88.5–89	812
Cbzo-Gly·DL-Ala·Gly·OCH$_2$CN	145	802
Cbzo-Gly·Gly·O—C$_6$H$_4$—NO$_2$	163–165	799
Cbzo-Gly·Gly·SC$_6$H$_5$	117	170
Cbzo-Gly·Gly·Gly·SCH$_2$CO$_2$H	175–176	812
Cbzo-Gly·Gly·DL-Phe·O—C$_6$H$_4$—SO$_2$CH$_3$	90–92	812*b*
Cbzo-Gly·L-Leu·Gly·OCH$_2$CN	80–82	812*c*
Cbzo-Gly·L-Leu·Gly·O—C$_6$H$_4$—NO$_2$	155.5–156.5	812*c*
Cbzo-Gly·L-Leu·Gly·S—C$_6$H$_4$—NO$_2$	159	800
Cbzo-Gly·L-Leu·Gly·Gly·L-Leu·Gly·S—C$_6$H$_4$—NO$_2$	194–195	812*a*
Cbzo-Gly·L-Leu·Gly·D-Leu·Gly·S—C$_6$H$_4$—NO$_2$	150–152	812*a*
Cbzo-Gly·L-Leu·Gly·L-Leu·Gly·S—C$_6$H$_4$—NO$_2$	184	800, 811
Cbzo-Gly·DL-Phe·SC$_6$H$_5$	94	795
Cbzo-Gly·L-Phe·S—C$_6$H$_4$—NO$_2$	154–155[h]	800
Cbzo-Gly·DL-Phe·Gly·O—C$_6$H$_4$—NO$_2$	171–172	812*b*
Cbzo-Gly·DL-Phe·Gly·O—C$_6$H$_4$—SO$_2$CH$_3$	161–162.5	812*b*
Cbzo-DL-Leu·OCH$_2$CN	83–85	805
Cbzo-L-Leu·OCH$_2$CN	84–85[i]	805

TABLE 10–40 (*continued*)

Active Ester	Melting Point, °C.	Ref.
Cbzo-L-Leu·O—C₆H₄—NO₂	95	799
Cbzo-DL-Leu·S—C₆H₄—NO₂	98	812a
Cbzo-D-Leu·S—C₆H₄—NO₂	106–107	812a
Cbzo-L-Leu·S—C₆H₄—NO₂	107	800
Cbzo-L-Leu·Gly·S—C₆H₄—NO₂	118	800
Cbzo-L-Leu·D-Phe·OCH₂CN	102–103	719
Cbzo-L-Leu·D-Phe·O—C₆H₄—CN	160	799
Cbzo-L-Leu·D-Phe·O—C₆H₄—NO₂	165–166	799
Cbzo-DL-Phe·O—C₆H₄—CN	88.5–89	812b
O,N-diCbzo-L-Tyr·OCH₂CN	99[j]	802
O,N-diCbzo-L-Tyr·OCH₂CO₂CH₂CH₃	100[k]	802
Cbzo-L-Val·O—C₆H₄—NO₂	63	799
p-NO₂-Cbzo-Gly·OCH₂CN	77–79	677
p-NO₂-Cbzo-DL-Leu·OCH₂CN	68	802
p-NO₂-Cbzo-DL-Leu·OCH₂—C₆H₄—NO₂	75	802
Phth-β-Ala·OCH₂CN	97	802
Phth-L-Ala·O—C₆H₄—NO₂	127	797
Phth-DL-Glu·OH └—SC₆H₅	184	481
Phth-L-Glu·OH └—SC₆H₅	190–192[l]	481
Phth-DL-Glu·(SC₆H₅)₂	109–110	481
Phth-DL-Glu·Gly·OH └—SC₆H₅	60–64	481

CHEMICAL PROCEDURES FOR SYNTHESIS OF PEPTIDES 1045

TABLE 10-40 (continued)

Active Ester	Melting Point, °C.	Ref.
Phth-Gly·OCH₂CN	132–133.5	677
Phth-Gly·OCH₂C≡CH	80–82	813
Phth-Gly·OC₆H₅	124–125	797, 799
Phth-Gly·SC₆H₅	103–106	797
Phth-Gly·O—(2-NO₂-C₆H₄)	158–160	797
Phth-Gly·O—(3-NO₂-C₆H₄)	170–172	797
Phth-Gly·O—(4-NO₂-C₆H₄)	180–181.5	797
Phth-Gly·O—(3,4-diNO₂-C₆H₃)	217	797
Phth-D-Leu·O—(4-NO₂-C₆H₄)	82	797
Phth-L-Leu·O—(4-NO₂-C₆H₄)	82	797
Tosyl-Gly·OCH₂CN	94	802
Tosyl-L-Glu-NH₂·OCH₂CN	117^m	802
Tosyl-DL-Met·OCH₂CN	85	802
Tosyl-DL-Met·OCH₂CO₂CH₂CH₃	–	802
TFA-DL-Ala·OCH₂CN	44–45	814
TFA-L-Ala·OCH₂CN	58–60^n	814
TFA-Gly·OCH₂CN	82–83	814
TFA-Gly·SC₆H₅	80–81.5	569
TFA-Gly·Gly·OCH₂CN	128–129	814
diTFA-L-Lys·OCH₂CN	102–104°	814
TFA-DL-Phe·OCH₂CN	78–79	814
TFA-L-Phe·OCH₂CN	70–72^p	814
TFA-L-Pro·OCH₂CN	oil^q	814
TFA-L-Val·OCH₂CN	44–46^r	814
Trityl-Gly·OCH₂CN	90.5–91	806
Trityl-Gly·O—(naphthyl)	127–128	799

TABLE 10-40 (continued)

Active Ester	Melting Point, °C.	Ref.
Trityl-Gly·Gly·OCH$_2$CN	157.5	806
Trityl-Gly·Gly·SC$_6$H$_5$	128	546
Trityl-Gly·Gly·SCH$_2$C$_6$H$_5$	120	546
Trityl-Gly·Gly·Gly·OCH$_2$CN	135.5-136	806
Trityl-Gly·Gly·Gly·Gly·OCH$_2$CN	172.5-173.5	806
Trityl-Gly·DL-Met·SCH$_2$C$_6$H$_5$	86	546
Trityl-Gly·DL-Phe·Gly·OCH$_2$CN	164-165.5	812b
Trityl-L-Val·L-(N$^\varepsilon$-Tos-Lys)·L-Leu·D-Phe· L-Pro·O—⟨ ⟩—NO$_2$	–	814a
Trityl-L-Val·L-(N$^\delta$-Tos-Orn)·L-Leu·D-Phe· L-Pro·O—⟨ ⟩—NO$_2$	–	814a
H·D-Ala·SC$_6$H$_5$·HCl	155-157	815
H·L-Ala·SC$_6$H$_5$·HCl	155-157	815
H·β-Ala·SC$_6$H$_5$·HCl	140	815
H·Gly·SC$_6$H$_5$·HCl	180 d.	809
H·Gly·S—⟨ ⟩—NO$_2$·HBr	194	811
H·Gly·SCH$_2$CO$_2$H·HBr	145-146·5	812
H·Gly·Gly·Gly·OCH$_2$CN·HCl	159-160	806
H·Gly·Gly·Gly·SCH$_2$CO$_2$H·HBr	180.5-181	812
H·Gly·Gly·Gly·Gly·OCH$_2$CN·HCl	155.5-156.5	806
H·Gly·DL-Leu·SC$_6$H$_5$·HCl	83-84	810
H·Gly·L-Leu·Gly·O—⟨ ⟩—NO$_2$·HBr	112-115	812c
H·Gly·DL-Val·SC$_6$H$_5$·HCl	154	810
H·DL-Leu·SC$_6$H$_5$·HCl	171-172	809
H·DL-Met·SC$_6$H$_5$·HCl	143	809
H·DL-Val·SC$_6$H$_5$	65-70	810
H·DL-Val·SC$_6$H$_5$·HCl	190 d.	809

^{a} $[\alpha]_D^{19} = -23°$ (4.2% in chloroform).
^{b} $[\alpha]_D^{20} = -14.5°$ (0.2% in ethanol).
^{c} $[\alpha]_D^{20} = -5.8°$ (0.5% in ethanol).
^{d} $[\alpha]_D^{23} = -27°$ (2% in acetic acid).
^{e} $[\alpha]_D^{19} = -25.5°$ (2% in dioxane).
^{f} $[\alpha]_D^{19} = +3.5°$ (8.5% in dioxane).
^{g} $[\alpha]_D^{20} = +3.6°$ (3.1% in tetrahydrofuran).
^{h} $[\alpha]_D^{20} = -67.0°$ (4.5% in dioxane).
^{i} $[\alpha]_D^{23} = -27.4°$ (5% in chloroform).
^{j} $[\alpha]_D = +2°$ (in chloroform).
^{k} $[\alpha]_D = +3°$ (in chloroform).
^{l} $[\alpha]_D^{18} = -18°$ (4% in dioxane).
^{m} $[\alpha]_D = -21°$ (in acetone).
^{n} $[\alpha]_D^{21} = -74°$ (2.3% in ethanol).
^{o} $[\alpha]_D^{21} = -33.5°$ (1.8% in ethanol).
^{p} $[\alpha]_D^{21} = -20.8°$ (1.8% in ethanol).
^{q} $[\alpha]_D^{21} = -86.6°$ (3.3% in ethanol).
^{r} $[\alpha]_D^{21} = -56.8°$ (1.9% in ethanol).

subject to the disproportionation or decomposition so often encountered with other active intermediates, their utilization for the synthesis of cyclic peptides is of especial value. Although the marked steric hindrance provided by the bulky trityl group does not permit the general use of active esters of tritylamino acids in the peptide coupling step (546), alternative use of the trifluoracetyl group leads to highly satisfactory results (814). Finally, it should be noted that, while active esters may often be implicated in coupling reactions without the accompaniment of racemization where optically active residues are involved, this is by no means an inviolate rule. Thus, for example, the synthesis of Cbzo·L-CySBz·L-Tyr·L-Ileu·OEt from the condensation either of Cbzo·L-CySBz·L-Tyr·OCH$_2$CN with H·L-Ileu·OEt or of Cbzo·L-CySBz·OCH$_2$CN with H·L-Tyr·L-Ileu·OEt proceeds in the absence of detectable racemization (804), whereas marked optical inactivation ensues during condensation of Cbzo·Gly·L-Ala·S—⟨ ⟩—NO$_2$ with H·L-Phe·Gly·OH. To what extent the structure of the active ester group, the constitution of the amino acid residues, or yet other factors might contribute to the process cannot be evaluated from presently available data.

Related Methods. In 1898, Pawlewski (816) demonstrated the ability of thioacids to act as active acylating agents when treatment of a series of aromatic amines (LXIV) with thioacetic acid (LXIII) led to the ready formation of the corresponding acetyl-amide (LXV) and the concomitant evolution of hydrogen sulfide:

$$CH_3COSH + NH_2Ar \rightarrow CH_3CO-NHAr + H_2S$$
LXIII   LXIV   LXV   LXVI

That acylated thioamino acids exhibit comparable behavior was announced in 1952 by Cronyn and Jiu (817), who converted phthalylglycine (LXVII) into phthalylthioglycine (LXIX) upon passage of a stream of hydrogen sulfide into a cold solution of the pertinent mixed carboxylic-carbonic acid anhydride (LXVIII; R = C$_2$H$_5$OCO) in methylene chloride. An essentially identical procedure was described in a neighboring publication by Sheehan and Johnson (818), who in addition reported that the same compound could alternatively be procured via the action of sodium hydrosulfide on phthalylglycyl chloride (LXVIII; R = Cl) in dimethylformamide solution; treatment of the thio acid (LXIX) with glycine methyl ester hydrochloride either (*a*) as a solution in methylene chloride containing a tertiary amine, or (*b*) in aqueous sodium bicarbonate, gave the desired peptide derivative (LXX; R′ = CH$_2$CO$_2$Me). Further exploitation of thio acids of the type described above for the synthesis of peptides has been extremely limited. However, it is of interest to note in this connection that the preparation of several free amino thio acids (LXXII) has been described by Wieland and his collaborators (819–821); thus thiogylcine, -alanine, -β-alanine, -γ-aminobutyric acid, -ε-aminocaproic acid, -isoleucine, -methionine, -tryptophan, and -valine were prepared by the action of hydrogen sulfide on the corre-

$$\underset{\text{LXVII}}{\text{Phth}\diagup\text{NCH}_2\text{CO}_2\text{H}} \rightarrow \underset{\text{LXVIII}}{\text{Phth}\diagup\text{NCH}_2\text{COR}} \xrightarrow{\text{H}_2\text{S}}$$

$$\underset{\text{LXIX}}{\text{Phth}\diagup\text{NCH}_2\text{CO—SH}} \xrightarrow{\text{NH}_2\text{R}'} \underset{\text{LXX}}{\text{Phth}\diagup\text{NCH}_2\text{CO—NHR}'}$$

sponding amino acid thiophenyl ester (LXXI) either in an alkaline aqueous medium or in an inert organic solvent containing a tertiary base.

$$\underset{\text{LXXI}}{\text{NH}_2\text{CHRCO—SC}_6\text{H}_5} + \underset{\text{LXVIa}}{\text{H}_2\text{S}} \rightarrow \underset{\text{LXXII}}{\overset{\oplus}{\text{H}_3\text{N}}\text{CHRCO}\overset{\ominus}{\text{S}}} + \text{C}_6\text{H}_5\text{SH}$$

39. Methods Applicable to Amino Acid Residues with Secondary Functional Groups. At this point, it should be clear that, although the above mentioned coupling procedures (Sections 10–26 to 10–38) may be considered general, their applicability to the synthesis of any given peptide derivative is contingent upon the absence of interfering reactive groups in the side-chain moieties of the amino acid residues involved. Toward this end, peptide-forming reactions which implicate the glycine, alanine, leucine, phenylalanine, proline, tryptophan, or methionine residues pose few problems and hence require no further elaboration here; consideration has already been given to those situations wherein the steric hindrance imposed by the valine and the isoleucine residues might afford special difficulties. However, where the hydroxyl functions of serine, threonine, hydroxyproline, and tyrosine, the ω-basic substituents of arginine, lysine, and histidine, the ω-carboxyl moieties of aspartic and glutamic acids, or the sulfur atoms of cysteine and cystine appear as interfering secondary functional groups, adequate masking of their reactivity with a suitable blocking substituent becomes a necessary prelude to the coupling step. In this connection, care must be taken to select a protecting group which can be removed under conditions that will lead neither to hydrolysis of the labile peptide bonds nor racemization of existing asymmetric residues within the molecule. It is with such protection of reactive secondary groups that the discussion below is primarily concerned.

Aromatic and Aliphatic Hydroxyl Groups. The conditions employed for the azide (Section 10–26), phosphorus oxychloride (Section 10–34), and carbodiimide (Section 10-36) methods are not, at the same time, conducive to auxiliary reactions which might involve the hydroxyl function of hydroxyamino acid residues. Hence it has become possible to utilize these coupling methods successfully in syntheses wherein the unprotected hydroxyl moiety of a serine (444, 501, 631, 699, 718, 785), threonine (454, 524, 687, 769), hydroxyproline (169, 524, 769), or tyrosine (400, 537, 700, 769) residue may appear as a constituent of either the amine or the carboxylic acid reactant. Additionally, the free phenolic-hydroxyl group of the tyrosine residue has appeared to suffer no detectable alteration in syntheses which either involved tetraethyl pyrophosphite (Section 10-31) as the condensing agent (82, 446, 722) or employed an active ester (Section 10-38) (804) or a mixed carboxylic-carbonic acid anhydride (Section 10-29) (822) as the reactive intermediate. Nevertheless, inasmuch as the conditions required for the conversion of an acylated amino acid or peptide to the corresponding acid chloride or mixed anhydride intermediate may also lead to acylation or marked chemical alteration of the hydroxyl group, indiscriminate use of the different coupling procedures with reactants which possess unmasked hydroxyl substituents should be rigidly avoided. With this in mind, it is worthy of note that the mixed carboxylic-carbonic acid anhydride-mediated condensation of carbobenzoxy-L-hydroxyproline with glycylglycine ethyl ester was shown to lead to the acylated tripeptide ester in some 38% yield (823); although the desired coupling reaction was apparently achieved, the fact that the isolation of the product occurred in less than the 80-90% yield customarily given by this procedure is presumably explicable on the basis of complicating side reactions which involve the free hydroxyl group. However, in view of the more appreciable reactivity of the amino than of the hydroxyl substituent under the conditions ordinarily employed in the peptide coupling step, no comparable difficulties should be encountered when the acid chloride or mixed anhydride is condensed with an amine which incorporates a hydroxyamino acid residue (168, 400, 657, 700, 734, 824). As illustrative of this point, demonstration has been made that the treatment of a dioxane solution of serine ester (II) with phthalyl- or tosylglycyl chloride in the presence of diethylamine many proceed with the formation of either the N-acylglycyl- (I) or the O,N-diacylglycylserine ester (III), dependent upon whether one equivalent or two equivalents of the acid chloride is used (825):

$$\underset{\text{I}}{\text{RCO—NHCHCO}_2\text{Et}}\overset{\text{RCOCl}}{\underset{(C_2H_5)_2NH}{\longleftarrow}}\underset{\text{II}}{\overset{\text{CH}_2\text{OH}}{\text{NH}_2\text{CHCO}_2\text{Et}}}\overset{2\text{RCOCl}}{\underset{2(C_2H_5)_2NH}{\longrightarrow}}\underset{\text{III}}{\overset{\text{CH}_2\text{OCOR}}{\text{RCO—NHCHCO}_2\text{Et}}}$$

Shortly after the development of the carbobenzoxy procedure (128), it was recognized that, if the reactivity of the hydroxyl function of hydroxyamino acids could be suitably masked with a selectively removable blocking substituent, then it would be feasible to incorporate such residues into peptide derivatives through the use of otherwise inapplicable coupling procedures. Early efforts in this direction were pointed toward the development of acyl blocking substituents for the phenolic-hydroxyl group of N-carbobenzoxy-L-tyrosine which, under mild conditions, would be susceptible to preferential cleavage and hence would permit the incorporation of N-terminal tyrosine residues into the peptide molecule. Although a large number of O-acylated N-carbobenzoxy-L-tyrosine derivatives have been developed which could admirably serve such requirement, practical considerations have limited their routine use principally to those derivatives which embody the early described O-carbobenzoxy (826) or O-acetyl (378) moieties, or the more recently introduced O-tosyl (446) substituent. Preparation of the first of these derivatives, O,N-dicarbobenzoxy-L-tyrosine (VI; R = $C_6H_5CH_2OCO$), was achieved by Abderhalden and Bahn (826) in 1933 upon treatment of a cold aqueous alkaline solution of L-tyrosine with an excess of carbobenzoxy chloride (procedure 10–103); the same procedure or minor modifications thereof have since been employed for O,N-dicarbobenzoxy-DL- (379), O,N-ditosyl-L- (126, 430), O,N-dicarboallyloxy-L- (460), O,N-dibenzylsulfonyl-L- (and DL-) (601), and O,N-di-*p*-nitrocarbobenzoxy-DL-tyrosine (362). The hitherto most extensively utilized of the diacyltyrosines, O-acetyl-N-carbobenzoxy-L-tyrosine (VI; R = CH_3CO), was secured in 1934 by Bergmann, Zervas, Salzmann, and Schleich (378) through the saponification of N-carbobenzoxy-L-tyrosine ethyl ester (IV) in aqueous alkali, followed by treatment *in situ* of the sodium salt (V) so derived with acetic anhydride. Some twenty-five years later, Katsoyannis, Gish, and du Vigneaud (446) described

O-tosyl-N-carbobenzoxy-L-tyrosine (VI; R = H_3C—⟨ ⟩—SO_2), potentially the most versatile of this class of derivatives. Preparation of this intermediate was effected by the action of *p*-toluenesulfonyl chloride on an alkaline solution of the copper complex of L-tyrosine (X), followed by N-carbobenzoxylation in aqueous alkali of the O-tosyl-L-tyrosine (VIII) thereupon formed (procedure 10–104).

Illustrative procedure 10–103 (379). O,N-Dicarbobenzoxy-L-tyrosine. A solution of 11.5 g. of L-tyrosine in 60 ml. of 2*N* sodium hydroxidei s treated over a period of 1 hr. with 25 g. of carbobenzoxy chloride (procedure 10–27) and 40 ml. of 4*N* sodium hydroxide, added in alternate and portionwise amounts. The reaction mixture is stirred vigorously and kept at 0°, while the introduction of the latter two reactants is so regulated as to maintain the *p*H between 9 and 11. After the addition of reagents is complete, the solution is brought to room temperature and then extracted twice with 100-ml. portions of ether. Acidification of the aqueous layer to Congo red with 4*N* hydrochloric acid leads to the separation of the desired O,N-dicarbobenzoxy derivative which, in turn, is extracted with two 100-ml. portions of ether. The combined ethereal extracts are dried over anhydrous sodium sulfate, concentrated *in vacuo*, and the crystalline residue recrystallized twice from carbon tetrachloride; yield, 25.3 g. (89%); m.p. 117°; $[\alpha]_D^{20} = -5°$ (10% in glacial acetic acid).

Illustrative procedure 10–104 (446). N-Carbobenzoxy-O-tosyl-L-tyrosine. To a solution of 18 g. (0.1 mole) of L-tyrosine in 200 ml. (0.2 mole) of *N* sodium hydroxide is added a solution of 12.5 g. (0.05 mole) of cupric sulfate pentahydrate in 50 ml. of water. Such mixture is treated with a solution of 19 g. (0.1 mole) of *p*-toluenesulfonyl chloride in 40 ml. of ether and then shaken vigorously for 3.5 hr. The copper complex which deposits is isolated by filtration, washed with water, and finally dissolved in 200 ml. of concentrated hydrochloric acid. After several hours in the cold, the crystalline hydrochloride salt of O-tosyl-L-tyrosine is collected by filtration and subsequently dissolved in 1 l. of water. Upon adjustment of the *p*H of the solution to 6 with ammonium hydroxide, O-tosyl-L-tyrosine deposits as a crystalline product which, after several hours of cooling, is filtered, washed with water, and recrystallized from boiling water (1 g. solute per 100 ml. solvent); yield 12.5 g. (37%); m.p. 215–217°; $[\alpha]_D^{22} = +9.0°$ (3.0% in *N* HCl).

A mixture of 3.35 g. (0.01 mole) of O-tosyl-L-tyrosine, 10 ml. of *N* sodium hydroxide, 15 ml. of *N* sodium carbonate, and 80 ml. of *N* sodium bicarbonate (*p*H 9) is warmed for several minutes and then cooled to 0°. The suspension is treated with 2 g. of carbobenzoxy chloride (procedure 10–27) added in portions over a period of 1 hr., with vigorous stirring and cooling. After the final addition, the reaction mixture is stirred for 30 min. longer, acidified with hydrochloric acid, and stirred for 15 min. The precipitate is filtered, washed with water, dried *in vacuo*, and purified by precipitation from ethyl acetate with hexane; yield, 3.8 g. (83%); m.p. 124–126°; $[\alpha]_D^{25} = -27°$ (1% in dimethylformamide).

Implication of the above-mentioned derivatives in the peptide-forming step has generally involved the conversion of the O,N-diacylated tyrosine to the corresponding acid chloride or mixed anhydride intermediate, followed by treatment of the latter with a suitably constituted amine in an aqueous or organic medium to yield the desired O,N-diacylated peptide

(378, 446, 637, 700, 822, 826). Such O,N-diacyltyrosines have proved of value, too, as parent compounds for the corresponding O-acyl-N-carboxy-tyrosine anhydrides, which have been employed both for the stepwise synthesis of simple peptides (353) and in polymerization reactions (369, 379) (Section 10–10). In any event, the O-acetyl group is selectively split from its linkage in the O,N-diacylated peptide derivative under the mild alkaline conditions ordinarily used for the saponification of fatty acid esters (353, 369, 378, 637, 700) or through the action of hydrazine (637); the O-tosyl and O-carbobenzoxy groups, on the other hand, have been cleaved upon treatment of the former with a mixture of sodium in liquid ammonia (446), and of the latter with a glacial acetic acid–hydrogen bromide mixture (369, 379, 822), aqueous alkali (369, 379), or hydrogen in the presence of palladium catalyst (826). Fission of such groups will be considered in greater detail below.

As in the case of tyrosine, O-acylation of the other hydroxyamino acids may be readily achieved. Toward this end, Sakami and Toennies (827) demonstrated in 1942 that the O-acetyl derivatives of L-hydroxyproline, DL-serine (XII), DL-threonine, and L-tyrosine could be conveniently prepared in high yield and in the absence of accompanying racemization upon treatment of the pertinent amino acid with a mixture of acetic anhydride and perchloric acid in glacial acetic acid solution (procedure 10–105); acetylation of only the hydroxyl function was realized because of the presence of perchloric acid, which served both to effectively block the acylation of the amino group and catalytically promote the desired reaction. More recently, Sheehan, Goodman, and Hess (524) prepared O-acetyl-L-serine (XII) through the action of hydrogen chloride gas on a suspension of L-serine (XIa) in an excess of glacial acetic acid (procedure 10–105); treatment of a suspension

$$\underset{\text{XI}}{\underset{|}{\text{NH}_2\text{CHCO}_2\text{H}}}^{\text{CH}_2\text{OH}} \xrightarrow[\text{2. C}_5\text{H}_{11}\text{NH}_2]{\text{1. Ac}_2\text{O,AcOH,HClO}_4} \underset{\text{XII}}{\underset{|}{\text{NH}_2\text{CHCO}_2\text{H}}}^{\text{CH}_2\text{OCOCH}_3} \xleftarrow[\text{2. (C}_2\text{H}_5)_3\text{N}]{\text{1. AcOH,HCl}} \underset{\text{XIa}}{\underset{|}{\text{NH}_2\text{CHCO}_2\text{H}}}^{\text{CH}_2\text{OH}}$$

of (XII) with phthalic anhydride in hot dioxane yielded N-phthalyl-O-acetyl-L-serine. The related O-acetyl derivative of N-carbobenzoxy-DL-serine was prepared sometime earlier by Frankel and Halmann (377) via the action of acetyl chloride on carbobenzoxy-DL-serine in hot benzene solution, while O,N-dicarbobenzoxy-DL-serine was isolated by Levene and Schormüller (503) as early as 1934 from the mother liquors of the reaction mixture used for the N-carbobenzoxylation of DL-serine under Schotten-Baumann conditions. In contradistinction to the analogous tyrosine derivatives, none of the afore-mentioned O,N-diacylserines has been extensively exploited for the synthesis of N-terminal serine peptide derivatives. Thus the utilization of the O-acetyl-N-phthalyl derivative has been hitherto confined to a single

N,N'-di*cyclo*hexylcarbodiimide-induced condensation with L-phenylalanine methyl ester (524), while the O-acetyl-N-carbobenzoxy and O,N-dicarbobenzoxy derivatives have been implicated in polymerization studies subsequent to their conversion to the corresponding O-acyl-N-carboxyserine anhydrides upon treatment with phosphorus pentachloride in ether solution (377) (see Section 10-10). No data are yet available on the comparable use of O-acylated threonine or hydroxyproline derivatives in synthetic peptide procedures.

Illustrative procedure 10–105 (397, 827). O-Acetyl-DL-serine. A mixture of 4.99 g. of 60.4% perchloric acid and 2.52 g. of 98.7% acetic anhydride is diluted to 50 ml. with 100% acetic acid (prepared by removal of water from glacial acetic acid with acetic anhydride), and 2.5 g. of DL-serine dissolved therein. Such solution is cooled to 0° and treated first with 12 g. of 98.7% acetic anhydride and, after 1.5 hr., with 1 ml. of water. After the reaction mixture has stood for an additional hour, 3.48 g. of amylamine is added thereto. Finally, the addition of 300 ml. of ether leads to the deposition of the desired O-acetyl derivative; yield, 3.1 g. (91%); m.p. 144° d. Recrystallization may be effected from 50% ethanol. Comparable procedures have been employed for the preparation of the O-acetyl derivatives of L-hydroxyproline (m.p. 179–181° d.), DL-threonine (m.p. 146–149° d.), and L-tyrosine (m.p. 213–214° d.) (827).

O-Acetyl-L-serine (524). A solution of 3.5 g. of L-serine in 150 ml. of glacial acetic acid is saturated with hydrogen chloride gas at 0°. After the reaction mixture has stood for 15 hr. at room temperature, the solvent is removed under reduced pressure and the entire process repeated once. The residual O-acetyl-L-serine hydrochloride is crystallized from ethanol–ether; yield, 5.2 g. (99%); m.p. 160° d.; $[\alpha]_D^{27} = -7.4°$ (2.2% in ethanol). When a solution of 3.0 g. of this product in ethanol is treated with 1.62 g. of triethylamine, a precipitate of O-acetyl-L-serine is obtained which, after filtration, is recrystallized from water–ethanol; yield, 2.42 g. (98%); m.p. 167–168° d.; $[\alpha]_D^{27} = +9.2°$ (1.8% in 0.1N hydrochloric acid).

By virtue of the fact that certain substituents in ether linkage are susceptible to ready preferential cleavage under mild conditions, these may serve to mask the reactivity of the hydroxyl function of hydroxyamino acid residues. Previous discussion in this connection was concerned with O-linkages between the acid-labile tetrahydropyranyl group and serine or tyrosine residues (Section 10-38). Since the O-benzyl moiety suffers ready scission from its

$$CH_2=CHCO_2CH_3 \xrightarrow{Br_2} CH_2BrCHBrCO_2CH_3 \xrightarrow[\text{ether}]{C_6H_5CH_2ONa} C_6H_5CH_2OCH_2CHBrCO_2CH_3 \xrightarrow{\text{saponification}}$$
$$\text{XIII} \qquad\qquad \text{XIV} \qquad\qquad \text{XV}$$

$$C_6H_5CH_2OCH_2CHBrCO_2H \xrightarrow{NH_3} C_6H_5CH_2OCH_2CH(NH_2)CO_2H$$
$$\text{XVI} \qquad\qquad \text{XVII}$$

ether linkage upon catalytic hydrogenation, this group too should suffice as an acceptable blocking substituent. That such is indeed the case was shown in a series of investigations by Okawa (398, 504, 828), who synthesized (formulas XIII to XVII) and resolved O-benzyl-DL-serine (Section 36-4) (XVII) and successfully utilized the carbobenzoxy derivative of the L-antipode for the synthesis of several N-terminal serine peptides (procedure 10–106). An interesting aspect of these studies was the finding that, while the implication of the unmasked N-carbobenzoxyserine reactant in N,N'-di*cyclo*hexylcarbodiimide-mediated coupling reactions was associated both with an appreciable amount of side reaction and extremely poor yields of product, the alternative use of O-benzyl substituted serine derivatives permitted the desired reaction to proceed in high yield in the absence of the detrimental reactions. A later study by Zahn and Diehl (678) reaffirmed the marked side-product formation which arises from coupling reactions involving unmasked N-acylated serine as a reactant and N,N'-di*cyclo*hexylcarbodiimide as the condensing agent. O-Benzyl-DL-serine as its ethyl ester and N-carbobenzoxy derivatives (829), as well as O-benzyl-L-tyrosine in the form of its methyl ester and N-carbobenzoxy derivatives (830), have recently been employed successfully in coupling reactions involving phosphazo intermediates (Section 10–33). Synthesis of O-benzyl-N-carbobenzoxy-L-tyrosine (XX) was effected through the action of benzyl bromide on the copper complex of L-tyrosine (XVIII) in aqueous alkali, removal of copper ions by treatment with hydrogen sulfide gas, and N-carbobenzoxylation of the O-benzyl-L-tyrosine (XIX) so derived.

OH   OCH$_2$C$_6$H$_5$ OCH$_2$C$_6$H$_5$
| | |
[ring] 1. C$_6$H$_5$CH$_2$Br, NaOH   [ring]   Cbzo Cl   [ring]
        ─────────────────→   ─────→
        2. H$_2$S   NaOH
| | |
CH$_2$ CH$_2$ CH$_2$
| | |
NH$_2$CHCO$_2$·½Cu   NH$_2$CHCO$_2$H   Cbzo—NHCHCO$_2$H
XVIII   XIX   XX

Illustrative procedure 10–106 (504). N-Carbobenzoxy-O-benzyl-L-seryl-L-tyrosine methyl ester. A mixture of 1.51 g. of L-tyrosine methyl ester hydrochloride (procedure 10–48) and 0.9 ml. of triethylamine is treated with 10 ml. of tetrahydrofuran, the reaction mixture shaken for several minutes, the precipitate of triethylamine hydrochloride removed by filtration, and the filtrate treated with 1.34 g. of N,N'-di*cyclo*hexylcarbodiimide (procedure 10–84) and 1.65 g. of N-carbobenzoxy-O-benzyl-L-serine, m.p. 98°. Preparation of the latter reactant is achieved *via* resolution of O-benzyl-DL-serine (Section 36-4) followed by conversion of the L-antipode to its N-carbobenzoxy derivative (see procedures 10–28 and 10–30). After the reaction mixture has stood for 4 hr. at room temperature, the precipitated N,N'-di*cyclo*hexylurea is removed by filtration, 0.15 ml. of acetic acid is added to the filtrate, and, after 1 hr., the resulting precipitate is filtered off. Evaporation of the solvent *in vacuo* leaves a residue which is taken up in ethyl acetate and, after removal of the undissolved material, sufficient petroleum ether is added to cause crystallization of the desired peptide derivative. Recrystallization is effected from ethyl acetate–petroleum ether; yield, 1.8 g. (72%); m.p. 111–112°; $[\alpha]_D^{15} = +15.5°$ (2.8% in 99% ethanol).

In a few isolated instances, the lactone formation which certain N-acylated hydroxyamino acids can undergo has been advantageously exploited in the peptide-forming step. Thus in 1957 Patchett and Witkop (487) reported that carbobenzoxy-L-allohydroxyproline lactone (XXII) could be induced to undergo aminolysis, with the formation of ethyl carbobenzoxy-L-allohydroxyprolylglycinate (XXIII), upon treatment with a mixture of glycine ethyl ester hydrochloride, anhydrous magnesium sulfate, and triethylamine in refluxing benzene; the D-allo dipeptide derivative was secured in a comparable manner. Preparation of the requisite lactone reactant (XXII) was readily effected through the action of N,N'-di*cyclo*hexylcarbodiimide on carbobenzoxyallohydroxyproline (XXI) in methylene chloride solution. No analogous lactone formation is possible with the corresponding normal forms of carbobenzoxyhydroxyproline in consequence of the *trans* position

$$
\begin{array}{ccc}
\text{CH}_2\text{—CHOH} & \text{CH}_2\text{—CH—O} & \text{CH}_2\text{—CH—OH} \\
|\quad\quad\; | & |\quad\quad\quad | & |\quad\quad\; | \\
\;\;\;\text{CH}_2 & \;\;\;\text{CH}_2\;\; & \;\;\;\text{CH}_2 \\
|\quad\quad\; | & |\quad\quad\quad | & |\quad\quad\quad\quad\quad\quad\quad\quad | \\
\text{Cbzo—N——CHCO}_2\text{H} & \text{Cbzo—N——CH——CO} & \text{Cbzo—N——CHCO—NHCH}_2\text{CO}_2\text{Et} \\
\text{XXI} & \text{XXII} & \text{XXIII}
\end{array}
$$

$$\xrightarrow{\text{NH}_2\text{CH}_2\text{CO}_2\text{Et}}$$

of the hydroxyl and the carboxyl functions relative to the plane of the pyrrolidine ring (Section 2–32). However, a comparable type of behavior is elicited by both the normal and the allo forms of carbobenzoxy-DL-γ-hydroxyglutamic acid lactone (XXVI) which, under the influence of methanolic ammonia, undergo amide (XXVII) formation with simultaneous scission of the lactone ring (485). It is worthy of note that, although the lactone of carbobenzoxy-allo-γ-hydroxyglutamic acid (XXVI) arises spontaneously upon carbobenzoxylation of the free amino acid (XXIV) under the usual Schotten-Baumann conditions, the normal form of the amino acid yields the expected acylaminodicarboxylic acid (XXV) under like circumstances. Conversion of the latter compound to its respective lactone derivative (XXVI) is conveniently achieved by azeotropic removal of water from the molecule with the aid of refluxing toluene. That the lactones of the

$$
\begin{array}{cccc}
\text{CO}_2\text{H} & \text{CO}_2\text{H} & \text{CO}_2\text{H} & \text{CO}_2\text{H} \\
| & | & | & | \\
\text{CHOH} & \text{CHOH} & \text{CHO} & \text{CHOH} \\
| & | & |\quad\;\; & | \\
\text{CH}_2 & \text{CH}_2 & \text{CH}_2\;\; & \text{CH}_2 \\
| & | & |\quad\;\; & | \\
\text{NH}_2\text{CHCO}_2\text{H} & \text{Cbzo—NHCHCO}_2\text{H} & \text{Cbzo—NHCH——CO} & \text{Cbzo—NHCHCONH}_2 \\
\text{XXIV} & \text{XXV} & \text{XXVI} & \text{XXVII}
\end{array}
$$

$$\xrightarrow[\text{NaOH}]{\text{Cbzo Cl}} \quad \xrightarrow[\Delta]{\text{toluene}} \quad \xrightarrow{\text{MeOH-NH}_3}$$

normal and allo forms of dicarbobenzoxy-DL-hydroxylysine undergo analogous aminolysis when subjected to the action of warm methanolic ammonia or a warm solution of either glycine amide or alanine amide in dioxane was recently shown by Zahn and Zürn (830a).

ω-Amino Substituents. The discussion below is concerned primarily with the preparation of peptide derivatives which incorporate a lysine or an ornithine residue, although it is applicable as well to syntheses in which other varieties of α,ω-diamino acids may participate. Peptide linkages which include such diaminomonocarboxylic acid residues may involve either the α-amino (XXVIII), the ω-amino (XXIX), or the α-carboxyl (XXX) substituent, in addition to any combination thereof. However, the major

$$\begin{array}{ccc}
-\text{NH} & -\text{NHCHRCO}-\text{NH} & -\text{NH} \\
| & | & | \\
(\text{CH}_2)_x & (\text{CH}_2)_x & (\text{CH}_2)_x \\
| & | & | \\
-\text{NHCHRCO}-\text{NHCHCO}- & -\text{NHCHCO}- & -\text{NHCHCO}-\text{NHCHRCO}- \\
\text{XXVIII} & \text{XXIX} & \text{XXX}
\end{array}$$

portion of study to date has centered about those linkages which involve the α-amino and the α-carboxyl functions. Peptide derivatives of the general type represented by (XXX) are most conveniently prepared by the initial conversion of the pertinent diamino acid (XXXI) to its corresponding

$$\begin{array}{ccc}
\text{NH}_2 & \text{RCO}-\text{NH} & \text{RCO}-\text{NH} \\
| & | & | \\
(\text{CH}_2)_x \xrightarrow[\text{OH}^-]{\text{RCOCl}} & (\text{CH}_2)_x \xrightarrow{\text{NH}_2\text{R}'} & (\text{CH}_2)_x \\
| & | & | \\
\text{NH}_2\text{CHCO}_2\text{H} & \text{RCO}-\text{NHCHCO}_2\text{H} & \text{RCO}-\text{NHCHCO}-\text{NHR}' \\
\text{XXXI} & \text{XXXII} & \text{XXXIII}
\end{array}$$

$N^α, N^ω$-diacylated derivative (XXXII), followed by condensation of the latter with a suitably constituted amine to yield the desired peptide derivative (XXXIII). For the purpose at hand, the selectively removable N-acyl blocking substituents previously described (Sections 10–13 to 10–21) prove adequate. Thus, although the $N^α, N^ε$-dicarbobenzoxy derivative of L-lysine (XXXII; R = $C_6H_5CH_2O$, $x = 4$) (358) has hitherto been implicated almost exclusively in the synthesis of N-terminal lysine peptides (491, 507, 626, 649, 660, 667, 697, 706, 715, 723, 734, 831–834), the dicarboallyloxy (460), di-*p*-nitrocarbobenzoxy (362), dibenzylsulfonyl (601), dicarbo*cyclo*pentyloxy (464), ditrifluoroacetyl (570), and ditrityl (550) derivatives should also suffice here. With the exception of the last two compounds, the aforementioned diacyllysines may be generally prepared by treatment of one equivalent of lysine with two equivalents of the requisite acid chloride under Schotten-Baumann conditions. Synthesis of α,ε-ditrifluoroacetyllysine, on the other hand, is effected via the interaction of ε-trifluoroacetyllysine with trifluoroacetic anhydride in trifluoroacetic acid solution at 0° (see Section 10–17), while ditrityllysine is formed by the action of trityl chloride on a chloroform solution of lysine methyl ester in the presence of a tertiary base, followed by saponification of the trityllysine methyl ester so derived (550).

CHEMICAL PROCEDURES FOR SYNTHESIS OF PEPTIDES 1057

Finally, it should be noted that the preparation of α,δ-dicarbobenzoxy-ornithine (XXXII; R = C$_6$H$_5$CH$_2$O, $x = 3$) has permitted the synthesis of peptide derivatives which contain an N-terminal ornithine residue (373, 421).

The synthesis of peptide derivatives wherein both the α- and the ω-amino functions of an α,ω-diamino acid are to be bound in peptide linkage poses little difficulty because the desired product may be secured simply upon the condensation of two equivalents of an acylated amino acid or peptide with one equivalent of the pertinent diamino acid ester. However, for the synthesis of peptides in which the α-amino but not the ω-amino function is to participate in the peptide linkage, it has been customary to employ an N^ω-acylated diamino acid derivative as the amine reactant. Special methods are required here to mask the reactivity of the ω-amino group while at the same time keeping the α-amino function available for coupling during the peptide-forming step. A unique approach to this problem was provided by Bergmann, Zervas, and Ross (358), who exploited the property of carbobenzoxyamino acid chlorides readily to eliminate benzyl chloride with the formation of the corresponding N-carboxy-α-amino acid anhydrides (Section 10-10). Thus the action of phosphorus pentachloride on a solution of α,ε-dicarbobenzoxy-L-lysine (XXXIV; $x = 4$) in ether led to the corresponding acid chloride (XXXV) which, upon being heated at 50 to 60°, was converted to the N-carboxy-anhydride derivative (XXXVI); whereas treatment of the latter compound with methanolic HCl proceeded with the formation of ε-carbobenzoxy-L-lysine methyl ester hydrochloride (XXXVII; R = CH$_3$, $x = 4$) (procedure 10-107), treatment with water yielded the ε-carbobenzoxylated amino acid (XL; R' = C$_6$H$_5$CH$_2$OCO, $x = 4$). A comparable reaction sequence has since been utilized to secure the benzyl ester hydrochlorides of ε-carbobenzoxy-L- and D-lysine (XXXVII; R = CH$_2$C$_6$H$_5$, $x = 4$) (667) as well as the L- (373) and DL-form (372) of δ-carbobenzoxyornithine methyl ester hydrochloride (XXXVII; R = CH$_3$, $x = 3$).

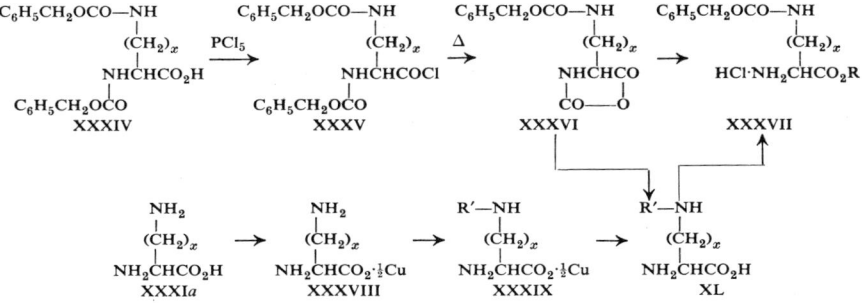

Illustrative procedure 10-107 (358). ε-Carbobenzoxy-L-lysine methyl ester hydrochloride. A solution of 25 g. of L-lysine dihydrochloride in 171 ml. of 2N sodium hydroxide, when treated with 60 g. of carbobenzoxy chloride and 142 ml. of 4N sodium hydroxide under Schotten-Baumann conditions, ultimately yields 45 g. of α,ε-dicarbobenzoxy-L-lysine as an ether-soluble syrup (see procedure 10–29). Such syrup, when dissolved in 175 ml. of dry ether and subsequently treated with 26 g. of phosphorus pentachloride in the manner described under procedure 10–17, is converted to ε-carbobenzoxy-N-carboxy-L-lysine anhydride. The latter compound is secured in 28.1-g. yield after recrystallization from ethyl acetate-petroleum ether; m.p. 100° d. To 23.1 g. of the N-carboxy-anhydride in 15 ml. of absolute methanol is added 151 ml. of a methanol solution which is N in hydrogen chloride. Carbon dioxide is evolved upon warming the reaction mixture to 50°. The reacting solution is stored at room temperature overnight and then concentrated to a residual syrup at 40–50° *in vacuo*. Crystallization occurs when the residue is scratched in the presence of a little ether; yield, 24.5 g. Recrystallization is effected from hot acetone; m.p. 117°.

An alternative route to ω-acylated diamino acid derivatives takes advantage of the fact that, while the α-amino and α-carboxyl functions of the copper salt of an α,ω-diamino acid are bound in a stable chelate structure with copper, the ε-amino function remains free to react with acylating agents. Such a system was first applied by Kurtz (835) to the isolation of lysine as its insoluble ε-benzoyl derivative from protein hydrolysates, and has since been employed for the synthesis of ε-carbobenzoxy-L- (457), ε-carboallyloxy-L- (and DL-) (460), and ε-tosyl-L-lysine (393) (procedure 10–108), as well as for the δ-carbobenzoxy-L- (373), δ-carbobenzoxy-DL- (421), and δ-tosyl-L-ornithine (423) derivatives. Routine use of this procedure generally involves the preliminary interaction of the α,ω-diamino acid (XXXIa) ($\omega > \beta$; *cf.* Chapter 6) with cupric carbonate in aqueous solution, with the copper complex of the amino acid (XXXVIII) so formed then being converted to its corresponding insoluble ω-acylated derivative (XXXIX) upon treatment with the pertinent acid chloride (R'Cl) in aqueous sodium hydroxide solution; decomposition of (XXXIX) with hydrogen sulfide gas then yields the desired ω-acylamino acid (XL) (see procedure 10–108). Although this procedure is apparently satisfactory when applied to the synthesis of ε-acylated derivatives of lysine, poor yields of the δ-acyl and appreciable formation of the α,δ-diacyl derivatives have been noted where ornithine is involved, presumably because of the incomplete stability of the copper complex of the latter under the reaction conditions employed (421). However, use of magnesium oxide in lieu of sodium hydroxide as the base has been reported to result in yields of δ-carbobenzoxy-DL-ornithine which are in excess of 90 % of theory (429); a comparable procedure was also satisfactorily applied to the synthesis of γ-carbobenzoxy-L-α,γ-diaminobutyric acid. Conversion of several of the afore-mentioned ω-acyl-α,ω-diamino acids to their corresponding methyl or ethyl ester derivatives has been achieved through the action of methanolic or ethanolic HCl (373, 393, 423).

Illustrative procedure 10-108 (393).   ε-Tosyl-L-lysine.   To a hot solution of 24 g. of L-lysine hydrochloride in 1500 ml. of water is slowly added 40 g. of cupric carbonate in portionwise amounts. Upon completion of the addition, the reaction mixture is refluxed for 2 hr., filtered while hot, and the solid residue washed with 150 ml. of hot water. After cooling, the combined filtrate and washings are treated with 42 g. of sodium bicarbonate and a solution of 37.8 g. of tosyl chloride in 1500 ml. of acetone, and the resulting mixture is stirred vigorously for 10 hr. The copper complex which deposits is collected, washed thoroughly and successively with water, acetone, and ether, and air-dried; yield, 30 to 33 g. A suspension of 30 g. of the finely ground complex in 500 ml. of boiling water is treated with a stream of hydrogen sulfide, with rapid stirring, until decomposition of the complex is complete (*ca.* 0.5 hr.); boiling is continued until the excess hydrogen sulfide is removed. The mixture, after treatment with 5 g. of charcoal and 15 ml. of 6N hydrochoric acid, is filtered through a fine paper, the pH of the filtrate adjusted to 6 with 4N sodium hydroxide, and the product collected after several hours and washed first with water, then ethanol; yield, 21.2 g. Purification may be effected by precipitation of the material from its solution in hydrochloric acid by the addition of sodium hydroxide; m.p. 237–238° d., $[\alpha]_D^{21} = +13.6°$ (3% in 2N hydrochloric acid).

The more general availability of a variety of ε-acyllysine derivatives afforded by the use of copper complex intermediates has encouraged the utilization of α,ε-diacyllysine derivatives wherein the constitution of the two component acyl substituents differ. Preparation of the latter compounds may be easily achieved by treatment of the pertinent ε-acyllysine with the requisite acid chloride in an alkaline aqueous medium. It was by such procedure that du Vigneaud and co-workers (393) prepared α-carbobenzoxy-ε-tosyl-L-lysine (XLII) via the α-carbobenzoxylation of ε-tosyl-L-lysine (XLI) (procedure 10–109); the related α-tosyl-ε-carbobenzoxy-L-lysine was prepared in a similar manner (429). Since the nature of compounds of this type is such that one of the acyl blocking substituents may be selectively removed while the other is left intact, a greater degree of flexibility is lent to the peptide-building process. Thus, for example, the condensation of (XLII) with glycine ethyl ester through the use of phosphite ester intermediates (Section 10–31) yields the desired dipeptide derivative (XLIII); subsequent

Tos—NH
|
(CH₂)₄   —Cbzo Cl→
| aq. NaOH
NH₂CHCO₂H
XLI

Tos—NH
|
(CH₂)₄   ——→
|
Cbzo—NHCHCO₂H
XLII

Tos—NH
|
(CH₂)₄   —HBr—HOAc→
|
Cbzo—NHCHCO—NHCHRCO₂Et
XLIII

Tos—NH
|
(CH₂)₄
|
HBr·NH₂CHCO—NHCHRCO₂Et
XLIV

treatment of the latter compound with a glacial acetic acid–hydrogen bromide mixture proceeds with selective cleavage of the carbobenzoxy moiety and hence provides a product (XLIV) whose α-amino group is now available for further coupling purposes (393).

Illustrative procedure 10-109 (393). α-Carbobenzoxy-ε-tosyl-L-lysine. A solution of 12 g. of ε-tosyl-L-lysine in 40 ml. of N sodium hydroxide is cooled to 0° and stirred while a total of 8.5 g. of carbobenzoxy chloride and 50 ml. of N sodium hydroxide is added in alternate and portionwise amounts over a period of 1 hr. Stirring is continued for an additional 30 min. and sufficient water added to dissolve the oily precipitate of the sodium salt of the product. The reaction mixture is then washed with ether, the aqueous layer acidified to pH 1.7 with 6N hydrochloric acid, and the resulting product extracted into ethyl acetate. After drying over magnesium sulfate, the ethyl acetate solution is concentrated *in vacuo* to a pale-green, viscous oil; yield, 18 g. Crystallization of the compound is effected from ethyl acetate-hexane; m.p. 85–88°, $[\alpha]_D^{21} = -13.3°$ (1% in 5% sodium bicarbonate). For the preparation of ε-tosyl-L-lysine, see procedure 10-108 above.

Brief mention should be given to several other ornithine and lysine derivatives which might prove of utility in synthetic peptide procedures. Preparation of δ-trifluoroacetyl-L-ornithine (570) and ε-trifluoroacetyl-DL-lysine (procedure 10-44) via the action of ethyl thiotrifluoroacetate on a solution of the pertinent amino acid in a weakly alkaline aqueous medium, and of α-trifluoroacetyl-L-ornithine (570) and α-trifluoroacetyl-DL-lysine (procedure 10-41) upon treatment of the amino acid with trifluoroacetic anhydride in trifluoroacetic acid solution at 0°, has been considered previously (Section 10-17) and need not be reiterated here. Somewhat more tedious manipulations are required for the synthesis of ε-trityl-L- (and DL-) lysine, namely, (*a*) the interaction of trityl chloride, lysine methyl ester hydrochloride, and triethylamine in chloroform solution to give α,ε-ditrityl-lysine methyl ester, (*b*) partial detritylation of the latter compound in a refluxing acetone–hydrochloric acid mixture, and (*c*) saponification of the ε-trityllysine methyl ester so derived (550). α-Formyl-L-lysine became available upon treatment of ε-carbobenzoxy-L-lysine with acetic anhydride in 98% formic acid solution, followed by decarbobenzoxylation of the intermediate α-formyl-ε-carbobenzoxy-L-lysine through catalytic reduction (42); reaction of the last-mentioned compound with biotinyl chloride followed by removal of the α-formyl group on mild acid hydrolysis yielded ε-N-biotinyl-L-lysine (biocytin).

The Imidazole Nucleus. The preparation of peptide derivatives (XLVII) wherein the α-amino group of histidine is bound in peptide linkage to the C-terminal end of another amino acid residue affords little difficulty by virtue of the ready condensation which histidine methyl ester (XLVI) or other amines which incorporate a histidine residue may undergo with suitably activated acylated amino acids (XLV) or peptides. In contradistinction to comparable syntheses which involve α,ω-diamino acid residues, prior masking of the basicity of the histidine residue does not form a necessary prerequisite to its implication in the peptide-forming step. That syntheses of such type may be effected was demonstrated in 1932 by Bergmann, Zervas, and Greenstein (626), who prepared dicarbobenzoxy-L-lysyl-L-histidine methyl

$$\underset{\text{XLV}}{\text{R—NHCHR'COX}} + \underset{\text{XLVI}}{\overset{\text{MeO}_2\text{CCHCH}_2-\text{C}=\text{CH}}{\underset{\text{NH}_2}{|}\underset{\text{CH}}{\overset{|}{\text{N}}}\underset{}{\overset{|}{\text{NH}}}}} \rightarrow \underset{\text{XLVII}}{\text{R—NHCHR'CO—NH}} \quad \underset{\text{XLVIII}}{\overset{\text{MeO}_2\text{CCHCH}_2-\text{C}=\text{CH}}{\underset{\text{N}}{|}\underset{\text{CH}}{\overset{|}{\text{N}}}\underset{}{\overset{|}{\text{NH}}}}} + \text{HX}$$

ester (XLVII; R = Cbzo, R' = CbzoNH(CH$_2$)$_4$) via the action of dicarbobenzoxy-L-lysine azide (XLV; X = N$_3$) on L-histidine methyl ester (XLVI) in chloroform solution. A number of other N-terminal histidine peptide derivatives have since been analogously secured through application of the azide (Section 10–26) (537, 690, 713, 718), acid chloride (Section 10–27) (359, 836, 837), acid anhydride (Section 10–29) (508, 838), and carbodiimide (Section 10–36) (504, 714, 718) methods. Inasmuch as experience has shown that these reactions proceed in a generally satisfactory manner with neither undue complication nor the requirement for additional manipulation, their extensive discussion here would only prove superfluous. A few practical points are worthy of note, however. Thus, when histidine methyl ester is one of the reactants involved in the peptide-forming step, it may be employed either (*a*) as the free base, isolated after neutralization of a solution of the dihydrochloride salt in water with a sodium hydroxide–sodium carbonate mixture (718) or in methanol with sodium methylate (141, 231) (procedure 10–110), or (*b*) as a solution of the dihydrochloride salt in a suitable solvent medium which contains two equivalents of a tertiary base. It should be noted, too, that the presence of a basic imidazole nucleus in the coupling product does not permit the reaction mixture to be subjected to the dilute acid wash which is so frequently employed to remove unchanged amine reactant; several washes with water are generally substituted instead.

Illustrative procedure 10–110 (141, 231). L-Histidine methyl ester (free base). A solution of 24.2 g. of L-histidine methyl ester dihydrochloride (procedure 10–49) in 250 ml. of hot absolute methanol is quickly cooled and a solution of 4.6 g. of sodium in 100 ml. of methanol rapidly added thereto before crystallization can occur. Separation of sodium chloride is aided by the addition of an equal volume of ether. After filtration, the filtrate is concentrated to dryness *in vacuo*. The residue is taken up in chloroform, the solution is filtered, and the filtrate, when taken to dryness *in vacuo*, yields the desired product as a syrupy residue.

If peptide derivatives (LI) are desired in which the α-carboxyl group of a histidine residue is united in peptide linkage with the α-amino function of another amino acid residue, then the requisite coupling reaction may be achieved via an azide-mediated condensation of the pertinent amine (L) with either an N-acylhistidine (XLIX) or an N-acylated peptide which incorporates a histidine residue. In this connection, it may be recalled that the standard azide procedure involves the conversion of a hydrazide to an azide through the action of nitrous acid in an acidic medium, followed by

$$\underset{\underset{\text{XLIX}}{\overset{\diagdown\diagup}{\text{CH}}}}{\overset{\text{CH}=\text{C}-\text{CH}_2\text{CHNH}-\text{COR}}{\underset{\text{NH}\quad\text{N}}{|}\quad\underset{\text{CO}_2\text{H}}{|}}} + \text{NH}_2\text{CHR}'\text{CO}- \rightarrow \underset{\underset{\text{LI}}{\overset{\diagdown\diagup}{\text{CH}}}}{\overset{\text{CH}=\text{C}-\text{CH}_2\text{CHNH}-\text{COR}}{\underset{\text{NH}\quad\text{N}}{|}\quad\underset{\text{CO}-\text{NHCHR}'\text{CO}-}{|}}}$$

extraction of the azide intermediate into an inert organic solvent (Section 10–26). However, in consequence of the basicity possessed by the imidazole nucleus, azide derivatives which incorporate a histidine residue are not extractable from acidic solution. It was with this latter point in mind that Holley and Sondheimer (695), in 1954, prepared carbobenzoxy-L-histidine azide in aqueous solution according to the standard procedure and subsequently extracted the desired azide intermediate into ethyl acetate after basification of the aqueous solution with potassium carbonate; treatment of the ethyl acetate extracts with an amino acid ester then yielded the pertinent dipeptide derivative. The carbobenzoxy-L-histidine hydrazide employed was secured by the acylation of L-histidine methyl ester with carbobenzoxy chloride in chloroform solution containing triethylamine, followed by the action of hydrazine on an ethanolic solution of the oily carbobenzoxy-L-histidine methyl ester so derived (procedure 10–111). Such procedure or minor modifications thereof have since been successfully utilized for the synthesis of a wide variety of N-terminal histidine peptides (537, 621, 713, 714, 718). Especially worthy of note is the convenient modification of Hofmann and co-workers (713), who carried out the condensation of carbobenzoxy-L-histidine azide with a free amino acid or peptide in an alkaline aqueous medium, and of Davis (621), who did not effect a preliminary extraction of the azide intermediate prior to the coupling step but, rather, treated its acidic aqueous solution directly with a solution of the pertinent amino acid ester and excess triethylamine in chloroform (procedure 10–112).

Illustrative procedure 10–111 (695). Carbobenzoxy-L-histidine hydrazide. A solution prepared from 1.50 g. (6.2 millimoles) of L-histidine methyl ester dihydrochloride (procedure 10–49), 12.4 ml. of purified chloroform, and 1.73 ml. (12.4 millimoles) of redistilled triethylamine is cooled in ice and treated with 0.68 ml. (3.1 millimoles) of freshly prepared carbobenzoxy chloride (procedure 10–27). The mixture is stirred for 2 min., 0.87 ml. (6.2 millimoles) of triethylamine is added, and, after the solid material has dissolved, 0.68 ml. more carbobenzoxy chloride is added. A few minutes later, the reaction mixture is removed from the ice bath, stored at room temperature for 30 min., and washed three times with 5 ml. of water. The chloroform layer is dried over anhydrous sodium sulfate and concentrated to dryness *in vacuo*. Absolute ethanol is added and evaporated thrice, and the residual oil dissolved in 3 ml. of absolute ethanol to which 0.62 ml. of 100% hydrazine hydrate is subsequently added. Crystallization of the desired hydrazide commences after about 30 min. at room temperature. After some 24 hr. the mixture is chilled, filtered, and the precipitate washed with ether and dried *in vacuo*; yield, 0.93 to 1.17 g. (50–62%). A melting point of 171–173° is obtained after recrystallization of the product from boiling water.

Illustrative procedure 10–112 (621). Carbobenzoxy-L-histidylglycine benzyl ester. A solution of 3.03 g. of carbobenzoxy-L-histidine hydrazide (procedure 10–111) in 100 ml. of 0.24N hydrochloric acid is cooled to 0° and converted to the azide upon treatment with 1.24 g. of sodium nitrite. After 2 min., a solution of 2.1 g. of glycine benzyl ester hydrochloride (procedure 10–57) and 2.8 ml. of triethylamine in 50 ml. of cold chloroform is added with vigorous stirring. After some 30 min. of stirring in the cold, the chloroform layer is separated, washed with water, dried over anhydrous sodium sulfate, and concentrated to dryness *in vacuo*. The residue is dissolved in ether and the desired product precipitated therefrom by the addition of petroleum ether; yield, 3.5 g. (80%); m.p. 134–136°.

The phosphite amide (Section 10–31) and carbodiimide (Section 10–36) procedures provide additional means whereby the C-terminal end of a histidine residue may be combined in peptide linkage with the N-terminus of another amino acid residue. Thus, Schwarz, Bumpus, and Page (508) described the preparation of Cbzo·L-Val·L-Tyr·L-Ileu·L-His·L-Pro·L-Phe·OMe in over 60% yield from the treatment of H·L-Pro·L-Phe·OMe with diethyl chlorophosphite and triethylamine in ethyl acetate solution, followed by the interaction of the diethyl phosphite amide derivative so obtained with Cbzo·L-Val·L-Tyr·L-Ileu·L-His·OH in diethyl phosphite solution. Additionally, Okawa (828) observed that the N,N'-dicyclohexylcarbodiimide-mediated condensation of N-carbobenzoxy-O-benzyl-L-seryl-L-histidine with L-leucine methyl ester in a dioxane–tetrahydrofuran mixture proceeded readily to give the pertinent tripeptide derivative in some 64% yield. Successful use of the carbodiimide reagent in the latter instance was feasible because the marked solubility of the N-carbobenzoxy-O-benzyl-L-seryl-L-histidine reactant in various inert organic solvents, e.g., dioxane and chloroform, permitted a homogeneous coupling reaction; like reaction sequence with N-carbobenzoxy-L-histidine is handicapped by virtue of its insolubility in suitable organic solvents.

Since the imidazole ring of histidine is weakly basic, with a pK of approximately 6, it may undergo substitution reactions under certain conditions. Such reactions bring to mind the classical study of Bergmann and Zervas (839) in 1928 on *im*-N,α-N-diacylated histidines. These investigators observed that treatment of N-benzoyl-L-histidine methyl ester (LII; R = C_6H_5, R^1 = CH_3) with hippuryl chloride in benzene solution led to the formation of the corresponding *im*-N-hippuryl derivative (LIII; R^2 =

$$\underset{\text{LII}}{\underset{\underset{\text{CH}}{\overset{\text{NH}}{\diagdown}}\overset{\diagup}{\text{N}}}{\overset{\text{CH}=\text{C}-\text{CH}_2\text{CHNH}-\text{COR}}{\overset{|}{\underset{|}{\text{CO}_2\text{R}^1}}}}} \longrightarrow \underset{\text{LIII}}{\underset{\underset{\text{CH}}{\overset{\text{R}^2\text{CO}-\text{N}}{\diagdown}}\overset{\diagup}{\text{N}}}{\overset{\text{CH}=\text{C}-\text{CH}_2\text{CHNH}-\text{COR}}{\overset{|}{\underset{|}{\text{CO}_2\text{R}^1}}}}} \xrightarrow{\text{NH}_2\text{R}^3} \underset{\text{LIV}}{\text{R}^2\text{CO}-\text{NHR}^3}$$

$C_6H_5CONHCH_2$). That the new amide linkage so derived was particularly sensitive to aminolysis was evidenced by the fact that the interaction of (LIII) in chloroform solution with the sodium salt of glycine in aqueous solution permitted the ultimate isolation of N-benzoyl-L-histidine methyl ester and benzoylglycylglycine (LIV; $R^2 = C_6H_5CONHCH_2$, $R^3 = CH_2CO_2H$) from the chloroform and aqueous layers, respectively. Similar acyl transfer of the acetyl group to the α-amino function of an amino acid residue was shown when N-benzoyl-*im*-N,α-N-diacetyl-L-histidine methyl ester (LIII; $R = C_6H_5$, $R^1 = R^2 = CH_3$) was treated with L-arginine, glycine, and ethyl glycinate under comparable conditions. The essential validity of these findings was reaffirmed about a quarter of a century later by Wieland and Schneider (840), who prepared *im*-N,α-N-di(carbobenzoxyglycyl)-L-histidine methyl ester (LIII; $R^1 = CH_3$, $R = R^2 = C_6H_5CH_2OCONHCH_2$) from carbobenzoxyglycine and histidine methyl ester via the mixed carboxylic-carbonic acid anhydride procedure and demonstrated the ability of such product to transfer its *im*-N-carbobenzoxyglycyl moiety to the amino functions of aniline and alanine methyl ester. Reactions of this type provided the basis of a rather novel coupling procedure developed in 1958 by Anderson and Paul (840a), who employed N,N'-carbonyldiimidazole in lieu of the N-acylated histidine derivative. These investigators observed that the former reagent undergoes ready interaction with the carboxyl function of N-acylated amino acids in tetrahydrofuran solution at room temperature according to the following reaction scheme:

$$\underset{\substack{\text{carboxylic}\\\text{acid}}}{\text{RCO}_2\text{H}} + \underset{\text{N,N'-carbonyldiimidazole}}{\left[\begin{array}{c}\text{N}=\\ \text{N}-\overset{\overset{\text{O}}{\|}}{\text{C}}-\text{N}\\ =\text{N}\end{array}\right]} \rightarrow \underset{\text{acylimidazole}}{\text{RCO}-\text{N}\left[\begin{array}{c}=\text{N}\\ \end{array}\right]} + \underset{\substack{\text{carbon}\\\text{dioxide}}}{\text{CO}_2} + \underset{\text{imidazole}}{\text{HN}\left[\begin{array}{c}=\text{N}\\ \end{array}\right]}$$

The acyl-imidazole so derived, when treated *in situ* with an amino acid, either as its ester derivative in an organic medium or as its alkali metal salt in aqueous solution, then reacts to yield the desired N-acylated peptide derivative. In this connection, it is worthy of note that the yields of product obtained through the use of the tetraethyl pyrophosphite method (Section 10-31) could sometimes be considerably improved and the rate of peptide bond formation approximately doubled when imidazole was present in molar equivalent quantities to the substituted amino acid or peptide reactants; no like improvement was observed in the case of the azide or the mixed carboxylic-carbonic acid anhydride procedures (840b).

CHEMICAL PROCEDURES FOR SYNTHESIS OF PEPTIDES

Inasmuch as the basic character of the imidazole nucleus imparts an appreciable dipolar character to N-carbobenzoxyhistidine (Chapter 4), this compound is generally insoluble in most of the common organic solvents and hence is of limited applicability in synthetic peptide processes. This difficulty would be circumvented if the basicity of the imino group of the imidazole nucleus could be adequately masked prior to the peptide coupling step. Toward this end, Patchornik, Berger, and Katchalski (483) prepared dicarbobenzoxy-L-histidine (LVI) by the action of two equivalents of carbobenzoxy chloride on one equivalent of L-histidine (LV) in aqueous solution at 0° and at pH 9 to 10, followed by adjustment of the pH of the reaction mixture to 2.4 (procedure 10–113); that the basicity of the imidazole nucleus in such a product is not completely repressed is attested to by the amphoteric nature of the dicarbobenzoxy derivative as well as by its isolation as the corresponding methyl ester hydrochloride derivative (LIX) after treatment either with methanolic HCl or with diazomethane followed by hydrogen chloride. Although crude im-N,α-N-dicarbobenzoxy-L-histidine undergoes rapid decomposition at room temperature with the production of N-carbobenzoxy-L-histidine (LVII), it is considerably more stable after crystallization from methanol or ethanol. As is the case with the other im-N,α-N-diacyl-histidine derivatives described above, dicarbobenzoxy-L-histidine (LVI) suffers ready decarbobenzoxylation upon treatment with such nucleophilic reagents as ammonia and aniline, with the formation of the corresponding benzylurethan (LX; R = H or C_6H_5) and N-carbobenzoxy-L-histidine (LVII); the latter product (LVII) is obtained as well by the action of ethanolic potassium hydroxide on (LVI) (procedure 10–114). In a brief communi-

cation, Akabori, Okawa, and Sakiyama (841) independently described the synthesis of im-N,α-N-dicarbobenzoxy-L-histidine and exploited the ready solubility of this compound in such inert organic solvents as ethyl acetate, dioxane, chloroform, and tetrahydrofuran for coupling purposes with various amino acid esters. The di$cyclo$hexylcarbodiimide-induced condensation of dicarbobenzoxy-L-histidine (LVI) with L-leucine methyl ester, O-benzyl-L-serine methyl ester, L-glutamic acid diethyl ester, L-threonine methyl ester, and L-methionine methyl ester, in dioxane or chloroform solution, gave the desired dipeptide derivative (LVIII) in some 68–85% yield.

Illustrative procedure 10–113 (483). *im*-N,α-N-Dicarbobenzoxy-L-histidine. To an ice-cooled solution of 10.5 g. of L-histidine hydrochloride hydrate in 50 ml. of 2N sodium hydroxide is added a total of 17 ml. of carbobenzoxy chloride (procedure 10–27) in ten equal portions. After each addition of the latter reagent, the reaction mixture is shaken vigorously for 2 min. with intermittent cooling, and its *p*H is maintained between 9 and 10 by treatment with 2N sodium hydroxide; approximately 60 ml. of alkali is required. Upon completion of the reaction, the mixture is acidified to *p*H 2.4 with cold 4N hydrochloric acid. The white precipitate which forms is caused to coagulate through vigorous shaking, recovered by filtration and *immediately* recrystallized from methanol. The desired product crystallizes with one molecule of methanol of solvation; yield, 16 g. (70%); m.p. 105–107° d.; $[\alpha]_D^{20} = +15.3°$ (6.3% in 80% acetone–20% methanol). When ethanol is employed as the crystallization solvent, the product is solvated with one molecule of ethanol (483); crystallization from acetone–water gives the unsolvated material (841). It should be noted that *crystalline dicarbobenzoxyhistidine is extremely unstable upon storage, and after several weeks in vacuo at room temperature undergoes nearly complete decomposition to N-carbobenzoxyhistidine*; a similar decomposition occurs within several hours if crystallization of the crude product is delayed (483).

Illustrative procedure 10–114 (483). N-Carbobenzoxy-L-histidine. To a suspension of 4.69 g. of *im*-N,α-N-dicarbobenzoxy-L-histidine·1EtOH (procedure 10–113) in 10 ml. of ethanol is added 10 ml. of 1.0N alcoholic potassium hydroxide and the reaction mixture stored at room temperature for 5 min. The mixture is then neutralized with 10 ml. of 1.0N aqueous perchloric acid and the precipitated potassium perchlorate filtered off. After concentration of the filtrate *in vacuo* to a volume of about 5 ml., 20 ml. of ethanol and 20 ml. of benzene are added thereto and the mixture concentrated to dryness *in vacuo*. The residual material is treated with 15 ml. of hot ethanol and any insoluble potassium perchlorate removed by filtration. Crystallization of the desired product is induced by the addition of 10 ml. of acetone to the filtrate; yield, 2.3 g. (80%). A melting point of 166–167° d. is obtained upon recrystallization from ethanol; $[\alpha]_D^{22} = -25°$ (6% in 6N hydrochloric acid).

That the benzyl group of *im*-N-benzyl-L-histidine may be removed by the reductive action of sodium in liquid ammonia was demonstrated by du Vigneaud and Behrens (842), who prepared this compound (LXII) through treatment of a solution of L-histidine hydrochloride (LXI) in liquid ammonia with sodium, followed by the addition of benzyl chloride to the reaction mixture (procedure 10–115). A means for masking the reactivity of the imidazole nucleus of histidine is thereupon provided. Conversion of *im*-N-benzyl-L-histidine (LXII) to its N-carbobenzoxy derivative (LXIII) may be readily effected upon treatment with carbobenzoxy chloride under Schotten-Baumann conditions (see procedure 10–28); the desired product gives a melting point of 216° d. after crystallization from pyridine (369).

CHEMICAL PROCEDURES FOR SYNTHESIS OF PEPTIDES 1067

Demonstration that this material may adequately serve as the parent compound in the preparation of poly-L-histidine was given by Patchornik, Berger, and Katchalski (370), who converted it to the corresponding N-carboxy anhydride hydrochloride (LXIV) via the action of phosphorus pentachloride in dioxane solution. Polymerization of (LXIV) occurred readily at room temperature upon the addition of triethylamine in dioxane, while removal of the *im*-N-benzyl groups from the polymer (LXV) so derived was ultimately effected via the sodium-liquid ammonia technique. Use of *im*-N-benzyl-

substituted histidine derivatives should likewise prove of utility in the stepwise synthesis of peptides, although applications in this direction have been hitherto neglected.

Illustrative procedure 10–115 (842). *im*-N-Benzyl-L-histidine. Twenty grams of L-histidine monohydrochloride monohydrate is placed in 200 ml. of dry liquid ammonia in a 500-ml. 3-necked round-bottom flask fitted with a mercury seal mechanical stirrer, and the mixture subsequently cooled in a trichloroethylene–dry ice bath. Small pieces of sodium are added to the mixture until the appearance of a permanent blue color denotes that it is present in excess; about 9 g. of sodium are here required. Upon discharge of the blue color by the addition of a small amount of histidine, a light-brown solution which contains a white precipitate remains. This solution is stirred vigorously while 12 ml. of benzyl chloride is slowly added dropwise from a small separatory funnel. After an additional 30 min. of stirring, the bulk of the ammonia is allowed to evaporate spontaneously; evacuation of the flask aids in the removal of the final traces of ammonia. The residual material is dissolved in 100 ml. of ice water, the solution immediately extracted with ether to remove the excess benzyl chloride, and the aqueous layer aerated until the odor of ether is no longer in evidence. After filtration of the solution, dilute sulfuric acid is added slowly thereto with stirring until precipitation begins (*p*H 8.0–8.5). The mixture is then stored at 4° for 3 hr., filtered, and the precipitate recrystallized from 70% ethanol; yield, 13.4 g. (57%); m.p. 248–249°

(with softening at 243°); $[\alpha]_D^{34} = +20.5°$ (2% in water containing 1 equivalent of HCl).

The Guanidino Group. By virtue of the complex nature of the guanidino group, the incorporation of the highly basic arginine molecule into synthetic peptides has posed more formidable problems than have been encountered with any of the other protein-derived amino acids. According to presently available synthetic schemes, the successful union of an arginine residue with another amino acid residue in peptide linkage requires that the basicity of the former be adequately masked prior to its implication in the peptide-forming step. For such purpose, the basicity of the guanidino function is customarily suppressed via (*a*) substitution with a nitro function, (*b*) salt formation with a hydrogen halide, or (*c*) acylation. The first of these techniques was introduced by Bergmann, Zervas, and Rinke (492) who, in 1934, exploited the strongly electronegative character of the nitro function to depress effectively the basicity of the guanidino group and thereupon facilitate the incorporation of the arginine residue into peptides. Preliminary experiments in this direction revealed that nitro-L-arginine (LXVII), secured by the direct nitration of arginine (LXVI) in a cold fuming nitric acid–fuming sulfuric acid mixture (see Section 22-4), could be converted back to the parent amino acid without any detectable loss in optical activity upon palladium-catalyzed

$$\underset{\text{LXVI}}{\underset{|}{\underset{\text{NH}_2\text{CHCO}_2\text{H}}{\underset{|}{(\text{CH}_2)_3\text{NH}}}}\text{HN}{=}\text{CNH}_2} \xrightarrow[\text{H}_2]{\text{HNO}_3} \underset{\text{LXVII}}{\underset{|}{\underset{\text{NH}_2\text{CHCO}_2\text{H}}{\underset{|}{(\text{CH}_2)_3\text{NH}}}}\text{HN}{=}\text{CNHNO}_2} \xrightarrow[\text{aq. NaOH}]{\text{Cbzo}-\text{NHCH}_2\text{COCl}} \underset{\text{LXVIII}}{\underset{|}{\underset{\text{Cbzo}-\text{NHCH}_2\text{CO}-\text{NHCHCO}_2\text{H}}{\underset{|}{(\text{CH}_2)_3\text{NH}}}}\text{HN}{=}\text{CNHNO}_2}$$

reduction. This state of affairs permitted the synthesis of peptide derivatives wherein the nitroarginine residue could be ultimately transformed into the desired arginine residue. Thus carbobenzoxyglycylnitro-L-arginine (LXVIII), formed by the action of carbobenzoxyglycyl chloride on nitro-L-arginine (LXVII) in aqueous alkali, was smoothly converted to glycyl-L-arginine (isolated as the sulfate) upon hydrogenation at normal temperature and pressure in the presence of palladium black catalyst. A variety of C-terminal arginine peptide derivatives have since been analogously secured via the azide-mediated (678, 713), mixed anhydride-mediated (491, 541), and carbodiimide-mediated (678) condensation of a carbobenzoxyamino acid with either nitro-L-arginine, or suitably substituted ester or peptide derivatives thereof, in inert organic solvents or in alkaline aqueous media. Worthy of note in this connection is the preparation by Hofmann and co-workers (713) of Cbzo-L-Glu-NH$_2$·L-His·L-Phe·L-NO$_2$-Arg·OH through the action of carbobenzoxy-L-glutamine azide on L-histidyl-L-phenylalanyl-nitro-L-arginine in aqueous solution containing triethylamine as the base.

Although the nitroarginine technique of Bergmann, Zervas, and Rinke (492) provided a means whereby C-terminal arginine peptides could be made

CHEMICAL PROCEDURES FOR SYNTHESIS OF PEPTIDES 1069

generally available, its successful application to the preparation of N-terminal arginine peptides did not occur until some twenty years after its introduction. As the conditions imposed by the conversion of carbobenzoxynitro-L-arginine to the corresponding acid chloride or azide derivatives also lead to marked side reactions, early attempts to implicate these reactive intermediates in the peptide-forming step proved unfruitful (843). However, with the introduction of the mixed carboxylic-carbonic acid anhydride method (Section 10–29) during the 1950's, a route was afforded whereby the C-terminus of the nitroarginine residue could be combined in peptide linkage with the amino function of another amino acid residue. Such means was first utilized by Hofmann, Rheiner, and Peckham (491, 844) who, in 1953, successfully converted carbobenzoxynitro-L-arginine (LXIX) to its corresponding mixed anhydride (LXX) through the action of ethyl chlorocarbonate and a tertiary amine in dioxane solution; treatment of (LXX) *in situ* with the methyl and ethyl esters of a variety of amino acids yielded the corresponding dipeptide

$$\underset{\text{LXIX}}{\text{Cbzo—NHCHCO}_2\text{H} \atop \underset{\text{HN=CNHNO}_2}{|} \atop (\text{CH}_2)_3\text{NH}} \xrightarrow[\text{(C}_4\text{H}_9)_3\text{N}]{\text{C}_2\text{H}_5\text{OCOCl}} \underset{\text{LXX}}{\text{Cbzo—NHCHCO—O—CO}_2\text{C}_2\text{H}_5 \atop \underset{\text{HN=CNHNO}_2}{|} \atop (\text{CH}_2)_3\text{NH}} \xrightarrow{\text{NH}_2\text{CHRCO}_2\text{Et}}$$

$$\underset{\text{LXXI}}{\text{Cbzo—NHCHCO—NHCHRCO}_2\text{Et} \atop \underset{\text{HN=CNHNO}_2}{|} \atop (\text{CH}_2)_3\text{NH}}$$

derivatives (LXXI). Similar syntheses were independently described shortly thereafter by van Orden and Smith (541), and these were subsequently extended by Berse and Piche (513), who employed the *p*-nitrocarbobenzoxy group as the N^α-blocking substituent, and by Zahn and Diehl (678), who employed N,N'-di*cyclo*hexylcarbodiimide as the condensing agent in lieu of an intermediate mixed anhydride. In an extensive study by Izumiya and Makisumi (845), a comparison of the mixed anhydride- and carbodiimide-induced condensations of carbobenzoxynitro-L-arginine with various amino acid benzyl esters revealed yields of product ranging from 40 to 50% for the former and from 70 to 80% for the latter method (procedure 10–116), respectively. A novel feature associated with these later syntheses is that catalytic reduction of the carbobenzoxynitro-L-arginylamino acid benzyl esters, so secured, proceeded with the removal of the carbobenzoxy, benzyl ester, and nitro groups in a single operation.

Illustrative procedure 10–116 (845). Carbobenzoxynitro-L-arginyl-L-glutamic acid dibenzyl ester. Carbobenzoxynitro-L-arginine is prepared from nitro-L-arginine (see Section 22–4) according to the directions given for the glycine derivative in procedure 10–28. The crude crystalline material so obtained is washed with ice water, triturated with ether, and then recrystallized from dilute ethanol; m.p. 134–136°; $[\alpha]_D^{27} = -3.5°$ (1.0% in methanol) (491). A solution of 2.12 g. of carbobenzoxynitro-L-arginine in 24 ml. of tetrahydrofuran is treated with a solution of 3.0 g. of L-glutamic acid dibenzyl ester p-toluenesulfonate (see procedure 10–56) and 0.84 ml. of triethylamine in 24 ml. of chloroform. To the mixture is added 1.26 g. of N,N'-dicyclohexylcarbodiimide (procedure 10–84) with stirring for several minutes at room temperature. A precipitate of N,N'-dicyclohexylurea forms and is filtered off after about 4 hr., washed with a little chloroform, and the combined filtrate and washings washed successively with water, 4% sodium bicarbonate solution, water, 2% hydrochloric acid, and water. The chloroform layer is then dried over anhydrous sodium sulfate and concentrated to dryness *in vacuo*. Crystallization of the residue is effected from a methanol-ether-petroleum ether mixture; yield, 2.91 g. (73%); m.p. 107–109° (with partial melting at 87°); $[\alpha]_D^{26} = -11.0°$ (2% in acetic acid).

That the highly basic character of the guanidino group of arginine may be advantageously exploited in the synthesis of N-terminal arginine peptides was reported independently by two groups of investigators (363, 471) in the same issue of the journal which carried the initial communication of Hofmann, Rheiner, and Peckham (844). The rationale here applied (363) was that

Since the pK of the guanidino group is about 12.5 as compared to a pK of about 8 for the α-amino group of amino acid esters, a pK of about 9 for ammonia and a pK of about 5 for aniline, the guanidino group would remain largely bound to a proton in the presence of equivalent amounts of these or any other bases of comparable strength. Thus one should be able to mask the reactivity of the guanidino group by combining it with a proton, and keeping it in a positively charged form, either as the zwitterionic salt or as a hydrochloride or similar salt, while permitting an acid chloride or other reactive group to react selectively with a discharged α-amino group or other group of similar basicity.

With this in mind, Gish and Carpenter (363) treated p-nitrocarbobenzoxy-L-arginine (LXXIII; R = NO$_2$—⟨ ⟩—CH$_2$O) with thionyl chloride and coupled the acid chloride hydrochloride (LXXIV) so derived with aniline, ammonia, or an amino acid ester, in a suitable organic solvent, to obtain the desired peptide derivative (LXXV; X = Cl). Anderson (471), on the other hand, masked the guanidino group of carbobenzoxy-L-arginine (LXXIII; R = C$_6$H$_5$CH$_2$O) as the hydrobromide salt (LXXII) and utilized

NH$_2$R', tetraethyl pyrophosphite, diethyl phosphite

HN=CNH$_2$·HBr   HN=CNH$_2$ HN=CNH$_2$·HCl   HN=CNH$_2$·H
| HBr | SOCl$_2$ | NH$_2$R' |
(CH$_2$)$_3$NH ⇄ (CH$_2$)$_3$NH → (CH$_2$)$_3$NH → (CH$_2$)$_3$NH
| | | |
RCO—NHCHCO$_2$H   RCO—NHCHCO$_2$H   RCO—NHCHCOCl   RCO—NHCHCO—NHR
LXXII   LXXIII   LXXIV   LXXV

the condensing action of the tetraethyl pyrophosphite reagent in diethyl phosphite solution (Section 10–31) to couple the latter (LXXII) with an amino acid ester. An analogous procedure has been since employed by du Vigneaud, Gish, and Katsoyannis (510, 846) for the incorporation of an arginine residue into the synthetic precursor derivatives of arginine-vasopressin, e.g.,

Cbzo·CySBz·Tyr·Phe·Glu-NH$_2$·Asp-NH$_2$·OH + H·CySBz·Pro·Arg·Gly·NH$_2$·HBr

$\quad\quad\quad\quad\quad\quad\quad\quad$ | pyrophosphite method
$\quad\quad\quad\quad\quad\quad\quad\quad$ ↓

Cbzo·CySBz·Tyr·Phe·Glu-NH$_2$·Asp-NH$_2$·CySBz·Pro·Arg·Gly·NH$_2$·HBr

More recently, the condensing action of the ethyl chlorophosphite (Section 10–31) and the N,N'-di*cyclo*hexylcarbodiimide reagents (Section 10–36) have been satisfactorily utilized to mediate peptide bond formation between a carbobenzoxy-L-arginine hydrohalide and an amino acid ester (758, 847), as well as between a carbobenzoxyamino acid and an L-arginine ester hydrohalide (678, 847).

If the basicity of the guanidino moiety of arginine could be adequately suppressed through combination with suitable acyl blocking substituents, then an alternative synthetic route to arginine peptides would be available. It is pertinent to note that the basic character of the guanidino group in such N$^\alpha$,N$^\omega$-diacylated L-arginines as the dibenzoyl (848), dibenzenesulfonyl (849), di-*p*-nitrocarbobenzoxy (362), and dibenzylsulfonyl (601) derivatives is by no means completely masked. This fact was established as early as 1928 both by Felix and Dirr (848) and by Zervas and Bergmann (142), who described the hydrochloride salt of N$^\alpha$,N$^\omega$-dibenzoylarginine, and it has been more recently reaffirmed by Gish and Carpenter (363), who determined the apparent dissociation constants of N$^\alpha$,N$^\omega$-di-*p*-nitrocarbobenzoxyarginine and reported a fruitless attempt to employ this compound in the peptide-forming step. Investigations directed toward the synthesis of L-arginyl-L-arginine by Professor Leonidas Zervas (458, 459) in 1956 and again in 1957–1958 during a stay in the writers' Laboratory afforded an opportunity to reinvestigate the potential utility of the N$^\omega$-acylated arginines as intermediates in the synthesis of peptides. Toward this end, an attempt was made to secure the hitherto undescribed N$^\alpha$,N$^\omega$-dicarbobenzoxy derivative of L-arginine by treatment of a *strongly alkaline* solution of the amino acid (LXXVI) with 2 to 4 equivalents of carbobenzoxy chloride under Schotten-Baumann conditions. During the reaction an insoluble material precipitated which was filtered in the cold, washed with cold sodium carbonate solution, and taken up in alcohol-free chloroform; concentration of the solution *in vacuo* yielded an oily residue which solidified on treatment with ether. Elemental analyses of the crude material unexpectedly conformed to the composition possessed by sodium tricarbobenzoxy-L-argininate. The latter material could be converted either (*a*) to the corresponding free acid (LXXVII) upon purification from an ethanolic solution of sodium acetate followed by neutralization of the crystalline sodium salt with sulfuric acid (procedure 10–117), or (*b*) to N^α,N^ω-dicarbobenzoxy-L-arginine (LXXVIII) upon treatment with a solution of potassium hydroxide in methanol (procedure 10–118). In any event, the ready accessibility of an $N^\alpha,N^\omega,N^\omega$-tricarbobenzoxylated (LXXVII) and an N^α,N^ω-dicarbobenzoxylated (LXXVIII) arginine, wherein the reactivity of the strongly basic guanidino function is either virtually completely or only partially suppressed by a selectively removable acyl substituent, unveiled compounds which potentially qualified as intermediates in the synthesis of N-terminal arginine peptides.

$$\underset{\text{LXXVI}}{\begin{array}{c} HN{=}CNH_2 \\ | \\ NH \\ | \\ (CH_2)_3 \\ | \\ NH_2CHCO_2H \end{array}} \xrightarrow[\text{aq. NaOH}]{CbzoCl} \underset{\text{LXXVII}}{\begin{array}{c} Cbzo{-}N{=}CNH{-}Cbzo \\ | \\ NH \\ | \\ (CH_2)_3 \\ | \\ Cbzo{-}NHCHCO_2H \end{array} \quad or \quad \begin{array}{c} HN{=}CNH{-}Cbzo \\ | \\ N{-}Cbzo \\ | \\ (CH_2)_3 \\ | \\ Cbzo{-}NHCHCO_2H \end{array}} \xrightarrow[\text{MeOH}]{KOH} \underset{\text{LXXVIII}}{\begin{array}{c} HN{=}CNH{-}Cbzo \\ | \\ NH \\ | \\ (CH_2)_3 \\ | \\ Cbzo{-}NHCHCO_2H \end{array}}$$

Illustrative procedure 10–117 (459, 904). $N^\alpha,N^\omega,N^\omega$-Tricarbobenzoxy-L-arginine. A solution of 35 g. of L-arginine (free base) (Section 22–4) in 200 ml. of N sodium hydroxide is cooled to $-10°$ and treated, with vigorous stirring, with 100 ml. of precooled $2N$ sodium hydroxide and 27 ml. of freshly prepared carbobenzoxy chloride. Some 3 to 4 min. later, a second addition of 100 ml. of precooled $2N$ sodium hydroxide and 27 ml. of carbobenzoxy chloride is effected. Three more identical additions are made at 5-min. intervals and the vigorous stirring and cooling continued for 20–30 min. beyond the final addition. The white precipitate which forms during the reaction is filtered off in the cold room, pressed sharply to remove the liquid, washed with 100 ml. of ice-cold 5% sodium carbonate solution, and the residue again pressed sharply. The crude sodium salt so secured is dissolved in about 800 ml. of chloroform and, after removal of the slight water layer, is washed successively with two 100-ml. portions of 5% sodium carbonate, two 100-ml. portions of $2N$ sulfuric acid and several times with water, and is then dried at room temperature. After drying over anhydrous sodium sulfate, the chloroform fraction is concentrated to dryness under reduced pressure at 35–40°, complete removal of final traces of chloroform being ensured by the addition of absolute ethanol followed by concentration *in vacuo*. To the residual syrup is added 200–220 ml. of a hot ethanolic solution of 27 g. of sodium acetate trihydrate, and the mixture first boiled for 2 min. with stirring and then permitted to stand at room temperature for some 12–20 hr., during which time the desired crystalline sodium salt (needles) separates. This is filtered off, washed with 30 ml. of absolute ethanol, and the wet cake extracted into 100 ml. of boiling ethyl acetate. Upon chilling the solution at 4°, a solid deposits which is filtered off, washed with 20 ml. of cold ethyl acetate, and then redissolved, while yet moist, in the minimal amount of hot absolute ethanol. A highly pure sodium salt of tricarbobenzoxy-L-arginine precipitates which, after some 24 hr. at 4°, is filtered over suction and washed first with a little cold absolute ethanol, and then ether; yield, 21–24 g.

Five grams of the above-described crystalline sodium salt is suspended in 200 ml. of ethyl acetate and slowly brought into solution by vigorously shaking with 50 ml. of 2% sulfuric acid. The ethyl acetate layer is separated and washed, first with 50 ml. of 2% sulfuric acid, then three times with water, dried over anhydrous sodium sulfate, and then concentrated to dryness *in vacuo*. A crystalline residue is secured which is stirred with petroleum ether and subsequently recovered by filtration over suction; yield, 3.8 g.; m.p. 135°. The melting point is raised to 138–139° after two recrystallizations from ethyl acetate; $[\alpha]_D^{25} = +15.5°$ (1% in alcohol-free chloroform).

Illustrative procedure 10–118 (459, 904). N^α, N^ω-Dicarbobenzoxy-L-arginine. The carbobenzoxylation of 34.8 g. of L-arginine (free base) is achieved under Schotten-Baumann conditions, as described in procedure 10–117, and the precipitate of the sodium salt of tricarbobenzoxy-L-arginine which forms is filtered over suction *in the cold* and washed with 200 ml. of cold 5% sodium carbonate solution. The wet precipitate is dissolved in approximately 500 ml. of 95% ethanol containing 15 g. of potassium hydroxide, with simultaneous cooling in an ice bath and stirring. After the solution has stood at room temperature for 2 hr., about 300 ml. of water is added and the reaction mixture is concentrated to about 300–400 ml. *in vacuo* at 30–35°. About 400 ml. of water and an excess of acetic acid are added, the mixture is cooled, and the syrup which results is washed several times with ice water by decantation. The syrup is then dissolved in approximately 400–500 ml. of hot methanol and the solution permitted to cool first at room temperature and finally in the cold. A precipitate of the desired compound ensues which is recovered and washed with methanol; yield, 52 g.; m.p. 147°. Purification is effected by solution of the substance in dilute potassium carbonate, acidification, and subsequent crystallization of the precipitated gum from hot methanol; m.p. 150°.

With the above in mind, it becomes clear that, in view of the effectively suppressed basicity of the guanidino moiety of tricarbobenzoxy-L-arginine, a convenient synthetic route to N-terminal arginine peptides is available. Indeed, the condensation of tricarbobenzoxy-L-arginine, via the mixed carbonic-carboxylic acid anhydride (Section 10–29) and the di*cyclo*hexylcarbodiimide (Section 10–36) methods, with the benzyl esters of L-alanine, L-aspartic acid, L-glutamic acid, glycine, L-isoleucine, D-alloisoleucine, L-leucine, L-phenylalanine, L-tyrosine, and L-valine proceeded smoothly and without complication, and permitted the isolation of the corresponding tricarbobenzoxy-L-arginylamino acid benzyl esters in high yield (459, 904). Subsequent palladium black-catalyzed hydrogenolysis (Section 10–44) of the condensation products led to the simultaneous removal of the carbobenzoxy and benzyl ester substituents with the formation of the free dipeptides. An alternative route to the latter compounds involved the di*cyclo*hexylcarbodiimide-induced condensation of N^α, N^ω-dicarbobenzoxy-L-arginine with the hydrochloride salt of an amino acid ester, *in the absence of added base*, followed by the successive saponification and catalytic hydrogenolysis of the N^α,N^ω-dicarbobenzoxy-L-arginylamino acid ester so derived. No appreciable coupling reaction was observed when the amino acid ester reactant was present as the free base; such a situation is explicable on the basis of a migration of protons from the amino acid ester to the dipolar N^α,N^ω-dicarbobenzoxyarginine as a prelude to the actual condensation. Hence, both $N^\alpha,N^\omega,N^\omega$-tri- and N^α,N^ω-dicarbobenzoxyarginine may satisfactorily serve in the preparation of N-terminal arginine peptides.

During the course of the above-described condensation of N^α,N^ω-dicarbobenzoxy-L-arginine with an amino acid ester, a crystalline by-product precipitated whose elemental analytical values and chemical properties unequivocally identified it as N^α,N^ω-dicarbobenzoxyanhydro-L-arginine (LXXIX; R = Cbzo, R′ = H); $[\alpha]_D^{25} = -12.4°$ in chloroform; m.p. 147° (904). Synthesis of the latter compound (LXXIX) could be readily achieved in excellent yield either by the interaction of N^α,N^ω-dicarbobenzoxy-L-arginine (LXXVIIIa) with di*cyclo*hexylcarbodiimide in the presence of catalytic amounts of a strong acid or via the action of a tertiary base on N^α,N^ω-dicarbobenzoxy-L-arginine chloride hydrochloride. Treatment of either (LXXVIIIa) or (LXXIX; R = Cbzo, R′ = H) with acetic anhydride at room temperature led to the formation of an intermediate (LXXIX; R = Cbzo, R′ = CH₃CO) which, when treated with cold 5N hydrochloric acid, decomposed into a mixture of products (LXXX; R = Cbzo, R′ = CH₃CO) wherefrom N-acetyl-N′-carbobenzoxyurea and α-carbobenzoxy-L-ornithine hydrochloride ($[\alpha]_D^{25} = -11.5°$ in water) could be isolated. Substance (LXXIX; R = Cbzo, R′ = CH₃CO) presumably arose as a result

```
                         Ac₂O ↓
   HN=CNH—Cbzo      R′N=CNHR              R′NHCONHR        HN=CNH₂
        |                |                    and               |
        NH               N────       HCl     NH₂(HCl)           NH
        |         →      |           ──→      |                  |
       (CH₂)₃           (CH₂)₃               (CH₂)₃            (CH₂)₃
        |                |                    |                  |
   Cbzo—NHCHCO₂H     RNHCH────CO         RNHCHCO₂H         NH₂CHCO₂H
      LXXVIIIa           LXXIX                 LXXX            LXXVIa
```

of the preliminary activation of the carboxyl group of dicarbobenzoxyarginine (LXXVIIIa) by the condensing agent, followed by an intramolecular cyclization. Such formation of an anhydroarginine derivative is reminiscent of the observation by Bergmann and Köster (296) in 1926 that L-arginine (LXXVIa), when treated with an excess of acetic anhydride at the boiling temperature, is converted to triacetylanhydro-DL-arginine (LXXIX; R = R′ = CH₃CO), which decomposes to a mixture (LXXX; R = R′ = CH₃CO) composed of N,N′-diacetylurea and α-acetylornithine after treatment with water. An analogous situation prevails in the conversion of nitro-L-arginine to N^α-acetylanhydronitro-DL-arginine by the action of acetic anhydride in boiling glacial acetic acid (848a). The intramolecular cyclization which accompanies reactions of this type may be ascribed to the fact that the basicity of the guanidino moiety of the precursor arginine derivative is not completely masked. In this connection, it becomes pertinent to note that the treatment of the exhaustively protected tricarbobenzoxy-L-arginine with acetic anhydride does not lead to the formation of a corresponding anhydro derivative (905).

The afore-mentioned $N^\alpha,N^\omega,N^\omega$-tricarbobenzoxy- and N^α,N^ω-dicarbobenzoxy-L-arginine may also serve as useful intermediates for the synthesis of C-terminal arginine peptides after removal of the N^α-carbobenzoxy substituent by an appropriate method (459, 904). Thus, treatment of the former compound (LXXXI; $R = C_6H_5CH_2OCO$) with thionyl chloride, followed by hydrolysis of the N-carboxy-anhydride (LXXXII) so derived, proceeds with the formation of N^ω,N^ω-dicarbobenzoxy-L-arginine (LXXXIII;

```
C₆H₅CH₂OCO—NHC=NR            C₆H₅CH₂OCO—NHC=NR            C₆H₅CH₂OCO—NHC=NR
           |                             |                             |
           NH         SOCl₂              NH        R'OH                NH
           |          ———→               |         ———→                |
         (CH₂)₃                        (CH₂)₃                        (CH₂)₃
           |                             |                             |
C₆H₅CH₂OCO—NHCHCO₂H                    NHCHCO                       NH₂CHCO₂R'
                                         |   |
                                         CO—O
        LXXXI                           LXXXII                        LXXXIII
```

$R = C_6H_5CH_2OCO$, $R' = H$). Similar treatment of N^α,N^ω-dicarbobenzoxy-L-arginine (LXXXI; $R = H$) with thionyl chloride or with phosphorus pentachloride in chloroform solution, followed by the action of aqueous acetic acid, methanol, or benzyl alcohol upon the intermediate N^ω-carbobenzoxy-L-arginine N-carboxyanhydride (LXXXII; $R = H$), leads to the ultimate isolation, respectively, of the free acid (LXXXIII; $R = R' = H$), the methyl ester (LXXXIII; $R = H$, $R' = CH_3$), and the benzyl ester (LXXXIII; $R = H$, $R' = C_6H_5CH_2$) of N^ω-carbobenzoxy-L-arginine (procedure 10–119). The last-mentioned compound has been utilized in the synthesis of L-arginyl-L-arginine (850, 904). For such purpose, tricarbobenzoxy-L-arginine was coupled with N^ω-carbobenzoxy-L-arginine benzyl ester via both the mixed anhydride (459) and dicyclohexylcarbodiimide (850, 904) methods. This process led to a mixture of products wherefrom tricarbobenzoxy-L-arginyl-N^ω-carbobenzoxy-L-arginine benzyl ester could be isolated in a satisfactory degree of purity only after repeated recrystallization from various solvents; side product formation in such situation is not unexpected in view of the fact that the benzyl ester of N^ω-carbobenzoxy-L-arginine possesses at least two reactive groups capable of partaking in the coupling reaction, namely, one at the α-position and the other at the guanidino nucleus. However, when an identical condensation was effected in the presence of one equivalent of a strong acid, the desired dipeptide derivative was secured directly in both satisfactory yield and a high degree of purity (procedure 10–120); such occurrence presumably arose from the proton-mediated neutralization of the basic guanidino nucleus prior to the peptide-forming reaction. Catalytic hydrogenolysis of the coupling product in methanol–acetic acid solution and in the presence of freshly prepared palladium black (Section 10–44) permitted the ultimate isolation of the desired L-arginyl-L-arginine as its dipicrolonate derivative (procedure 10–163).

Illustrative procedure 10–119 (459, 904). N^ω-Carbobenzoxy-L-arginine benzyl ester. A suspension of 22.0 g. of dry N^α,N -dicarbobenzoxy-L-arginine (dried at 78° for 2 hr). in 120 ml. of anhydrous chloroform is cooled to $-10°$ and treated with 11.0 g. of phosphorus pentachloride. The reaction mixture is shaken in the cold until all of the latter reagent disappears and is then stored at room temperature for 1 hr., during which time a syrupy precipitate forms. The mixture is evaporated to dryness under reduced pressure at about 55°, the residue treated with a little chloroform, and the evaporation repeated. Removal of the benzyl chloride and phosphorus oxychloride from the residual material is effected upon washing the latter several times with petroleum ether by decantation. After removal of the traces of petroleum ether by evaporation *in vacuo*, 100 ml. of benzyl alcohol containing 3.5 g. of hydrogen chloride gas is added to the syrupy residue which then begins to dissolve slowly with the evolution of carbon dioxide. The reaction mixture is stored at room temperature for 3 hr., after which time the benzyl ester hydrochloride is precipitated as a syrup by the addition of ether. This is dissolved in a small amount of water, the solution is treated with an excess of anhydrous potassium carbonate, and the liberated free ester is extracted into ethyl acetate. Concentration of the ethyl acetate extracts *in vacuo*, followed by the addition of petroleum ether, results in the deposition of N^ω-carbobenzoxy-L-arginine benzyl ester in the form of prisms. Recrystallization of the product is effected from ethyl acetate; m.p. 129–130° (corr.); yield, 11.2 g. (58%).

Illustrative procedure 10–120 (904). $N^\alpha,N^\omega,N^{\omega'}$-Tricarbobenzoxy-L-arginyl-N^{ω}-carbobenzoxy-L-arginine benzyl ester. A suspension of 8.7 g. of tricarbobenzoxy-L-arginine (procedure 10–117), 6.0 g. of N^ω-carbobenzoxy-L-arginine benzyl ester (procedure 10–119), and 2.6 g. of *p*-toluenesulfonic acid in 30 ml. of dioxane is treated with 3.3 g. of N,N′-di*cyclo*hexylcarbodiimide (procedure 10–84) at room temperature and the reaction mixture is shaken thoroughly. As the reaction is mildly exothermic, the mixture is maintained at room temperature by periodic immersion in an ice bath. After storage at room temperature overnight, the insoluble precipitate of di*cyclo*hexylurea is removed by filtration and washed with a little dioxane. To the combined filtrate and washings are added 1 ml. of acetic acid and a few drops of water and, after storage for 30 min. at room temperature, the slight turbidity which develops is removed by filtration. The clear filtrate is concentrated to dryness under reduced pressure and the residue taken up in a large volume of ethyl acetate. The resulting solution is washed twice with dilute aqueous triethylamine, once with water, twice with dilute acetic acid and finally three times with water. After removal of water droplets by passage through a dry filter paper, the organic layer is evaporated *in vacuo* and the residue treated with a little methanol which is removed *in vacuo*. A crystalline material ensues which is recrystallized twice from hot ethyl acetate; yield, 6.2 g. (43%); m.p. 162–164°.

Although it has long been known that the action of such reagents as cyanamide (851, 852), guanidine (853), O-methylisourea (854–856), or S-methylisothiourea (857) on an amino group readily converts it to a guanidino group, this reaction has been only rarely exploited for the synthesis of arginyl peptides. In this connection, it has been shown that the action of O-methylisourea on L-lysyl-L-glutamic acid in methanol proceeds with guanidination only at the ε-amino function of the lysine residue and the concomitant formation of homoarginylglutamic acid (858). S-Methylisothiourea has been employed in comparable manner to convert the L-ornithine residue of tyrocidine to an L-arginine residue (859), and it has been implicated in the conversion of poly-DL-ornithine to poly-DL-arginine under similar conditions (860). More recently, Barrass and Elmore (429) prepared the L- and DL-forms of N^α-tosylarginylglycine (LXXXVI; R = CH_2CO_2H) by the action of either O-methylisourea or S-methylisothiourea on the corresponding form of α-tosylornithylglycine (LXXXV) in alkaline solution at room temperature; the latter reactant was secured via decarbobenzoxylation of α-tosyl-δ-carbobenzoxyornithylglycine (LXXXIV). A comparable procedure was used for the synthesis of N^α-tosyl-L-homoarginylglycine.

```
    Cbzo—NH                    NH₂                                    NHC(=NH)NH₂
      |           Pd, H₂        |          NH₂C(=NH)OMe or               |
     (CH₂)₃       ———→         (CH₂)₃      ——————————————→             (CH₂)₃
      |                         |          NH₂C(=NH)SMe                  |
   Tos—NHCHCO—NHR            Tos—NHCHCO—NHR                          Tos—NHCHCO—NHR
      LXXXIV                     LXXXV                                  LXXXVI
```

The Sulfhydryl and Disulfide Functions. Since substitution at both amino or both carboxyl functions of the symmetrical cystine molecule can involve either the same or different substituents, derivatives of this amino acid may be classified as symmetrical (LXXXVII and LXXXVIII), unsymmetrical (LXXXIX and XC), or combinations thereof. While a variety of symmetrical cystine peptides are presently accessible via a number of different synthetic

```
      NH—R¹                NH—                 NH—R¹                NH—
        |                    |                    |                    |
   SCH₂CHCO—          SCH₂CHCO—R²           SCH₂CHCO—           SCH₂CHCO—R²
        |                    |                    |                    |
   SCH₂CHCO—          SCH₂CHCO—R²           SCH₂CHCO—           SCH₂CHCO—R⁴
        |                    |                    |                    |
      NH—R¹                NH—                 NH—R³                NH—
      LXXXVII             LXXXVIII             LXXXIX                XC
```

routes, the development of preparative methods which might lead to unsymmetrical cystine peptides has hitherto been generally ignored. Thus, during the first decade of the present century, Fischer (219, 228) and his collaborators applied the α-haloacyl halide method (Section 10–7) to the synthesis of peptides wherein the two halves of a cystine residue were symmetrically bound in peptide linkage with the C-terminal end of a glycine, alanine, or leucine residue. Similar linkages are presently achieved with little difficulty through the condensation of two molecules of an acylated amino acid or peptide, via an appropriate coupling procedure, with one molecule of cystine or a suitable derivative thereof. A general synthetic route to symmetrical N-terminal cystine peptides, on the other hand, had to await the introduction of the carbobenzoxy group in 1932. Toward this end, Bergmann and Zervas (128) demonstrated that bis-carbobenzoxy-L-cystine as its acid chloride (XCII; X = Cl) or azide (XCII; X = N₃) derivatives couples smoothly with glycine ethyl ester in an inert organic solvent to yield the desired bis-carbobenzoxy-L-cystinylbisglycine ethyl ester (XCI; R = CH₂CO₂Et). Similar condensation of bis-carbobenzoxy-L-cystinyl bis-chloride with various amino acids or their pertinent ester or peptide derivatives, either in an aqueous alkaline medium or an inert organic solvent, has since permitted the description of an impressive variety of N-terminal cystine peptides (10, 189, 477, 861–865). Worthy of especial note is the implication of the original Bergmann-Zervas synthesis as the initial step in the classical synthesis of glutathione by Harington and Mead (10). A variation of this approach involves the conversion of bis-carbobenzoxy-L-cystinyl bis-chloride (XCII; X = Cl) to its respective N-carboxy-α-amino acid anhydride (XCIII) (Section 10–10) prior to the condensation with a suitably constituted amine (353). Conversion of cystine peptides

```
       Cbzo—NH              Cbzo—NH              NHCO                 NH₂
          |                    |                    \                    |
          |                    |                     O                   |
       SCH₂CHCO—NHR         SCH₂CHCOX            SCH₂CHCO             SCH₂CHCO—NHR
       |              NH₂R  |              Δ     |            NH₂R     |
       SCH₂CHCO—NHR   ←———  SCH₂CHCOX      ——→   SCH₂CHCO     ——→      SCH₂CHCO—NHR
          |                    |                     \                   |
          |                    |                      O                  |
       Cbzo—NH              Cbzo—NH              NHCO                 NH₂
          XCI                  XCII                XCIII                XCIV
```

to the corresponding cysteine derivatives may be achieved through the reductive action of either phosphonium iodide in glacial acetic acid (10), zinc and acid (866), or sodium in liquid ammonia (867).

Although an unprotected cysteine residue has often been employed during the peptide-forming step, such practice is best avoided because of the likelihood of partial oxidation of the sulfhydryl function with the attendant purification problems this would entail. A particular advantage would therefore be gained if, during the course of the reaction, the reactivity of the sulfhydryl function could be masked with a blocking substituent which in

CHEMICAL PROCEDURES FOR SYNTHESIS OF PEPTIDES

turn could be removed selectively at the terminal stage of the reaction sequence. That replacement of the sulfhydryl hydrogen atom with a benzyl group would adequately serve such a purpose was demonstrated by du Vigneaud and co-workers (690, 862), who converted S-benzyl-L-cysteine (XCVII; R = OH) and S-benzyl-L-cysteinylglycine (XCVII; R = NHCH$_2$CO$_2$H) to the corresponding sulfhydryl compounds (XCVI) by reductive cleavage of the benzyl thioether linkage through the action of metallic sodium in liquid ammonia. Subsequent oxidation of the sulfhydryl compound (XCVI) so derived proceeded with the formation of the corresponding disulfide derivative (XCV). Preparation of the desired S-benzylcysteine derivatives (XCVII) may be readily achieved upon treatment of cysteine (XCVI; R = OH), cystine (XCV; R = OH), or peptide derivatives thereof with sodium in liquid ammonia, followed by the addition of benzyl chloride thereto (862, 867); an alternative preparation of S-benzylcysteine involves the interaction of cysteine and benzyl bromide under aqueous alkaline conditions, followed by adjustment of the pH of the reaction mixture slightly toward the acidic side of 7 (see Section 24–4 for a detailed description of the preparation of S-benzyl-L-cysteine). The high degree of promise

$$(-SCH_2CH(NH_2)CO-R)_2 \underset{O_2}{\overset{Na-NH_3}{\rightleftarrows}} HSCH_2CH(NH_2)CO-R \xrightarrow[Na-NH_3]{C_6H_5CH_2Cl} C_6H_5CH_2SCH_2CH(NH_2)CO-R$$

XCV XCVI XCVII

shown by the use of these materials in synthetic peptide procedures (see procedures 10–70 and 10–83) indicated that, even where the corresponding disulfide form might be employed, the alternative implication of the S-benzylated form would still be favored by virtue of both its greater stability and its greater tendency to yield crystalline derivatives with a high degree of purity. An added virtue of this technique resides in the fact that the carbobenzoxy (690) and p-toluenesulfonyl (842) substituents are also reduced by the action of sodium in liquid ammonia and hence may be cleaved simultaneously with the S-benzyl group in a single operation. This state of affairs was exploited by du Vigneaud and Miller (11) in 1936 for the conversion of N-carbobenzoxy-γ-glutamyl-S-benzyl-L-cysteinylglycine to glutathione. Worthy of note is the more recent utilization of S-benzylcysteine residues in two alternative syntheses of glutathione (475, 606), as well as in the synthesis of lysine-vasopressin (432), arginine-vasopressin (510), oxytocin (82, 868), and the isoglutamine isomer of the latter (623).

Although the protection afforded by the benzyl thioether linkage to the sulfhydryl function of a cysteine residue has been hitherto employed more than any other means during the synthesis of peptides which incorporate a cystine or a cysteine residue, the protection provided by several of the more recently introduced masking substituents are worthy of consideration in view of their considerable potential utility. As the procedures wherewith these newer masking substituents are initially introduced into the cysteine residue and ultimately removed therefrom vary markedly, each will be given separate consideration in the paragraphs which follow.

(*a*) *p*-Nitrobenzyl substituent. Despite the close structural relationship between the *p*-nitrobenzyl and the benzyl radicals, the former can be readily cleaved from its thioether linkage with the sulfhydryl function via catalytic hydrogenation, whereas the latter requires the reductive action of sodium in liquid ammonia to undergo like scission (512). The preparation of S-*p*-nitrobenzyl-L-cysteine (XCIX) is readily effected upon treatment of L-cysteine hydrochloride (XCVIII) with *p*-nitrobenzyl chloride in aqueous alkali, followed by adjustment of the *p*H of the reaction mixture to a slightly acidic range (procedure 10–121); esterification of (XCIX) with ethanolic

$$HSCH_2CH(NH_2 \cdot HCl)CO_2H \quad \xrightarrow[\text{aq. NaOH}]{NO_2-C_6H_4-CH_2Cl} \quad NO_2-C_6H_4-CH_2SCH_2CH(NH_2)CO_2H$$

XCVIII XCIX

HCl (procedure 10–48) converts it to the crystalline ethyl ester hydrochloride (m.p. 172–173°, $[\alpha]_D^{25} = +27.3°$ for a 1.0% solution in ethanol). No description of the use of S-*p*-nitrobenzyl-L-cysteine in synthetic peptide procedures has appeared at the present writing.

Illustrative procedure 10–121 (512). S-*p*-Nitrobenzyl-L-cysteine hydrate. A solution of 3.14 g. of L-cysteine hydrochloride in 60 ml. of *N* sodium hydroxide is stirred vigorously and cooled at 0° while a solution of 1.71 g. of *p*-nitrobenzyl chloride in 30 ml. of dioxane is added thereto, in five approximately equal portions, over a period of 30 min. The reaction mixture is then stirred at room temperature for an additional 30 min., after which time it is washed twice with ether and acidified to litmus with concentrated hydrochloric acid. Removal of the organic solvent from the aqueous solution *in vacuo* is followed within a few hours by the deposition of the desired product. The latter is obtained in some 60% yield after recrystallization from hot water; m.p. 233–234°.

(*b*) S-Thiophenyl substituent. In 1956, Sakakibara and Tani (647, 869) synthesized S-thiophenyl-L-cysteine (C) via the action of benzenesulfenyl chloride on an ethanolic suspension of L-cysteine hydrochloride (XCVIIIa) and sodium bicarbonate (procedure 10–122). By virtue of its possession of a disulfide linkage, this substance may be readily converted to L-cysteine either by reductive methods, e.g., tin and hydrochloric acid, or upon alteration of the disulfide-sulfhydryl equilibrium with an excess of a mercaptan, e.g., ethyl thioglycolate. However, in consequence of the unsymmetrical nature of its disulfide linkage, S-thiophenylcysteine exhibits a relatively marked instability toward both mineral acids and alkalis, and hence should prove of only limited utility for the stepwise synthesis of peptides which incorporate a cysteine or cystine residue. Thus the material

CHEMICAL PROCEDURES FOR SYNTHESIS OF PEPTIDES   1081

in cold aqueous N sodium hydroxide or in boiling hydrochloric acid undergoes gradual decomposition with the concomitant formation of L-cystine and diphenyldisulfide. Comparable decomposition arises from the action of a solution of dry hydrogen chloride in glacial acetic acid. Despite these apparent shortcomings, S-thiophenyl-L-cysteine has proved of value in polymerization reactions. In this connection, a polymer of L-cysteine (CII) has been successfully prepared through the conversion of S-thiophenylcysteine (C) to its corresponding N-carboxyanhydride derivative (CI) by phosgenation in dioxane solution (Section 10–10), followed by simultaneous polymerization and reduction of (CI) upon heating in ethyl thioglycolate solution; some cysteine anhydride formation accompanied the reaction.

$$\underset{\substack{\text{XCVIIIa}}}{\underset{\substack{| \\ \text{NH}_2\cdot\text{HCl}}}{\text{HSCH}_2\text{CHCO}_2\text{H}}} \xrightarrow[\text{in EtOH}]{\text{C}_6\text{H}_5\text{SCl}} \underset{\substack{\text{C} \\ | \\ \text{NH}_2}}{\text{C}_6\text{H}_5\text{SSCH}_2\text{CHCO}_2\text{H}} \xrightarrow{\text{COCl}_2} \underset{\substack{\text{CI} \\ | \\ \text{NH—CO}}}{\text{C}_6\text{H}_5\text{SSCH}_2\overset{\overset{\displaystyle\text{O}}{|}}{\text{CH—CO}}} \longrightarrow \left[\underset{\substack{\text{CII} \\ | \\ \text{CH}_2\text{SH}}}{\text{—NHCHCO—}}\right]_x \text{H} \quad \text{OH}$$

Illustrative procedure 10–122 (647, 869). **S-Thiophenyl-L-cysteine.** The benzenesulfenyl chloride reactant is first prepared by passing a slow stream of dry chlorine gas through 150 ml. of carbon tetrachloride, with vigorous stirring and cooling in a salt–ice mixture, while a solution of 5 g. of thiophenol in 50 ml. of carbon tetrachloride is slowly added thereto (870). Excess chlorine and solvent are removed under reduced pressure at a temperature not exceeding 40°, and the residual syrup is taken up in 30 ml. of dry ether. Inasmuch as the product is extremely unstable to the action of water, all the afore-mentioned operations are carried out with the rigid exclusion of moisture. The ethereal solution of benzenesulfenyl chloride is then added, with vigorous stirring and cooling, to a precooled suspension of 6.2 g. of L-cysteine hydrochloride and 3.8 g. of powdered sodium bicarbonate in 120 ml. of absolute ethanol. Upon completion of the addition, the reaction mixture is permitted to stand at room temperature for several hours and the deposit of sodium chloride removed by filtration. Treatment of the filtrate with 5 ml. of pyridine leads to the precipitation of the desired product, which is recovered by centrifugation, washed well with alcohol, and dried. Recrystallization is effected from $0.5N$ hydrochloric acid; yield, 8.1 g. (88%); m.p. 192° d.; $[\alpha]_D^{18} = -78.3°$ (0.4% in N hydrochloric acid).

(c) *Trityl group.* Peptide bond formation between S,N-ditrityl-L-cysteine (CIII) and an amino acid or peptide ester may be readily induced through the condensing action of di*cyclo*hexylcarbodiimide (Section 10–36). Preferential removal of the N-trityl substituent from the S,N-ditrityl-L-cysteine residue (CIV → CV) proceeds via the action of hydrochloric acid in 80% acetone solution for 10 min. under reflux and thereupon makes the amino function of the cysteine residue available for coupling with the carboxyl end of another amino acid residue. This sequence of events has been exploited for the synthesis of both glutathione (549) and oxytocin (673). A description of the synthesis of S,N-ditrityl-L-cysteine (CIII) was reported in 1956 by Amiard, Heymes, and Velluz (549), who isolated the desired compound as its diethylamine salt after treatment of an aqueous solution of L-cysteine hydrochloride with an ethereal solution of trityl chloride in the presence of diethylamine (procedure 10-123); detritylation of (CIII) to S-trityl-L-cysteine may be mediated by the action of hot 50% acetic acid.

$$(C_6H_5)_3C-NH \atop (C_6H_5)_3C-SCH_2\overset{|}{C}HCO_2H \atop \text{CIII}} \xrightarrow{NH_2R} {(C_6H_5)_3C-NH \atop (C_6H_5)_3C-SCH_2\overset{|}{C}HCO-NHR \atop \text{CIV}} \xrightarrow[CH_3COCH_3]{HCl}$$

$$(C_6H_5)_3C-SCH_2\overset{\overset{NH_2}{|}}{C}HCO-NHR \atop \text{CV}$$

Illustrative procedure 10-123 (549). S,N-Ditrityl-L-cysteine. To a solution of 25 g. of L-cysteine hydrochloride in 480 ml. of water is added a solution of 80 ml. of diethylamine in 480 ml. of ether, with vigorous stirring and cooling at 0°. After the solution has been cooled to −5°, 120 g. of trityl chloride is added thereto and the entire mixture stirred for a period of 3 hr. All of the above operations are carried out under a stream of nitrogen. The reaction mixture is extracted into chloroform and the chloroform extracts washed with water, dried over sodium sulfate, and concentrated to dryness *in vacuo*. The residual material is dissolved in ethanol, 1 ml. of diethylamine added, and the diethylamine salt of S,N-ditrityl-L-cysteine precipitated therefrom upon treatment with ether; yield, 76 g. (70%); $[\alpha]_D^{20} = +71°$ (2% in chloroform).

(*d*) *Carbobenzoxy group.* The lack of success experienced by Berger, Noguchi, and Katchalski (365) in 1956, during attempts to debenzylate poly-S-benzyl-L-cysteine to poly-L-cysteine through the reductive action of either sodium in liquid ammonia or phosphonium iodide in glacial acetic acid, led to a search for a more suitable masking substituent for the sulfhydryl function. Such search terminated with the finding that the S-carbobenzoxy group of poly-S-carbobenzoxy-L-cysteine (CVIII) was susceptible to facile cleavage by the sodium–liquid ammonia system. Preparation of the desired precursor polymer (CVIII) was accomplished by the polymerization in dry benzene solution of N-carboxy-S-carbobenzoxy-L-cysteine anhydride (CVII) which, in turn, was formed through either the action of phosphorus pentachloride on N,S-dicarbobenzoxy-L-cysteine in benzene solution or

$$\underset{\text{CVI}}{\begin{array}{c} NH-CO_2CH_2C_6H_5 \\ | \\ CHCO_2H \\ | \\ CH_2SCO_2CH_2C_6H_5 \end{array}} \xrightarrow{PCl_5} \underset{\text{CVII}}{\begin{array}{c} NH-CO \\ | \diagdown \\ O \\ | \diagup \\ CH-CO \\ | \\ CH_2SCO_2CH_2C_6H_5 \end{array}} \xrightarrow{} \underset{\text{CVIII}}{\left[\begin{array}{c} -NHCHCO- \\ | \\ CH_2 \\ | \\ SCO_2CH_2C_6H_5 \end{array} \right]_x} \begin{array}{c} H OH \end{array}$$

the phosgenation of S-carbobenzoxy-L-cysteine in dry dioxane. N,S-Dicarbobenzoxy-L-cysteine (CVI) was prepared by the condensation of two moles of carbobenzoxy chloride with one mole of L-cysteine in cold aqueous alkali at pH 9–10 (procedure 10-124), whereas S-carbobenzoxy-L-cysteine arose from the interaction of one mole of L-cysteine with one mole of carbobenzoxy chloride in aqueous sodium bicarbonate (procedure 10-125). Neither the N,S-di- nor the S-monocarbobenzoxylated cysteines have as yet been utilized during the stepwise synthesis of peptides.

Illustrative procedure 10–124 (365). N,S-Dicarbobenzoxy-L-cysteine. To a solution of 12.0 g. of L-cysteine hydrochloride in 115 ml. of $2N$ sodium hydroxide are added, simultaneously, 27 ml. of carbobenzoxy chloride (procedure 10-27) and 43 ml. of $2N$ sodium hydroxide over a period of 30 min., with vigorous stirring and cooling in an ice bath. The rate of introduction of the alkali is so regulated as to maintain the pH of the reaction mixture between 9 and 10. The sodium salt of the dicarbobenzoxycysteine, which settles out as a heavy oil, is separated by decantation and washed with ether, and then acidified with dilute hydrochloric acid under cooling. After extraction of the desired product into 200 ml. of ethyl acetate, the organic layer is washed with water, dried over sodium sulfate, and concentrated *in vacuo*. The residue solidifies on trituration with petroleum ether and is crystallized from 100 ml. of carbon tetrachloride; yield, 21 g. (71%); m.p. 97–98°; $[\alpha]_D^{20} = -32.4°$ (8.5% in glacial acetic acid).

Illustrative procedure 10–125 (365). S-Carbobenzoxy-L-cysteine. An ice-cooled solution of 8.8 g. of L-cysteine hydrochloride in 100 ml. of N aqueous sodium bicarbonate is covered with 50 ml. of ether and 8.6 g. of carbobenzoxy chloride (procedure 10-27) added thereto, in a single portion, with vigorous stirring. After 1 hr. at 0°, the temperature is allowed to rise to 10°, at which point it is maintained for an additional hour. The crystalline mass is filtered over suction, washed with water, sucked as dry as possible, washed with acetone and ether, and finally dried *in vacuo*; yield, 9.5 g. (67%); m.p. 177°, unchanged on recrystallization from aqueous acetic acid (1 : 1); $[\alpha]_D^{20} = -50°$ (1% in glacial acetic acid).

(*e*) Thiazolidine intermediates. That the conversion of cysteine to its corresponding 4-carboxy-2:2-dimethylthiazolidine derivative affords a means of protection for the sulfhydryl function, while at the same time leaving the α-amino or α-carboxyl group available for condensation with another amino acid residue, was announced in a brief communication by Sheehan and Armstrong (871) in 1952 and through a more comprehensive report by King, Clark-Lewis, and Wade (872) in 1957. The hydrochloride salt of the crucial thiazolidine intermediate (CXIV) may be conveniently prepared in high yield via the hydrogen chloride-catalyzed interaction of L-cysteine hydrochloride (XCVIII*b*) with acetone (872–874) (procedure 10-126). Utilization of intermediate (CXIV) for the synthesis of peptides wherein the C-terminal end of a cysteine residue is to be joined in peptide linkage with the amino function of another amino acid residue requires that the secondary amino group of the thiazolidine ring be appropriately masked prior to the

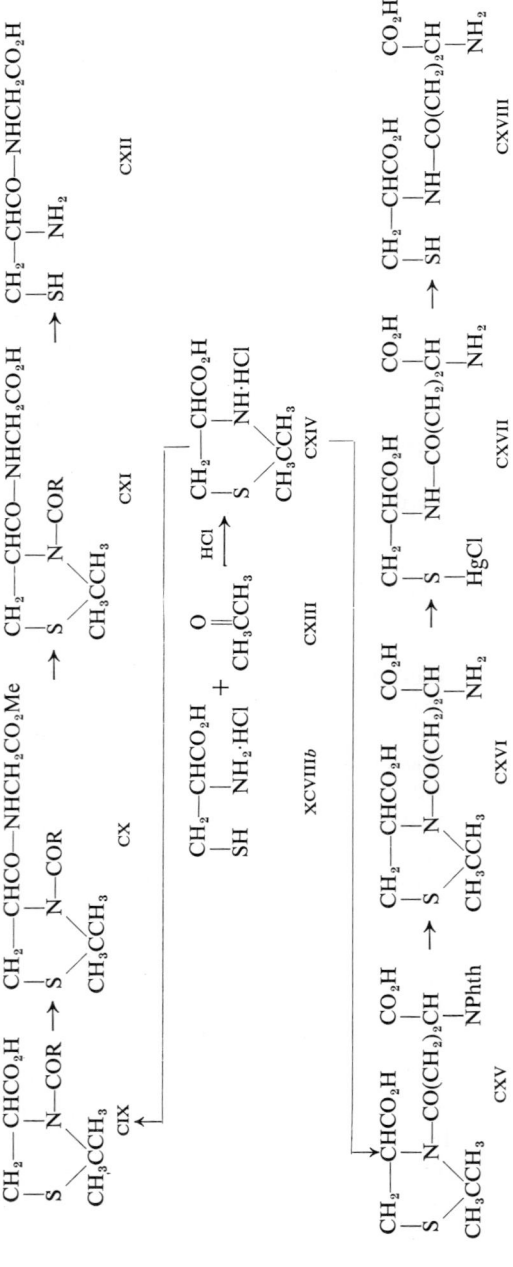

coupling stage. Toward this end, 3-formyl-4-carboxy-2:2-dimethylthiazolidine (CIX; R = H) may be secured by the treatment of a mixture of (CXIV) and anhydrous sodium formate in formic acid solution with acetic anhydride (872, 874) (procedure 10–127). The corresponding 3-carbobenzoxy derivative (CIX; R = $C_6H_5CH_2O$) is also available through the interaction of (CXIV) with carbobenzoxy chloride in dry pyridine solution (875) (procedure 10–128). Condensation of the appropriate 3-acylated thiazolidine derivative (CIX) with a suitably constituted amine may be satisfactorily achieved via the mixed carboxylic-carbonic acid anhydride (Section 10–29) and the carbodiimide (Section 10–36) methods in the absence of apparent racemization (872, 874). Thus, for example, the use of a methylene chloride solution of ethyl chlorocarbonate and triethylamine to activate the carboxyl function of the 3-formyl derivative (CIX; R = H), followed by treatment of the mixed anhydride so derived with glycine methyl ester, permits the subsequent isolation of the optically active L-N-(3-formyl-2:2-dimethylthiazolidine-4-carboxy)-glycine methyl ester (CX; R = H) in some 89% yield (procedure 10–129); on the other hand, employment of phosphorus trichloride as the condensing agent (Section 10–33) leads to a wholly racemic product (533). The desired cysteinyl peptide (CXII) is readily obtained by saponification of the ester group of (CX), followed by simultaneous removal of the formyl group and rupture of the thiazolidine ring of the resulting free acid (CXI) by mild acid hydrolysis.

For the synthesis of peptide linkages which involve the N-terminal end of a cysteine residue, the secondary amino function of 4-carboxy-2:2-dimethylthiazolidine (CXIV) may be condensed with a suitably activated acylated amino acid or peptide. A case in point is the facile formation of L-4-carboxy-2:2-dimethyl-3-(phthalyl-γ-L-glutamyl)-thiazolidine (CXV) from the interaction of phthalyl-L-glutamic anhydride with (CXIV) in glacial acetic acid in the absence of base (874). Dephthalylation of (CXV) via the action of hydrazine leads to the corresponding 3-aminoacyl-4-carboxy-2:2-dimethylthiazolidine (CXVI) which, in turn, undergoes rupture upon treatment with a heavy metal salt, such as mercuric chloride, to yield the mercuric mercaptide of the corresponding aminoacylcysteine (CXVII). Decomposition of the latter compound with hydrogen sulfide then proceeds with the liberation of the desired C-terminal cysteine derivative (CXVIII). An analogous reaction sequence is involved in the conversion of L-4-N-methoxycarbonyl-methylcarbamoyl-2:2-dimethyl-3-(phthalyl-γ-L-glutamyl)-thiazolidine (CX; R = $CH_2CH_2CH(N—Phth)CO_2H$ to glutathione (872).

Illustrative procedure 10–126 (872). L-4-Carboxy-2:2-dimethylthiazolidine hydrochloride. A suspension of 5 g. of powdered L-cysteine hydrochloride in 350 ml. of acetone is boiled for 30 min., whereupon the amino acid dissolves and large plates of the thiazolidine hydrochloride separate from the hot acetone. Filtration of the chilled suspension yields 6 g. (95%) of product melting at 164–165°;

recrystallization of the material from acetone raises the melting point to 168–170° d. On a larger scale (20 g. of L-cysteine hydrochloride) the yield of thiazolidine is about 80% (872, 874).

Illustrative procedure 10–127 (872). L-4-Carboxy-3-formyl-2:2-dimethylthiazolidine. To a suspension of 37.4 g. of L-4-carboxy-2:2-dimethylthiazolidine hydrochloride (procedure 10–126) and 13 g. of anhydrous sodium formate in 175 ml. of 90% formic acid is added 84 ml. of acetic anhydride, dropwise, over a period of 1 hr. with stirring and cooling to maintain the temperature below 20°. The reaction mixture is permitted to stand overnight, after which time the product is collected by filtration and the filtrate evaporated under reduced pressure and then diluted with water to give a further crop of crystals; yield, 32.5 g. (90%). Recrystallization may be effected from water; m.p. 225° d.; $[\alpha]_D^{21} = -181°$ (2.4% in 0.333N sodium carbonate).

Illustrative procedure 10–128 (875). L-4-Carboxy-3-carbobenzoxy-2:2-dimethylthiazolidine. A solution of 500 mg. of L-4-carboxy-2:2-dimethylthiazolidine hydrochloride (procedure 10–126) in 60 ml. of dry pyridine is cooled in an ice bath and 1.8 ml. of carbobenzoxy chloride (procedure 10–27) added dropwise thereto with vigorous stirring. After the addition is complete, the stirring is continued for another 15 min. and the reaction mixture then concentrated to a syrup *in vacuo*. The residue is dissolved in chloroform and the solution washed with water, dried, and concentrated under reduced pressure; the oily residue is washed with hexane and the solvent removed *in vacuo*. A residual material remains which is dissolved in 10 ml. of ether. Treatment of the ethereal solution with 1.5 equivalents of benzylamine leads to the precipitation of the desired compound as its benzylamine salt. The latter is recrystallized from 20 ml. of benzene upon dilution with 100 ml. of hexane; yield, 275 mg.; m.p. 124–128°.

Illustrative procedure 10–129 (874). L-N-(3-Formyl-2:2-dimethylthiazolidine-4-carboxy)-glycine methyl ester. A solution of 0.945 g. of L-4-carboxy-3-formyl-2:2-dimethylthiazolidine (procedure 10–127) and 0.70 ml. of triethylamine in 10 ml. of purified methylene chloride is treated with 0.54 g. of freshly distilled ethyl chloroformate at −8°. The mixture is stirred at this temperature for 18 min., during which time a large amount of triethylamine hydrochloride separates. A precooled solution of 0.627 g. of glycine methyl ester hydrochloride and 0.70 ml. of triethylamine in 40 ml. of methylene chloride is added to the reaction mixture, which is first stirred for 20 min. at −5°, then for 2 hr. at room temperature. After this time, the mixture is diluted with 100 ml. of methylene chloride and washed thoroughly with 10-ml. portions of 5% hydrochloric acid, 5% sodium bicarbonate, and water. The methylene chloride layer is dried and evaporated under reduced pressure to an oily residue, which solidifies readily on scratching. Recrystallization from carbon tetrachloride–petroleum ether gives 1.16 g. (89%) of colorless prisms; m.p. 108–109.5°; $[\alpha]_D^{28} = -155.0°$ (3.5% in methanol).

(*f*) N-Acyl-α-amino-β-propiothiolactone intermediates. In a communication by Flěs, Markovac-Prpic, and Tomašic (875a), it was reported that, whereas the interaction of equimolar amounts of aluminum chloride and N-phthalyl-S-benzyl-L-cysteinyl chloride in warm benzene gives rise to a polythioester [—SCH₂CH(NPhth)CO—]ₓ·H₂O, the use of two or more molar equivalents of the aluminum halide leads to the successive debenzylation and intramolecular cyclization of the acid chloride reactant with the formation of L-α-phthalimido-β-propiothiolactone (m.p. 141–143°, $[\alpha]_D^{20}$ = −162° in benzene and −106° in dioxane); the DL-form (m.p. 138–139°) of the latter compound could be prepared in a comparable manner. That L-α-phthalimido-β-propiothiolactone may prove of utility for the preparation of cysteinyl peptides was indicated when its interaction with amines and with ethanolic-HCl yielded the corresponding amide and ethyl ester ($[\alpha]_D$ = −56° in benzene), respectively, of N-phthalyl-L-cysteine; thus, treatment of the thiolactone with L-methionine ethyl ester in dioxane solution at room temperature permitted the ultimate isolation of N-phthalyl-L-cysteinyl-L-methionine ethyl ester in some 32% yield. The pertinent reaction sequence is given in what follows:

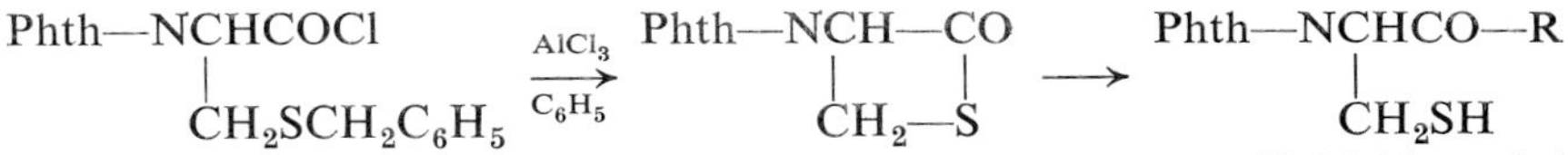

Phth—NCHCOCl   AlCl₃   Phth—NCH—CO   Phth—NCHCO—R
    | C₆H₅ | | ⟶ |
CH₂SCH₂C₆H₅   CH₂—S   CH₂SH
N-phthalyl-S-benzyl-   L-α-phthalimido-   N-phthalyl-L-cysteinyl
L-cysteinyl chloride   β-propiothiolactone   derivative

where R = NHCH(CH₂CH₂SCH₃)CO₂C₂H₅ or OC₂H₅.

(g) *S-Tetrahydropyranyl substituent*. That the adduct which forms between mercaptans and dihydropyran (875b) provides another means for masking the sulfhydryl function of cysteine residues during peptide synthesis arises from the recent study of Holland and Cohen (875c). Preparation of the pertinent S-tetrahydropyranyl derivative may be achieved upon interaction of dihydropyran with either the ester or the N-acylated derivative of cysteine in methylene chloride solution containing hydrogen chloride as a catalyst, as in the following:

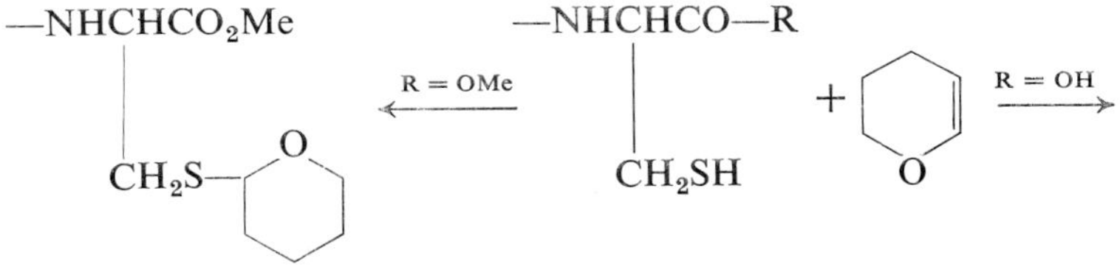

—NHCHCO₂Me   —NHCHCO—R
   | R = OMe | R = OH
CH₂S—⟨O⟩ ⟵   CH₂SH + ⟨O⟩ ⟶

S-tetrahydropyranyl derivative   cysteine derivative   dihydropyran

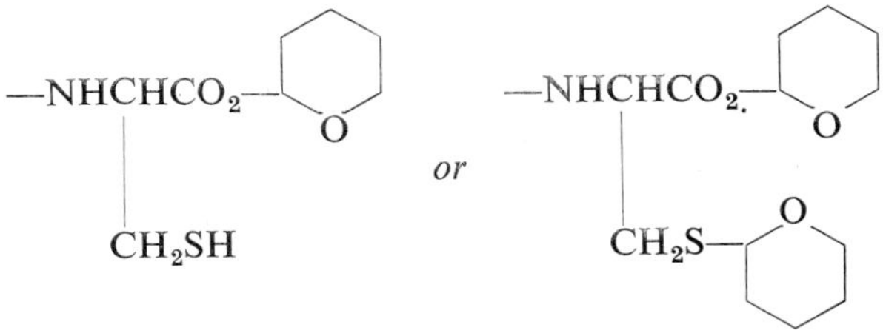

—NHCHCO₂—⟨O⟩   —NHCHCO₂—⟨O⟩
   | or |
CH₂SH   CH₂S—⟨O⟩

O-tetrahydropyranyl ester   O,S-di(tetrahydropyranyl) derivative

If the carboxyl group of the cysteine residue is blocked with an ester function, the S-tetrahydropyranyl derivative is obtained directly. However, if the carboxyl group is free, this group is first esterified preferentially by the dihydropyran reagent, the corresponding S-tetrahydropyranyl derivative being obtained only in the presence of excess dihydropyran. In contrast to the S-benzyl substituent which undergoes facile cleavage in the sodium–liquid ammonia system, the S-tetrahydropyranyl substituent exhibits a relatively slow rate of cleavage when subjected to the action of this same reagent. On the other hand, the latter blocking group may be rapidly removed by hydrolysis with dilute acid (875b) or, better, by decomposition with aqueous silver nitrate (875c); the products of the last-mentioned cleavage are the silver mercaptide of the cysteine derivative and δ-hydroxyvaleraldehyde. Application of this interesting masking substituent to the preparation of cysteine peptides has not been sufficiently extensive to warrant further comment at the present time.

(*h*) S-Benzylthiomethyl group. Use of the benzylthiomethyl group for the protection of the sulfhydryl function of cysteine residues during peptide synthesis has been recommended by Pimlott and Young (875d). The preparation of S-benzylthiomethyl-L-cysteine

$$(C_6H_5CH_2SCH_2\text{—}SCH_2CH(NH_2)CO_2H)$$

m.p. 193°, $[\alpha]_D^{19} = -39.8°$ in 2.4N HCl) may be readily achieved either (*a*) by reducing L-cystine via the action of sodium in liquid ammonia and adding benzylthiomethyl chloride ($C_6H_5CH_2SCH_2Cl$) to the resulting solution or (*b*) by refluxing a mixture of L-cysteine hydrochloride and benzylthiomethyl chloride in dry methanol and subsequently saponifying the product so derived. Treatment of S-benzylthiomethyl-L-cysteine with thionyl chloride in methanol leads to the corresponding amino acid methyl ester hydrochloride

$$(C_6H_5CH_2SCH_2\text{—}SCH_2CH(NH_2\cdot HCl)CO_2CH_3, \text{ m.p. } 145\text{–}146°)$$

whilst the action of carbobenzoxy chloride in aqueous alkali yields the N-carbobenzoxylated amino acid

$$(C_6H_5CH_2SCH_2\text{—}SCH_2CH(NH\text{—}Cbzo)CO_2H)$$

which may be isolated as its crystalline di*cyclo*hexylamine salt (m.p. 118.5–119°, $[\alpha]_D^{19} = +6.5°$ in ethanol). Although the cleavage of the S-benzylthiomethyl substituent can be readily effected by treatment with mercuric chloride in a warm acidic aqueous medium, the group is stable to the action of aqueous alkali, hydrogen bromide in glacial acetic acid, and warm 2N hydrochloric acid. Removal of this group from a cysteine peptide derivative has not been described hitherto.

The discussion above has been primarily concerned with studies directed toward the preparation of peptide derivatives which incorporate either a cysteine residue or a symmetrically substituted cystine residue of the variety depicted in formulas (LXXXVII) and (LXXXVIII). In contrast to such studies, the development of methods which would permit the synthesis of unsymmetrical open-chain derivatives of the type represented in formulas (LXXXIX) and (XC) has hitherto received only scant attention. Thus an attempt by Fischer and Gerngross (219) in 1909 to prepare monoglycyl- and monoleucyl-L-cystine via aminolysis of their respective mono-α-halocyl-L-cystine precursors culminated in the isolation, in each instance, of a material that was presumed to be the desired product. Such presumption was none the less tinged with an element of doubt since the amorphous physical appearance of the isolated materials, as well as the marked deviation of their elemental analytical values from the calculated values, led to the admitted conclusion that each was grossly contaminated. That the synthesis did not rigorously follow the expected course was indicated by the fact that free cystine could be isolated from the reaction mixture in appreciable amount, a phenomenon that was ascribed to the hydrolysis of the reactant α-haloacylamino acid. No successful synthesis of an unsymmetrical open-chain peptide of cystine had been reported for nearly 50 years since this early but somewhat unrewarding effort.

Recent investigation of methods which might be applied to the synthesis of unsymmetrical cystine peptides, by Zervas, Benoiton, and Weiss (876) in this Laboratory tends to explain in part both the unsatisfactory results obtained by Fischer and Gerngross (219) as well as some of the difficulties which might be encountered in syntheses of this type. The key intermediate upon which these studies were based was monocarbobenzoxy-L-cystine (CXX), formed by the action of a large excess of L-cystine (CXIX) with carbobenzoxy chloride under Schotten-Baumann conditions; isolation of the monoacylated derivative required adjustment of the pH of the reaction mixture to 6, removal of the highly insoluble excess cystine by filtration, readjustment of the pH of the filtrate to 3.2, and recovery of the deposited monocarbobenzoxy-L-cystine (procedure 10–130). Esterification of the latter product (CXX) with methanolic-HCl and with benzyl alcohol in the presence of p-toluenesulfonic acid yielded the corresponding bis-methyl ester hydrochloride (CXXI; R = CH_3, X = HCl) and bis-benzyl ester p-toluenesulfonate (CXXI; R = $CH_2C_6H_5$, X = p-$CH_3C_6H_4SO_3H$) derivatives, respectively. Treatment of (CXXI) with trityl chloride and triethylamine in chloroform solution led, in turn, to the pertinent bis-ester of N-trityl-N'-carbobenzoxy-L-cystine (CXII). An attempt to prepare the corresponding α-monohydrazide (here assuming that the appreciable steric hindrance provided by the bulky trityl group would prevent reactivity of the vicinal ester moiety) by interaction of (CXXII) with several equivalents of hydrazine in methanolic solution proceeded, instead, with the rapid deposition of bis-trityl-L-cystine bis-methyl ester (CXXIV) in nearly quantitative amount; concentration of the mother liquors permitted the subsequent isolation of bis-carbobenzoxy-L-cystine bis-hydrazide (CXXV). The action of hydrazine had apparently triggered a disulfide rearrangement between two molecules of (CXXII) to yield one molecule each of the symmetrical compounds (CXXIV and CXXV). That the reaction was base-catalyzed was evidenced by the fact that precipitation of the bis-tritylcystine derivative (CXXIV) could alternatively be induced by the addition of only a trace of either hydrazine or alkali to a methanolic solution of (CXXII). Analogous disulfide interchange was revealed by monocarbobenzoxy-L-cystine (CXX) which, after treatment with diethylamine in aqueous solution for some 2 hours, was converted to a mixture of free cystine (CXIXa) and dicarbobenzoxy-cystine (CXXIII) to the extent of some 40%; under the less alkaline conditions

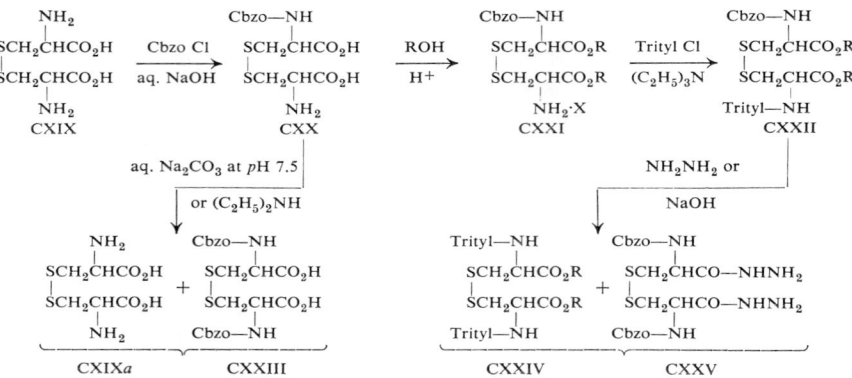

imposed by an aqueous solution of (CXX) adjusted to pH 7.5 with sodium carbonate, some 3 days were required for only 25% of (CXX) to undergo comparable rearrangement; on the other hand, no detectable interchange was noted after 5 days of storage at pH 6.5 (procedure 10–130).

Illustrative procedure 10–130 (299, 876). Preparation and disulfide interchange reactions of monocarbobenzoxy-L-cystine. One hundred grams (0.42 mole) of L-cystine is dissolved in 1 l. of cold 1.65N sodium hydroxide. The solution is placed in an ice bath and 25 ml. of carbobenzoxy chloride (procedure 10–27) added thereto over a period of 1 hr. with vigorous stirring. After an additional 20 min., the reaction mixture is carefully adjusted to pH 6 with 6N hydrochloric acid and the stirring and cooling continued for 20 min. longer. The precipitate of excess L-cystine is filtered over suction and washed with 100 ml. of water. The combined filtrate and washings are adjusted to exactly pH 3.2 with 6N hydrochloric acid and, after cooling at 4° for several hours, filtered and the precipitate washed copiously with alcohol and then ether. The product is suspended and shaken in 100 ml. of N hydrochloric acid for 1 hr. in order to remove the final traces of free cystine. After recovery of the insoluble product by filtration, it is dissolved in the required amount of aqueous diethylamine (15 g. per 300 ml.) and the solution treated immediately with an excess of acetic acid. Crystallization begins after a few minutes and, after storage for several hours in the cold, the deposit is collected by filtration. The product is obtained in a 15–30 g. yield after washing first with ethanol, then with ether, and drying *in vacuo*; $[\alpha]_D^{23} = -120°$ (1% in N sodium hydroxide).

The following experiments reveal the tendency of monocarbobenzoxy-L-cystine to undergo disulfide interchange under alkaline conditions:

(a) A mixture of 3.7 g. of monocarbobenzoxy-L-cystine, 4 ml. of water, 4.5 ml. of diethylamine, and 8 ml. of isopropyl alcohol is shaken at room temperature for 2 hr. and 20 ml. of N sodium hydroxide then added thereto. After 15 min., the reaction mixture is acidified to pH 2 with hydrochloric acid and the resulting suspension first extracted with ethyl acetate and then filtered to give 1.6 g. of the unchanged monocarbobenzoxyamino acid. The aqueous filtrate is adjusted to pH 6 with sodium hydroxide, cooled, and filtered; crystallization of the precipitate from the acid solution by neutralization with alkali yields 200 mg. of L-cystine. The above ethyl acetate extracts are dried over anhydrous sodium sulfate and concentrated *in vacuo* to a residual material which is crystallized first from a chloroform–petroleum ether mixture and subsequently from chloroform to yield 1 g. of bis-carbobenzoxy-L-cystine; m.p. 121°. Such results lead to the conclusion that a minimum of some 40% disulfide interchange has taken place under these conditions.

(b) A solution of 3.7 g. of monocarbobenzoxy-L-cystine is adjusted to pH 7.5 with sodium carbonate and stored for 3 days at room temperature. Recovery of the bis-carbobenzoxy-L-cystine as in (a) above yields 600 mg. of material. This corresponds to an interchange of some 24%. However, storage of a solution of monocarbobenzoxy-L-cystine at pH 6.5 for 5 weeks at room temperature leads to no appreciable formation of interchange products.

That disulfide interchange of cystine and its derivatives may occur in neutral, basic, and strongly acidic solution was initially reported by Ryle and Sanger (877), who demonstrated the formation of mono(dinitrophenyl)-cystine (by photometric measurements) from the interaction of cystine and bis(dinitrophenyl)cystine. The same investigators also established that the disulfide interchange between the last-mentioned compound and cystinyl-bis-glycine led to the production of mono(dinitrophenyl)cystinylglycine. The rate and extent of interchange in basic solution was shown to increase with an increase in pH. The afore-mentioned results obtained in this Laboratory (876) are not only reminiscent of the alkali-catalyzed disulfide interchange described by Ryle and Sanger (877) with the dinitrophenyl derivatives of cystine, but also explain the large amount of cystine formation noted by Fischer and Gerngross during the aminolysis of mono-α-halo-acylcystine. In any event, the findings indicate that the successful synthesis of unsymmetrical peptides of cystine is contingent upon the establishment of reaction conditions that would not be conducive to rearrangements about the disulfide linkage. Toward this end, conditions similar to those previously employed for the synthesis of monocarbobenzoxy-L-cystine (procedure 10–130) also sufficed for the preparation of monocarbobenzoxyglycyl-L-cystine (procedure 10–131). Thus the treatment of an excess of L-cystine with carbobenzoxyglycyl chloride in aqueous dioxane under alkaline conditions permitted the ultimate isolation of pure monocarbobenzoxyglycyl-L-cystine (876). Decarbobenzoxylation of the latter by the action of anhydrous hydrogen bromide in glacial acetic acid (Section 10–46; procedure 10–167) yielded the desired monoglycyl-L-cystine in addition to a small amount of free cystine which could be readily removed through fractional crystallization. Although this route made available for the first time a pure, crystalline unsymmetrical open-chain peptide of cystine, its application to the synthesis of peptides of more diverse structure is admittedly limited. The development of more general alternative approaches is clearly desirable; however, this is made difficult by the extensive disulfide interchange which can occur under the conditions ordinarily employed for peptide syntheses.

Illustrative procedure 10–131 (876). Mono(carbobenzoxyglycyl)-L-cystine. Carbobenzoxyglycyl chloride is prepared by shaking an *ice-cooled* mixture of 10.5 g. of carbobenzoxyglycine (procedure 10–28) and 11.2 g. of phosphorus pentachloride in 60 ml. of absolute ether until solution is complete (about 20–30 min.), filtering the reaction mixture, concentrating the filtrate to dryness under reduced pressure at a temperature not exceeding 10°, and washing the residue twice with dry petroleum ether; the washed residue crystallizes upon storage at −10° under petroleum ether to yield 8.8 g. of the acid chloride which, in turn, is recrystallized from ether–petroleum ether; m.p. 43°. This product is added in four equal portions, with vigorous stirring, to a solution of 36.0 g. (0.15 mole) of L-cystine in a mixture of 95 ml. of 4N sodium hydroxide and 95 ml. of dioxane at 0°. The pH of the solution is adjusted to 6 with hydrochloric acid within 10 min. of the initial addition of acid chloride, and the dioxane is subsequently removed from the reaction mixture by evaporation under reduced pressure. After treatment of the concentrate with 50 ml. of water, the cystine is filtered off with the help of a filter aid and the filtrate adjusted to pH 1.8 with concentrated hydrochloric acid. The mixture is then washed twice with ethyl acetate and the aqueous fraction carefully brought to pH 3.2 with lithium hydroxide solution. The resulting solution (approximately 150 ml.), after storage in the cold overnight, yields 5.5 g. of the desired product, which is collected over suction and washed first with cold water then with ethanol; an additional 1.0 g. of product is recovered by concentration of the filtrate followed by the addition of ethanol thereto. Recrystallization is accomplished from water by the addition of ethanol; m.p. 178–180° d.; $[\alpha]_D^{25} = -136°$ (2% in water containing 1 eq. of hydrochloric acid).

ω-Carboxyl Functions. Although coupling procedures which involve aspartic or glutamic acid residues will be the primary concern of the following paragraphs, the discussion will often also be applicable to syntheses wherein other residues which incorporate an ω-carboxyl function participate.

Condensations which implicate the amino function of such monoaminodicarboxylic acids and the carboxyl group of an acylated amino acid or peptide afford no especial difficulties, since the reactivity of the two carboxyl groups of the former reactant can be conveniently suppressed prior to the peptide-forming step. However, when the peptide linkage is to involve one or the other carboxyl function of a monoaminodicarboxylic acid residue, then conditions must be employed which would permit the preferential activation of the pertinent carboxyl function in order that the coupling reaction may assume the desired course. Toward this end, systems have been designed wherein the carboxyl function which is not to participate (a) is combined in an intramolecular cyclic anhydride ring, (b) is masked as its ester derivative, or (c) is free, during the peptide-forming step. The differences between each of these systems are sufficiently diverse to permit their separate consideration below.

(a) *Syntheses involving intramolecular anhydrides.* It was not until the introduction of the carbobenzoxy group by Bergmann and Zervas (128) in 1932 that a practicable synthetic route to peptides which incorporate either an N-terminal glutamic or an N-terminal aspartic acid residue became generally accessible. A unique feature of the procedure, as initially employed by these investigators, rests upon the use of the intramolecular cyclic anhydrides of carbobenzoxy-L-aspartic (CXXVII; $x = 1$) and carbobenzoxy-L-glutamic (CXXVII; $x = 2$) acids as the acylation agents. Preparation of these reactive intermediates is readily achieved via the action of acetic anhydride on the corresponding acylamino acid (CXXVI) either with warming (128) or preferably at room temperature (609, 610) (procedure 10–132); the desired reaction proceeds in the absence of racemization. Since nucleophilic attack by an amine or an amino acid ester may theoretically occur at one or the other carbonyl carbon atom of the anhydride ring (CXXVII), the coupling reaction could conceivably proceed with the formation of the α-amide (CXXVIII), the ω-amide (CXXIX), or a mixture of the two. The early assumption that such reactions are directed primarily

$$\begin{array}{cc}
\text{Cbzo—NHCHCO}_2\text{H} & \text{Cbzo—NHCHCO—O} \\
| & | \quad\quad | \\
(\text{CH}_2)_x\text{CO}_2\text{H} \xrightarrow{\text{Ac}_2\text{O}} & (\text{CH}_2)_x\text{—CO} \xrightarrow{\text{NH}_2\text{R}} \\
\text{CXXVI} & \text{CXXVII}
\end{array}$$

$$\begin{array}{ccc}
\text{Cbzo—NHCHCO—NHR} & & \text{Cbzo—NHCHCO}_2\text{H} \\
| & + & | \\
(\text{CH}_2)_x\text{CO}_2\text{H} & & (\text{CH}_2)_x\text{CO—NHR} \\
\text{CXXVIII} & & \text{CXXIX}
\end{array}$$

toward the α-carbonyl carbon atom was based on the finding that the carbobenzoxy derivatives of L-isoasparagine (CXXVIII; $x = 1$, $R = H$), L-isoglutamine (CXXVIII; $x = 2$, $R = H$), α-L-glutamylglycine ethyl ester, and diethyl α-L-glutamyl-L-glutamate were the only products isolated from the reaction of carbobenzoxy-L-aspartic or carbobenzoxy-L-glutamic anhydride with the pertinent amine (128, 726, 878). That this is not an invariable occurrence was subsequently indicated by the fact that, while the α-isomer occasionally is obtained as the sole product, the isolation of mixtures which contain the α and ω forms in varying proportion is even more common (378, 455, 609, 610, 838, 879–882). Thus, for example, although the early interaction of carbobenzoxy-L-glutamic anhydride with ammonia led to the ultimate preparation of the pure isoglutamine derivative (CXXVIII; $x = 2$, R = H) (128), the crude product was shown by Melville (882) to contain some 14% of the isomeric γ-amide (CXXIX; $x = 2$, R = H); additionally, a report by Bergmann, Zervas, Salzmann, and Schleich (378) indicated that the interaction of carbobenzoxy-L-aspartic anhydride and tyrosine ethyl ester in pyridine solution resulted in the formation chiefly of ethyl carbobenzoxy-β-L-aspartyl-L-tyrosinate. In any event, when the coupling product is composed of a mixture of the α and ω derivatives, fractional extraction with aqueous sodium carbonate according to the method of Le Quesne and Young (609, 610) permits the separation of the pure isomeric forms (procedure 10–133). Advantage is taken of the greater acidity possessed by the form with the free α-carboxyl group (CXXIX) than by its corresponding γ-isomer (CXXVIII).

Illustrative procedure 10–132 (610). Carbobenzoxy-L-glutamic anhydride. A suspension of 20 g. of carbobenzoxy-L-glutamic acid (see procedures 10–28 and 10–30) in 50 ml. of acetic anhydride is permitted to stand at room temperature, with occasional shaking, until solution is complete. The solvent is then removed *in vacuo* at 50–60° and the residue dissolved in a mixture of 40 ml. of dry chloroform and 40 ml. of ether by warming. After storage of the solution for 1 hr. at 0°, the desired product is filtered off over suction; yield, 13.0 g. (70%); m.p. 93–94°; $[\alpha]_D = -45.1°$ (10% in glacial acetic acid).

Illustrative procedure 10–133 (610). Carbobenzoxy-α-L-glutamyl-L-valine ethyl ester. A solution of 1.1 g. of L-valine ethyl ester hydrochloride (procedure 10–48) and 1.5 g. of potassium bicarbonate in 10 ml. of water, covered with 10 ml. of ethyl acetate, is stirred mechanically while a solution of 1.5 g. of carbobenzoxy-L-glutamic anhydride (procedure 10–132) in 10 ml. of ethyl acetate is added portionwise thereto during 2–3 min.; stirring is continued for 2 hr. and the reaction mixture then stored overnight. After this time, the aqueous layer is separated, acidified with 5N hydrochloric acid and finally extracted twice with ethyl acetate. The ethyl acetate layer is washed with water and then successively extracted with aqueous sodium carbonate (four portions each containing 0.06 g., then 0.5 g.); each of the separate sodium carbonate solution extracts is acidified with 5N hydrochloric acid. The oil which separates from the last fraction soon crystallizes, while repetition of the fractional extraction procedure on the oil obtained from the penultimate extraction gives more solid material. Recrystallization from ethyl acetate yields carbobenzoxy-α-L-glutamyl-L-valine ethyl ester; yield, 1.0 g. (32%); m.p. 119–121°. The melting point is raised to 122–124° by further recrystallization.

In contrast to the behavior exhibited by carbobenzoxyglutamic anhydride, the condensation of phthalylglutamic anhydride (CXXXI; $x = 2$) with different amines appears to be directed almost exclusively toward the formation of the corresponding γ-amide derivative (CXXXII; $x = 2$). Such behavior was initially described in 1949 by King and Kidd (527), who obtained phthalyl-L- (and DL-) glutamine (CXXXII; $x = 2$, R = H) as the only isolable product upon treatment of a solution of the precursor anhydride (CXXXI) (procedure 10–134) in dioxane with dry ethereal ammonia (procedure 10–135); phthalyl-γ-DL-glutamylglycine was prepared via the action of phthalyl-DL-glutamic anhydride on glycine in hot glacial acetic acid, while the interaction of the corresponding L-anhydride with diethyl L-glutamate in ether–dioxane solution at room temperature yielded diethyl phthalyl-γ-L-glutamyl-L-glutamate. That the γ-directed course of the aminolysis reaction was indeed of general nature was subsequently reaffirmed by King and his collaborators (607, 872) and by others (535, 874, 883, 884). Analogous studies with phthalylaspartic anhydride (CXXXI; $x = 1$) by Tanenbaum (885) revealed that the direction of ring opening during the aminolysis reaction is governed to a marked extent by the nature of the solvent employed. Thus, whereas the ring opening of phthalylaspartic anhydride with ammonia in aqueous alcohol proceeds with the predominant formation of phthalylisoasparagine (CXXXIII; $x = 1$, R = H), comparable reaction in anhydrous ether leads to the asparagine derivative (CXXXII; $x = 1$, R = H) almost exclusively; on the other hand, aminolysis in aqueous ether yields a mixture of phthalylasparagine and

phthalylisoasparagine. Thus the preferential susceptibility to aminolysis revealed by one or the other carbonyl group under the conditions stated appears to be due to a competition between the α-directed and the γ-directed reactions, the former predominating under the influence of a polar solvent. On this basis, the suggestion was offered that the presence of water or of aqueous alcohol leads to an acid-catalyzed attack by ammonium ion at the α-carbonyl position, while the ω-carbonyl position is more susceptible to base-catalyzed attack (885).

Illustrative procedure 10-134 (527). Phthalyl-L-glutamic anhydride. A solution of 7.5 g. of phthalyl-L-glutamic acid (procedure 10-35) in 20 ml. of acetic anhydride is heated on a steam bath for 5 min. Concentration of the solution under reduced pressure, followed by treatment of the residual material with ether, permits isolation of the desired product as stout prisms; yield, 4.65 g. (67%); m.p. 195-196°.

Illustrative procedure 10-135 (527). Phthalyl-L-glutamine. A solution of 4.9 g. of phthalyl-L-glutamic anhydride (procedure 10-134) in 40 ml. of warm dioxane is cooled in water and treated with small quantities of dry ethereal ammonia in excess. When precipitation is complete, the bulky ammonium salt is collected by filtration over suction and is washed with ether, then dissolved in a little water. Acidification of the aqueous solution to Congo red with 5N hydrochloric acid leads to the slow separation of the desired product which, after several hours at 4°, is collected over suction; yield, 4 g. (77%). The product melts at 163° after crystallization from water; $[\alpha]_D^{18} = -16.9°$ in 0.33N sodium carbonate.

The action of such anhydride-forming reagents as acetic anhydride or thionyl chloride on the acetyl (292), trifluoroacetyl (568, 573), phenylacetyl (886, 887), carbobenzoxy (128), *p*-nitrobenzoyl (608, 888), *p*-nitrocarbobenzoxy (509), and phthalyl (527) derivatives of glutamic acid proceeds with the formation of the corresponding intramolecular cyclic anhydride of the type depicted in formula (CXXXIV). Certain α-ester derivatives of N-

```
R—NHCH—C=O        R—N——CHCO₂R'       R—N——CHCO·O·COCH₃    R—N——CHCOR'
     |     \           |      |                |      |                |      |
    CH₂     O         O=C    CH₂              O=C    CH₂              O=C    CH₂
     |     /           \     /                 \     /                 \     /
    CH₂-C=O             CH₂                     CH₂                     CH₂
    CXXXIV              CXXXV                  CXXXVI                  CXXXVII
```

acylated glutamic acids, on the other hand, are converted to the N-acylpyroglutamic (N-acylpyrrolid-5-one-2-carboxylic) acids (CXXXV) upon comparable exposure to dehydrating conditions; for example, benzyl N-carbobenzoxypyroglutamate (CXXXV; R = C₆H₅CH₂OCO, R' = C₆H₅CH₂) is formed under certain circumstances upon treatment of the α-benzyl ester of carbobenzoxy-L-glutamic acid with phosphorus pentachloride (889). In contradistinction to the behavior exhibited by other unesterified acylglutamic acids, tosylglutamic acid undergoes facile conversion to N-tosylpyroglutamic acid (CXXXV; R = H₃C—⟨ ⟩—SO₂, R' = H) rather than the anticipated intramolecular anhydride (CXXXIV), when subjected to the action of a suitable dehydrating agent. Such anomalous behavior was initially observed in 1940 by Harington and Moggridge (434), who secured the mixed anhydride of tosylpyroglutamic and acetic acids

(CXXXVI; R = H₃C—⟨C₆H₄⟩—SO₂) upon the interaction of tosyl-L-glutamic acid with acetic anhydride or acetyl chloride. Mild hydrolysis of the mixed anhydride in 70% aqueous dioxane permitted the isolation of tosylpyroglutamic acid (CXXXV; R = H₃C—⟨C₆H₄⟩—SO₂, R′ = H), which could be transformed into the corresponding acid chloride (CXXXVII; R′ = Cl) upon treatment with phosphorus pentachloride. The same acid chloride as well as its precursor carboxylic acid may be more conveniently prepared via the action of thionyl chloride on tosylglutamic acid (procedures 10–136 and 10–137). In any event, treatment of tosylpyroglutamyl chloride with ammonia led to the formation of tosylpyroglutamic acid amide (CXXXVII; R = H₃C—⟨C₆H₄⟩—SO₂, R′ = NH₂) (procedure 10–138), which underwent ring cleavage in the presence of one equivalent of warm aqueous alkali to yield tosyl-L-isoglutamine (procedure 10–139). Thus was provided the groundwork upon which the future development of one of the most convenient and trustworthy methods for the preparation of N-terminal glutamyl peptides was based.

Illustrative procedure 10–136 (436). Tosyl-L-pyroglutamic acid. Tosyl-L-glutamic acid is first prepared via the simultaneous addition of 250 ml. of 4N sodium hydroxide and a solution of 190 g. of *p*-toluenesulfonyl chloride in 500 ml. of acetone to a solution of 147 g. of L-glutamic acid in 500 ml. of 4N sodium hydroxide; removal of the acetone under reduced pressure, acidification of the warm aqueous solution to Congo red, and subsequent storage at 0° for some 12 hr. yields a crystalline material (264 g.) which melts at 140–142° after two recrystallizations from water and at 145–146° after further recrystallization. A suspension of 30.1 g. of *p*-toluenesulfonyl-L-glutamic acid in 50 ml. of pure redistilled thionyl chloride is shaken until a clear solution ensues (6–10 hr.). The reaction mixture is diluted with 50 ml. of ether, filtered through a sintered glass funnel, the slight residue washed with an additional 50 ml. of ether, and the combined filtrate and washings treated with petroleum ether to turbidity. When crystallization commences, an additional 350 ml. of petroleum ether is slowly added. After cooling at 0° the precipitate is filtered off, washed with petroleum ether and dried *in vacuo* over sodium hydroxide pellets and paraffin wax; yield, 26.1 g. (92%); m.p. 127–129°.

Illustrative procedure 10–137 (436, 443). Tosyl-L-pyroglutamyl chloride. A suspension of 30.1 g. of tosyl-L-glutamic acid (see procedure 10–136) in 50 ml. of thionyl chloride is refluxed until a clear solution is obtained, and then for an additional 15 min. The excess thionyl chloride is removed by distillation *in vacuo*, the residual material taken up in benzene, and the benzene then distilled off. An oily residue remains which is dissolved in 100 ml. of boiling ether and the ethereal solution cooled to 0°, treated with 100 ml. of petroleum ether and chilled at 0° for 1 hr. The crystalline product (26.8 g.) is recovered by filtration; m.p. 103–105°.

Recrystallization from benzene raises the melting point to 106–107°. A metastable form of the same compound melts at 83–85°.

Illustrative procedure 10–138 (434, 435, 443). Tosyl-L-pyroglutamic acid amide. A solution of 5.3 g. of tosyl-L-pyroglutamyl chloride (procedure 10–137) in 10 ml. of chloroform is cooled in an ice bath and treated with successive portions of a solution of ammonia in chloroform (saturated at 0°) until a strong odor of ammonia persists. After standing for 10 min. at 0°, the reaction mixture is treated with 2N hydrochloric acid and the precipitate then filtered over suction and washed successively with water, 96% ethanol, and finally ether; yield, 4.8 g. (96.5%); m.p. 192–193°. Recrystallization from water raises the melting point to 194–195°.

Illustrative procedure 10–139 (434). Tosyl-L-isoglutamine. A mixture of 1 equivalent of tosyl-L-pyroglutamic acid amide (procedure 10–138) and 1 equivalent of N sodium hydroxide is warmed over a steam bath for 5 min., cooled, and acidified with hydrochloric acid. The desired product, which separates in some 90–95% yield, forms needles upon crystallization from aqueous ethanol. A melting point range of 158–170° is shown by the compound, presumably as a result of cyclization during heating.

During 1953–1954, du Vigneaud and his co-workers (435, 716) in the United States and Rudinger (436, 890) in Czechoslovakia independently exploited the N-tosylpyroglutamic acid of Harington and Moggridge (434) as a key intermediate for the synthesis of peptides which incorporate an N-terminal glutamine residue, or wherein either the α- or the γ-carboxyl function of a glutamic acid residue is bound in amide linkage with an amine or another amino acid residue. Thus, by virtue of the marked facility with which the pyrrolidone ring of tosylpyroglutamic acid suffers simultaneous cleavage and aminolysis at the carbonyl carbon atom, the formation of N-tosyl-γ-glutamyl derivatives (CXLIII) could be readily achieved upon the conversion of tosyl-L-glutamic acid (CXXXVIII) to tosyl-L-pyroglutamic acid (CXLII) (procedure 10–136), followed by interaction of the latter with a suitably constituted amine in either an aqueous (procedure 10–140) or an organic (procedure 10–141) medium. The preparation of the corresponding α-glutamyl derivatives (CXLIV and CXLV), on the other hand, requires activation of the carboxyl function of tosylpyroglutamic acid prior to its implication in the peptide-forming step. For the purpose at hand, the acid chloride derivative (CXL) formed by the action of phosphorus pentachloride or thionyl chloride on tosyl-L-glutamic acid (CXXXVIII) proves eminently satisfactory; this synthesis presumably occurs with the intermediate formation of tosylglutamyl dichloride (CXXXIX; m.p. 74–75° d.), which may be either isolated as such or induced to undergo intramolecular cyclization to the desired compound with the concomitant loss of hydrogen chloride (686). Condensation of (CXL) with an amino acid ester in an inert organic solvent (436) or with an amino acid in a weakly alkaline aqueous medium (435, 868) yields the pertinent tosylated pyroglutamyl derivative (CXLI)

CHEMICAL PROCEDURES FOR SYNTHESIS OF PEPTIDES 1099

(procedure 10–142) which, under the influence of aqueous alkali, undergoes ready ring scission with the formation of the corresponding tosyl-α-glutamyl derivative (CXLIV); saponification of ester groups within the molecule accompanies the alkali treatment (procedure 10–143). If, however, the tosylated pyroglutamyl intermediate (CXLI) is exposed to the action of aqueous ammonia, then ring cleavage leads to the production of the glutaminyl derivative (CXLV). A comparable series of reactions cannot

Tos—NHCHCO₂H   Tos—NHCHCOCl   Tos—N——CHCOCl   Tos—N——CHCO—NHR
      | SOCl₂ | | | NH₂R | |
      CH₂   ——→   CH₂   Δ   O=C   CH₂   ——→   O=C   CH₂
      | or PCl₅ | ——→   \\ /   \\ /
      CH₂CO₂H   CH₂COCl   CH₂   CH₂
    CXXXVIII   CXXXIX   CXL   CXLI

      | Ac₂O or
      | SOCl₂   NaOH | NH₃
      ↓   ┌───────┘   ↓
Tos—N——CHCO₂H   Tos—NHCHCO₂H   Tos—NHCHCO—NHR   Tos—NHCHCO—NHR
    | | NH₂R | | |
  O=C   CH₂   ——→   CH₂   CH₂   CH₂
    \\ /   Δ | | |
     CH₂   CH₂CO—NHR   CH₂CO₂H   CH₂CO—NH₂
    CXLII   CXLIII   CXLIV   CXLV

be applied to tosylaspartic acid, since treatment of this material with dehydrating agents leads to tosylaspartic anhydride (434). Such behavior is explicable on the basis that an intramolecular cyclization involving the nitrogen atom here would necessitate the formation of a highly strained four-membered ring.

Illustrative procedure 10–140 (435). Tosyl-L-glutamine. A solution of 0.5 g. of tosyl-L-pyroglutamic acid (procedure 10–136) in 10 ml. of aqueous ammonia is permitted to stand overnight at room temperature, then evaporated to dryness under reduced pressure. Acidification of the residue gives 0.41 g. of product; m.p. 157–159°. Crystallization from ethyl acetate raises the melting point to 164–165°; $[\alpha]_D^{21} = +8.5°$ (2.4% in 0.5N potassium bicarbonate).

Illustrative procedure 10–141 (890). *p*-Toluenesulfonyl-γ-L-glutamylglycine ethyl ester. A mixture of 14.15 g. (0.05 mole) of anhydrous tosyl-L-pyroglutamic acid (procedure 10–136), 7.0 g. (0.05 mole) of glycine ethyl ester hydrochloride (procedure 10–48), 75 ml. of acetonitrile, and 15 ml. (0.11 mole) of N-ethylpiperidine is refluxed for 3 hr., cooled, and the solvent removed under reduced pressure. The oily residue is rubbed with 50 ml. of dilute hydrochloric acid and the white crystalline precipitate which forms is filtered over suction, washed with water, and dissolved in 5% sodium bicarbonate solution. Any insoluble matter is removed by filtration, and the main product precipitated from the filtrate by acidification with concentrated hydrochloric acid; yield, 15.4 g. (80%); m.p. 190–191°. The product melts at 191° after crystallization from aqueous ethanol.

Illustrative procedure 10–142 (890). Tosyl-L-pyroglutamylglycine ethyl ester. To a solution of 15.1 g. of tosyl-L-pyroglutamyl chloride (procedure 10–137) in 100 ml. of chloroform are added 7.7 g. of glycine ethyl ester hydrochloride (procedure 10–48) and 9.0 g. of sodium bicarbonate, and the resulting suspension is layered with 40 ml. of water. The reaction mixture is shaken until the evolution of carbon dioxide ceases (about 10 min.) and then permitted to stand for an additional 30 min. with occasional shaking. The chloroform layer is separated, washed twice with 50-ml. portions of dilute hydrochloric acid, and evaporated to dryness. A crystalline residue is secured which is recrystallized from the minimal amount of 96% ethanol; yield, 15.6 g. (85%); m.p. 132–133°.

In addition to the afore-mentioned compound, the tosyl-L-pyroglutamyl derivatives of glycine benzyl ester (m.p. 90–92°) and L-tyrosine ethyl ester monohydrate (m.p. 133°) have been prepared in comparable manner (436); catalytic reduction of the former compound permits the isolation of tosyl-L-pyroglutamylglycine (m.p. 198–200°). The preparation of tosyl-L-pyroglutamyl-L-asparagine (m.p. 150–151°, $[\alpha]_D^{21} = -42.7°$ in $0.5N$ KHCO$_3$), on the other hand, is effected in a weakly alkaline aqueous medium (435, 868). Condensation of this material with S-benzyl-L-cysteine ethyl ester via the mixed anhydride or pyrophosphite method yields tosyl-L-pyroglutamyl-L-asparaginyl-S-benzyl-L-cysteine ethyl ester (m.p. 186–187°) (868). The methyl ester (m.p. = 150°, $[\alpha]_D^{23} = +11.6°$ in dioxane), ethyl ester (m.p. = 150°, $[\alpha]_D^{22} = -17.0°$ in dioxane) and free acid (m.p. = 89–90°) of tosyl-L-pyroglutamyl-S-benzyl-L-cysteine have also been described (432a).

Illustrative procedure 10–143 (890). Tosyl-L-α-glutamylglycine. A solution of 3.68 g. of tosyl-L-pyroglutamylglycine ethyl ester (procedure 10–142) in 20 ml. of acetone is cooled to 0° and treated with a mixture of 7.5 ml. of $4N$ sodium hydroxide and 12.5 ml. of methanol. The solution is evaporated to a small volume under reduced pressure and a temperature not exceeding 40°. Acidification of the residual solution with hydrochloric acid leads to the deposition of an oil. The latter is separated by decantation, dissolved in 7.5 ml. of $4N$ sodium hydroxide, and the resulting solution permitted to stand for 10 min., then acidified. The desired product crystallizes as needles; yield, 2.60 g. (72%); m.p. 213°.

•In 1950, a novel route to N-terminal α-glutamyl peptide derivatives was provided by the observation that the pyrrolidone ring of an unacylated pyroglutamic acid derivative suffers facile cleavage at the lactam linkage when subjected to the action of ethanolic hydrogen chloride (648). The case in point involved the initial conversion of ethyl L-pyroglutamate (CXLVI) to the corresponding hydrazide (CXLVII) upon treatment with hydrazine in absolute ethanol. Interaction of (CXLVII) with nitrous acid then yielded the azide which, in turn, underwent ready condensation with diethyl L-glutamate to give diethyl L-pyroglutamyl-L-glutamate (CXLVIII; R = CH(CO$_2$Et)CH$_2$CH$_2$CO$_2$Et). Simultaneous ring scission and esterification of the latter to triethyl L-α-glutamyl-L-glutamate (CXLIX; R = CH-(CO$_2$Et)CH$_2$CH$_2$CO$_2$Et) occurred upon treatment with ethanolic hydrogen chloride; use of the latter reagent permitted the analogous conversion of L-pyroglutamic acid amide (CXLVIII; R = H) to ethyl L-isoglutaminate (CXLIX; R = H), albeit in low yield (509, 648). The utilization of unacylated pyroglutamyl derivatives has received little attention in syntheses other

CHEMICAL PROCEDURES FOR SYNTHESIS OF PEPTIDES 1101

$$\underset{\text{CXLVI}}{\underset{\text{NH}}{\overset{\text{H}_2\text{C}\text{———}\text{CH}_2}{\overset{|}{\text{O}=\text{C}}\quad\overset{|}{\text{CHCO}_2\text{Et}}}}} \xrightarrow{\text{NH}_2\text{NH}_2} \underset{\text{CXLVII}}{\underset{\text{NH}}{\overset{\text{H}_2\text{C}\text{———}\text{CH}_2}{\overset{|}{\text{O}=\text{C}}\quad\overset{|}{\text{CHCO}\text{—NHNH}_2}}}} \xrightarrow[\text{2. NH}_2\text{R}]{\text{1. HNO}_2}$$

$$\underset{\text{CXLVIII}}{\underset{\text{NH}}{\overset{\text{H}_2\text{C}\text{———}\text{CH}_2}{\overset{|}{\text{O}=\text{C}}\quad\overset{|}{\text{CHCO}\text{—NHR}}}}} \xrightarrow[\text{HCl}]{\text{EtOH}} \underset{\text{CXLIX}}{\overset{\text{HCl}\cdot\text{NH}_2\text{CHCO}\text{—NHR}}{\underset{\text{CH}_2\text{CO}_2\text{Et}}{\overset{|}{\text{CH}_2}}}}$$

than those cited, presumably as a consequence of the subsequent introduction of more satisfactory procedures which utilized N-tosylated pyroglutamyl derivatives.

In addition to the afore-mentioned phthalylated and carbobenzoxylated aspartic and glutamic anhydrides, the anhydrides of p-nitrocarbobenzoxy-L- (509), N-benzyl-DL- (558), and trifluoroacetyl-L-aspartic acid (576) have been described, as have the corresponding derivatives of p-nitrocarbobenzoxy-L- (509), phenylthiocarbonyl-L- (579), and trifluoroacetyl-L-glutamic acid (568, 573). Studies with these compounds have added further weight to the previously discussed thesis that the extent to which the α- or the ω-carbonyl carbon atom is attacked by amines or amino acid esters is governed, at least in part, by the nature of the blocking substituent as well as by the reaction conditions employed. Thus the action of aqueous ammonia, anhydrous ammonia in dioxane, or ethanolic ammonium hydroxide on p-nitrocarbobenzoxy-L-aspartic anhydride and the corresponding L-glutamic acid derivative was shown by Chambers and Carpenter (509) to lead to a mixture of the α-amide and the ω-amide derivatives wherein the proportion of the former component definitely exceeded that of the latter; the direction of ring opening in favor of α-substitution is reminiscent of the behavior earlier observed with the carbobenzoxy derivatives. On the other hand, the action of aqueous or acetone solutions of amines or amino acid esters on N-benzyl-DL-aspartic anhydride was reported by Zilkha and Liwschitz (558) to proceed with the formation of the β-derivative, accompanied in some instances by the α-isomer; however, only the pertinent isoasparagine derivative was isolated when ammonia was employed. No data on the behavior exhibited by either phenylthiocarbonyl-L-glutamic anhydride (579) or trifluoroacetyl-L aspartic anhydride (576) toward various amines is presently available. In contrast, studies on the interaction of trifluoroacetyl-L-glutamic anhydride with different amines have been made and have, indeed, afforded some very interesting results. Thus the action of aniline on this anhydride (CLI) in tetrahydrofuran solution was shown by Weygand and Leising (568) to yield the α-anilide derivative (CL; R = C_6H_5). A subsequent report by

Weygand and Reiher (573) revealed that, when a comparable reaction was carried out in which di*cyclo*hexylamine was employed in lieu of aniline, the reaction did not yield the anticipated di*cyclo*hexylamide but led, rather, to the deposition of a material which dissolved upon repeated washing with water; isolation and analysis of the water-soluble material permitted its identification as racemic pyrrolidonecarboxylic acid (CLIII). The suggestion was offered that the latter compound arose as a result of the fact that the marked activation of the imide-hydrogen atom by the strongly electronegative CF_3 group led to salt formation with di*cyclo*hexylamine and hence

$$CF_3CO-NHCHCO-NHR \atop {\overset{|}{C}H_2} \atop {\overset{|}{C}H_2CO_2H}$$
CL

$\leftarrow$

$$CF_3CO-NHCHCO-O \atop {\overset{|}{C}H_2} \atop {\overset{|}{C}H_2-CO}$$
CLI

$\rightarrow$

$$\left[CF_3CO-N{\overset{\diagdown}{}}{\underset{OC}{}}{\overset{\diagup}{CH_2}}{\underset{\diagdown}{}}CHCO_2^- \atop {\underset{CH_2 \ R_2NH_2^+}{}} \right]$$
CLII

$\rightarrow$

$$NH-CHCO_2H \atop OC{\overset{\diagdown}{}}{\overset{\diagup}{CH_2}} \atop CH_2$$
CLIII

permitted intramolecular nucleophilic attack by the imide-nitrogen atom on the C_5-atom with the concomitant formation of an N,N-diacylamide (CLII). Facile cleavage of the latter compound to (CLIII) by the hydrolytic action of water was ascribed to the general instability of compounds of this type, while racemization at the C_2-carbon atom was attributed to a mobilization of the C_2-hydrogen atom. In any event, it became clear that the course of the reaction of an acylated glutamic or aspartic anhydride with an amine may be markedly influenced by the nature of the amine as well as by the nature of the acyl substituent and of the solvent medium employed.

Table 10–41 (p. 1140) lists the melting points of the various acylated aspartic and glutamic acid anhydrides alluded to above, as well as those of the tosylpyroglutamic acids.

(b) *Syntheses involving half-ester derivatives*. An alternative route to aspartyl and glutamyl peptide derivatives of the above-described type arises from the studies of Bergmann, Zervas, and Salzmann (602) in 1933. The method here suggested involves the preferential masking of one or the other carboxyl function of an acylated aspartic or glutamic acid with an ester moiety (CLIV or CLVII) prior to the peptide-forming step; the desired peptide derivative (CLV or CLVI) is then secured upon condensation of the unaltered carboxyl function of the acylated dicarboxylic acid derivative with a suitably constituted amine via an appropriate coupling procedure. Although the initial study was confined to the conversion of the α-benzyl

$$\begin{array}{cc}
\text{RCO—NHCHCO}_2\text{H} & \xrightarrow{\text{NH}_2\text{R}^2} \quad \text{RCO—NHCHCO—NHR}^2 \\
\quad | & \quad \quad \quad \quad \quad \quad \quad | \\
\text{(CH}_2)_x\text{CO}_2\text{R}^1 & \quad \quad \quad \quad \quad \text{(CH}_2)_x\text{CO}_2\text{R}^1 \\
\text{CLIV} & \quad \quad \quad \quad \quad \quad \text{CLV} \\
\\
\text{RCO—NHCHCO}_2\text{R}^1 & \xleftarrow{\text{NH}_2\text{R}^2} \quad \text{RCO—NHCHCO}_2\text{R}^1 \\
\quad | & \quad \quad \quad \quad \quad \quad \quad | \\
\text{(CH}_2)_x\text{CO—NHR}^2 & \quad \quad \quad \quad \quad \text{(CH}_2)_x\text{CO}_2\text{H} \\
\text{CLVI} & \quad \quad \quad \quad \quad \quad \text{CLVII}
\end{array}$$

esters of carbobenzoxy-L-aspartic and L-glutamic acids (CLVII; R = $C_6H_5CH_2O$, $R^1 = C_6H_5CH_2$, $x = 1$ or 2) to their respective acid chloride intermediates, followed by interaction of the latter with ammonia to give the corresponding L-asparagine and L-glutamine derivatives (CLVI; $R^2 = H$), subsequent application of the method has led to derivatives wherein the ω-carboxyl group of aspartic or glutamic acid is bound in peptide combination with another amino acid residue (378, 726, 836). For the purpose at hand, the α-benzyl esters of carbobenzoxy-L-aspartic and L-glutamic acids may be prepared by the action of the pertinent acylamino acid anhydride on benzyl alcohol (602), although the glutamic acid derivative is generally so obtained as a syrup (presumably because of contamination with the γ-substituted isomer) which may be crystallized after fractional extraction with aqueous sodium carbonate (610); the latter compound may be alternatively prepared in a high degree of purity by the carbobenzoxylation of glutamic acid α-benzyl ester in an alkaline aqueous medium (662). In comparable syntheses, the α-methyl or α-ethyl ester derivatives of carbobenzoxy-L-aspartic or L-glutamic acid (CLVII; R = $C_6H_5CH_2O$, $R^1 = CH_3$ or C_2H_5) may be employed in lieu of the corresponding α-benzyl ester derivatives (10, 475, 609); in addition, the acid chloride procedure may be replaced by other coupling methods (475, 891). Thus, for example, the early synthesis of glutathione by Harington and Mead (10) involved a condensation of the γ-acid chloride of carbobenzoxy-L-glutamic acid α-methyl ester with ethyl S-benzyl-L-cysteinylglycinate as an intermediate step; an analogous synthesis by Goldschmidt and Jutz (475) directed toward the same compound involved a phosphazo intermediate as the condensing agent. In addition, the action of the γ-acid chloride of carbobenzoxy-α-glutamyl peptides on ammonia has permitted the synthesis of the corresponding glutaminyl derivatives (882), while the o-phenylene chlorophosphite-mediated condensation of the γ-carboxyl group of a carbobenzoxy-α-glutamyl peptide ester with an amino acid ester has led to derivatives in which both carboxyl groups of the glutamic acid residue are united in peptide combination (891). For the synthesis of α-glutamyl peptide derivatives (CLV), the γ-methyl ester of carbobenzoxy-L-glutamic acid (CLIV; R = $C_6H_5CH_2O$, $R^1 = CH_3$) has been employed in a manner comparable to that given above for the corresponding α-derivatives (677).

TABLE 10-41
Intramolecular Anhydrides of Acylglutamic and Acylaspartic Acids

Compound	M.P., °C.	Ref.
Aspartic acid derivatives		
N-Bz-DL-aspartic anhydride·HCl	157	558
Cbzo-L-aspartic anhydride	109–111[a]	128, 602, 609
p-NO₂-Cbzo-DL-aspartic anhydride	163–164.5	509
Phth-L-aspartic anhydride	227–228[b]	528, 885
Tos-DL-aspartic anhydride	148	434
TFA-L-aspartic anhydride	133–134[c]	576
Glutamic acid derivatives		
Cbzo-DL-glutamic anhydride	108–109	610
Cbzo-L-glutamic anhydride	94[d]	10, 128, 610
p-NO₂-Cbzo-L-glutamic anhydride	156–158[e]	509
Phth-DL-glutamic anhydride	195–196 d.	527
Phth-L-glutamic anhydride	196–198[f]	523, 527, 533
PhTC-L-glutamic anhydride	166–168	579
Tos-DL-pyroglutamic acid[g]	169–170	433
Tos-DL-pyroglutamic acid·H₂O[g]	122–130	433
Tos-D-pyroglutamic acid[g]	128–130	433
Tos-D-pyroglutamic acid·H₂O[g]	68–69	433
Tos-L-pyroglutamic acid[g]	129–130	436
Tos-L-pyroglutamic acid·H₂O[g]	68–70	436
TFA-L-glutamic anhydride	70[h]	568, 573

[a] $[\alpha]_D^{19} = -39.8°$ (4.1% in acetic acid) (128).
[b] $[\alpha]_D^{15} = -60°$ (0.3% in dimethylformamide), m.p. = 210–213° (528).
[c] $[\alpha]_D^{22} = -22.3°$ (0.6% in tetrahydrofuran).
[d] $[\alpha]_D^{19} = -44.1°$ (5.5% in acetic acid) (128).
[e] $[\alpha]_D^{24} = -34.2°$ (2.5% in dioxane).
[f] $[\alpha]_D^{21} = -43.1°$ (1.8% in dioxane).
[g] Pyroglutamic acid = pyrrolid-5-one-2-carboxylic acid.
[h] $[\alpha]_D^{20} = -38.5°$ (1.3% in tetrahydrofuran).

The half-ester derivatives of a number of acylated aspartic and glutamic acids which incorporate an N-acyl substituent other than the carbobenzoxy group have also been applied, with varying degrees of success, to the synthesis of α- and ω-peptide derivatives of aspartic and glutamic acids. For this purpose, the pertinent N-phthalyl or N-trityl derivatives have proved most satisfactory. Thus the fact that the treatment of phthalylglutamic anhydride (CLVIII) with methanol leads to the virtually exclusive formation of the γ-ester derivative of phthalylglutamic acid (CLIX) (892) was profitably exploited for the synthesis of α-glutamyl peptides during 1957 by King, Clark-Lewis, and Wade (533) (procedure 10–144); the thionyl chloride-

Phth=NCHCO   Phth=NCHCO₂H   Phth=NCHCOCl   Phth=NCHCO—NHR
     | \ | | |
    CH₂   O   MeOH   CH₂   SOCl₂   CH₂   NH₂R   CH₂
     | /   ──────→ | ─────→ | ──────→ |
    CH₂CO   CH₂CO₂Me   CH₂CO₂Me   CH₂CO₂Me
    CLVIII   CLIX   CLX   CLXI

mediated conversion of the methyl ester derivative to the corresponding acid chloride (CLX), followed by interaction of the latter with an amino acid ester, yielded the desired α-glutamyl peptide derivative (CLXI) (procedure 10–145). In an alternative approach, advantage may be taken of the steric hindrance imposed by the bulky trityl group in order to procure the essential half-ester intermediates (CLXII and CLXV). The hindrance permits the facile preparation of the α-esters of tritylglutamic and aspartic acids (CLXII; $x = 1$ or 2) by virtue of the protection against saponification which it affords to the α-ester moiety of α,ω-diesters of tritylglutamic and aspartic acids (CLXIII; $x = 1$ or 2) under conditions that induce rapid hydrolysis at the ω-ester position (675, 790); additionally, treatment of dibenzyl trityl-L-glutamate (CLXIII; $R = C_6H_5CH_2$, $x = 2$) with methanolic sodium methoxide leads to (CLXIV), which undergoes ready hydrogenolysis to trityl-L-glutamic acid α-methyl ester in the presence of palladium catalyst (675).

Trityl—NHCHCO₂R   OH⁻   Trityl—NHCHCO₂R   NaOMe
        | ←────── | ──────→
     (CH₂)ₓCO₂H   (CH₂)ₓCO₂R
        CLXII   CLXIII

Trityl—NHCHCO₂Me   H₂   Trityl—NHCHCO₂Me
        | ──────→ |
     (CH₂)₂CO₂CH₂C₆H₅   Pd   (CH₂)₂CO₂H
        CLXIV   CLXV

The tritylated half-esters so derived have been utilized with particular success in the preparation of asparaginyl, glutaminyl, and isoglutaminyl peptides (790). It might further be noted that β-aspartyl and γ-glutamyl peptide derivatives are likewise available through analogous use of the α-ethyl ester derivatives of trifluoroacetyl-L-aspartic and glutamic acids which, in turn, arise from the action of ethanol on the corresponding trifluoroacetylamino acid anhydride (477, 576). Although the γ-methyl ester of tosylglutamic acid may be secured in pure form via methanolysis of the lactam bond of tosylpyroglutamic acid with a methanolic solution of sodium methoxide, this derivative has not been hitherto involved in the synthesis of glutamyl peptides.

Illustrative procedure 10–144 (533). Phthalyl-L-glutamic acid γ-methyl ester. The addition of 15 g. of phthalyl-L-glutamic anhydride (procedure 10–134) to

200 ml. of methanol is followed, after the solid has completely dissolved, by boiling the solution for some 15 min. and subsequently evaporating the reaction mixture to dryness under reduced pressure. Crystallization of the solid residue from benzene-petroleum ether yields the desired product as prisms; yield, 13.5 g. (80%); m.p. 135–136°. The melting point is raised to 136–137° after recrystallization from ethyl acetate-petroleum ether; $[\alpha]_D^{20} = -40.5°$ (2.7% in chloroform).

Illustrative procedure 10–145 (533). Phthalyl-α-L-glutamylglycine dimethyl ester. A solution of 2 g. of phthalyl-L-glutamic acid γ-methyl ester (procedure 10–144) in 6 ml. of thionyl chloride is permitted to stand at room temperature for 14 hr., after which time the excess thionyl chloride is removed by distillation under reduced pressure. Removal of the last traces of thionyl chloride is effected by two more distillations after the addition of dry benzene. The residual syrupy acid chloride is dissolved in 15 ml. of dry benzene and the resulting solution added dropwise to a stirred solution of 0.9 g. of glycine methyl ester hydrochloride and 2.1 ml. of triethylamine in 10 ml. of dry chloroform. After storage overnight, the solvent is removed under reduced pressure and the residue is washed successively with water, aqueous sodium hydrogen carbonate, and water. The desired product is crystallized from ethyl acetate-petroleum ether; yield, 2.2 g. (85%); m.p. 80–82°. Recrystallization from the same solvent mixture raises the melting point to 82–83°; $[\alpha]_D^{21} = -3.1°$ (1.4% in chloroform).

Although the aforementioned use of half-ester derivatives seemingly provides an unequivocal route to aspartyl and glutamyl peptides of known structure, the danger of isomerization nevertheless exists under certain conditions. Thus it was pointed out by Cason (893) in 1948 that the acid chlorides derived from monoesters of aliphatic dicarboxylic acids exhibit a marked propensity to undergo ready isomerization with the interchange of the alkoxy group and the chlorine atom. A case in point is the ready rearrangement to a mixture of the two structural isomers (CLXVII and CLXVIII) shown by either of the ester acid chlorides related to the two half-esters of α-butyl-α-ethylglutaric acid (CLXVI) upon storage; the acid chlorides were not identified as such but rather were converted to the corresponding keto esters (CLXIX and CLXX) prior to the isolation step. As the danger of comparable isomerization presumably exists where the half-

$$\underset{\text{CLXVI}}{\begin{array}{c}\text{CO}_2\text{CH}_3\\|\\(\text{CH}_2)_2\\|\\\text{C}_2\text{H}_5\overset{|}{\text{C}}\text{C}_4\text{H}_9\\|\\\text{CO}_2\text{H}\end{array}} \xrightarrow{\text{SOCl}_2} \underset{\text{CLXVII}}{\begin{array}{c}\text{CO}_2\text{CH}_3\\|\\(\text{CH}_2)_2\\|\\\text{C}_2\text{H}_5\overset{|}{\text{C}}\text{C}_4\text{H}_9\\|\\\text{COCl}\end{array}} + \underset{\text{CLXVIII}}{\begin{array}{c}\text{COCl}\\|\\(\text{CH}_2)_2\\|\\\text{C}_2\text{H}_5\overset{|}{\text{C}}\text{C}_4\text{H}_9\\|\\\text{CO}_2\text{CH}_3\end{array}} \xrightarrow{(\text{C}_4\text{H}_9)_2\text{Cd}} \underset{\text{CLXIX}}{\begin{array}{c}\text{CO}_2\text{CH}_3\\|\\(\text{CH}_2)_2\\|\\\text{C}_2\text{H}_5\overset{|}{\text{C}}\text{C}_4\text{H}_9\\|\\\text{COC}_4\text{H}_9\end{array}} + \underset{\text{CLXX}}{\begin{array}{c}\text{COC}_4\text{H}_9\\|\\(\text{CH}_2)_2\\|\\\text{C}_2\text{H}_5\overset{|}{\text{C}}\text{C}_4\text{H}_9\\|\\\text{CO}_2\text{CH}_3\end{array}}$$

ester of an acylated glutamic or aspartic acid is involved, use of the acid chloride method is best avoided; unfortunately, little knowledge is as yet available regarding the extent of rearrangement, if any, which occurs with other coupling procedures. That rearrangement may also take place during alkaline degradation of the condensation product was demonstrated by Battersby and Robinson (893). This phenomenon arises from the fact that either of the structural isomers, (CLXXI) or (CLXXII), may be transformed into the same imide structure (CLXXIII) which, in turn, may then undergo hydrolysis in both possible directions to yield a mixture of isomeric products (CLXXIV and CLXXV). It would therefore be well advised to employ the benzyl esters, which can be cleaved by catalytic hydrogenolysis, wherever possible.

$$\begin{array}{c}
\text{—NHCHCO}_2\text{R} \\
\mid \\
(\text{CH}_2)_x\text{CO—NH—} \\
\text{CLXXI}
\end{array} \xrightarrow{OH^-} \begin{array}{c}
\text{—NHCH——CO} \\
\mid \quad\quad\quad \searrow \\
\quad\quad\quad\quad\quad \text{N—} \\
\quad\quad\quad\quad\quad\nearrow \\
(\text{CH}_2)_x\text{—CO} \\
\text{CLXXIII}
\end{array} \xleftarrow{OH^-} \begin{array}{c}
\text{—NHCHCO—NH—} \\
\mid \\
(\text{CH}_2)_x\text{CO}_2\text{R} \\
\text{CLXXII}
\end{array}$$

$$\begin{array}{c}
\text{—NHCHCO}_2\text{H} \\
\mid \\
(\text{CH}_2)_x\text{CO—NH—} \\
\text{CLXXIV}
\end{array} \xleftarrow{OH^-} \quad\quad\quad \xrightarrow{OH^-} \begin{array}{c}
\text{—NHCHCO—NH—} \\
\mid \\
(\text{CH}_2)_x\text{CO}_2\text{H} \\
\text{CLXXV}
\end{array}$$

(c) *Syntheses involving half-azide intermediates.* A third approach directed toward the combination of either the α- or the γ-carboxyl group of glutamic acid in peptide linkage with another amino acid residue was independently introduced during 1948–1950 by Hegedüs (606) and by Le Quesne and Young (691). This approach involves the use of an acylated glutamic acid wherein one carboxyl function remains free while the other is converted to its hydrazide derivative. Preparation of the α- and γ-hydrazide derivatives of carbobenzoxy-L-glutamic acid (CLXXVII and CLXXXI) may be readily achieved upon treatment of the precursor methyl or ethyl ester (CLXXVI and CLXXX; $R^1 = CH_3$ or C_2H_5) with hydrazine (procedure 10–146) (606, 691, 692). For the purposes of coupling, the pertinent half-hydrazide (CLXXVII or CLXXXI) is first converted to the corresponding azide derivative (CLXXVIII or CLXXXII) by the action of nitrous acid and then treated with a suitably constituted amine (see procedure 10–61). Although such reaction route was first successfully employed by Hegedüs (606) for the synthesis of glutathione and has since been applied by others (605, 606, 679, 691–693), the desired α- or γ-glutamyl peptide derivatives (CLXXIX and CLXXXIII) are not invariably isolated as the sole products. That mixtures of α- and γ-glutamyl peptide derivatives may indeed arise from coupling reactions which involve the γ-azide of carbobenzoxyglutamic acid was shown by Sachs and Brand (724); the mechanism whereby rearrangement may occur has been discussed previously (Section 10–26) and need not be reiterated here. However, this difficulty is not always encountered, although the exact conditions under which the reaction proceeds with the formation of a single isomer on the one hand, or a mixture of the isomeric α- and γ-derivatives on the other, are still obscure. A variation

$$\underset{\text{CLXXVI}}{\overset{\text{RCO—NHCHCO}_2\text{R}^1}{\underset{(\text{CH}_2)_2\text{CO}_2\text{H}}{|}}} \xrightarrow{\text{NH}_2\text{NH}_2} \underset{\text{CLXXVII}}{\overset{\text{RCO—NHCHCONHNH}_2}{\underset{(\text{CH}_2)_2\text{CO}_2\text{H}}{|}}} \xrightarrow{\text{HNO}_2}$$

$$\underset{\text{CLXXVIII}}{\overset{\text{RCO—NHCHCON}_3}{\underset{(\text{CH}_2)_2\text{CO}_2\text{H}}{|}}} \xrightarrow{\text{NH}_2\text{R}^2} \underset{\text{CLXXIX}}{\overset{\text{RCO—NHCHCO—NHR}^2}{\underset{(\text{CH}_2)_2\text{CO}_2\text{H}}{|}}}$$

$$\underset{\text{CLXXX}}{\overset{\text{RCO—NHCHCO}_2\text{H}}{\underset{(\text{CH}_2)_2\text{CO}_2\text{R}^1}{|}}} \xrightarrow{\text{NH}_2\text{NH}_2} \underset{\text{CLXXXI}}{\overset{\text{RCO—NHCHCO}_2\text{H}}{\underset{(\text{CH}_2)_2\text{CONHNH}_2}{|}}} \xrightarrow{\text{HNO}_2}$$

$$\underset{\text{CLXXXII}}{\overset{\text{RCO—NHCHCO}_2\text{H}}{\underset{(\text{CH}_2)_2\text{CON}_3}{|}}} \xrightarrow{\text{NH}_2\text{R}^2} \underset{\text{CLXXXIII}}{\overset{\text{RCO—NHCHCO}_2\text{H}}{\underset{(\text{CH}_2)_2\text{CO—NHR}^2}{|}}}$$

of the above approach which might prove less erratic involves the conversion of the free carboxyl group of the reactant half-hydrazide (CLXXVII or CLXXXI) to its ester derivative prior to the nitrous acid treatment. Such a reaction route was successfully utilized by Sorm and Rudinger (894), who treated the α-methyl ester γ-azide derivative of carbobenzoxy-L-glutamic acid with both ethyl glycinate and ethyl tyrosinate to obtain the desired peptide derivatives.

Illustrative procedure 10–146 (692). Carbobenzoxy-γ-L-glutamyl hydrazide. Carbobenzoxy-L-glutamic acid γ-ethyl ester is first prepared as follows (367): To a mixture of 40 g. of γ-ethyl L-glutamate (procedure 10–50) and 40 g. of sodium bicarbonate in 600 ml. of water, cooled in a salt-ice bath, is added 40 ml. of carbobenzoxy chloride (procedure 10–27). The reaction mixture is stirred at 0° to −5° for 3 hr. and at room temperature for an additional 2 hr., extracted with ether, and the aqueous layer acidified with hydrochloric acid. The product is then extracted into ether, the ethereal extracts concentrated to dryness, and the residual material recrystallized twice from carbon tetrachloride; yield, 47 g.; m.p. 87°. To 35 g. of the carbobenzoxy-L-glutamic acid γ-ethyl ester so procured is added 35 ml. of 85% hydrazine hydrate, and the mixture heated over a steam bath for 15 min. After the addition of 700 ml. of ice-cold water to the reaction mixture the solution is acidified to pH 1 with 6N hydrochloric acid and then quickly readjusted to pH 3.8 with 10N sodium hydroxide. The desired hydrazide, which begins to crystallize immediately, is filtered off after some 4 hr. storage at 4°. Recrystallization is effected from the minimal amount of boiling water; yield, 26 g.; m.p. 177–178°.

40. Physical Constants of Acylated Peptide Esters. The coupling procedures described above (Sections 10–26 to 10–39) have been implicated in

CHEMICAL PROCEDURES FOR SYNTHESIS OF PEPTIDES

the preparation of hundreds of acylated peptide esters of most diverse type. Table 10–42 lists the melting point and optical rotation data of a major portion of the methyl, ethyl, and benzyl ester derivatives of N-acylated peptides with selectively removable N-acyl blocking groups (Sections 10–13 and 10–21) which had been described up to the end of 1958. The compilation should by no means be considered complete, but rather as representative of the various types of derivatives which are synthetically available. Where two or more separate groups of investigators have described the same compound, an *italicized reference number* in the tables of this chapter identifies the group from which the physical constants were selected. If, however, gross differences in the melting point or optical rotation values are reported by independent investigators, alternative values are cited in a footnote to the table   In any event, the possibility should be continually borne in mind that acylated peptide esters may occasionally exist as dimorphic forms which exhibit different melting points; these forms should, of course, exhibit the same optical rotation values.

Abbreviations for the compounds listed in Table 10–42 have been defined in Table 10–1; abbreviations for additional amino acid residues are: α-amino-n-butyric acid, α-NH$_2$-n-But; α-aminoisobutyric acid, α-NH$_2$-isoBut; nitroarginine, NO$_2$-Arg; S-benzylcysteine, CySBz; the γ-benzyl, γ-methyl, and γ-ethyl esters of glutamic acid, Glu-OBz, Glu-OMe, and Glu-OEt; γ-hydroxyglutamic acid, γ-OH-Glu; δ-hydroxylysine, δ-OH-Lys; isovaline, Ival; phenylserine, Phser; 3:4-dihydroxyphenylalanine, 3:4-di-OH-Phe; α,ε-diaminopimelic acid, α,ε-diNH$_2$-Pim; O-acetylserine, O-Ac-Ser; O-benzylserine, O-Bz-Ser; O-acetyltyrosine, O-Ac-Tyr; O-benzoyltyrosine, O-Bzoyl-Tyr; O-benzyltyrosine, O-Bz-Tyr; 3:5-diiodotyrosine, I$_2$-Tyr. Use of such abbreviations for the representation of peptide structures has been described in Section 10–1. Compounds which incorporate monoaminodicarboxylic acid residues, i.e., glutamic and aspartic acids, deserve added consideration. Thus, the abbreviation Glu-NH$_2$ is used to designate the glutaminyl residue (—NHCH(CH$_2$CH$_2$CONH$_2$)CO—), where a *hyphen* between Glu and NH$_2$ denotes combination by way of the γ-carboxyl function. The isoglutamine residue

(NH$_2$CH(CH$_2$CH$_2$CO$_2$H)CONH$_2$)

on the other hand, is denoted by Glu·NH$_2$, where a *center dot* between Glu and NH$_2$ represents a linkage at the α-carboxyl function. Glutamine and isoglutamine thereupon become H·(Glu-NH$_2$)·OH and H·Glu·NH$_2$ respectively. According to this scheme, compounds such as glycylglutaminylglycine and glycylisoglutaminylglycine would be designated H·Gly·(Glu-NH$_2$)·Gly·OH and H·Gly·(Glu-Gly·OH)·NH$_2$ or H·Gly·Glu·NH$_2$ respec-
└—Gly·OH
tively, while glycyl-α-glutamylglycine and glycyl-γ-glutamylglycine would

be designated H·Gly·Glu·Gly·OH for the former compound and H·Gly·(Glu-Gly·OH)·OH or H·Gly·Glu·OH for the latter. In like manner, the α- and
$$\overset{\llcorner}{\text{—Gly·OH}}$$
γ-ethyl esters of glutamic acid become H·Glu·OEt and H·(Glu-OEt)·OH respectively. Analogous formulations prevail for derivatives involving the α- and β-carboxyl groups of aspartic acid.

The compounds given in Table 10-42 (pp. 1112 to 1148) are categorized in the following order according to the N-acyl substituents which they bear:

1. N-benzyl (or N,N-dibenzyl)
2. benzylsulfonyl
3. benzylthiocarbonyl
4. carbobenzoxy
5. carboallyloxy
6. *p*-nitrocarbobenzoxy
7. carbo-*t*-butyloxy
8. carbo*cyclo*pentyloxy
9. carbo*cyclo*hexyloxy
10. phenylthiocarbonyl
11. phthalyl
12. *p*-toluenesulfonyl
13. triphenylmethyl
14. *o*-nitrophenoxyacetyl

Each compound within a given category is arranged in alphabetical order according to the parent name of the amino acid residue most closely adjacent to the N-acyl substituent. The widespread preference for the carbobenzoxy group is strikingly evidenced by the fact that the derivatives which incorporate this acyl substituent form some 75% of the total listed, whereas the next most frequently employed blocking groups, i.e., phthalyl and tosyl, number less than 6% each. Included in the table are only those compounds which are well-defined and which have been well-characterized. Epimeric mixtures such as ethyl carbobenzoxy-DL-leucyl-L-leucinate and methyl phthalyl-L-alanyl-DL-valinate have been deliberately omitted, as these are neither pure compounds nor do they reveal the physical characteristics of pure compounds. Thus, for example, although the former epimeric mixture may possess elemental values which attest to its analytical purity, it will none the less exhibit an optical rotation value which falls somewhere between the values shown by the optically pure D-L and L-L stereomers, according to the proportion of each of the two stereochemical forms present. It is somewhat ironical that, despite the ready availability of optically pure amino acids as starting materials, descriptions of the synthesis of such epimeric materials accompanied by carefully done elemental analyses, melting points, and optical rotation data are common even in the current chemical literature.

41. Preparation and Physical Constants of Acylated Amino Acid and Peptide Amides. Amide derivatives of acylated amino acids or peptides (III; $R^3 = H$) may be generally procured through two alternative synthetic routes. The first is concerned with the condensation of an acylated amino acid or peptide (I; $R^2 = H$) with ammonia (II; $R^3 = H$), an amino acid amide (II; $R^3 = CHR^4CONH_2$), or a peptide amide via an appropriate coupling procedure; inasmuch as application of such a route involves essentially the same techniques as were employed in the above-described syntheses of acylated peptide esters (Sections 10–26 to 10–39), its further elaboration is not necessitated here. The second method involves the

$$-\text{NHCHR}^1\text{CO}_2\text{R}^2 + \text{NH}_2\text{R}^3 \rightarrow -\text{NHCHR}^1\text{CO}-\text{NHR}^3$$
$$\text{I} \qquad\qquad \text{II} \qquad\qquad \text{III}$$

ammonolysis of the methyl, ethyl, or benzyl ester derivative of an acylated amino acid or peptide (I; $R^2 = CH_3$, C_2H_5, or $C_6H_5CH_2$). In routine practice, the pertinent acylated-ester (see Tables 10–32 and 10–42) is dissolved in 10–20 volumes of methanol previously saturated with ammonia gas at zero to $-5°$, and the reaction mixture is then permitted to stand in a sealed vessel at room temperature for several days, during which time the desired amide is formed (procedure 10–147). It is often expedient from the vantage points of convenience and over-all yield to effect the ammonolysis reaction without prior crystallization or purification of the acylated-ester intermediate (procedure 10–148). Where the ester reactant either possesses limited solubility in methanolic NH_3 or is not susceptible to ready ammonolytic cleavage by this medium, the use of other systems such as ethanolic NH_3 or liquid ammonia may occasionally prove more fruitful. Although the reaction rate is markedly accelerated by an elevation of the temperature, such a condition at the same time leads to an increased danger of cleavage at the peptide bonds, especially with the highly labile longer chain polypeptides. In any event, the relative rates at which the various acylated esters undergo ammonolysis are conditioned in part by the degree of steric hindrance imposed by the side-chain moiety of the C-terminal amino acid residue and, in the case of N-acylated amino acid esters, by the N-acyl blocking substituent. Thus, for example, a greater susceptibility to attack by ammonia is exhibited where the side chain of the amino acid residue bearing the ester group affords little hindrance as in glycine or alanine, rather than appreciable hindrance as in valine or isoleucine; additionally, the virtually complete resistance to the action of ammonia generally revealed by N-tritylated amino acid esters is not encountered with the corresponding N-carbobenzoxy analogs which possess a less bulky N-acyl substituent.

Illustrative procedure 10–147 (916). Carbobenzoxyglycyl-L-tyrosine amide. A solution of 7.8 g. of carbobenzoxyglycyl-L-tyrosine ethyl ester (procedure 10–80) in 75 ml. of methanol, previously saturated with ammonia gas at 0°, is stored in a pressure bottle at room temperature for 2 days. After this time, the reaction mixture is concentrated under reduced pressure and a temperature not exceeding 40° to a syrupy residue which crystallizes from ethanol-water; yield, 5.3 g.; m.p. 170°.

Illustrative procedure 10–148 (916). Carbobenzoxy-L-phenylalanine amide. An excess of solid sodium carbonate is added to a solution of 10 g. of L-phenylalanine ethyl ester hydrochloride (procedure 10–48) in the minimal amount of water

(*discussion continued on p. 1149*)

TABLE 10-42
Acylated Peptide Esters

Compound	Config.	M.P., °C.	$[\alpha]_D$, deg.	Temp., °C.	Concn. and Solvent	Ref.
N-Benzyl (Bz) derivatives						
N-Bz·Asp·Gly·OEt	DL	146	—	—	—	555
N-Bz·Asp·OH	DL	140[a]	—	—	—	555, 558
└─Gly·OEt						
N-Bz·Asp·β-Ala·OEt	DL	140	—	—	—	895
N,N-diBz·(α-NH₂-n-But)·Gly·OEt	DL	140	—	—	—	552
N,N-diBz·Gly·Glu·(OEt)₂	L	120–122	—	—	—	552
N,N-diBz·Gly₂·OEt	—	160–161	—	—	—	552
N,N-diBz·Gly·Ser·OEt	DL	160	—	—	—	552
N,N-diBz·Gly·Try·OMe	DL	120	—	—	—	552
N,N-diBz·Gly·Val·OEt	DL	140–145	—	—	—	552
Benzylsulfonyl (BzSO₂) derivative						
BzSO₂·Leu₂·OEt	L-L	122–123	−48.7	27	3.3%, EtOH	601
Benzylthiocarbonyl (BzTC) derivatives						
BzTC·Ala·Gly·OEt	DL	120–121	—	—	—	580
BzTC·Ala·Gly·OEt	L	105–106	—	—	—	580
BzTC·Gly₂·OEt	—	119–120	—	—	—	580
BzTC·Gly·Phe·OEt	DL	108–109	—	—	—	580
Carbobenzoxy (Cbzo) derivatives						
Cbzo·Ala₂·OBz	L-L	138	—	—	—	666

Cbzo·Ala$_2$·OEt	D-D	116	—	—	—	666
Cbzo·Ala$_2$·OEt	D-L	92	—	—	—	666
Cbzo·Ala$_2$·OEt	L-D	92	—	—	—	666
Cbzo·Ala$_2$·OEt	L-L	116	—	—	—	666, 896
Cbzo·Ala$_3$·OBz	3 D	201.5	—	—	—	703
Cbzo·Ala$_3$·OBz	D-L-L	173	—	—	—	703
Cbzo·Ala$_3$·OBz	L-D-L	148–149	—	—	—	703
Cbzo·Ala$_3$·OBz	L-L-D	180.5	—	—	—	703
Cbzo·Ala$_3$·OBz	3 L	201.5	—	—	—	703
Cbzo·Ala$_3$·OEt	L-D-L	142	—	—	—	703
Cbzo·Ala$_3$·OEt	L-L-D	176	—	—	—	703
Cbzo·Ala$_3$·OEt	3 L	192	—	—	—	703
Cbzo·Ala$_4$·OBz	D-3 L	191–192	—	—	—	897
Cbzo·Ala$_4$·OBz	L-D-2 L	181.5	—	—	—	897
Cbzo·Ala$_4$·OBz	2 L-D-L	213–214	—	—	—	897
Cbzo·Ala$_4$·OBz	4 L	246	—	—	—	897
Cbzo·Ala$_5$·OBz	5 L	254	—	—	—	897
Cbzo·Ala$_6$·OBz	6 L	>260 d.	—	—	—	897
Cbzo·Ala·(α-NH$_2$-n-But)·OEt	L-L	77	—	—	—	468
Cbzo·Ala·Glu-NH$_2$·OMe	L-L	154–156	—	—	—	619
Cbzo·Ala·Glu·OBz	D-L	132–135	+4.8	24	1.7%, HOAc	891
Cbzo·Ala·Glu·OBz	L-L	147–149	−21.2	24	1.6%, HOAc	891
Cbzo·Ala·Glu·(OBz)$_2$	D-L	112–113	+3.8	23	2%, HOAc	898
Cbzo·Ala·Glu·(OBz)$_2$	L-D	112–113	−3.7	23	2%, HOAc	898
Cbzo·Ala·Glu·(OBz)$_2$	L-L	104–105	−16.6	23	2%, HOAc	898
Cbzo·Ala·Glu·OBz	D-L	169–171	+19.7	24	2%, HOAc	891
└─Ala·OBz	D					
Cbzo·Ala·Glu·OBz	D-L	156–158	−7.9	24	2%, HOAc	891
└─Ala·OBz	L					

TABLE 10-42 (*continued*)

Compound	Config.	M.P., °C.	[α]$_D$, deg.	Temp., °C.	Concn. and Solvent	Ref.
Carbobenzoxy (Cbzo) derivatives (*continued*)						
Cbzo·Ala·Glu·OBz ⌐Ala·OBz	L-L D	148–150	+4.0	23	2%, HOAc	891
Cbzo·Ala·Glu·OBz ⌐Ala·OBz	L-L L	150–151	−28.8	23	2%, HOAc	891
Cbzo·Ala·Gly·OBz	D	112	—	—	—	666
Cbzo·Ala·Gly·OBz	L	111	—	—	—	666
Cbzo·Ala·Gly·OEt	DL	81	—	—	—	723, 740, 769 769a, 774
Cbzo·Ala·Gly·OEt	D	98	—	—	—	466
Cbzo·Ala·Gly·OEt	L	97.5–98	−24.4	20	1.0%, EtOH	466, 613a, 666 808b
Cbzo·β-Ala·Gly·OEt	—	95–96	—	—	—	899
Cbzo·Ala·Gly·OMe	DL	74–76	—	—	—	900
Cbzo·Ala·Gly·Ala·Gly·OBz	D-D	204–205	+20.3	25	1%, MeOH	704
Cbzo·Ala·Gly·Ala·Gly·OBz	L-L	202–204	−20.5	25	1%, MeOH	704
Cbzo·Ala·Gly$_2$·OBz	D	116	—	—	—	705
Cbzo·Ala·Gly$_2$·OBz	L	114–116	—	—	—	705
Cbzo·Ala·Gly$_2$·OEt	DL	113	—	—	—	769a
Cbzo·Ala·Gly·Val·CySBz·OBz	3 L	186–187	−53.8	20	1%, HOAc	875c
Cbzo·β-Ala·His·Gly·OEt	L	154–156	—	—	—	621
Cbzo·β-Ala·His$_2$·OMe	L-L	160–161	—	—	—	621
Cbzo·Ala·Leu·OMe	D-L	72–73	−9	27	1%, EtOH	467

Compound	Config.	M.p.	[α]	%	Solvent	Ref.
Cbzo·Ala·(Nε-Cbzo-Lys)·OMe	D-L	130	—	—	—	667
Cbzo·Ala·(Nε-Cbzo-Lys)·OMe	L-D	128	—	—	—	667
Cbzo·Ala·(Nε-Cbzo-Lys)·OMe	L-L	90	—	—	—	667
Cbzo·Ala·(Nε-Cbzo-Lys)·Ala·OBz	L-2 D	173–174	—	—	—	706
Cbzo·Ala·(Nε-Cbzo-Lys)·Ala·OBz	L-D-L	160–161	—	—	—	706
Cbzo·Ala·(Nε-Cbzo-Lys)·Ala·OBz	3 L	183–184	—	—	—	706
Cbzo·Ala·(Nε-Cbzo-Lys)·Ala·OEt	3 L	191–192	—	—	—	706
Cbzo·Ala·(Nε-Cbzo-Lys)·Ala$_2$·OBz	L-D-2 L	166–167	—	—	—	901
Cbzo·Ala·(Nε-Cbzo-Lys)·Ala$_2$·OBz	4 L	198	—	—	—	901
Cbzo·Ala·(Nε-Cbzo-Lys)·Ala$_3$·OBz	L-D-3 L	213–214	—	—	—	901
Cbzo·Ala·(Nε-Cbzo-Lys)·Ala$_3$·OBz	5 L	238–239	—	—	—	901
Cbzo·Ala·Gly·Phe·OEt	L-L	123–124	—	—	—	902
Cbzo·Ala·Nval·OEt	D-L	90	—	—	—	468
Cbzo·Ala·Nval·OEt	L-L	108	—	—	—	468
Cbzo·Ala·Phe·OEt	L-L	97–98	—	—	—	808b, 903
Cbzo·β-Ala·Phe·OEt	DL	88–89	—	—	—	899
Cbzo·Ala·Ser·OMe	L-L	134–135	—	—	—	432a, 631
Cbzo·Ala·Ser·Val·CySBz·OBz	4 L	187–188	—	—	—	432a
Cbzo·Ala·Tyr·OEt	D-L	105–107	—	—	—	660
Cbzo·Ala·Tyr·OEt	L-L	138–139	—	—	—	903
Cbzo·Ala·(O-Ac-Tyr)·Gly·OEt	L-L	178–178.5	—	—	—	495
Cbzo·(α-NH$_2$-n-But)·Gly·OEt	L	114	−25	16	2.7%, EtOH	58
Cbzo·(α-NH$_2$-n-But)·Phe·OEt	L-L	94–95	—	—	—	660
α,ω,ω-triCbzo·Arg·Ala·OBz	L-L	171–172	—	—	—	904
Cbzo·NO$_2$-Arg·Ala·OBz	L-L	163–164	−23.5	26	2%, HOAc	845
Cbzo·NO$_2$-Arg·β-Ala·OBz	L	142–143	−9.2	26	2%, HOAc	845
Cbzo·NO$_2$-Arg·Ala·OMe	L-L	157–159	−18.8	25	1%, MeOH	491
α,ω,ω-triCbzo·Arg·(ω-Cbzo-Arg)·OBz	L-L	162–164	—	—	—	459, 850, 904
α,ω,ω-triCbzo·Arg·(ω-Cbzo-Arg)·OMe	L-L	135	—	—	—	459

TABLE 10-42 (continued)

Compound Carbobenzoxy (Cbzo) derivatives (continued)	Config.	M.P., °C.	[α]_D, deg.	Temp., °C.	Concn. and Solvent	Ref.
α,ω,ω-triCbzo·Arg·Asp·(OBz)₂	L-L	159–160	—	—	—	904
Cbzo·NO₂·Arg·Asp·(OBz)₂	L-L	114–115	+2.0	20	2%, HOAc	845
Cbzo·NO₂·Arg·Asp·(OEt)₂	L-L	122–123	−3.8	19	2%, acetone	845
Cbzo·NO₂·Arg·Glu·(OBz)₂	L-L	107–109	−11.0	26	2%, HOAc	845
α,ω,ω-triCbzo·Arg·Glu·(OBz)₂	L-L	120–121	—	—	—	459
Cbzo·NO₂·Arg·Glu·(OEt)₂	L-L	110–111	−7.5	19	2%, acetone	491, 541, 845
α,ω,ω-triCbzo·Arg·Gly·OBz	L	118–120	—	—	—	904
Cbzo·NO₂·Arg·Gly·OBz	L	152–154	−13.9	25	1%, MeOH	541, 678
Cbzo·NO₂·Arg·Gly·OEt	L	124–126	—	—	—	541
Cbzo·NO₂·Arg·Gly·OMe	L	70–73	−13.8	29	3.6%, MeOH	491
α,ω,ω-triCbzo·Arg·allo-Ileu·OBz	L-D	128–130	—	—	—	904
α,ω,ω-triCbzo·Arg·Ileu·OBz	L-L	147–150	—	—	—	904
α,ω,ω-triCbzo·Arg·Leu·OBz	L-L	158–160	—	—	—	904
Cbzo·NO₂·Arg·Leu·OBz	L-L	154–155	−22.1	26	2%, HOAc	845
Cbzo·NO₂·Arg·Leu·OMe	L-L	162–163.4	−23.4	30	1%, MeOH	491, 541
Cbzo·Arg·Leu·OMe·HBr·H₂O	L-L	90–92	−20.3	23	2%, MeOH	471
Cbzo·Arg·Leu·OMe·HCl	L-L	92–94	−21.6	25	2%, MeOH	758
α,ω,ω-triCbzo·Arg·Phe·OBz	L-L	168–170	—	—	—	904
Cbzo·NO₂·Arg·Phe·OEt	L-L	141–143	—	—	—	541
Cbzo·NO₂·Arg·Phe·OMe	L-L	132–133	−8.2	25	1.2%, MeOH	491
Cbzo·Arg·Try·OMe·HCl	L-L	140–150 d.	+5.8	23	2.0%, MeOH	471a

Cbzo·NO₂·Arg·Try·OMe	L-L	83–85	−0.5	29	1.5%, MeOH	491
α,ω,ω-triCbzo·Arg·Tyr·OBz	L-L	166–168	—	—	—	904
Cbzo·NO₂·Arg·Tyr·OBz	L-L	41–43	−4.9	20	2%, HOAc	845
Cbzo·NO₂·Arg·Tyr·OEt	L-L	139–141	—	—	—	541
Cbzo·NO₂·Arg·Tyr·OMe	L-L	159–160	−3.6	28	1.2%, MeOH	491
α,ω,ω-triCbzo·Arg·Val·OBz	L-L	129–131.5	—	—	—	904
Cbzo·Asp-NH₂·NO₂·Arg·OMe	L-L	170–173	+5	24	2%, HOAc	714
Cbzo·Asp-NH₂·NO₂·Arg·Val·Tyr·OMe	4 L	202–206	−4	23	0.9%, DMF	714
Cbzo·Asp-NH₂·NO₂·Arg·Val·Tyr·Ileu·His·Pro·Phe·OMe	8 L	190–205	−29	23	0.5%, DMF	714
Cbzo·Asp-NH₂·NO₂·Arg·Val·Tyr·Val·His·Pro·Phe·OMe	8 L	205–210 d.	−27	—	–, DMF	718a
Cbzo·Asp-NH₂·NO₂·Arg·Val·Tyr·Val·His·Pro·Phe·His·Leu·OMe	10 L	180–195 d.	−55	—	0.7%, MeOH (0.01 N in HCl)	638a
Cbzo·Asp-NH₂·CySBz·OBz	L-L	185–187	—	—	—	674
Cbzo·Asp-NH₂·CySBz·OEt	L-L	188–190	—	—	—	674
Cbzo·Asp-NH₂·CySBz·OMe	L-L	196	−31.9	19	2.4%, pyridine	472, 482a, 791a, 868, 906
Cbzo·Asp-NH₂·Gly·OBz	L	181–183	—	—	—	482
Cbzo·Asp-NH₂·Gly·OEt	L	184–185	—	—	—	674
Cbzo·Asp-NH₂·Leu·OBz	L-L	154	—	—	—	672
Cbzo·Asp-NH₂·Ser·OMe	L-L	139–140	—	—	—	907
Cbzo·Asp-NH₂·Ser·Gly·OEt	L-L	139–140	—	—	—	907
Cbzo·Asp·OBz└─Ala·OMe	L L	102	—	—	—	908
Cbzo·Asp·OMe·NO₂·Arg·Val·Tyr·Ileu·His·Pro·Phe·OMe	8 L	188–192	−32.5	25	0.5%, DMF	508

TABLE 10-42 (continued)

Compound	Config.	M.P., °C.	$[\alpha]_D$, deg.	Temp., °C.	Concn. and Solvent	Ref.
Carbobenzoxy (Cbzo) derivatives (continued)						
Cbzo·Asp·OBz	L	160	—	—	—	474
└CyS·OEt	L					
┌CyS·OEt	L					
Cbzo·Asp·OBz	L					
Cbzo·Asp·CySBz·OEt	L-L	114–116	—	—	—	674
Cbzo·Asp·OH	L	146–147	—	—	—	674
└CySBz·OEt	L					
Cbzo·Asp·Glu·(OEt)$_2$·H$_2$O	L-L	82–84	—	—	—	609
Cbzo·Asp·OBz	L	153	—	—	—	727
└CySBz·Gly·OMe	L					
Cbzo·Asp·OH·H$_2$O	L	71–73	—	—	—	609
└Glu·(OEt)$_2$	L					
Cbzo·Asp·Gly·(OBz)$_2$	L	98	—	—	—	672
Cbzo·Asp·OBz	L	101	—	—	—	726
└Gly·OEt	L					
Cbzo·Asp·Gly·OBz	L	164	—	—	—	726
└Gly·OBz	L					
Cbzo·Asp·Gly·OEt	L	120–122[b]	—	—	—	609, 726, 878
Cbzo·Asp·OH	L	122–124	—	—	—	609
└Gly·OEt	L					

Cbzo·Asp·His·OMe	L-L	95–105 d.	—	—	—	838
Cbzo·Asp-OBz·(N$^\alpha$-Tos-Lys)·OBz	L-L	120–122	—	—	—	439a
Cbzo·Asp·Ser·Gly·Glu·(OEt)$_2$	3 L	182	—	—	—	907
Cbzo·Asp·Tyr·OEt	L-L	142–144	—	—	—	609
Cbzo·Asp·OH └─Tyr·OEt	L L	203	—	—	—	128
Cbzo·Asp·OMe·OH └─Tyr·OMe	L L	136	—	—	—	378
Cbzo·Asp·OBz └─Tyr·OEt	L L	128	—	—	—	378
Cbzo·Asp·OH └─Tyr·OEt	L L	200–201	—	—	—	609
Cbzo·Asp·Val·OMe	L-L	102–104	−8.4	19	2.3%, H$_2$O + 1 eq. NaOH	880
Cbzo·Asp·OH └─Val·OMe	L L	163–164.5	−13.3	19	2.2%, H$_2$O + 1 eq. NaOH	880
Cbzo·CyS·Asp·(OEt)$_2$	L-L	145	—	—	—	189
Cbzo·CyS·Asp·(OEt)$_2$	L-L	72–76	—	—	—	189
Cbzo·CyS·CySH·OEt	L-L					
Cbzo·CyS·CySH·OEt	L-L					
Cbzo·CyS·Glu·(OEt)$_2$	L-L	145	—	—	—	189
Cbzo·CyS·Glu·(OEt)$_2$	L-L					
Cbzo·CyS·Glu·(OEt)$_2$	L-L	139	—	—	—	189
Cbzo·CyS·Glu·(OMe)$_2$	L-L					
Cbzo·CyS·Glu·(OMe)$_2$	L-L					

TABLE 10-42 (continued)

Compound	Config.	M.P., °C.	$[\alpha]_D$, deg.	Temp., °C.	Concn. and Solvent	Ref.
Carbobenzoxy (Cbzo) derivatives (continued)						
Cbzo·CyS·Gly·OEt	L	166	—	—	—	10, 128, 477, 495
┌Cbzo·CyS·Gly·OEt	L		—	—	—	
└Cbzo·CyS·Gly·OBz	L	167–168	—	—	—	474
┌Cbzo·CyS·Gly·OBz	L					
└Cbzo·CyS·Tyr·OEt	L-L	168–175	—	—	—	189
Cbzo·CyS·Tyr·OEt	L-L		—	—	—	432a
Cbzo·CySBz·Ala·OEt	L-L	117.5	—	—	—	432a
Cbzo·CySBz·Ala·OMe	L-L	128.5–129	—	—	—	432a
Cbzo·CySBz·Ala·Ser.OMe	3 L	195–196	—	—	—	432a
Cbzo·CySBz·Ala·Ser·Val·CySBz·OBz	5 L	200–202	—	—	—	432a
Cbzo·(CySBz)₂·OBz	L-D	128–129	+2.5	24	1%, acetone	390
Cbzo·(CySBz)₂·OBz	L-L	129–130	−45.0	21	1%, acetone	390
Cbzo·(CySBz)₂·OEt	D-L	103	−4.9	26	2%, acetone	473
Cbzo·(CySBz)₂·OEt	L-D	103	+5.1	26	2%, acetone	473
Cbzo·(CySBz)₂·OEt	L-L	105	−55.3	26	2%, acetone	390, 473
Cbzo·(CySBz)₂·OMe	L-L	140	—	—	—	432a
Cbzo·CySBz·Gly·OEt	L	98–99	−26.8	20	6%, HOAc	390, 432a, 475 759a, 769
Cbzo·CySBz·Gly·OBz	L	127–128	−28.3	19	1%, acetone	432a

Compound	Config	M.p. (°C)	[α]	Conc	Solvent	Ref
Cbzo·CySBz·Gly·CySBz·OBz	L-L	161	−34.7	20	2.6%, dioxane	390
Cbzo·CySBz·Gly·CySBz·OEt	L-L	125–126	—	—	—	390
Cbzo·CySBz·Gly₂·OEt	L	114–115	−12.9	20	3.2%, EtOH	390
Cbzo·CySBz·Gly₂·OMe	L	110	—	—	—	390
Cbzo·CySBz·Gly₂·CySBz·OBz	L-L	175	−29.6	20	2.7%, pyridine	390
Cbzo·CySBz·Gly₂·CySBz·OEt	L-L	135	—	—	—	390
Cbzo·CySBz·Gly₃·OEt	L	122–123	−2.2	20	4.6%, dioxane	390
Cbzo·CySBz·Gly₃·CySBz·OBz	L-L	157–158	−30.6	20	2.9%, dioxane	390
Cbzo·CySBz·Gly₄·CySBz·OBz	L-L	205–206	−29.7	20	1.1%, pyridine	390, 711
Cbzo·CySBz·Gly₅·OBz	L	207	—	—	—	390
Cbzo·CySBz·Gly₅·OEt	L	198–199	—	—	—	390
Cbzo·CySBz·Gly₅·CySBz·OBz	L-L	224–226	−27.2	22	1%, HOAc	472
Cbzo·CySBz·Pro·(Nε-Tos-Lys)·Gly·OEt	3 L	106–109	−26.0	21.5	3%, CHCl₃	393
Cbzo·CySBz·(O-Benzoyl-Tyr)·OEt	L-L	164–166	+26.0	23	4.4%, CHCl₃	646, 804
Cbzo·CySBz·Tyr·OEt	L-L	103–104	+26.0	22	3.4%, CHCl₃	804
Cbzo·CySBz·(O-Bz-Tyr)·OMe	L-L	150·5	—	—	—	830
Cbzo·CySBz·Tyr·OMe	L-L	89	—	—	—	472
Cbzo·CySBz·Tyr·Ileu·OEt	3 L	141–142	−18	21	4%, HOAc	707, 804
Cbzo·CySBz·Tyr·Ileu·OMe	3 L	159.5–160ᵉ	−34.8	23	1.5%, MeOH	472, 623
Cbzo·CySBz·Tyr·Leu·OMe	3 L	128	−39.4	20	2.9%, MeOH	629
Cbzo·CySBz·Tyr·Phe·OMe	3 L	154	−33.7	19	1.5%, MeOH	629
Cbzo·CySBz·Tyr·Val·OMe	3 L	132	−36.4	19	2.9%, MeOH	629, 708
Cbzo·Glu·Ala·OBz	L-D	148–151	+8.8	23	1.3%, HOAc	891
Cbzo·Glu·OBz·Ala·OBz	L-D	120–121	+2.6	23	2%, HOAc	898
Cbzo·Glu·OBz	L	124–125	+14.7	25	2%, HOAc	898
└─Ala·OBz	D					
Cbzo·Glu·Ala·OBz	L-L	153–154	−25.8	25	1.1%, HOAc	891
Cbzo·Glu·OBz·Ala·OBz	L-L	102–104	−21.2	23	2%, HOAc	898

TABLE 10-42 (continued)

Compound	Config.	M.P., °C.	$[\alpha]_D$, deg.	Temp., °C.	Concn. and Solvent	Ref.
Carbobenzoxy (Cbzo) derivatives (continued)						
Cbzo·Glu·OBz └─Ala·OBz	L L	124–126	−16.2	26	2%, HOAc	898
Cbzo·Glu·OH └─Ala·OBz	L L	82–85	—	—	—	692
Cbzo·Glu·OH └─Ala·OEt	L L	112–113	—	—	—	605
Cbzo·Glu·Ala·OEt	L-L	149–150	—	—	—	881
Cbzo·Glu-NH₂·Ala·OEt	L-L	195–197	—	—	—	619
Cbzo·Glu·Ala·OBz └─Ala·OBz	L-D D	169–170	+23.3	23	2%, HOAc	891
Cbzo·Glu·Ala·OBz └─Ala·OBz	L-D L	189–190	−5.9	23	2%, HOAc	891
Cbzo·Glu·Ala·OBz └─Ala·OBz	L-L D	186–187	+3.3	23	2%, HOAc	91
Cbzo·Glu·Ala·OBz └─Ala·OBz	L-L L	200–201	−37.8	28	2%, HOAc	891
Cbzo·Glu·Ala·OBz └─Gly·OBz	L-D	182–183	+11.6	23	2%, HOAc	891
Cbzo·Glu·Ala·OBz └─Gly·OBz	L-L	182–183	−15.7	23	2%, HOAc	891
Cbzo·Glu-NH₂·Asp-NH₂·CySBz·OMe	3 L	239	−38.6	20	2.4%, HOAc	472, 482a, 868
Cbzo·Glu·Asp·(OEt)₂	L-L	118–120	—	—	—	610

Compound		m.p.	[α]	T	solvent	ref
Cbzo·Glu·CySH·OBz	L-L	148	—	—	—	474
Cbzo·Glu·CySBz·OBz	L-L	144	—	—	—	474
Cbzo·Glu-NH₂·CySBz·OBz	L-L	187–190	—	—	—	432a, 474
Cbzo·Glu·OMe	L	97	—	—	—	10
└CySH·OEt	L					
Cbzo·Glu·OEt·CySBz·OMe	L-L	130	—	—	—	767
Cbzo·Glu-NH₂·CySBz·OMe	L-L	204	−30.3	19	2.4%, HOAc	428a, 629, 906
Cbzo·Glu-NH₂·(CySBz)₂·OEt	3 L	181–185	—	—	—	432a
Cbzo·Glu·OH	L	173	—	—	—	10
└CySH·Gly·OEt	L					
Cbzo·Glu·OEt·CySBz·Gly·OEt	L-L	125–127	—	—	—	767
Cbzo·Glu·OEt	L	105–107	—	—	—	475
└CySBz·Gly·OEt	L					
Cbzo·Glu·OH	L	102–105	—	—	—	692
└Glu·(OBz)₂	L					
Cbzo·Glu·OBz	L	129.5–131	+3.3	23	2%, HOAc	898
└Glu·(OBz)₂	D					
Cbzo·Glu·OBz	L	140.5–142	−5.2	23	2%, HOAc	898
└Glu·(OBz)₂	L					
Cbzo·Glu·OBz·Glu·(OBz)₂	L-L	104–105	−10.4	23	2%, HOAc	898
Cbzo·Glu·OBz	L	148–151	−6.5	24	1.4%, HOAc	891
└Glu·OBz	L					
Cbzo·Glu·OH	D	177	+18.1	20	2.7%, MeOH	679
└Glu·OBz	D					
Cbzo·Glu·OH	L	177–178	−18.0	20	4.8%, MeOH	679
└Glu·OBz	L					
Cbzo·Glu·OMe	D	104–106	+30.0	20	2.5%, MeOH	679
└Glu-OMe·OBz	D					

TABLE 10-42 (continued)

Specific Rotation

Compound	Config.	M.P., °C.	$[\alpha]_D$, deg.	Temp., °C.	Concn. and Solvent	Ref.
Carbobenzoxy (Cbzo) derivatives (continued)						
Cbzo·Glu·OMe	L	105–106	−30.0	20	5.0%, MeOH	679
└─Glu·OMe·OBz	L	137	—	—	—	128, 610, 691
Cbzo·Glu·Glu·(OEt)$_2$	L-L	62–68	—	—	—	691
Cbzo·Glu·OH	L					
└─Glu·(OEt)$_2$	L	92–93	−22.7	15	1.15%, EtOH	767, 909
Cbzo·Glu·OEt	L					
└─Glu·(OEt)$_2$	L	104–105	−35.0	15	1.47%, EtOH	767, 879
Cbzo·Glu·OEt·Glu·(OEt)$_2$	L-L	181	—	—	—	767, 882
Cbzo·Glu·NH$_2$·Glu·(OEt)$_2$	L-L	81–82	−11.8	25	2.2%, HOAc	677
Cbzo·Glu·OMe·Glu·(OEt)$_2$	L-L	255	−41.8	19	2.4%, HOAc	629
Cbzo·Glu·NH$_2$·Glu·NH$_2$·CySBz·OMe	3 L	147–149	−5.3	28	2%, HOAc	891
Cbzo·Glu·OBz	L					
└─Glu·(OBz)$_2$	L	146	—	—	—	879
Cbzo·Glu·Glu·OEt·Glu·(OEt)$_2$	3 L	147–148	−33.3	18	1.5%, EtOH	881
Cbzo·Glu·Glu·OMe·Glu·(OEt)$_2$	3 L	114–116	—	—	—	767
Cbzo·Glu·OEt·Glu·OEt·Glu·(OEt)$_2$	3 L	113–114	—	—	—	767, 909
Cbzo·Glu·OEt	L					
└─Glu·(OEt)$_2$	L					
Cbzo·Glu·OEt·Glu·OEt·Glu·(OEt)$_2$	3 L	128	—	—	—	879

Compound		mp	[α]	Yield	Solvent	Ref
Cbzo·Glu·OEt	L	168–169.5	—	—	—	767
└Glu·OEt	L					
└Glu·OEt	L					
└Glu·(OEt)$_2$	L					
Cbzo·Glu·OEt·Glu·OEt·Gly·OEt	L-L	143–144	—	—	—	767
Cbzo·Glu·OMe·Glu·OMe·Gly·OEt	L-L	140–141	−20.6	25	2.2%, HOAc	677
Cbzo·Glu·OBz	L	104–105	—	—	—	474
└Gly·OBz						
Cbzo·Glu·OH	L	94–95	—	—	—	692
└Gly·OBz						
Cbzo·Glu·OEt·Gly·OBz	L	112–113	—	—	—	482
Cbzo·Glu·Gly·OEt	L	127	—	—	—	691, 726, 878, 882
Cbzo·Glu·NH$_2$·Gly·OEt	L	167^d	—	—	—	767, 882
Cbzo·Glu·OH	L	107–109	—	—	—	691, 693
└Gly·OEt						
Cbzo·Glu·OEt·Gly·OEt	L	94–94.5	−11.4	22	4.4%, HOAc	767
Cbzo·Glu·OMe	L	89–90	—	—	—	894
└Gly·OEt						
Cbzo·Glu·OMe·Gly·OEt	L	94	−14.4	19	2.9%, HOAc	677
Cbzo·Glu·OEt·Gly·Glu·(OEt)$_2$	L-L	121	−10.5	22	3.4%, 96% EtOH	677
Cbzo·Glu·OMe·Gly·Glu·(OEt)$_2$	L-L	94	−10.0	23	4.2%, 96% EtOH	677
Cbzo·Glu·Gly$_2$·OEt	L	139–140	—	—	—	455, 610, 882
Cbzo·Glu·NH$_2$·Gly$_2$·OEt	L	172–180^e	—	—	—	619, 882
Cbzo·Glu·OH	L	92–94	—	—	—	691
└Gly$_2$·OEt						
Cbzo·Glu·OEt·Gly$_2$·OEt	L	112–114	—	—	—	767

TABLE 10-42 (continued)

Compound	Config.	M.P., °C.	$[\alpha]_D$, deg.	Temp., °C.	Concn. and Solvent	Ref.
Carbobenzoxy (Cbzo) derivatives (continued)						
Cbzo·Glu·OEt	L	104–105	—	—	—	767
└Gly₂·OEt						
Cbzo·Glu·Gly·OEt	L	153	−27.8	20	1.6%, acetone	774
└Gly·OEt						
Cbzo·Glu·OH	L	112–115	—	—	—	692
└Leu·OBz	L					
Cbzo·Glu·Leu·OEt	L-L	94–96	—	—	—	610
Cbzo·Glu·NH₂·Leu·OMe	L-L	163–164	—	—	—	619
Cbzo·Glu·Met·OMe	L-L	114–115	—	—	—	627
Cbzo·Glu·Phe·OEt	L-D	131	—	—	—	709
Cbzo·Glu·Phe·OEt	L-L	144	—	—	—	709
Cbzo·Glu·NH₂·Phe·OEt	L-L	138	—	—	—	709
Cbzo·Glu·NH₂·Ser·OMe	L-L	182–185	—	—	—	619
Cbzo·Glu·Tyr·OEt	L-L	176	—	—	—	378, 894
Cbzo·Glu·OH	L	172–176	—	—	—	691
└Tyr·OEt	L					
Cbzo·Glu·NH₂·Tyr·OMe	L-L	198–201	—	—	—	619
Cbzo·Glu·Tyr·Gly·OEt	L-L	193–194	—	—	—	709
Cbzo·Glu·Val·OEt	L-L	122–124	—	—	—	610
Cbzo·Glu·NH₂·Val·OMe	L-L	173–175	—	—	—	619
Cbzo·Gly·Ala·OBz	DL	91–92	—	—	—	769

Cbzo·Gly·Ala·OEt	DL	53–55	—	—	—	704, 774
Cbzo·Gly·Ala·OEt	D	66	—	—	—	666
Cbzo·Gly·Ala·OEt	L	65	—	—	—	666, 710
Cbzo·Gly·β-Ala·OEt	—	63	—	—	—	723, 899
Cbzo·Gly·Ala₂·OEt	L-D	126	—	—	—	703
Cbzo·Gly·Ala₂·OEt	L-L	128	—	—	—	703
Cbzo·Gly·Ala·Gly·OBz	DL	165–166	—	—	—	704
Cbzo·Gly·Ala·Gly·OBz	D	144	—	—	—	703
Cbzo·Gly·Ala·Gly·OBz	L	144–145	−27.5	25	2%, MeOH	703, 717a
Cbzo·Gly·Ala·Gly·OEt	DL	179	—	—	—	774
Cbzo·Gly·Ala·Gly·OEt	L	145	—	—	—	703
Cbzo·Gly·Ala·Gly₂·OMe	DL	144–145	—	—	—	803
Cbzo·Gly·β–Ala·His·OMe	L	168–169	—	—	—	621
Cbzo·Gly·Ala·Leu·OMe	L-L	111.5–113.5	—	—	—	494, 710
Cbzo·Gly·Ala·Leu·Glu·(OMe)₂	3 L	149	—	—	—	710
Cbzo·Gly·(α-NH₂-n-But)·OEt	DL	46	—	—	—	774
Cbzo·Gly·(α-NH₂-isoBut)·OEt	—	84	—	—	—	466
Cbzo·Gly·NO₂-Arg·OEt	L	112–114	−6.9	25	1.7%, MeOH	678
Cbzo·Gly·Asp·(OBz)₂	L	85–86	—	—	—	672
Cbzo·Gly·Asp·Gly·OEt	L	148	—	—	—	878
Cbzo·Gly·CySBz·OBz	L	97	−22.0	20	0.18%, EtOH	390
Cbzo·Gly·CySBz·OEt	L	80	−45.9	20	−, MeOH	774
Cbzo·Gly·CySBz·OEt	L	80	−34.5	19	0.43%, EtOH	390, 759a
Cbzo·Gly·Glu·(OEt)₂	L	53–55	−11.9	20	2.5%, 96% EtOH	677
Cbzo·Gly·Glu·Gly·OEt	L	169	—	—	—	878
Cbzo·Gly·Glu·OEt·Gly₂·OEt	L	172–173	—	—	—	767
Cbzo·Gly·Glu·OEt·Tyr·OEt	L-L	169	—	—	—	709
Cbzo·Gly₂·OBz	—	110	—	—	—	665

TABLE 10-42 (continued)

Carbobenzoxy (Cbzo) derivatives (continued)

Compound	Config.	M.P., °C.	$[\alpha]_D$, deg.	Temp., °C.	Concn. and Solvent	Ref.
Cbzo·Gly₂·OEt	—	80–81	—	—	—	495, 697, 722, 723, 758, 759, 759a, 768, 769, 769a, 774, 808
Cbzo·Gly₂·OMe	—	63–65	—	—	—	769, 900
Cbzo·Gly₂·β-Ala·OEt	—	142	—	—	—	899
Cbzo·Gly₂·Ala·OMe	DL	97	—	—	—	910
Cbzo·Gly₂·Ala·Gly·OMe	DL	166	—	—	—	910
Cbzo·Gly₂·Ala·Gly₂·OMe	DL	200	—	—	—	910
Cbzo·Gly₂·CySBz·OBz	L	115.5–116[f]	−32.3	21	1%, EtOH	390, 711
Cbzo·Gly₃·OBz	—	162[g]	—	—	—	390, 665
Cbzo·Gly₃·OEt	—	166–167	—	—	—	697, 711, 723, 757, 759a, 768, 769a, 774, 832, 911
Cbzo·Gly₃·OMe	—	151–155	—	—	—	413
Cbzo·Gly₃·CySBz·OBz	L	150–151	−18.0	22	1%, dioxane	711
Cbzo·Gly₄·OEt	—	205[h]	—	—	—	723, 774
Cbzo·Gly₄·OMe	—	214.5	—	—	—	806
Cbzo·Gly₄·CySBz·OBz	L	217–218.5	−24.5	23	1%, HOAc	472
di(Cbzo·Gly)·His·OMe	L	146–147 d.	—	—	—	840

Cbzo·Gly₂·Hypro·OBz	L	123–127	—	—	—	169
Cbzo·Gly₂·Leu·OMe	D	95–96	—	—	—	911
Cbzo·Gly₂·Leu·OMe	L	93–94	—	—	—	911
Cbzo·Gly₂·Phe·OEt	DL	78–80	—	—	—	758
Cbzo·Gly₂·Phe·OEt·H₂O	DL	105	—	—	—	761, *812b*
Cbzo·Gly₂·Phe·OEt	L	73–74	—	—	—	902
Cbzo·Gly₂·Pro·OBz	L	87	—	—	—	169
Cbzo·Gly·His·Gly·OEt	L	172–173	—	—	—	537
Cbzo·Gly·His·Gly·Ser·OMe	L-L	184–185	—	—	—	537
Cbzo·Gly·His·Ser·OMe	L-L	163–165	—	—	—	537
Cbzo·Gly·His·Tyr·OMe	L-L	208	—	—	—	537
Cbzo·Gly·Leu·OEt	DL	52	—	—	—	723, 769, *774*
Cbzo·Gly·Leu·OMe	L	64–66	—	—	—	912
Cbzo·Gly·Leu·OEt	L	108–108.5	—	25	3%, EtOAc	495, 694, 758, *769a*, *812c*
Cbzo·Gly·Leu·Gly·OMe	DL	107–108	—	—	—	697, 758
Cbzo·Gly·Leu·Gly·OMe	D	131	—	—	—	878
Cbzo·Gly·Leu·Gly·OMe	L	132–133	−36.1	25	5%, MeOH	697, 722, 758, 878
Cbzo·Gly·Leu·Gly₂·Leu·Gly·OEt	L-L	186–188	—	—	—	*812c*
Cbzo·Gly·Leu·Gly·Leu·OMe	L-L	88–90	—	—	—	694
Cbzo·Gly·Leu·Gly·Leu·OMe	L-D	117–118	—	—	—	694
Cbzo·Gly·Leu₂·OMe	L-L	133–134	−47.4	25	2%, MeOH	694, 697, 758
Cbzo·Gly·Leu₂·OMe	L	87–89	—	—	—	833
Cbzo·Gly·(Nᵃ-Cbzo-Lys)·OBz	L	97	—	—	—	358, *613a*, *667*
Cbzo·Gly·(Nᵋ-Cbzo-Lys)·OMe	DL	106	—	—	—	723
di(Cbzo·Gly)·Lys·OMe	L	120–122	—	—	—	706
Cbzo·Gly·(Nᵋ-Cbzo-Lys)·Gly·OBz	L	146	—	—	—	358
Cbzo·Gly·(Nᵋ-Cbzo-Lys)·Gly·OEt	L	134	—	—	—	774
Cbzo·Gly·Nleu·OEt	DL					

TABLE 10-42 (continued)

Compound	Config.	M.P., °C.	$[\alpha]_D$, deg.	Temp., °C.	Concn. and Solvent	Ref.
Carbobenzoxy (Cbzo) derivatives (continued)						
Cbzo·Gly·Phe·OBz	L	74	—	—	—	665
Cbzo·Gly·Phe·OEt	DL	92	—	—	—	697, 721, 722, 723, 734, 757, 758, 759, 761, 774, 832, 913
Cbzo·Gly·Phe·OMe	DL	83–84	—	—	—	900
Cbzo·Gly·Phe·Ala·OMe	L-L	124–125	—	—	—	611a
Cbzo·Gly·Phe·Gly·OEt	DL	132–134	—	—	—	721, 734, 758, 812b
Cbzo·Gly·Phe·Gly·OEt	L	118–119	−12.3	24	2%, EtOH	495, 697, 722, 758, 785, 788
Cbzo·Gly·Phe·Gly$_2$·OEt	DL	174–176	—	—	—	721, 722, 808a
Cbzo·Gly·Ser·OBz	DL	141–142	—	—	—	913a
Cbzo·Gly·(O-Bz-Ser)·OEt	DL	84	—	—	—	828
Cbzo·Gly·Ser·OMe	L	96	—	—	—	537, 631
Cbzo·Gly·Ser·Gly·OBz	DL	169–170	—	—	—	913a
Cbzo·(O-Bz-Ser)·His·Leu·OMe	3 L	152–153	−20.1	13	1%, EtOH	828

CHEMICAL PROCEDURES FOR SYNTHESIS OF PEPTIDES 1131

Compound	Config	m.p.	$[\alpha]$	t	solvent	Ref.
Cbzo·Gly·Tyr·OEt	L	126–127	+19.2	24	5%, EtOH	697, 700, 721, 722, 734, 757, 758, 761, 769, 914
Cbzo·Gly·(O-Bz-Tyr)·OMe	L	81	—	—	—	830
Cbzo·His·Ala·OEt	L-L	149.5–152	−25.0	22	1%, EtOH	695
Cbzo·His·β-Ala·OEt	L	122–123	—	—	—	621
im,N-diCbzo·His·Glu·(OEt)₂	L-L	78–80	+0.2	22	2.9%, EtOAc	841
Cbzo·His·Gly·OBz	L	134–136	—	—	—	621
Cbzo·His·Gly·OEt	L	113–114	—	—	—	621
Cbzo·His·Gly₂·OEt	L	180–181	—	—	—	621
Cbzo·His₂·OMe	L-L	74–75	—	—	—	621
Cbzo·His·Hypro·OMe	L-L	75–76	—	—	—	621
Cbzo·His·Leu·OMe	L-L	125–128	−25.5	22	1%, EtOH	621, 695
im,N-diCbzo·His·Leu·OMe	L-L	101–103	+21.4	22	2.9%, EtOAc	841
im,N-diCbzo·His·Met·OMe	L-L	110–113	+9.1	22	2.8% HOAc	841
Cbzo·His·Phe·OMe	L-L	161–163	−15.8	23	1.9%, DMF	471a, 621, 713
Cbzo·His·Phe·NO₂·Arg·Try·Gly·OBz	4 L	183–185	−29.0	27	0.9%, DMF	791
Cbzo·His·Ser·OMe	L-L	140–142	—	—	—	695
im,N-diCbzo·His·(O-Bz-Ser)·OMe	L-L	113–115	+19.8	22	3.0%, EtOAc	841
im,N-diCbzo·His·Thr·OMe	L-L	148–150	+12.7	22	3.1%, EtOAc	841
Cbzo·His·Tyr·OEt	L-L	94–95	—	—	—	621
Cbzo·Hypro·Ala·OMe	L-L	105	—	—	—	642
Cbzo·Hypro·Asp·(OEt)₂	L-L	81–82	—	—	—	642
Cbzo·Hypro·Gly·OBz	L	153	—	—	—	169, 471
Cbzo·Hypro·Gly₂·OEt	L	144–145	−11.1	21	1%, EtOH	823
Cbzo·Hypro·Leu·OMe	L-L	132–133	—	—	—	642

TABLE 10-42 (continued)

Compound	Config.	M.P., °C.	$[\alpha]_D$, deg.	Temp., °C.	Concn. and Solvent	Ref.
Carbobenzoxy (Cbzo) derivatives (continued)						
Cbzo·Hypro·Phe·OEt	L-L	102–103	—	—	—	642
Cbzo·Hypro·Phe·OMe	L-L	114–115	−29.2	27	2.8%, EtOH	524
Cbzo·Ileu·Ala·OBz	L-D	171	−0.7	27	2%, HOAc	454
Cbzo·allo-Ileu·Ala·OBz	D-D	162	+36.0	27	2%, HOAc	454
Cbzo·allo-Ileu·Ala·OBz	L-D	149	+4.6	27	2%, HOAc	454
Cbzo·Ileu·His·OMe	L-L	186–189	−44.2	25	1%, MeOH–NHCl(1:1)	508
Cbzo·Ileu·His·OMe·HCl·H$_2$O	L-L	174–175 d.	−34	24	1.0%, H$_2$O	714
Cbzo·Ileu·His·Pro·Phe·OMe	4 L	105–110	−56	22	1.0%, MeOH	714
Cbzo·Ileu$_2$·OBz	L-L	118–119	−37.3	25	2.0%, MeOH	914a
Cbzo·Leu·Ala·OMe	L-D	129–130	−1	27	4%, EtOH	466, 467
Cbzo·Leu·Ala·OMe	L-L	95–96	−38	22	1%, EtOH	466, 467
Cbzo·Leu·Ala·Val·Phe·Gly·OEt	4 L	223–225	−43.8	24	2.2%, HOAc	915
Cbzo·Leu·Ala·Val·Phe·Gly·Pro·OBz	5 L	210–212	−53.5	22	2.1%, HOAc	915
Cbzo·Leu·CySBz·Gly·OBz	L-L	151–152	—	—	—	432a
Cbzo·Leu·Gly·OEt	DL	94–95^i	—	—	—	495, 613a, 769, 805
Cbzo·Leu·Gly·OEt	L	104–105	−26.4	25	5%, EtOH	495, 613a, 625, 697, 717, 721 722, 734, 758, 759a, 805, 808, 808b, 878

Compound	Config	mp	[α]	T	Solvent	Ref
Cbzo·Leu·Gly·OMe	L	92–94		25	5%, MeOH	758
Cbzo·Leu·Gly₂·OEt	DL	102				611a
Cbzo·Leu·Gly₂·OEt	L	103–104.5	−11	25	5%, 95% EtOH	179, 611a, 878
Cbzo·Leu·Gly₃·OEt	L	75				611a
Cbzo·Leu·Gly·Leu·OMe	L-L	89–91				694
Cbzo·Leu₂·OMe	L-D	81.5–82.5	+2.3	24	1%, EtOH	622
Cbzo·Leu₂·OMe	L-L	97–98.5	−35.3	24	10%, EtOH	622, 625, 721, 734, 757, 834
Cbzo·Leu₂·Gly·OMe	L-L	108				455
Cbzo·Leu·Phe·OEt	D-L	114–115				660
Cbzo·Leu·Phe·OEt	L-D	107.5–108.5	−16.9	23	1%, EtOH	373, 622, 698, 719
Cbzo·Leu·Phe·OEt	L-L	95–96	−21.6	23	1%, EtOH	622, 808b
Cbzo·Leu·Phe·OMe	L-D	112				423, 698
Cbzo·Leu·Phe·Pro·OEt	3 L	134–136				698
Cbzo·Leu·Phe·Pro·OMe	L-D-L	40–42	−42.2	22	2.7%, MeOH	423, 698
Cbzo·Leu·Try·OMe	D-L	125–127				696
Cbzo·Leu·Tyr·OBz	L-D	151.5–153	+5.1	25	0.5%, MeOH	679a
Cbzo·Leu·Tyr·OEt	L-D	122–123.5	+29.7	25	1%, MeOH	679a
Cbzo·Leu·Tyr·OEt	L-L	115–117	−15.2	24	5%, EtOH	721, 722, 734, 758
Cbzo·Leu·(O-Bz-Tyr)·OMe	L-L	109				830
Cbzo·Leu·Val·OMe	L-D	102–102.5	−7.9	25	1%, EtOH	622
Cbzo·Leu·Val·Glu·(OEt)₂	3 L	177–178	−43.0	25	3%, HOAc	718, 915a
diCbzo·Lys·Ala·OBz	L-L	132				667
diCbzo·Lys·Ala·OEt	L-D	131.5				667
diCbzo·Lys·Ala·OEt	L-L	119				667
diCbzo·Lys·NO₂-Arg·OMe	L-L	70–72	−10.6	29	3.6%, MeOH	491
diCbzo·Lys·Asp·(OEt)₂	L-L	142				831

TABLE 10-42 (continued)

Compound	Config.	M.P., °C.	$[\alpha]_D$, deg.	Temp., °C.	Concn. and Solvent	Ref.
Carbobenzoxy (Cbzo) derivatives (continued)						
diCbzo·Lys·Glu·(OEt)₂	L-L	105	—	—	—	626
diCbzo·Lys·Gly·OBz	L	125	—	—	—	667
diCbzo·Lys·Gly·OEt	DL	83	—	—	—	723
diCbzo·Lys·Gly·OEt	L	92–93	−12.0	24	4%, EtOH	667, 697, 721, 734, 831, 832, 834
diCbzo·Lys·Gly·OMe	L	122–123	—	—	—	833
diCbzo·Lys·Gly₂·Glu·(OEt)₂	L-L	134–135	−9.5	17	1.5%, EtOH	649
diCbzo·Lys·His·OMe	L-L	138–140	—	—	—	626
diCbzo·Lys·(Nᵋ-Cbzo-Lys)·OBz	L-L	139–142	—	—	—	833
diCbzo·Lys·(Nᵋ-Cbzo-Lys)·OEt	L-L	117–117.5	−5.6	18	2.5%, acetone	584a
diCbzo·Lys·(Nᵋ-Cbzo-Lys)·OMe	L-D	134	—	—	—	667
diCbzo·Lys·(Nᵋ-Cbzo-Lys)·OMe	L-L	123	−8.1	20	4.5%, EtOH	667, 715
diCbzo·Lys·(Nᵋ-Cbzo-Lys)₂·OBz	L-2 D	151–152	—	—	—	706
diCbzo·Lys·(Nᵋ-Cbzo-Lys)₂·OBz	L-D-L	141–142	—	—	—	706
diCbzo·Lys·(Nᵋ-Cbzo-Lys)₂·OBz	3 L	153–154ʲ	—	—	—	706, 715
diCbzo·Lys·(Nᵋ-Cbzo-Lys)₂·OMe	3 L	160–162ᵏ	−10.4	20	5%, HOAc	706, 715
diCbzo·Lys·(Nᵋ-Cbzo-Lys)₃·OBz	4 L	170–172	—	—	—	715
diCbzo·Lys·(Nᵋ-Cbzo-Lys)₃·OMe	4 L	156–157	—	—	—	715
diCbzo·Lys·(Nᵋ-Cbzo-Lys)₄·OBz	5 L	177–178	—	—	—	715
diCbzo·Lys·Phe·OEt	L-L	131	—	—	—	660
diCbzo·Lys·Tyr·OEt	L-L	140–142ˡ	−6.2	20	5%, MeOH	660, 834

Compound	Config	M.p. (°C)	[α]	Conc.	Solvent	Ref.
diCbzo·Lys·Tyr·OMe	L-L	131–133	—	—	—	584a, 834
diCbzo·Lys·Tyr·Leu·OBz	3 L	130.5–132	—	—	—	584a
diCbzo·Lys·Tyr·(N$^\varepsilon$-Cbzo-Lys)·OBz	3 L	131–132	—	—	—	584a
diCbzo·Lys·Val·OEt	L-L	109–110	−17.4	22	2.9%, EtOH	507
diCbzo·Lys·Val·Phe·Gly·OEt	3 L	199–200	−21.4	24	2%, HOAc	507
Cbzo·Met·Glu·(OEt)$_2$	L-L	95–96	−20.9	25	1.3%, EtOH	444
Cbzo·Met·Gly·OEt	DL	72–74	—	—	—	627
Cbzo·Met·Gly·OEt	D	93–95	—	—	—	627
Cbzo·Met·Gly·OEt	L	95–96	−20.0	27	4.6%, EtOH	444, 627
Cbzo·Met·Gly·OMe	DL	79–81	—	—	—	900
Cbzo·Met·Gly$_2$·OEt	L	131–132	—	—	—	627
Cbzo·Met$_2$·OMe	L-D	112–114	+12.4	20	1%, MeOH	490
Cbzo·Met$_2$·OMe	L-L	104–105	−28.0	19	1%, MeOH	490, 627
Cbzo·Met$_3$·OMe	3 L	153	−38.0	17	1%, MeOH	490
Cbzo·Met·Tyr·OEt	L-L	109–111	—	—	—	627
diCbzo·Met·Orn·Leu·OMe	L-L	83–84	−18	20	2.8%, EtOH	373
diCbzo·Orn·Leu·Phe·Pro·OMe	2 L-D-L	86–88	—	—	—	421
Cbzo·Phe·Ala·OMe	L-L	130–131	—	—	—	611a
Cbzo·Phe·NO$_2$-Arg·OMe	L-L	160–161	−16.2	28	1.1%, MeOH	491
Cbzo·Phe·Glu·(OEt)$_2$	L-L	126–127	−11.4	25	2%, EtOH	709, 758
Cbzo·Phe·Gly·OBz	L	137–139	−8.4	25	2%, HOAc	507, 665, 758
Cbzo·Phe·Gly·OEt	DL	97.5–99	—	—	—	758, 808b, 812b
Cbzo·Phe·Gly·OEt	D	109–111	—	—	—	313
Cbzo·Phe·Gly·OEt	L	110–111	−16.9	25	5%, EtOH	495, 682, 697, 700, 758, 769a, 808b
Cbzo·Phe·Gly$_2$·OEt	DL	144	—	—	—	759, 774
Cbzo·Phe·Leu·OMe	D-D	109	—	—	—	469
Cbzo·Phe$_2$·OBz	L-L	149–150	+8.4	25	2%, CHCl$_3$	914a

TABLE 10-42 (*continued*)

Compound	Config.	M.P., °C.	$[\alpha]_D$, deg.	Temp., °C.	Concn. and Solvent	Ref.
Carbobenzoxy (Cbzo) derivatives (*continued*)						
Cbzo·Phe₂·OEt	L-L	140	—	—	—	916
Cbzo·Phe·Tyr·OEt	L-L	159–160	−9.4	24	10%, EtOH	721, 916
Cbzo·Pro·Gly·OEt	DL	59–60	—	—	—	170
Cbzo·Pro·Gly₂·OEt	L	120–120.5	−23.1	21	1%, EtOH	170, 823
Cbzo·Pro·Gly₃·OEt	L	108–109	—	—	—	170
Cbzo·Pro·Gly·Phe·OMe	L-L	92–93	—	—	—	611*a*
Cbzo·Pro·Leu·OEt	L-L	68–69	—	—	—	717
Cbzo·Pro·Leu·Gly·OBz	L-L	116–117	—	—	—	717
Cbzo·Pro·Leu·Gly·OEt	L-L	148–149	−79.8	23	2.5%, EtOH	717, 865
Cbzo·Pro·(Nᵉ-Tos-Lys)·OEt	L-L	122.5–123.5	−29.1	22	1%, CHCl₃	393
Cbzo·Pro·(Nᵉ-Tos-Lys)·Gly·OEt	L-L	151–151.5	−56.0	21	1%, HOAc	393
Cbzo·Pro·(Nᵉ-Tos-Lys)·Gly·OEt·H₂O	L-L	129–130	—	—	—	393
Cbzo·Pro·Phe·His·Leu·OMe	4 L	185–187	−60	—	1.0%, MeOH	638*a*
Cbzo·Pro·Val·(Nᵟ-Tos-Orn)·Leu·Tyr·Pro·OMe	4 L-D-L	199–201	−84.0	20	0.5%, MeOH	679*a*
Cbzo·Ser·Ala·OMe	L-L	113–114	—	—	—	501
Cbzo·Ser·Ala·Glu·(OEt)₂	3 L	135	—	—	—	631
Cbzo·(O-Bz-Ser)·CyS·OMe	L-L	101–102	+22.2	15	2.7%, EtOAc	504
Cbzo·(O-Bz-Ser)·CyS·OMe	L-L					
Cbzo·Ser·Glu·(OEt)₂	L-L	85–86	—	—	—	498, *501*
Cbzo·Ser·Gly·OBz	DL	100–101	—	—	—	913*a*
Cbzo·Ser·Gly·OBz	L	102	—	—	—	501

Compound		m.p. (°C)	[α]	conc.	solvent	ref.
Cbzo·Ser·Gly·OEt	DL	86–87	—	—	—	498, 537, 704
Cbzo·Ser·Gly·OEt	L	106–107	—	—	—	501, 785
Cbzo·Ser·Gly·OMe	L	105–106	—	—	—	699, 907
Cbzo·Ser·Gly·Ala·OEt	D-L	153–154	−5	25	2%, MeOH	717a
Cbzo·Ser·Gly·Ala·OEt	L-L	128–129	−23.5	25	2%, MeOH	717a
Cbzo·Ser·Gly·Ala·Gly·Ala·Gly·OBz	3 L	250–251	−50.5	25	1%, HOAc	717a
Cbzo·Ser·Gly·Glu·(OEt)$_2$	L-L	106–107	—	—	—	631, 907
Cbzo·Ser·Gly$_2$·OBz	L	151–153	—	—	—	699
Cbzo·Ser·Gly·Ser·OMe	L-L	173	—	—	—	631
Cbzo·Ser·His·OMe	L-L	121–122	−12.0	27	2%, HOAc	718
Cbzo·(O-Bz-Ser)·His·OMe	L-L	110	+7.2	15	4.9%, 99% EtOH	504
Cbzo·(O-Bz-Ser)·His·Leu·OMe	3 L	152–153	−20.1	13	1%, EtOH	828
Cbzo·Ser·His·Leu·Val·Glu·(OEt)$_2$	5 L	213	−46.3	27	3%, EtOH	718
Cbzo·(O-Bz-Ser)·His·Leu·Val·Glu·(OEt)$_2$	5 L	192–193	−34.5	13	1%, HOAc	915a
Cbzo·Ser·Met·OMe	L-L	101–102	—	—	—	444
Cbzo·Ser$_2$·OMe	L-L	143–145	—	—	—	501
Cbzo·Ser·Tyr·OMe	L-L	115–116	+13.5	21	2.0%, DMF	471a, 537
Cbzo·(O-Bz-Ser)·Tyr·OMe	L-L	111–112	+15.5	15	2.8%, 99% EtOH	504
Cbzo·Ser·Tyr·Ser·OMe	3 L	191–192	−3.9	25	1.8%, pyridine	444, 471a
Cbzo·Ser·Tyr·Ser·Met·OMe	4 L	190 d.	−39.0	27	0.7%, MeOH	444
Cbzo·Thr·Ala·OBz	L-D	147	−0.6	27	2%, HOAc	454
Cbzo·allo-Thr·Ala·OBz	L-D	142–143	+8.3	27	2%, HOAc	454
Cbzo·Thr·His·OMe	L-L	120–121	−16	28	4.3%, HOAc	504a
Cbzo·Thr·His·Leu·Val·Glu·(OEt)$_2$	5 L	222–224	−51	28	1.9%, EtOAc	504a
Cbzo·Try·Gly·OEt	L	120	—	—	—	621
Cbzo·Try·Gly·OMe	L	158–159	−11.0	27	2.0%, HOAc	791
Cbzo·Try·(N^ε-Cbzo-Lys)·Leu·Ala·Val·Phe·Gly·Pro·OBz	7 L	246–248	−43.6	22	1.4%, HOAc	915
Cbzo·(O-Ac-Tyr)·Asp·(OEt)$_2$	L-L	144	—	—	—	378

TABLE 10-42 (continued)

Compound	Config.	M.P., °C.	$[\alpha]_D$, deg.	Temp., °C.	Concn. and Solvent	Ref.
Carbobenzoxy (Cbzo) derivatives (continued)						
Cbzo·Tyr·CySBz·OEt	L-L	168.5-169[m]	—	—	—	646, 917
O,N-diCbzo·Tyr·Gly·OEt	L	164-165	−2	21	4%, $CHCl_3$	803
Cbzo·(O-Ac-Tyr)·Gly·OEt	L	127	—	—	—	700
Cbzo·(O-Bz-Tyr)·Gly·OEt	L	137	—	—	—	830
Cbzo·Tyr·Gly$_2$·OEt	L	165-167	+6.5	24	2%, HOAc	700, 722, 758
Cbzo·Tyr·His·OMe	L-L	165-166	−14.0	24	1%, MeOH	537
O,N-diCbzo·Tyr·Ileu·OEt	L-L	163-164	+9.0	23	4.3%, $CHCl_3$	804
Cbzo·(O-Ac-Tyr)·Leu·OMe	L-L	143	—	—	—	584a
Cbzo·(O-Ac-Tyr)·Phe·OEt	L-L	170	—	—	—	916
Cbzo·Tyr·Ser·OMe	L-L	152	−3.1	23	2.2%, MeOH	471a, 537
Cbzo·Tyr$_2$·OEt	L-L	159-160.5	—	—	—	637
Cbzo·Tyr$_2$·OMe	L-L	174-175	—	—	—	637
Cbzo·(O-Ac-Tyr)·Tyr·OEt	L-L	160-161	—	—	—	378
Cbzo·(O-Ac-Tyr)·Tyr$_2$·OEt	3 L	211	—	—	—	637
Cbzo·(O-Ac-Tyr)·Tyr$_3$·OEt	4 L	236-237	—	—	—	637
Cbzo·Val·CySBz·OBz	L-L	155.5-156.5	−17.4	20	1.0%, $CHCl_3$	432a, 875c
Cbzo·Val·Gly·OEt	DL	144-145[n]	—	—	—	380, 506, 697, 758, 769
Cbzo·Val·Gly·OEt	L	166	—	—	—	613a, 808b
Cbzo·Val·Gly·OMe	DL	130-132	—	—	—	900
Cbzo·Val·His·OMe	L-L	165-166	−22	23	2.0%, EtOH	638a
Cbzo·Val·His·Pro·Phe·OMe	4 L	95-150	−56	—	1.0%, MeOH	718a

Compound	Config	m.p.	[α]	Temp	Solvent	Ref
Cbzo·Val·(Nᵉ·Tos·Lys)·OMe	L-L	130	−8	18	1.0%, HOAc	626a
Cbzo·Val·(Nᵉ·Tos·Lys)·Leu·Phe·Pro·OMe	3 L-D-L	208–208.5	−48	23	1.1%, HOAc	626a
Cbzo·Val·(N^δ·Cbzo·Orn)·OMe	L-L	155–156	0	18	2.5%, CHCl₃	373, 421
Cbzo·Val·(N^δ·Tos·Orn)·OMe	L-L	145	—	—	—	423, 719
Cbzo·Val·(N^δ·Tos·Orn)·Leu·Phe·Pro·OMe	3 L-D-L	184	−52.3	23	0.9%, HOAc	423
Cbzo·Val·[N^δ·Tos·Orn)·Leu·Phe·Pro]₂·OMe	[3 L-D-L]₂	209–211	−111.1	27	1.1%, MeOH	423
Cbzo·Val·(N^δ·Tos·Orn)·Leu·Tyr·OEt	3 L-D	182–185.5	−17.0	25	1%, MeOH	679a
Cbzo·Val·(N^δ·Tos·Orn)·Leu·Tyr·Pro·OMe	3 L-D-L	154–156	−56	25	2%, MeOH	679a
Cbzo·Val·[N^δ·Tos·Orn)·Leu·Tyr·Pro]₂·OMe	[3 L-D-L]₂	218–220	−112	25	0.5%, MeOH	679a
Cbzo·Val·Phe·Gly·OEt	L-L	191.5–192	−22.5	24	2.1%, HOAc	507
Cbzo·Val·Tyr·OEt	L-L	145–147	+34	23	4.0%, CHCl₃	638a
Cbzo·Val·Tyr·OMe	L-L	155.5–156°	+10.2	25	4.8%, pyridine	508, 714
Cbzo·Val·Tyr·Ileu·His·OMe	4 L	213–217	+6.0	25	5%, DMF	508
Cbzo·Val·Tyr·Ileu·His·Pro·Phe·OMe	6 L	162–167	−66.3	25	1.0%, MeOH	508
Cbzo·Val·Tyr·Val·OMe	3 L	194–196	−24	—	4.1%, HOAc	638a
Cbzo·Val·Tyr·Val·His·OMe	4 L	228–230 d.	−31	—	2.1%, HOAc	638a
Cbzo·Val·Tyr·Val·His·Pro·Phe·OMe	6 L	155	−57	—	2% EtOH	718a
Cbzo·Val·Tyr·Val·His·Pro·Phe·His·Leu·OMe	8 L	150–170	−73	—	1.0%, EtOH	638a
Cbzo·Val₂·OBz	L-L	116	−44.3	25	2.0%, MeOH	914a

Carboallyloxy (Callo) derivative

Compound	Config	m.p.	[α]	Temp	Solvent	Ref
Callo·Met₃·OMe	3 L	121–123	−41.0	21	2% MeOH	490

p-Nitrocarbobenzoxy (p-NO₂-Cbzo) derivatives

Compound	Config	m.p.	[α]	Temp	Solvent	Ref
p-NO₂-Cbzo·Arg·Glu·(OEt)₂·HCl	L-L	139–140	−9.8	25	0.9%, 95% EtOH	363
p-NO₂-Cbzo·NO₂-Arg·Glu·(OEt)₂	L-L	110	+2.2	22	2%, acetone	513
p-NO₂-Cbzo·NO₂-Arg·Gly·OEt·H₂O	L	106–107	+7.1	22	1.2%, acetone	513
p-NO₂-Cbzo·NO₂-Arg·Leu·OEt	L-L	154–155	−3.0	22	1.3%, acetone	513
p-NO₂-Cbzo·Arg·Leu·OMe·HCl	L-L	167–169	−15.2	24	1% 95% EtOH	513
p-NO₂-Cbzo·NO₂-Arg·Phe·OEt	L-L	165	+8.8	22	0.7%, acetone	513

TABLE 10-42 (continued)

Compound	Config.	M.P., °C.	$[\alpha]_D$, deg.	Temp., °C.	Concn. and Solvent	Ref.
p-Nitrocarbobenzoxy (*p*-NO₂-Cbzo) derivatives (continued)						
p-NO₂-Cbzo·NO₂-Arg·Tyr·OEt	L-L	139–140	+9.1	22	2.6%, acetone	513
p-NO₂-Cbzo·CyS·Gly·OEt	L	160–161	−76.6	25	1.1%, acetone	512
p-NO₂-Cbzo·CyS·Gly·OEt	L					
p-NO₂-Cbzo·CyS·Phe·OEt	L-L	173–174	−37.8	25	0.6%, acetone	512
p-NO₂-Cbzo·CyS·Phe·OEt	L-L					
p-NO₂-Cbzo·CySBz·Pro·(Nᵋ-Tos-Lys)·Gly·OEt	3 L	114–117	−20.1	24	3%, CHCl₃	393
p-NO₂-Cbzo·Gly·Glu·(OBz)₂	L	94–95	−14.3	19	1.3%, 96% EtOH	677
p-NO₂-Cbzo·Gly·Glu·(OEt)₂	L	85–87	−8.2	21	1.3%, 96% EtOH	677
p-NO₂-Cbzo·Gly·Glu·(OMe)₂	L	154–160	+5.4	19	1.6%, dioxane	677
p-NO₂-Cbzo·Gly·Leu·OMe	L	59–62	−26.5	26	1%, EtOH	462
p-NO₂-Cbzo·Leu·Gly·OEt	DL	90–91	–	–	–	803
p-NO₂-Cbzo·Leu₂·OMe	L-L	79.5–81.5	−24.1	24	1%, EtOH	462
Carbo-*t*-butyloxy (C-*t*-Buo) derivatives						
C-*t*-Buo·Ala·Gly·OMe	DL	101–102	–	–	–	464
C-*t*-Buo·Gly·Phe·OEt	DL	102–103	–	–	–	465
C-*t*-Buo·Gly·Phe·OMe	DL	89–92	–	–	–	464
C-*t*-Buo·Gly·Phe·Gly·OEt	L	98–99	−10.9	25	2%, MeOH	465
C-*t*-Buo·Leu·Gly·OMe	L	128–131	–	–	–	464
C-*t*-Buo·Leu₂·OEt	L-L	130–133	–	–	–	464

C-t-Buo·Phe·β-Ala·OEt	DL	102–106	—	—	—	464
C-t-Buo·Phe·Gly·OEt	L	89.5–90	−4.3	25	2%, EtOH	465
C-t-Buo·Phe·Gly·OMe	DL	150–152	—	—	—	464
C-t-Buo·Val·Gly·OMe	DL	113–114	—	—	—	464

Carbo*cyclo*pentyloxy (C-*cy*-Peo) derivatives

C-*cy*-Peo·Ala·Gly·OMe	DL	84–87	—	—	—	464
C-*cy*-Peo·β-Ala·Phe·OMe	DL	102–105	—	—	—	464
C-*cy*-Peo·Gly₂·OMe	—	67–70	—	—	—	464
C-*cy*-Peo·Gly·Phe·OMe	DL	104–105	—	—	—	464
C-*cy*-Peo·Ileu·Gly·OMe	L	144–146	—	—	—	464
C-*cy*-Peo·Ileu·His·OMe	L-L	199–203	—	—	—	464
C-*cy*-Peo·Leu₂·OEt	L-L	139–140	—	—	—	464
C-*cy*-Peo·Met·Gly·OMe	DL	78–100	—	—	—	464
C-*cy*-Peo·Nval·Gly·OMe	DL	93–95	—	—	—	464
C-*cy*-Peo·(O-Ac-Tyr)·Gly·OMe	L	143–147	—	—	—	464
C-*cy*-Peo·Val·Gly·OMe	DL	135–136	—	—	—	464
C-*cy*-Peo·Val·Gly·OMe	L	149–154	—	—	—	464
C-*cy*-Peo·Val·Leu·Gly·OMe	L-L	172–177	—	—	—	464
C-*cy*-Peo·Val·Ser·OMe	L-L	149–155	—	—	—	464

Carbo*cyclo*hexyloxy (C-*cy*-Hexo) derivatives

C-*cy*-Hexo·Gly·Leu·OMe	L	158–159	—	—	—	464
C-*cy*-Hexo·Phe·Gly·OMe	DL	113–115	—	—	—	464

Formyl derivatives

Formyl·(CySBz)₂·OMe	L-L	116–117	—	—	—	432a
Formyl·Phe·Gly·OEt	DL	98.5–99	—	—	—	586
Formyl·Phe·Gly·OEt	L	131–132	+4.4	26	2.3%, EtOH	586
Formyl·(O-Ac-Tyr)·Leu·OBz	L-L	156–157	—	—	—	584a
Formyl·(O-Ac-Tyr)·(Nᵋ-Cbzo-Lys)·OBz	L-L	157	—	—	—	584a

TABLE 10-42 (*continued*)

Compound	Config.	M.P., °C.	$[\alpha]_D$, deg.	Temp., °C.	Concn. and Solvent	Ref.
Formyl derivatives (*continued*)						
Formyl·Val·Gly·OEt	L	156–157	—	—	—	586
Formyl·Val·Phe·OMe	L-L	148–149.5	−43.2	28	1.5%, MeOH	586
Formyl·Val·Phe·Gly·OEt	L-L	187–188	−12.5	28	0.9%, HOAc	586
Phenylthiocarbonyl (PhTC) derivatives						
PhTC·Gly·Ala·OMe	DL	116^p	—	—	—	578, 579
PhTC·Gly·CySH·OEt	—	114	—	—	—	578
PhTC·Gly$_2$·OEt	—	127^q	—	—	—	578, 579
Phthalyl (Phth) derivatives						
Phth·Ala·Gly·OEt	L	136.5–137	—	—	—	808b
Phth·Ala·Gly$_2$·OEt	L	165–166.5	−16.1	17	1.3%, EtOH	808b
Phth·Ala·Pro·OBz	L-L	101–102	−135	27	—, EtOH	785
Phth·CySH·Met·OEt	L-L	108–109	−42.3	24	0.6%, benzene	875a
Phth·Glu·OH	L	162	—	—	—	527
└Glu·(OEt)$_2$	L					
Phth·Glu·OMe·Gly·OMe	L	82–83	−3.1	21	1.4%, CHCl$_3$	533
Phth·Glu·OH	DL	157–158	—	—	—	533
└Gly·OMe						
Phth·Glu·OH	L	177.5–179	−25	—	2%, EtOH	535
└Tyr·OEt	L					
Phth·Gly·Ala·OEt	L	206–207	—	—	—	797
Phth·Gly·CySBz·OEt	L	165	−29.0	20	0.1%, EtOH	390, 808b

CHEMICAL PROCEDURES FOR SYNTHESIS OF PEPTIDES

Compound	Config	M.p. (°C)	[α]	T (°C)	Solvent	References
Phth·Gly·Glu·(OBz)$_2$	L	90–93	–17.1	20	2%, 96% EtOH	677
Phth·Gly·Glu·(OEt)$_2$	L	143	–17.8	22	2.1%, 96% EtOH	677
Phth·Gly·Glu·(OMe)$_2$	L	158–160	–16.2	22	0.6%, 96% EtOH	677, 536, 723, 740, 758, 759, 774, 788, 791a, 797, 798, 808a, 808b, 918
Phth·Gly$_2$·OEt	–	194–195	–	–	–	522, 731
Phth·Gly$_2$·OMe	–	203–204	–	–	–	536
Phth·Gly$_2$·CySBz·OEt	L	187–188	–9.1	20	0.8%, CHCl$_3$	413, 536, 791a, 808b, 919
Phth·Gly$_3$·OEt	–	229–230	–	–	–	536
Phth·Gly$_2$·Leu·OEt	L	156–157	+21.2	29	3.3%, CHCl$_3$	537
Phth·Gly·His·OMe	L	199–201	–	–	–	526
Phth·Gly·(3:4-di-OH-Phe)·OMe	DL	196–197 d.	–	–	–	721, 722, 734, 758
Phth·Gly·Leu·OEt	L	144–145	–26.5^r	24	2%, EtOH	734, 757, 758
Phth·Gly·Phe·OEt	DL	148–152	–	–	–	808b
Phth·Gly·Phe·OEt	L	148.5–149.5	–	–	–	537, 685
Phth·Gly·Ser·OMe	DL	225	–	–	–	535, 721, 734, 797
Phth·Gly·Tyr·OEt	L	163–164^s	+43.0	24	2%, EtOH	808b
Phth·Gly·Val·OMe	L	188–189.5	–9.2	22	0.6%, EtOAc	808b
Phth·Leu·Gly·OEt	L	118–118.5	–6.7	24	1%, EtOH	522, 758, 785, 788, 808a, 808b
Phth·Phe·Gly·OEt	L	160–161	–146	26	2%, EtOH	721
Phth·Phe·Gly$_2$·OEt	DL	162–163	–	–	–	785, 788
Phth·Phe·Leu·OEt	L-L	108–109	–115	26	–, EtOH	788
Phth·Phe$_2$·OMe	L-L	101–102	–128	26	–, EtOH	524
Phth·(O-Ac-Ser)·Phe·OMe	L-L	131–132	+14.7	27	2.6%, EtOH	

TABLE 10-42 (continued)

Compound	Config.	M.P., °C.	$[\alpha]_D$, deg.	Temp., °C.	Concn. and Solvent	Ref.
Phthalyl (Phth) derivatives (continued)						
Phth·Thr·Leu·OBz	L-L	109–110	−16.7	26	5.1%, EtOH	524
Phth·Thr·Phe·OMe	L-L	153–154	+1.9	27	6.6%, DMF	524
Phth·Thr·Phe₂·OMe	3 L	147–148	−25.6	27	1.8%, EtOH	524
Phth·Val·(N^δ-Cbzo-Orn)·OMe	L-L	104.5–105	—	—	—	544
Phth·Val·(N^δ-Cbzo-Orn)·Leu·Phe·Pro·OMe	3 L-D-L	117–119	—	—	—	544
Phth·Val₃·OMe	3 L	163.5–164.5	+21.6	30	2.6%, CHCl₃	543a
Phth·Val₃·OMe	2 L-D	176–177	−9.8	28	2.9%, CHCl₃	543a
Phth·Val₃·OMe	L-D-L	156.5–157.5	+64.2	26	2.7%, CHCl₃	543a
Phth·Val₃·OMe	L-2 D	158–159	+53.8	25	2.6%, CHCl₃	543a
Phth·Val₃·OMe	3 D	163–164.5	−21.7	28	2.8%, CHCl₃	543a
Phth·Val₃·OMe	2 D-L	176–177	+9.7	28	2.6%, CHCl₃	543a
Phth·Val₃·OMe	D-2 L	158–159	−53.0	25	2.4%, CHCl₃	543a
Phth·Val₃·OMe	D-L-D	156.5–157.5	−63.2	26	2.6%, CHCl₃	543a
p-Toluenesulfonyl (Tos) derivatives						
Tos·CySBz·Tyr·OEt	L-L	109–110	+3.7	19	2.4%, 95% EtOH	400, 432
Tos·CySBz·Tyr·Gly·OEt	L-L	134.5	—	—	—	400
Tos·CySBz·Tyr·Ileu·OMe	3 L	193–194	—	—	—	400, 868, 919a
Tos·CySBz·Tyr·Leu·OEt	3 L	154	—	—	—	400
Tos·CySBz·(O-Ac-Tyr)·Leu·OEt	3 L	166–168	—	—	—	400
Tos·CySBz·Tyr·Leu·OMe	3 L	193	—	—	—	400
Tos·CySBz·Tyr·Leu·Gly·OEt	3 L	194–195	—	—	—	400
Tos·CySBz·Tyr·Phe·OMe	3 L	180–181	−42.6	22	1.2%, MeOH	482a
Tos·Glu-NH₂·Asp-NH₂·CySBz·OBz	3 L	228–229	−30.7	23	1%, DMF	482a, 906

Compound	Config.	m.p.	[α]	conc.	solvent	Ref.
Tos·Glu-NH₂·Asp-NH₂·CySBz·OBz	3 L	193–195	—	—	—	868
Tos·Glu-NH₂·CySBz·OEt	L-L	178–180	+26.1	22	1.0%, dioxane	432a
Tos·Glu-NH₂·(CySBz)₂·OBz	3 L	176–177	—	—	—	432a
Tos·Glu·NH₂	L	178	+25.0	21	1.5%, HOAc	701
└─Gly·OBz						
Tos·Glu-NH₂·Gly·OEt	L	169–170	−2	—	1%, DMF	803
Tos·Glu·NH₂	L	190	+27.9	21	0.5%, HOAc	701
└─Gly·OEt						
Tos·Glu·OEt·Gly·OEt	L	109	—	—	—	890
Tos·Glu·OH	D	189–190	—	—	—	433
└─Gly·OEt						
Tos·Glu·OH	L	191	—	—	—	890
└─Gly·OEt						
Tos·Glu·OMe·Gly·OMe	L	99–100	—	—	—	890
Tos·Glu·OH	L	181–182	—	—	—	890
└─Tyr·OEt						
Tos·Ileu·Gly·OEt	L	160–161	—	—	—	438
Tos·Ileu·Leu·OMe	L-L	147–148	—	—	—	438
Tos·(Nᵋ-Cbzo-Lys)·Gly·OBz	L	127.5–128.5	—	—	—	429
Tos·(Nᵋ-Cbzo-Lys)·Gly·OEt	L	103–104	—	—	—	429
Tos·(Nᵟ-Cbzo-Orn)·Gly·OBz	L	132–133	—	—	—	429
Tos·(Nᵟ-Cbzo-Orn)·Gly·OEt	DL	124.5–125.5	—	—	—	429
Tos·(Nᵟ-Cbzo-Orn)·Gly·OEt	L	132.5–133.5	—	—	—	429
Tos·Pro·Leu·Gly·OEt	L-L	145–146	—	—	—	717
Tos·Thr·Thr·OMe	D-D	182–184	+16.0	20	2%, MeOH	687
Tos·Thr·Thr·OMe	L-L	182–183	−15.9	17	2%, MeOH	687
Tos·Val·(Nᵟ-Cbzo-Orn)·OMe	L-L	187	0	20	1.8%, CHCl₃	421
Tos·Val·Orn·Leu·Phe·Pro·OMe·HCl	3 L-D-L	236	−94.6	18	1%, MeOH	421
Tos·Val·(Nᵟ-Cbzo-Orn)·Leu·Phe·Pro·OMe	3 L-D-L	201	—	—	—	421

TABLE 10-42 (continued)

Compound	Config.	M.P., °C.	$[\alpha]_D$, deg.	Temp., °C.	Concn. and Solvent	Ref.
Trifluoroacetyl (TFA) derivatives						
TFA·Ala$_2$·OEt	L-L	139	−77.8	9	1%, EtOH	573, 814
TFA·Ala$_3$·OEt	3 L	241–243	−79.4	22	0.3%, EtOH	814
TFA·Ala·Gly·OEt	DL	115–116	—	—	—	568, 571, 573, 814
TFA·Ala·Gly·OEt	L	99–101	−58.8	15	1.6%, EtOH	573, 814
TFA·CyS·Gly·OEt	L	190.5–191	−130	20	2%, acetone	477
TFA·CyS·Gly·OEt └CySH·Gly·OEt	L	165.5	−41.7	20	0.7%, EtOH	477
TFA·Glu·OEt └CyS·Gly·OEt	L	226	−21.3	20	0.5%, HOAc	477
TFA·Glu·OEt └CyS·Gly·OEt	L					
TFA·Glu·OEt └Glu·(OEt)$_2$	L	84	−5.6	23	0.7%, tetrahydrofuran	576
TFA·Gly$_2$·OEt	—	145	—	—	—	568, 573, 814
TFA·Gly$_3$·OEt	—	232–234	—	—	—	814
TFA·Phe·Gly·OEt	DL	131–133	—	—	—	814
TFA·Pro·Gly·OEt	L	113	−68.2	17	0.5%, tetrahydrofuran	576
TFA·Pro·Gly·OEt	DL	112–114	—	—	—	814

Compound	Config	mp (°C)	[α]	Temp	Solvent	Ref
TFA·Val·Ala·OEt	L-L	135–137	−53.0	22	1.3%, EtOH	814
TFA·Val·Gly·OEt	L	141	−64.4	15	1%, EtOH	573, 814
TFA·Val·Gly·OEt	DL	144–145	—	—	—	571
Triphenylmethyl (Trityl) derivatives						
Trityl·Ala·Gly·OEt	DL	147–148	—	—	—	547
Trityl·Ala·Gly·OEt	L	155–165	—	—	—	548
Trityl·Arg·Try·OMe·HCl	L-L	170	+14.6	22	5.3%, DMF	471a
Trityl·Asp-NH₂·(CyS-Trityl)·Pro·Leu·Gly·OMe	4 L	—	−77	20	1%, CHCl₃	790
Trityl·Asp-NH₂·Gly·OBz	L	160	−71	20	1%, CHCl₃	790
Trityl·Asp-NH₂·Gly·OEt	L	182	—	—	—	548a
Trityl·(CyS-Trityl)·Pro·Leu·Gly·OMe	3 L	130 d.	+112	20	2%, CHCl₃	673
Trityl·(CyS-Trityl)·Tyr·OEt	L-L	183ᵗ	+77	20	2%, CHCl₃	673
Trityl·(CyS-Trityl)·Tyr·Ileu·Glu·OMe· Asp·OMe·(CyS-Trityl)·Pro·Leu·Gly·OMe	8 L	120	0	20	2%, CHCl₃	673
Trityl·Glu-NH₂·Asp-NH₂·OBz	L-L	170	−5.5	25	1%, EtOH	790
Trityl·Glu·OMe·Asp·OMe· (CyS-Trityl)·Pro·Leu·Gly·OMe	5 L	130	−26	20	2%, CHCl₃	673
Trityl·Glu-NH₂·Asp-NH₂· (CyS-Trityl)·Pro·Leu·Gly·OMe	5 L	—	−35	20	1%, CHCl₃	790
Trityl·Glu·NH₂ └─Gly·OBz	L	160	+27	20	1%, CHCl₃	790
Trityl·Glu·OMe·Leu·OMe	L-L	121–122	+10.0	30	2%, MeOH	675
Trityl·Gly·Ala·OMe	DL	135	—	—	—	548
Trityl·Gly₂·OBz	—	153	—	—	—	548
Trityl·Gly₂·OEt	—	162	—	—	—	545, 546, 547, 548, 806
Trityl·Gly₂·OMe	—	165	—	—	—	548
Trityl·Gly₃·OEt	—	185.5–186	—	—	—	806
Trityl·Gly₄·OEt	—	180.5 d.	—	—	—	806
Trityl·Gly₂·Phe·OEt	DL	149	—	—	—	546

TABLE 10-42 (continued)

Compound	Config.	M.P., °C.	$[\alpha]_D$, deg.	Temp., °C.	Concn. and Solvent	Ref.
Triphenylmethyl (Trityl) derivatives *(continued)*						
Trityl·Gly·(N$^\varepsilon$-Cbzo-Lys)·OMe	L	75 d.	−11.9	21	2.0%, pyridine	471a
Trityl·Gly·(N$^\varepsilon$-Cbzo-Lys)·Pro·Val·OMe	3 L	65 d.	−33.5	21	2.0%, MeOH	471a
Trityl·Gly·Phe·Gly·OEt	DL	149–149.5	–	–	–	812b
Trityl·Gly·Phe·Gly·OEt	L	140	–	–	–	548a
Trityl·Gly·Try·OMe	DL	164–165	–	–	–	547
N,N'-diTrityl·His·Phe·OMe	L-L	95 d.	+18.0	22	2.8%, MeOH	471a
N,N'-diTrityl·His·Phe·Arg·Try·OMe·HCl	4 L	170–178 d.	−27.6	21	1.3%, DMF	471a
Trityl·Try·Gly·OEt	DL	203	–	–	–	789
Trityl·Val·(N$^\varepsilon$-Tos-Lys)·Leu·Phe·Pro·OMe	3 L-D-L	111	−28	24	1.0%, MeOH	626a
Trityl·[Val·(N$^\varepsilon$-Tos-Lys)·Leu·Phe·Pro]$_2$·OMe	[3 L-D-L]$_2$	–	−49	23	0.9%, MeOH	626a
Trityl·Val·(N$^\delta$-Tos-Orn)·Leu·Phe·Pro·OMe	3 L-D-L	123.5–125.5	–	–	–	719
Trityl·[Val·(N$^\delta$-Tos-Orn)·Leu·Phe·Pro]$_2$·OMe	[3 L-D-L]$_2$	140–142	−67	23	0.7%, MeOH	719
o-Nitrophenoxyacetyl (o-NO$_2$-Phoac) derivatives						
o-NO$_2$-Phoac·Gly$_2$·OEt	–	142–143.5	–	–	–	494
o-NO$_2$-Phoac·Phe·Leu·OMe	L-L	164–167	–	–	–	494

[a] M.p. = 201° (558).
[b] M.p. = 113° (726); m.p. 128° (878).
[c] M.p. = 135° (472).
[d] M.p. = 151–152° (767).
[e] M.p. = 150–152° (882).
[f] M.p. = 100–101° (390).
[g] M.p. = 148° (390).
[h] Appears to have dimorphous form melting at 185° (723, 774).
[i] M.p. = 85–86° (805); m.p. = 91° (495).
[j] M.p. = 161–162° (715).
[k] M.p. = 142–145° (707).
[l] M.p. = 106–107° (660).
[m] M.p. = 142–145° (646).
[n] M.p. = 105–106° (380); m.p. = 148.5–149.5 (697, 758).
[o] M.p. = 144–147°, $[\alpha]_D^{24} = +54°$ (1.1% in chloroform) (714).
[p] M.p. = 121–123° (579).
[q] M.p. = 131–133° (579).
[r] $[\alpha]_D = -29.0°$ (2% in ethanol) (721, 758).
[s] M.p. = 167°, $[\alpha]_D = +38°$ (1.3% in ethanol) (797); m.p. = 174–176° (535); m.p. = 164–165°, $[\alpha]_D^{24} = +46.0°$ (2% in ethanol) (721).
[t] M.p. = 135° (673).

CHEMICAL PROCEDURES FOR SYNTHESIS OF PEPTIDES 1149

and the resulting slurry is rapidly extracted several times into ice-cold ethyl acetate. The ethyl acetate solution is dried over anhydrous sodium sulfate and then treated with 4 g. of magnesium oxide and 8 g. of carbobenzoxy chloride (procedure 10–27) with stirring in the cold. The excess carbobenzoxy chloride is destroyed by the addition of a little pyridine, and the ethyl acetate layer is then washed successively with dilute hydrochloric acid, water, dilute sodium bicarbonate solution, and water. After drying over anhydrous sodium sulfate, the ethyl acetate layer is concentrated under reduced pressure to a syrup which is taken up in 50 ml. of methanol previously saturated at 0° with gaseous ammonia. The solution is stored in a pressure bottle for 2 days at room temperature and concentrated *in vacuo* to give 6.5 g. of a crystalline material; m.p. 167°.

Table 10–43 lists the melting point and specific rotation values of several acylated amino acid and dipeptide amides. Preparation of these compounds was achieved principally through the methods cited above. By virtue of the facile cleavage which the trifluoroacetyl and phthalyl groups undergo in the presence of ammonia, amides which incorporate these groups cannot be prepared by ammonolysis of the precursor acylated ester; in such instances, the desired amide derivative may be secured via a reaction of the pertinent reactants mediated by a suitable condensing agent. Amide derivatives of tritylamino acids may be obtained through the di*cyclo*hexylcarbodiimide-induced condensation of the parent tritylamino acid and ammonia. Although the ammonolysis of carbobenzoxylated amino acid and peptide esters (V) generally proceeds satisfactorily with the formation of the desired amide (IV), certain exceptions are known. Thus an attempt by Fruton and Bergmann (916) to prepare carbobenzoxy-L-phenylalanylglycine amide (IV; R = $C_6H_5CH_2$) by treatment of the precursor acylated dipeptide ethyl ester (V) with methanolic NH_3 yielded the amide of 5-benzylhydantoin-3-acetic acid (VI; R = $C_6H_5CH_2$) instead (procedure 10–149); a similar situation was subsequently observed by Dekker, Taylor, and Fruton (627) during attempts to convert, in a comparable manner, ethyl carbobenzoxy-L-leucylglycinate (V; R = $(CH_3)_2CHCH_2$) and ethyl carbobenzoxy-L-methionylglycinate (V; R = $CH_3SCH_2CH_2$) to the corresponding amide derivatives.

$$\underset{\text{IV}}{\overset{\displaystyle C_6H_5CH_2OCO}{\underset{\displaystyle RCHCO-NHCH_2CONH_2}{|\atop NH\atop |}}} \quad \overset{NH_3}{\underset{CH_3OH}{\longleftarrow}} \quad \underset{\text{V}}{\overset{\displaystyle C_6H_5CH_2OCO}{\underset{\displaystyle RCHCO-NHCH_2CO_2Et}{|\atop NH\atop |}}} \quad \overset{NH_3}{\underset{CH_3OH}{\longrightarrow}}$$

$$\underset{\text{VI}}{\overset{\displaystyle CO-N-CH_2CONH_2}{\underset{\displaystyle RCH}{|\quad\;\;|\atop NH\quad CO\atop \diagdown\;\diagup}}} \quad + \underset{\text{VII}}{C_6H_5CH_2OH}$$

Such reactions, which proceed with concomitant cleavage of benzyl alcohol

(discussion continued on p. 1158)

TABLE 10-43
Amide Derivatives of Acylamino Acids and Peptides

Compound	Config.	M.P., °C.	$[\alpha]_D$, deg.	Temp., °C.	Concn. and Solvent	Ref.
N-Benzyl (Bz) derivative						
N-Bz·Asp·NH$_2$	DL	180	—	—	—	555
Benzylsulfonyl (BzSO$_2$) derivative						
BzSO$_2$·Met·NH$_2$	L	141–142	+14.4	25	1%, butanone	601
Carbobenzoxy (Cbzo) derivatives						
Cbzo·β-Ala·NH$_2$	—	164	—	—	—	899
Cbzo·Ala·Gly·NH$_2$	DL	125	—	—	—	920a
Cbzo·β-Ala·Gly·NH$_2$	—	176	—	—	—	899
Cbzo·Ala·Gly·Phe·NH$_2$	L-L	224–225	—	—	—	902
Cbzo·β-Ala·His·NH$_2$	L	179–180	—	—	—	621
Cbzo·Ala·Leu·NH$_2$	D-L	187–188	−6.0	30	1%, EtOH	467
Cbzo·Ala·Leu·NH$_2$	L-L	188–189	−41	30	1%, EtOH	467
Cbzo·Ala·Phe·NH$_2$	L-L	210–211	—	—	—	902
Cbzo·Ala·Tyr·NH$_2$	L-L	216	—	—	—	902
diCbzo·(α,ε-diNH$_2$-Pim)·(NH$_2$)$_2$	DL	223–224	—	—	—	478
Cbzo·NO$_2$-Arg·NH$_2$	L	219–220	—	—	—	541
α,ω,ω-triCbzo·Arg·NH$_2$	L	182–185	—	—	—	904
Cbzo·Asp·NH$_2$	L	164	+6.9	18	1.5%, HOAc	128, 609
Cbzo·Asp·(NH$_2$)$_2$	L	219–223 d.	—	—	—	683
Cbzo·CySBz·Ala·NH$_2$	L-L	181	—	—	—	432a
Cbzo·CySBz·Pro·Leu·Gly·NH$_2$	3 L	170–171	—	—	—	717

Compound		m.p.				Ref.
Cbzo·CySBz·Tyr·Ileu·Glu·NH₂	8 L	241	−51.5	19	2.5%, HOAc	82, 472
Asp·NH₂·CySBz·Pro·Leu·Gly·NH₂						
Cbzo·CySBz·Tyr·Ileu·Glu·NH₂	8 L	234.5–236.5	−44.1	21.7	1%, DMF	623
⌐Asp·NH₂·CySBz·Pro·Leu·Gly·NH₂						
Cbzo·CySBz·Tyr·Ileu·Glu·NH₂·Glu·NH₂· CySBz·Pro·Leu·Gly·NH₂	8 L	260	—	—	—	629
Cbzo·CySBz·Tyr·Leu·Glu·NH₂·Asp-NH₂· CySBz·Pro·Leu·Gly·NH₂	8 L	228	−54.9	19	2.7%, HOAc	629
Cbzo·CySBz·Tyr·Phe·Glu·NH₂·Asp·NH₂· CySBz·Pro·Leu·Gly·NH₂	8 L	228[a]	−51.8	19	2.5%, HOAc	629, 846
Cbzo·CySBz·Tyr·Val·Glu·NH₂·Asp·NH₂· CySBz·Pro·Leu·Gly·NH₂	8 L	232	—	—	—	629, 708
Cbzo·CySBz·Pro·(N^ε-Tos-Lys)·Gly·NH₂	3 L	101–104	−29.3	21	1%, CHCl₃	88, 393
Cbzo·Glu·NH₂	L	175	—	—	—	128, 481, 610, 682a
Cbzo·Glu·(NH₂)₂	DL	181–183	—	—	—	921
Cbzo·Glu·OBz·NH₂	L	126–127	—	—	—	922
Cbzo·(γ-OH-Glu)·NH₂	DL	149–150	—	—	—	485
Cbzo·(allo-γ-OH-Glu)·NH₂	DL	160–161	—	—	—	485
Cbzo·Glu·OMe·NH₂	L	118–120	−5.7	24	1%, MeOH	683
Cbzo·Glu·NH₂	L	187.5–188	+7.3	21	3%, DMF	623
⌐Asp·NH₂·OH	L					
Cbzo·Glu·NH₂·Asp·NH₂·CySBz·Pro·Arg·Gly· NH₂·HBr	5 L	—	−34.8	22	1%, DMF	482a
Cbzo·Glu·NH₂·Asp·NH₂·CySBz·Pro·Leu·Gly· NH₂	5 L	206	—	—	—	472
Cbzo·Glu·NH₂·Asp·NH₂·CySBz·Pro·Leu·Gly· NH₂·½H₂O	5 L	209–210	—	—	—	868

TABLE 10-43 (continued)

Specific Rotation

Compound	Config.	M.P., °C.	$[\alpha]_D$, deg.	Temp., °C.	Concn. and Solvent	Ref.
Carbobenzoxy (Cbzo) derivatives (continued)						
Cbzo·Glu·NH₂	5 L	212–214	—	—	—	623
└─Asp·NH₂·CySBz·Pro·Leu·Gly·NH₂						
Cbzo·Glu·NH₂·Glu·NH₂·CySBz·Pro·Leu·Gly·NH₂	5 L	238	—	—	—	629
Cbzo·Glu·Leu·NH₂	L-L	165–169	—	—	—	912
Cbzo·Glu·Phe·NH₂	L-L	185–187	—	—	—	923
Cbzo·Glu·Tyr·NH₂	L-L	181	—	—	—	709
Cbzo·Glu·NH₂·Tyr·NH₂	L-L	240	—	—	—	709
Cbzo·Gly·NH₂	—	138–139	—	—	—	684, 795, 924
Cbzo·Gly·β-Ala·NH₂	—	179	—	—	—	899
Cbzo·Gly·Ala·NH₂	DL	146–147	—	—	—	830a, 920a
Cbzo·Gly·Glu·Gly·NH₂	L	175	—	—	—	700
Cbzo·Gly₂·NH₂	—	179–181	—	—	—	916
Cbzo·Gly₃·NH₂	—	220	—	—	—	911
Cbzo·Gly₂·Leu·NH₂	L	181–182	—	—	—	912
Cbzo·Gly₂·Phe·NH₂	L	196–197	—	—	—	902
Cbzo·Gly·His·NH₂	L	212–213 d.	—	—	—	925
Cbzo·Gly·Hypro·NH₂	L	208	—	—	—	169
Cbzo·Gly·Glu·NH₂	L	185	—	—	—	878
Cbzo·Gly·Leu·NH₂	L	123–124	—	—	—	912
Cbzo·Gly·(Nᵋ-Cbzo-Lys)·NH₂	L	134–138	—	—	—	358, 833
Cbzo·Gly·(Nᵋ-Cbzo-Lys)·Gly·NH₂	L	90–95	—	—	—	358

Cbzo·Gly·Met·NH₂	L	131–134	—	—	—	627
Cbzo·Gly·Phe·NH₂	L	130	—	—	—	916
Cbzo·Gly·Phe·Gly·NH₂	DL	161.5–162	—	—	—	812b
Cbzo·Gly·Phe·Gly·NH₂	L	178	—	—	—	700
Cbzo·Gly·Phe·Gly·Phe·Gly·NH₂	L-L	192–193	—	—	—	902
Cbzo·Gly·Pro·NH₂	L	150–151	—	—	—	169
Cbzo·Gly·Try·NH₂	L	145	—	—	—	505
Cbzo·Gly·Tyr·NH₂	L	170	—	—	—	916
Cbzo·Gly·Tyr·Gly·NH₂	L	192	—	—	—	700
Cbzo·Gly·Val·NH₂	L	181	—	—	—	920a
Cbzo·His·NH₂·½H₂O	DL	196–197	—	—	—	621
Cbzo·His·Leu·NH₂	L	183–184	—	—	—	621
Cbzo·His·Phe·NH₂	L-L	203–204	—	—	—	621
Cbzo·His·Tyr·NH₂·½H₂O	L-L	205–206	—	—	—	621
diCbzo·(δ-OH-Lys)·NH₂	DL	154	—	—	—	830a
diCbzo·(δ-allo-OH-Lys)·Gly·NH₂	DL	83–85	—	—	—	830a
Cbzo·tert-Leu·NH₂	D	—	−15.5	26	2%, EtOH	371
Cbzo·Leu·NH₂	D	123–124	—	—	—	926
Cbzo·Leu·NH₂	L	122–123	—	—	—	926
Cbzo·Leu·Ala·NH₂	L-D	181–182	−6.0	22	1%, EtOH	467
Cbzo·Leu·Ala·NH₂	L-L	189	−26.0	27	0.6%, EtOH	467
Cbzo·Leu·Gly·NH₂	DL	138–139	—	—	—	805
Cbzo·Leu·Gly·NH₂	L	80	−10.5	19	1.8%, CHCl₃	472
Cbzo·Leu·Phe·NH₂	L-L	176–178	—	—	—	660
diCbzo·Lys·NH₂	L	155	0	17	0.7%, pyridine	358, 649
diCbzo·Lys·Gly·NH₂	L	135	—	—	—	833
diCbzo·Lys·(Nᵉ-Cbzo-Lys)·NH₂	L-L	203–204	—	—	—	833
diCbzo·Lys·(Nᵉ-Cbzo-Lys)·Tyr·NH₂	3 L	188	—	—	—	584a
diCbzo·Lys·Phe·NH₂	L-L	170	—	—	—	660

TABLE 10-43 (continued)

Carbobenzoxy (Cbzo) derivatives (continued)

Compound	Config.	M.P., °C.	$[\alpha]_D$, deg.	Temp., °C.	Concn. and Solvent	Ref.
diCbzo·Lys·Tyr·NH$_2$	L-L	183	—	—	—	584a, 660
Cbzo·Met·NH$_2$	DL	119–121	—	—	—	627
Cbzo·Met·NH$_2$	D	125	—	—	—	627
Cbzo·Met·NH$_2$	L	125	—	—	—	627
Cbzo·Met·Gly·NH$_2$	L	120–122	—	—	—	627
Cbzo·Met$_2$·NH$_2$	L-L	196	—	—	—	627
Cbzo·Phe·NH$_2$	L	167	+12.0	20	1%, CHCl$_3$	793, 916
Cbzo·Phe·Gly·NH$_2$	L	134	—	—	—	916
Cbzo·Phe$_2$·NH$_2$	L-L	230	—	—	—	916
Cbzo·Phe·Tyr·NH$_2$	L-L	221	—	—	—	916
Cbzo·Pro·NH$_2$	DL	117	—	—	—	927
Cbzo·Pro·NH$_2$	D	94	+33.9	23	2%, EtOH	927
Cbzo·Pro·NH$_2$	L	94	−33.8	23	2%, EtOH	927
Cbzo·Pro·Leu·Gly·NH$_2$	L-L	163	−71.9	20	2.5%, EtOH	472, 717, 86
Cbzo·Pro·(N$^\epsilon$-Tos-Lys)·Gly·NH$_2$	L-L	183–185	—	—	—	393
Cbzo·Pro·Phe·NH$_2$	L-L	180–181	—	—	—	660
Cbzo·Pro·Tyr·NH$_2$	L-L	172–173	—	—	—	660
Cbzo·Ser·NH$_2$	L	132–133	+14.4	26	5%, EtOH	501
Cbzo·Ser·Phe·NH$_2$	L-L	189	—	—	—	928
Cbzo·Thr·NH$_2$	L	82–83	—	—	—	627
Cbzo·Try·NH$_2$	L	187–188	—	—	—	612
Cbzo·Try·Gly·NH$_2$	L	135–136	—	—	—	621

Compound	Config.	M.p. (°C)	[α]	c	Solvent	Ref.
Cbzo·Tyr·Gly·NH₂	L	116	—	—	—	700
Cbzo·Tyr·Gly₂·NH₂	L	218	—	—	—	700
Cbzo·Tyr·Phe·NH₂	L-L	220	—	—	—	916
Cbzo·Tyr₂·NH₂	L-L	187–189	—	—	—	916
Cbzo·Val·Gly·NH₂	DL	166	—	—	—	920a

Carboallyloxy (Callo) derivatives

Compound	Config.	M.p. (°C)	[α]	c	Solvent	Ref.
Callo·Gly·NH₂	—	107–107.5	—	—	—	684
Callo·Leu·NH₂	DL	83–85	—	—	—	684

p-Nitrocarbobenzoxy (p-NO₂-Cbzo) derivatives

Compound	Config.	M.p. (°C)	[α]	c	Solvent	Ref.
p-NO₂-Cbzo·Arg·Gly·NH₂·picrate	L	165–168	−3.8	22	1%, acetone-H₂O (4:1)	510, 511
p-NO₂-Cbzo·CySBz·Pro·Arg·Gly·NH₂·picrate	3 L	182–185	−47.7	22	1%, acetone-H₂O (4:1)	510, 511
p-NO₂-Cbzo·Asp·NH₂	DL	162–163	—	—	—	509
p-NO₂-Cbzo·Glu·NH₂	L	166–170	+4.0	24	10%, DMF	509
p-NO₂-Cbzo·Ileu·Glu-NH₂·Asp-NH₂·CySBz·Pro·Leu·Gly·NH₂	6 L	242–243	—	—	—	868

Carbo-t-butyloxy (C-t-Buo) derivatives

Compound	Config.	M.p. (°C)	[α]	c	Solvent	Ref.
C-t-Buo·Leu·NH₂	L	136–140	—	—	—	464
C-t-Buo·Val·NH₂	DL	146–148	—	—	—	464

Phthalyl (Phth) derivatives

Compound	Config.	M.p. (°C)	[α]	c	Solvent	Ref.
Phth·Asp·NH₂	L	220–222	—	—	—	885
Phth·Asp-OMe·NH₂	DL	141	—	—	—	685
Phth·Glu·NH₂	DL	170–172	—	—	—	607
Phth·Glu-OBz·NH₂	DL	126–128	—	—	—	607
Phth·Gly·NH₂	—	259–260	—	—	—	740
Phth·Gly₂·NH₂	—	252–253 d.	—	—	—	798
Phth·Leu·Gly·NH₂	D	188	+24	—	1%, MeOH	798

TABLE 10-43 (*continued*)

Compound	Config.	M.P., °C.	$[\alpha]_D$, deg.	Temp., °C.	Concn. and Solvent	Ref.
p-Toluenesulfonyl (Tos) derivatives						
Tos·Arg·NH$_2$·HCl	L	—	—	—	—	422
Tos·CySBz·Tyr·Ileu·Glu-NH$_2$·Asp-NH$_2$· CySBz·Pro·Leu·Gly·NH$_2$·H$_2$O	8 L	242–244	—	—	—	868
Tos·CySBz·Tyr·Phe·Glu-NH$_2$·Asp-NH$_2$· CySBz·Pro·(N$^\epsilon$-Tos-Lys)·Gly·NH$_2$	8 L	226–230	−23.0	18	2.1%, DMF	88, 432
Tos·Glu·NH$_2$	DL	158–170	—	—	—	434
Tos·Glu·(NH$_2$)$_2$	L	220–221 d.	+16.2	22	1.8%, HOAc	435, 686
Tos·Glu-OMe·NH$_2$	L	164–165	—	—	—	436
Tos·Glu-NH$_2$·Asp·CySBz·NH$_2$	3 L	222–226	—	—	—	868
Tos·Glu-NH$_2$·CySBz·NH$_2$	L-L	226	—	—	—	432*a*
Tos·Glu·OH └─Gly·NH$_2$	L	208	—	—	—	890
Tos·Ileu·Glu-NH$_2$·Asp-NH$_2$·CySBz·Pro·Leu· Gly·NH$_2$	6 L	236.5–237.5	—	—	—	82
Tos·(N$^\epsilon$-Cbzo-Lys)·NH$_2$	L	157–158	—	—	—	439*b*
Tos·(N$^\epsilon$-Cbzo-Lys)·Gly·NH$_2$	L	164.5–165.5	—	—	—	429
Tos·(N$^\delta$-Cbzo-Orn)·NH$_2$	DL	143–144	—	—	—	439*b*
Tos·(N$^\delta$-Cbzo-Orn)·NH$_2$	L	135–136	—	—	—	439*b*
Tos·(N$^\delta$-Cbzo-Orn)·Gly·NH$_2$	DL	192–193	—	—	—	429
Tos·Val·Orn·Leu·Phe·Pro·NH$_2$·HCl	3 L-D-L	268–270 d.	—	—	—	421

Trifluoroacetyl (TFA) derivatives					
TFA·Ala·NH₂	DL	172	—	—	—	573
TFA·Asp·NH₂	L	191	−29.9	19	1.2%, MeOH	576
TFA·Tyr·NH₂	L	228–228.5 d.	+39.8	27	2%, EtOH	577
Triphenylmethyl (Trityl) derivatives					
Trityl·(CyS-Trityl)·Tyr·Ileu·Glu-NH₂·Asp-NH₂·(CyS-Trityl)·Pro·Leu·Gly·NH₂	8 L	—	+5.0	—	2%, CHCl₃	673
Trityl·Glu-OMe·NH₂	L	120	+26.0	20	1%, CHCl₃	790
Trityl·Gly·(Nᵉ-Cbzo-Lys)·Pro·Val·NH₂	3 L	110 d.	−39.0	21	2.6%, MeOH	471a
N,N′-diTrityl·His·Phe·Arg·Try·Gly·(Nᵉ-Cbzo-Lys)·Pro·Val·NH₂	7 L	180	−27.9	21	2.0%, DMF	471a

[a] M.p. = 210–212°, $[\alpha]_D^{21} = -48.1°$ (0.8% in DMF) (846).

(VII), are reminiscent of the previously discussed (Section 10–6) alkali-mediated conversion of ethyl carboethoxyglycylglycinate to carbonyl-bisglycine via hydantoin-3-acetic acid as a transient intermediate. However, experience has shown that, apart from the exceptions noted above, the ammonolysis of acylated amino acid and peptide esters more often than not leads to the desired amide derivatives.

Illustrative procedure 10–149 (916). Amide of 5-benzylhydantoin-3-acetic acid. A solution of 4.4 g. of carbobenzoxy-L-phenylalanylglycine ethyl ester (procedure 10–77) in 50 ml. of methanol, previously saturated with ammonia gas at 0°, is stored in a pressure bottle for 2 days at room temperature. Concentration of the reaction mixture yields a crystalline residue which melts at 218° after recrystallization from hot water; yield, 2.4 g.

42. Preparation and Physical Constants of Acylated Peptides (Free Acids). Previous discussion was concerned in part with the preparation of N-acylated peptides (III) *via* the condensation of an acylated amino acid or peptide (I) with a free amino acid or peptide (II) in an alkaline medium under the influence of a suitable condensing agent. An alternative route to these same compounds involves the conversion of an appropriate ester derivative of an acylated peptide (IV; $R' =$ alkyl) to the corresponding free acid (III)

$$RCO_2H + NH_2 \cdots CO_2H \rightarrow RCO-NH \cdots CO_2H \leftarrow RCO-NH \cdots CO_2R'$$
$$\text{I} \qquad \text{II} \qquad\qquad \text{III} \qquad\qquad \text{IV}$$

by selective cleavage of the ester moiety. Toward this end, saponification of the methyl, the ethyl, or, less frequently, the benzyl ester derivative of an acylated peptide (IV; $R' = CH_3$, C_2H_5 or $C_6H_5CH_2$) with a slight excess of alkali, followed by acidification of the resulting alkali metal salt of the carboxylic acid, has been most commonly employed. In routine practice, the pertinent acylated peptide ester is shaken with 1 to 2 equivalents of aqueous alkali at room temperature or in the cold until complete solution is effected and the reaction mixture then neutralized with a slight excess of mineral acid (procedure 10–150) or, in the presence of the highly acid-susceptible N-trityl and N-formyl groups, with either acetic acid or *exactly one equivalent* of a mineral acid. In the case of some of the more sparingly soluble esters, it is sometimes convenient to use a mixture of aqueous alkali with a water-miscible organic solvent such as methanol, ethanol, or dioxane as the reaction solvent in order to expedite solution (procedures 10–151 and 10–152). The rate of saponification will of course vary with the degree of steric hindrance imposed by the side chain of the amino acid residue bearing the ester group. Hence the time required for completion of the reaction may vary from only a few minutes, as in the case of a C-terminal glycine residue, to several hours where more hindered residues, e.g., isoleucine or valine, are implicated. With the notable exceptions of N-phthalylated derivatives which undergo partial hydrolysis in strongly alkaline media

CHEMICAL PROCEDURES FOR SYNTHESIS OF PEPTIDES 1159

to the corresponding phthalamic acids, and trifluoroacetyl derivatives which exhibit a marked tendency toward hydrolytic fission of the acyl substituent under only mildly alkaline conditions, selective saponification of the ester group as described above may be considered generally applicable to the N-acylated peptide esters listed in Table 10–42. It should be kept in mind, however, that other alkali-susceptible groups such as the O-acyl substituents of O-acylated hydroxyamino acid residues and the ω-ester functions of α-aminodicarboxylic acid residues will undergo hydrolysis under the same conditions (Section 10–39); additionally, the action of alkali will lead to cleavage at the imide linkage of the pyrrolidone ring of a pyroglutamic acid residue with the concomitant formation of an α-glutamyl derivative (procedure 10–143).

Illustrative procedure 10–150 (700). Carbobenzoxyglycyl-L-tyrosine. One gram of finely pulverized carbobenzoxyglycyl-L-tyrosine ethyl ester (procedure 10–80) is shaken with 7 ml. of N sodium hydroxide for 15 min. at room temperature, the reaction mixture filtered, and the filtrate acidified with N hydrochloric acid with cooling. The resulting syrup is extracted into ethyl acetate and the latter solution extracted with aqueous sodium bicarbonate solution. Careful acidification of the aqueous extracts, with cooling, results in the deposition of the desired product. Recrystallization is effected from ethyl acetate; m.p. 107°.

Carbobenzoxy-α-L-glutamyl-L-valine (610). A solution of 0.8 g. of carbobenzoxy-α-L-glutamyl-L-valine ethyl ester (procedure 10–133) in 5 ml. of N sodium hydroxide is permitted to stand at room temperature for 1 hr. and then acidified with 5N hydrochloric acid. An oil precipitates which soon crystallizes. After some 30 min., the product is filtered off, washed with water, air-dried, and finally washed with boiling ether; yield, 0.5 g. (68%). Recrystallization is effected from ethyl acetate–petroleum ether; m.p. 131–133°.

Illustrative procedure 10–151 (473). Carbobenzoxy-S-benzyl-L-cysteinyl-S-benzyl-L-cysteine. A mixture of 454 g. of carbobenzoxy-S-benzyl-L-cysteinyl-S-benzyl-L-cysteine ethyl ester (procedure 10–70) in 4.6 l. of dioxane and 480 ml. of 2N sodium hydroxide is shaken for 5 hr. at 5° and the clear solution then treated with 167 ml. of 6N hydrochloric acid. The reaction mixture is condensed to a small volume *in vacuo* at a temperature not exceeding 40° and water added thereto. An oil appears which solidifies slowly upon agitation with a glass rod. The solid material is filtered over suction, washed with water, dried, and subsequently crystallized from ethyl acetate by the careful addition of petroleum ether; yield, 355 g.; m.p. 152°; $[\alpha]_D^{26} = -50.6°$ (2% in acetone).

Illustrative procedure 10–152 (547, 548). Tritylglycylglycine. Two grams of tritylglycylglycine ethyl ester (procedure 10–102) is boiled under reflux for 2 min. with 20 ml. of 20% methanolic potassium hydroxide solution. After dilution with 20 ml. of water and removal of the methanol by distillation *in vacuo*, the solution is cooled and then acidified with acetic acid. The desired product precipitates in the form of a gel which, after filtration, is transformed into fine needles upon treatment with a little ether. Recrystallization is effected from ethanol in an over-all yield which is greater than 90% of theory; m.p. 180°.

Precaution must sometimes be observed in the alkaline saponification of N-carbobenzoxylated peptide esters (V) wherein a glycine residue is adjacent to the N-terminal amino acid residue, since different products can here arise depending upon both the amount of alkali employed and the time permitted for the saponification to continue (759a). Whereas the use of one molar equivalent of alkali at room temperature should generally lead to the corresponding free acid in satisfactory yield, progressively poorer yields of the desired product are likely to be encountered as the amount of alkali is increased. Thus, for example, the saponification of carbobenzoxyglycylglycine ethyl ester with one equivalent of 0.5N sodium hydroxide at room temperature gives the expected acid in 85% yield; however, the use of two equivalents of alkali permits the ultimate isolation of the desired carbobenzoxyglycylglycine in only 47% yield after one hour, whilst none of the latter can be isolated if the reaction time is prolonged to five hours (759a). Such a situation may be attributed to the fact that, in peptide derivatives of this type (V), alkali induces the elimination of benzyl alcohol from the carbobenzoxy group with a concomitant rearrangement of the molecule to either the urea derivative (VI) or the hydantoin-3-acetic acid derivative (VII).

$$C_6H_5CH_2OCO-NHCHRCO-NHCH_2CO_2Et \qquad \underset{\underset{NHCH_2CO_2H}{\diagdown}}{\overset{NHCHRCO_2H}{\diagup}}CO \qquad \underset{\underset{CO}{\diagdown}}{\overset{RCH-CO}{\diagup}}\underset{}{N}H\underset{}{N}CH_2CO_2H$$

$$\qquad\qquad V \qquad\qquad\qquad\qquad\qquad VI \qquad\qquad\qquad VII$$

This phenomenon is reminiscent of the rearrangements previously shown to occur with carboethoxylated and carbomethoxylated peptide derivatives in alkaline media (Section 10–6). Under the mild saponification conditions routinely employed in synthetic peptide procedures, no similar rearrangements should ordinarily be expected to occur for those peptide sequences in which the amino acid residue adjacent to the N-terminal residue is other than glycine.

The marked susceptibility of the N-phthalyl group to partial hydrolysis under alkaline conditions has led to the utilization of auxiliary methods for the cleavage of ester groups from derivatives which incorporate this masking substituent. In this connection, both acid hydroylsis of the methyl, ethyl, and benzyl ester derivatives and catalytic hydrogenolysis of the benzyl ester derivative have been successfully employed. Despite the extremely mild conditions imposed by the latter of these methods, its use with N-phthalylated peptide derivatives has been hitherto restricted to the debenzylation of dibenzyl phthalylglycyl-L-glutamate (677); as catalytic reduction also leads to the facile scission of the carbobenzoxy, p-nitrocarbobenzoxy, carboallyloxy, and N-benzyl substituents, the method has been more extensively exploited for the preparation of free peptides from benzyl ester intermediates which embody these N-acyl blocking groups (Section 10–44). Removal of the ester moiety from N-phthalylated dipeptide esters has been most commonly achieved through the hydrolytic action of dilute aqueous hydrochloric acid either alone or in admixture with acetone (procedure 10–153) (522, 524, 533, 535, 536, 677, 797). As completion of the hydrolytic process may generally require several hours at elevated temperatures, the method is not to be recommended for the more labile longer-chain polypeptide derivatives. Analogous use of dilute hydrochloric acid in 50% ethanol has permitted simultaneous cleavage of the ester group and opening of the pyrrolidone ring of tosyl-L-pyroglutamylglycine ethyl ester (VIII) to yield the corresponding tosyl-α-glutamylamino acid (IX) (procedure 10–154). The relatively high

$$H_3C-\langle\rangle-SO_2-NH-CHCO-NHCH_2CO_2Et \quad\quad H_3C-\langle\rangle-SO_2-NHCHCO-NHCH_2CO_2H$$

VIII

IX

stability revealed by N-phthalyl and N-tosyl derivatives in the presence of hot mineral acid is apparently not shared by their formyl and carbobenzoxy analogs, among others, which exhibit a marked propensity to undergo deacylation under the hydrolytic influence of this same reagent.

Illustrative procedure 10–153 (524). Phthalyl-L-threonyl-L-phenylalanine. To a solution of 0.84 g. (0.0021 mole) of phthalyl-L-threonyl-L-phenylalanine methyl ester (procedure 10–86) in 30 ml. of acetone is added 10 ml. of water and 5 ml. of concentrated hydrochloric acid. The solution is refluxed for 2.5 hr. and the acetone removed by distillation. The residual mixture is extracted with ethyl acetate and the ethyl acetate fraction extracted with an aqueous sodium bicarbonate solution. After acidification of the aqueous layer, the product is re-extracted into ethyl acetate, the solution dried over anhydrous sodium sulfate, and the solvent removed under reduced pressure. Recrystallization of the resulting crystalline mass from ethanol–water yields 0.51 g. (64%) of the desired material; m.p. 207–208°; $[\alpha]_D^{27} = +23.2°$ (1.7% in ethanol).

Illustrative procedure 10–154 (890). Tosyl-α-L-glutamylglycine. A solution of 1.84 g. of tosyl-L-pyroglutamylglycine ethyl ester (procedure 10–142) in 5 ml. of hot ethanol is treated with 5 ml. of 7% aqueous hydrochloric acid and the mixture heated over a water bath in an open flask for 2 hr. Upon being cooled, the contents of the flask set to a mass of crystals which are collected over suction with the aid of a little water; yield, 1.45 g. (91%). A melting point of 210° is shown after crystallization of the material from its solution in alkali by the addition of acid (see procedure 10–143).

Table 10–44 lists the melting points and specific rotation values of several acylated peptides which have been prepared through the procedures described above.

(discussion continued on p. 1187)

TABLE 10-44
Acylated Peptides (Free Acids)

Compound	Config.	M.P., °C.	$[\alpha]_D$, deg.	Temp., °C.	Concn. and Solvent	Ref.
N-Benzyl (Bz) derivatives						
Bz·Ala·Gly·OH	DL	234–235	—	—	—	551
Bz·Asp·Gly·OH	DL	187	—	—	—	555
diBz·(α-NH₂-n-But)·Gly·OH	DL	175	—	—	—	552
diBz·Gly·Glu·OH	L	176–178	—	—	—	552
diBz·Gly₂·OH	—	138–140	—	—	—	551, 552
diBz·Gly₃·OH	—	—	—	—	—	551
diBz·Gly·Ser·OH	DL	165 d.	—	—	—	552
diBz·Gly·Ser·OH·HCl	DL	165 d.	—	—	—	551
diBz·Gly·Try·OH	DL	165–168	—	—	—	552
diBz·Gly·Val·OH	DL	127–128	—	—	—	552
Bz·Try·Gly·OH	DL	198–200	—	—	—	551
Benzylsulfonyl (BzSO₂) derivatives						
BzSO₂·Leu₂·OH	L-L	140–141	−52.9	24	1%, N NaOH	601
BzSO₂·Met₂·OH	L-D	136–137	−51.3	26	1%, N NaOH	929
BzSO₂·Met₂OH	L-L	107–108	−25.2	26	1%, N NaOH	929
Benzylthiocarbonyl (BzTC) derivative						
BzTC·Gly₂·OH	—	177–178	—	—	—	580
Carboallyloxy (Callo) derivative						
Callo·Leu₂·OH	L-L	113–114	−25.1	22	2%, CHCl₃	930

Carbobenzoxy (Cbzo) derivatives					
Cbzo·Ala₂·OH	D-D	153	—	—	—	666
Cbzo·Ala₂·OH	D-L	116	—	—	—	468
Cbzo·Ala₂·OH	L-D	116.5	—	—	—	666
Cbzo·Ala₂·OH	L-L	152–153	—	—	—	896
Cbzo·Ala₂·OH	L	165	—	—	—	466
Cbzo·Ala·(α-NH₂-isoBut)·OH	L-L	171–172	−9.4	25	1.3%, MeOH	491
Cbzo·Ala·NO₂-Arg·OH	3 L	97–101	+5.5	19	2%, acetone	845
Cbzo·Ala·NO₂-Arg·Asp·OH	D-L	141	—	—	—	468
Cbzo·Ala·(α-NH₂-n-But)·OH	L-L	154	—	—	—	468
Cbzo·Ala·(α-NH₂-n-But)·OH	D-L-D	118–120	−4.5	23	2%, HOAc	891
Cbzo·Ala·Glu·Ala·OH	D-L-L	210–212	−11.4	22	2%, HOAc	891
Cbzo·Ala·Glu·Ala·OH	L-L-D	157–159	−29.5	24	2%, HOAc	891
Cbzo·Ala·Glu·Ala·OH	3 L	130–140	−31.6	24	2%, HOAc	891
Cbzo·Ala·Gly·OH	DL	133	—	—	—	712, 723, 774
Cbzo·Ala·Gly·OH	D	(see ref. 896)	—	—	—	466
Cbzo·Ala·Gly·OH	L	132	−17.4	17	5%, EtOH	466, 613a, 875c
						896
Cbzo·β-Ala·Gly·OH	—	146–149	—	—	—	899
Cbzo·β-Ala·Gly₂·OH	—	184–185	—	—	—	899
Cbzo·Ala·Gly·Tyr·OH	L-L	128	—	—	—	931
Cbzo·Ala·His·OH	L-L	131	—	—	—	359
Cbzo·β-Ala·His·OH	L	160–161	—	—	—	690
Cbzo·Ala·His·OH·2H₂O	L-L	131	—	—	—	359
Cbzo·β-Ala·His·Gly·OH	L	166–167	—	—	—	621
Cbzo·β-Ala·Leu·OH	L	111	—	—	—	899
Cbzo·Ala·(Nᵉ-Cbzo-Lys)·OH	D-L	162	—	—	—	667
Cbzo·Ala·(Nᵉ-Cbzo-Lys)·OH	L-L	134	—	—	—	667
Cbzo·Ala·Nval·OH	D-L	151	—	—	—	468

TABLE 10-44 (continued)

Carbobenzoxy (Cbzo) derivatives (continued)

Compound	Config.	M.P., °C.	$[\alpha]_D$, deg.	Temp., °C.	Concn. and Solvent	Ref.
Cbzo·Ala·Nval·OH	L-L	145	—	—	—	468
Cbzo·β-Ala·Phe·OH	DL	142	—	—	—	899
Cbzo·Ala·Phe·OH	D-L	74	—	—	—	468
Cbzo·Ala·Phe·OH	L-L	122[a]	—	—	—	468, 903
Cbzo·β-Ala·Pro·OH	L	91–93	—	—	—	899
Cbzo·Ala·Ser·OH	L-L	204–205	—	—	—	631
Cbzo·Ala·Tyr·OH	L-L	149–150	—	—	—	903
Cbzo·Ala·(O-Ac-Tyr)·OH	L-L	145.5–146.5	—	—	—	495
Cbzo·Arg·Ala·OH	L-L	207–208	−5.9	29	1.8%, pyridine	491
Cbzo·NO₂-Arg·Asp·OH	L-L	97–101	+5.5	19	2%, acetone	845
Cbzo·Arg·Glu·OH	L-L	211–212	—	—	—	541
α,ω-diCbzo·Arg·Glu·OH	L-L	160	—	—	—	904
Cbzo·NO₂-Arg·Glu·OH	L-L	224–225	0	27	1%, pyridine	491
Cbzo·NO₂-Arg·Gly·OH	L	111–113	−16.8	28	1%, MeOH	491, 541
Cbzo·Arg·Leu·OH	L-L	223–224 d.	−26.0	24	2%, 0.4N HBr	471
Cbzo·NO₂-Arg·Leu·OH	L-L	165–167	−5.0	27	1.7%, pyridine	491, 541
Cbzo·NO₂-Arg·Phe·OH	L-L	225–226	+13.1	29	0.6%, pyridine	491, 541
Cbzo·NO₂-Arg·Try·OH	L-L	202–203	+20.8	30	1.5%, pyridine	491
Cbzo·NO₂-Arg·Tyr·OH	L-L	171–173	+17.9	28	3.5%, pyridine	491
Cbzo·Asp-NH₂·NO₂-Arg·OH	L-L	98–103	+7	22	2%, MeOH	714
Cbzo·Asp-OMe·NO₂-Arg·OH	L-L	78–85	−7.4	25	5%, pyribine	508
Cbzo·Asp-NH₂·NO₂-Arg·Val·Tyr·OH	4 L	165–170 d.	0	23	0.4%, MeOH	714

Compound	Config.	m.p. (°C)	[α]	t (°C)	Solvent	Ref.
Cbzo·Asp·NO₂·Arg·Val·Tyr·Ileu·His·Pro·Phe·OH	8 L	192–196	−28.4	25	1·0% DMF	508
Cbzo·Asp-NH₂·CySBz·OH	L-L	200	—	—	—	472, 868
Cbzo·Asp·OH └CySBz·Gly·OH	L	168–170	—	—	—	727
Cbzo·Asp·Glu·OH	L-L	151–152	—	—	—	609
Cbzo·Asp·OH └Glu·OH	L	153–157	—	—	—	609
Cbzo·Asp-NH₂·Gly·OH	L	166–169	—	—	—	674
Cbzo·Asp·Gly·OH	L	162–165	—	—	—	609, 726, 878
Cbzo·Asp·OH └Gly·OH	L	160–162	—	—	—	474, 609, 726
Cbzo·Asp·His·OH	L-L	171	—	—	—	838
Cbzo·Asp·Tyr·OH	L-L	149–151	—	—	—	609
Cbzo·Asp·OH └Tyr·OH	L	110	—	—	—	128, 378
Cbzo·Asp·Val·OH	L-L	138–140	0	—	−, 1 eq. aq. NaOH	880
Cbzo·Asp·OH └Val·OH	L	172–173	−24.8	20	2.4%, 1 eq. aq. NaOH	880
Cbzo·CySBz·Asp·NH₂·OH	L-L	180–181	—	—	—	674
Cbzo·(CySBz)₂·OH	D-L	110	+4.6	26	2%, acetone	473
Cbzo·(CySBz)₂·OH	L-D	111	−4.1	26	2%, acetone	473
Cbzo·(CySBz)₂·OH	L-L	152ᵇ	−50.6	26	2%, acetone	390, 473
Cbzo·CySBz·Glu-NH₂·OH	L-L	188–189	—	—	—	474
Cbzo·CySBz·Glu·OEt·OH	L-L	88	—	—	—	474
Cbzo·CySBz·Gly·OH	L	94–96ᶜ,ᵈ	−35	18	2%, EtOH	390, 481, 606, 759a
Cbzo·CySBz·Gly·CySBz·OH	L-L	148–150	—	—	—	390
Cbzo·CySBz·Gly₂·OH	L	129–130	−9.4	20	0.21%, EtOH	390

TABLE 10-44 (continued)

Compound	Config.	M.P., °C.	$[\alpha]_D$, deg.	Temp., °C.	Concn. and Solvent	Ref.
Carbobenzoxy (Cbzo) derivatives (continued)						
Cbzo·CySBz·Pro·OH	L-L	—	−80.8	22	3%, CHCl$_3$	393
Cbzo·CySBz·Tyr·OH	L-L	199–201	−17[e,f]	22	3.9%, pyridine	472, 646, 791a, 797, 804
Cbzo·CySBz·(O-Bz-Tyr)·OH	L-L	170.5	—	—	—	830
Cbzo·CySH·Tyr·OH	L-L	160–162	—	—	—	646
Cbzo·CySBz·Tyr·Ileu·OH	3 L	164–166[g]	−11	23	3.8%, HOAc	472, 623, 629, 707, 804
Cbzo·CySBz·Tyr·Leu·OH	3 L	140	—	—	—	629
Cbzo·CySBz·Tyr·Phe·Glu-NH$_2$·Asp-NH$_2$·OH	5 L	214	−29.0	24	1%, DMF	510, 822
Cbzo·CySBz·(O-Tos-Tyr)·Phe·Glu-NH$_2$·Asp-NH$_2$·OH	5 L	217–219	−33.5	25	1%, DMF	446
Cbzo·CyS·CySBz·OH	L-L	120	−53.0	20	0.13%, EtOH	390
Cbzo·CyS·CySBz·OH	L-L					
Cbzo·CyS·Gly·OH	L	176–177[h]	−129	24	−, MeOH	476, 861, 862
Cbzo·CyS·Gly·OH	L					
Cbzo·CyS·Gly$_2$·OH	L	210	—	—	—	863
Cbzo·CyS·Gly$_2$·OH	L					

Cbzo·CyS·Pro·Leu·Gly·OH	3 L	—	—	—	865
|————————————|					
Cbzo·CyS·Pro·Leu·Gly·OH	3 L	—	—	—	
Cbzo·CyS·Tyr·OH	L	158	—	—	646
|——————|					
Cbzo·CyS·Tyr·OH	L				
Cbzo·CyS·Val·OH	L-D	165–172[i]	−86.8	23	1%, DMF	476, 864
Cbzo·CyS·Val·OH	L-D				
Cbzo·Glu·Ala·OH	L-L	178–179	—	—	—	881
Cbzo·Glu·OH	L	150–154	—	—	—	605
|—Ala·OH					
Cbzo·Glu·NH₂·Ala·OH	L-L	209–213	—	—	—	619
Cbzo·Glu·OH	L	166–168 d.	−19	20	3.2%, HOAc	58
|—(α-NH₂-n-But)·Gly·OH	L				
Cbzo·Glu·Asp·OH	L-L	171–174	—	—	—	610
Cbzo·Glu·NH₂·Asp-NH₂·OH	L-L	206	—	—	—	868
Cbzo·Glu·NH₂·Asp-NH₂·CySBz·OH	3 L	217–219[j]	—	—	—	472, 868
Cbzo·Glu·CySBz·OH	L-L	183	−40.0	15	1%, EtOH	767
Cbzo·Glu·CySH·Gly·OH	L-L	118–120	—	—	—	481
Cbzo·Glu·OH	L	166 d.	—	—	—	10
|—CySH·Gly·OH	L				
Cbzo·Glu·CySBz·Gly·OH	L-L	191–192	—	—	—	767, 932
Cbzo·Glu·OH	L	78–82[k]	−23	—	1%, EtOH	475, 606
|—CySBz·Gly·OH	L				
Cbzo·Glu·Glu·OH	L-L	176	—	—	—	128, 767, 879
Cbzo·Glu·NH₂·Glu·OH	L-L	184–185	—	—	—	767
Cbzo·Glu·Glu·OEt·OH	L-L	157–158	—	—	—	879

TABLE 10-44 (continued)

Compound	Config.	M.P., °C.	$[\alpha]_D$, deg.	Temp., °C.	Concn. and Solvent	Ref.
Carbobenzoxy (Cbzo) derivatives (continued)						
Cbzo·Glu·OMe	L	117–118	−9.3	20	6%, MeOH	679
└Glu·OMe·OH	L					
Cbzo·Glu·Glu·OH·H₂O	3 L	163–165	−17.1	18	1.3%, EtOH	881
Cbzo·Glu·OEt·Glu·OH	L-L	120–122	—	—	—	933
└CySAc·Gly·OH	L					
Cbzo·Glu·OBz	L	157–159	−13.5	31	1.9%, 95% EtOH	934
└Glu·NH₂·OH	L					
Cbzo·Glu·Gly·OH	L	143	—	—	—	726, 767
Cbzo·Glu·OH	L	159–161	—	—	—	691, 693, 726, 767
└Gly·OH						
Cbzo·Glu·NH₂·Gly·OH	L	180–181[l]	—	—	—	482, 767, 882
Cbzo·Glu·OEt·Gly·OH	L	54	—	—	—	482
Cbzo·Glu·Gly₂·OH	L	142	—	—	—	455
Cbzo·Glu·OH	L	124–127	—	—	—	691
└Gly₂·OH						
Cbzo·Glu·NH₂·His·Phe·OH	3 L	208–210 d.	−31.0	24	0.9%, N HCl	713
Cbzo·Glu·OBz·His·Phe·NO₂-Arg·OH	4 L	185–187 d.	−2.4	29	1.7%, HOAc	713
Cbzo·Glu·NH₂·His·Phe·NO₂-Arg·OH	4 L	170 d.	−4.7	29	1.1%, HOAc	713
Cbzo·Glu·NH₂·Glu·NH₂·OH	L-L	177–178	—	—	—	20a
Cbzo·Glu·OMe·Glu·NH₂·OH·2H₂O	L-L	184–185	—	—	—	20a
Cbzo·Glu·OMe·Glu·NH₂·Glu·NH₂·OH	3 L	175–180 d.	—	—	—	20a

Cbzo·Glu·OH	L	132–134[m]	—	—	605
└─Leu·OH	L			
Cbzo·Glu·NH₂·Leu·OH	L-L	178–181	—	—	619
Cbzo·Glu·Met·OH	L-L	135–136	—	—	627
Cbzo·Glu·Phe·OH	L-D	122	—	—	709
Cbzo·Glu·Phe·OH	L-L	162	—	—	709
Cbzo·Glu·NH₂·Phe·OH	L-L	180	—	—	709
Cbzo·Glu·NH₂·Ser·OH	L-L	199–202	—	—	619
Cbzo·Glu·Tyr·OH	L-L	185	—	—	378, 894
Cbzo·Glu·(I₂-Tyr)·OH	L-L	188	—	—	709
Cbzo·Glu·OH	L	—	—	—	894
└─Tyr·OH	L			
Cbzo·Glu·NH₂·Tyr·OH	L-L	183–185	—	—	619
Cbzo·Glu·Tyr·Gly·OH	L-L	182	—	—	709
Cbzo·Glu·Val·OH	L-L	131–133	—	—	610
Cbzo·Glu·OH	L	153–156	—	—	605
└─Val·OH	L			
Cbzo·Glu·NH₂·Val·OH	L-L	176–183	—	—	619
Cbzo·Gly·Ala·OH	DL	176[n]	—	—	495, 731, 774, 795
Cbzo·Gly·Ala·OH	D	119[o]	—	—	666, 705
Cbzo·Gly·Ala·OH	L	119.5[o,p]	—	—	495, 666, 705, 935
Cbzo·Gly·β-Ala·OH	—	140	—	—	723, 899
Cbzo·Gly·Ala₂·OH	L-D	146	—	—	703
Cbzo·Gly·Ala₂·OH	L-L	172	—	—	703
Cbzo·Gly·Ala·Gly·OH	DL	176[q]	—	—	731, 774
Cbzo·Gly·β-Ala·Gly·OH	—	177–180	—	—	899

TABLE 10-44 (continued)

Carbobenzoxy (Cbzo) derivatives (continued)

Compound	Config.	M.P., °C	$[\alpha]_D$, deg.	Temp., °C	Concn. and Solvent	Ref.
Cbzo·Gly·Ala·Phe·Gly·OH	L-L	175	−31.7	21	2.5%, $CH_3OCH_2CH_2OH$	495
Cbzo·Gly·(α-NH_2-n-But)·OH	DL	158	—	—	—	774
Cbzo·Gly·NO_2-Arg·OH	L	145	+3.2	25	1.1%, HOAc	491, 492, 541
Cbzo·Gly·Asp-NH_2·OH	L	129.5–131	—	—	—	674
Cbzo·Gly·CyS·OH	L	176–180 d.	−136	25	2.0%, H_2O	876
H·CyS·OH						
Cbzo·Gly·CyS·OH	L	142	—	—	—	936, 937
	L					
Cbzo·Gly·CyS·OH	L	141–143	—	—	—	759a
Cbzo·Gly·CySBz·OH	DL	120–121	−24	18	1.2%, EtOH	390, 759a
Cbzo·Gly·CySBz·OH	L	160–162	—	—	—	444, 923
Cbzo·Gly·Glu·OH	L	98–100	—	—	—	878
Cbzo·Gly·Glu·Gly·OH	L	173	—	—	—	709
Cbzo·Gly·Glu·Tyr·OH	L-L	178–179	—	—	—	128, 495, 723, 768, 769a, 774
Cbzo·Gly_2·OH	—					
Cbzo·Gly·Gly·Ala·OH	DL	184	—	—	—	910
Cbzo·Gly_2β-Ala·OH	—	187–189	—	—	—	899
Cbzo·Gly·Gly_2·Ala·Gly_2·OH	DL	192	—	—	—	910

Compound		m.p.				Ref.
Cbzo·Gly₂·CySBz·OH	L	161–162	—	—	—	390
Cbzo·Gly₂·Glu·OEt·OH	L	144–146	—	—	—	893
Cbzo·Gly₃·OH	—	196	—	—	—	495, 723, 774, 878
Cbzo·Gly₄·OH	—	230	—	—	—	723, 741, 774, 806, 878
Cbzo·Gly₃·Leu·Gly·OH	L	225	—	—	—	878
Cbzo·Gly₂·Phe·OH	DL	129	—	—	—	731, 812b
Cbzo·Gly₂·Phe·OH	L	146	—	—	—	665
Cbzo·Gly₂·Pro·OH	L	137	—	—	—	170
Cbzo·Gly·His·OH	L	175	—	—	—	837
Cbzo·Gly·His·Tyr·OH	L-L	223–224 d.	—	—	—	537
Cbzo·Gly·Hypro·OH	L	124–124.5	—	—	—	169
Cbzo·Gly·allo-Hypro·OH	L	187–188	—	—	—	657
Cbzo·Gly·(α-NH₂·isoBut)·OH	—	154	—	—	—	466
Cbzo·Gly·Ileu·OH	DL	108	—	—	—	723, 774
Cbzo·Gly·Ileu·OH	L	114–115	+14.3	22	5%, EtOH	938
Cbzo·Gly·Leu·OH	DL	125–126	—	—	—	506, 723, 759a, 774
Cbzo·Gly·Leu·OH	D	101–102	—	—	—	469
Cbzo·Gly·Leu·OH	L	143–144ʳ	−9.5	25	5%, EtOH	723, 758, 769a, 812c, 938
Cbzo·Gly·Leu·Gly·OH	DL	161	—	—	—	495
Cbzo·Gly·Leu·Gly·OH	L	110	−14.7	19	4%, DMF	800, 811, 812c
Cbzo·Gly·Leu·Gly₂·Leu·Gly·OH	L-L	155–158	—	—	—	812c
Cbzo·Gly·Leu·Gly·Leu·Gly·OH	L-D	—	−4.0	27	4.5%, EtOH	812a
Cbzo·Gly·Leu·Gly·Leu·Gly·OH	L-L	206–207	—	—	—	800, 811
Cbzo·Gly·Leu₂·OH	L-D	144–145	—	—	—	694
Cbzo·Gly·Leu₂·OH	L-L	137	—	—	—	694

TABLE 10-44 (continued)

Compound	Config.	M.P., °C.	$[\alpha]_D$, deg.	Temp., °C.	Concn. and Solvent	Ref.
Carbobenzoxy (Cbzo) derivatives (continued)						
Cbzo·Gly·(N$^\epsilon$-Cbzo-Lys)·OH	DL	121	—	—	—	723
Cbzo·Gly·(N$^\epsilon$-Cbzo-Lys)·OH	L	75	—	—	—	613a, 667
Cbzo·Gly·(N$^\epsilon$-Cbzo·Gly-Lys)·OH	DL	134	—	—	—	723
Cbzo·Gly·Met·OH	DL	124	—	—	—	769, 774
Cbzo·Gly·Met·OH	D	107–109	—	—	—	627
Cbzo·Gly·Met·OH	L	110–111	—	—	—	627
Cbzo·Gly·Phe·OH	DL	161	—	—	—	613a, 712, 721, 723, 757, 759, 774, 795, 913, 939
Cbzo·Gly·Phe·OH	D	—	−39.0	25	—, EtOH	913
Cbzo·Gly·Phe·OH	L	126	+41.9	14	2.5%, EtOH	495, 613a, 712, 800, 913, 923
Cbzo·Gly·Phe·Ala·OH	L-L	165–166	−8.6	22	2%, MeOH	611a
Cbzo·Gly·Phe·Gly·OH	DL	141–142	—	—	—	712, 800, 812b
Cbzo·Gly·Phe·Gly·OH	L	162.5–163	−14.6	21	1.3%, EtOH	495, 507, 712, 800
Cbzo·Gly·Pro·OH	DL	129–130	—	—	—	170, 705
Cbzo·Gly·Pro·OH	L	156	—	—	—	170, 940
Cbzo·Gly·Pro·Gly·OH	DL	133.5	—	—	—	170
Cbzo·Gly·Pro·Gly·OH	L	144–145	−80.9	21	1%, H$_2$O	170, 823, 941

Cbzo·Gly·Ser·OH	L	124	—	—	—	631
Cbzo·Gly·(O-Bz-Ser)·OH	DL	136	—	—	—	829
Cbzo·Gly·Try·OH	L	142	—	—	—	505
Cbzo·Gly·Tyr·OH	L	107	—	—	—	700
Cbzo·Gly·(O-Bz-Tyr)·OH	L	142	—	—	—	830
Cbzo·Gly·Tyr·Gly·OH	L	134	—	—	—	931
Cbzo·Gly·Val·OH	DL	146^s	—	—	—	506, *721, 723, 731, 774, 939*
Cbzo·Gly·Val·Gly·OH	DL	193	—	—	—	942
Cbzo·His·Ala·OH	L-L	211–214 d.	−6	22	1%, 50% EtOH	695
Cbzo·His·Leu·OH	L-L	185–188	−7	22	1%, EtOH	695
Cbzo·His·Phe·OH	L-L	230–231	—	—	—	621, 713
Cbzo·His·Phe·NO$_2$Arg·OH	3 L	222–223	−13.8	26	8.5%, HOAc	713
Cbzo·His·Tyr·OH·½H$_2$O	L-L	232–233	—	—	—	621
Cbzo·Hypro·Ala·OH	L-L	194–195	—	—	—	642
Cbzo·Hypro·Asp·OH	L-L	166–167	—	—	—	642
Cbzo·Hypro·Glu·OH	L-L	64.5–66.5	—	—	—	642
Cbzo·Hypro·Gly$_2$·OH	L	159.5–160	−53.9	21	1%, H$_2$O	823
Cbzo·Hypro·Leu·OH	L-L	146–147	—	—	—	642
Cbzo·Hypro·Phe·OH	L-L	134–135	—	—	—	642
Cbzo·Hypro·Tyr·OH	L-L	134–135	—	—	—	642
Cbzo·Ileu·Glu·NH$_2$·OH	L-L	184–185	−18.8	21	1.3%, 0.5N KHCO$_3$	438
Cbzo·Ileu·Glu·NH$_2$·Asp·NH$_2$·OH	3 L	203–204	−35.5	21	1%, 0.5N KHCO$_3$	438
Cbzo·Ileu·Phe·OH	L-L	166–167	—	—	—	456
Cbzo·Leu·Ala·OH	L-L	152–153	−25	27	1%, EtOH	467, 915
Cbzo·Leu·Ala·Val·Phe·Gly·OH	4 L	237–242 d.	−44.4	22	2.3%, HOAc	915
Cbzo·Leu·Asp·NH$_2$·OH	L-L	162–163	—	—	—	672, *674*
Cbzo·Leu·Glu·Leu·OH·½H$_2$O	3 L	105	—	—	—	881
Cbzo·Leu·Gly·OH	DL	162–163	—	—	—	613*a*, *805, 812a*

TABLE 10-44 (continued)

Specific Rotation

Compound	Config.	M.P., °C.	$[\alpha]_D$, deg.	Temp., °C.	Concn. and Solvent	Ref.
Carbobenzoxy (Cbzo) derivatives (continued)						
Cbzo·Leu·Gly·OH	D	116–117	+25.9	22	2%, EtOH	812a
Cbzo·Leu·Gly·OH	L	115	—	—	—	495, 613a, 800, 805, 878
Cbzo·Leu·Gly$_2$·OH	D	144	—	—	—	878
Cbzo·Leu·Gly$_2$·OH	L	144	—	—	—	179, 611a, 878
Cbzo·Leu·Gly$_3$·OH	L	158–159	—	—	—	611a
Cbzo·Leu·(1-Bz-His)·OH	L-L	177–178	—	—	—	484
Cbzo·Leu·Ileu·OH	L-D	70–71	−29.6	25	1%, EtOH	622
Cbzo·Leu·Ileu·OH	L-L	101–101.5	−12.0	27	1%, EtOH	622
Cbzo·Leu·Leu·OH	L-L	114–116^t	−30.8	23	5%, MeOH	622, 834
Cbzo·Leu·Phe·OH	L-D	114–115^u	−39.5	23	1%, EtOH	423, 622, 719
Cbzo·Leu·Phe·OH	L-L	119–121	—	—	—	622
Cbzo·Leu·(O-Bz-Tyr)·OH	L-L	174	—	—	—	830
Cbzo·Leu·Val·OH	L-L	108–109	−15.0^v	22	1%, EtOH	622, 718, 915a
diCbzo·Lys·Ala·OH	L-D	159	—	—	—	667
diCbzo·Lys·Ala·OH	L-L	150	—	—	—	667
diCbzo·Lys·NO$_2$-Arg·OH	L-L	142–145	−6.2	27	2.6%, pyridine	491
diCbzo·Lys·Glu·OH	L-L	130	—	—	—	626
diCbzo·Lys·Gly·OH	DL	127	—	—	—	723
diCbzo·Lys·Gly·OH	L	158–159	−11.4	16	5%, MeOH	613a, 667, 831, 834
diCbzo·Lys·His·OH	L-L	157–162	—	—	—	626

Compound	Config	M.p. (°C)	[α]	conc	solvent	Ref.
diCbzo·Lys·(Nᵋ-Cbzo-Lys)·OH	L-D	146	—	—	—	667
diCbzo·Lys·(Nᵋ-Cbzo-Lys)·OH	L-L	145–147	−1.5	20	5%, HOAc	667, 715
diCbzo·Lys·(Nᵋ-Cbzo-Lys)₂·OH	3 L	173–174	—	—	—	715
diCbzo·Lys·(Nᵋ-Cbzo-Lys)₃·OH	4 L	162–163	—	—	—	715
diCbzo·Lys·Tyr·OH	L-L	141–142	+6.0	17	5%, MeOH	834
diCbzo·Lys·Val·OH	L-L	70–73	−7.0	22	2.4%, EtOH	507
diCbzo·Lys·Val·Phe·Gly·OH	3 L	173–175	−22.0	24	2.4%, HOAc	507
Cbzo·Met·Glu·OH	L-L	138–140	−13.5	28	1%, EtOH	444
Cbzo·Met·Gly·OH	DL	141–143	—	—	—	627
Cbzo·Met·Gly·OH	D	129–130	—	—	—	627
Cbzo·Met·Gly·OH	L	135–136	−16.0	26	2.2%, EtOH	444, 627
Cbzo·Met·Gly₂·OH	L	137–138	—	—	—	627
Cbzo·Met₂·OH	L-L	118–120	−18.4	20	2%, MeOH	490, 627
Cbzo·Met·Tyr·OH	L-L	137–138.5	—	—	—	627
diCbzo·Orn·Leu·OH·2H₂O	L-L	63–64	−14	17	4.2%, MeOH	373
Cbzo·Phe·Ala·OH	L-L	—	−11.0	22	2%, EtOH	611a
Cbzo·Phe·NO₂-Arg·OH	L-L	185–186ʷ	+1.5	27	1.6%, pyridine	491, 541
Cbzo·Phe·Glu·OH	L-L	180	—	—	—	709
Cbzo·Phe·Glu·NH₂·Asp·NH₂·OH	3 L	223–225	−26.0	21	0.1%, 0.5N KHCO₃	440
Cbzo·Phe·Gly·OH	DL	158–159	—	—	—	943
Cbzo·Phe·Gly·OH	D	150–151	+9.7	25	—, HOAc	313
Cbzo·Phe·Gly·OH	L	154	−10.2	18	4.3%, HOAc	313, 495, 712, 916
Cbzo·Phe·Gly₂·OH	L	109	—	—	—	665
Cbzo·Phe·Gly₃·OH	L	114–115	—	—	—	665
Cbzo·Phe·Gly·Phe·OH	L-L	150–151	—	—	—	665
Cbzo·Phe·His·OH	L-L	198–200 d.	—	—	—	456
Cbzo·Phe·His·Leu·OH	3 L	—	+30.5	24	1%, HOAc	484
Cbzo·Phe·(1-Bz-His)·OH	L-L	140–141	—	—	—	484

TABLE 10-44 (continued)

Compound	Config.	M.P., °C.	$[\alpha]_D$, deg.	Temp., °C.	Concn. and Solvent	Ref.
Carbobenzoxy (Cbzo) derivatives (continued)						
Cbzo·Phe·(1-Bz-His)·Asp·OH	3 L	193–196 d.	—	—	—	484
Cbzo·Phe·(1-Bz-His)·Leu·OH	3 L	163–165	—	—	—	484
Cbzo·Phe·Pro·OH	L-L	109.5–110.5	—	—	—	642
Cbzo·Pro·NO₂·Arg·OH	L-L	197–198	−32.7	30	3.9%, MeOH	491
Cbzo·Pro·Gly·OH	DL	125	—	—	—	170
Cbzo·Pro·Gly·OH	L	122–123	−63.2	21	5%, MeOH	170, 613a
Cbzo·Pro·Gly₂·OH	L	134–135	−56.0	21	1%, H₂O	823
Cbzo·Pro·Gly·Phe·OH	L-L	160	—	—	—	611a
Cbzo·Pro·Hypro·OH	L-L	217–218.5	—	—	—	642
Cbzo·Pro·Leu·Gly·OH	L-L	163.5–164	−85.2	23.5	2%, 95% EtOH	865
Cbzo·Pro·(Nᵋ-Tos-Lys)·OH	L-L	—	−22.6	21	1%, CHCl₃	393
Cbzo·Pro·Phe·OH	L-L	126–127	−49	22	2.5%, CHCl₃	638a
Cbzo·Pro₂·OH	L-L	186–187	—	—	—	168
Cbzo·Pro·Val·OH	L-L	134–135	−58	18	2.8%, MeOH	373
Cbzo·Ser·Ala·OH	L-L	161–162	—	—	—	501
Cbzo·Ser·Ala·Glu·OH	3 L	192–193	—	—	—	631
Cbzo·Ser·Glu·OH	L-L	152–153	—	—	—	501
Cbzo·Ser·Gly·OH	L	131	—	—	—	501
Cbzo·Ser·Gly·Glu·OH	L-L	140–141ˣ	—	—	—	444, 631
Cbzo·(O-Bz-Ser)·His·OH	L-L	164	+20.7	13	1%, HOAc	828
Cbzo·(O-Bz-Ser)·His·Leu·OH	L-L	172–173	—	—	—	828
Cbzo·Ser·Met·OH	3 L	128–129	−24.2	26	3.2%, satd. NaHCO₃	444

Compound	Config	M.p. (°C)	[α]	T (°C)	Solvent	Ref
Cbzo·Ser·Met·Glu·OH	3 L	117–121	−22.5	25	1%, EtOH	444
Cbzo·Ser₂·OH	L-L	186–187	—	—	—	501, 631
Cbzo·Ser·Tyr·OH	L-L	189–190	+37.4	24	1.9%, EtOH	444, 537
Cbzo·Ser·Tyr·Glu·OH	3 L	—	−23.5	25	1%, EtOH	444
Cbzo·Ser·Tyr·Met·Glu·OH	4 L	—	−22.7	25	1%, HOAc	444
Cbzo·Ser·Tyr·Ser·OH	3 L	182	−10.5	20	1.9%, MeOH	471a
Cbzo·Ser·Tyr·Ser·Met·Glu·OH	5 L	—	−13.2	25	1%, HOAc	444
Cbzo·Ser·Tyr·Ser·Met·Glu·OBz·OH	5 L	173ʸ	−23	23	1.0%, MeOH	471a
Cbzo·Try·Ala·OH	L-L	155	−13.2	21	4%, EtOH	495, 505
Cbzo·Try·Gly·OH	L	158–159	—	—	—	505, 791
Cbzo·Try·(Nᵉ-Cbzo-Lys)·OH	L-L	130.5–131.5	0	—	−, HOAc	915
Cbzo·Try·Pro·OH	L-L	128–130	—	—	—	505
Cbzo·Try₂·OH	L-L	207	—	—	—	505
Cbzo·Try·Try·OH	L-L	135–140 d.	—	—	—	505
Cbzo·Tyr·CySBz·OH	L-L	166ᶻ	—	—	—	646, 917
Cbzo·Tyr·CySH·OH	L-L	120	—	—	—	646
Cbzo·Tyr·CyS·OH	L-L	150 d.	—	—	—	646
Cbzo·Tyr·CyS·OH	L-L	100	—	—	—	700
Cbzo·Tyr·Gly·OH	L	163.5	—	—	—	830
Cbzo·(O-Bz-Tyr)·Gly·OH	L	168	—	—	—	826
O,N-diCbzo·Tyr·Gly·OH	L	213–215	—	—	—	931
Cbzo·Tyr·Gly₂·OH	L	199	—	—	—	537
Cbzo·Tyr·His·OH	L-L	—	—	—	—	822
O,N-diCbzo·Tyr·Phe·Glu-NH₂·Asp-NH₂·OH	4 L	219–220	−21.0	21	1%, DMF	822
Cbzo·(O-Tos-Tyr)·Phe·Glu-NH₂·Asp-NH₂·OH	4 L	218–220	−16.6	25	1%, DMF	446
Cbzo·Tyr·Ser·OH	L-L	148	+8.1	20	1.8%, EtOH	471a
Cbzo·Try₂·OH	L-L	148	—	—	—	378
Cbzo·(O-Ac-Tyr)₂·OH	L-L	209–210	—	—	—	637

TABLE 10-44 (continued)

Compound	Config.	M.P., °C.	$[\alpha]_D$, deg.	Temp., °C.	Concn. and Solvent	Ref.
Carbobenzoxy (Cbzo) derivatives (continued)						
Cbzo·Tyr₃·OH	3 L	182–183	—	—	—	637
Cbzo·Tyr₄·OH	4 L	224–225 d.	—	—	—	637
Cbzo·Val·Glu·Val·OH·½H₂O	3 L	245	—	—	—	881
Cbzo·Val·Gly·OH	DL	160–162^{aa}	—	—	—	380, 900
Cbzo·Val·Gly·OH	L	146	−24.2	22	5%, MeOH	613a
Cbzo·Val·Gly₂·OH	DL	178–179	—	—	—	380
Cbzo·Val·His·OH·HCl	L-L	122–125	−23	24	4.2%, H₂O	638a
Cbzo·Val·(N$^\delta$-Cbzo-Orn)·OH	L-L	193–195	−11.0	20	0.9%, HOAc	373
Cbzo·Val·(N$^\delta$_Tos-Orn)·OH	L-L	150	—	—	—	423
Cbzo·Val·(N$^\delta$_Tos-Orn)·Leu·Phe·Pro·OH	3 L-D-L	157	−53.9	25	1%, HOAc	423
Cbzo·[Val·(N$^\delta$-Tos-Orn)·Leu·Phe·Pro]₂·OH	[3 L-D-L]₂	223–224	−103.4	27	0.7%, MeOH	423
Cbzo·[Val·(N$^\delta$-Tos-Orn)·Leu·Tyr·Pro]₂·OH	[3 L-D-L]₂	230–235 d.	−113.4	25	0.5%, MeOH	679a
Cbzo·Val·Tyr·OH	L-L	161–163	+26	22	4·0%, pyridine	638a
Cbzo·Val·Tyr·Ileu·His·OH	4 L	212–215	+8.4	25	1.2%, DMF	508
Cbzo·Val·Tyr·Val·OH	3 L	222–224	−26	23	4.2%, EtOH	638a
Cbzo·Val·Tyr·Val·His·OH	4 L	236–238 d.	−10	—	2.1%, HOAc	638a
Cbzo·Val₂·OH	L-D	184–185	−21.3	25	1.5%, N KOH	625
Cbzo·Val₂·OH	L-L	139.5–140	−36.6	20	3.2%, N KOH	625
p-Nitrocarbobenzoxy (p-NO₂-Cbzo) derivatives						
p-NO₂-Cbzo·Arg·Glu·OH	L-L	141–143	−15.9	26	1%, 6N HCl	363
p-NO₂-Cbzo·NO₂·Arg·Glu·OH	L-L	136–137	+6.6	22	3.2%, pyridine	513

p-NO₂·Cbzo·Arg·Gly·OH·H₂O	L	128–129	+11.3	22	1.8%, pyridine	513
p-NO₂·Cbzo·Arg·Leu·OH·3H₂O	L-L	167.5–169	−6.3	24	0.9%, dioxane-H₂O (1:1)	363
p-NO₂·Cbzo·NO₂·Arg·Leu·OH	L-L	193–194	—	—	—	513
p-NO₂·Cbzo·NO₂·Arg·Phe·OH	L-L	255–256	+14.0	22	1.5%, pyridine	513
p-NO₂·Cbzo·NO₂·Arg·(β-Phser)·OH	L-L	219–220	+5.3	22	1.2%, pyridine	513
p-NO₂·Cbzo·NO₂·Arg·Tyr·OH	L-L	239–240	+22.4	22	1.5%, pyridine	513
p-NO₂·Cbzo·CyS·Gly·OH	L	111–113	−79.8	25	1.3%, acetone	512
p-NO₂·Cbzo·CyS·Gly·OH	L	—	—	—	—	—
p-NO₂·Cbzo·CyS·Phe·OH	L-L	118–120	−49.1	25	2.5%, acetone	512
p-NO₂·Cbzo·CyS·Phe·OH	L-L	—	—	—	—	—
p-NO₂·Cbzo·Gly·Leu·OH	L	118–120.5	−15.6	27	1%, N NaOH	462
p-NO₂·Cbzo·Leu₂·OH	L-L	89.5–91	−33.3	24	1%, N NaOH	462
Carbo-t-butyloxy (C-t-Buo) derivatives						
C-t-Buo·Ala·Gly·OH	DL	168–170	—	—	—	464
C-t-Buo·Gly·Leu·OH	L	112–116	—	—	—	464
C-t-Buo·Gly·Met·OH	DL	138–140	—	—	—	464
C-t-Buo·Gly·Phe·OH	DL	131.5–132.5	—	—	—	464, 465
C-t-Buo·Gly·Try·OH	DL	157–159	—	—	—	464
C-t-Buo·Leu₂·OH	L-L	153–155	—	—	—	464
C-t-Buo·Met·Glu·OBz·OH	L-L	—	−13.3	20	2%, MeOH	471a
C-t-Buo·Met·Gly·OH	DL	138–141	—	—	—	464
C-t-Buo·Phe·β-Ala·OH	DL	173–175	—	—	—	464
C-t-Buo·Phe·Gly·OH	DL	180–181	—	—	—	464
C-t-Buo·Val·Gly·OH	DL	132–135	—	—	—	464

TABLE 10-44 (continued)

Compound	Config.	M.P., °C.	$[\alpha]_D$, °C.	Temp., °C.	Concn. and Solvent	Ref.
Carbocyclopentyloxy (C-cy-Peo) derivatives						
C-cy-Peo·Ala·Gly·OH	DL	158–159	—	—	—	464
C-cy-Peo·β-Ala·Phe·OH	DL	140–145	—	—	—	464
C-cy-Peo·Gly·β-Ala·Leu·Thr·OH	L-D	158–164	—	—	—	464
C-cy-Peo·Gly·Phe·OH	DL	129–131	—	—	—	464
C-cy-Peo·Ileu·Gly·OH	L	135–138	—	—	—	464
C-cy-Peo·Met·Gly·OH	DL	150–153	—	—	—	464
C-cy-Peo·Nval·Gly·OH	DL	125–128	—	—	—	464
C-cy-Peo·Pro·Gly·OH	DL	190–192	—	—	—	464
C-cy-Peo·Val·Gly·OH	DL	155–158	—	—	—	464
C-cy-Peo·Val·Leu·Gly·OH	L-L	180–189	—	—	—	464
C-cy-Peo·Val·Ser·OH	L-L	183–186	—	—	—	464
Carbocyclohexyloxy (C-cy-Hexo) derivatives						
C-cy-Hexo·Gly·Leu·Gly·OH	L	191–193	—	—	—	464
C-cy-Hexo·Phe·Gly·OH	DL	160–161	—	—	—	464
Formyl derivatives						
Formyl·Phe·Gly·OH	L	—	+15.1	28	2.2%, 0.5N Na$_2$CO$_3$	586
Formyl·Val·Gly·OH	L	207–208	−50.9	28	1.3%, 70% EtOH	586
Formyl·Val·Phe·OH	L-L	203–204	−31.4	28	0.8%, MeOH	586
p-Methoxybenzyloxycarbonyl (p-Meo-Cbzo) derivatives						
p-Meo-Cbzo·Gly·Met·OH	DL	137–139	—	—	—	464
p-Meo-Cbzo·Met·Gly·OH	DL	122–125	—	—	—	464

Phthalyl (Phth) derivatives					
Phth·Ala·Asp-NH₂·OH	L-L	201–202	—	—	—	674
Phth·CySBz·Gly·OH	L	164–165	—	—	—	533
Phth·Glu·OH	DL	206–207	—	—	—	527, 533
└─Gly·OH					
Phth·Glu·OH	DL	165–167	—	—	—	883
└─Gly₂·OH·H₂O					
Phth·Glu·OH	DL	186–188 d.	—	—	—	883
└─Gly₂·OH					
Phth·Glu·OH	L	207–209	—	—	—	535
└─Tyr·OH					
Phth·Gly·Ala·OH	L	223–224	—	—	—	536, 731
Phth·Gly·Ala·OH	DL	195	—	—	—	797
Phth·Gly·Asp-NH₂·OH	L	208–209	—	—	—	674, 685, 798
Phth·Gly·Glu·OH·H₂O	DL	194–196	+4.7	22	9.1%, 96% EtOH	677
Phth·Gly₂·OH	L	231–232	—	—	—	518, 522, 536, 752, 797
Phth·Gly·His·OH	—	258	—	—	—	537
Phth·Gly·Leu·OH	L	104–106	—	—	—	791a
Phth·Gly·Phe·OH	L	197–199	—	—	—	518, 740, 752
Phth·Gly·Ser·OH	DL	199	—	—	—	685
Phth·Gly·Tyr·OH	DL	235–237	—	—	—	535
Phth·Leu·Asp-NH₂·OH	L	210–212	—	—	—	674
Phth·Leu·Glu-NH₂·OH	L-L	123–126	—	—	—	674
Phth·Leu·Gly·OH·2H₂O	L-L	164–165	−37.8	20	2.8%, N Na₂CO₃	536
Phth·Phe·Gly·OH	L	163.5–167[bb]	—	—	—	495
Phth·Phe·Gly·OH	DL	186–187[cc]	−140	20	1.7%, EtOH	495, 522
Phth·Phe·Gly₂·OH	L	244–245.5	—	—	—	518
Phth·Thr·Phe·OH	DL	207–208	+23.2	27	1.7%, EtOH	524

TABLE 10-44 (continued)

Compound	Config.	M.P., °C.	$[\alpha]_D$, deg.	Temp., °C.	Concn. and Solvent	Ref.
Phthalyl (Phth) derivatives (continued)						
Phth·Val₂·OH	L-L	141–142.5	+59.3	27	2.8%, CHCl₃	543a
Phth·Val₂·OH	L-D	137–139	+48.4	25	2.7%, CHCl₃	543a
Phth·Val₂·OH	D-L	137.5–139.5	−49.6	25	3.2%, CHCl₃	543a
Phth·Val₂·OH	D-D	141–142.5	−59.2	25	2.4%, CHCl₃	543a
p-Toluenesulfonyl (Tos) derivatives						
Tos·Ala·Gly·OH	DL	149–150	—	—	—	127, 712, 794, 944
Tos·Ala·Leu·OH	L-L	186	−30.5	20	—, EtOH	127
Tos·(α,γ-diNH₂-*n*-But)·OH	L	219–221 d.	−18.4	21	3%, *N* HCl	429
Tos·Arg·Gly·OH·1½H₂O	L	—	−36.8	21	1.3%, 10% H₂SO₄	429
Tos·Arg·Gly·OH·2H₂O	DL	265–266 d.	—	—	—	429
Tos·(*homo*-Arg)·Gly·OH	L	262–264 d.	−33.2	21	1.7%, *N* HCl	429
Tos·CySBz·Tyr·OH	L-L	155–156	+28.2	18	2.1%, EtOH	400, 432
Tos·CySBz·Tyr·Gly·OH·H₂O	L-L	125	—	—	—	400
Tos·CySBz·Tyr·Phe·OH	3 L	205–206	−37.5	23	1%, MeOH	482a
Tos·CySBz·Tyr·Phe·Glu·NH₂·Asp·NH₂·OH·½H₂O	5 L	203–205	+4.4	21	2.1%, DMF	432
Tos·CySBz·Tyr·Phe·Glu·NH₂·Asp·NH₂·OH	5 L	203–204	+4.4	21	2%, DMF	88
Tos·CySBz·Tyr·Phe·Glu·NH₂·Asp·NH₂·CySBz·OH	6 L	213–214	−24.4	24	0.9%, 90% tetrahydrofuran	482a
Tos·CySBz·Tyr·Ileu·OH·H₂O	3 L	119–123	—	—	—	400

Compound	Config	M.p. (°C)	[α]	T (°C)	Solvent	Ref.
Tos·CySBz·Tyr·Leu·OH	3 L	93–101	—	—	—	400
Tos·Glu·NH₂·Asp·NH₂·OH	L-L	197–198[dd]	−11.4	21	2.1%, 0.5N KHCO₃	435, 868
Tos·Glu·NH₂·Asp·NH₂·CySBz·OH·½H₂O	3 L	181–183	—	—	—	868
Tos·Glu·NH₂·CySBz·OH	L-L	183	+13.6	21	2%, 0.5N KHCO₃	432a
Tos·Glu·Gly·OH	L	217	—	—	—	890
Tos·Glu·NH₂·Gly·OH	L	205	−23.4	21	5.2%, 0.5N KHCO₃	701, 890
Tos·Glu·OH └─Gly·OH	D	166–167	—	—	—	433
Tos·Glu·OH └─Gly·OH	L	171–172	—	—	—	890
Tos·Glu·NH₂ └─Gly·OH	L	171	−27.3	21.5	1.7%, 0.5N KHCO₃	701
Tos·Glu·Tyr·OH	L-L	218–219	—	—	—	890
Tos·Glu·OH └─Tyr·OH	L	120–130[ee]	—	—	—	890
Tos·Gly·Ala·OH	L	167	—	—	—	127
Tos·Gly₂·OH	—	178.5	—	—	—	127, 794
Tos·Gly₂·Glu·OBz·OH	L	101–103	+9.4	22	3.7%, EtOH	676
Tos·Gly·Leu·OH·H₂O	DL	87	—	—	—	127
Tos·Gly·Leu·OH	DL	81–82	—	—	—	127
Tos·Gly·Phe·OH	DL	144–145	—	—	—	495
Tos·Gly·Phe·OH	L	160.5	+50.3	16	2.6%, EtOH	495
Tos·Gly·Phe·Glu·OBz·OH	L-L	146–147	−20.9	16	2%, EtOH	676
Tos·Gly·Phe·Gly·OH	DL	192	—	—	—	495
Tos·Gly·Pro·OH	L	183–184	−71	27	1%, 0.5N KHCO₃	944
Tos·Ileu·Glu·NH₂·OH	L-L	203–204	−3.1	21	1.1%, 0.5N KHCO₃	438
Tos·Ileu·Glu·NH₂·Asp·NH₂·OH	3 L	223	−30.7	21	1.8%, 0.5N KHCO₃	438
Tos·Ileu·Gly·OH	L	—	−26.7	21	1.1%, 0.5N KHCO₃	438
Tos·Ileu·Leu·OH	L-L	163–165	−24.7	21	1.1%, 0.5N KHCO₃	438

TABLE 10-44 (continued)

Specific Rotation

Compound	Config.	M.P., °C.	$[\alpha]_D$, deg.	Temp., °C.	Concn. and Solvent	Ref.
p-Toluenesulfonyl (Tos) derivatives (continued)						
Tos·Leu·Gly·OH	DL	121.5	—	—	—	127
Tos·(N$^\varepsilon$-Cbzo-Lys)·Gly·OH	L	120–121^{ff}	—	—	—	429
Tos·Lys·Gly·OH·H$_2$O	L	242–244 d.	−29.8	23	2.3%, N HCl	429
Tos·Orn·Gly·OH	DL	220–222 d.	—	—	—	429
Tos·Orn·Gly·OH	L	205 d.	−31.4	22	1.2%, N HCl	429
Tos·(N$^\delta$-Cbzo-Orn)·Gly·OH	DL	155–156	—	—	—	429
Tos·(N$^\delta$-Cbzo-Orn)·Gly·OH	L	164.5–165.5	—	—	—	429
Tos·Phe·Arg·OH	L-L	256	—	—	—	471a
Tos·Phe·Glu·NH$_2$Asp·NH$_2$·OH	3 L	193–195	−26.0	21	2%, 0.5N KHCO$_3$	440, 822
Tos·Pro·Hypro·OH	L-L	224–224.5	−198	36	1%, 0.5N KHCO$_3$	944
Tos·Val·Gly·OH	DL	174–175	—	—	—	944
Trifluoroacetyl (TFA) derivatives						
TFA·Gly$_2$·OH	—	185	—	—	—	570, 573
TFA·Gly$_3$·OH	—	233–235 d.	—	—	—	814
TFA·Gly·Phe·OH	DL	152.5–155	—	—	—	569
Triphenylmethyl (Trityl) derivatives						
Trityl·Ala·Gly·OH	L	180 d.^{gg}	—	—	—	548
Trityl·(CyS-Trityl)·Pro·Leu·OH	3 L	120 d.	+80.0	20	2%, CHCl$_3$	673
Trityl·(CyS-Trityl)·Tyr·OH	L-L	146–148	+87.5	20	2%, CHCl$_3$	673
Trityl·(CyS-Trityl)·Tyr·Ileu·OH	3 L	150–155	+51	20	2%, CHCl$_3$	673

CHEMICAL PROCEDURES FOR SYNTHESIS OF PEPTIDES 1185

Compound	Config.	m.p. (°C)	[α]	conc.	solvent	Ref.
Trityl·Glu·OH	L	—	—	—	—	549
└(CyS-Trityl)·Gly·OH	L	—	—	—	—	—
Trityl·Glu·NH₂·Gly·OH	L	130	+25	20	1%, EtOH	790
Trityl·Glu·NH₂	L	175	+55	—	1%, EtOH	790
└Gly·OH						
Trityl·Glu·Tyr·OH	L-L	130	+19	25	1%, 1 eq. NaOH in 75% MeOH	675
Trityl·Gly₂·OH	—	180ʰʰ	—	—	—	545, 546, 548, 806
Trityl·Gly₃·OH	—	205ⁱⁱ	—	—	—	806
Trityl·Gly₄·OH	—	—	—	—	—	806
Trityl·Gly·(1-Bz-His)·OH	L	198–201	—	—	—	484
Trityl·Gly·(Nᵉ-Trityl-Lys)·OH	L	130	+22.0	20	2%, CHCl₃	550
Trityl·Gly·(Nᵉ-Cbzo-Lys)·OH	L	110	−7.1	21	2.0%, pyridine	471a
Trityl·Gly·(Nᵉ-Trityl-Lys)·Glu·OH	L-L	130–140	+47	20	2%, CHCl₃	550
Trityl·Gly·(Nᵉ-Cbzo-Lys)·Pro·Val·OH	3 L	100 d.	−35.5	22	2.2%, MeOH	471a
Trityl·Gly·Met·OH	DL	111	—	—	—	546
Trityl·Gly·Phe·OH	L	210–215 d.ʲʲ	—	—	—	548
Trityl·Gly·Phe·Gly·OH	DL	130–132	—	—	—	812b
Trityl·Gly·Phe·Gly·OH	L	205–210 d.ᵏᵏ	—	—	—	548
N,N′-diTrityl·His·Gly·OH	L	155–160	+17	—	2%, CHCl₃	789
N,N′-diTrityl·His·Phe·OH	L-L	154 d.	−11.0	20	1.1%, CHCl₃	471a
N,N′-diTrityl·His·Phe·Arg·Try·OH	4 L	200–210 d.	−21	22	1.1%, DMF	471a
Trityl·(Nᵉ-Trityl-Lys)·Glu·OH	L-L	150	+4	20	2%, EtOH	550
Trityl·Val·(Nᵉ-Tos-Lys)·Leu·Phe·Pro·OH	3 L-D-L	138	−36	22	1.4%, MeOH	626a
Trityl·[Val·(Nᵉ-Tos-Lys)·Leu·Phe·Pro]₂·OH	[3 L-D-L]₂	137–138	−62	22	1.2%, MeOH	626a
Trityl·[Val·(Nᵟ-Tos-Orn)·Leu·Phe·Pro]₂·OH	[3 L-D-L]₂	133–134	—	—	—	719

TABLE 10-44 (continued)

Compound	Config.	M.P., °C.	$[\alpha]_D$, deg.	Temp., °C.	Concn. and Solvent	Ref.
o-Nitrophenoxyacetyl (o-NO₂-Phoac) derivatives						
o-NO₂-Phoac·Gly·Ala·Leu·OH	L-L	184–186	—	—	—	494
o-NO₂-Phoac·Gly₂·OH	—	209.5–213.5 d.	—	—	—	494
o-NO₂-Phoac·Gly₃·OH	—	215–217 d.	—	—	—	494
o-NO₂-Phoac·Phe·Leu·OH	L-L	161–164.5	−23.0	23	0.9%, EtOH	494

[a] M.p. = 56–58° (903).
[b] M.p. = 147°, $[\alpha]_D^{19} = -39.0°$ (0.2% in EtOH) (390).
[c] M.p. = 80–82°, $[\alpha]_D = -35°$ (2% in EtOH) (606).
[d] M.p. = 153–154°, $[\alpha]_D^{20} = -11.4°$ (2.6% in EtOH) (390).
[e] $[\alpha]_D = -6.4°$ (1.4% in 0.5N KHCO₃) (797).
[f] $[\alpha]_D^{22} = +5.5°$ (2% in N NaOH) (472).
[g] M.p. = 185–186°, $[\alpha]_D^{24} = -10.1°$ (3.9% in HOAc) (623).
[h] M.p. = 161–163° (861); m.p. = 182–183° (862).
[i] M.p. = 145–147°, $[\alpha]_D^{29} = -42.5°$ (in MeOH) (476).
[j] M.p. = 190° (472).
[k] M.p. = 125° (475).
[l] M.p. = 172–173° (482).
[m] A dimorphous form melts at 83–85° (605).
[n] M.p. = 183° (495).
[o] M.p. = 135° (705).
[p] M.p. = 133°, $[\alpha]_D^{19} = -9.5°$ (4.4% in EtOH) (495).
[q] M.p. = 145° (731).
[r] Dimorphous form melts at 100–101° (758); $[\alpha]_D^{16} = -17.9°$ (in N sodium hydroxide) (723).
[s] M.p. = 127–128° (939).
[t] M.p. = 98–101°, $[\alpha]_D^{22} = -24.7°$ (1% in EtOH) (622).
[u] M.p. = 76° (119); m.p. = 64–66° (719).
[v] $[\alpha]_D^{25} = -18.7°$ (4% in EtOH) (718); $[\alpha]_D^{13} = -18.5°$ (1% in EtOH) (915a).
[w] M.p. = 171.5–173° (541).
[x] M.p. = 106–107° (444).
[y] M.p. = 165° (505).
[z] Dimorphous form melts at 132–133° (917).
[aa] M.p. = 138–139° (380).
[bb] Dimorphous form melts at 128–133° (495).
[cc] M.p. = 183–185°, $[\alpha]_D^{28} = -148.5°$ (1.5% in EtOH) (522).
[dd] M.p. = 207–209° (868).
[ee] Melting point is variable, sometimes going as high as 140°.
[ff] Dimorphous form melts at 140–141°.
[gg] Softens at 115–120°.
[hh] M.p. = 186° (546); m.p. = 168° (806).
[ii] Melts at 114–115° and hardens at 138°.
[jj] Softens at 80–90°.
[kk] Softens at 90°.

Removal of N-Acyl Blocking Substituents

43. Preparation and Physical Constants of Peptides, Peptide Esters, Peptide Amides, and Amino Acid Amides. Free peptides, peptide esters, peptide amides, and amino acid amides may be generally procured through selective deacylation of the corresponding N^{α}-acylated precursors (see Tables 10-42 to 10-44). Methods whereby such deacylation is most frequently achieved include catalytic hydrogenolysis, chemical reduction with such reagents as Raney nickel or sodium in liquid ammonia, acid or alkaline hydrolysis, aminolysis, hydrazinolysis, and oxidation. Specific employment of each of these methods will be described in the sections which follow (Sections 10-44 to 10-48). Prior to such description, however, it would bode well to emphasize that, while more than one procedure may sometimes be applicable to the removal of a particular blocking substituent, choice of the procedure to be utilized for the preparation of a given compound often cannot be indiscriminately made but is, rather, governed by a combination of factors. Thus, for example, subjection of a carbobenzoxy-dipeptide benzyl ester (II) to palladium-catalyzed hydrogenolysis, the reductive action of sodium in liquid ammonia, or the action of hydrogen bromide in glacial acetic acid leads, respectively, to the formation of the free dipeptide (I) in the former two instances and of the dipeptide benzyl ester hydrobromide (III) in the latter instance. However, if the parent acylated dipeptide deri-

$$NH_2CHRCO\text{—}NHCHR'CO_2H \leftarrow Cbzo\text{—}NHCHRCO\text{—}NHCHR'CO_2Bz \rightarrow$$
$$\text{I} \qquad\qquad\qquad\qquad \text{II}$$

$$HBr\cdot NH_2CHRCO\text{—}NHCHRCO_2Bz$$
$$\text{III}$$

vative (II) incorporates an S-benzylcysteine residue, then catalytic hydrogenolysis is totally inhibited, the action of the glacial acetic–hydrogen bromide system proceeds as above with the removal only of the N-acyl group, whereas the reductive action of sodium in liquid ammonia results in the scission of the S-benzyl moiety as well as of the N-acyl and benzyl ester groups. Hence it becomes clear that prior to the selection of a synthetic route to a particular derivative, consideration must be given to the nature of the reactant and the limitations of the procedure employed.

Earlier sections of this chapter have been concerned with synthetic procedures for peptides, as well as their ester and amide derivatives, which do not involve the final removal of an acyl blocking group (Sections 10-4 to 10-11). Peptide esters may, in addition, be procured via treatment of the pertinent free peptide with alcoholic HCl or through the use of some other suitable esterification procedure, although such route to these compounds is rarely employed. Although peptides, peptide esters, and peptide amides are most conveniently prepared through deacylation of the N^{α}-acylated precursor, amino acid amides are best procured via ammonolysis of amino acid ester hydrochlorides (procedure 10–155) or the free base procured therefrom (procedure 10–156). Where the amino acid ester hydrochloride is the parent compound, its association with excess adherent hydrogen halide should be carefully avoided in order to prevent contamination of the final product with the difficultly removable ammonium chloride; several recrystallizations of the reactant amino acid ester hydrochloride, followed by drying *in vacuo* at room temperature over sodium hydroxide pellets, should obviate this danger. As in the preparation of the previously discussed acylated amino acid and peptide amides (Section 10–41), the rate of ammonolysis is here dependent upon the degree of steric hindrance imposed by the side chain of the amino acid residue bearing the ester group. Thus, for example, an attempt to prepare the highly hindered DL-*tert*-leucine amide (IV) by treatment of the precursor methyl ester hydrochloride with a ten-fold volume of methanolic ammonia for 8 days at room temperature culminated in the recovery of the unchanged starting material (371); the amide derivatives of the less hindered glycine and alanine residues, on the other hand, are readily secured in a shorter space of time under these same conditions. Treatment of γ-ethyl glutamate (V) with aqueous ammonia does not yield glutamine but, rather, leads to an intramolecular cyclization with the formation of pyrrolidonecarboxylic acid (VI) (604).

$$\underset{\text{IV}}{\text{CH}_3\text{—}\overset{\overset{\displaystyle\text{CH}_3}{|}}{\underset{\underset{\displaystyle\text{CH}_3}{|}}{\text{C}}}\text{CH}(\text{NH}_2)\text{CONH}_2} \qquad \underset{\text{V}}{\text{EtO}_2\text{C}\overset{\text{H}_2\text{N—CHCO}_2\text{H}}{\underset{\text{CH}_2}{\diagdown\diagup}}\text{CH}_2} \quad \xrightarrow{\text{aq. NH}_3} \quad \underset{\text{VI}}{\text{OC}\overset{\text{HN———CHCO}_2\text{H}}{\underset{\text{CH}_2}{\diagdown\diagup}}\text{CH}_2}$$

Illustrative procedure 10–155 (912). L-Leucine amide hydrochloride. A recrystallized preparation of 10 g. of L-leucine methyl ester hydrochloride (procedure 10–48) is allowed to stand in a pressure bottle at room temperature for 2 days with 50 ml. of anhydrous methanol which had previously been saturated with ammonia gas at 0°. The solution is then concentrated to dryness *in vacuo* at a temperature not exceeding 40° and the evaporation repeated several times after the addition, each time, of about 25 ml. of methanol. The residual crystals are filtered with the aid of absolute ether; yield, 8.5 g. Recrystallization from methanol–ether gives thin plates; m.p. 236–237°.

Illustrative procedure 10–156 (509). Amino acid amide acetates. Five grams of the pertinent amino acid methyl or ethyl ester hydrochloride (procedures 10–48 and 10–49) is dissolved in 10–15 ml. of methanol and treated with 1 equivalent of redistilled triethylamine. About 200 ml. of anhydrous ether is added and the mixture cooled for 1 hr. in an ice–salt bath. The precipitate of triethylamine hydrochloride is then removed by filtration and washed with ether. Concentration of the combined filtrate and washings under reduced pressure gives the free ester, which is transferred to a pressure flask containing 50 ml. of methanol previously saturated with ammonia at 0°. After 3 days, the solvent is removed under reduced pressure and the residue repeatedly dissolved in small portions of methanol, then evaporated to dryness under reduced pressure. The latter evaporation process is repeated with benzene and the crude product ultimately obtained dissolved in a small amount of methanol to which 1 equivalent of glacial acetic acid is added. Treatment of the latter solution with ethyl acetate leads to the precipitation of the desired amino acid amide acetate which is recrystallized from methanol–ethyl acetate. The melting points and yields of the various amino acid amide acetates prepared in this manner are: DL-alanine, 136–137°, 77%; DL-aspartic acid (diamide), 136–137°, 54%; glycine, 122–124°, 69%; DL-histidine, 151–152°, 50%; DL-leucine, 140–141°, 65%; DL-methionine, 143–146°, 27%; DL-phenylalanine, 139–140°, 29%; DL-serine, 117–119°, 57%; DL-tryptophan, 126–127°, 56%; DL-tyrosine, 159–161°, 64%; and DL-valine, 140–143°, 66%.

Tables 10–45 to 10–47 list several of the peptides, peptide esters, peptide amides, and amino acid amides which have been prepared by the methods discussed in this chapter. Description of the amide and ester derivatives has most frequently been given in the form of the corresponding acetate or hydrohalide salts, and occasionally as the free base or the picrate, sulfate, picrolonate, or other salts; peptides which incorporate a basic amino acid residue, e.g., arginine, lysine or histidine, have also been generally described as salts with organic or inorganic acids.

44. Catalytic Hydrogenolysis. *Principle.* The reductive action of hydrogen, under the catalytic influence of palladium black, palladized charcoal, or palladous oxide, may be utilized to effect the facile cleavage of the benzyl moiety from its covalent linkage with an oxygen, a nitrogen and, in certain instances, a sulfur atom. Such reaction has been most prominently exploited for the quantitative scission of the carbobenzoxy substituent from its amide linkage with the α-amino function of a suitably constituted amino acid or peptide derivative (I → IV; X = H). During this process, the benzyl residue is eliminated as toluene (II; X = H), and carbon dioxide (III) is simultaneously evolved, presumably as a consequence of spontaneous breakdown of a transitory N-carboxyamino acid intermediate (128).

$$X-\text{C}_6\text{H}_4-\text{CH}_2\text{OCO}-\text{NHCHRCO}-\text{NH}\cdots \rightarrow X-\text{C}_6\text{H}_4-\text{CH}_3 + CO_2 + NH_2\text{CHRCO}-\text{NH}\cdots$$

I   II   III   IV

Deacylation is achieved in like manner where the hydroxyl function of a hydroxyamino acid residue, e.g., tyrosine (826), the ω-amino function of a diamino acid residue, e.g., lysine (626), or the guanidino moiety of an arginine residue (459, 904, 905) is masked with a carbobenzoxy subsitutuent. Comparable reductive degradation may be effected in the case of the analogous *p*-nitrocarbobenzoxy (I; X = NO₂) (363, 462), *p*-bromocarbobenzoxy

(*discussion continued on p. 1231*)

TABLE 10-45
Methyl, Ethyl, and Benzyl Ester Derivatives of Unacylated Peptides

Compound	Config.	M.P., °C.	$[\alpha]_D$, deg.	Temp., °C.	Concn. and Solvent	Ref.
H·Ala·Gly·OEt·HCl	L	156	—	—	—	613a
H·Ala·Gly₂·OEt	L	103	—	—	—	353
H·Ala·Gly₂·OMe·HCl	DL	153	—	—	—	416
H·Ala·Gly·Val·CySBz·OBz·HBr	3 L	178–179	—	—	—	875c
H·Ala·Ser·Val·CySBz·OBz·HBr	4 L	180–182	—	—	—	432a
H·Ala·Tyr·OEt·HCl	D-L	—	+4.9	25	2%, H₂O	660
H·Ala·Tyr·OEt·HCl	L-L	—	+6.4	25	2%, H₂O	660
H·Asp·NH₂·Arg·Val·Tyr·Val·His·Pro·Phe·OMe·HCOOH	8 L	200 d.	−67.7	—	1%, H₂O	718a
H·Asp·NH₂·CySBz·OMe·HBr	L-L	125–126	−22.5	23	1%, H₂O	482a
H·Asp·NH₂·(CyS-Trityl)·Pro·Leu·Gly·OMe·HCl	4 L	—	−23	20	1%, CHCl₃	790
H·Asp·Gly·OEt	L	232	—	—	—	878
H·Arg·Try·OMe·2HCl	L-L	150 d.	−6.7	20	2.1%, H₂O	471a
H·Asp·OH └─β-Ala·OEt	DL	188	—	—	—	895
H·Asp·Gly·OEt	DL	175–176	—	—	—	555
H·Asp·OH └─Gly·OEt	DL	238	—	—	—	555
H·(CySBz)₂·OEt·HBr	L-L	145–147	—	—	—	432a
H·CySBz·Gly·OBz·HBr	L	124	—	—	—	432a
H·CySBz·Pro·Leu·Gly·OBz·HCl	3 L	193–194	−73.5	23	1%, EtOH	798, 865
H·CySH·Gly·OEt·HI	L	111–113	—	—	—	477

H·(CyS-Trityl)·Gly·OEt·HCl	L	100	—	—	—	549
H·(CyS-Trityl)·Pro·Leu·Gly·OMe·HCl	3 L	150	−17	20	2%, CHCl$_3$	673
H·CyS·Gly·OEt	L	72–73	—	—	—	353
H·CyS·Gly·OEt	L					
H·Glu·OMe·Asp·OMe·(CyS-Trityl)·Pro·Leu·Gly·OMe·HCl	5 L	125	−30	20	2%, CHCl$_3$	673
H·Glu·OEt	L	132–133	−5.6	26	4%, H$_2$O	767, 909
└─Glu·(OEt)$_2$·HCl						
H·Glu·OEt	L	147–150	—	—	—	767, 909
└─Glu·OEt						
└─Glu·(OEt)$_2$·HCl						
H·Glu·Gly·OEt	L	151	—	—	—	878
H·Glu·OMe·Gly·OEt·HCl	L	91–91.5	+32.0	19	5%, H$_2$O	677
H·Glu·OEt·Gly$_2$·OEt·HBr	L	144–146	—	—	—	767
H·Glu·Tyr·OEt	L-L	144	—	—	—	709
H·Gly·Ala·Gly·OBz·HBr	DL	194–195	—	—	—	704
H·Gly·Ala·Gly·OBz·HBr	L	214–216	−54.5	25	2%, H$_2$O	717a
H·Gly·Glu·(OEt)$_2$·HCl	L	113–115	−13.7	18	8.9%, 96% EtOH	649, 677
H·Gly·Glu·Gly·OEt	—	—	—	—	—	878
H·Gly$_2$·OBz·HBr	—	144	—	—	—	665
H·Gly$_2$·OBz·HCl	—	160	—	—	—	548, 699
H·Gly$_2$·OEt	—	85–86	—	—	—	165
H·Gly$_2$·OEt·HCl	—	185–186	—	—	—	179, 415
H·Gly$_2$·OMe	—	250 d.	—	—	—	164
H·Gly$_2$·Ala·OMe·HBr	DL	176–178	—	—	—	910
H·Gly$_2$·CySBz·OBz·HI	L	139–140	−40.3	23	0.8%, EtOH	711
H·Gly$_2$·Glu·(OEt)$_2$·HCl	L	160–161	−16.5	17	1.3%, EtOH	649
H·Gly$_3$·OBz·HBr	—	174–175	—	—	—	665

TABLE 10-45 (*continued*)

Compound	Config.	M.P., °C.	$[\alpha]_D$, deg.	Temp., °C.	Concn. and Solvent	Ref.
H·Gly₃·CySBz·OBz·HI	L	164–167	−14.7	22	1%, EtOH	711
H·Gly₃·OEt	—	107	—	—	—	165
H·Gly₃·OEt·HBr	—	191	—	—	—	415
H·Gly₃·OEt·HCl	—	215–216 d.	—	—	—	165, 353, 415, 919
H·Gly₃·OMe	—	110	—	—	—	164, 165
H·Gly₃·OMe·HCl	—	197	—	—	—	165
H·Gly₄·CySBz·OBz·HI	L	166–168	−24.2	20	0.8%, HOAc	472
H·Gly₄·OEt	—	—[a]	—	—	—	165
H·Gly₄·OEt·HCl	—	213–214	—	—	—	165, 415
H·Gly₅·OEt	—	—	—	—	—	165
H·Gly₅·OEt·HCl	—	236–237 d.	—	—	—	165, 415
H·Gly₆·OEt	—	—[a]	—	—	—	165
H·Gly₆·OEt·HCl	—	239–240 d.	—	—	—	165
H·Gly₃·Pro·OEt·HBr	DL	241	—	—	—	170
H·Gly₃·Pro·OEt·HBr	L	179–181 d.	−60.0	25	2.2%, H₂O	170
H·Gly₂·Phe·OEt·HOAc	L	121–122	—	—	—	902
H·Gly₂·Phe·OEt·HCl	DL	139–140	—	—	—	812b
H·Gly₂·Pro·OEt·HCl	L	112–114	—	—	—	170
H·Gly·Leu·OEt·HBr	L	178	−36.3	27	6%, EtOH	769a
H·Gly·Lys·OMe·2HCl	L	177	—	—	—	358
H·Gly·Phe·OBz·HBr	L	193	—	—	—	665
H·Gly·Phe·OMe·HCl	DL	166	—	—	—	415

Compound	Config	M.p. (°C)	[α]	T (°C)	Solvent	Ref
H·Gly·Phe·OEt·HCl	L	—	+7.2	29	2%, H_2O	928
H·Gly·Pro·OEt·HCl	DL	137 d.	—	—	—	170
H·Gly·Pro·Gly·OEt·HCl	DL	213 d.	—	—	—	170
H·Gly·Pro·Gly·OEt·HCl	L	214	−104.0	25	1.5%, H_2O	170
H·Gly·Tyr·OEt·HOAc	L	—	+16.2	29	2%, H_2O	928
H·Gly·Tyr·OEt·HCl	L	245	+17.1	22	2%, H_2O	660, 914
H·Gly·Tyr·OMe·HCl	L	223 d.	—	—	—	415
H·His·Phe·OMe·2HBr	L-L	165 d.	+13.5	23	2.3%, 4N HCl	471a
H·(α-NH₂-isoBut)·Phe·OEt·HCl	L	—	−18.1	22	2%, H_2O	660
H·(α-NH₂-isoBut)·Tyr·OEt·HCl	L	—	−9.1	22	2%, H_2O	660
H·Ileu·His·Pro·Phe·OMe·2HBr	4 L	130–140	+18	22	1.0%, H_2O	714
H·Leu·Ala·Phe·Gly·Pro·OBz·HBr·3H_2O	5 L	250 d.	−65.3	23	0.7%, H_2O	915
H·Leu·Phe·OEt·HCl	D-L	—	−43.3	22	2%, H_2O	660
H·Leu·Phe·OEt·HCl	L-D	216	—	—	—	698
H·Leu·Phe·OEt·HCl	L-L	—	−3.8	22	2%, H_2O	660
H·Leu·Phe·Pro·OEt	3 L	—	—	—	—	698
H·Leu·Phe·Pro·OMe·HCl	L-D-L	240 d.	−38.9	20	2%, MeOH	698, 719
H·Leu·Tyr·OEt·HCl	L-D	205–207	+18.3	25	2%, MeOH	679a
H·Leu·Tyr·Pro·OMe·HCl	L-D-L	239–241 d.	−51.0	21	2%, MeOH	679a
H·Leu·Val·Glu·(OEt)₂·HCl	3 L	238–239	−25.5	25	2%, EtOH	718
H·Leu·Val·Glu·(OEt)₂·HBr	3 L	220	−30.5	13	2%, EtOH	915a
H·Lys·Phe·OEt·2HCl	L-L	—	+14.5	22	2%, H_2O	660
H·Lys·Tyr·OEt·2HCl	L-L	—	+16.9	22	2%, H_2O	660
H·Lys·Val·Phe·Gly·OEt·2HBr	3 L	216–218	—	—	—	507
H·(Nᵉ·Tos·Lys)·Gly·OEt	L	86.5–88	−6.0	21	3%, $CHCl_3$	393
H·(Nᵉ·Tos·Lys)·Gly·OEt·HBr	L	176.5–177.5	+16.7	21	2%, H_2O	393
H·(Nᵉ·Tos·Lys)·Gly·OEt·HCl	L	204–206	+18.9	21	3.4%, H_2O	393
H·Orn·Leu·Phe·Pro·OMe	2 L-D-L	—	—	—	—	421

1194 CHEMISTRY OF THE AMINO ACIDS

TABLE 10-45 (continued)

Specific Rotation

Compound	Config.	M.P., °C.	$[\alpha]_D$, deg.	Temp., °C.	Concn. and Solvent	Ref.
H·Phe·Gly·OEt·HBr	L	134–135	+41.8	25	1%, H_2O	465, 495, 682, 722
H·Phe·Gly·OEt·HCl	DL	152–153	—	—	—	812b
H·Phe·Gly$_2$·OEt·HCl	DL	239–240 d.	—	—	—	415
H·Phe·Pro·OEt·HCl	L-L	174	—	—	—	698
H·Pro·Gly·OEt·HCl	DL	95–96	—	—	—	170
H·Pro·Gly·OEt·HCl	L	119–120	−39.5	22	2.4%, H_2O	170
H·Pro·Gly$_2$·OEt	L	109	—	—	—	170
H·Pro·Gly$_3$·OEt	L	161–162	—	—	—	170
H·Pro·Gly$_3$·OEt·HCl	L	188 d.	−14.0	24	1.7%, H_2O	170
H·Pro·(N$^\varepsilon$-Tos-Lys)·Gly·OEt	L-L	81–84	−32.5	20	2.5%, EtOH	88, 393
H·Pro·Phe·OEt·HCl	L-L	—	−40.9	22	2%, H_2O	660
H·Pro·Phe·OMe·HCl	L-L	162.5–163.5	−41.8	25	2.5%, H_2O	508, 714
H·Pro·Tyr·OEt·HCl	L-L	—	−29.3	22	2%, H_2O	660
H·Pro·Val·OMe·HBr	L-L	80 d.	−60.0	21	2.0%, H_2O	471a
H·Pro·Val·(N$^\delta$-Tos-Orn)·Leu·Tyr·Pro·OMe·HCl	4 L-D-L	206–213	−83.0	25	0.5%, 0.01N HCl	679a
H·Ser·Gly·Ser·OMe·HCl	L-L	174–175	−4.1	24	2%, H_2O	631
H·Ser·Tyr·Ser·OMe·HCl	L-L	135	+10.2	20	2.6%, MeOH	471a
H·Try·Gly·OBz·HCl	3 L	172–174	+27.0	25	1.2%, EtOH	791
H·Tyr·Leu·OBz·HCl	L-L	169–172	−16.7	19	1.6%, EtOH	584a
H·(O-Ac-Tyr)·Leu·OMe·HCl	L-L	—	—	—	—	584a
H·Tyr·(N$^\varepsilon$-Cbzo-Lys)·OBz	L-L	119–120	—	—	—	584a
H·Tyr·(N$^\varepsilon$-Cbzo-Lys)·OBz·HCl	L-L	158.5–160	—	—	—	584a
H·Tyr·Ser·OMe·HCl	L-L	130–135 d.	+12.2	22	2.0%, MeOH	471a

H·Tyr₂·OEt·HCl	L-L	216 d.	—	—	—	637
H·Tyr₂·OMe·HCl	L-L	210	—	—	—	637
H·Tyr₃·OEt·HCl	3 L	231–231.5 d.	—	—	—	637
H·Val·CySBz·OBz·HBr	L-L	184.5–185.5	−37.1	20	1.0%, MeOH	432a, 875c
H·Val·(Nᵋ-Tos-Lys)·Leu·Phe·Pro·OMe·HCl	3 L-D-L	140	—	—	—	626a
H·Val·(N^δ-Tos-Orn)·Leu·Phe·Pro·OMe·HCl	3 L-D-L	—	−48.0	24	0.9%, 0.01N HCl	423, 719
H·[Val·(N^δ-Tos-Orn)·Leu·Phe·Pro]₂·OMe	[3 L-D-L]₂	220–222 d.	−113.7	27	0.2%, EtOH	423
H·Val·(N^δ-Tos-Orn)·Leu·Tyr·Pro·OMe·HCl	3 L-D-L	—	−52.1	25	0.01%, 0.01N HCl	679a
H·Val·Phe·OMe·HCl	L-L	196–196.5	+26.6	28	2.8%, H₂O	586
H·Val·Phe·Gly·OEt·HBr	L-L	210–211	+29.2	25	2%, H₂O	507
H·Val·Tyr·OMe·HBr	L-L	208–209	+31.0	23	1.1%, MeOH	714
H·Val·Tyr·Ileu·His·Pro·Phe·OMe·2HCl	6 L	181–187	−14.1	25	1%, MeOH	508
H·Val·Tyr·Val·His·Pro·Phe·OMe	6 L	135–140 d.	−55	—	0.9%, MeOH	718a
H·Val·Tyr·Val·His·Pro·Phe·His·Leu·OMe	8 L	—	−70	—	1.2%, MeOH	638a
H·Val₃·OMe·HCl	3 L	225–228 d.	+48.8	22	2.1%, H₂O	543a
H·Val₃·OMe·HCl	2 L-D	220–224 d.	+16.3	21	2.0%, H₂O	543a
H·Val₃·OMe·HCl	3 D	226–228 d.	−51.2	22	2.3%, H₂O	543a

[a] No definite melting point.

TABLE 10-46
Amino Acid and Peptide Amides

Compound	Config.	M.P., °C.	$[\alpha]_D$, deg.	Temp., °C.	Concn. and Solvent	Ref.
H·Ala·NH₂	L	71–72	—	—	—	945
H·Ala·NH₂·HOAc	DL	136–137	—	—	—	509
H·β-Ala·NH₂·HOAc	—	118	—	—	—	899
H·Ala·NH₂·HBr	DL	175	—	—	—	616
H·Ala·NH₂·HCl	DL	—	—	—	—	946
H·Ala·NH₂·HCl	L	196–199	—	—	—	899
H·β-Ala·Gly·NH₂·HOAc	—	118–120	—	—	—	899
H·Ala·Gly·Phe·NH₂	L-L	—	—	—	—	902
H·Ala·Leu·NH₂·HOAc	D-L	249–250	−35	26	1.5%, H₂O	467
H·Ala·Leu·NH₂·HOAc	L-L	250 d.	−9	28	2%, H₂O	467
H·Ala·Phe·NH₂·HOAc	L-L	—	+33.4	27	1.5%, H₂O	902
H·Ala·Tyr·NH₂·HOAc	L-L	—	+30.2	27	1.2%, H₂O	902
H·(α-NH₂-n-But)·NH₂·HCl	DL	222–223	—	—	—	612
H·Asp·NH₂	DL	—	—	—	—	555
H·Asp·NH₂	L	—	+15.5[a]	18	1.5%, 0.1N HCl	128, 576, 885
H·Asp·NH₂·NH₂·HOAc	DL	136–137	—	—	—	509
H·Arg·NH₂·2HCl·H₂O	L	—	+13.8	24	1%, H₂O	904, 947
H·Arg·Gly·NH₂·dipicrate	L	209–210	+15.9	24	1%, acetone–H₂O (1:1)	511
H·CySBz·NH₂·HCl	DL	112	—	—	—	616
H·CySBz·Pro·Leu·Gly·NH₂	3 L	136–137[b]	−50.8[b]	20	3.3%, EtOH	865, 868
H·CySBz·Pro·Leu·Gly·NH₂·H₂O	3 L	—	—	—	—	717

Compound		m.p.	$[\alpha]_D$	°C	conc., solvent	Ref.
H·CySBz·Pro·(N$^\epsilon$-Tos-Lys)·Gly·NH$_2$	3 L	—	−13.6	21	2%, CHCl$_3$	393
H·CyS·Tyr·Ileu·Glu-NH$_2$·Asp-NH$_2$·CyS·Pro·Leu·Gly·NH$_2$ (oxytocin)	8 L	—	−26.1	22	0.5%, H$_2$O	82, 673, 868
H·CyS·Tyr·Ileu·(Glu-Asp-NH$_2$·CyS·Pro·Leu·Gly·NH$_2$)·NH$_2$·HOAc (isoglutamine-oxytocin)	8 L	—	+33.0	21.5	0.6%, H$_2$O	623
H·CyS·Tyr·Phe·Glu-NH$_2$·Asp-NH$_2$·CyS·Pro·Leu·Gly·NH$_2$ (oxypressin)	8 L	—	−33	22	0.6%, 0.1N HOAc	846
H·CyS·Tyr·Phe·Glu-NH$_2$·Asp-NH$_2$·CyS·Pro·Lys·Gly·NH$_2$ (lysine-vasopressin)	8 L	—	−47.5	20	1%, H$_2$O	432
α,ε-Diaminopimelic acid diamide	DL	—	—	—	—	478, 920
H·Glu·NH$_2$	DL	—	—	—	—	607
H·Glu·NH$_2$	L	—	+20.5	21	6.1%, H$_2$O	128, 435, 509, 790, 882, 922
H·Glu-NH$_2$·Asp-NH$_2$·CySBz·Pro·Leu·Gly·NH$_2$	5 L	145	−67.3	19	2.3%, HOAc	472, 868
H·Glu-NH$_2$·Glu-NH$_2$·CySBz·Pro·Leu·Gly·NH$_2$	5 L	—	—	—	—	629
H·Glu·OEt·NH$_2$·HCl	L	197–198	+21.2	26	2%, H$_2$O	648
H·Glu·OH	L	196–197	—	—	—	890
H·Glu·NH$_2$ —Gly·NH$_2$	L	183	+15.3	21.5	2%, H$_2$O	701
H·Glu·NH$_2$ —Gly·OH		—	—	—	—	485
H·(γ-OH-Glu)·NH$_2$	DL	—	—	—	—	485
H·(allo-γ-OH-Glu)·NH$_2$	DL	—	+6.7	27	2.1%, H$_2$O	912
H·Glu·Leu·NH$_2$	L-L	175–177	—	—	—	924
H·Glu·Phe·NH$_2$	L-L	185–186	—	—	—	945
H·Gly·NH$_2$	—	67–68	—	—	—	509
H·Gly·NH$_2$·HOAc	—	122–124	—	—	—	830a
H·Gly·Ala·NH$_2$	DL	126–127	—	—	—	

TABLE 10-46 (continued)

Compound	Config.	M.P., °C.	[α]_D, deg.	Temp., °C.	Concn. and Solvent	Ref.
H·Gly₂·NH₂·HOAc	—	—	—	—	—	916
H·Gly₃·NH₂·HOAc	—	—	—	—	—	911
H·Gly₂·Phe·NH₂	L	—	—	—	—	902
H·Gly·His·NH₂·2HCl·H₂O	L	—	—	—	—	925
H·Gly·Leu·NH₂·HCl	L	210 d.	−19.0	26	5%, H₂O	912
H·Gly·Lys·NH₂·2HBr	L	—	—	—	—	833
H·Gly·(Nᵉ-Cbzo-Lys)·Pro·Val·NH₂·HCl	3 L	130 d.	−62.0	21	2.2%, MeOH	471a
H·Gly·Met·NH₂·HOAc	L	108–110	—	—	—	627
H·Gly·Phe·NH₂·HOAc	D	—	−28.5	25	5%, H₂O	902
H·Gly·Phe·NH₂·HOAc	L	—	+28.8	26	5%, H₂O	916
H·Gly·Phe·Gly·Phe·NH₂	L-L	—	+17.6	27	2% pyridine	902
H·Gly·Tyr·NH₂·HOAc	L	—	+28.0	22	10%, H₂O	916
H·Gly·(O-Me-Tyr)·NH₂·HOAc	L	—	+39.5	22	2%, H₂O	660
H·Gly·Tyr·Gly·NH₂·HCl	L	89–90	—	—	—	700
H·Gly·Val·NH₂·HBr	DL	180	—	—	—	920a
H·His·NH₂·HOAc	DL	151–152	—	—	—	509
H·His·NH₂·HCl	DL	233 d.	—	—	—	616
H·His·NH₂·2HCl	L	260–261	+22.0	20	1%, H₂O	621
H·His·Phe·Arg·Try·Gly·(Nᵉ-Cbzo-Lys)·Pro·Val·NH₂·HCl	7 L	100	−37.3	22	2.0%, MeOH	471a
H·Hypro·NH₂	L	139	—	—	—	169
H·Ileu·NH₂·HCl	D	246–247	−21.0	24	1%, H₂O	622
H·Ileu·NH₂·HCl	L	246 d.	+21.2	20	1%, H₂O	622
H·Leu·NH₂	DL	105–106	—	—	—	945
H·Leu·NH₂·HOAc	DL	140–141	—	—	—	509
H·Leu·NH₂·HOAc	D	128–129	−9.2	24	5%, H₂O	612, 926

Compound	Config.	M.p. (°C)	[α]	T (°C)	Solvent	Ref.
H·Leu·NH$_2$·HOAc	L	125-126	—	—	—	926
H·Leu·NH$_2$·HBr	L	—	+8.7	25	5%, H$_2$O	464
H·*tert*-Leu·NH$_2$·HCl	DL	337	—	—	—	371
H·Leu·NH$_2$·HCl	D	—	-10.9	25	2%, H$_2$O	254
H·Leu·NH$_2$·HCl	L	236-237	+9.5^c	25	5%, H$_2$O	254, 912
H·Leu·Ala·NH$_2$·HOAc	L-L	250-255 d.	+4.0	21	1%, H$_2$O	467
H·Leu·Gly·NH$_2$	DL	97-98	—	—	—	805
H·Leu·Gly·NH$_2$·HBr	DL	200-202	—	—	—	805
H·Leu·Phe·NH$_2$·HOAc	L-L	—	—	—	—	660
H·Leu·Tyr·NH$_2$·HOAc	L-L	—	+6.2	27	2.1%, pyridine	902
H·Lys·NH$_2$·2HCl	L	250-260 d.	—	—	—	584a, 833
H·(N$^\epsilon$-Cbzo-Lys)·NH$_2$·HCl	L	203	—	—	—	358
H·Lys·Gly·NH$_2$·2HBr	L	—	—	—	—	833
H·Lys·Lys·Tyr·NH$_2$·3HCl	3 L	—	—	—	—	584a
H·Lys·Phe·NH$_2$·2HCl	L-L	—	+38.0	22	2%, H$_2$O	660
H·Lys·Tyr·NH$_2$·2HBr	L-L	—	+17.3	18	2%, H$_2$O	660
H·Lys·Tyr·NH$_2$·2HCl	L-L	250-253	—	—	—	584a
H·Met·NH$_2$·HOAc	DL	143-146	—	—	—	509
H·Met·NH$_2$·HOAc	D	101-102	—	—	—	627
H·Met·NH$_2$·HOAc	L	103	—	—	—	627
H·Nleu·NH$_2$·HCl	DL	234-235 d.	—	—	—	612
H·Nval·NH$_2$·HCl	DL	240	—	—	—	612
H·Phe·NH$_2$	DL	137-139	—	—	—	586
H·Phe·NH$_2$·HOAc	DL	139-140	—	—	—	509
H·Phe·NH$_2$·HCl	DL	238-239 d.	—	—	—	586
H·Phe·NH$_2$·HOAc	D	—	+34.8	25	2%, H$_2$O	924
H·Phe·NH$_2$·HOAc	L	119-120	—	—	—	916
H·Phe·Gly·NH$_2$·HOAc	L	—	+68.2	23	5%, H$_2$O	916
H·Phe$_2$·NH$_2$	L-L	138	—	—	—	916
H·Phe·Tyr·NH$_2$	L-L	180	—	—	—	916
H·Pro·NH$_2^d$	DL	99	—	—	—	927

TABLE 10-46 (continued)

Compound	Config.	M.P., °C.	$[\alpha]_D$, deg.	Temp., °C.	Concn. and Solvent	Ref.
H·Pro·NH₂	L	99	—	—	—	927
H·Pro·NH₂·HCl	L	182	−70.7	23	2%, EtOH	169, 509, 927
H·Pro·Leu·Gly·NH₂·½H₂O	L-L	122–123	—	—	—	717
H·Pro·Leu·Gly·NH₂·HBr	L-L	191–192	—	—	—	717
H·Pro·Phe·NH₂·HCl	L-L	—	−15.8	22	2%, H₂O	660
H·Ser·NH₂·HOAc	DL	117–119	—	—	—	509
H·Ser·Phe·NH₂·HCl	L-L	—	+26.7	29	2%, H₂O	928
H·Ser·Tyr·NH₂·HCl	L-L	—	+30.0	29	2%, H₂O	928
H·Try·NH₂	DL	120–121	—	—	—	634
H·Try·NH₂·HOAc	DL	126–127	—	—	—	509
H·Try·NH₂	L	167–170	−7.9	20	2%, EtOH	948
H·Try·NH₂·HCl	L	257–260 d.	+24.0	26	1.6%, H₂O	612
H·Tyr·NH₂·HOAc	DL	159–161	—	—	—	509
H·Tyr·NH₂·HOAc	L	177	—	—	—	926
H·Tyr·Gly·NH₂·HOAc	L	—	+70.9	22	6%, H₂O	916
H·Tyr₂·NH₂·HOAc	L-L	—	—	—	—	916
H·Val·NH₂·HOAc	DL	140–143	—	—	—	509
H·Val·NH₂·HBr	DL	—	—	—	—	464
H·Val·NH₂·HCl	DL	245	—	—	—	622
H·Val·NH₂·HCl	D	268–269 d.	−28.3	24	1%, H₂O	622
H·Val·NH₂·HCl	L	268 d.	+28.3	20	1%, H₂O	622
H·Val·Gly·NH₂·HBr	DL	228	—	—	—	920a

^{a} $[\alpha]_D^{18} = +9.7°$ (0.5% in H₂O) (576).
^{b} M.p. = 69.5–71.5°; $[\alpha]_D^{23} = -47.7°$ (1% in EtOH) (865).
^{c} $[\alpha]_D^{25} = +10.8°$ (3% in N HCl) (254).
^{d} See Section 35-4 for new synthesis of the acetate.

CHEMICAL PROCEDURES FOR SYNTHESIS OF PEPTIDES 1201

TABLE 10-47
Free Peptides

Compound	Config.	$[\alpha]_D$, deg.	Temp., °C	Concn. and Solvent	Ref.
N-Alanyl derivatives					
H·Ala$_2$·OH	D-D	+37.9	24	2%, 0.5N HCl	666
H·Ala$_2$·OH	D-L	−71.1	25	2%, H$_2$O	196, 468
H·Ala$_2$·OH	L-D	+74.1[a]	23	2%, 0.5N HCl	666, 949
H·Ala$_2$·OH	L-L	−37.3[b]	24	2%, 0.5N HCl	156, 198, 666, 896, 949
H·β-Ala·β-Ala·OH	—	—	—	—	899
H·Ala$_3$·OH	3 D	+85.9	24	2%, 0.5N HCl	703
H·Ala$_3$·OH	D-2 L	−115.2	23	2%, 0.5N HCl	703
H·Ala$_3$·OH	L-D-L	+37.0	23	2%, 0.5N HCl	703
H·Ala$_3$·OH	2 L-D	−4.6	23	2%, 0.5N HCl	703
H·Ala$_3$·OH	3 L	−85.4[c]	23	2%, 0.5N HCl	703, 950
H·Ala$_4$·OH	D-3 L	−145.1	22	2%, 0.5N HCl	897
H·Ala$_4$·OH	L-D-2 L	−14.2	21	2%, 0.5N HCl	897
H·Ala$_4$·OH	2 L-D-L	−5.0	25	2%, 0.5N HCl	897
H·Ala$_4$·OH	4 L	−120.5	20	2.2%, 2N HCl	950
H·Ala$_4$·OH·H$_2$O	4 L	−131.0	25	2%, 0.5N HCl	897
H·Ala$_5$·OH	5 L	−149.7[d]	23	2%, 0.5N HCl	897, 950
H·Ala$_6$·OH	6 L	−156.6	23	0.9%, 0.5N HCl	897
H·Ala$_2$·Gly·OH	D-D	+47.2	20	3%, H$_2$O	951
H·Ala$_2$·Gly·OH	L-L	−48.1	22	2%, H$_2$O	353

TABLE 10-47 (continued)

N-Alanyl derivatives (continued)

Compound	Config.	$[\alpha]_D$, deg.	Temp., °C	Concn. and Solvent	Ref.
H·Ala·CyS·OH	D-L	−227.9	20	1%, N HCl	617, 952
H·Ala·CyS·OH | H·Ala·CyS·OH	D-L L-L	 −137.4	 20	 1.3%, N HCl	 617
H·Ala·CyS·OH | H·Ala·CyS·OH	L-L D-L	 −52.8	 25	 2%, H_2O	 468
H·Ala·(α-NH₂-n-But)·OH	L-L	−8.0	25	2%, H_2O	468
H·Ala·(α-NH₂-isoBut)·OH	L	+34.5	20	2%, H_2O	466
H·Ala·Arg·OH·HOAc	L-L	+8.7	27	3.3%, H_2O	491
H·Ala·Glu·OH	D-L	−32.9	23	1–2%, 0.5N HCl	898
H·Ala·Glu·NH₂·OH	D-L	−20.1	15	5%, H_2O	953
H·Ala·Glu·OH	L-D	+32.4	23	1–2%, 0.5N HCl	898
H·Ala·Glu·OH	L-L	−9.3	24	1–2%, 0.5N HCl	898
H·Ala·Glu·NH₂·OH	L-L	+9.3	18	1%, H_2O	953
H·Ala·Glu·Ala·OH	D-L-D	−13.3	24	2%, 0.5N HCl	891

H·Ala·Glu·OH
   |
   Ala·OH
	D-L
	
	D
		+7.6	24	2%, 0.5N HCl	891

H·Ala·Glu·Ala·OH	D-2 L	−63.8	24	2%, 0.5N HCl	891

H·Ala·Glu·OH
   |
   Ala·OH
	D-L
	
	L
		−47.5	24	2%, 0.5N HCl	891

H·Ala·Glu·Ala·OH	2 L-D	+6.9	24	2%, 0.5N HCl	891

H·Ala·Glu·OH └──Ala·OH	L-L	+26.2	24	2%, 0.5N HCl	891
H·Ala·Glu·Ala·OH	D	−41.7	24	2%, 0.5N HCl	891
H·Ala·Glu·OH └──Ala·OH	3 L	−29.9	25	2%, 0.5N HCl	891
H·Ala·Gly·OH	L-L L DL	—	—	—	127, 353, 416, 464, 547, 551, 573, 900
H·Ala·Gly·OH	D	−23.5^e	24	2%, 0.5N HCl	466, 666
H·Ala·Gly·OH	L	+22.6^f	24	2%, 0.5N HCl	215, 251, 353, 466, 548, 613a, 666, 949
H·β-Ala·Gly·OH	—	—	—	—	899
H·Ala·Gly·Ala·OH	L-L	−19.5	20	3.7%, H$_2$O	935
H·Ala·Gly$_2$·OH	D	−31.6	25	10%, H$_2$O	705
H·Ala·Gly$_2$·OH	L	+32.4	25	10%, H$_2$O	157, 215, 353, 705
H·β-Ala·Gly$_2$·OH	—	—	—	—	899
H·Ala·Gly$_2$·Ala·Gly$_2$·OH	L-L	+13.2	21	8%, H$_2$O	157
H·Ala·Gly$_2$·OH	L	+27.0	20	3%, H$_2$O	216
H·Ala·Gly$_3$·OH	L-L	−11.2	20	2.3%, H$_2$O	954
H·Ala·Gly·Leu·OH	L-L	+41.9	20	4.6%, H$_2$O	229, 931
H·Ala·Gly·Tyr·OH	3 L	−32	20	0.7%, H$_2$O	875c
H·Ala·Gly·Val·CySBz·OH	D	−20.4	28	2%, H$_2$O	862
H·β-Ala·His·OH	L	+20.5	25	2%, H$_2$O	690
H·β-Ala·His·OH	D-L	−2.5	24	1%, H$_2$O	359
H·Ala·His·OH·(½H$_2$SO$_4$)	L-L	+27.0	27	1%, H$_2$O	359
H·Ala·His·OH	L-L	+14.1	25	−, H$_2$O	359
H·Ala·His·OH·(½H$_2$SO$_4$)	L	+12.3	30	5%, H$_2$O	50
H·β-Ala·(1-Me-His)·OH	L	—	—	—	621
H·β-Ala·His·Gly·OH·HNO$_3$					

TABLE 10-47 (continued)

Specific Rotation

Compound	Config.	$[\alpha]_D$, deg.	Temp., °C	Concn. and Solvent	Ref.
N-Alanyl derivatives (continued)					
H·Ala·Ileu·OH	L-L	+6.1	20	3.8%, N HCl	955
H·Ala·Leu·OH	D-D	—	—	—	469
H·Ala·Leu·OH	L-L	−17.0	21	5%, H_2O	127, 230, 467
H·β-Ala·Leu·OH	L	−31.0	26	1.5%, H_2O	899
H·Ala·Leu·Gly·OH	L-L	−30.4	20	2.1%, H_2O	954
H·Ala·Leu·Ileu·OH	3 L	−24.9	20	4.9%, N HCl	956
H·Ala·Leu₂·OH	3 D	+62.0	25	3.2%, N NaOH	198
H·Ala·Leu·Val·OH	3 L	−60.2	19	4.4%, H_2O	957
H·Ala·Lys·OH·HCl	D-L	−30.4	24	2%, 0.5N HCl	667
H·Ala·Lys·OH	D-L	−27.9	25	2%, 6N HCl	949
H·Ala·Lys·OH·HCl	L-L	−7.4	24	2%, 0.5N HCl	667
H·Ala·Lys·OH	L-L	−7.2	25	2%, 6N HCl	949
H·Ala·Lys·Ala·OH·HCl	L-2 D	+12.4	24	2%, 0.5N HCl	706
H·Ala·Lys·Ala·OH·HCl	L-D-L	+14.2	19	2%, 0.5N HCl	706
H·Ala·Lys·Ala·OH·HCl	3 L	−42.5	25	2%, 0.5N HCl	706
H·Ala·Lys·Ala₂·OH·2HCl	4 L	−78.0	24	2%, 0.5N HCl	901
H·Ala·Lys·Ala₂·OH·HCl	L-D-2 L	−18.6	24	2%, 0.5N HCl	901
H·Ala·Lys·Ala₃·OH·HCl	L-D-3 L	−62.0	27	2%, 0.5N HCl	901
H·Ala·Lys·Ala₃·OH·HCl·H_2O	5 L	−109.3	23	2%, 0.5N HCl	901
H·Ala·Nval·OH	D-L	−47.4	25	2%, H_2O	468
H·Ala·Nval·OH	L-L	−5.0	25	2%, H_2O	468
H·β-Ala·Phe·OH	DL	—	—	—	464

Compound	Config	[α]	Temp	Solvent	Ref
H·Ala·Pro·OH	L-L	−114.4	25	2.7%, H_2O	940
H·β-Ala·Pro·OH	L	−93.3	26	1.5%, H_2O	899
H·Ala·Ser·OH	L-L	+11.5	23	1.7%, H_2O	631
H·Ala·Try·OH	L-L	+18.7	20	6%, H_2O	226, 958
H·Ala·Tyr·OH	L-L	+43.1	20	2%, H_2O	216
H·Ala·(I$_2$-Tyr)·OH	L-L	+62.9	20	7.8%, NH_4OH	216
H·Ala·Tyr·Gly·OH	L-L	+18.5	22	2%, H_2O	353
H·Ala·Val·OH	L-L	−5.9	20	10%, H_2O	185

N-α-Aminobutyryl derivatives

Compound	Config	[α]	Temp	Solvent	Ref
H·(α-NH$_2$-n-But)·Gly·OH	DL	—	—	—	552
H·(α-NH$_2$-n-But)·Gly·OH	L	+72	16	2.8%, H_2O	58

N-Arginyl derivatives

Compound	Config	[α]	Temp	Solvent	Ref
H·Arg·Ala·OH·HOAc	L-L	+9.7	32	2.4%, H_2O	*491, 845, 904*
H·Arg·Arg·OH·dipicrolonate	L-L	+5.5	25	1%, DMF	850, *904*
H·Arg·Asp·OH·2H$_2$O	L-L	+32.1	24	1%, H_2O	845, *904*
H·Arg·Glu·OH	L-L	+25.1^h	22	1.9%, H_2O	*491, 513*
H·Arg·Glu·OH·H$_2$O	L-L	+27.2	19	1%, H_2O	541
H·Arg·Glu·OH·2H$_2$O	L-L	+22.0	25	1%, H_2O	363
H·Arg·Glu·OH·4H$_2$O	L-L	+21.4	24	1%, H_2O	845, *905*
H·Arg·Gly·OH·2HOAc	L	+37.6^i	25	1%, H_2O	*491, 513, 904*
H·Arg·Gly·OH·(½H$_2$SO$_4$)	L	+14.2	19	1%, H_2O	541
H·Arg·Ileu·OH·HOAc	L-L	+17.4	24	1%, H_2O	904
H·Arg·Leu·OH·HOAc	L-L	+10.3	25	1%, H_2O	363, *491, 513, 845, 904*
H·Arg·Leu·OH·HBr·H$_2$O	L-L	+8.6	24	2%, H_2O	471
H·Arg·Leu·OH·HCl	L-L	+10.2	19	1%, H_2O	541
H·Arg·Phe·OH·HOAc	L-L	+29.3	25	1%, H_2O	*491, 513, 904*
H·Arg·Phe·OH·HCl	L-L	+36.6	19	1%, H_2O	541

TABLE 10-47 (continued)

Compound	Config.	$[\alpha]_D$, deg.	Temp., °C	Concn. and Solvent	Ref.
N-Arginyl derivatives (continued)					
H·Arg·(β-Phser)·OH·HOAc	L-L	+39.7	22	0.7%, H_2O	513
H·Arg·Try·OH·HOAc	L-L	+5.1	28	4.9%, H_2O	491
H·Arg·Tyr·OH·HOAc	L-L	+32.0	25	1%, H_2O	491, 513, 845, 904
H·Arg·Val·OH·HOAc	L-L	+15.8	24	1%, H_2O	904
N-Aspartyl and asparginyl derivatives					
H·Asp·β-Ala·OH	DL	—	—	—	895
H·Asp·OH ⌐Ala·OH	L L	—	—	—	908
H·Asp·NH₂·Arg·Val·Tyr·Ileu·His·Pro·Phe·OH	8 L	−44.0	22	0.6%, H_2O	714
H·Asp·Arg·Val·Tyr·Ileu·His·Pro·Phe·OH	8 L	—	—	—	508
H·Asp·Arg·Val·Tyr·Val·His·Pro·Phe·OH·HOAc·2H₂O	8 L	−53.8	—	1%, H_2O	718a
H·Asp·NH₂·Arg·Val·Tyr·Val·His·Pro·Phe·OH·HOAc	8 L	−58.0	—	1%, H_2O	718a
H·Asp·Arg·Val·Tyr·Val·His·Pro·Phe·His·Leu·OH·HOAc·5H₂O	10 L	−67.5	—	1.7%, H_2O	638a
H·Asp·NH₂·Arg·Val·Tyr·Val·His·Pro·Phe·His·Leu·OH·HOAc·5H₂O	10 L	−68	—	1.7%, H_2O	638a
H·Asp·NH₂·CySH·OH	L-L	—	—	—	674
H·Asp·OH ⌐CySH·Gly·OH	L L	−29.0	25	1%, H_2O	727

H·Asp·Glu·OH	L-L	+5.6	25	3.4%, H_2O	609
H·Asp·OH └─Glu·OH	L	—	—	—	609
H·Asp-NH_2·Gly·OH	L	+53.0	27	4.6%, H_2O	482
H·Asp·Gly·OH	DL	—	—	—	555
H·Asp·OH └─Gly·OH	DL	—	—	—	555
H·Asp-NH_2·Gly·OH	L	+55.0	20	1%, H_2O	674, 790
H·Asp·Gly·OH	L	+38.0	25	2%, H_2O + 1 eq. HCl	609, 672
H·Asp·Gly·OH·H_2O	L	+36.7	23	1.9%, H_2O + 1 eq. HCl	726
H·Asp·OH └─Gly·OH	L	+7.2[g]	22	2.4%, H_2O + 1 eq. HCl	609, 726
H·Asp·Gly·OH └─Gly·OH	L	+33.8	23	2.3%, H_2O + 1 eq. HCl	726
H·Asp·His·OH·2H_2O	L-L	−6.0	30	1%, H_2O	838
H·Asp·OH └─His·OH	L	+38.0	27	1%, H_2O	836
H·Asp-NH_2·Leu·OH	L-L	−9.8	25	5%, H_2O	672, 790
H·(N$^\epsilon$-Asp-Lys)·OH·2H_2O	L-L	+13.2	20	1.4%, 0.5N HCl	439a
H·Asp·Tyr·OH·H_2O	L-L	+17.8	21	2.6%, H_2O + 1 eq. HCl	609
H·Asp·OH └─Tyr·OH	L	+60.1	18	2.3%, H_2O + 1 eq. HCl	128
H·Asp·Val·OH	L-L	+14	20	2.3%, HOAc	880
H·Asp·OH └─Val·OH	L	−10	20	1.5%, H_2O	880

TABLE 10-47 (continued)

Specific Rotation

Compound	Config.	$[\alpha]_D$, deg.	Temp., °C.	Concn. and Solvent	Ref.
N-Cysteinyl and cystinyl derivatives					
H·CySH·Asp-NH₂·OH	L-L	—	—	—	674
H·CyS·CyS·OH (cyclocystinyl)	L-L	−29	25	1%, N HCl	473, 959
H·CySBz·CySBz·OH	D-L	+1.5	26	0.5%, N NaOH	473
H·CySBz·CySBz·OH	L-D	−1.8	—	0.5%, N NaOH	473
H·CySBz·CySBz·OH	L-L	−14.1^j	26	2%, N NaOH	390, 473
H·CySH·CySH·OH·1½HCl·H₂O	L-L	+35.0	22	1%, 0.2N HCl	193
H·CyS·CyS·OH	D-L	+190	26	1%, N HCl	473
⎯⎯⎯⎯ (as parallel structure)					
H·CyS·CyS·OH	D-L				
H·CyS·CyS·OH	L-D	−187	26	1%, N HCl	473
⎯⎯⎯⎯ (as parallel structure)					
H·CyS·CyS·OH	L-D				
H·CyS·CyS·OH	L-L	−58.7	26	1%, N HCl	473
⎯⎯⎯⎯ (as parallel structure)					
H·CyS·CyS·OH	L-L				
H·CyS·CyS·OH·H₂O	L-L	−60	22	1%, N HCl	193
⎯⎯⎯⎯ (as parallel structure)					
H·CyS·CyS·OH·H₂O	L-L				
H·CyS·CyS·OH·HCl·2H₂O	L-L	—	—	—	193
⎯⎯⎯⎯ (as parallel structure)					
H·CyS·CyS·OH·HCl·2H₂O	L-L				
H·CySH·Glu-NH₂·OH	L-L	+6.6	—	3%, H₂O	474

H·CyS·Glu·NH₂·OH	L-L	−13.9	—	3%, H₂O	474
H·CyS·Glu·NH₂·OH	L-L				
H·CySH·Gly·OH·H₂O	L	+46.1	28	2.9%, H₂O	874
H·CySH·Gly·OH·HCl	L	+21.5	25	2%, H₂O	960
H·CySBz·Gly·OH	L	+27.0[k]	—	2%, N NaOH	476, 606, 862
H·CyS-Trityl·Gly·OH	L	+17.5	20	2%, 0.1N NaOH-MeOH (1:9)	549
H·CyS·Gly·OH	L	−68.5[l]	21	1%, H₂O	353, 512, 861, 862
H·CyS·Gly·OH	L				
H·CyS·Gly₂·OH·H₂O	L	−55.0	20	1%, N HCl	863
H·CyS·Gly₂·OH·H₂O	L				
H·CyS·Gly₄·CyS·OH	L-L	−67	22	0.5%, N H₂SO₄	711
H·CySH·Phe·OH	L-L	−8.9	25	2%, N HCl	512
H·CyS·Phe·OH·HCl	L-L	−57.3	25	0.8%, N HCl	512
H·CyS·Phe·OH·HCl	L-L				
H·CyS·Tyr·OH	L-L	−50.8	25	5%, N HCl	646, 830
H·CyS·Tyr·OH	L-L	+15.8	21	5%, N HCl	646, 804, 917
H·CySH·Tyr·OH	L-L	+8.5	21	2%, 5% HOAc	707
H·CySH·Tyr·Ileu·OH	3 L	+23.5[m]	23	1.6%, 2.5N HCl	476, 864
H·CySBz·Val·OH	L-D				

N-Glutamyl and glutaminyl derivatives

H·Glu·Ala·OH	L-D	+79.7	24	1–2%, 0.5N HCl	898

TABLE 10-47 (continued)

Compound	Config.	$[\alpha]_D$, deg.	Temp., °C	Concn. and Solvent	Ref.
N-Glutamyl and glutaminyl derivatives (continued)					
H·Glu·OH └Ala·OH	L D	+63.1	24	1–2%, 0.5N HCl	898
H·Glu·Ala·OH	L-L	+7.3^n	27	1–2%, 0.5N HCl	881, 898
H·Glu·OH └Ala·OH	L L	−26.4^o	26	2%, H$_2$O	605, 692, 898
H·Glu-NH$_2$·Ala·OH	L-L	+8	24	1%, N HCl	619
H·Glu·Ala·OH └Ala·OH	L-D D	+92.2	25	2%, 0.5N HCl	891
H·Glu·Ala·OH └Ala·OH	L-D L	+34.5	25	2%, 0.5N HCl	891
H·Glu·Ala·OH └Ala·OH	L-L D	+32.8	23	2%, 0.5N HCl	891
H·Glu·Ala·OH └Ala·OH	L-L L	−15.4	24	2%, 0.5N HCl	891
H·Glu·Ala·OH └Glu·OH	L-L L	+7.9	26	2%, 0.5N HCl	891
H·Glu·Ala·OH └Gly·OH	L-D	+61.2	26	2%, 0.5N HCl	891
H·Glu·OH └(α-NH$_2$-n-But)·OH	— L	—	—	—	58
H·Glu·OH └(α-NH$_2$-n-But)·Gly·OH·½H$_2$O	L L	−29	20	2.4%, H$_2$O	58
H·Glu·Asp·OH	L-L	+30.2	18	2.3%, H$_2$O	610

Compound	Config	[α]	Temp	Solvent	Ref
H·Glu·OH	L	+19.5	18	2%, H₂O + 1 eq. HCl	691
└Asp·OH	L				
H·Glu-NH₂·Asp-NH₂·OH	L-L	+17.1^p	21	1.5%, H₂O	435, 790, 868
H·Glu-NH₂·Asp-NH₂·CySBz·OH	3 L	−26	25	1%, H₂O	482a
H·Glu·CySBz·OH	L-L	—	—	—	767
H·Glu·CySH·OH	L-L	+3.2	18	2%, H₂O	481
H·Glu·OH	L	+13.6	—	1.1%, H₂O	10, 874
└CySH·OH	L				
H·Glu·OH	L	+2.9	28	2.5%, H₂O	874
└CySH·OH·HCl	L				
H·Glu-NH₂·CySH·OH	L-L	−9.8	—	3%, H₂O	474
H·Glu-NH₂·CySBz·OH	L-L	—	—	—	432a
H·Glu·CySH·Gly·OH·H₂O	L-L	+2.5	25	2%, H₂O	932
H·Glu·OH	D	−34.6	15	1.9%, H₂O	961
└CySH·Gly·OH	L				
H·Glu·OH	L	−21.3	27	2%, H₂O	10, 11, 475, 477, 549, 606, 872
└CySH·Gly·OH	L				
H·Glu·OH	L	−120	—	1%, H₂O	10
└CyS·OH	L				
└CyS·OH	L				
H·Glu·OH	L				
H·Glu-NH₂·CyS·OH	L-L	−119	—	1%, 0.046N HCl	474
H·Glu-NH₂·CyS·OH	L-L				
H·Glu·OH	L	+8.7	23	1%, 0.5N HCl	934
└Glu-NH₂·OH	L				
H·Glu·Glu·OH	L-D	+56.4	24	1-2%, 0.5N HCl	898

TABLE 10-47 (continued)

Compound	Config.	$[\alpha]_D$, deg.	Temp., °C	Concn. and Solvent	Ref.
N-Glutamyl and glutaminyl derivatives (continued)					
H·Glu·OH └─Glu·OH	L D	+36.7	22	1–2%, 0.5N HCl	898
H·Glu·Glu·OH	L-L	+18.2^q	24	1–2%, 0.5N HCl	128, 767, 898
H·Glu·OH └─Glu·OH	L L	+3.8^r	24	1–2%, 0.5N HCl	679, 691, 692, 898
H·Glu·NH$_2$·Glu·OH	L-L	+15	18	4.8%, N HCl	767, 882
H·Glu·OH └─Glu·OH·H$_2$O	L L	+3.6	22	1.6%, N HCl	767
H·Glu·Glu·Glu·OH	3 L	−7.2	19	1.4%, H$_2$O	881
H·Glu·OH └─Glu·OH └─Glu·OH	L L L	−7.2	24	2%, 0.5N HCl	891
H·Glu·OH └─Gly·OH	DL	—	—	—	527
H·Glu·OH └─Gly·OH	D	+8.1	21	3%, H$_2$O	433
H·Glu·Gly·Gly·OH	L	+79.5	—	2%, H$_2$O	675, 726, 890
H·Glu·OH └─Gly·OH	L	+11.1	14	2.5%, H$_2$O	675, 691, 692, 693, 767, 890
H·Glu·NH$_2$·Gly·OH	L	+78	22	1.7%, H$_2$O	482, 619, 701, 767, 790, 882, 890
H·Glu·OH └─Gly$_2$·OH·H$_2$O	DL	—	—	—	883

H·Glu·Gly₂·OH	L	—	—	—	610, 767
H·Glu·OH └Gly₂·OH	L	+9.4	12	2.8%, H₂O	691, 767
H·Glu·His·Phe·Arg·OH	4 L	−5.0	26	2.0%, H₂O	713
H·Glu·Leu·OH	L-L	+8.6	18	1.8%, H₂O + 1 eq. HCl	610, 675
H·Glu·OH └Leu·OH	L	−17.6^s	26	2%, H₂O	605, 675, 692
H·Glu·NH₂·Leu·OH	L-L	+11.5	22	1%, N HCl	619, 790
H·Glu·NH₂·OH └Leu·OH	L	+2	25	2%, 50% EtOH	790
H·Glu·Met·OH	L-L	+18.8	25	1.1%, H₂O	627
H·Glu·Phe·OH	L-L	+27.0	25	2%, H₂O + 1 eq. HCl	962
H·Glu·Tyr·OH	L-L	+30.1	19	2.3%, H₂O + 1 eq. HCl	378, 675, 890
H·Glu·OH └Tyr·OH	L	+25.6	15	2.1%, H₂O	675, 691, 894
H·Glu·Val·OH	L-L	+24.5	15	2.7%, H₂O + 1 eq. HCl	610
H·Glu·OH └Val·OH	L	0	19	2.4%, H₂O	605
H·Glu·NH₂·Val·OH	L-L	+22.5	22	1%, N HCl	619
N-Glycyl derivatives					
H·Gly·Ala·OH	DL	—	—	—	127
H·Gly·Ala·OH	L	−59.3^t	25	2%, 0.5N HCl	214, 253, 666, 797, 935, 949, 957
H·Gly·Ala₂·OH	L-D	−14^u	23	2%, 6N HCl	703, 949

TABLE 10-47 (continued)

Compound	Config.	$[\alpha]_D$, deg.	Temp., °C	Concn. and Solvent	Ref.
N-Glycyl derivatives (continued)					
H·Gly·Ala₂·OH	L-L	−103.0^v	23	2%, 0.5N HCl	703, 949
H·Gly·Ala₂·Gly·OH	D-D	+104.8	20	2.9%, H₂O	951
H·Gly·Ala·Gly·OH	DL	—	—	—	330
H·Gly·Ala·Gly·OH	D	+65.5	24	2%, 0.5N HCl	703
H·Gly·Ala·Gly·OH	L	−65.3	24	2%, 0.5N HCl	215, 703
H·Gly·β-Ala·Gly·OH	—	—	—	—	899, 963, 964
H·Gly·Ala·Gly·Tyr·OH	L-L	+18.4	20	2.6%, H₂O	215, 931
H·Gly·Ala·Leu·OH	L-L	−87	22	0.6%, 0.1N HCl	494, 954
H·Gly·Ala·Leu·Glu·OH	3 L	—	—	—	710
H·Gly·Ala·Leu·Ileu·OH	3 L	−80.6	20	0.9%, N HCl	956
H·Gly·Ala·Tyr·OH	L-L	−4.8	20	4.3%, H₂O	216
H·Gly·(α-NH₂-isoBut)·OH	—	—	—	—	254, 466
H·Gly·(α-NH₂-n-But)·OH	D	+31.0	26	2%, H₂O	254
H·Gly·(α-NH₂-n-But)·OH	L	−31.0	25	2%, H₂O	253
H·Gly·Arg·OH·HOAc	L	+1.6	25	4.3%, H₂O	491
H·Gly·Arg·OH·(½H₂SO₄)	L	—	—	—	492
H·Gly·Asp-NH₂·OH	DL	—	—	—	685
H·Gly·Asp·OH	DL	—	—	—	674
H·Gly·Asp·OH	D	−12.5	25	2%, H₂O	253
H·Gly·Asp-NH₂·OH	L	−7.8	27	5%, H₂O	143, 253, 482, 674
H·Gly·Asp·OH	L	+12.0	25	5%, H₂O	218, 253, 613a, 672
H·Gly·Asp-NH₂·Leu·OH	L-L	−46.8	20	4.8%, N HCl	144

Compound	Config.	[α]	Temp.	Conc.	Refs.
H·Gly·CySH·OH·HCl	L	+2.5	25	2%, H_2O	518, 866, 960
H·Gly·CyS·OH	L	−189	25	1%, H_2O	876
H·CyS·OH·1½H_2O	L	—	—	—	674
H·Gly·Glu·NH_2·OH	DL	—	—	—	221, 253, 552, 649, 677
H·Gly·Glu·OH	L	−6.8	25	5%, H_2O	
H·Gly·Glu·NH_2·OH·H_2O	L	−2.4	27	5.8%, H_2O	482, 953
H·Gly·Glu·Gly·OH	L	—	—	—	878
H·Gly·Glu·NH_2·Gly·OH	L	−28.4	19	6%, H_2O	953
H·Gly·Glu·Tyr·OH	L-L	—	—	—	709
H·Gly_2·OH	—	—	—	—	10, 103, 127, 253, 464, 494, 518, 547, 548, 551, 552, 573, 665, 751, 900, 965
H·Gly_2·OH·HCl·H_2O	—	—	—	—	179
H·Gly_2·Ala·OH	DL	—	—	—	330, 910
H·Gly_2·Ala·OH	D	+36.5	25	2%, H_2O	254
H·Gly_2·Ala·OH	L	−36.3	25	2%, H_2O	254
H·Gly_2·β-Ala·OH	—	—	—	—	899
H·Gly_2·Ala·Gly·OH	D	+53.7	20	3%, H_2O	966
H·Gly·CyS·OH	L	−108[w]	24	0.8%, N HCl	228, 590, 617, 866, 936
H·Gly·CyS·OH	L	—	—	—	212, 494, 551, 665, 814
H·Gly_3·OH	—	—	—	—	213
H·Gly_4·OH	—	—	—	—	806
cyclo-Gly_4	—	—	—	—	

TABLE 10-47 (continued)

Specific Rotation

Compound	Config.	$[\alpha]_D$, deg.	Temp., °C	Concn. and Solvent	Ref.
N-Glycyl derivatives (continued)					
H·Gly₅·OH	—	—	—	—	213
H·Gly₆·OH	—	—	—	—	156
cyclo-Gly₆	—	—	—	—	806
H·Gly₃·Leu·Gly·OH	L	−28.4	24	2.5%, H_2O	878
H·Gly₃·Pro·OH·½H_2O	L	−78.5	24	1.2%, H_2O	170
H·Gly₂·Hypro·OH	L	−97.7	26	2.8%, H_2O	169
H·Gly₂·Leu·OH	DL	—	—	—	330
H·Gly₂·Leu·OH	D	+27.5	26	2%, H_2O	911
H·Gly₂·Leu·OH	L	−28.0	26	2%, H_2O	911
cyclo-(Gly₂·Leu)	D	—	—	—	918
H·Gly₂·Leu·Gly·OH	L	−43.2	24	2.5%, H_2O	878
cyclo-(Gly₂·Leu·Gly₂·Leu)	L-L	−44.4	25	0.3%, HOAc	812a, 812c
cyclo-(Gly₂·Leu·Gly·Leu)	L-D	—	—	—	812a
cyclo-(Gly₂·Leu·Gly·Leu)	L-L	−8.7	20	3%, trifluoroacetic acid	811, 812a
H·Gly₂·Phe·OH	DL	—	—	—	330
H·Gly₂·Phe·OH	L	+35.6	25	1%, H_2O	665
cyclo-(Gly₂Pro)	DL	—	—	—	967
H·Gly₂·Pro·OH·½H_2O	L	−101.5^x	26	2.2%, H_2O	169
H·Gly₂·Thr·OH	DL	—	—	—	968
H·Gly₂·Try·OH	DL	—	—	—	751
H·Gly₂·Tyr·OH	L	+42.3	20	1.6%, H_2O	931
H·Gly·His·OH·HCl	L	+25.0	26	1%, H_2O	837

H·Gly·His·Tyr·OH	L-L	—	—	—	537
H·Gly·Hypro·OH	L	−128.4	26	1.8%, H_2O	169
H·Gly·allo-Hypro·OH	L	−86.0	21	2.4%, H_2O	657
H·Gly·(O-Me-Hypro)·OH	L	−99.5	21	1%, H_2O	657
H·Gly·Ileu·OH	D	+14.0	25	2%, H_2O	253, 969, 970
H·Gly·allo-Ileu·OH	D	+5.4	26	2%, H_2O	254
H·Gly·Ileu·OH	L	−14.1	25	2%, H_2O	253, 955, 970
H·Gly·allo-Ileu·OH	L	−5.2	25	2%, H_2O	253
H·Gly·Ival·OH	DL	—	—	—	254
H·Gly·Ival·OH	D	+7.0	26	4%, 2.5N HCl	254
H·Gly·Ival·OH	L	−7.1	26	4%, 2.5N HCl	254
H·Gly·Leu·OH	DL	—	—	—	127
H·Gly·Leu·OH	D	+35.7	25	3%, H_2O	469
H·Gly·Leu·OH	L	−36.3	25	2%, H_2O	223, 253, 462, 625, 723
H·Gly·*tert*-Leu·OH	DL	—	—	—	371
H·Gly·Leu·Ala·OH	L-L	−59.0	20	2.5%, H_2O	954
H·Gly·Leu·CyS·OH	L-L	−108.9	20	0.7%, H_2O	617
H·Gly·Leu·CyS·OH	L-L	—	—	—	330
H·Gly·Leu·Gly·OH	DL	+42.6	26	2%, H_2O	911
H·Gly·Leu·Gly·OH	D	−41.8	22	1.9%, H_2O	464, 694, 878
H·Gly·Leu·Gly·OH	L	−52.6	26	1.5%, N HCl	694, 971
H·Gly·Leu·Gly·Leu·OH	L-L	0	22	1.5%, N HCl	694
H·Gly·Leu·Gly·Leu·OH	L-D	−66.7[y]	22	1.7%, N HCl	694, 972
H·Gly·Leu$_2$·OH	L-L	−78.6	20	2%, N NaOH	972
H·Gly·Leu$_3$·OH	3 L	−118.1	20	2.5%, N NaOH	972
H·Gly·Leu$_4$·OH	4 L	−9.0	25	2%, 6N HCl	949
H·Gly·Lys·OH	L				

TABLE 10-47 (continued)

Specific Rotation

Compound	Config.	$[\alpha]_D$, deg.	Temp., °C	Concn. and Solvent	Ref.
N-Glycyl derivatives (continued)					
H·Gly·Lys·OH·HCl	L	−12.8	25	2%, 0.5N HCl	550, 613a, 667
H·Gly·Lys·OH·($\frac{1}{2}$H$_2$SO$_4$)	L	−10.0	25	5%, H$_2$O	253
H·(N$^\varepsilon$-Gly-Lys)·OH·HOAc	L	+85	16	1.1%, H$_2$O	972a
H·(N$^\varepsilon$-Cbzo·Gly-Lys)·OH	L	+8.7	16	1.0%, HOAc	972a
H·(N$^\varepsilon$-Tos·Gly-Lys)·OH	L	+12	25	1.4%, HOAc	439
H·Gly·Lys·Glu·OH	L-L	−33	20	1%, H$_2$O	550
H·Gly·Lys·Gly·OH·HCl	L	−32.1	25	2%, 0.5N HCl	706
H·Gly·Met·OH	DL	—	—	—	253, 464
H·Gly·Met·OH	D	+10.2	26	2%, H$_2$O	254, 627
H·Gly·Met·OH	L	−10.2	25	2%, H$_2$O	253, 627, 973
H·Gly·Nleu·OH	D	+16.2	26	2%, H$_2$O	254
H·Gly·Nleu·OH	L	−16.0	25	2%, H$_2$O	253
H·Gly·Nval·OH	D	+27.6	26	2%, H$_2$O	254
H·Gly·Nval·OH	L	−27.5	25	2%, H$_2$O	253
H·Gly·Phe·OH	DL	—	—	—	415, 464, 518, 613a, 900
H·Gly·Phe·OH	D	−41.7	21	2%, H$_2$O	962
H·Gly·Phe·OH	L	+41.5	25	2%, H$_2$O	224, 253, 548, 613a, 665
H·Gly·Phe·Ala·OH	L-L	−5.0	20	2%, N HCl	611a
H·Gly·Phe·Glu·OH	D-L	−11.3	20	4.7%, H$_2$O	974
H·Gly·Phe·Glu·OH	L-L	−4.7	20	4.7%, H$_2$O	974
H·Gly·Phe·Gly·OH	DL	—	—	—	330

H·Gly·Phe·Gly·OH	L	+15.7	25	5.6%, 0.2N HCl	548, 548a
H·Gly·Pro·OH	DL	—	—	—	170, 705
H·Gly·Pro·OH	L	−113.8	20	3.9%, H_2O	940
H·Gly·Pro·Gly·OH·$2H_2O$	DL	—	—	—	170
H·Gly·Pro·Gly·OH	L	−108.4	21	1%, H_2O	823, 941
H·Gly·Ser·OH	DL	—	—	—	502, 551, 552, 829, 913a
H·Gly·Ser·OH	D	+9.2	25	5%, H_2O	253
H·Gly·Ser·OH	L	−9.2	27	−, H_2O	253, 502, 631
H·Gly·(O-Bz-Ser)·OH	DL	—	—	—	829
H·Gly·Ser·Gly·OH	DL	—	—	—	913a
H·Gly·Thr·OH	DL	—	—	—	968
H·Gly·Thr·OH	D	+16.0	25	2%, H_2O	253
H·Gly·Thr·OH	L	−16.2	25	2%, H_2O	253
H·Gly·Try·OH	DL	—	—	—	464, 547, 552, 751
H·Gly·Try·OH	D	−34.2	26	2%, 5N HCl	254
H·Gly·Try·OH	L	+34.3	25	2%, 5N HCl	226, 253, 975
H·Gly·Try·OH	D	−44.2	26	2%, H_2O	254
H·Gly·Tyr·OH	L	+44.0	25	1%, H_2O	213, 253, 830, 962
H·Gly·(I$_2$-Tyr)·OH	L	+52.7	20	5%, NH_4OH	220
H·Gly·Tyr·Gly·OH	L	+24.1	20	4.1%, H_2O	931
H·Gly·Val·OH	DL	—	—	—	552, 965
H·Gly·Val·OH	D	+20.0	25	2%, H_2O	253
H·Gly·Val·OH	L	−19.9	25	2%, H_2O	185, 253, 976
H·Gly·Val·Gly·OH·$1\frac{1}{2}H_2O$	DL	—	—	—	942
N-Histidyl derivatives					
H·His·Ala·OH	L-L	−27	22	1%, 0.1N NaOH	695
H·His·Gly·OH	L	+25	—	2%, H_2O	789
H·His·Gly·OH·HCl·$\frac{1}{2}H_2O$	L	−8.4^z	20	1%, H_2O	621

TABLE 10-47 (continued)

Specific Rotation

Compound	Config.	$[\alpha]_D$, deg.	Temp., °C	Concn. and Solvent	Ref.
N-Histidyl derivatives (continued)					
H·His·Leu·OH	L-L	+13	—	2%, N HCl	695, 789
H·His·Phe·OH	L-L	+33.8	27	2.6%, N HCl	713
H·His·Phe·OH·HCl·H$_2$O	L-L	−2.1	20	1%, H$_2$O	621
H·His·Phe·Arg·OH	3 L	+3.0	25	2.8%, H$_2$O	713
H·His·Phe·NO$_2$-Arg·OH	3 L	+23.2	25	1.9%, N HCl	713
H·His·Phe·Arg·Try·Gly·OH·HOAc·2H$_2$O	4 L	−10.0	27	0.9%, N HCl	791
N-Hydroxyprolyl and allohydroxyprolyl derivatives					
H·Hypro·Ala·OH	L-L	−60.3	22	1%, H$_2$O	642
H·Hypro·Asp·OH	L-L	−23.3	22	1%, H$_2$O	642
H·Hypro·Glu·OH	L-L	−35.8	22	1%, H$_2$O	642
H·Hypro·Gly·OH	L	−22.4	26	7.7%, H$_2$O	169
H·allo-Hypro·Gly·OH	D	+11.3	20	1%, H$_2$O	487
H·allo-Hypro·Gly·OH	L	−11.1^{aa}	20	1%, H$_2$O	487
H·Hypro·Gly$_2$·OH	L	−13.2	21	1%, H$_2$O	823
H·Hypro·Leu·OH	L-L	−62.5	20	1%, N HCl	642
H·Hypro·Phe·OH	L-L	−30.8	20	1%, N HCl	642
H·Hypro·Try·OH	L-L	—	—	—	769
H·Hypro·Tyr·OH	L-L	−8.7	22	1%, H$_2$O	642
N-Isoleucyl and alloisoleucyl derivatives					
H·allo-Ileu·Ala·OH	D-D	−23.9	27	2%, H$_2$O	454
H·Ileu·Ala·OH	L-D	+81.5	27	2%, H$_2$O	454
H·allo-Ileu·Ala·OH	L-D	+92.0	27	2%, H$_2$O	454

Compound	Config	[α]	Temp	Solvent	Ref
H·Ileu·Asp-NH₂·OH	L-L	+21.2	25	5%, H₂O	464
H·Ileu₂·OH	L-L	+17.1	25	1%, H₂O + 1 eq. HCl	914a
H·Ileu·Gly·OH	L	+33.6	20	6%, H₂O	955
H·Ileu·Phe·OH	L-L	—	—	—	456
N-Leucyl derivatives					
H·Leu·β-Ala·OH	DL	—	—	—	963
H·Leu·β-Ala·OH	L	+28.0	26	5%, H₂O	899
H·Leu·Ala·OH	L-D	+80	27	1%, H₂O	466, 467
H·Leu·Ala·OH	L-L	+22.9	24	5%, MeOH	157, 466, 467
H·Leu·Ala·CyS·OH	3 L	−115.3	20	0.7%, H₂O	617
H·Leu·Ala·CyS·OH	3 L	−17.3	20	1.2%, H₂O	954
H·Leu·Ala·Gly·OH	L-L	−56.3	23	0.7%, 3N HCl	915
H·Leu·Ala·Val·Phe·Gly·Pro·OH·3H₂O	5 L	−53.8	20	5%, H₂O	144
H·Leu·Asp-NH₂·OH	D-L	+15.7	25	5%, H₂O	144, 672, 674
H·Leu·Asp-NH₂·OH	L-L	+27.1	20	6%, H₂O	218
H·Leu·Asp·OH	L-L	−9.7	20	1%, *N* HCl	432a
H·Leu·CySBz·Gly·OH	L-L	+10.5	24	2%, *N* HCl	229, 912
H·Leu·Glu·OH	L-L	+12.6	18	3.7%, *N* HCl	674, 953
H·Leu·Glu-NH₂·OH	L-L	−26.8	19	1.4%, 0.5*N* HCl	881
H·Leu·Glu·Leu·OH·H₂O	3 L	—	—	—	127, 613a, 805
H·Leu·Gly·OH	DL	+85.8	24	2%, H₂O	157, 613a, 805, 878
H·Leu·Gly·OH	L	+20.3	20	10%, H₂O	223, 977
H·Leu·Gly·Ala·OH	L-L	+55.3	20	5%, H₂O	218
H·Leu·Gly·Asp·OH	L-L	—	—	—	611a
H·Leu·Gly₂·OH	DL				

TABLE 10-47 (continued)

Specific Rotation

Compound	Config.	$[\alpha]_D$, deg.	Temp., °C	Concn. and Solvent	Ref.
N-Leucyl derivatives (continued)					
H·Leu·Gly₂·OH	L	+57.7	25	5%, H₂O	158, *179*, 353, 611a
H·Leu·Gly₃·OH	L	+45.9	20	9.6%, H₂O	*157*, 611a
H·Leu·Gly₆·OH	L	+5.2	20	3.7%, 0.1N NaOH	158
H·Leu·Gly₇·OH	L	+6.3	20	6%, H₂O + 1 eq. NaOH	230
H·Leu·Gly₃·Leu·OH	L-L	+21.3	20	2.4%, H₂O	223
H·Leu·Gly·Ileu·OH	L-D	+41.2	20	2%, 0.2N HCl	978
H·Leu·Gly·Ileu·OH	L-L	+26.5	20	3%, H₂O	969, 978
H·Leu·Gly·Leu·OH	L-L	+5.6	26	2.5%, *N* HCl	694, 971
H·Leu·Gly·Try·OH	L-L	+32.3	20	8%, *N* HCl	226
H·Leu·His·OH	L-L	+32.1	18	5%, H₂O	231
H·Leu·Ileu·OH	L-D	+58.4	24	1%, H₂O	*622*, 969
H·Leu·Ileu·OH	L-L	+20.9^{bb}	23	1%, H₂O	*622*, 955, 956
H·Leu₂·OH·H₂O	L-D	+74.4	27	1%, *N* HCl	*622*, 625
H·Leu₂·OH	D-D	+13.9	25	4.5%, *N* NaOH	198, 232
H·Leu₂·OH	D-L	−68.0	20	9.4%, *N* HCl	232
H·Leu₂·OH	L-D	+68.9	20	9.7%, *N* HCl	232
H·Leu₂·OH	L-L	−13.4	23	1%, *N* NaOH	157, *462*, 464, 601, *622*, 625, 834, 930, *979*
H·Leu·CyS·OH	L-L	−136.6	20	4%, *N* HCl	219, 617
H·Leu·CyS·OH (disulfide)	L-L				

H·Leu₂·Gly·OH	L-L	—	—	—	455
H·Leu₃·OH	3 D	+46.0	25	6.5%, N NaOH	198
H·Leu₃·OH	3 L	−51.4	20	3.1%, N NaOH	972
H·Leu₄·OH	4 L	−90.0	20	7.6%, N NaOH	972
H·(Nᵋ-Tos·Leu-Lys)·OH·HCl	L-L	−17	25	1.2%, HOAc	439
H·Leu·Phe·OH·2H₂O	L-D	+25.0^cc	17	2.4%, HOAc	373, 622
H·Leu·Phe·OH·H₂O	L-L	+9.7	26	1%, H₂O	622
H·Leu·Pro·Tyr·OH	3 L	−7.5	25	2.1%, H₂O	980
H·Leu·Try·OH	L-L	+4.5	20	7%, N HCl	226
H·Leu·Try·Glu·OH	3 L	+17.4	20	4%, N HCl	981
H·Leu·Tyr·OH	L-L	+22.6	25	1%, H₂O	216, 830
H·Leu·Val·OH·H₂O	L-D	+55.3	24	1%, H₂O	622
H·Leu·Val·OH·H₂O	L-L	+18.2^dd	23	1%, N HCl	185, 622, 957
N-Lysyl derivatives					
H·Lys·Ala·OH·HCl	L-D	+80.4	24	2%, 0.5N HCl	667
H·Lys·Ala·OH	L-D	+70.9	26	2%, 6N HCl	949
H·Lys·Ala·OH	L-L	−1.9	25	2%, 6N HCl	949
H·Lys·Ala·OH·HCl	L-L	+2.7	24	2%, 0.5N HCl	667
H·Lys·Arg·OH·2HOAc	L-L	+15.5	25	2.1%, H₂O	491
H·Lys·Asp·OH	L-L	+23	20	1.3%, H₂O	831
H·Lys·Glu·OH	L-L	+22.9	19	3.1%, H₂O	550, 626
H·Lys·Gly·OH	L	+31.1	24	2%, 6N HCl	949
H·Lys·Gly·OH·HCl	L	+40.7	25	2%, 0.5N HCl	550, 613a, 667
H·Lys·Gly·OH·(½H₂SO₄)	L	+30.0	22	1.5%, H₂O	831
H·Lys·Gly₂·Glu·OH	L-L	+33.5	20	1%, H₂O	649
H·Lys·His·OH·(½H₂SO₄)	L-L	+35.3	20	1.3%, H₂O	626
H·Lys₂·OH	L-L	+5.6	25	2%, 6N HCl	715, 949
H·Lys₂·OH	L-D	+39.6	23	2%, 6N HCl	949

TABLE 10-47 (continued)

Specific Rotation

Compound	Config.	$[\alpha]_D$, deg.	Temp., °C	Concn. and Solvent	Ref.
N-Lysyl derivatives (*continued*)					
H·Lys$_2$·OH·3HCl·H$_2$O	L-L	+8.2	24	2%, 0.5N HCl	667
H·Lys$_2$·OH·2HCl	L-D	+44.7	24	2%, 0.5N HCl	667
H·Lys$_2$·OH·3HBr	L-L	—	—	—	833
H·N$^\epsilon$-(diCbzo-Lys)·Lys·OH (sulfate salt)	L-L	—	—	—	972a
H·Lys$_3$·OH·3HCl	L-2 D	+54.9	22	2%, 0.5N HCl	706
H·Lys$_3$·OH·3HCl	L-D-L	+27.7	22	2%, 0.5N HCl	706
H·Lys$_3$·OH·3HCl	3 L	−2.2	24	2%, 0.5N HCl	706
H·Lys$_3$·OH	3 L	—	—	—	715
H·Lys$_4$·OH	4 L	—	—	—	715
H·Lys$_5$·OH	5 L	—	—	—	715
H·Lys·Tyr·OH·HOAc	L-L	+17.0	15	5%, H$_2$O	834
H·Lys·Tyr·Lys·OH·2HCl	3 L	+22.4	20	1.6%, 0.5N HCl	584a
H·Lys·Val·Phe·Gly·OH·EtOH·LiBr	3 L	−8.3	24	2%, N HCl	507
N-Methionyl derivatives					
H·Met·Glu·OH	L-L	+18.6	28	2.6%, N HCl	444, 982
H·Met·Glu·OBz·OH	L-L	+16.1	22	1.9%, N HCl	471a
H·Met·Gly·OH	DL	—	—	—	464, 627, 789
H·Met·Gly·OH	D	−88.0	23	1.1%, H$_2$O	627
H·Met·Gly·OH	L	+86.8^{ee}	21	2%, H$_2$O	444, 627
H·Met·Gly$_2$·OH	L	+73.1	23	1.9%, H$_2$O	627
H·Met$_2$·OH	L-D	+75.8	25	1%, H$_2$O	929
H·Met$_2$·OH	L-L	+27.0	24	2%, H$_2$O	490, 627, 929

H·Met₃·OH	3 L	−70	16	1%, H₂O	490
H·Met·Tyr·OH	L-L	+18.6	22	2.1%, 0.2N HCl	627
N-Phenylalanyl derivatives					
H·Phe·Ala·OH	L-L	+12.8	20	2%, H₂O	611a
H·Phe·β-Ala·OH	DL	–	–	–	464
H·Phe·Arg·OH·HOAc	L-L	+7.0	23	3.2%, H₂O	491
H·Phe·NO₂-Arg·OH·½H₂O	L-L	+22.5	21	8.9%, H₂O	713
H·Phe·Glu·OH	L-L	+20.3	20	4.8%, H₂O	123
H·Phe·Glu-NH₂·Asp-NH₂·OH	3 L	+0.1	21	4.9%, 0.15N HCl	440
H·Phe·Gly·OH	DL	–	–	–	464, 495, 943
H·Phe·Gly·OH·H₂O	L	+95.6[ff]	22	2.1%, H₂O	224, 507, 522, 665, 586
H·Phe·Gly·OH·2H₂O	L	+100.0	20	2.4%, H₂O	495
H·Phe·Gly₂·OH	DL	–	–	–	518
H·Phe·Gly₂·OH	L	+79.4	25	1.8%, H₂O	665
H·Phe·Gly₃·OH	L	+65.3	25	2%, H₂O	665
H·Phe·Gly·Phe·OH·H₂O	L-L	+45.5	25	1.7%, N HCl	665
H·Phe·Hypro·OH	L-L	−29.1	20	1%, H₂O	642
H·Phe·Leu·OH	D-D	–	–	–	469
H·Phe·Leu·OH	L-L	−21	22	1%, 1% NaHCO₃	494
H·(Nᵉ-Phe-Lys)·OH·½H₂O	L-L	+47.1	13	1.1%, H₂O	972a
H·(Nᵉ-Cbzo-Phe-Lys)·OH	L-L	–	–	–	972a
H·Phe·Pro·OH	D-L	−96	18	2.4%, HOAc	373
N-Prolyl derivatives					
H·Pro·Ala·OH	L-L	−66.3	20	4.9%, H₂O	980
H·Pro·Arg·OH·HOAc	L-L	−28.6	27	2.6%, H₂O	491
H·Pro·Asp·OH	L-L	−34.8	23	1%, H₂O	642
H·Pro·Glu·OH	L-L	−49.0	25	2%, H₂O	941

TABLE 10-47 (continued)

Specific Rotation

Compound	Config.	$[\alpha]_D$, deg.	Temp., °C	Concn. and Solvent	Ref.
N-Prolyl derivatives (continued)					
H·Pro·Gly·OH	DL	—	—	—	464
H·Pro·Gly·OH	L	−22.5	20	0.1%, H_2O	168, 170, 576, 613a, 980, 983
H·Pro·Gly$_2$·OH	L	−22.1	21	1%, H_2O	823
H·Pro·Gly·Phe·OH	L-L	+14.8	18	2%, H_2O	611a
H·Pro·Gly·Hypro·OH	L	−160.3	21	1%, H_2O	823
H·Pro·Leu·OH	L-L	−73.5	20	0.7%, N HCl	168
H·Pro·Phe·OH	L-L	−41.7	25	1.7%, $6N$ HCl	200, 252, 508, 980, 638a
H·Pro$_2$·OH	L-L	−160.2	21	1%, H_2O	823
H·Pro·Ser·OH	L-L	−47.9	20	3.1%, H_2O	980
H·Pro·Tyr·OH	L-L	−7.8	20	1.7%, H_2O	168, 983
H·Pro·Val·OH·H_2O	L-L	−61	20	1.7%, H_2O	373
N-Seryl derivatives					
H·Ser·Ala·OH	L-L	−30.4	26	6%, N HCl	501
H·Ser·Ala·Glu·OH	3 L	−32.9	24	2%, H_2O	631
H·Ser·Glu·OH	L-L	−9.4	25	6%, N HCl	501
H·Ser·Gly·OH	DL	—	—	—	913a, 984
H·Ser·Gly·OH	L	+30.2	26	6%, N HCl	501
H·Ser·Gly·OH	DL	—	—	—	984
H·(O-Bz-Ser)·Gly·OH	3 L	−54.5	25	2%, H_2O	717a
H·Ser·Gly·Ala·Gly·Ala·Gly·OH·1½H_2O	L	+32.5	25	5.4%, N HCl	699
H·Ser·Gly$_2$·OH	L-L	+20.4	24	2%, H_2O	631
H·Ser·Gly·Glu·OH					

H·Ser·Gly·Ser·OH	L-L	+25.2	25	1.1%, H$_2$O	631
H·Ser·His·LH·HBr	L-L	+26.4	13	3%, H$_2$O	828
H·Ser·His·Leu·OH·H$_2$O	3 L	−25.3	13	1%, H$_2$O	828
H·Ser·His·Leu·Val·Glu·OH·H$_2$O	5 L	−55.8	25	1%, H$_2$O	718, 915a
H·Ser·Met·OH	L-L	−11.4	27	5.6%, N HCl	444
H·Ser·Met·Glu·OH	3 L	−26.1	25	1%, H$_2$O	444, 982
H·Ser$_2$·OH	L-L	+14.2	25	7%, N HCl	501
H·Ser·Tyr·OH	L-L	+38.4	24	1%, H$_2$O	444, 537
H·Ser·Tyr·Met·Glu·OH	4 L	−8.6	25	1%, H$_2$O	444
H·Ser·Tyr·Ser·Met·Glu·OH	5 L	−20.6	25	2%, 2N HCl	444, 982
N-Threonyl and allothreonyl derivatives					
H·Thr·Ala·OH	L-D	+95.3	27	2%, H$_2$O	454
H·allo-Thr·Ala·OH	L-D	+87.5	27	2%, H$_2$O	454
H·Thr·His·Leu·Val·Glu·OH·H$_2$O	5 L	—	—	—	504a
N-Tryptophyl derivatives					
H·Try·Glu·OH	L-L	+34.4	20	4.5%, H$_2$O	981
H·Try·Gly·OH	DL	—	—	—	551, 789
H·Try·Gly·OH	L	+81.7	26	1.7%, H$_2$O	226, 791
H·Try·Lys·Leu·Ala·Val·Phe·Gly·Pro·OH·HOAc·6H$_2$O	7 L	+15.3	24	0.8%, H$_2$O	915
N-Tyrosyl derivatives					
H·Tyr·Arg·OH	D-L	−105.7	23	6.4%, 0.2N HCl	125
H·Tyr·Asp·OH	L-L	+20.4	19	3.6%, H$_2$O + 1 eq. HCl	378
H·Tyr·CySH·OH	L-L	+22.6	23	5%, N HCl	646, 917
H·Tyr·CyS·OH	L-L	−70.8	23	5%, N HCl	646
H·Tyr·CyS·OH	L-L				

TABLE 10-47 (continued)

Compound	Config.	$[\alpha]_D$, deg.	Temp., °C	Concn. and Solvent	Ref.
N-Tyrosyl derivatives (continued)					
H·Tyr·Gly·OH	L	+82.6[gg]	22	2%, H_2O	353, 803, 826, 830, 931, 962
H·Tyr·Gly$_2$·OH	L	+43.1	22	2.7%, 20% HCl	353, 931
H·Tyr·Leu·OH	L-L	+6.3	21	3.2%, 0.5N HCl	584a
H·Tyr·Phe·Glu-NH$_2$·Asp-NH$_2$·OH·HBr	4 L	+6.3	21	1%, H_2O	822
H·Tyr·Ser·OH	L-L	+24.2	22	1.6%, N HCl	471a
H·Tyr$_2$·OH	L-L	+30.1	19	4%, H_2O + 1 eq. HCl	353, 378
H·Tyr$_3$·OH·2H$_2$O	3 L	—	—	—	637
H·Tyr$_4$·OH	4 L	—	—	—	637
N-Valyl derivatives					
H·Val·CySBz·OH·H$_2$O	L-L	—	—	—	432a
H·Val·Glu·OH	L-L	+3.2	19	1.5%, H_2O	881
H·Val·Glu·Val·OH·2H$_2$O	3 L	−16.6	19	2.2%, 0.5N HCl	881
H·Val·Gly·OH	DL	—	—	—	464, 900
H·Val·Gly·OH	L	+102	18	2%, H_2O	185, 586, 613a
H·Val·Gly$_2$·OH	DL	—	—	—	380
H·Val·His·OH	L-L	+46	24	4.2%, H_2O	638a
H·Val·Leu·Gly·OH	L-L	—	—	—	464
cyclo-[Val·Lys·Leu·Phe·Pro]$_2$·2HCl·H$_2$O	[3 L-D-L]$_2$	—	—	—	626a
cyclo-[Val·(N$^\epsilon$-Tos-Lys)·Leu·Phe·Pro]$_2$·$\frac{1}{2}$H$_2$O	[3 L-D-L]$_2$	−226	22	1.0%, HOAc	626a, 814a
H·Val·Orn·OH·HCl·$\frac{1}{2}$H$_2$O	L-L	+19	19	2%, H_2O	373

Compound	Config	[α]	T	Solvent	Ref
H·Val·Orn·Leu·Phe·Pro·OH·2HCl	3 L-D-L	−62.4	26	0.5%, 0.5N HCl	423
H·[Val·(N^δ-Tos-Orn)·Leu·Phe·Pro]₂·2H₂O	[3 L-D-L]₂	−191	23	1%, HOAc	814a
cyclo-[Val·Orn·Leu·Phe·Pro]₂·2HCl	[3 L-D-L]₂	−289	24	0.4%, 70% EtOH	719
H·[Val·Orn·Leu·Phe·Pro]₂·OH·3HCl	[3 L-D-L]₂	−89.2	26	0.3%, 0.5N HCl	423
cyclo-[Val·Orn·(N^δ-Tos-Orn)·Leu·Phe·Pro]₂·2H₂O	[3 L-D-L]₂	−188.0	24	0.7%, HOAc	719
H·[Val·Orn·Leu·Tyr·Pro]₂·2H₂O	[3 L-D-L]₂	−143	—	0.03%, 70% MeOH	679a
H·Val·Tyr·OH·2MeOH	L-L	+49	24	4.2%, H₂O	638a
H·Val·Tyr·Val·OH	3 L	+24	—	3.3%, 0.1N HCl	638a
H·Val·Tyr·Val·His·OH·H₂O	4 L	−6	24	2.5%, H₂O	638a
H·Val₂·OH	D-D	−10.8	25	2.0%, H₂O	914a
H·Val₂·OH	L-D	+59.5	25	2.0%, H₂O	625, 914a
H·Val₂·OH	D-L	−62.1	25	2.0%, H₂O	185, 914a
H·Val₂·OH	L-L	+10.8^hh	25	2.0%, H₂O	625, 914a, 971
H·Val₂·OH·HCl	L-L	+13.6	25	2.9%, H₂O	543a
H·Val₂·OH·HCl	L-D	+51.1	24	2.7%, H₂O	543a
H·Val₂·OH·HCl	D-L	−51.7	24	3.3%, H₂O	543a
H·Val₂·OH·HCl	D-D	−12.8	25	5.2%, H₂O	543a
H·Val₃·OH	3 L	−41.8	21	2.7%, N HCl	543a
H·Val₃·OH	2 L-D	+2.4	33	1.7%, N HCl	543a
H·Val₃·OH	L-D-L	+39.9	33	3.9%, N HCl	543a
H·Val₃·OH	L-2 D	+73.6	33	3.3%, N HCl	543a
H·Val₃·OH	3 D	+41.3	21	2.8%, N HCl	543a
H·Val₃·OH	2 D-L	−0.4	33	1.8%, N HCl	543a
H·Val₃·OH	D-2 L	−71.9	33	3.6%, N HCl	543a
H·Val₃·OH	D-L-D	—	—	—	543a

TABLE 10-47 (continued)

^{a} $[\alpha]_D^{24} = +67.2°$ (2% in 6N HCl) (949).
^{b} $[\alpha]_D^{26} = -38.3°$ (2% in 6N HCl) (949); $[\alpha]_D^{20} = -21.7°$ (in water) (896).
^{c} $[\alpha]_D^{18} = -72.2°$ (3.5% in 2N HCl) (950).
^{d} $[\alpha]_D^{24} = -136.4°$ (1.9% in 2N HCl) (950).
^{e} $[\alpha]_D^{23} = -50.7°$ (4.3% in H$_2$O) (466).
^{f} $[\alpha]_D^{23} = +51.3°$ (2.5% in H$_2$O) (548); $[\alpha]_D^{24} = +13.8°$ (2% in 6N HCl) (949).
^{g} $[\alpha]_D^{20} = +13.9°$ (2.6% in 1 eq. aq. HCl) (609).
^{h} $[\alpha]_D^{25} = +24.8°$ (1.9% in H$_2$O) (491).
^{i} $[\alpha]_D^{28} = +38.9°$ (5.8% in H$_2$O) (491); $[\alpha]_D^{22} = +47.1°$ (0.9% in H$_2$O) (513).
^{j} $[\alpha]_D^{20} = -18.0°$ (0.8% in HOAc) (390).
^{k} $[\alpha]_D^{30} = +74°$ (in H$_2$O) (476).
^{l} $[\alpha]_D^{27} = -86.0°$ (1% in N HCl) (862).
^{m} $[\alpha]_D^{29} = +14.5°$ (in 50% EtOH) (476).
^{n} $[\alpha]_D^{19} = +10.1°$ (1.4% in H$_2$O) (881).
^{o} $[\alpha]_D^{24} = -11.5°$ (1–2% in 0.5N HCl) (898); $[\alpha]_D^{18} = -22.1°$ (5% in H$_2$O) (605).
^{p} $[\alpha]_D^{25} = +24°$ (1% in H$_2$O) (790).
^{q} $[\alpha]_D^{18} = +19.9°$ (2% in H$_2$O + 1 eq. HCl) (128).
^{r} $[\alpha]_D^{18} = +3.9°$ (4.6% in H$_2$O + 1 eq. HCl) (679); $[\alpha]_D^{17} = +6°$ (1% in H$_2$O + 1 eq. HCl) (691).
^{s} $[\alpha]_D^{25} = -14°$ (2% in H$_2$O) (675); $[\alpha]_D^{19} = -13.5°$ (2.3% in H$_2$O) (605).
^{t} $[\alpha]_D^{24} = -52.9°$ (2% in 6N HCl) (949); $[\alpha]_D^{25} = -51.0°$ (2% in H$_2$O) (253).
^{u} $[\alpha]_D^{23} = -21.7°$ (2% in 0.5N HCl) (703).
^{v} $[\alpha]_D^{23} = -87.9°$ (2% in 6N HCl) (949).
^{w} $[\alpha]_D^{24} = -87.7°$ (0.7% in N NaOH) (590).
^{x} $[\alpha]_D^{22} = -92.9°$ (2.1% in H$_2$O) has been reported for the monohydrate (170).
^{y} $[\alpha]_D^{20} = -67.0°$ (2.9% in EtOH) (972).
^{z} $[\alpha]_D = -43.5°$ (1% in 0.1N NaOH) (695).
^{aa} $[\alpha]_D^{20} = -21.0°$ (1% in H$_2$O) has been reported for the monohydrate (985).
^{bb} $[\alpha]_D^{24} = +26.1°$ (1% in N HCl) (622).
^{cc} $[\alpha]_D^{23} = +29.7°$ (1% in HOAc) (622).
^{dd} $[\alpha]_D^{23} = +17.7°$ (1% in H$_2$O) (622).
^{ee} $[\alpha]_D^{26} = +83.0°$ (1.9% in H$_2$O) (444).
^{ff} $[\alpha]_D$ values in H$_2$O of $+84.4°$ (522), $+52.4°$ (224), and $+93.5°$ (665) have also been reported.
^{gg} $[\alpha]_D^{23} = +70°$ (3% in H$_2$O) (803); $[\alpha]_D^{25} = +69.1°$ (1% in H$_2$O + 1 eq. HCl).
^{hh} $[\alpha]_D^{20} = -54°$ (4.3% in H$_2$O) (971). This was probably the D-L form due to inversion during synthesis.

CHEMICAL PROCEDURES FOR SYNTHESIS OF PEPTIDES 1231

(I; X = Br) (461), and *p*-chlorocarbobenzoxy (I; X = Cl) (514), in addition to the carbophenyloxy (C₆H₅—OCO—) (514) and carbo-*p*-tolyloxy (H₃C—C₆H₄—OCO—) (514) derivatives; as the reaction with *p*-nitrocarbobenzoxy derivatives proceeds with the concomitant reduction of the nitro group to an amino function, it follows that *p*-toluidine (II; X = NH₂) rather than *p*-nitrotoluene is obtained as one of the products of the reaction (462). Catalytic hydrogenolysis may also be utilized to eliminate the carboallyloxy (CH₂=CHCH₂OCO—) (460) and trityl ((C₆H₅)₃C—) (548) groups. Such cleavage of the former group suffers a severe disadvantage in that the simultaneous hydrogenation of the allyl residue to a non-hydrogenolyzable propyl residue occurs and hence limits the amount of isolable product (460, 514). On the other hand, reductive cleavage of the trityl group to triphenylmethane ((C₆H₅)₃CH) proceeds quantitatively, but the rate at which the degradation takes place is markedly slower than that encountered with benzyloxycarbonyl derivatives (548, 843).

If, in addition, the benzyl group is implicated in ether linkage as in an O-benzylserine (504, 828, 829, 984) or O-benzyltyrosine (830) residue, in oxycarbonyl linkage with a carbon atom as in a benzyl ester derivative (602, 705), or if it is attached directly to the amino function as in an N^α-benzylamino acid residue (551, 552, 555, 565), then the hydrogenolysis proceeds with the generation of a free hydroxyl function (V → VI), carboxyl group (VII → VIII) or amino function (IX → X), respectively. Although the *p*-nitrobenzyl group is comparably cleaved from its thioether linkage with the

RO—CH₂—C₆H₅ → ROH   RCO₂CH₂—C₆H₅ → RCO₂H
     V   VI   VII   VIII

C₆H₅—CH₂—NHR → NH₂R   RS—CH₂—C₆H₄—X → RSH
        IX   X   XI   XII

sulfhydryl function of a cysteine residue (XI; X = NO₂), no detectable rupture of the analogous derivative with an unsubstituted benzyl group (XI; X = H) has been observed under like conditions (512). Finally, it should be noted that palladium-catalyzed reduction permits the removal of the nitro group from the nitroarginine residue (XIII) during the final stage in the synthesis of arginine containing peptides; the reaction presumably proceeds with the initial formation of a hydrazino intermediate (XIV) which, in turn, undergoes further degradation to one molecule each of the desired arginine residue (XV) and ammonia (XVI) (492).

$$\text{NO}_2\text{NH}-\underset{\underset{\text{XIII}}{\|}}{\overset{\text{NH}}{\text{C}}}-\underset{|}{\overset{\text{NH}-}{\text{N}}}\text{H(CH}_2)_3\overset{|}{\text{CHCO}}- \rightarrow \left[\text{NH}_2\text{NH}-\underset{\underset{\text{XIV}}{\|}}{\overset{\text{NH}}{\text{C}}}-\underset{|}{\overset{\text{NH}-}{\text{N}}}\text{H(CH}_2)_3\overset{|}{\text{CHCO}}-\right] \rightarrow$$

$$\text{NH}_2-\underset{\underset{\text{XV}}{\|}}{\overset{\text{NH}}{\text{C}}}-\underset{|}{\overset{\text{NH}-}{\text{N}}}\text{H(CH}_2)_3\overset{|}{\text{CHCO}}- + \underset{\text{XVI}}{\text{NH}_3}$$

Experimental Conditions. Cleavage of the carbobenzoxy, *p*-nitrocarbobenzoxy, *p*-bromocarbobenzoxy, *p*-chlorocarbobenzoxy, carbophenyloxy, and carbo-*p*-tolyloxy substituents from their linkage with an oxygen or a nitrogen atom may be readily effected via catalytic hydrogenolysis at room temperature and atmospheric pressure. Reaction proceeds in each instance with the absorption of one mole of hydrogen and the evolution of one mole of carbon dioxide per mole of acyl substituent, except with the *p*-nitrocarbobenzoxy group in which case the absorption of two additional moles of hydrogen is required for the reduction of the nitro group to an amino function. Palladium black has hitherto proved the catalyst of choice, although palladous oxide and a preparation of 5–20% palladium on charcoal have also been satisfactorily employed. A highly active palladium black catalyst may be prepared upon reduction of a solution of palladous chloride with formic acid according to the directions given in procedure 10–157; as the active catalyst is pyrophoric and undergoes inactivation in the dry state, its storage is best achieved under water. Although a preparation of 10% palladium on charcoal is presently available on the commercial market, its activity has in the writers' experience shown considerable variation from batch to batch and hence is not to be generally recommended. On the other hand, the relatively recent use of palladous oxide in lieu of palladium black has proved quite satisfactory; preparation of palladous oxide is readily effected via the thermally controlled fusion of palladous chloride and sodium nitrate (procedure 10–158). Irrespective of the kind of catalyst employed, however, the hydrogenolysis may be carried out in any of a number of types of apparatus either commercially accessible or easily assembled from the equipment ordinarily available in the chemical laboratory. By virtue of the extreme sensitivity of palladium catalyst to poisoning by traces of sulfur, an all-glass apparatus is preferable, although connections which involve rubber stoppers or rubber tubing may be safely employed if the rubber has been previously desulfurized by soaking in 10–20% alkali for a week, followed by copious washing with distilled water until a neutral reaction to litmus is noted. An apparatus which has been satisfactorily used in the writers' Laboratory is illustrated in Figure 10–7 (see procedure 10–159). In any event, whatever the form of equipment employed, provision should be made both for the passage of a stream of pure hydrogen through the system and for the convenient determination of the carbon dioxide evolved during the course of the hydrogenation.

CHEMICAL PROCEDURES FOR SYNTHESIS OF PEPTIDES

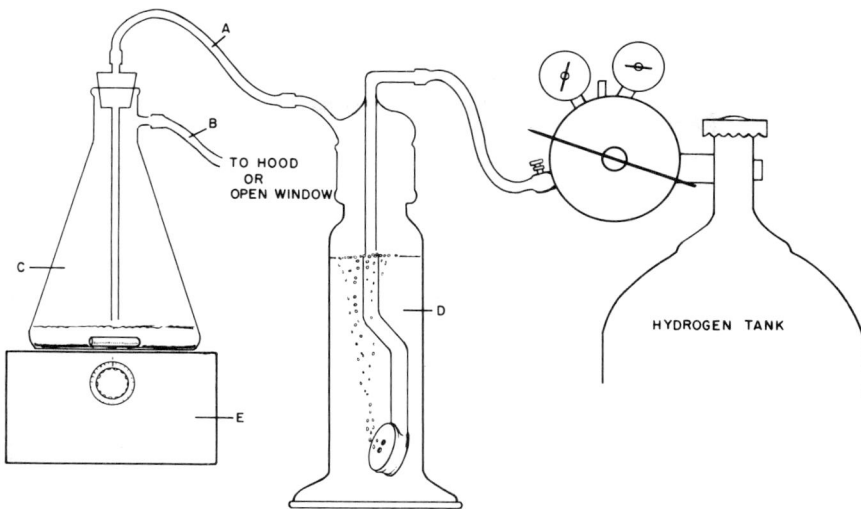

Figure 10-7. Catalytic hydrogenolysis apparatus. (A) gas inlet tube, (B) gas outlet tube, (C) reaction flask (suction flask), (D) gas wash bottle, (E) magnetic stirrer.

Illustrative procedure 10–157 (986). Palladium black catalyst. Twelve grams of palladium metal (sheet) is cut into thin strips 0.5 inch long and then placed in a 500-ml. Kjeldahl flask containing 50 ml. of *aqua regia* (1 part of nitric acid to 3 parts of hydrochloric acid). The mixture is permitted to stand at room temperature for some 10–15 min. and then heated over the steam bath, first gently and then more vigorously, until all the metal has dissolved. The solution is evaporated to dryness at 130–140° in a paraffin bath, the residual material treated with 30 ml. of concentrated hydrochloric acid, and the evaporation repeated. After two repetitions of the latter treatment with hydrochloric acid, the residue is dissolved in 60–100 ml. of 5N hydrochloric acid and the solution filtered into 1200 ml. of water maintained at 90° in a 5-l. Florence flask. To the hot solution is *slowly* added 3.6 ml. of formic acid with *vigorous and immediate agitation*. This is followed by the portionwise addition of 5N potassium hydroxide (approximately 200 ml.), with vigorous shaking, until the reaction mixture is alkaline to litmus. Formic acid is then added dropwise until a just slightly alkaline reaction to litmus is observed. After cooling under tap water, the granular deposit of palladium black is separated by decantation and washed 8–9 times with distilled water. The catalyst is stored under distilled water in a tightly stoppered container until ready for use; *it should never be permitted to dry*. As the catalyst is readily poisoned by traces of sulfur, its contact with sulfur-containing materials, e.g., rubber stoppers or rubber tubing, or certain gases sometimes present in the laboratory air, e.g., hydrogen sulfide, should be rigidly avoided.

Illustrative procedure 10–158 (987). Palladous oxide catalyst. In a 150-ml. casserole, 50 g. of chemically pure sodium nitrate and a solution of palladous chloride corresponding to 2 g. of palladium are thoroughly mixed, evaporated to dryness, and then further heated until fused. The mixture fuses at 270–280°, and when the temperature reaches 350–370° a vigorous evolution of oxides of nitrogen occurs with considerable foaming. After this evolution of gas, which lasts for 3–5 min., the temperature is raised rapidly and maintained between 575° and 600° for 5 min. As the temperature may be followed by the evolution of gases, the process may be readily effected by heating with a single Meker burner. The melt is then permitted to cool, dissolved in 200 ml. of distilled water, and the palladous oxide filtered off. Since the oxide shows a marked tendency to become colloidal in pure water, washing of the catalyst with this solvent must be avoided. It is therefore thoroughly washed with a 1% sodium nitrate solution and dried in a vacuum desiccator over sulfuric acid. A total of about 45 min. is required for the preparation of the catalyst, including filtration and washing.

If this process is properly executed, the filtrates from the fusions should be clear and colorless. Palladous nitrate and chloride give a deep-brown color in concentrated solutions which becomes light yellow on dilution, and this color can be used as an index for the completeness of precipitation. If the filtrate possesses a yellowish-orange opalescence, some of the oxide has become colloidal. In order to recover palladium from the filtrate, it can either be evaporated to dryness and re-fused or rendered slightly alkaline with sodium carbonate and precipitated by heating with formaldehyde. A small amount of the oxide invariably adheres to the casserole during the fusion process and cannot be removed by ordinary means, but is readily dissolved by boiling hydrobromic acid.

In practice, the catalytic reduction of a pertinent N-acylated peptide is generally achieved in anhydrous or aqueous solutions of methanol, ethanol, glacial acetic acid, or some other suitable solvent; the addition of a few drops of glacial acetic acid expedites the reaction. Typical manipulations involved in the conversion of an N-carbobenzoxylated peptide to the corresponding free peptide are described in procedure 10–159; such a procedure is of course applicable to the hydrogenolysis of derivatives which incorporate the analogous *p*-nitro-, *p*-chloro-, and *p*-bromo-carbobenzoxy as well as the carbophenyloxy and carbo-*p*-tolyloxy groups. As given, the procedure should require approximately 2 hours for the removal of the carbobenzoxy substituent, although such time may vary quite considerably with the activity and the amount of catalyst employed, the temperature, and the pressure, among other factors. At any rate, completion of the desired reaction may be readily detected by the point of cessation of carbon dioxide evolution. Inasmuch as the reaction proceeds quantitatively with the generation of volatile co-products (toluene + carbon dioxide), ultimate evaporation of the solvent under reduced pressure yields the desired peptide in a high degree of purity. It should be kept in mind that the hydrogenolysis procedure, as presented here, is subject to numerous variations, e.g., procedure 10–160.

Illustrative procedure 10–159. Catalytic hydrogenolysis of a carbobenzoxypeptide. A suspension containing about 1 g. of palladium catalyst (procedure

10–157) is placed in the reaction flask (Fig. 10–7) and the catalyst washed several times with methanol by decantation. To the flask is then added a solution of 0.02 mole of the pertinent carbobenzoxy-peptide in methanol containing 4 or 5 drops of glacial acetic acid and a magnetic stirring bar. The terminal end of the gas inlet tube is adjusted so as to lie just slightly *above* the surface of the solution. In order to safeguard against the possibility of explosion of a mixture of oxygen and hydrogen gas, precaution should be taken at this stage to ensure that no catalyst adheres to the walls of the flask or is exposed above the surface of the solution. With all stoppers and connections tightly secured, a moderately rapid stream of hydrogen gas is permitted to pass through the system for some 5 min., *in the absence of stirring*, in order to flush out the atmospheric oxygen; the proper rate of flow of gas is ascertained with the aid of a gas wash bottle containing distilled water. The effluent gases should be permitted to escape to the outside through an explosion-proof hood or an open window and their contact with open flames or sparks rigidly avoided. Stirring is then commenced and the effluent gases tested for carbon dioxide by periodic passage through a saturated barium hydroxide solution. The formation of a white precipitate of barium carbonate signals the start of the reaction. Comparable tests are effected each 30 min. until completion of the hydrogenolysis, as indicated by cessation of carbon dioxide evolution. If the free peptide precipitates during the course of the hydrogenation, sufficient water should be added to achieve its solution. At the termination of the reaction, the catalyst is removed by filtration, washed with a little water, and the combined filtrate and washings are concentrated *in vacuo* at 40°. The desired peptide so obtained is recrystallized from water–alcohol or some other suitable solvent medium.

Illustrative procedure 10–160 (610). α-L-Glutamyl-L-valine. A solution of 0.7 g. of carbobenzoxy-α-L-glutamyl-L-valine (procedure 10–150) in aqueous methanol is catalytically reduced according to the directions given in procedure 10–159. The desired peptide separates during the reduction and is recovered, together with admixed catalyst, by filtration upon completion of the hydrogenolysis. Extraction of the solid material with boiling water, followed by the addition of ethanol to the aqueous extracts, leads to recovery of the product as shiny plates; yield, 0.45 g. Recrystallization is effected from aqueous ethanol; $[\alpha]_D^{15} = +24.5°$ (2.7% in water containing 1 molecular equivalent of hydrochloric acid).

Application of the afore-mentioned hydrogenolysis scheme to the methyl ester, ethyl ester, or amide derivative of a suitable N^α-acylated peptide requires the addition of at least 1 molar equivalent of acid (generally hydrochloric or acetic acid) per molar equivalent of amino group liberated; the pertinent peptide ester (procedure 10–161) or peptide amide (procedure 10–162) is then isolated as its corresponding hydrochloride or acetate salt, although the latter has been recommended because of its frequently more desirable crystallization properties (916). If, however, the N^α-acylated peptide benzyl esters are subjected to like catalytic hydrogenolysis, then reaction proceeds with the simultaneous scission of the N-acyl and benzyl ester moieties and the concomitant generation of the free peptide (procedure 10–163); as a rule, about 0.5 g. of palladium catalyst should be used per

0.01 mole of the group to be reduced. By virtue of the fact that the cleavage of the benzyl ester group is not accompanied by the evolution of carbon dioxide gas, it is generally good practice here either to employ a hydrogenation apparatus designed to permit the course of the reaction to be followed by quantitative hydrogen gas uptake or to allow the hydrogenolysis to proceed for about twice the period of time required for the complete removal of the carbobenzoxy group. Comparable situation applies to the fission of the O-benzyl moiety from its ether linkage with the hydroxyl function of a serine or a tyrosine residue, the N-benzyl moiety from its linkage with the nitrogen atom of an amino function, and the S-p-nitrobenzyl moiety from its thioether linkage with a sulfhydryl group; in the former two instances, one molecular equivalent of hydrogen is consumed per mole of benzyl group cleaved, while the reductive cleavage of the S-p-nitrobenzyl substituent, on the other hand, requires a total consumption of three molecular equivalents of hydrogen by virtue of the following reaction (512):

$$NO_2-\langle\rangle-CH_2-SR \xrightarrow[Pd]{3H_2} HOHN-\langle\rangle-CH_3 + RSH + H_2O$$

XVII XVIII XIX XX

As the reductive removal the nitro function from a nitroarginine residue (procedure 10–164) and the trityl group from an N-tritylated amino acid residue occurs at an appreciably slower rate than does the cleavage of an O- or N-benzyl substituent, somewhat longer periods of hydrogenolysis are generally necessitated here.

Illustrative procedure 10–161 (928). Glycyl-L-tyrosine ethyl ester acetate. Two grams of carbobenzoxyglycyl-L-tyrosine ethyl ester (procedure 10–80) in 25 ml. of absolute methanol is treated with 1.2 molecular equivalents of glacial acetic acid and the mixture subjected to catalytic hydrogenolysis according to procedure 10–159. After reduction is complete, the mixture is filtered, the catalyst washed with a little methanol, and the combined filtrate and washings concentrated to dryness *in vacuo* at a temperature not exceeding 40°. Treatment of the residual material with ether is succeeded by filtration of the crystalline product; yield, 1.5 g.; $[\alpha]_D^{29} = +16.2$ (2% in water).

Illustrative procedure 10–162 (916). Glycyl-L-tyrosine amide acetate. A solution of 1.85 g. of carbobenzoxyglycyl-L-tyrosine amide (procedure 10–147) and 0.3 ml. of glacial acetic acid in 25 ml. of methanol is subjected to catalytic reduction according to the directions outlined in procedure 10–159. After completion of the reaction and removal of the catalyst, the filtrate is concentrated under reduced pressure at a temperature not exceeding 40° to a crystalline mass; yield, 1.4 g. Recrystallization is effected from methanol-ethyl acetate; $[\alpha]_D^{22} = +28.0°$ (10% in water).

Illustrative procedure 10–163 (904). L-Arginyl-L-arginine dipicrolonate. A suspension of 4.78 g. of $N^\alpha,N^\omega,N^\omega$-tricarbobenzoxy-L-arginyl-N^ω-carbobenzoxy-L-arginine benzyl ester (procedure 10–120) in about 150 ml. of methanol containing

CHEMICAL PROCEDURES FOR SYNTHESIS OF PEPTIDES

2–3 ml. of acetic acid is subjected to catalytic hydrogenolysis according to procedure 10–159. The reaction mixture is filtered, the catalyst washed several times with 5% acetic acid, and the combined filtrate and washings again filtered. The filtrate so secured is diluted to 300 ml. with water; each ml. of solution thereupon contains approximately 5.5 mg. of arginylarginine. A 200-ml. aliquot of the aforementioned solution is concentrated to a heavy syrup *in vacuo* at a temperature not exceeding 40°. The evaporation process is repeated twice more after the addition each time of a little water. To a solution of the residual syrup in 50 ml. of water is added 500 ml. of a saturated picrolonic acid solution (prepared by stirring 5.5 g. of recrystallized picrolonic acid (from hot ethanol) in 500 ml. of water overnight at room temperature and filtering off the undissolved material). A bright-yellow precipitate of the dipicrolonate forms almost immediately which, after some 12 hr. storage in the dark, is recovered by filtration, washed with ice water until a colorless filtrate is obtained, and air-dried in the dark; yield, 2.25 g. (79%); $[\alpha]_D^{25} = +5.5°$ (1% in dimethylformamide).

Illustrative procedure 10–164 (845). L-Arginyl-L-glutamic acid. To a mixture of 40 ml. of methanol, 10 ml. of glacial acetic acid, and 5 ml. of water is added 1.99 g. of carbobenzoxy-nitro-L-arginyl-L-glutamic acid dibenzyl ester (procedure 10–116) and the reaction mixture subjected to catalytic reduction for some 10 hr. according to the directions outlined in procedure 10–159. After this time, the catalyst is removed by filtration and the filtrate concentrated to dryness *in vacuo* below 40°. The residual material is treated with absolute ethanol, filtered, and finally crystallized from 50% ethanol. The desired product is obtained as the tetrahydrate; yield, 0.99 g. (88%); $[\alpha]_D^{21} = +20.9°$ (2% in water).

Scope and Limitations. Since its introduction by Bergmann and Zervas (128) in 1932, the carbobenzoxy substituent has been selected as the N-acyl blocking group of choice for the synthesis of a wider variety of peptides and peptide derivatives than have all other blocking groups combined. The pre-eminent position assumed by this substituent among the techniques of synthetic peptide chemistry may, in large part, be ascribed both to its facile scission by catalytic hydrogenolysis under conditions so mild as to preclude the possibility either of rupture of the highly labile peptide bonds or racemization of optically active residues, and to the fact that the only end products of the reductive process are the desired peptide (or peptide derivative) and volatile co-products, uncontaminated with the inorganic salts so generally characteristic of peptide preparations obtained by the earlier methods. Inasmuch as the hydrogenolysis proceeds quantitatively, the yield of the desired product in practice frequently ranges from 80 to 90% of theory or greater. An added virtue possessed by the method is that the hydrogenolysis of the methyl or ethyl ester derivatives of carbobenzoxylated peptides leads to the corresponding free peptide esters and hence permits ready access to intermediates which may be utilized for elongation of the peptide chain. As the use of carbobenzoxy-peptide benzyl esters in like reaction proceeds with the simultaneous removal of the N-carbobenzoxy and benzyl ester moieties, the need for a prior saponification step in syntheses directed toward the free peptide is obviated. Indeed, the improved over-all yield of product generally observed here, as well as the ready availability of amino acid benzyl esters as reactants (Section 10–23), often makes this synthetic route the preferable one. Although there has been a tendency in recent years to advocate the employment of other "carbobenzoxy-like" N-acyl substituents such as the *p*-nitro-, *p*-chloro-, or *p*-bromocarbobenzoxy, the carboallyloxy, the carbophenyloxy, and the carbo-*p*-tolyloxy groups, the accumulated years of experience gained with the carbobenzoxy group makes it for the most part virtually irreplaceable.

Although the carbobenzoxy group has proved of inestimable value in providing a means whereby peptides previously unknown or prepared only with great difficulty could be conveniently secured, an early attempt at its application to the synthesis of peptides which incorporate a cystine residue was without success. Thus White (861) in 1934 reported an effort to decarbobenzoxylate biscarbobenzoxycystinylbisglycine by reduction with hydrogen in the presence of platinum or palladium black as catalyst. Notwithstanding the fact that cystine may be reduced to cysteine by palladium-catalyzed hydrogenolysis (988), it is now generally accepted that the efficiency of palladium or platinum as a catalyst suffers a marked diminution whenever sulfur is present. That catalytic hydrogenation may none the less be employed to cleave quantitatively the carbobenzoxy group from peptide derivatives which incorporate a methionine residue was demonstrated by Dekker, Taylor, and Fruton (627), although completion of the hydrogenolysis required both a prolonged time and the addition of fresh catalyst during the course of the reduction. Successful utilization of a similar technique with carbobenzoxylated derivatives which incorporate a disulfide linkage as in cystine, a thioether bond as in S-benzylcysteine, or a sulfhydryl function as in cysteine has not been described. However, replacement of the carbobenzoxy with a *p*-nitrocarbobenzoxy substituent in such compounds was shown by Berse, Boucher, and Piche (512) to permit facile hydrogenolysis of the acyl substituent; this situation was ascribed to the marked labilization of the acyl group which results from a strong inductive effect of the nitro function. Thus treatment of an aqueous solution of the sodium salt of bis(*p*-nitrocarbobenzoxy)-L-cystine or a peptide derivative thereof with hydrogen in the presence of palladium black at room temperature and atmospheric pressure led to the corresponding cystinyl or cysteinyl derivative, dependent upon whether the reaction was arrested after the absorption of six or seven molecular equivalents of hydrogen; the co-product in each instance was *p*-tolylhydroxylamine $\left(\text{HONH}-\!\!\!\bigcirc\!\!\!-\text{CH}_3\right)$. Employment of ethanol as the reaction solvent resulted in the absorption of only four molecular equivalents of hydrogen and the precipitation of cystine or the pertinent cystinyl peptide from the reaction mixture. It is of interest that the greater susceptibility toward hydrogenolysis revealed by the *p*-nitrocarbobenzoxy group than by the carbobenzoxy group is not characteristic of related blocking substituents, which reveal rates of cleavage in this order: carbobenzoxy > *p*-chlorocarbobenzoxy > carbophenyloxy > carbo-*p*-tolyloxy (514).

45. Chemical Reduction. *Principle.* The reductive action of metallic sodium in liquid ammonia on a carbobenzoxy-peptide (I; R = OH) or a carbobenzoxy-peptide amide (I; R = NH$_2$) proceeds with the scission of the N-acyl substituent and the liberation of the desired peptide derivative (II) (690); decomposition of the carbobenzoxy group is accompanied by the formation of dibenzyl (III) in addition to small amounts of toluene (IV)

⟨⟩—CH$_2$OCO—NH···COR → NH$_2$···COR + ⟨⟩—CH$_2$CH$_2$—⟨⟩ + ⟨⟩—CH$_3$
        I   II   III   IV

(690, 989). Reductive degradation of the O- and N-tosyl (446, 842), the N-carboallyloxy (460), and the N-benzylsulfonyl (601) substituents may be achieved in a similar manner; cleavage of the last-mentioned group may, in addition, be effected via the action of Raney nickel in alkaline 80% ethanol (601). Application of the sodium-liquid ammonia technique to derivatives which incorporate a disulfide linkage (V) (690, 862, 867), a thiobenzyl linkage (VI) (11, 690, 862), or an S-carbobenzoxy linkage (VII) (365) as in a cystine, S-benzylcysteine, or S-carbobenzoxycysteine residue, respectively, leads to the generation in each case of a free sulfhydryl function (VIII). Under the reductive influence of these same reagents, the benzyl

RS—SR   ⟨⟩—CH$_2$—SR   ⟨⟩—CH$_2$OCO—SR   RSH
 V   VI   VII   VIII

group of a 1-benzylhistidine residue undergoes facile cleavage from the imidazole nucleus (842).

Experimental Conditions. Reductive cleavage of the N- or S-carbobenzoxy, O- or N-tosyl, N carboallyloxy, N-benzylsulfonyl, and N- or S-benzyl substituents, as well as the disulfide linkage of a cystine residue, is readily achieved upon treatment of a solution of the pertinent compound in liquid ammonia with small pieces of sodium; although no hard and fast rule exists, a convenient concentration in practice appears to be 0.01 mole of reactant per 100–200 ml. of liquid ammonia. Reaction is generally effected in a Dewar flask or an ordinary round-bottom 3-necked flask in either the presence or absence of external cooling, but with vigorous stirring. Completion of the reductive reaction is signaled by the appearance of a permanent blue color which marks the presence of an excess of sodium. Destruction of the excess sodium, with concomitant dissipation of the blue color, is achieved upon the addition of a sufficient quantity of an ammonium salt, e.g., ammonium chloride or ammonium acetate, to the reaction mixture. Upon evaporation of the ammonia, a residue remains which is composed of the desired product admixed with large quantities of sodium salts; where the reductive degradation involves the N-tosyl and presumably also the N-benzylsulfonyl groups, inorganic sulfite and sulfate ions appear as co-products (890). At this point, it is pertinent to note that no general method can be said to exist which permits the isolation of amino acids, peptides, and peptide amides from such reaction mixtures. The isolation problem may often be solved by exploiting some specific property of the product, such as its ability to form an insoluble picrate (842) or mercury salt (11, 473), although the general applicability of this scheme is obviously limited. In most instances, however, it is of essence that the inorganic salts be removed prior to the isolation step. Toward this end, the use of ion exchange resins (435, 890), and countercurrent distribution (cf. 82) appears to offer considerable promise, although the employment of more classical techniques may also prove effective. Thus, for example, the considerably greater solubility exhibited by sodium iodide toward alcohol than is ordinarily shown by a peptide permits separation of the sodium ions from the reaction mixture after treatment of the latter with hydriodic acid; the separation of sulfate and chloride ions, on the other hand, may be achieved via precipitation with barium and silver ions, respectively. In any event, it should be clear that the exact method of separation utilized will vary with the individual circumstances. A method which has been satisfactorily employed in several instances is detailed in procedure 10–165; *as liquid ammonia is extremely corrosive upon contact with skin or eyes, a saturated solution of boric acid should be constantly at hand for first aid purposes.*

Illustrative procedure 10–165 (890). α-L-Glutamylglycine. Into a 3-necked flask fitted with a stirrer and a drying tube filled with sodium hydroxide pellets is placed 3.58 g. (0.01 mole) of tosyl-α-L-glutamylglycine (procedures 10–143 and 10–154); the careful addition of about 120 ml. of liquid ammonia follows. With rapid stirring, the solution is gradually treated with sodium metal in thin slices of about 0.1 g. each until a dark-blue coloration, stable for more than 3 min., indicates the end of the reaction; the consumption of sodium to this point is about 1.3–1.5 g. (0.055–0.065 gram atoms). Ammonium acetate is then added to the solution until the blue color disappears, after which time the ammonia is allowed to evaporate spontaneously with continued stirring. The last traces of free ammonia are removed by evacuating the flask at the water pump with warming to 40°. The dry residue is then dissolved in 20 ml. of ice water and treated with 10 g. of a carboxylate ion exchanger (Amberlite IRC–50) in the form of its ammonium salt. After 30 min., the ion exchanger is filtered off, washed with water, and the combined filtrate and washings evaporated to about 15 ml. under reduced pressure at a temperature less than 40°. To the residual solution is added M barium acetate (about 5–10 ml.) until precipitation is complete; the precipitate is removed by filtration, washed with cold water, and the combined filtrate and washings again evaporated *in vacuo*, if necessary, to a volume of 10–30 ml. The solution is poured onto a 3 by 8 cm. column of coarse-grained ion exchanger (Amberlite IRC-50 as its ammonium salt), with the rate of flow adjusted to 20–30 drops per minute. The column is washed with distilled water until the total volume of eluate amounts to 150 ml. Evaporation of the solution to a small volume under reduced pressure at 40°, followed by the addition of excess ethanol, yields the desired peptide. Recrystallization is achieved from water–ethanol; yield 1.40 g. (68.5%); $[\alpha]_D^{21} = +80°$ (2.2% in water).

For the reductive fission of the N-tosyl group, metallic lithium, barium, or calcium has been used in lieu of sodium (890). However, the yields of product secured in this alternative procedure are generally lower than those obtained with sodium.

Scope and Limitations. The sodium–liquid ammonia technique for the reductive cleavage of an N-carbobenzoxy or N-tosyl substituent, an S-benzyl moiety, or a disulfide linkage, as devised by du Vigneaud and his collaborators (11, 690, 842, 862, 867) has proved invaluable in the synthesis of peptides which incorporate a cysteine or a cystine residue. Reaction in each case proceeds with the liberation of a free sulfhydryl function and hence often permits convenient isolation of the desired peptide by its precipitation from the reaction mixture as the insoluble mercury salt (cf. 11, 473, 990). Decomposition of an aqueous suspension of the latter with hydrogen sulfide, followed by removal of the mercury sulfide precipitate via filtration, then leaves a solution of the pertinent cysteine peptide uncontaminated with inorganic metallic salts. Isolation of the cysteine peptide may be achieved either as such, or after its oxidation to the corresponding cystine analog through aeration of the aqueous solution at pH 7.5 to 8.5 until a negative sulfhydryl reaction is noted with the sodium nitroprusside or ferric chloride reagents. In the latter connection, it might be added that, if two or more cysteine residues are contained within the parent peptide molecule, then the possibility of intramolecular as well as intermolecular disulfide formation exists, the occurrence of one or the other being governed by both the pH and the concentration of the solution. Thus, for example, the sodium–liquid ammonia mediated reduction of S-benzyl-L-cysteinyl-S-benzyl-L-cysteine (IX) leads to L-cysteinyl-L-cysteine (X) which, upon aeration as a 0.15% solution in water at pH 6.5, undergoes facile intramolecular disulfide formation to give a cyclic monopeptide (XI) designated *cyclo*-L-cystinyl (procedure 10–166); however, if a pH of 8.5 and a concentration of 0.6% are employed, then an appreciable amount of intermolecular disulfide formation occurs between two molecules of reactant with the production of a dimer which may possess a parallel structure (XII), an antiparallel structure (XIII), or a mixture of both. The oxidation at pH 6.5 is reminiscent of the intramolecular disulfide formation reported by du Vigneaud and his coworkers (82) as the terminal step in the synthesis of oxytocin; it is not unlikely that such oxidation, under other conditions of pH, could lead to polymeric materials united via disulfide linkages. However, irrespective

$$\underset{\text{IX}}{C_6H_5CH_2SCH_2\overset{\overset{\displaystyle NH_2}{|}}{C}HCO-NH\overset{\overset{\displaystyle CO_2H}{|}}{C}HCH_2SCH_2C_6H_5} \overset{H}{\longrightarrow}$$

$$\underset{\text{X}}{HSCH_2\overset{\overset{\displaystyle NH_2}{|}}{C}HCO-NH\overset{\overset{\displaystyle CO_2H}{|}}{C}HCH_2SH} \xrightarrow[pH\ 6.5]{O} \underset{\text{XI}}{\underset{|\quad\quad\quad|}{\overset{NH_2CHCO-NHCHCO_2H}{CH_2S\text{------}SCH_2}}}$$

$$\downarrow \overset{O}{pH\ 8.5}$$

$$\underset{\text{XII}}{\overset{SCH_2CH(NH_2)CO-NHCH(CO_2H)CH_2S}{\underset{SCH_2CH(NH_2)CO-NHCH(CO_2H)CH_2S}{|\quad\quad\quad\quad\quad\quad\quad\quad\quad\quad|}}} \text{ and/or } \underset{\text{XIII}}{\overset{SCH_2CH(NH_2)CO-NHCH(CO_2H)CH_2S}{\underset{SCH_2CH(CO_2H)NH-COCH(NH_2)CH_2S}{|\quad\quad\quad\quad\quad\quad\quad\quad\quad\quad|}}}$$

of the course which the subsequent oxidation of sulfhydryl functions may take, reductive scission of blocking groups by the action of sodium in liquid ammonia provides a route whereby peptides which incorporate cystine and cysteine residues become more readily available.

Illustrative procedure 10–166 (473, 959). *cyclo*-L-Cystinyl. To a solution of 15 g. of S-benzyl-L-cysteinyl-S-benzyl-L-cysteine (procedure 10–170) in 500 ml. of liquid ammonia is added 4.5 g. of metallic sodium in small pieces. The blue color is discharged by the addition of 13 g. of ammonium sulfate and the ammonia then permitted to evaporate. A solid residue is obtained which is dissolved in 450 ml. of cold 0.7N sulfuric acid and the slight amount of insoluble material removed by filtration. Ninety milliliters of mercuric sulfate solution (prepared by mixing 200 g. of mercuric sulfate, 50 ml. of 10N sulfuric acid, 40 ml. of concentrated sulfuric acid, and 600 ml. of water in the order given (990)) is added with stirring and the resulting precipitate removed by centrifugation and washed with oxygen-free water. Decomposition of the mercury derivative is effected by treatment of its suspension in water with hydrogen sulfide gas, and, after removal of the mercuric sulfide by filtration, the solution is freed from excess hydrogen sulfide by evaporation *in vacuo*. The pH of the solution, which at this point is about 1.5, is adjusted to 6.5 by the addition of baryta. After filtration of the barium sulfate through a pad of filter aid, the clear filtrate is diluted to a volume of 5.5 l. with distilled water and the pH again checked. A stream of clean air is then bubbled through the solution until a positive sulfhydryl color reaction with sodium nitroprusside or ferric chloride is no longer evidenced (about 4–12 hr.). The pH of the solution is then adjusted to 5 by the addition of sulfuric acid, the precipitate of barium sulfate removed by filtration, the filtrate evaporated *in vacuo* and at a low temperature to a small bulk, and the crystals are filtered off. Recrystallization is effected by dissolving the solid in a large volume of warm water, filtering off the traces of insoluble impurity, and re-evaporating to a small bulk; yield, 72%; $[\alpha]_D^{25} = -29.3°$ (1% in N hydrochloric acid).

Although the reductive action of sodium in liquid ammonia may be utilized to remove a pertinent blocking group from a peptide or peptide amide derivative, use of the corresponding peptide ester in such process is precluded by virtue of the fact that it would be subject to at least partial ammonolysis under the conditions imposed by the reaction. While the reductive process generally leads to no racemization where optically active residues are involved, a noteworthy exception was cited by Brenner and Pfister (490) when the optically inactive tripeptide resulted from the cleavage of the carbobenzoxy group from carbobenzoxy-L-methionyl-L-methionyl-L-methionine. In consequence of the large amount of salt formation which necessarily accompanies reductions effected by the sodium-liquid ammonia technique and the attendant purification problems posed thereby, employment of this procedure for the removal of blocking groups is not recommended where alternative methods such as catalytic hydrogenolysis (Section 10–44) would suffice. This should not be construed to imply that the method is of utility only for the synthesis of peptides and peptide derivatives which incorporate a cystine or a cysteine residue. Thus, for example, the relatively recent introduction of tosylpyroglutamic acid as an intermediate in the synthesis of α- and γ-glutamyl peptides (Section 10–39) has emphasized the important role of the sodium-liquid ammonia technique for the selective cleavage of the tosyl group. In such situations, the use of ion exchange resins, countercurrent distribution, fractional crystallization, and the classical techniques of inorganic chemistry generally are required for the removal of inorganic salts.

46. Hydrolytic and Non-hydrolytic Cleavage with Acid. *Principle.* The action of a mixture of phosphonium iodide (PH_4I) in warm glacial acetic acid on an N-carbobenzoxy-peptide (I; $R = C_6H_5CH_2$, $R' = OH$), or its corresponding amide (I; $R' = NH_2$) or methyl, ethyl, or benzyl ester derivatives (I; $R' = OCH_3$, OC_2H_5 or $OCH_2C_6H_5$), leads to the facile cleavage of the N-acyl substituent with the concomitant formation of benzyl iodide (III; $R = C_6H_5CH_2$, $X = I$), carbon dioxide (IV), and the hydriodide salt

$$\underset{\text{I}}{\text{ROCO—NH} \cdots \text{COR}'} + \underset{\text{II}}{2HX} \rightarrow \underset{\text{III}}{RX} + \underset{\text{IV}}{CO_2} + \underset{\text{V}}{HX \cdot NH_2 \cdots \text{COR}'}$$

of the unacylated peptide, peptide amide, or peptide ester (V) (10, 474). The non-hydrolytic cleavage is presumably mediated through the catalytic action of the hydriodic acid (II; $X = I$) which arises from the interaction of phosphonium iodide and glacial acetic acid. Comparable scission of the N-carbobenzoxy group may be effected somewhat more smoothly at room temperature via the action of hydriodic acid (991), hydrogen bromide (514, 664, 665, 722), or hydrogen chloride (664) in glacial acetic acid, although other organic solvents such as dioxane (664), nitromethane (900), carbon tetrachloride (755), diethyl phosphite (465), or ethanol (637, 664) also suffice here. Use of the last-mentioned medium is accompanied by esterification of unmasked carboxyl functions (637, 664). Other blocking groups susceptible to cleavage by the afore-mentioned reagents include the N-carboallyloxy (460, 514), N-*p*-chlorocarbobenzoxy (514), N-carbo-*tert*-butyloxy (464, 465), N-carbo*cyclo*pentyloxy (464), N-carbo*cyclo*hexyloxy (464), O-carbobenzoxy (369, 379, 822), and O-benzyl (828) substituents. Whereas somewhat more drastic conditions are required in the case of the N-tosyl group, its removal may none the less be achieved upon treatment with a phosphonium iodide-concentrated hydriodic acid mixture at 50–65° (127). Cleavage of the N-tosyl group also results from the action of a hydrogen bromide-phenol-glacial acetic acid mixture either for prolonged periods at room temperature (992) or for some 2–4 hours at 65–70° (366); no detectable cleavage of this group is apparent upon storage at room temperature in the presence of methanolic hydrogen chloride for many hours or even upon treatment with this reagent at 100° (514). A striking contrast is revealed with the N-formyl group which, although extremely resistant to scission by solutions of hydrogen halide in glacial acetic acid for periods of several days at 20° (514), is none the less highly susceptible to cleavage by alcoholic or aqueous solutions of hydrogen chloride under conditions which do not lead to rupture of the labile peptide linkage (514, 584, 586, 993). The N-trityl group, on the other hand, is readily cleaved as triphenylcarbinol ((C$_6$H$_5$)$_3$COH) upon brief warming in dilute acetic acid or upon treatment with one or more equivalents of hydrogen chloride in an aqueous or organic medium at room temperature (545–549, 673). Selective hydrolytic fission of the N-carbobenzoxy group may be achieved under the influence of warm concentrated hydrochloric acid (718, 861).

Experimental Conditions. Treatment of an N-carbobenzoxylated peptide, peptide amide, or peptide ester with a concentrated solution of hydrogen bromide in glacial acetic acid generally results in the virtually quantitative scission of the N-acyl substituent after some 15 minutes to 1 hour at room temperature (procedure 10–167); the N-carbo-*t*-butyloxy group is cleaved at an appreciably faster rate than its N-carbobenzoxy analog under the same conditions (464, 465), while somewhat slower rates of cleavage are revealed by the N-carboallyloxy (514), N-*p*-chlorocarbobenzoxy (514), N-carbo*cyclo*pentyloxy (464), and N-carbo*cyclo*hexyloxy (464) substituents. Termination of the reaction is denoted by a cessation of carbon dioxide evolution. As the presence of moisture can lead to hydrolytic cleavage of some of the less sterically hindered peptide bonds (900), best practice demands the use of thoroughly dried reactants and the maintenance of anhydrous conditions during the course of the reaction. A simple procedure for the removal of water usually associated with commercial glacial acetic acid preparations is to freeze the reagent in an ice bath, decant off the unfrozen aqueous layer, and finally permit the reagent to thaw in an atmosphere protected from moisture with a calcium chloride drying tube. Isolation of the hydrobromide salt of the desired peptide, peptide amide, or peptide ester is conveniently achieved by precipitation upon the addition of anhydrous ether to the reaction mixture. Conversion of the peptide hydrobromide to the free peptide may be effected upon treatment of an ethanolic or methanolic solution of the salt with ammonia, pyridine, aniline, lithium hydroxide, or some other suitable base. Although glacial acetic acid has been popularly selected as the reaction solvent of choice in the process described above, any of a large number of inert anhydrous media may be employed in its stead; the use of anhydrous ethanol should be avoided, however, not only in consequence of the esterification which accompanies the reaction, but also because the immiscibility of anhydrous ether in an ethanolic solution of hydrogen bromide does not permit direct precipitation of the desired product (664).

Illustrative procedure 10–167. Decarbobenzoxylation with hydrogen bromide in glacial acetic acid. To 0.01 mole of an N-carbobenzoxylated peptide, or its corresponding amide or ester derivative, is added 10 g. of a saturated solution of dry hydrogen bromide in glacial acetic acid and the reaction vessel protected from atmospheric moisture with a calcium chloride drying tube. Carbon dioxide begins to evolve soon after the addition of the reagent. Upon cessation of gas evolution (about 15 min. to 1 hr.), 100 ml. of dry ether is added to precipitate the amine hydrobromide formed. After several hours of storage in the cold, the hydrobromide salt is filtered off and washed with several portions of anhydrous ether. The hydrobromide salts of the peptide amides and peptide esters are stored as such, while the corresponding salt of the unsubstituted peptides is converted to the free peptide by precipitation from methanol, ethanol, or some other suitable solvent system upon treatment with a base such as aniline, ammonium hydroxide, lithium hydroxide, or pyridine.

Although cleavage of a suitably constituted N-carboalkyloxy substituent, whether with the phosphonium iodide-glacial acetic acid system or via the action of hydrogen chloride, hydrogen iodide, or hydrogen bromide in an anhydrous organic solvent, is similar in principle, certain attributes associated with the hydrogen bromide-acetic acid reagent have made its general employment most advantageous. Thus, for example, whereas scission of the N-carbobenzoxy group proceeds smoothly at room temperature within a few minutes with the hydrogen bromide system, elevated temperatures are required with the phosphonium iodide reagent while a like reaction catalyzed by hydrogen chloride either consumes more time or necessitates the use of higher temperatures (664). The hydrogen iodide-glacial acetic acid reagent, on the other hand, is relatively unstable. In any event, the hydrobromides ultimately obtained as products not only are more readily crystallized and less likely to be hygroscopic than the analogous hydrochloride derivatives, but are also less sensitive to discoloration than are the corresponding hydriodides (722).

Deformylation via acid hydrolysis or alcoholysis proceeds at a rate which varies, in each instance, with the nature of the amino acid residues involved (584). Thus, for example, a 40- to 60-minute half-life is revealed with the methyl esters of formylvaline, -leucine, and -glycine in molar solutions of hydrogen chloride in methanol. In practice, removal of the N-formyl substituent is generally achieved by treatment of the pertinent peptide derivative with a slight excess of hydrogen chloride in methyl, ethyl, or benzyl alcohol (with the corresponding ester derivatives), or in aqueous dioxane (with the free acid) for some 16 to 48 hours at room temperature or for somewhat shorter periods at elevated temperatures (514, 584, 586, 993). Such a reaction assumes especial importance in view of the relatively recent introduction of L-4-carboxy-3-formyl-2:2-dimethylthiazolidine as an intermediate in the synthesis of peptides which incorporate a cysteine residue (see Section 10–39). A case in point involves the simultaneous removal of the formyl and isopropylidene moieties from L-N-(3-formyl-2:2-dimethylthiazolidine-4-carboxy)-glycine (VI), upon mild acid solvolysis, with the formation of L-cysteinylglycine (VII). Detailed description of the latter synthesis is given in procedure 10–168.

$$\begin{array}{c}
CH_2\text{—}CHCO\text{—}NHCH_2CO_2H \\
| \quad\quad | \\
S \quad\quad NCHO \\
\diagdown \diagup \\
H_3C\text{—}C\text{—}CH_3
\end{array}
\xrightarrow[\text{aq. dioxane}]{\text{HCl in}}
\begin{array}{c}
CH_2CHCO\text{—}NHCH_2CO_2H \\
| \quad\quad | \\
SH \quad NH_2
\end{array}$$

VI   VII

Illustrative procedure 10–168 (874). L-Cysteinylglycine monohydrate. L-N-(3-Formyl-2:2-dimethylthiazolidine-4-carboxy)-glycine methyl ester (procedure 10–129) is first saponified by treating a solution of 4.16 g. (16.0 mmoles) of the substance in 42 ml. of dioxane with 16.0 ml. of 1.0N sodium hydroxide, storing the reaction mixture at room temperature for 50 min., adding an additional 1.2 ml. of 1.0N sodium hydroxide thereto, and acidifying the solution with an equivalent amount of N hydrochloric acid after a further 15 min. Removal of the solvents under reduced pressure yields a colorless residue which, after being triturated twice with 20 ml. portions of ethyl acetate and twice with 6-ml. portions of water, is dried and recrystallized from a methanol-carbon tetrachloride mixture; yield, 3.36 g. (87%); m.p. 152–153.5°; $[\alpha]_D^{26} = -169°$ (2% in water). A solution of 3.20 g. (13 mmoles) of the L-N-(3-formyl-2:2-dimethylthiazolidine-4-carboxy)-glycine, so derived, in a mixture of 14.0 ml. of N hydrochloric acid and 50 ml. of 1 : 1 dioxane-water is refluxed under nitrogen for 2 hr. The mixture is cooled, neutralized with an equivalent amount of N lithium hydroxide under an atmosphere of nitrogen, and immediately lyophilized. The residual material is washed thoroughly first with ethyl acetate, then with ethanol, and dried under vacuum. Recrystallization is effected from 1 : 1 methanol-water (oxygen-free) under an atmosphere of nitrogen; yield, 1.4 g. (55%); $[\alpha]_D^{28} = +46.1°$ (2.9% in water).

Acid-mediated cleavage of the trityl substituent from its linkage with a nitrogen atom occurs at a rate which exceeds that exhibited by any of the N-acyl substituents heretofore mentioned. Such striking lability to the action of acid is attested to by the fact that quantitative scission of the N-trityl group does not necessarily require the catalytic action of mineral acids but may, indeed, proceed rapidly upon gentle warming in the presence of aqueous acetic acid. For practical purposes, detritylation is conveniently achieved either upon heating the pertinent derivative in 50% acetic acid (1.0 mmole per ml.) over the steam bath for 1–2 minutes (procedure 10–169), or upon treating a suspension of one molecular equivalent of the derivative in alcohol or acetone with one molecular equivalent of hydrochloric acid, followed by boiling for 1 minute or storage at room temperature for only a few minutes (545–549, 673). Although the S-trityl group is apparently stable to the action of warm aqueous acetic acid, both the N-and the S-trityl groups are readily cleaved by hydrogen chloride in chloroform solution (549).

Illustrative procedure 10–169 (548). Glycylglycine. A suspension of 0.005 mole of tritylglycylglycine (procedure 10–152) in 5 ml. of 50% acetic acid is heated for 1–2 min. over a steam bath, during which time solution of the compound occurs and triphenylcarbinol precipitates. Water is added, the carbinol removed by filtration, and the filtrate evaporated to dryness *in vacuo*. The desired dipeptide is obtained in some 94% yield upon treatment of the residual material with ethanol and subsequent filtration.

Scope and Limitations. The hydrogen bromide-glacial acetic acid system provides a most excellent means for the removal of the carbobenzoxy and related groups from a suitable peptide derivative, not only because of the experimental simplicity which it affords, but also because the products to which it ultimately leads are generally both satisfactory in yield and high in chemical as well as stereochemical purity. Conditions imposed by the method are sufficiently mild to permit such sensitive groups as ethyl and methyl esters, amides, and thiolesters to remain largely unaltered. Although acidolysis of the benzyl ester function may be mediated by the hydrogen bromide-glacial acetic acid reagent upon prolonged storage at room temperature or for shorter periods at elevated temperatures, such reaction does not occur to any appreciable extent under the conditions ordinarily employed for the removal of the carbobenzoxy substituent. Indeed, the rates at which the N-carbobenzoxy and the benzyl ester moieties undergo cleavage are sufficiently divergent to permit the ready preparation of the benzyl esters of amino acids (see procedure 10–53) and peptides from the corresponding N-acylated precursors (664, 665); hence, intermediates which are of value for coupling purposes become easily accessible. A singular advantage possessed by the hydrogen bromide-glacial acetic acid reagent rests in its ability to selectively cleave the carbobenzoxy substituent from derivatives which incorporate such reducible groups as a nitro function and an S-benzyl moiety (procedure 10–170). However, the extreme lability of the indole nucleus of tryptophan to the action of mineral acid, and the striking propensity of methionine to undergo conversion to S-benzylcysteine by virtue of the rapid displacement of the S-methyl group by a benzylcarbonium ion, do not permit the satisfactory use of this reagent with N-carbobenzoxylated derivatives which incorporate either of these amino acid residues (900; cf. 993a). Side reactions of this type are of minor consequence for the more rapidly cleaved N-carbo-*tert*-butyloxy derivatives (464); it is of interest that, in contrast to the carbobenzoxy group, the carbo-*tert*-butyloxy group is resistant to reduction via catalytic hydrogenation or the action of sodium in liquid ammonia and hence should be of value for the synthesis of complex peptides where a combination of blocking groups and their selective removal is desirable (465). Certain of the advantages inherent in the use of the hydrogen bromide rather than the hydrogen chloride, hydriodide, and phosphonium iodide reagents have been alluded to earlier and need not be reiterated here. It should be noted, however, that acid-catalyzed decompositions in the presence of water (718, 861) or alcohols (637) may be accompanied by appreciable rupture of the peptide bonds (514, 900) and hence are not to be generally recommended.

Illustrative procedure 10–170 (473). S-Benzyl-L-cysteinyl-S-benzyl-L-cysteine. To 1.77 l. of a saturated solution of dry hydrogen bromide in glacial acetic acid is added 350 g. of carbobenzoxy-S-benzyl-L-cysteinyl-S-benzyl-L-cysteine (procedure 10–151). The mixture is permitted to stand at 25° with occasional shaking for 1 hr. and then treated with several volumes of dry ether. The dipeptide hydrobromide which separates is filtered off, washed with dry ether, and dissolved in dilute hydrobromic acid. Treatment of the latter solution with dilute ammonium hydroxide to pH 6 leads to the deposition of the free peptide, which is recovered by filtration. Crystallization is effected by bringing a suspension of the crude peptide into solution in 20 l. of 30% ethanol by the careful addition of dilute ammonia and subsequently adding dilute hydrochloric acid thereto, with stirring, to a pH of 6; the crystallization procedure is repeated once more. The final yield is 213 g.; m.p. 170–172° (corr.); $[\alpha]_D^{26} = -141.1°$ (2% in N sodium hydroxide).

In contradistinction to the behavior revealed by the N-trityl, N-formyl, N-carbobenzoxy, and related blocking substituents, the N-tosyl group shows a marked resistance to the action of alcoholic hydrogen chloride, even under reflux (514, 993). The latter substituent is nevertheless susceptible to acidolysis by hydrogen bromide in glacial acetic acid (366, 992), although the rate of cleavage is appreciably slower than with the analogous

N-carbobenzoxy derivatives. While the rate of cleavage is markedly increased at elevated temperatures, this is of little practicable worth by virtue of the concomitant increased tendency of peptide bonds to undergo decomposition (514). A comparable problem is posed by the use of the phosphonium iodide-glacial acetic acid reagent, which mediates a very slow acidolysis of the N-tosyl group at 50° but an extremely rapid scission of this same substituent at 100° as a result of the reductive action which accompanies the acidolysis at this temperature (514). On the other hand, removal of the N-tosyl group by treatment with a warm mixture of phosphonium iodide in concentrated hydriodic acid is largely a reductive process (127). In any event, the somewhat drastic conditions required should ordinarily preclude the use of the phosphonium iodide reagent for the removal of the N-tosyl group from peptide derivatives.

47. Alkaline Hydrolysis and Hydrazinolysis. *Principle.* Treatment of a suitably constituted N-phthalylated peptide or its corresponding amide derivative (II) with hydrazine, either in boiling ethanol (518, 965) or in aqueous sodium carbonate at room temperature (527), leads to cleavage of the acyl group with the concomitant formation of phthalhydrazide (III) in addition to the desired peptide or peptide amide (IV). Comparable dephthalylation may be mediated by phenylhydrazine (994) or N-methylhydrazine (995) in lieu of hydrazine, although the addition of a tertiary base, e.g., tri-*n*-butylamine, as a catalyst is required in such instances. However, the action of alkali on a phthalyl derivative (II) causes a rupture of the five-membered ring with the formation of a phthalamic acid derivative (I) which no longer reacts with hydrazine in the desired manner. Sensitivity to alkaline media is shown too by N-trifluoroacetyl derivatives, which undergo

facile deacylation in the presence of dilute aqueous or alcoholic solutions of alkali or ammonia (567–569, 573).

Experimental Conditions. In practice, dephthalylation of an appropriate derivative is most conveniently achieved by refluxing its solution in ethanol with 1–2 equivalents of hydrazine for 1–2 hours (procedure 10–171). Since the phthalhydrazide formed during the reaction is acidic, subsequent evaporation of the reaction mixture yields the corresponding amine salt of phthalhydrazide; decomposition of the latter with dilute acetic acid or hydrochloric acid leads to the almost complete precipitation of the highly insoluble phthalhydrazide and hence permits the desired amine to be recovered upon evaporation of the filtrate (518, 965). An alternative approach is afforded by refluxing an ethanolic solution of an N-phthalyl peptide with 1.5 to 2 equivalents of phenylhydrazine and 1 equivalent of tri-n-butylamine for 2 hours (994). Subsequent treatment of the reaction mixture with 1.5 volumes of methylethylketone and 1 equivalent of glacial acetic acid results in the crystallization of the desired peptide, while the soluble N-phenylphthalhydrazide remains behind in solution. Somewhat less drastic conditions for dephthalylation are imposed by treatment of a solution of the pertinent derivative in aqueous sodium carbonate with 1 equivalent of hydrazine at room temperature for 2 days (procedure 10–172); neutralization of the reaction mixture with hydrochloric acid causes precipitation of the phthalhydrazide and leaves a solution which contains the peptide together with sodium chloride. As separation of the latter two materials might sometimes prove cumbersome, it is generally good practice to use hydriodic acid for the neutralization and thus take advantage of the fact that the relatively high solubility of sodium iodide in cold alcohol, in which the free peptide invariably shows a sparing solubility, will enable removal of the inorganic material (527).

Illustrative procedure 10–171 (518). Glycylglycine. A suspension of 2.62 g. (0.01 mole) of phthalylglycylglycine (procedure 10–65) in 30 ml. of ethanol is treated with 10 ml. of M alcoholic hydrazine hydrate and the mixture heated under reflux for 1 hr. After this time, the mixture is evaporated to dryness, the residue warmed to 50° for 10 min. with 25 ml. of approximately $2N$ hydrochloric acid, and the mixture permitted to cool to room temperature during 30 min. The phthalhydrazide is removed by filtration and glycylglycine hydrochloride monohydrate obtained by concentrating the filtrate under reduced pressure. After crystallization of the latter from ethanol, it is dissolved in 100 ml. of water and converted to the free dipeptide by passage through a column of Amberlite IR-4B acid-adsorbing resin. Concentration of the halogen-free effluent to a volume of 20 ml., followed by the addition of ethanol thereto, leads to the recovery of 1.07 g. (87%) of glycylglycine.

Illustrative procedure 10–172 (527). L-Glutamine. To a solution of 1.35 g. of sodium carbonate in 25 ml. of water are added 5.4 g. of phthalyl-L-glutamine (procedure 10–135) and 2 g. of 50% hydrazine hydrate and the reaction mixture then set aside for 2 days at room temperature. After this time, the solution is neutralized with $2N$ hydrochloric acid, the precipitate of phthalhydrazide removed by filtration, and the chloride ion in the filtrate eliminated by shaking with 7.5 g. of silver carbonate for several hours. Filtration of the mixture yields a clear solution which is exactly neutralized by 2N hydriodic acid and concentrated at 30° under reduced pressure. The addition of alcohol precipitates the L-glutamine in some 67% yield. Recrystallization of the latter is achieved by rendering its aqueous solution turbid with ethanol, followed by storage in the cold for several hours; $[\alpha]_D^{22} = +5.6°$ in water.

Hydrolytic cleavage of the amide bond between a trifluoroacetyl group and a nitrogen atom occurs with facility at room temperature and a pH greater than 10 (567–569, 573). The rate at which the alkaline hydrolysis of an N-trifluoroacetylamino acid occurs is influenced, to a marked extent, by the nature of the component amino acid residue. Thus, for example, while the extent of hydrolysis observed for N-trifluoroacetylglycine is about 45% after some 38 minutes in 40% aqueous ethanol at pH 12.0–12.1 and room temperature, only a 5% cleavage of N-trifluoroacetyl-DL-phenylalanine is attained under the same conditions (569). Hence the conditions under which the quantitative deacylation of a trifluoroacetylated peptide derivative is to be achieved should be expected to vary with the nature of the individual compound. In practice, a solution of the pertinent peptide derivative is stored in an aqueous or alcoholic solution of alkali (procedure 10–173) or ammonia (procedure 10–174) at room temperature until quantitative deacylation has been achieved. The time of storage may vary from several minutes to several days, according to the constitution of the reactant and the conditions employed; the paucity of presently available data unfortunately does not permit any more definite rules to be drawn in this regard.

Illustrative procedure 10–173 (569). L-Phenylalanine anilide. To a solution of 91.1 mg. of N-trifluoroacetyl-L-phenylalanine anilide (procedure 10–66) in 5.0 ml. of 95% ethanol is added 1.0 ml. of N sodium hydroxide. The basic solution is allowed to stand for 48 hr. at room temperature and subsequently acidified with N hydrochloric acid. On evaporation to dryness, the solid residue is washed with 2 ml. of dilute aqueous ammonia and the product crystallized from 4 ml. of 50% aqueous ethanol; yield, 37.0 mg. (57%); m.p. 73–74°; $[\alpha]_D^{26} = +22.1°$ (1.0% in ethanol).

Illustrative procedure 10–174 (573). Glycylglycine. A solution of 0.42 g. of the dicyclohexylamine salt of trifluoroacetylglycylglycine (procedure 10–69) in 10 ml. of 12% ammonium hydroxide is permitted to stand for 30 min. at room temperature and the liberated dicyclohexylamine then extracted into petroleum ether. The aqueous layer is concentrated to dryness *in vacuo*, the residue taken up in a little water, and the evaporation repeated. After treatment of the residual material with 5 ml. of ethanol, the desired crystalline product is recovered by filtration; yield, 116 mg. (85%).

Scope and Limitations. Selective removal of the phthalyl group via hydrazinolysis has been employed in the preparation of only a few di- and tripeptides which incorporate some of the less complex amino acids; no data are as yet available with derivatives which incorporate serine, threonine, hydroxyproline, histidine, lysine, arginine, or tryptophan residues, among others. That the dephthalylation process may not be invariably successful even in the case of simple peptide derivatives is attested to, for example, by the complete failure of the hydrazine treatment to remove the protecting group from phthalylglycylglycyl-L-asparagine (674). Several other shortcomings engendered by the use of the phthalyl group warrant mention here. Thus the low temperature saponification of ester groups cannot be utilized in the case of phthalylated peptide esters since such treatment leads to an opening of the phthalyl ring with the concomitant formation of the corresponding phthalamic acid derivative which, in turn, cannot be deacylated by the action of hydrazine. Although acid hydrolysis of ester groups may be used in these instances, such a condition is sufficiently drastic to cause appreciable hydrolysis of the more sensitive amide and peptide linkages simultaneously (674). Moreover, since the action of hydrazine converts an ester moiety to a hydrazide, free peptide esters cannot be prepared by deacylation of the corresponding phthalyl derivative.

As the trifluoroacetyl group has not been extensively employed for the synthesis of peptides to the present time, a proper evaluation of its practicable worth is not yet feasible.

48. Special Cleavage Methods. (*a*) Oxidation. Selective cleavage of the N-benzyl-, N-phenyl-, and N-methylthiocarbonyl substituents may be achieved upon treatment of the pertinent N-acylated peptide (I; R = $C_6H_5CH_2$, C_6H_5, and CH_3 respectively), or its ester derivative, with 2.5 moles of perbenzoic acid for 1 hour at 0° in acetic acid-benzene, benzene-tetrahydrofuran, or dioxane, preferably in the presence of some 2% water (580). Oxidation presumably proceeds via an intermediate of the type represented by (VI) which, under the influence of water, undergoes decomposition with the evolution of carbon dioxide and the formation of the free peptide (II) or peptide ester. Isolation of the free peptide from the reaction mixture is accomplished in excellent yield by absorption on a Dowex 50 cation exchange resin, followed by elution with dilute ammonia; in the case of peptide esters, alkaline saponification of the ester moiety precedes the isolation step. Unlike its carbobenzoxy analog, the benzylthiocarbonyl substituent is insensitive to the action of hydrogen bromide in glacial acetic acid.

$$2RSCO\text{—}NHCHRCO\cdots \xrightarrow{5O} RS\cdot O\cdot CO\text{—}NHCHRCO\cdots$$
$$\text{I}$$

$$\xrightarrow{2H_2O} RS\cdot O\cdot CO\text{—}NHCHRCO\cdots$$

$$2NH_2CHRCO\cdots + RSO_3H + RSO_2H + 2CO_2$$

II   III   IV   V   VI

(b) Intramolecular aminolysis. Preferential removal of the N-o-nitrophenoxyacetyl and N-chloroacetyl substituents from suitably constituted peptide derivatives (VII and XII) is based upon their conversion, respectively, to the corresponding N-o-aminophenoxyacetyl (VIII) and N-o-aminophenylglycyl (XIII) derivatives, both of which undergo facile intramolecular cyclization with the formation of the lactam of o-aminophenoxyacetic acid (IX) in the former case, the lactam of o-aminophenylglycine (XIV) in the latter, and the concomitant liberation of the free peptide (X and Xa) in both (494). Thus reduction of an N-o-nitrophenoxyacetyl-peptide (VII) by hydrogenation in the presence of platinum catalyst yields the N-o-aminophenoxyacetyl analog (VIII), which, upon treatment with boiling water at 100° for 1 hour and subsequent cooling, leads to the precipitation of o-aminophenoxyacetic acid lactam (IX); subsequent evaporation of the solution permits the recovery of the desired free peptide (X). In the case of N-chloroacetyl derivatives (XII), treatment with 2 molecules of o-phenylenediamine (XI) dihydrochloride and 5 molecules of lithium hydroxide in aqueous solution for 1 hour at 100°, followed by chilling the reaction mixture, leads to the deposition of o-aminophenylglycine lactam and permits the ultimate isolation of the free peptide (Xa) from the filtered solution; reaction presumably proceeds with the transitory formation of the N-o-aminophenylglycine intermediate (XIII).

49. An Approach to the Determination of the Optical Purity of Peptides.
The optical purity of a peptide refers to the optical purity of its constituent amino acids, for if these are not pure there is not one peptide but a mixture of two or more diastereomers. In Section 10–25, the requirement for amino acids of a high degree of optical purity *prior* to their synthetic combination into peptides was strongly emphasized. If, however, the method of synthesis itself leads to some racemization of one or more of the amino acid residues in the peptide (cf. Sections 10–28 and 10–29) it might appear that this requirement was excessive. On the other hand, it is clear that, unless the original amino acid reactants are optically pure, it would be rather difficult in the event that an optically mixed peptide were secured to know whether to ascribe this condition to the method of synthesis employed or to the prior state of the reactants.

If it can be assumed that the desired prior condition of optically pure amino acid reactants is met, it follows that the determination of the optical purity of the amino acid residues in a synthetic peptide will serve to answer the question whether the synthesis of the peptide was or was not accompanied by racemization. In order to acquire this information, the peptide must first be hydrolyzed to its constituent amino acids, and the optical purity of these former residues subsequently determined. Obviously, the method of hydrolysis must itself lead to no racemization at all, while the method of determining the optical purity of the amino acids must involve agents which are (*a*) absolutely optically specific, (*b*) highly sensitive, and (*c*) completely uninhibited in the presence of a large excess of the antipodal amino acid.

The use of refluxing strong acid as a hydrolytic agent over a period of several days (996) is quite contra-indicated inasmuch as appreciable racemization occurs under such conditions. The criterion of optical rotation to determine optical purity (see Section 10–25) is relatively ineffective because of the range of error involved and because of the need of some unequivocal reference standard. The use of microbiological growth procedures to determine the amount of an L-amino acid in a possible mixture of L- and D-amino acids is questionable because of the crudity of the measurements, the large range of error, and the possibility of inhibitory reactions due to the presence of the insusceptible D-isomers. Thus *L. arabinosus* has been employed to determine L-valine in the presence of D-valine (996), although it had already been shown that the growth of this organism is inhibited by D-valine (997). An isomeric mixture composed, for example, of 95% L-amino acid and 5% D-amino acid, is more accurately defined by a method suitable for determining the 5% due to the D-isomer than by one which depends upon the quantitative estimation of the 95% of the L-isomer and the assumption that the undetermined 5% is due to the D-isomer.

In the writers' experience, the simplest and at the same time the most sensitive approach to the problem of the determination of the optical purity of peptides lies in the use of renal aminopeptidase (Chapter 20) as a hydrolyzing agent, followed by the application of snake venom L-amino acid oxidase or renal D-amino acid oxidase to the hydrolysis products (254). As with all enzymic techniques, the method is limited to susceptible substrates, i.e., the peptide whose optical purity is under consideration must be readily and completely hydrolyzed by the aminopeptidase, and the *antipodes* of the hydrolysis products must be susceptible to the action of the oxidases (cf. Chapter 19). Thus there is little use in attempting to determine the optical purity of glycyl-D-proline, even were this substrate easily cleaved by aminopeptidase, because the possible presence of L-proline in the hydrolysis products could not be detected in view of its insusceptibility to snake venom L-amino acid oxidase.

Still another limitation is involved in the nature of the peptide, which for the present purposes must be designed to be optically homogeneous, i.e., it must involve *susceptible potential antipodes* either L or D in configuration but not both. Thus the peptide may be L-leucyl-L-leucine, D-leucyl-D-leucine, or L-leucylglycyl-L-leucine, etc., but not L-leucyl-D-leucine or D-leucyl-L-leucine, etc. These optically mixed peptides may well be completely hydrolyzed by aminopeptidase; but, (a) if one residue undergoes more racemization than the other, this can be detected only by an increase in oxygen consumption through the agency of one oxidase and a decrease in oxygen through the agency of the other oxidase, the increase or decrease representing a relatively small difference between two large numbers and hence subjected to considerable error, and, (b) if both residues undergo the same amount of partial racemization, it will be obviously impossible to detect this fact through the use of the oxidases. The peptides to be investigated by this procedure must therefore be optically homogeneous, but, even if some D-leucine is detected in the peptidase-induced hydrolysate of L-leucyl-L-leucine, it would not be possible to determine whether it was derived by racemization of the N-terminal residue or the C-terminal residue of the peptide, or both. This constitutes a further limitation on the procedure when applied to peptides not only optically but also chemically homogeneous. This limitation could be removed in certain restricted cases by the employment of a structurally as well as an optically specific enzyme such as L-tyrosine decarboxylase (Chapter 20). Thus the hydrolysate of D-leucyl-D-tyrosine would yield D-leucine and D-tyrosine. Any L-leucine or L-tyrosine present would be detected without discrimination between the two by snake venom L-amino acid oxidase. The subsequent employment, on another aliquot of the hydrolysate, of L-tyrosine decarboxylase would however detect exclusively only the L-tyrosine if present. This procedure is obviously limited to peptides containing residues whose antipodes are specifically susceptible to certain amino acid decarboxylases.

The first application of the general procedure was in the determination of the optical purity of several glycyl-L- and D-amino acids, originally prepared by the classic Fischer procedure, which were found to be completely hydrolyzed by renal aminopeptidase and completely inert, after hydrolysis, to the action of that oxidase specific for the optical antipode (254); glycine is of course inert to both L- and D-amino acid oxidases. More recently, the following peptides were prepared in the writers' Laboratory by Dr. W. K. Paik by the mixed anhydride procedure (Section 10–29) employing isobutylchloroformate: L-leucyl-L-leucine, D-leucyl-D-leucine, L-valyl-L-valine, and D-valyl-D-valine. These compounds were analytically and chromatographically pure, and the enantiomorphic forms possessed optical rotations equal in magnitude and opposite in sign. The optical purity of the valine and leucine isomers which had been employed in the peptide syntheses had previously been determined and found to be greater than 99.9% (Chapter 19). No free amino acid was present in the final peptide preparations, as revealed not only by paper chromatography but also by the negative results obtained by Van Slyke CO_2-ninhydrin determinations (Chapter 12). Mixtures were prepared of 100 μmoles of the peptide with or without 1 μmole of L- or D-amino acid, renal aminopeptidase, and either L- or D-amino acid oxidase, and the oxygen consumption followed until it ceased. No catalase was added inasmuch as the aminpoeptidase preparation had sufficient adherent catalase activity present. Under these conditions, 1 μmole of amino acid when oxidized consumes 11.2 μl. of oxygen. Some aminopeptidase activity was also present in the D-amino acid oxidase preparation. After the oxygen uptake had terminated, an aliquot of the mixture was subjected to Van Slyke CO_2-ninhydrin analysis to be certain that all of the peptide had been hydrolyzed.

The results of this study were of interest (998). Of three preparations of L-leucyl-L-leucine, one (which had been crystallized from water four times) gave a hydrolysate which did not react with D-amino acid oxidase, but consumed 10.5 μl. of oxygen in the presence of 1 μmole of added D-leucine and 21.9 μl. in the presence of 1 μmole of added D-leucyl-D-leucine, and hence could be considered optically pure (greater than 99%). Of two other preparations of this peptide (which had been crystallized only once), one gave a hydrolysate which by itself consumed 10.3 μl. of oxygen, and 20.3 μl. in the presence of 1 μmole of added D-leucine, while the other preparation gave a hydrolysate which by itself consumed 41.3 μl. of oxygen, and 51.8 μl. in the presence of 1 μmole of added D-leucine. Thus the former of these two preparations of L-leucyl-L-leucine was racemized to the extent of yielding 1% D-leucine in the hydrolysate, and the latter to the extent of yielding 4% D-leucine in the hydrolysate, and neither could be considered optically pure if the standard is better than 99%. Yet all three preparations of L-leucyl-L-leucine were derived from the same stock of L-leucine, and it must therefore be concluded that in the course of the synthesis of the peptide some racemization

CHEMICAL PROCEDURES FOR SYNTHESIS OF PEPTIDES 1257

occurred, most probably at the coupling stage. The exact amount of racemization, which might vary from preparation to preparation, is not likely to be known in view of the fractionation of the diastereomeric mixture on crystallization from water.

In the same manner as described, the optical purity of the preparation of L-valyl-L-valine (crystallized four times from water) was determined; the hydrolysis mixture consumed 12.9 μl. of oxygen in the presence of 1 μmole of added D-valine, and hence the peptide contained less than 1 part in 100 of the D-isomer, and within the present definition could be considered optically pure. The optical purity of the preparation of D-leucyl-D-leucine which had been crystallized from water four times was tested in like manner except that *Bothrops atrox* L-amino acid oxidase was used in place of the renal D-amino acid oxidase. This preparation yielded a hydrolysate with aminopeptidase which consumed 8.8 μl. of oxygen in the presence of 1 μmole of added L-leucine and 25.8 μl. of oxygen in the presence of 1 μmole of added, optically pure L-leucyl-L-leucine, and hence could be considered optically pure ($>99\%$).

Illustrative procedure 10-175 (998). The standard procedure for checking the optical purity of susceptible peptides is as follows. There is placed in the conventional Warburg flask a mixture consisting of 2 ml. of water containing 100 μmoles of the peptide to be tested, 0.1 ml. of either water or an aqueous solution containing 1 μmole of added L- or D-amino acid or L-L- or D-D-peptide, 2 ml. of 0.1M borate buffer at pH 8.05, and 0.4 ml. of renal aminopeptidase suspension (Chapter 20). Close to 0.5 ml. of an aqueous solution of either *Bothrops atrox* venom or hog renal D-amino acid oxidase (Chapter 20) is placed in the side arm of the vessel, and 0.2 ml. of 20% KOH is added to the center cup. After temperature equilibrium is reached (at 37°), the oxidase in the side arm is added and the oxygen consumption recorded until it stops. When this stage is reached, the reaction is discontinued and 0.5 ml. of the mixture is removed and subjected to analysis in the manometric apparatus for the amount of CO_2 evolved after treatment with ninhydrin (Chapter 12). Under these conditions, 1 μmole of amino acid consumes 11.2 μl. of oxygen, while the complete hydrolysis of 100 μmoles of a dipeptide should yield close to 200 μmoles of carbon dioxide.

Preparation of Selected Derivatives

50. Glutamine and Asparagine. Although asparagine and glutamine are generally classified as α-amino acids, and have been obtained commercially by isolation from suitable plant tissues, their synthesis has for the most part been achieved through application of the techniques of peptide chemistry. The first synthesis of this type was accomplished in 1933 by Bergmann, Zervas, and Salzmann (602), who prepared L-glutamine (IV; $x = 2$; $[\alpha]_D^{19} = +8.0°$ in water) via palladium-catalyzed hydrogenolysis of benzyl carbobenzoxy-L-glutaminate (VIII; $R = C_6H_5CH_2OCO$, $R^1 = C_6H_5CH_2$). The latter compound arose from the treatment of carbobenzoxy-L-glutamic anhydride (X) (procedure 10–132) with benzyl alcohol at 100° to yield carbobenzoxy-L-glutamic acid α-benzyl ester (XI) which was subsequently coupled with ammonia by way of its corresponding acid chloride derivative (XII). L-Asparagine (IV; $x = 1$; $[\alpha]_D^{17} = +20.6°$ in 1 equivalent of 0.1N HCl) was synthesized from carbobenzoxy-L-aspartic anhydride (X; $R = C_6H_5CH_2OCO$) through an identical reaction sequence by the same investigators. A variation of the original glutamine procedure was described some two years later by Harington and Mead (10), who first saponified the benzyl carbobenzoxy-L-glutaminate (VIII) of Bergmann, Zervas, and Salzmann and subsequently removed the acyl substituent from the carbobenzoxy-L-glutamine (III) so derived by the action of phosphonium iodide in glacial acetic acid. That carbobenzoxy-L-glutamine may be more conveniently secured by the ammonolysis of carbobenzoxy-L-glutamic acid γ-ethyl ester (II; $R^2 = C_2H_5$) with liquid ammonia was shown during the same year by Nienburg (999), who prepared the parent compound (II) through the carbobenzoxylation of γ-ethyl L-glutamate (I); catalytic hydrogenolysis of (III) yielded the desired L-glutamine (IV; $[\alpha]_D = +8.3°$ in water). In a subsequent modified procedure by Miller and Waelsch (482), the ammonolysis step was more conveniently effected in concentrated aqueous ammonia. A novel means of obtaining carbobenzoxy-L-glutamine (III) was reported by Fruton (1000), who exploited the fact that the specificity of the proteolytic enzyme papain is adapted to the hydrolytic cleavage of amide linkages involving the α-carboxyl function of N-acylated L-glutamic acids, with no concomitant alteration of γ-amide linkages. Thus the ammonolysis of dimethyl carbobenzoxy-L-glutamate (VI; $R = C_6H_5CH_2OCO$, $R^1 = R^2 = CH_3$) led to the diamide derivative (VII; m.p. 194–196°) which, when subjected to the hydrolytic action of cysteine-activated papain, suffered cleavage of the α-amide group and permitted the ultimate isolation of carbobenzoxy-L-glutamine (III); L-glutamine (IV;

$$\begin{array}{cccc}
\text{NH}_2\text{CHCO}_2\text{H} & \text{R—NHCHCO}_2\text{H} & \text{R—NHCHCO}_2\text{H} & \boxed{\text{NH}_2\text{CHCO}_2\text{H}} \\
| & | & | & | \\
(\text{CH}_2)_x\text{CO}_2\text{R}^2 \rightarrow & (\text{CH}_2)_x\text{CO}_2\text{R}^2 \rightarrow & (\text{CH}_2)_x\text{CO—NH}_2 \rightarrow & \boxed{(\text{CH}_2)_x\text{CO—NH}_2} \\
\text{I} & \text{II} & \text{III} & \text{IV} \\
\uparrow & \uparrow & \uparrow & \uparrow \\
\text{NH}_2\text{CHCO}_2\text{H} & \text{R—NHCHCO}_2\text{R}^1 & \text{R—NHCHCO—NH}_2 & \text{R—NHCHCO}_2\text{R}^1 \\
| & | & | & | \\
(\text{CH}_2)_x\text{CO}_2\text{H} \rightarrow & (\text{CH}_2)_x\text{CO}_2\text{R}^2 \rightarrow & (\text{CH}_2)_x\text{CO—NH}_2 & (\text{CH}_2)_x\text{CO—NH}_2 \\
\text{V} & \text{VI} & \text{VII} & \text{VIII} \\
\downarrow & & & \uparrow \\
\text{R—NHCHCO}_2\text{H} & \text{R—NHCH—CO} & \text{R—NHCHCO}_2\text{R}^1 & \text{R—NHCHCO}_2\text{R}^1 \\
| & | \quad \searrow & | & | \\
& \qquad \text{O} \rightarrow & & \\
(\text{CH}_2)_x\text{CO}_2\text{H} & (\text{CH}_2)_x\text{CO} & (\text{CH}_2)_x\text{CO}_2\text{H} \rightarrow & (\text{CH}_2)_x\text{COCl} \\
\text{IX} & \text{X} & \text{XI} & \text{XII}
\end{array}$$

$[\alpha]_D^{23} = +6.0°$ in water) was recovered upon catalytic hydrogenolysis of the latter.

Intermediates which contain blocking substituents other than the carbobenzoxy group have also been utilized for the preparation of glutamine and asparagine. In this connection, previous discussion (Section 10–39) was concerned with the preparation of glutamine via both the reduction of tosyl-L-glutamine (procedure 10–140) with sodium in liquid ammonia and the hydrazinolysis of phthalyl-L-glutamine (procedure 10–172). That DL-asparagine (IV; $x = 1$) may be obtained by the reduction with sodium in liquid ammonia of tosyl-DL-asparagine (III; $R = p\text{-}CH_3C_6H_4SO_2$) was demonstrated by Bovarnick (1001), who procured the latter compound upon treatment of tosyl-DL-aspartic anhydride (X) with benzyl alcohol at 100°, fractionation of the ensuing mixture of α- and β-benzyl esters, and ammonolysis of the tosyl-DL-aspartic acid β-benzyl ester (II; $R^2 = C_6H_5CH_2$) so derived with aqueous ammonia. The same compound (XVI) was secured by Frankel, Liwschitz, and Amiel (556) by the initial conversion of maleic anhydride (XIII) to maleamic acid (XIV) by the action of ammonia in dioxane, treatment of (XIV) with one molecular equivalent of benzylamine

```
CH—CO           CHCO₂H           C₆H₅CH₂NHCHCO₂H      NH₂CHCO₂H
   \                |                    |                    |
    O  —NH₃→        |         →          |          →         |
   /                |                    |                    |
CH—CO           CHCO—NH₂            CH₂CO—NH₂            CH₂CO—NH₂
 XIII              XIV                   XV                  XVI
```

first in boiling dioxane and subsequently in boiling toluene, and, finally, palladium-catalyzed reduction of the N-benzyl-DL-asparagine (XV) resulting from such treatment. L-Asparagine (IV; $x = 1$), on the other hand, was prepared by Weygand, Klinke, and Eigen (576) by the simultaneous deacylation and de-esterification of trifluoroacetyl-L-asparagine ethyl ester (VIII; $R = CF_3CO$, $R^1 = C_2H_5$) with baryta at room temperature; the synthesis of (VIII) was carried out by treating trifluoroacetyl-L-aspartic anhydride (X) with ethanol, converting the β-carboxyl group of the resulting α-ethyl ester (XI; $R = C_2H_5$) to the corresponding acid chloride (XII), and treating the latter with ammonia. A procedure described by Amiard, Heymes, and Velluz (675) for the preparation of L-glutamine (IV; $x = 2$; $[\alpha]_D = +7°$ in water) involved the ammonolysis of trityl-L-glutamic acid γ-methyl ester (II; $R = (C_6H_5)_3C$, $R^2 = CH_3$) with methanolic ammonia, followed by detritylation of the resulting trityl-L-glutamine (III) with warm 50% acetic acid; (II) was obtained by the selective saponification of dibenzyl trityl-L-glutamate (VI; $R^1 = R^2 = C_6H_5CH_2$) with sodium methoxide in methanol, followed by catalytic reduction of the benzyl ester moiety of the trityl-L-glutamic acid α-benzyl ester γ-methyl ester (VI; $R^1 = C_6H_5CH_2$, $R^2 = CH_3$) arising thereby.

One of the simplest and most convenient preparations of L-glutamine (XX) has been described by Akabori and Narita (1002). The method involves the initial conversion of L-glutamic acid (XVII) to its γ-methyl ester (XVIII), treatment of the latter with hydrazine in absolute ethanol and, finally, Raney nickel-induced reduction of the γ-hydrazide of glutamic acid (XIX) so derived. The reaction, which apparently proceeds with the absence of racemization, is depicted in the following (procedure 10–176):

$$\begin{array}{cccc} \text{NH}_2\text{CHCO}_2\text{H} & \text{NH}_2\text{CHCO}_2\text{H} & \text{NH}_2\text{CHCO}_2\text{H} & \text{NH}_2\text{CHCO}_2\text{H} \\ | & \rightarrow \quad | & \rightarrow \quad | & \rightarrow \quad | \\ (\text{CH}_2)_2\text{CO}_2\text{H} & (\text{CH}_2)_2\text{CO}_2\text{CH}_3 & (\text{CH}_2)_2\text{CO}\text{—NHNH}_2 & (\text{CH}_2)_2\text{CO}\text{—NH}_2 \\ \text{XVII} & \text{XVIII} & \text{XIX} & \text{XX} \end{array}$$

Illustrative procedure 10–176 (1002). L-Glutamine. To a suspension of 14 g. of finely powdered γ-methyl L-glutamate (see procedures 10–50 and 10–51) in 40 ml. of absolute ethanol is added 5 g. of hydrazine hydrate. The reaction mixture is warmed gently, and soon after solution is complete the γ-hydrazide of L-glutamic acid begins to crystallize out. Recrystallization is effected from 50% ethanol in an over-all yield of about 90% of theory; m.p. 164°; $[\alpha]_D^{29} = +11.4°$ (5.4% in acetic acid). To 10 g. of the L-glutamic acid γ-hydrazide so derived in 300 ml. of 50% ethanol is added Raney nickel, freshly prepared from 40 g. of Ni-Al (1 : 1). The reaction mixture is refluxed for 30 min., cooled, and the Raney nickel removed by filtration and thoroughly washed with hot water. Treatment of the combined filtrate and washings with a small quantity of dimethylglyoxime, followed by brief warming, results in a disappearance of the blue color of the nickel-glutamine complex and the precipitation of red nickel-dimethylglyoxime. The latter is removed by filtration, the filtrate concentrated to a small volume at a temperature not exceeding 40°, and the concentrate decolorized with a small amount of activated charcoal, filtered, and treated with 2 volumes of ethanol. After storage overnight in the cold, 4.1 g. of L-glutamine may be recovered as tiny needles. Recrystallization is effected from aqueous ethanol; $[\alpha]_D^{13} = +8.6°$ (4.0% in water).

51. O- and N-Phosphoamino Acids and Peptides. *O-Derivatives.* Several proteins, such as vitellin, casein, and pepsin, contain phosphorus in a form that appears as inorganic phosphate when these proteins are hydrolyzed (1003). By methods of partial hydrolysis in acid at 100° it has been determined that much if not all of this phosphorus is bound to certain amino acid residues in the proteins, for isolation procedures from these digests have yielded crystalline preparations of O-phospho-L-serine (1004–1009) and, more recently, of O-phospho-L-threonine (1010). Although hydroxyproline, tyrosine, and hydroxylysine also contain hydroxyl groups, no evidence has yet been brought forward that these compounds at any time have been involved in phosphate linkages, and no samples of these amino acids have yet been isolated which are phosphorylated at the respective hydroxyl groups. It is perhaps significant that natural O-phosphorlyation has involved only amino acids with the hydroxyl in the β-position.

CHEMICAL PROCEDURES FOR SYNTHESIS OF PEPTIDES

However, all the hydroxyamino acids can be synthetically O-phosphorylated by a general procedure first developed by Levene and Schormüller in 1934 (503) (cf. 1011), and later improved by Plimmer (1012). This involved mixing the amino acid with nearly 100% phosphoric acid and phosphorus pentoxide at 100°. A typical preparation is given in procedure 10–177. The reactions involved are, in general terms,

$$\text{HORCH(NH}_2\text{)CO}_2\text{H} + \text{H}_3\text{PO}_4 + \text{P}_2\text{O}_5 \xrightarrow{\Delta} \text{HO}-\underset{\underset{\text{O}}{\|}}{\overset{\overset{\text{ORCH(NH}_2\text{)CO}_2\text{H}}{|}}{\text{P}}}-\text{OH}$$

I   II   III   IV

Illustrative procedure 10–177 (1012). O-Phospho-L-tyrosine. Five grams of L-tyrosine is mixed intimately with 35 g. of phosphoric acid and 5 g. of phosphorous pentoxide, and the mixture heated on the water bath in the absence of moisture for about 1 hr. The syrup on cooling is treated with ice-cold water to 500 ml. A solution of baryta is added to a *p*H of about 8, and the precipitated barium phosphate filtered off. The clear filtrate is evaporated *in vacuo* to about 20 ml., and the condensate treated with ethanol to 60%, resulting in a precipitation of the barium salt of O-phospho-L-tyrosine. This is filtered off, dissolved in the minimum amount of water, and the solution treated with a saturated solution of basic lead acetate until a precipitate no longer forms. The lead salt of O-phospho-L-tyrosine is filtered off, washed with a little ice water, suspended in 100 ml. of water, and decomposed with a stream of H_2S gas to saturation of the medium. Lead sulfide is filtered off with the aid of charcoal, the filtrate condensed *in vacuo* to about 20 ml., and ethanol added to 80%. Free O-phospho-L-tyrosine crystallizes readily and is recrystallized from water-ethanol to obtain the pure product. The O-phospho derivatives of serine, threonine, and hydroxyproline may be prepared by an essentially similar process (1012). The α-amino group does not appear to be affected by this procedure.

The phosphorylating conditions described above are rather severe, and agents more susceptible to control such as the substituted phosphoryl chlorides have generally been preferred. These agents, however, substitute readily at the amino group. Thus, Neuberg and Oertel in 1914 (1013) and Winnick and Scott some time later (1014) found that phosphorus oxychloride reacted with the α-amino group of free amino acids and peptides to form the corresponding N-phosphoro derivatives; the yields were quite low, and the preparation of pure substances was difficult. Better results in terms of yield and purity were obtained when di(alkyl or aryl)phosphorochloridates were employed with the esters of the amino acids (1015, 1016). When diisopropylphosphorochloridate (VI) was treated with excess serine or threonine ester (V), the agent combined preferentially with the amino rather than with the hydroxyl group, and the respective N-diisopropylphosphoroamino acid ester (VII) was formed and isolated in the crystalline state (1017). In refluxing these compounds in 2N HCl an N → O acyl shift occurred, together with hydrolysis of the ester group, and in this way O-phosphoserine (VIII; R = H) and O-phosphothreonine (VIII; R = CH$_3$) were prepared, the yields being relatively small:

$$\text{RCH(OH)CH(NH}_2\text{)CO}_2\text{Et} + \text{(Alk O)}_2\text{POCl} \longrightarrow \text{RCH(OH)CH[(Alk O)}_2\text{OP·NH]CO}_2\text{Et} \xrightarrow[\Delta]{\text{HCl}}$$
$$\text{V} \qquad\qquad \text{VI} \qquad\qquad\qquad \text{VII}$$

$$\text{RCH[O·P(OH)}_2\text{O]CH(NH}_2\text{)CO}_2\text{H} + 2\text{Alk OH}$$
$$\text{VIII} \qquad\qquad\qquad \text{IX}$$

For the O-phosphorylation of hydroxyamino acids while in peptide linkage neither of the two procedures described was at all suitable, for it would not be expected that the peptide linkages would survive the hot acid treatment involved. It was obvious that a minimum of difficulty would be encountered if the amino group could be blocked in some reversible manner, and the phosphorylating agent allowed to react directly on the hydroxyl group. The use of the N-carbobenzoxy group for the former purpose was first described by Posternak and Grafl in 1945 (1018). N-Carbobenzoxy-L-tyrosine ethyl ester was treated in cold pyridine solution with phosphorus oxychloride to yield N-carbobenzoxy-O-phospho-L-tyrosine ethyl ester. The carbobenzoxy group was removed with phosphonium iodide in glacial acetic acid, and the resulting O-phosphotyrosine ethyl ester hydriodide neutralized. Isolation of the compound successively as the barium and lead salts, followed by removal of the latter with H$_2$S gas, saponification of the ester, and subsequent acidification, led finally to the isolation of free O-phosphotyrosine in good yield. Several peptides of O-phosphotyrosine with glycine were successfully prepared by this general procedure (1018). A little over a decade later, Riley, Turnbull, and Wilson (498) applied this procedure to the preparation of O-phosphoserine, O-phosphothreonine, and of peptides thereof, employing diphenylphosphorochloridate as the phosphorylating agent, and dry hydrobromic acid in glacial acetic acid as the agent to remove the N-carbobenzoxy group from the N-carbobenzoxy-O-(diphenylphospho)serine or -threonine ester. Use of the benzyl ester of the amino acid, in place of the ethyl ester, reduced the number of steps involved and permitted through the use of catalytic hydrogen, the simultaneous removal of the N-carbobenzoxy and benzyl ester groups. The process for carbobenzoxylated esters of amino acids (X) and peptides (XV) is

$$\text{HORCH(NHCbzo)CO}_2\text{Et} \xrightarrow{\text{(PhO)}_2\text{PO·Cl}} \text{[O·P(OPh)}_2\text{O]RCH(NHCbzo)CO}_2\text{Et} \xrightarrow{\text{HX+HOAc}}$$
$$\text{X} \qquad\qquad\qquad\qquad\qquad \text{XI}$$

$$\text{[O·P(OPh)}_2\text{O]RCH(NH}_2\text{·HX)CO}_2\text{Et} \xrightarrow[\text{HOAc}]{\text{NaOH}} \text{[O·P(OH)}_2\text{O]RCH(NH}_2\text{)CO}_2\text{H} + 2\text{PhOH}$$
$$\text{XII} \qquad\qquad\qquad\qquad\qquad \text{XIII} \qquad\qquad\qquad \text{XIV}$$

where Cbzo = C$_6$H$_5$CH$_2$OCO, Ph = C$_6$H$_5$, and X = halogen;

HORCH(NHCbzo)CONHCHRCO₂Et $\xrightarrow{(PhO)_2PO \cdot Cl}$
XV

[O·P(OPh)₂O]RCH(NHCbzo)CONHCHRCO₂Et $\xrightarrow{HX+HOAc}$
XVI

[O·P(OPh)₂O]RCH(NH₂·HX)CONHCHRCO₂Et $\xrightarrow[\text{Amberlite IR-120(H}^+)]{\text{NaOH}}$
XVII

[O·P(OH)₂O]RCH(NH₂)CONHCHRCO₂H + PhOH
XVIII   XIVa

Carboxylic esterification of phosphate forms another type of O–P linkage (Section 10–30). This has been achieved synthetically by Black and Wright (1019) in the case of β-L-aspartyl phosphate through the interaction of N-carbobenzoxy-L-aspartyl α-benzyl ester β-acid chloride (XIX) (602) with a mixture of 85% phosphoric acid and trisilver phosphate. On subjecting the resulting N-carbobenzoxy-L-aspartyl α-benzyl ester β-phosphate (XX) to catalytic hydrogenolysis, the desired β-aspartyl phosphate (XXI) could be obtained. This was not isolated but was stored in the solution (at pH 6–7) at −20° from which the palladium black catalyst had been filtered. There is a slow deterioration of the compound in such solutions even under these conditions.

Cbzo—NHCHCO₂CH₂C₆H₅   Cbzo—NHCHCO₂CH₂C₆H₅   NH₂CHCO₂H
         | $\xrightarrow{H_3PO_4}$ | $\xrightarrow{H_2}$ |
    CH₂COCl $\xrightarrow{Ag_3PO_4}$ CH₂CO·OPO₃   Pd   CH₂CO·OPO₃
      XIX   XX   XXI

N-Derivatives. There is no evidence at the present time that N–P linkages occur within the class of phosphoproteins, but this linkage is known to occur in the biologically important, smaller compounds, such as creatine phosphate and arginine phosphate. Indeed, the latter is the only amino acid with an N–P bond which has thus far been encountered in biological material. It is found in the muscles of invertebrates, and it probably fulfills the same role in these tissues as does creatine phosphate in the muscles of vertebrates. From 1 kg. of fresh crab muscle, Meyerhof and Lohmann (1020) were successful in isolating about 300–400 mg. of arginine phosphate as the barium salt, (C₆H₁₄O₅N₄P)₂Ba·2H₂O, with [α]_D for the salt in water = +2.0°, and, after addition of the equivalent amount of HCl to the barium present, = +5.0°. After removal of the barium with the equivalent amount of sulfuric acid, a crystalline picrate with m.p. 205° (d.), or picrolonate with m.p. 233–234° (d.) could be isolated.

The phosphate group is readily cleaved in the presence of excess, dilute mineral acid, particularly if molybdate is present, and this acid-lability is a general characteristic of the N–P bond (1021). Arginine phosphate is apparently quite inert to the action of arginase (1020), but it becomes completely susceptible after treatment with dilute HCl, i.e., after splitting off of the phosphate. On the basis of this phenomenon, Meyerhof and Lohmann were of the opinion that the phosphorus linkage was involved with one of the nitrogen atoms of the guanidino group, the α-amino group of the arginine phosphate being presumably free.

An improved preparation of arginine phosphate was later described by Ennor, Morrison, and Rosenberg (1022) by which some 10 g. of the compound (roughly half of that actually present) was isolated from 1 kg. of fresh crab muscle. The isolated material appeared to possess the empirical formulation, Ba phosphoarginine, H_2CO_3, H_2O, and could be represented as in (XXII).

$$\left[\begin{array}{c} H_2N^+ {=} C \begin{array}{c} NH-\overset{\overset{O}{\|}}{P}-O^- \\ | \\ O^- \end{array} \\ NH \\ | \\ (CH_2)_3 \\ | \\ CHNH_3^+ \\ | \\ COO^- \end{array}\right] Ba^{2+}, HCO_3^-$$

XXII

As noted above, early attempts to synthesize compounds of amino acids with phosphoric acid involved the interaction of the former with phosphorus oxychloride in aqueous medium. An excess of magnesium oxide was invariably present, and the products were isolated as amorphous magnesium salts, in low yield, and with elemental analyses which revealed the expected compositions in only quite approximate terms. Tyrosine, glycine, alanine, and glutamic acid were among the amino acids studied in this connection (1013, 1014). The subsequent use by Sciarini and Fruton (1015) of diphenylphosphorochloridate with the esters (XXIII) of such amino acids as glycine, DL-phenylalanine, and L-glutamic acid led to the isolation of crystalline, well-characterized products (XXIV). In this reaction, the free

$$RCH(NH_2)CO_2Et \xrightarrow{(PhO)_2PO \cdot Cl} RCH[NH \cdot PO(PhO)_2]CO_2Et$$
XXIII XXIV

amino acid ester in ethyl acetate solution was treated, mole per mole, with diphenylphosphorochloridate, the HCl released being neutralized with aqueous sodium bicarbonate. After the ethyl acetate layer was washed, it was dried and concentrated, and the reaction product crystallized by addition of petroleum ether; the melting points of the respective derivatives of the ethyl esters of the three amino acids mentioned above were 77–78°, 78–79°, and 73.5–74° (1015). Attempts to saponify these esters with a slight excess of sodium hydroxide revealed only the very considerable stability of the ester groups in these compounds, for in each case the unchanged starting material was recovered. More vigorous treatment with alkali gave mixtures of products which could not be separated satisfactorily.

Much the same results were subsequently noted by Wagner-Jauregg, O'Neill, and Summerson (1016), who used diisopropylphosphorochloridate as the phosphorylating agent with various amino acid esters. In these studies, as in those of Paplinger and Wagner-Jauregg (1017) which followed, an excess of the amino acid ester was present, the excess being employed to neutralize the HCl formed in the reaction. The respective derivatives with the ethyl esters of glycine and of serine melted at 28–29° and 48–50°, and with the methyl ester of threonine at 54–56° (1016, 1017). The use of alkali with these compounds was again unsuccessful; with $2N$ HCl, as noted above, the P–N bond was split, but in the case of the serine and threonine derivatives an N → O shift occurred and the liberated phosphate group anchored to the respective β-oxygen atoms (VII → VIII).

Some years earlier, Zervas (1023) had suggested the use of silver dibenzyl phosphate as a phosphorylating agent for certain halogenated derivatives of the sugars, the particular effectiveness of the agent being due to the ready, subsequent removal of the benzyl groups from the dibenzylphosphorylated compound by means of catalytic hydrogenolysis. On the basis of this suggestion, Atherton, Openshaw, and Todd (756) developed the use of dibenzylphosphorochloridate as an agent particularly suitable for the phosphorylation of amines. With this agent, Li (1024) prepared the N-dibenzylphosphoro derivatives of a number of amino acid esters, but only with those of DL-phenylalanine methyl ester and DL-tryptophan methyl ester was it seemingly possible, by means of catalytic hydrogenolysis (H_2 and PdO_2), to remove the benzyl groups. In this fashion, N-phospho-DL-phenylalanine methyl ester (m.p. 143–145°), and N-phospho-DL-tryptophan methyl ester (m.p. 130–132°) were prepared. It was still impossible, however, to saponify the ester groups of these compounds so as to obtain the free N-phosphoamino acids, and Li suggested that perhaps the use of the benzyl esters of the amino acids might remove this curious complication. It appeared therefore that, although it was quite possible to arrive synthetically at O-phosphoamino acids and peptides, the preparation of N-phosphoamino acids and peptides might prove to be a more difficult task.

A solution to the latter problem was offered in 1955 by Zervas and Katsoyannis (914) and by Zervas and Dilaris (1025). These investigators proposed a general procedure for the synthesis of N-phosphoamino acids and peptides through the employment of the new phosphorylating agents, di-*p*-nitrobenzylphosphorochloridate and di-*p*-iodobenzylphosphorochloridate. The compounds were treated with an excess of various amino acid esters in chloroform solution, the precipitated ester·HCl removed, and the washed and subsequently dried chloroform solution condensed; addition of hexane to the condensate resulted in separation of the respective products. Saponification of the carboxyl ester group in ethanolic alkali was followed by removal of the *p*-substituted benzyl groups in the same solvent through catalytic hydrogenation. In those instances where the benzyl ester of the amino acid or peptide was used, saponification of the coupled product prior to hydrogenation was unnecessary, and removal of all the benzyl groups could be accomplished in a single step in alcoholic trimethylamine solution.

$$\text{RCH[NH·PO}(C_6H_4XCH_2O)_2]CO_2CH_2C_6H_5 \xrightarrow[(CH_3)_3N]{H_2,\ Pd} \text{RCH(NH·PO·O}^-\cdot\text{OH)COO}^-\cdot Ba^{2+}$$
$$\text{XXV} \hspace{6cm} \text{XXVI}$$

where X = I or NO_2.

The appropriate phosphorylating reagents employed in the above reactions were prepared by heating the corresponding triester of phosphoric acid with barium or sodium iodide for a short time (1025) to yield the diester, which subsequently was treated with phosphorus pentachloride to give the phosphoryl chloride. The triester employed as starting material had been prepared by the interaction of silver phosphate with the appropriate *p*-substituted benzyl halide. The action of the *p*-iodobenzyl derivative on glycine benzyl ester gave a good yield of N-di(*p*-iodobenzyl)phosphoroglycine benzyl ester (XXV; R = H), m.p. 89°. On catalytic hydrogenation, pure N-phosphoglycine as the barium salt (XXVI; R = H) was obtained in a yield of 90% (914). L-Tyrosine and glycyl-L-tyrosine as the respective ethyl esters reacted with the *p*-iodobenzyl derivative to give good yields of the N-di(*p*-iodobenzyl)-phosphoroamino acid or peptide ester, with m.p. 143° and 127–128°, respectively. On saponification of the carboxylic ester group by standing for 15 minutes in 0.1*N* ethanolic sodium hydroxide, followed directly by catalytic hydrogenation in the presence of palladium black to remove the substituted benzyl groups, N-phospho-L-tyrosine and N-phosphoglycyl-L-tyrosine were formed and isolated in the pure state as the respective barium salts by the employment of barium iodide in methanol saturated with barium hydroxide. The respective yields were 85 and 95%. The pure barium salt of N-phosphoglycylglycine (yield 80%) was prepared from N-di(*p*-nitrobenzyl)phosphoroglycylglycine ethyl ester (m.p. 112–113°) in a similar manner (914). Table 10–48 lists several varieties of O- and N-phosphorylated amino acids and peptides.

52. Benzoylamino Acids. The extensive use of benzoylamino acids for characterization purposes, as well as for starting materials in the synthesis of benzoylated peptides employed in enzyme specificity studies, may be

TABLE 10-48
O-Phosphoamino Acids and Peptides

Compound	M.P., °C.	$[\alpha]_D$, deg.	Ref.
O-Phospho-L-serine (Ba salt)	–	+8.2 (10% HCl)	1004
O-Phospho-L-serine	167	+7.2 (H_2O)	1009
O-Phospho-DL-serine	166–167	–	1017
O-Phospho-L-serine (Ba salt)	–	+9.4 (10% HCl)	503
O-Phospho-DL-serine (Ba salt)	165–166	–	1012
O-Phospho-DL-serine	165–166	–	498
O-Phospho-L-serine (Ba salt)	–	+5.5 (HCl)	498
O-Phospho-L-serine	175–176	–	498
O-Phospho-DL-serylglycine	150–154	–	498
O-Phospho-L-seryl-L-glutamic acid	145–147	–	498
O-Phospho-DL-threonine	150–152	–	498
O-Phospho-L-threonine	–	−7.4 (H_2O)	1010
O-Phospho-L-tyrosine	225	−9.2 (2N HCl)	1012
O-Phospho-L-tyrosine	227	−8.8 (2N HCl)	1018
O-Phospho-L-hydroxyproline (anhydrous)	130–131	−28.8 (H_2O)	1012
O-Phospho-L-hydroxyproline (Ba salt)	–	−13.3 (10% HCl)	503
Glycyl-O-phospho-L-tyrosine	224–225	+27.9 (N H_2SO_4)	1018
O-Phospho-L-tyrosylglycine	178	+20.0 (N H_2SO_4)	1018
O-Phospho-L-tyrosylglycylglycine	182	+7.5 (N H_2SO_4)	1018
Glycyl-O-phospho-L-tyrosylglycine	198	+8.0 (N H_2SO_4)	1018

attributed both to the facility with which these compounds can be prepared and to their favorable crystallization properties. Preparation of a benzoylamino acid from the parent amino acid is most conveniently achieved via a Schotten-Baumann type reaction wherein benzoyl chloride is the acylating agent. Directions generally applicable to the benzoylation of a monoaminomonocarboxylic acid are detailed in procedure 10–178. Suitable modification of the procedure permits its extension to amino acids which incorporate more than one acidic or basic function; as the carbobenzoxylation of the more complex amino acids (Section 10–14) discussed earlier applies equally well here, no further elaboration is required.

Illustrative procedure 10–178. Benzoylation of α-amino acids. A solution of 0.1 mole of the pertinent amino acid in 60 ml. of 2N sodium hydroxide is chilled in an ice bath and treated with a total of 15 g. (0.11 mole) of benzoyl chloride and 60 ml. of 2N sodium hydroxide, in 10 equal and alternate portions, with vigorous intermittent shaking and cooling in an ice bath; the solution should be continually maintained at an alkaline pH by the addition of extra alkali when necessary. Upon completion of the addition of reagents, the reaction mixture is shaken for 15 min. at room temperature and then acidified to Congo red, with cooling, by dropwise treatment with concentrated hydrochloric acid. After some 2 hr. of storage at 4°, the precipitate is recovered by filtration, washed several times with ice water, and permitted to dry in the air overnight. Contaminating benzoic acid is removed from the product by boiling with 30–40 ml. of carbon tetrachloride for several minutes and subsequently filtering the slightly cooled mixture. Final purification of the residual material is effected by crystallization from ethanol-water or some other suitable medium. Yields in excess of 80% of theory are generally obtained.

Table 10–49 lists several of the more common benzoylamino acids which have been previously described.

REFERENCES

1. Fischer, E., *Ber.*, **39**, 530 (1906).
2. Braconnot, H., *Ann. chim. phys.*, [2] **13**, 113 (1820).
3. Hofmeister, F., *Ergeb. Physiol.*, I. Abt. Biochemie, p. 759 (1902).
4. Pauling, L., *Record Chem. Progr.*, **12**, 155 (1951).
5. Synge, R. L. M., *Quart. Revs. (London)*, **3**, 245 (1949).
6. Editorial Report on Nomenclature, *J. Chem. Soc.*, **1952**, 5075, 5089.
7. Brand, E., *Ann. N.Y. Acad. Sci.*, **47**, 189 (1946).
8. Sanger, F., *Advances in Protein Chem.*, **7**, 1 (1952).
9. Hopkins, F. G., *J. Biol. Chem.*, **84**, 269 (1929).
10. Harington, C. R., and Mead, T. H., *Biochem. J.*, **29**, 1602 (1935).
11. du Vigneaud, V., and Miller, G. L., *J. Biol. Chem.*, **116**, 469 (1936).
12. Hopkins, F. G., *Biochem. J.*, **15**, 286 (1921).
13. Mowat, J. H., Boothe, J. H., Hutchings, B. L., Stokstad, E. L. R., Waller, C. W., Angier, R. B., Semb, J., Casulich, D. B., and Subba Row, Y., *Ann. N.Y. Acad. Sci.*, **48**, 279 (1946).
14. Stokstad, E. L. R., Hutchings, B. L., and Subba Row, Y., *Ann. N.Y. Acad. Sci.*, **48**, 261 (1946).
15. Stokstad, E. L. R., Hutchings, B. L., Mowat, J. H., Boothe, J. H., Waller, C. W., Angier, R. B., Semb, J., Casulich, D. B., and Subba Row, Y., *Ann. N.Y. Acad. Sci.*, **48**, 269 (1946).
16. Hutchings, B. L., Stokstad, E. L. R., Bohonos, N., Sloane, N., and Subba Row, Y., *Ann. N.Y. Acad. Sci.*, **48**, 265 (1946).
17. Pfiffner, J. J., Calkins, D. G., Bloom, E. S., and O'Dell, B. L., *J. Am. Chem. Soc.*, **68**, 1392 (1946).
18. Pfiffner, J. J., Calkins, D. G., O'Dell, B. L., Bloom, E. S., Brown, R. A., Campbell, C. J., and Bird, O. D., *Science*, **102**, 228 (1945).
19. Rinderknecht, H., *Chem. & Ind.*, **1957**, 1384; Rinderknecht, H., Thomas, D., and Aslin, S., *Helv. Chim. Acta*, **41**, 1 (1958).
19a. Morris, C. J., and Thompson, J. F., *Arch. Biochem. Biophys.*, **73**, 281 (1958).
20. Dekker, C. A., Stone, D., and Fruton, J. S., *J. Biol. Chem.*, **181**, 719 (1949).
20a. Shiba, T., Imai, S., and Kaneko, T., *Bull. Chem. Soc. Japan*, **31**, 244 (1958).
21. Ohira, T., *J. Agr. Chem. Soc. Japan*, **16**, 293 (1940).
22. Kaneko, T., Shiba, T., Watarai, S., Imai, S., Shimada, T., and Ueno, K., *Chem. & Ind.*, **1957**, 986.
22a. Virtanen, A. I., and Ettala, T., *Acta Chem. Scand.*, **12**, 787 (1958).

TABLE 10-49
Benzoylamino Acids

Benzoylamino Acid	M.P., °C.	$[\alpha]_D$, deg.	Temp., °C	Concn. and Solvent	Ref.
DL-Alanine	165–166	—	—	—	1026, 1027
D-Alanine	150–151	−37.3[a]	20	—, H$_2$O + 1 eq. KOH	1027
L-Alanine	150–151	+37.1	20	9.3%, H$_2$O + 1 eq. KOH	1027
DL-Arginine (α-mono-)	315 d.	—	—	—	1028
DL-Arginine (α,ω-di-)	230	—	—	—	848
L-Arginine (α-mono-)	298 d.	−8.1	20	1.2%, H$_2$O + 1 eq. HCl	1029
L-Arginine (α,ω-di-)	244	+10.3	20	7%, 0.2M NaOH	142
DL-Aspartic acid	164–165[b]	—	—	—	1027, 1030
D-Aspartic acid	184–185	−37.6	20	10%, H$_2$O + 2 eq. KOH	1027
L-Aspartic acid	184–185	+37.4	20	9%, H$_2$O + 2 eq. KOH	1027
DL-Asparagine	190–192	—	—	—	589
DL-Cysteine	137	—	—	—	1031
DL-Cystine (bis-)	165–166	—	—	—	1031
L-Cystine (bis-)	195–196	−222	20	—, EtOH	1032
DL-Glutamic acid	155–157	—	—	—	1027
D-Glutamic acid	130–132	−18.7	20	10%, H$_2$O + 2 eq. KOH	1027

TABLE 10-47 (continued)

Benzoylamino Acid	M.P., °C.	$[\alpha]_D$, deg.	Temp., °C.	Concn. and Solvent	Ref.
L-Glutamic acid	137–139[c]	+17.2	20	10%, H_2O + 2 eq. KOH	1027
Glycine	187.5	—	—	—	1033
DL-Histidine	248 d.	—	—	—	1034
L-Histidine·H_2O	249	−47.4	20	—, 0.5M HCl	297, 1035, 1036
DL-Hydroxylysine (di-)	139–141	—	—	—	1037
D-Hydroxylysine (di-)	168–170	−4.0	25	1%, EtOH	1037, 1038
D-Allohydroxylysine lactone (di-)	196–198	—	—	—	1038
L-Hydroxylysine (di-)	172	—	—	—	1037
DL-Isoleucine	138–139	—	—	—	1039
DL-Alloisoleucine	118–119	—	—	—	1039
L-Isoleucine	116–117	+26.4	20	7.5%, 0.5M NaOH	1040
DL-Leucine	137–141	—	—	—	1041
D-Leucine	105–107	−6.4	20	9.5%, 0.5M KOH	1040, 1041
L-Leucine	105–107	+6.6	20	9.5%, 0.5M KOH	1040, 1041
DL-Lysine (α-mono-)	211[d]	—	—	—	854, 1042
DL-Lysine (ε-mono-)	268–270	—	—	—	1043, 1044
DL-Lysine (α,ε-di-)	145–146	—	—	—	1043, 1045
L-Lysine (α-mono-)	250 d.	+21.6	25	—, H_2O + 1 eq. NaOH	1046
L-Lysine (ε-mono-)	240 d.	+20.1[e]	19	1.9%, N HCl	1047, 1048
L-Lysine (α,ε-di-)	149–150	+3.1[f]	20	3.2%, 0.1N NaOH	1047
DL-Methionine	151	—	—	—	1049

DL-Ornithine (α,δ-di-)	187–188	–	–	–	238
L-Ornithine (α,δ-di-)	187–188	+8.8	–	10%, H_2O + 1 eq. KOH	142
DL-Phenylalanine	187–188	–	–	–	1050
D-Phenylalanine	145–146	−17.1	20	6.5%, N KOH	1050
L-Proline	158–159	−100.5	25	0.2%, EtOH	1039
DL-Serine	171	–	–	–	1051
L-Serine	147–149	+43.6	22	1%, EtOH	1031
DL-Threonine	143–144	–	–	–	1052
DL-Allothreonine	175–176	–	–	–	1052
D-Threonine	147–148	–	–	–	1052
L-Threonine	143–144[g]	+27.1	21	0.8%, H_2O	1053
DL-Tryptophan	193–194	–	–	–	1054
L-Tryptophan	104–105	–	–	–	659
DL-Tyrosine	195–197	–	–	–	1055
D-Tyrosine	165.5	−19.6	20	7.7%, H_2O + 1 eq. KOH	1055
L-Tyrosine	165–166	+19.3	20	8%, H_2O + 1 eq. KOH	1055
DL-Valine	132.5	–	–	–	152
L-Valine	131–132	+21.8	25	4.9%, EtOH	1056

[a] $[\alpha]_D^{20} = -3.3°$ (1% in water) (1027).
[b] M.p. = 172° (1030).
[c] Compound premelts at 128°.
[d] M.p. = 227–229° (1042).
[e] $[\alpha]_D = +27.2°$ (2.2% in 50% acetic acid) (1048).
[f] $[\alpha]_D^{15} = -8.6°$ (20% in methanol) (1047).
[g] M.p. = 147–148° (1052).

23. Hall, L. M., and Cohen, P. P., *Federation Proc.*, **15**, 266 (1956).
24. Hall, L. M., Metzenberg, R. L., and Cohen, P. P., *Nature*, **178**, 1468 (1956).
25. Tallan, H. H., Moore, S., and Stein, W. H., *J. Biol. Chem.*, **219**, 257 (1956).
26. Salkowski, E., and Salkowski, H., *Ber.*, **12**, 653 (1879).
27. Thierfelder, H., and Sherwin, C. P., *Ber.*, **47**, 2630 (1914).
28. Totani, G., *Z. physiol. Chem.*, **68**, 75 (1910).
29. von Liebig, J., *Ann. Physik*, **17**, Ser. 2, 389 (1829).
30. Henneberg, W., Stohmann, F., and Rautenberg, F., *Ann.*, **124**, 181 (1862).
31. Jaffe, M., *Ber.*, **10**, 1925 (1877); **11**, 406 (1878).
32. Ellinger, A., *Z. physiol. Chem.*, **29**, 334 (1900).
33. Jaffe, M., *Ber.*, **12**, 1092 (1879).
34. Baumann, E., and Preusse, C., *Z. physiol. Chem.*, **5**, 309 (1881).
35. Stoll, A., Hofmann, A., and Petrzilka, T., *Helv. Chim. Acta*, **34**, 1544 (1951).
36. Nelson, E. E., and Calvery, H. O., *Physiol. Revs.*, **18**, 297 (1938).
37. Guggisberg, H., *Mutterkorn, vom Gift zum Heilstoff*, S. Karger, Basel, 1954.
38. Birkinshaw, J. H., Raistrick, H., and Smith, G., *Biochem. J.*, **36**, 829 (1942).
39. Plattner, P. A., and Clauson-Kass, N., *Experientia*, **1**, 195 (1945).
40. Woolley, D. W., *J. Biol. Chem.*, **176**, 1291, 1299 (1948).
41. Plattner, P. A., and Clauson-Kass, N., *Helv. Chim. Acta*, **28**, 188 (1945).
41a. Brenner, M., Tamm, R., and Quitt, P., *Helv. Chim. Acta*, **41**, 763 (1958).
42. Wolf, D. E., Valiant, J., Peck, R. L., and Folkers, K., *J. Am. Chem. Soc.*, **74**, 2002 (1952).
43. Wright, L. D., Cresson, E. L., Skeggs, H. R., Wood, T. R., Peck, R. L., Wolf, D. E., and Folkers, K., *J. Am. Chem. Soc.*, **74**, 1996 (1952).
44. Baumann, L., and Ingvaldsen, T., *J. Biol. Chem.*, **35**, 263 (1918).
45. Barger, G., and Tutin, F., *Biochem. J.*, **12**, 402 (1918).
46. Gulewitsch, W., and Amiradzibi, S., *Ber.*, **33**, 1902 (1900).
47. Gulewitsch, W., and Amiradzibi, S., *Z. physiol. Chem.*, **30**, 565 (1900).
48. Linneweh, W., Keil, A. W., and Hoppe-Seyler, F. A., *Z. physiol. Chem.*, **183**, 11 (1924).
49. Linneweh, W., and Linneweh, F., *Z. physiol. Chem.*, **189**, 80 (1930).
50. Behrens, O. K., and du Vigneaud, V., *J. Biol. Chem.*, **120**, 517 (1937).
51. Ackermann, D., Timpe, O., and Poller, K., *Z. physiol. Chem.*, **183**, 1 (1929).
52. Kendo, K., *J. Biochem.*, **36**, 265 (1942).
53. Ono, T., and Hirohata, R., *Z. physiol. Chem.*, **304**, 77 (1956).
54. Imamura, H., *J. Biochem.*, **30**, 479 (1939).
55. Sobotka, H., *The Chemistry of the Sterids*, Williams and Wilkins Co., Baltimore, 1938.
56. Waley, S. G., *Proc. Chem. Soc.*, 25 (1957).
57. Waley, S. G., *Biochem. J.*, **64**, 715 (1956).
58. Waley, S. G., *Biochem. J.*, **67**, 172 (1957); **68**, 189 (1958).
59. Elliott, D. F., and Peart, W. S., *Nature*, **177**, 572 (1956).
60. Peart, W. S., *Biochem. J.*, **62**, 520 (1956).
61. Lentz, K. E., Skeggs, L. T., Woods, K. R., Kahn, J. R., and Shumway, N. P., *J. Exptl. Med.*, **104**, 183 (1956).
62. Skeggs, L. T., Lentz, K. E., Kahn, J. R., Shumway, N. P., and Woods, K. R., *J. Exptl. Med.*, **104**, 193 (1956).
63. Skeggs, L. T., Marsh, W. H., Kahn, J. R., and Shumway, N. P., *J. Exptl. Med.*, **99**, 275 (1954); Skeggs, L. T., Kahn, J. R., and Shumway, N. P., *ibid.*, **103**, 295, 301 (1956).
64. Fischer, E., and Reif, G., *Ann.*, **363**, 118 (1908).
65. Wintersteiner, O., and Pfiffner, J. J., *J. Biol. Chem.*, **111**, 599 (1935).

66. Butenandt, A., Karlson, P., and Zillig, W., *Z. physiol. Chem.*, **288**, 279 (1951).
67. Wieland, T., and Schön, W., *Ann.*, **593**, 157 (1955).
68. Lynen, F., and Wieland, V., *Ann.*, **533**, 93 (1937).
69. Wieland, H., and Witkop, B., *Ann.*, **543**, 171 (1940).
69a. Heinemann, B., Gourevitch, A. G., Lein, J., Johnson, D. L., Kaplan, M. A., Vanas, D., and Hooper, I. R., *Antibiotics Ann.*, **2**, 728 (1954–1955); Haskell, T. H., Maretzki, A., and Bartz, Q. R., *ibid.*, **2**, 784 (1954–1955); Sheehan, J. C., Zachau, H. G., and Lawson, W. B., *J. Am. Chem. Soc.*, **80**, 3349 (1958).
70. Consden, R., Gordon, A., Martin, A. J. P., and Synge, R. L. M., *Biochem. J.*, **41**, 596 (1947).
71. Battersby, A. R., and Craig, L. C., *J. Am. Chem. Soc.*, **73**, 1887 (1951).
72. Sanger, F., *Biochem. J.*, **40**, 261 (1946).
73. Gause, G. F., and Brazhnikova, M. G., *Sovyetskü, Gramistidin i lecheniye ran. Medgiz.*, Moscow (1943).
74. Paladini, A., and Craig, L. C., *J. Am. Chem. Soc.*, **76**, 688 (1954).
75. Battersby, A. R., cited in King, T. P., and Craig, L. C., *J. Am. Chem. Soc.*, **77**, 6627 (1955).
76. Hotchkiss, R. D., and Dubos, R. J., *J. Biol. Chem.*, **136**, 803 (1940); **141**, 155 (1941).
77. Biserte, B. G., and Dautrevaux, M., *Compt. rend.*, **242**, 1801 (1956).
78. Wilkinson, S., *Nature*, **164**, 622 (1949); Long, P. H., ed., *Ann. N.Y. Acad. Sci.*, **51**, Art. 5 (1949).
79. Vining, L. C., and Taber, W. A., *Can. J. Chem.*, **35**, 1109 (1957).
80. du Vigneaud, V., Ressler, C., and Trippett, S., *J. Biol. Chem.*, **205**, 949 (1953).
81. Tuppy, H., and Michl, H., *Monatsh. Chem.*, **84**, 1011 (1953).
82. du Vigneaud, V., Ressler, C., Swan, J. M., Roberts, C. W., and Katsoyannis, P. G., *J. Am. Chem. Soc.*, **76**, 3115 (1954).
83. Ott, I., and Scott, J., *J. Exptl. Med.*, **11**, 326 (1909).
84. Dale, H. H., *Biochem. J.*, **4**, 427 (1909).
85. Turner, R. A., Pierce, J. G., and du Vigneaud, V., *J. Biol. Chem.*, **191**, 21 (1951).
86. Popenoe, E. A., Lawler, H. C., and du Vigneaud, V., *J. Am. Chem. Soc.*, **74**, 3713 (1952).
87. du Vigneaud, V., Lawler, H. C., and Popenoe, E. A., *J. Am. Chem. Soc.*, **75**, 4880 (1953).
88. Bartlett, M. F., Jöhl, A., Roeske, R., Stedman, R. J., Stewart, F. H. C., Ward, D. N., and du Vigneaud, V., *J. Am. Chem. Soc.*, **78**, 2905 (1956).
89. Oliver, G., and Schäfer, A. E., *J. Physiol.*, **18**, 277 (1895).
90. Clarke, H. T., Johnson, J. R., and Robinson, R., eds., *The Chemistry of Penicillin*, Princeton Univ. Press, Princeton, N.J., 1949.
91. Fleming, A., *Brit. J. Exptl. Pathol.*, **10**, 226 (1929).
92. Hidy, P. H., Hodge, E. B., Young, V. V., Harned, R. L., Brewer, G. A., Phillips, W. F., Runge, W. F., Stavely, H. E., Pohland, A., Boaz, H., and Sullivan, H. R., *J. Am. Chem. Soc.*, **77**, 2345 (1955).
93. Buhs, R. P., Potter, I., Ormond, I., Lyons, J. E., Chaiet, L., Kuehl, F. A., Wolf, F. J., Trenner, N. R., Peck, R. L., Howe, E., Hunnewell, B. D., Downing, G., Newstead, E., and Folkers, K., *J. Am. Chem. Soc.*, **77**, 2344 (1955).
94. Schaal, E., *Ann.*, **157**, 26 (1871).
95. Grimaux, E., *Bull. soc. chim.*, **38**, 64 (1882).
96. Curtius, T., *Ber.*, **16**, 755 (1883).
97. Curtius, T., *Ber.*, **37**, 1284 (1904).
98. Schiff, H., *Ber.*, **30**, 2449 (1897); *Ann.*, **303**, 183 (1898); **307**, 231 (1899).
99. Schützenberger, P., *Compt. rend.*, **106**, 1407 (1888); **112**, 198 (1891).
100. Lilienfeld, L., *Arch. Physiol.*, 383, 555 (1894).

101. Balbiano, L., and Trasciatti, D., *Ber.*, **33**, 2323 (1900); Balbiano, L., *ibid.*, **34**, 1501 (1901); *Gazz. chim. ital.*, **32**, 410 (1902).
102. Leuchs, H., *Ber.*, **39**, 857 (1906).
103. Fischer, E., and Forneau, E., *Ber.*, **34**, 2868 (1901).
104. Wessely, F., *Z. physiol. Chem.*, **146**, 72 (1925).
105. Frankel, M., and Katchalski, E., *J. Am. Chem. Soc.*, **64**, 2264 (1942).
106. Frankel, M., and Katchalski, E., *Nature*, **144**, 330 (1939).
107. Frankel, M., and Katchalski, E., *J. Am. Chem. Soc.*, **64**, 2268 (1942).
108. Pacsu, E., *Nature*, **144**, 551 (1939).
109. Pacsu, E., and Wilson, E. J., *J. Org. Chem.*, **7**, 117 (1942).
110. Wilson, E. J., and Pacsu, E., *J. Org. Chem.*, **7**, 126 (1942).
111. Woodward, R. B., and Schramm, C. H., *J. Am. Chem. Soc.*, **69**, 1551 (1947).
112. Katchalski, E., *Advances in Protein Chem.*, **6**, 123 (1951).
113. Bamford, C. H., Elliott, A., and Hanby, W. E., *Synthetic Polypeptides*, Academic Press, New York, 1956.
114. Curtius, T., *J. prakt. Chem.*, **26**, 175 (1882).
115. Curtius, T., *Ber.*, **35**, 3226 (1902).
116. Curtius, T., and Lambotte, E., *J. prakt. Chem.*, **70**, 109 (1904).
117. Curtius, T., and Levy, L., *J. prakt. Chem.*, **70**, 89 (1904).
118. Curtius, T., and Curtius, H., *J. prakt. Chem.*, **70**, 158 (1904).
119. Curtius, T., and Gumlich, O., *J. prakt. Chem.*, **70**, 195 (1904).
120. Fischer, E., *Ber.*, **36**, 2094 (1903).
121. Fischer, E., and Otto, E., *Ber.*, **36**, 2106 (1903).
122. Greenstein, J. P., in *The Chemistry of the Amino Acids and Proteins*, Charles C. Thomas, Springfield, Ill., 2nd ed., p. 252, 1944.
123. Bergmann, M., Stern, F., and Witte, C., *Ann.* **449**, 277 (1926).
124. Bergmann, M., and Köster, H., *Z. physiol. Chem.*, **167**, 91 (1927).
125. Bergmann, M., Zervas, L., and du Vigneaud, V., *Ber.*, **62**, 1905 (1929).
126. Fischer, E., *Ber.*, **48**, 93 (1915).
127. Schoenheimer, R., *Z. physiol. Chem.*, **154**, 203 (1926).
128. Bergmann, M., and Zervas, L., *Ber.*, **65**, 1192 (1932).
129. Bergmann, M., and Fruton, J. S., *Advances in Enzymol.*, **1**, 63 (1941).
130. Bergmann, M., *Advances in Enzymol.*, **2**, 49 (1942).
131. Neurath, H., and Schwert, G. W., *Chem. Revs.*, **46**, 69 (1950).
132. Smith, E. L., in *The Enzymes*, Vol. I, Part 2, Academic Press, New York, p. 793, 1951.
133. Colowick, S. P., and Kaplan, N. O., eds., *Methods in Enzymology*, Vol. II, Academic Press, New York, pp. 3–423, 1955.
134. Marvel, C. S., and Horning, E. C., in *Organic Chemistry*, Vol. I, John Wiley and Sons, New York, 2nd ed., p. 701, 1942.
135. Kohler, H., *Ann.*, **134**, 369 (1865).
136. Kovacs, J., Könyves, I., and Pusztai, A., *Experientia*, **9**, 459 (1953).
137. Maillard, L. C., *Ann. chim.*, **1**, 519 (1914); **2**, 210 (1914).
138. Meyer, K. H., and Go, V., *Helv. Chim. Acta*, **17**, 1488 (1934).
139. Baniel, A., Frankel, M., Friedrich, I., and Katchalski, E., *J. Org. Chem.*, **13**, 791 (1948).
140. Shibata, K., *Acta phytochim.* (*Tokyo*), **2**, 39 (1925).
141. Fischer, E., and Suzuki, U., *Ber.*, **38**, 4173 (1905).
142. Zervas, L., and Bergmann, M., *Ber.*, **61**, 1195 (1928).
143. Fischer, E., and Koenigs, E., *Ber.*, **37**, 4585 (1904).
144. Fischer, E., and Koenigs, E., *Ber.*, **40**, 2048 (1907).
145. Fischer, E., and Suzuki, U., *Z. physiol. Chem.*, **45**, 405 (1905).

146. Bouveault, L., and Locquin, R., *Compt. rend.*, **141**, 115 (1905).
147. Hugonenq, L., and Morel, A., *Compt. rend.*, **140**, 505 (1905).
148. Bouveault, L., and Locquin, R., *Bull. soc. chim.*, **31**, 1180 (1904).
149. Adamson, D. W., *J. Chem. Soc.*, **1943**, 39.
150. Katchalski, E., Grossfeld, I., and Frankel, M., *J. Am. Chem. Soc.*, **68**, 879 (1946).
151. Fischer, E., *Ber.*, **34**, 433 (1901).
152. Slimmer, M. D., *Ber.*, **35**, 401 (1902).
153. Edlbacher, S., and Bonem, P., *Z. physiol. Chem.*, **145**, 69 (1925).
154. Kossel, A., and Staudt, W., *Z. physiol. Chem.*, **170**, 91 (1927).
155. Waldschmidt-Leitz, E., Schäffner, A., Schlatter, H., and Klein, W., *Ber.*, **61**, 299 (1928).
156. Fischer, E., *Ber.*, **39**, 453 (1906).
157. Fischer, E., *Ber.*, **39**, 2893 (1906).
158. Abderhalden, E., and Fodor, A., *Ber.*, **49**, 561 (1916).
159. Rees, P. S., Tong, D. P., and Young, G. T., *J. Chem. Soc.*, **1954**, 662.
160. Brockmann, H., Tummes, H., and von Metzsch, F. A., *Naturwiss.*, **41**, 37 (1954).
161. Ruggli, P., *Ann.*, **392**, 92 (1912).
162. Sluyterman, L. A., and Veenendaal, H. I., *Rec. trav. chim.*, **71**, 137 (1952).
163. Sluyterman, L. A., and Kooistra, M., *Rec. trav. chim.*, **71**, 277 (1952).
164. Brockmann, H., and Musso, H., *Chem. Ber.*, **87**, 581 (1954).
165. Rydon, H. N., and Smith, P. W. G., *J. Chem. Soc.*, **1955**, 2542.
166. Schramm, G., and Restle, H., *Makromol. Chem.*, **13**, 117 (1954).
167. Edsall, J. T., *J. Polymer Sci.*, **12**, 253 (1954).
168. Abderhalden, E., and Nienburg, H., *Fermentforsch.*, **13**, 573 (1933).
169. Smith, E. L., and Bergmann, M., *J. Biol. Chem.*, **153**, 627 (1944).
170. Rydon, H. N., and Smith, P. W. G., *J. Chem. Soc.*, **1956**, 3642; Smith, P. W. G., *ibid.*, **1957**, 3985.
171. Fischer, E., *Ber.*, **35**, 1095 (1902).
172. Bopp, H., *Ann.*, **69**, 28 (1849).
173. Hesse, O., and Limpricht, H., *Ann.*, **116**, 201 (1860).
174. Preu, I., *Ann.*, **134**, 372 (1865).
175. Erlenmeyer, E., and Lipp, A., *Ann.*, **219**, 179 (1883).
176. Mylius, F., *Ber.*, **17**, 286 (1884).
177. Meyer, P. J., *Ber.*, **10**, 1967 (1877).
178. Sannié, C., *Bull. soc. chim.*, **9**, 487 (1942).
179. Schott, H. F., Larkin, J. B., Rockland, L. B., and Dunn, M. S., *J. Org. Chem.*, **12**, 490 (1947).
180. Curtius, T., and Goebel, F., *J. prakt. Chem.*, **37**, 173 (1888).
181. Abderhalden, E., and Suzuki, S., *Z. physiol. Chem.*, **176**, 101 (1928).
182. Kapfhammer, J., and Matthes, K., *Z. physiol. Chem.*, **223**, 43 (1934).
183. Fischer, E., and Jacobs, W. A., *Ber.*, **39**, 2942 (1906).
184. Fischer, E., and Leuchs, H., *Ber.*, **35**, 3787 (1902).
185. Fischer, E., and Scheibler, H., *Ann.*, **363**, 136 (1908).
186. Huang, H. T., and Niemann, C., *J. Am. Chem. Soc.*, **72**, 921 (1950).
187. Fischer, E., *Ann.*, **340**, 126 (1905).
188. Abderhalden, E., and Hass, R., *Z. physiol. Chem.*, **153**, 146 (1926).
189. Greenstein, J. P., *J. Biol. Chem.*, **118**, 321 (1937).
190. Personal communication from Dr. Astbury.
191. du Vigneaud, V., Patterson, W. I., and Hunt, M., *J. Biol. Chem.*, **126**, 217 (1938).
192. Abenius, P. W., and Widman, O., *Ber.*, **21**, 1662 (1888).
193. Greenstein, J. P., *J. Biol. Chem.*, **121**, 9 (1937).
194. Fischer, E., *Ber.*, **38**, 605 (1905).

195. Fischer, E., and Kautzch, K., *Ber.*, **38**, 2375 (1905).
196. Fischer, E., and Raske, K., *Ber.*, **39**, 3981 (1906).
197. Fischer, E., and Schrauth, W., *Ann.*, **354**, 21 (1907).
198. Levene, P. A., Steiger, R. E., and Marker, R. E., *J. Biol. Chem.*, **93**, 605 (1931).
199. Bergmann, M., Zervas, L., and Köster, H., *Ber.*, **62**, 1901 (1929).
200. Bergmann, M., and Tietzman, J. E., *J. Biol. Chem.*, **155**, 535 (1944).
201. Schotten, C., *Ber.*, **17**, 2544 (1884); Baumann, E., *ibid.*, **19**, 3218 (1886).
202. Curtius, T., and Wüstenfeld, R., *J. prakt. Chem.*, **70**, 73 (1904).
203. Curtius, T., *J. prakt. Chem.*, **70**, 57 (1904).
204. Curtius, T., and van der Linden, C. F., *J. prakt. Chem.*, **70**, 137 (1904).
205. Curtius, T., and Müller, E., *J. prakt. Chem.*, **70**, 223 (1904).
206. Curtius, T., and Lenhard, W., *J. prakt. Chem.*, **70**, 230 (1904).
207. Fischer, E., and Bergell, P., *Ber.*, **36**, 2592 (1903).
208. Fischer, E., and Axhausen, W., *Ann.*, **340**, 123 (1905).
209. Fischer, E., *Untersuchungen über Aminosäuren, Polypeptide und Proteine*, Julius Springer, Berlin, p. 26, 1906.
210. Wessely, F., and Kemm, E., *Z. physiol. Chem.*, **174**, 306 (1928).
211. Wessely, F., Kemm, E., and Mayer, J., *Z. physiol. Chem.*, **180**, 64 (1929).
212. Fischer, E., *Ber.*, **36**, 2982 (1903).
213. Fischer, E., *Ber.*, **37**, 2486 (1904).
214. Fischer, E., and Schulze, A., *Ber.*, **40**, 943 (1907).
215. Fischer, E., *Ber.*, **41**, 850 (1908).
216. Abderhalden, E., and Hirszowski, A., *Ber.*, **41**, 2840 (1908).
217. Fischer, E., and Kropp, W., *Ann.*, **362**, 338 (1908).
218. Fischer, E., and Fiedler, A., *Ann.*, **375**, 181 (1910).
219. Fischer, E., and Gerngross, O., *Ber.*, **42**, 1485 (1909).
220. Abderhalden, E., and Guggenheim, M., *Ber.*, **41**, 1237 (1908).
221. Fischer, E., Kropp, W., and Stahlschmidt, A., *Ann.*, **365**, 181 (1909).
222. Leuchs, H., and Suzuki, U., *Ber.*, **37**, 3306 (1904).
223. Fischer, E., and Steingroever, J., *Ann.*, **365**, 167 (1909).
224. Fischer, E., and Schoeller, W., *Ann.*, **357**, 1 (1907).
225. Fischer, E., and Roesner, H., *Ann.*, **375**, 199 (1910).
226. Abderhalden, E., and Kempe, M., *Ber.*, **40**, 2737 (1907).
227. Fischer, E., *Ber.*, **41**, 2860 (1908).
228. Fischer, E., and Suzuki, U., *Ber.*, **37**, 4575 (1904).
229. Fischer, E., *Ber.*, **40**, 3704 (1907).
230. Fischer, E., *Ber.*, **40**, 1745 (1907).
231. Fischer, E., and Cone, L. H., *Ann.*, **363**, 107 (1908).
232. Fischer, E., and Koelker, A. H., *Ann.*, **354**, 39 (1907).
233. Fischer, E., *Ber.*, **37**, 3062 (1904).
234. Fischer, E., and Blank, P., *Ann.*, **354**, 1 (1907).
235. Fischer, E., and Schenkel, J., *Ann.*, **354**, 12 (1907).
236. Fischer, E., and Scheibler, H., *Ber.*, **41**, 2891 (1908).
237. Willstätter, R., *Ber.*, **33**, 1160 (1900).
238. Fischer, E., *Ber.*, **34**, 454 (1901).
239. Fischer, E., and Suzuki, U., *Ber.*, **37**, 2842 (1904).
240. Frankel, M., and Kuk, S., *Biochem. Z.*, **226**, 221 (1930).
241. Grassmann, W., Schoenebeck, O., and Auerbach, G., *Z. physiol. Chem.*, **210**, 1 (1932).
242. Abderhalden, E., and Sickel, H., *Z. physiol. Chem.*, **159**, 166 (1926).
243. Fischer, E., and Abderhalden, E., *Ber.*, **37**, 3071 (1904).
244. Fischer, E., and Gluud, W., *Ann.*, **369**, 247 (1909).
245. Liwschitz, Y., and Zilkha, A., *J. Am. Chem. Soc.*, **77**, 1265 (1955).

246. Bertho, A., and Maier, J., *Ann.*, **498**, 50 (1932).
247. Freudenberg, K., Eichel, H., and Leutert, F., *Ber.*, **65**, 1183 (1932).
248. Freudenberg, K., and Märkert, L., *Ber.*, **60**, 2447 (1927).
249. Brewster, P., Hiron, F., Hughes, E. D., Ingold, C. K., and Rao, P. A. D., *Nature*, **166**, 178 (1950).
250. Hinman, J. W., Caron, E. L., and Christensen, H. N., *J. Am. Chem. Soc.*, **72**, 1620 (1950).
251. Fischer, E., *Ber.*, **38**, 2914 (1905).
252. Fischer, E., and Luniak, A., *Ber.*, **42**, 4752 (1909).
253. Rao, K. R., Birnbaum, S. M., Kingsley, R. B., and Greenstein, J. P., *J. Biol. Chem.*, **198**, 507 (1952).
254. Robinson, D. S., Birnbaum, S. M., and Greenstein, J. P., *J. Biol. Chem.*, **202**, 1 (1953).
255. Greenstein, J. P., Birnbaum, S. M., and Otey, M. C., *J. Biol. Chem.*, **204**, 307 (1953).
256. Mohr, E., and Stroschein, F., *Ber.*, **42**, 2521 (1909).
257. Greenstein, J. P., *Advances in Enzymol.*, **3**, 117 (1948).
258. Plöchl, J., *Ber.*, **16**, 2815 (1883).
259. Rebuffat, O., *Gazz. chim. ital.*, **19**, 38 (1889).
260. Erlenmeyer, E., Jr., *Ber.*, **33**, 2036 (1900); **35**, 2483 (1902).
261. Carter, H. E., *Org. Reactions*, **3**, 198 (1946).
262. Erlenmeyer, E., Jr., and Halsey, J. T., *Ann.*, **307**, 138 (1899).
263. Erlenmeyer, E., Jr., and Kunlin, J., *Ann.*, **316**, 145 (1901).
264. Erlenmeyer, E., *Ann.*, **275**, 1, 8 (1893).
265. Erlenmeyer, E., and Früstück, E., *Ann.*, **284**, 36 (1895).
266. Erlenmeyer, E., *Ann.*, **307**, 70 (1899).
267. Fischer, H., and Hofmann, H. J., *Z. physiol. Chem.*, **245**, 139 (1936–1937).
268. Finar, I. L., and Libman, D. D., *J. Chem. Soc.*, **1949**, 2726.
269. Baltazzi, E., and Robinson, R., *Chem. & Ind.*, **1954**, 191.
270. Herbst, R. M., and Shemin, D., *Org. Syntheses*, Coll. Vol. **2**, 1 (1943).
271. Galat, A., *J. Am. Chem. Soc.*, **72**, 4436 (1950).
272. Bergmann, M., and Stern, F., *Ann.*, **448**, 20 (1926).
273. Carter, H. E., and Stevens, C. M., *J. Biol. Chem.*, **133**, 117 (1940).
274. Carter, H. E., and Risser, W. C., *J. Biol. Chem.*, **139**, 255 (1941).
275. Bain, D., Perkin, W. H., and Robinson, R., *J. Chem. Soc.*, **105**, 2392 (1914).
276. Gulland, J. M., and Virden, C. J., *J. Chem. Soc.*, **1928**, 1478.
277. Bergmann, M., Zervas, L., and Lebrecht, F., *Ber.*, **64**, 2315 (1931).
278. Bettzieche, F., and Menger, R., *Z. physiol. Chem.*, **172**, 56 (1927).
279. Carter, H. E., Handler, P., and Melville, D. B., *J. Biol. Chem.*, **129**, 359 (1939).
280. Bergmann, M., and Delis, D., *Ann.*, **458**, 76 (1927).
281. Bergmann, M., Schmitt, V., and Miekeley, A., *Z. physiol. Chem.*, **187**, 264 (1930).
282. Dakin, H. D., *J. Biol. Chem.*, **82**, 439 (1929).
283. Cornforth, J. W., in *The Chemistry of Penicillin*, Princeton Univ. Press, 1949.
284. Mohr, E., and Geis, T., *Ber.*, **41**, 798 (1908).
285. Mohr, E., *J. prakt. Chem.*, **80**, 521 (1908).
286. Lettre, H., and Fernholz, M. E., *Z. physiol. Chem.*, **266**, 37 (1940).
287. Bergmann, M., and Grafe, K., *Z. physiol. Chem.*, **187**, 196 (1930).
288. Mohr, E., *J. prakt. Chem.*, **81**, 49, 473 (1910).
289. Mohr, E., *J. prakt. Chem.*, **82**, 60, 322 (1910).
290. Bergmann, M., and Zervas, L., *Z. physiol. Chem.*, **175**, 154 (1928).
291. Carter, H. E., Handler, P., and Stevens, C. M., *J. Biol. Chem.*, **138**, 619 (1941).
292. Nicolet, B. H., *J. Am. Chem. Soc.*, **52**, 1192 (1930).
293. Harington, C. R., and Overhoff, J., *Biochem. J.*, **27**, 338 (1933).

293a. Barker, C. C., *Nature*, **168**, 908 (1951); *J. Chem. Soc.*, **1953**, 453; Swan, J. M., *Nature*, **169**, 826 (1952).
294. Karrer, P., and Widmer, R., *Helv. Chim. Acta*, **8**, 203 (1925).
295. Karrer, P., and Bussman, G., *Helv. Chim. Acta*, **24**, 645 (1941).
296. Bergmann, M., and Köster, H., *Z. physiol. Chem.*, **159**, 179 (1926).
297. Bergmann, M., and Zervas, L., *Biochem. Z.*, **203**, 280 (1928).
298. Greenstein, J. P., Levintow, L., Baker, C. G., and White, J., *J. Biol. Chem.*, **188**, 647 (1951).
299. Marshall, R., Winitz, M., Birnbaum, S. M., and Greenstein, J. P., *J. Am. Chem. Soc.*, **79**, 4438 (1957).
300. du Vigneaud, V., and Sealock, R. R., *J. Biol. Chem.*, **96**, 511 (1932).
301. du Vigneaud, V., and Meyer, C. E., *J. Biol. Chem.*, **98**, 295 (1932).
302. du Vigneaud, V., and Meyer, C. E., *J. Biol. Chem.*, **99**, 143 (1932–33).
303. Bergmann, M., Ensslin, H., and Zervas, L., *Ber.*, **58**, 1034 (1925).
304. Price, V. E., Levintow, L., Greenstein, J. P., and Kingsley, R. B., *Arch. Biochem.*, **26**, 92 (1950).
305. Robinson, D. S., and Greenstein, J. P., *J. Biol. Chem.*, **195**, 383 (1952).
306. Johnson, T. B., and Scott, W. M., *J. Am. Chem. Soc.*, **35**, 1136 (1913).
307. Csonka, F. A., and Nicolet, B. H., *J. Biol. Chem.*, **99**, 213 (1932–33).
308. Doherty, D. G., Tietzman, J. E., and Bergmann, M., *J. Biol. Chem.*, **147**, 617 (1943).
309. Bergmann, M., and Miekeley, A., *Z. physiol. Chem.*, **140**, 128 (1924).
310. Bergmann, M., Miekeley, A., and Kann, E., *Z. physiol. Chem.*, **146**, 247 (1925).
311. Bergmann, M., and Miekeley, A., *Ann.*, **458**, 40 (1927).
312. Bergmann, M., *Naturwiss.*, **51**, 941 (1932).
313. Behrens, O. K., Doherty, D. G., and Bergmann, M., *J. Biol. Chem.*, **136**, 61 (1940).
314. Bergmann, M., and Behrens, O. K., *J. Biol. Chem.*, **124**, 7 (1938).
315. Bergmann, M., and Grafe, K., *Z. physiol. Chem.*, **187**, 187 (1930).
316. Shemin, D., and Herbst, R. M., *J. Am. Chem. Soc.*, **60**, 1954 (1938).
317. Herbst, R. M., *J. Am. Chem. Soc.*, **61**, 483 (1939).
318. Nicolet, B. H., *J. Am. Chem. Soc.*, **57**, 1073 (1935).
319. Martell, A. E., and Herbst, R. M., *J. Org. Chem.*, **6**, 878 (1941).
320. Shive, W., and Shive, G. W., *J. Am. Chem. Soc.*, **68**, 117 (1946).
321. Bergmann, M. and Grafe, K., *Z. physiol. Chem.*, **187**, 183 (1930).
322. Gonçalves, J. M., and Greenstein, J. P., *Arch. Biochem.*, **16**, 1 (1948).
323. Böttinger, C., *Ber.*, **14**, 1599 (1881).
324. Price, V. E., Errera, M., and Greenstein, J. P., *Arch. Biochem.*, **17**, 51 (1948).
325. Fu, S-C. J., Levintow, L., Price, V. E., and Greenstein, J. P., *Arch. Biochem.*, **28**, 440 (1950).
326. Greenstein, J. P., and Carter, C. E., *J. Natl. Cancer Inst.*, **7**, 57 (1946).
327. Greenstein, J. P., and Price, V. E., *J. Biol. Chem.*, **175**, 963 (1948).
328. Price, V. E., and Greenstein, J. P., *Arch. Biochem.*, **14**, 249 (1947).
329. Price, V. E., and Greenstein, J. P., *J. Biol. Chem.*, **171**, 477 (1947); **173**, 337 (1948); **175**, 969 (1948).
330. Fodor, P. J., Price, V. E., and Greenstein, J. P., *J. Biol. Chem.*, **180**, 193 (1949).
331. Meister, A., and Greenstein, J. P., *J. Biol. Chem.*, **195**, 849 (1952).
332. Levintow, L., Fu, S-C. J., Price, V. E., and Greenstein, J. P., *J. Biol. Chem.*, **184**, 633 (1950).
333. Greenstein, J. P., Price, V. E., and Leuthardt, F. M., *J. Biol. Chem.*, **175**, 953 (1948).
334. Fruton, J. S., and Bergmann, M., *J. Biol. Chem.*, **166**, 449 (1946).
335. Herbst, R. M., *Advances in Enzymol.*, **4**, 75 (1944).
336. Waters, K. L., and Hartung, W. H., *J. Org. Chem.*, **12**, 469 (1947).

337. Weaver, W. E., and Hartung, W. H., *J. Org. Chem.*, **15**, 741 (1950); Hartung, W. H., Kramer, D. N., and Hager, G. P., *J. Am. Chem. Soc.*, **76**, 2261 (1954); Shen, L. M. C., and Hartung, W. H., *J. Org. Chem.*, **23**, 96 (1958).
338. Errera, M., and Greenstein, J. P., *J. Natl. Cancer Inst.*, **8**, 39 (1947).
339. Errera, M., and Greenstein, J. P., *Arch. Biochem.*, **15**, 445 (1947).
340. Fu, S-C. J., Price, V. E., and Greenstein, J. P., *Arch. Biochem. Biophys.*, **31**, 83 (1951).
341. Fu, S-C. J., and Greenstein, J. P., *Arch. Biochem. Biophys.*, **32**, 365 (1951).
342. Carter, C. E., and Greenstein, J. P., *J. Natl. Cancer Inst.*, **7**, 51 (1946).
343. Price, V. E., and Greenstein, J. P., *J. Natl. Cancer Inst.*, **7**, 275 (1947).
344. Fruton, J. S., Simmonds, S., and Smith, V. A., *J. Biol. Chem.*, **169**, 267 (1947).
345. Price, V. E., and Greenstein, J. P., *Arch. Biochem.*, **18**, 383 (1948).
346. Eiger, I. Z., and Greenstein, J. P., *Arch. Biochem.*, **19**, 467 (1948).
347. Nicolet, B. H., *Science*, **81**, 181 (1935).
348. Fu, S-C. J., and Greenstein, J. P., *J. Am. Chem. Soc.*, **77**, 4412 (1955).
349. Nicolet, B. H., *J. Wash. Acad. Sci.*, **28**, 84 (1938).
350. Gonçalves, J. M., Price, V. E., and Greenstein, J. P., *J. Natl. Cancer Inst.*, **7**, 443 (1947).
351. Curtius, T., and Sieber, W., *Ber.*, **54**, 1430 (1921); **55**, 1543 (1922).
352. Wessely, F., and Sigmund, F., *Z. physiol. Chem.*, **157**, 102 (1926).
353. Bailey, J. L., *Nature*, **164**, 889 (1949); *J. Chem. Soc.*, **1950**, 3461.
354. Leuchs, H., and Manasse, W., *Ber.*, **40**, 3235 (1907).
355. Leuchs, H., and Geiger, W., *Ber.*, **41**, 1721 (1908).
356. Katchalski, E., and Ben-Ishai, D., *J. Org. Chem.*, **15**, 1067 (1950).
357. Ben-Ishai, D., and Katchalski, E., *J. Am. Chem. Soc.*, **74**, 3688 (1952).
358. Bergmann, M., Zervas, L., and Ross, W. F., *J. Biol. Chem.*, **111**, 245 (1935).
359. Hunt, M., and du Vigneaud, V., *J. Biol. Chem.*, **124**, 699 (1938).
360. Go, V., and Tani, H., *Bull. Chem. Soc. Japan*, **14**, 510 (1939).
361. Hanby, W. E., Waley, S. G., and Watson, J., *J. Chem. Soc.*, **1950**, 3009.
362. Gish, D. T., and Carpenter, F. H., *J. Am. Chem. Soc.*, **75**, 950 (1953).
363. Gish, D. T., and Carpenter, F. H., *J. Am. Chem. Soc.*, **75**, 5872 (1953).
364. Berger, A., and Katchalski, E., *J. Am. Chem. Soc.*, **73**, 4084 (1951).
365. Berger, A., Noguchi, J., and Katchalski, E., *J. Am. Chem. Soc.*, **78**, 4483 (1956).
366. Poduska, K., Rudinger, J., and Sorm, F., *Collection Czechoslov. Chem. Communs.*, **20**, 1174 (1955).
367. Hanby, W. E., Waley, S. G., and Watson, J., *J. Chem. Soc.*, **1950**, 3239.
368. Becker, R. R., and Stahmann, M. A., *J. Biol. Chem.*, **204**, 737 (1953).
369. Overell, B. G., and Petrow, V., *J. Chem. Soc.*, **1955**, 232.
370. Patchornik, A., Berger, A., and Katchalski, E., *J. Am. Chem. Soc.*, **79**, 5227 (1957).
371. Izumiya, N., Fu, S-C. J., Birnbaum, S. M., and Greenstein, J. P., *J. Biol. Chem.*, **205**, 221 (1953).
372. Katchalski, E., and Spitnik, K., *J. Am. Chem. Soc.*, **73**, 2946 (1951).
373. Synge, R. L. M., *Biochem. J.*, **42**, 99 (1948).
374. Sela, M., and Katchalski, E., *J. Am. Chem. Soc.*, **76**, 129 (1954).
375. Berger, A., Kurtz, J., and Katchalski, E., *J. Am. Chem. Soc.*, **76**, 5552 (1954).
376. Sigmund, F., and Wessely, F., *Z. physiol. Chem.*, **157**, 91 (1926).
377. Frankel, M., and Halmann, M., *J. Chem. Soc.*, **1952**, 2735.
378. Bergmann, M., Zervas, L., Salzmann, L., and Schleich, H., *Z. physiol. Chem.*, **224**, 17 (1934).
379. Katchalski, E., and Sela, M., *J. Am. Chem. Soc.*, **75**, 5284 (1953).
380. Davis, J. W., *Ann. chim.*, **9**, 399 (1954).
381. Jones, H. W., and Lundgren, H. P., *J. Am. Chem. Soc.*, **73**, 5465 (1951).
382. Green, M., and Stahmann, M. A., *J. Biol. Chem.*, **197**, 771 (1952).

383. Smith, P. A. S., *Org. Reactions*, **3**, 337 (1946).
384. Fuchs, F., *Ber.*, **55**, 2943 (1922).
385. Levy, A. L., *Nature*, **165**, 152 (1950).
386. Farthing, A. C., and Reynolds, R. J. W., *Nature*, **165**, 647 (1950).
387. Farthing, A. C., *J. Chem. Soc.*, **1950**, 3213.
388. Schlögl, K., and Fabitschowitz, H., *Monatsh. Chem.*, **85**, 1061 (1954).
389. Coleman, D. W., *J. Chem. Soc.*, **1951**, 2294.
390. Hooper, K. C., Rydon, H. N., Schofield, J. A., and Heaton, G. S., *J. Chem. Soc.*, **1956**, 3148.
390a. Kurtz, J., Fasman, G. D., Berger, A., and Katchalski, E., *J. Am. Chem. Soc.*, **80**, 393 (1958).
391. Coleman, D., *J. Chem. Soc.*, **1950**, 3222.
392. Hopple, K. D., and Katz, J. J., *J. Am. Chem. Soc.*, **78**, 6199 (1956).
393. Roeske, R., Steward, F. H. C., Stedman, R. J., and du Vigneaud, V., *J. Am. Chem. Soc.*, **78**, 5883 (1956).
394. Petri, E. M., and Stavermann, A. J., *Rec. trav. chim.*, **71**, 385 (1952).
395. Schlögl, K., Wessely, F., and Korger, G., *Monatsh. Chem.*, **83**, 845 (1952).
396. MacDonald, R. N., and Tullock, C. W., U.S. Patent 2,630,423 (1953).
397. Frankel, M., Cordova, S., and Breuer, M., *J. Chem. Soc.*, **1953**, 1991.
398. Okawa, K., and Tani, K., *J. Chem. Soc. Japan*, **75**, 1199 (1954).
399. Patchornik, A., Sela, M., and Katchalski, E., *J. Am. Chem. Soc.*, **76**, 299 (1954).
400. Honzl, J., and Rudinger, J., *Collection Czechoslov. Chem. Communs.*, **20**, 1190 (1955).
401. Siegfried, M., *Z. physiol. Chem.*, **44**, 85 (1905); **46**, 401 (1906); **54**, 436 (1908).
402. Neuberg, C., and Kerb, J., *Biochem. Z.*, **40**, 498 (1912).
403. Frankel, M., and Katchalski, E., *J. Am. Chem. Soc.*, **65**, 1670 (1943).
404. Faurholt, C., *J. chim. phys.*, **22**, 1 (1925).
405. Meldrum, N. U., and Roughton, F. J. W., *J. physiol.*, **80**, 143 (1933).
406. Stadie, W. C., and O'Brien, H., *J. Biol. Chem.*, **112**, 723 (1936); **117**, 439 (1937).
407. Miller, E., Fankuchen, I., and Mark, H., *J. Appl. Phys.*, **20**, 531 (1949).
408. Katchalski, E., Grossfeld, I., and Frankel, M., *J. Am. Chem. Soc.*, **70**, 2094 (1948).
409. Hanby, W. E., Waley, S. G., and Watson, J., *Nature*, **161**, 132 (1948).
409a. Ballard, D. G. H., Bamford, C. H., and Weymouth, F. J., *Proc. Roy. Soc. (London)*, **A227**, 155 (1954).
410. Cook, A. H., Heilbron, I., and Levy, A. L., *J. Chem. Soc.*, **1948**, 201.
411. Cook, A. H., and Levy, A. L., *J. Chem. Soc.*, **1950**, 642.
412. Davis, A. C., and Levy, A. L., *J. Chem. Soc.*, **1951**, 2419.
413. Hofmann, K., Lindenmann, A., Magee, M. Z., and Khan, N. H., *J. Am. Chem. Soc.*, **74**, 470 (1952).
414. Billimoria, J. D., and Cook, A. H., *J. Chem. Soc.*, **1949**, 2323.
415. Cook, A. H., and Levy, A. L., *J. Chem. Soc.*, **1950**, 646.
416. Cook, A. H., and Levy, A. L., *J. Chem. Soc.*, **1950**, 651.
417. Cook, A. H., and Levy, A. L., *J. Chem. Soc.*, **1950**, 637.
418. Aubert, P., Jeffreys, R. A., and Knott, E. B., *J. Chem. Soc.*, **1951**, 2195.
419. Aubert, P., Knott, E. B., and Williams, L. A., *J. Chem. Soc.*, **1951**, 2185.
420. Fischer, E., and Lipschitz, W., *Ber.*, **48**, 360 (1915).
421. Harris, J. I., and Work, T. S., *Biochem. J.*, **46**, 582 (1950).
422. Bergmann, M., Fruton, J. S., and Pollok, H., *J. Biol. Chem.*, **127**, 643 (1939).
423. Erlanger, B. F., Sachs, H., and Brand, E., *J. Am. Chem. Soc.*, **76**, 1806 (1954).
424. Gibson, C. S., and Simonsen, J. L., *J. Chem. Soc.*, **107**, 798 (1915).
425. McChesney, E. W., and Swann, W. K., *J. Am. Chem. Soc.*, **59**, 1116 (1937).
426. Holley, R. W., and Holley, A. D., *J. Am. Chem. Soc.*, **71**, 2129 (1949).
427. Beecham, A. F., *J. Am. Chem. Soc.*, **79**, 3257 (1957).

CHEMICAL PROCEDURES FOR SYNTHESIS OF PEPTIDES

428. Fichter, F., and Schmid, M., *Helv. Chim. Acta*, **3**, 711 (1920).
429. Barrass, B. C., and Elmore, D. T., *J. Chem. Soc.*, **1957**, 3134.
430. Oseki, T., *J. Tokyo Chem. Soc.*, **41**, 8 (1920).
431. Freudenberg, K., and Noë, A., *Ber.*, **58**, 2399 (1925).
432. du Vigneaud, V., Bartlett, M. F., and Jöhl, A., *J. Am. Chem. Soc.*, **79**, 5572 (1957).
432a. Maclaren, J. A., Savige, W. E., and Swan, J. M., *Australian J. Chem.*, **11**, 345 (1958).
433. Rudinger, J., *Collection Czechoslov. Chem. Communs.*, **19**, 386 (1954).
434. Harington, C. R., and Moggridge, R. C. G., *J. Chem. Soc.*, **1940**, 706.
435. Swan, J. M., and du Vigneaud, V., *J. Am. Chem. Soc.*, **76**, 3110 (1954).
436. Rudinger, J., *Collection Czechoslov. Chem. Communs.*, **19**, 365 (1954).
437. Fischer, E., and Bergmann, M., *Ann.*, **398**, 96 (1913).
438. Katsoyannis, P. G., and du Vigneaud, V., *J. Am. Chem. Soc.*, **76**, 3113 (1954).
439. Theodoropoulos, D., and Craig, L. C., *J. Org. Chem.*, **21**, 1376 (1956).
439a. Swallow, D. L., Lockhart, I. M., and Abraham, E. P., *Biochem. J.*, **70**, 359 (1958).
439b. Barrass, B. C., and Elmore, D. T., *J. Chem. Soc.*, **1957**, 4830.
440. Popenoe, E. A., and du Vigneaud, V., *J. Am. Chem. Soc.*, **76**, 6202 (1954).
441. Kapfhammer, J., and Eck, R., *Z. physiol. Chem.*, **170**, 294 (1927).
442. Izumiya, N., *Bull. Chem. Soc., Japan*, **26**, 53 (1953).
443. Pravda, Z., and Rudinger, J., *Collection Czechoslov. Chem. Communs.*, **20**, 1 (1955).
444. Hofmann, K., Jöhl, A., Furlenmeier, A. E., and Kappler, H., *J. Am. Chem. Soc.*, **79**, 1636 (1957).
445. Brenner, M., Rüfenacht, K., and Sailer, E., *Helv. Chim. Acta*, **34**, 2102 (1951).
446. Katsoyannis, P. G., Gish, D. T., and du Vigneaud, V., *J. Am. Chem. Soc.*, **79**, 4516 (1957).
447. Bergell, P., *Z. physiol. Chem.*, **104**, 182 (1919).
448. Knoop, F., and Oesterlin, H., *Z. physiol. Chem.*, **170**, 186 (1927).
449. Rosenmund, K. W., and Zetzsche, F., *Ber.*, **54**, 2038 (1921).
450. Freudenberg, K., Dürr, W., and Hochstetter, H. von, *Ber.*, **61**, 1735 (1928).
451. Fischer, H. O. L., and Baer, E., *Ber.*, **65**, 337, 345 (1932).
452. du Vigneaud, V., and Meyer, C. E., *J. Biol. Chem.*, **98**, 295 (1932).
453. Cahill, W. M., and Burton, I. F., *J. Biol. Chem.*, **132**, 161 (1940).
454. Winitz, M., Bloch-Frankenthal, L., Izumiya, N., Birnbaum, S. M., Baker, C. G., and Greenstein, J. P., *J. Am. Chem. Soc.*, **78**, 2423 (1956).
455. Bergmann, M., Zervas, L., and Fruton, J. S., *J. Biol. Chem.*, **115**, 593 (1936).
456. Theodoropoulos, D., and Craig, L. C., *J. Org. Chem.*, **20**, 1169 (1955).
457. Neuberger, A., and Sanger, F., *Biochem. J.*, **37**, 515 (1943).
458. Zervas, L., Winitz, M., and Greenstein, J. P., *Arch. Biochem. Biophys.*, **65**, 573 (1956).
459. Zervas, L., Winitz, M., and Greenstein, J. P., *J. Org. Chem.*, **22**, 1515 (1957).
460. Stevens, C. M., and Watanabe, R., *J. Am. Chem. Soc.*, **72**, 725 (1950).
461. Channing, D. M., Turner, P. B., and Young, G. T., *Nature*, **167**, 487 (1951).
462. Carpenter, F. H., and Gish, D. T., *J. Am. Chem. Soc.*, **74**, 3818 (1952).
463. Gish, D. T., and Carpenter, F. H., *J. Am. Chem. Soc.*, **75**, 5872 (1953).
464. McKay, F. C., and Albertson, N. F., *J. Am. Chem. Soc.*, **79**, 4686 (1957).
465. Anderson, G. W., and McGregor, A. C., *J. Am. Chem. Soc.*, **79**, 6180 (1957).
466. Bergmann, M., Zervas, L., Fruton, J. S., Schneider, F., and Schleich, H., *J. Biol Chem.*, **109**, 325 (1935).
467. Polglase, W. J., and Smith, E. L., *J. Am. Chem. Soc.*, **71**, 3081 (1949).
468. Fu, S-C. J., Birnbaum, S. M., and Greenstein, J. P., *J. Am. Chem. Soc.*, **76**, 6054 (1954).
469. Smith, C. S., and Brown, A. E., *J. Am. Chem. Soc.*, **63**, 2605 (1941).
470. Greenstein, J. P., Izumiya, N., Winitz, M., and Birnbaum, S. M., *J. Am. Chem. Soc.*, **77**, 707 (1955).

471. Anderson, G. W., *J. Am. Chem. Soc.*, **75**, 6081 (1953).
471a. Guttmann, S., and Boissonnas, R. A., *Helv. Chim. Acta*, **41**, 1852 (1958); Boissonnas, R. A., Guttmann, S., Huguenin, R. L., Jaquenoud, P. A., and Sandrin, E., *ibid.*, **41**, 1867 (1958).
472. Boissonnas, R. A., Guttmann, S., Jaquenoud P. A., and Waller, J. P., *Helv. Chim. Acta*, **38**, 1491 (1955).
473. Izumiya, N., and Greenstein, J. P., *Arch. Biochem. Biophys.*, **52**, 203 (1954).
474. Harington, C. R., and Mead, T. H., *Biochem. J.*, **30**, 1598 (1936).
475. Goldschmidt, S., and Jutz, C., *Chem. Ber.*, **86**, 1116 (1953).
476. King, L. C., and Suydam, F. H., *J. Am. Chem. Soc.*, **74**, 5499 (1952).
477. Weygand, F., and Geiger, R., *Chem. Ber.*, **90**, 634 (1957).
478. Wade, R., Birnbaum, S. M., Winitz, M., Koegel, R. J., and Greenstein, J. P., *J. Am. Chem. Soc.*, **79**, 648 (1957).
479. Fruton, J. S., Irving, G. W., and Bergmann, M., *J. Biol. Chem.*, **133**, 703 (1940).
480. Levintow, L., Greenstein, J. P., and Kingsley, R. B., *Arch. Biochem. Biophys.*, **31**, 77 (1951).
481. Wieland, T., and Weidenmüller, H. L., *Ann.*, **597**, 111 (1955).
482. Miller, H. K., and Waelsch, H., *Arch. Biochem. Biophys.*, **35**, 176 (1952).
482a. Katsoyannis, P. G., Gish, D. T., Hess, G. P., and du Vigneaud, V., *J. Am. Chem. Soc.*, **80**, 2558 (1958).
483. Patchornik, A., Berger, A., and Katchalski, E., *J. Am. Chem. Soc.*, **79**, 6416 (1957).
484. Theodoropoulos, D., *J. Org. Chem.*, **21**, 1550 (1956).
485. Benoiton, L., Winitz, M., Birnbaum, S. M., and Greenstein, J. P., *J. Am. Chem. Soc.*, **79**, 6192 (1957).
486. Grassmann, W., and Wünsch, E., *Chem. Ber.*, **91**, 449, 462 (1958); Grassmann, W., Wünsch, E., and Riedel, A., *ibid.*, **91**, 455 (1958).
487. Patchett, A. A., and Witkop, B., *J. Am. Chem. Soc.*, **79**, 185 (1957); Witkop, B., and Foltz, C. M., *ibid.*, **79**, 192 (1957).
488. Fox, S. W., Fling, M., Wax, H., and Pettinga, C. W., *J. Am. Chem. Soc.*, **72**, 1862 (1950).
489. Dekker, C. A., and Fruton, J. S., *J. Biol. Chem.*, **173**, 471 (1948).
490. Brenner, M., and Pfister, R. W., *Helv. Chim. Acta*, **34**, 2085 (1951).
491. Hofmann, K., Peckham, W. D., and Rheiner, A., *J. Am. Chem. Soc.*, **78**, 238 (1956).
492. Bergmann, M., Zervas, L., and Rinke, H., *Z. physiol. Chem.*, **224**, 40 (1934).
493. Bergmann, M., Zervas, L., Rinke, H., and Schleich, H., *Z. physiol. Chem.*, **224**, 33 (1934).
494. Holley, R. W., and Holley, A. D., *J. Am. Chem. Soc.*, **74**, 1110, 3069 (1952).
495. Clayton, D. W., Farrington, J. A., Kenner, G. W., and Turner, J. M., *J. Chem. Soc.*, **1957**, 1398.
496. Zaoral, M., *Chem. Listy*, **48**, 1583 (1954).
497. Skinner, C. G., McCord, T. J., Ravel, J. M., and Shive, W., *J. Am. Chem. Soc.*, **78**, 2412 (1956).
498. Riley, G., Turnbull, J. H., and Wilson, W., *J. Chem. Soc.*, **1957**, 1373.
499. Baer, E., and Maurukas, J., *J. Biol. Chem.*, **212**, 25 (1955).
500. Nicolaides, E. D., Westland, R. D., and Wittle, E. L., *J. Am. Chem. Soc.*, **76**, 2887 (1954).
501. Fruton, J. S., *J. Biol. Chem.*, **146**, 463 (1942).
502. Moore, J. A., Dice, J. R., Nicolaides, E. D., Westland, R. D., and Wittle, E. L., *J. Am. Chem. Soc.*, **76**, 2884 (1954).
503. Levene, P. A., and Schormüller, A., *J. Biol. Chem.*, **105**, 547 (1934); **106**, 595 (1934).
504. Okawa, K., *Bull. Chem. Soc. Japan*, **29**, 488 (1956).
504a. Merrifield, R. B., *J. Biol. Chem.*, **232**, 43 (1958).

CHEMICAL PROCEDURES FOR SYNTHESIS OF PEPTIDES

505. Smith, E. L., *J. Biol. Chem.*, **175**, 39 (1948).
506. Kuhn, R., and Ruelius, H. W., *Chem. Ber.*, **85**, 38 (1952).
507. Vaughan, J. R., and Eichler, J. A., *J. Am. Chem. Soc.*, **75**, 5556 (1953).
508. Schwarz, H., Bumpus, F. M., and Page, I. H., *J. Am. Chem. Soc.*, **79**, 5697 (1957).
509. Chambers, R. W., and Carpenter, F. H., *J. Am. Chem. Soc.*, **77**, 1522 (1955).
510. du Vigneaud, V., Gish, D. T., and Katsoyannis, P. G., *J. Am. Chem. Soc.*, **76**, 4751 (1954).
511. Gish, D. T., and du Vigneaud, V., *J. Am. Chem. Soc.*, **79**, 3579 (1957).
512. Berse, C., Boucher, R., and Piche, L., *J. Org. Chem.*, **22**, 805 (1957).
513. Berse, C., and Piche, L., *J. Org. Chem.*, **21**, 808 (1956).
514. Boissonnas, R. A., and Preitner, G., *Helv. Chim. Acta*, **36**, 875 (1953).
514a. Schwyzer, R., Sieber, P., and Zatsko, K., *Helv. Chim. Acta*, **41**, 491 (1958).
515. Radenhausen, R., *J. prakt. Chem.*, **52**, 446 (1895).
516. Ing, H. R., and Manske, R. H., *J. Chem. Soc.*, **1926**, 2348.
517. Kidd, D. A., and King, F. E., *Nature*, **162**, 776 (1948).
518. Sheehan, J. C., and Frank, V. S., *J. Am. Chem. Soc.*, **71**, 1856 (1949).
519. Reese, L., *Ann.*, **242**, 1 (1887).
520. Fling, M., Minard, F. N., and Fox, S. W., *J. Am. Chem. Soc.*, **69**, 2466 (1947).
521. Billman, J. H., and Harting, W. F., *J. Am. Chem. Soc.*, **70**, 1473 (1948).
522. Sheehan, J. C., Chapman, D. W., and Roth, R. W., *J. Am. Chem. Soc.*, **74**, 3822 (1952).
523. Tipson, R. S., *J. Org. Chem.*, **21**, 1353 (1956).
524. Sheehan, J. C., Goodman, M., and Hess, G. P., *J. Am. Chem. Soc.*, **78**, 1367 (1956).
525. Wanag, G., and Veinbergs, A., *Ber.*, **75**, 1558 (1942).
526. O'Neill, J. J., Veitch, F. P., and Wagner-Jauregg, T., *J. Org. Chem.*, **21**, 363 (1956).
527. King, F. E., and Kidd, D. A. A., *J. Chem. Soc.*, **1949**, 3315.
528. Balenović, K., Gaspert, B., and Stimac, N., *Croat. Chem. Acta*, **29**, 93 (1957).
529. Gabriel, S., *Ber.*, **38**, 634 (1905); **44**, 59 (1911).
530. Fischer, E., *Ber.*, **40**, 489 (1907).
531. McKenzie, A., and Barrow, F., *J. Chem. Soc.*, **103**, 1331 (1913).
532. Hildescheimer, A., *Ber.*, **43**, 2796 (1910).
533. King, F. E., Clark-Lewis, J. W., and Wade, R., *J. Chem. Soc.*, **1957**, 886.
534. Fischer, E., *Ber.*, **34**, 2900 (1901).
535. Hanson, H., and Illhardt, R., *Z. physiol. Chem.*, **298**, 210 (1954).
536. King, F. E., Clark-Lewis, J. W., Wade, R., and Swindin, W. A., *J. Chem. Soc.*, **1957**, 873.
537. Fischer, R. F., and Whetstone, R. R., *J. Am. Chem. Soc.*, **76**, 5076 (1954).
538. Keil, W., *Z. physiol. Chem.*, **208**, 67 (1932).
539. Freytog, P., *Ber.*, **48**, 648 (1915).
540. Ulrich, A., *Ber.*, **37**, 1685 (1904).
541. Van Orden, H., and Smith, E. L., *J. Biol. Chem.*, **208**, 751 (1954).
542. Flěs, D., and Balenović, B., *J. Am. Chem. Soc.*, **78**, 3072 (1956).
543. Minard, F. N., and Fox, S. W., *J. Am. Chem. Soc.*, **71**, 1160 (1949).
543a. Shankman, S., and Schvo, Y., *J. Am. Chem. Soc.*, **80**, 1164 (1958).
544. Schumann, I., and Boissonnas, R. A., *Helv. Chim. Acta*, **35**, 2237 (1952).
545. Helferich, B., Moog, L., and Jünger, A., *Ber.*, **58**, 872 (1925).
546. Hillmann-Elies, A., Hillmann, G., and Jatzkewitz, H., *Z. Naturforsch.*, **8b**, 445 (1953).
547. Amiard, G., Heymes, R., and Velluz, L., *Bull. soc. chim.*, **1955**, 191.
548. Zervas, L., and Theodoropoulos, D. M., *J. Am. Chem. Soc.*, **78**, 1359 (1956).
548a. Stelekatos, G. C., Theodoropoulos, D. M., and Zervas, L., private communication.
549. Amiard, G., Heymes, R., and Velluž, L., *Bull. soc. chim.*, **1956**, 698.
550. Amiard, G., and Goffinet, B., *Bull. soc. chim.*, **1957**, 1133.

551. Velluz, L., Amiard, G., and Heymes, R., *Bull. soc. chim.*, **1954**, 1012.
552. Velluz, L., Anatol, J., and Amiard, G., *Bull. soc. chim.*, **1954**, 1449.
553. Velluz, L., Amiard, G., and Heymes, R., *Bull. soc. chim.*, **1955**, 201.
554. Anatol, J., and Torelli, V., *Bull. soc. chim.*, **1954**, 1446.
555. Liwschitz, Y., and Zilkha, A., *J. Am. Chem. Soc.*, **76**, 3698 (1954).
556. Frankel, M., Liwschitz, Y., and Amiel, Y., *J. Am. Chem. Soc.*, **75**, 330 (1953).
557. Liwschitz, Y., Zilkha, A., and Amiel, Y., *J. Am. Chem. Soc.*, **78**, 3067 (1956).
558. Zilkha, A., and Liwschitz, Y., *J. Chem. Soc.*, **1957**, 4397.
559. Kanao, S., *J. Pharm. Soc., Japan*, **66**, 6 (1944).
560. Mannich, C, and Kuphal, R., *Ber.*, **45**, 314 (1912).
561. Gavrilov, N., Koperina, A. W., and Klutcharova, M., *Bull. soc. chim.*, **1945**, 773.
562. Scheibler, H., and Baumgarten, P., *Ber.*, **55**, 1358 (1922).
563. Fischer, E., and Michel, L., *Ber.*, **49**, 1355 (1916).
564. Birkhofer, L., *Ber.*, **75**, 429 (1942).
565. Velluz, L., Amiard, G., and Heymes, R., *Bull. soc. chim.*, **1955**, 1283.
566. Swarts, F., *Bull. Acad. roy. Belgique, Classe des sciences*, [5] **8**, 343 (1922); *Chem. Zentr.*, **1**, 66 (1923).
567. Weygand, F., and Csendes, E., *Angew. Chem.*, **64**, 136 (1952).
568. Weygand, F., and Leising, E., *Chem. Ber.*, **87**, 248 (1954).
569. Schallenberg, E. F., and Calvin, M., *J. Am. Chem. Soc.*, **77**, 2779 (1955).
570. Weygand, F., and Geiger, R., *Chem. Ber.*, **89**, 647 (1956).
571. Weygand, F., and Glöckler, U., *Chem. Ber.*, **89**, 653 (1956).
572. Fones, W. S., *J. Org. Chem.*, **17**, 1661 (1952).
573. Weygand, F., and Reiher, M., *Chem. Ber.*, **88**, 26 (1955).
574. Fones, W. S., and Lee, M., *J. Biol. Chem.*, **210**, 227 (1954).
575. Hauptschein, M., Stokes, C. S., and Nodiff, E. A., *J. Am. Chem. Soc.*, **74**, 4005 (1952).
576. Weygand, F., Klinke, P., and Eigen, I., *Chem. Ber.*, **90**, 1896 (1957).
577. Shine, H. J., and Niemann, C., *J. Am. Chem. Soc.*, **74**, 97 (1952).
578. Ehrensvärd, G. C. H., *Nature*, **159**, 500 (1947).
579. Lindenmann, A., Khan, N. H., and Hofmann, K., *J. Am. Chem. Soc.*, **74**, 476 (1952).
580. Kollonitsch, J., Gabor, V., and Hajos, A., *Nature*, **177**, 841 (1956); *Chem. Ber.*, **89**, 2288 (1956).
581. Rivier, H., *Bull. soc. chim.*, [4] **1**, 733 (1907).
582. Schuller, W. H., and Niemann, C., *J. Am. Chem. Soc.*, **75**, 3425 (1953).
583. Crosby, D. G., and Niemann, C., *J. Am. Chem. Soc.*, **76**, 4458 (1954).
584. Waley, S. G., *Chem. & Ind.*, **1953**, 107; Zehra, A., *Ber.*, **23**, 3625 (1890).
584a. Waley, S. G., and Watson, J., *Biochem. J.*, **57**, 529 (1954).
585. King, F. E., Clark-Lewis, J. W., Kidd, D. A. A., and Smith, G. R., *J. Chem. Soc.*, **1954**, 1039.
586. Sheehan, J. C., and Yang, D-D. H., *J. Am. Chem. Soc.*, **80**, 1154 (1958).
587. Fodor, P. J., Price, V. E., and Greenstein, J. P., *J. Biol. Chem.*, **182**, 467 (1950); Biilmann, E., Jensen, K. A., and Jensen, H. B., *Bull. soc. chim.*, [5] **1**, 1661 (1934).
588. Micheel, F., Krzeminski, Z., Himmelman, W., and Kühlkamp, A., *Ann.*, **575**, 90 (1952).
589. Cherbuliez, E., and Chambers, I. F., *Helv. Chim. Acta*, **8**, 395 (1925).
590. Fruton, J. S., and Clarke, H. T., *J. Biol. Chem.*, **106**, 667 (1934); du Vigneaud, V., Dorfmann, R., and Loring, H. S., *ibid.*, **98**, 577 (1932).
591. Borek, B. A., and Waelsch, H., *J. Biol. Chem.*, **205**, 459 (1953).
592. Tabor, H., and Mehler, A. H., *J. Biol. Chem.*, **210**, 559 (1954).
593. Fischer, E., and Warburg, O., *Ber.*, **38**, 3997 (1905).
594. Abderhalden, E., and Weil, A., *Z. physiol. Chem.*, **77**, 435 (1912).
595. Locquin, R., *Bull. Soc. chim.*, [4] **1**, 598 (1907).

596. Windus, W., and Marvel, C. S., *J. Am. Chem. Soc.*, **53**, 3490 (1931).
597. Dalgleish, C. E., *J. Chem. Soc.*, **1952**, 137.
598. Abderhalden, E., and Sickel, H., *Z. physiol. Chem.*, **131**, 277 (1923).
599. Izumiya, N., and Nagamatsu, A., *Bull. Chem. Soc. Japan*, **25**, 265 (1952).
600. Fischer, E., *Ber.*, **39**, 2320 (1906).
601. Milne, H. B., and Peng, C-H., *J. Am. Chem. Soc.*, **79**, 639 (1957).
602. Bergmann, M., Zervas, L., and Salzmann, L., *Ber.*, **66**, 1288 (1933).
603. Curtius, T., and Goebel, F., *J. prakt. Chem.*, (2) **37**, 150 (1888).
604. Bergmann, M., and Zervas, L., *Z. physiol. Chem.*, **221**, 51 (1933).
605. Rowlands, D. A., and Young, G. T., *J. Chem. Soc.*, **1952**, 3937.
606. Hegedüs, B., *Helv. Chim. Acta*, **31**, 737 (1948).
607. King, F. E., Jackson, B. S., and Kidd, D. A. A., *J. Chem. Soc.*, **1951**, 243.
608. King, F. E., and Spensley, P. C., *J. Chem. Soc.*, **1950**, 3159.
609. Le Quesne, W. J., and Young, G. T., *J. Chem. Soc.*, **1952**, 24.
610. Le Quesne, W. J., and Young, G. T., *J. Chem. Soc.*, **1950**, 1954.
611. Barker, A. L., and Skinner, G. S., *J. Am. Chem. Soc.*, **46**, 403 (1925).
611a. Grassmann, W., Wünsch, E., and Riedel, A., *Chem. Ber.*, 455 (1958).
612. Smith, E. L., and Polglase, W. J., *J. Biol. Chem.*, **180**, 1209 (1949).
613. Greenstein, J. P., Winitz, M., Gullino, P., Birnbaum, S. M., and Otey, M. C., *Arch. Biochem. Biophys.*, **64**, 342 (1956).
613a. Grassmann, W., and Wünsch, E., *Chem. Ber.*, **91**, 449 (1958).
614. Piutti, A., and Magli, G., *Gazz. chim. ital.*, **36**, II, 740 (1906).
615. Sullivan, M. X., Hess, W. L., and Howard, H. W., *J. Washington Acad. Sci.*, **32**, 285 (1942).
616. Levintow, L., Price, V. E., and Greenstein, J. P., *J. Biol. Chem.*, **184**, 55 (1950).
617. Abderhalden, E., and Wybert, E., *Ber.*, **49**, 2449 (1916).
618. Hillmann, G., *Z. Naturforsch.*, **1**, 682 (1946).
619. Sondheimer, E., and Holley, R. W., *J. Am. Chem. Soc.*, **76**, 2816 (1954).
620. Pauly, H., *Z. physiol. Chem.*, **42**, 508 (1904).
621. Davis, N. C., *J. Biol. Chem.*, **223**, 935 (1956).
622. Smith, E. L., Spackman, D. H., and Polglase, W. J., *J. Biol. Chem.*, **199**, 801 (1952).
623. Ressler, C., and du Vigneaud, V., *J. Am. Chem. Soc.*, **79**, 4511 (1957).
624. Weil, K., and Kuhn, W., *Helv. Chim. Acta*, **29**, 784 (1946).
625. Nyman, M. A., and Herbst, R. M., *J. Org. Chem.*, **15**, 108 (1950).
626. Bergmann, M., Zervas, L., and Greenstein, J. P., *Ber.*, **65**, 1692 (1932).
626a. Schwyzer, R., and Sieber, P., *Helv. Chim. Acta*, **41**, 1582 (1958).
627. Dekker, C. A., Taylor, S. P., and Fruton, J. S., *J. Biol. Chem.*, **180**, 155 (1949).
628. Curtius, T., and Müller, E., *Ber.*, **37**, 1261 (1904).
629. Boissonnas, R. A., Guttmann, S., Jaquenoud, P. A., and Waller, J. P., *Helv. Chim. Acta*, **39**, 1421 (1956).
630. Mattocks, A. M., and Hartung, W. H., *J. Biol. Chem.*, **165**, 501 (1946).
631. Harris, J. I., and Fruton, J. S., *J. Biol. Chem.*, **191**, 143 (1951).
632. Dunn, F. W., *J. Biol. Chem.*, **227**, 575 (1957).
633. Kinoshita, M., and Umezawa, S., *J. Chem. Soc. Japan*, **72**, 382 (1951).
634. Holland, D. O., and Nayler, J. H. C., *J. Chem. Soc.*, **1953**, 285.
635. Brenner, M., Sailer, E., and Kocher, V., *Helv. Chim. Acta*, **31**, 1908 (1948).
636. Abderhalden, E., and Kempe, M., *Z. physiol. Chem.*, **52**, 207 (1907).
637. Barkdoll, A. E., and Ross, W. F., *J. Am. Chem. Soc.*, **66**, 951 (1944).
638. Fox, S. W., and Minard, F. N., *J. Am. Chem. Soc.*, **74**, 2085 (1952).
638a. Schwyzer, R., Iselin, B., Kappeler, H., Riniker, B., Rittel, W., and Zuber, H., *Helv. Chim. Acta*, **41**, 1273 (1958).
639. Johnson, T. B., and Ticknor, A. A., *J. Am. Chem. Soc.*, **40**, 636 (1918).

640. Piutti, A., *Gazz. chim. ital.*, **18**, 457 (1888).
641. Wegscheider, R., *Monatsh. Chem.*, **37**, 219 (1916).
642. Neuman, R. E., and Smith, E. L., *J. Biol. Chem.*, **193**, 97 (1951).
643. Curtius, T., and Koch, H., *J. prakt. Chem.*, [2] **38**, 473 (1888).
644. Koch, R., and Hanson, H., *Z. physiol. Chem.*, **292**, 180 (1953).
645. Cherbuliez, E., and Plattner, P., *Helv. Chim. Acta*, **12**, 317 (1929).
646. Harington, C. R., and Pitt Rivers, R. V., *Biochem. J.*, **38**, 417 (1944).
647. Sakakibara, S., and Tani, H., *Bull. Chem. Soc. Japan*, **29**, 85 (1956).
648. Angier, R. B., Waller, C. W., Hutchings, B. L., Boothe, J. H., Mowat, J. H., Semb, J., and Subba Row, Y., *J. Am. Chem. Soc.*, **72**, 74 (1950).
649. Prelog, V., and Wieland, P., *Helv. Chim. Acta*, **29**, 1128 (1946).
650. Chiles, H. M., and Noyes, W. A., *J. Am. Chem. Soc.*, **44**, 1798 (1922).
651. Friedman, O. M., and Seligman, A. M., *J. Am. Chem. Soc.*, **76**, 658 (1954).
652. Marvel, C. S., *Org. Syntheses*, **14**, 46 (1934).
653. Röhman, F., *Ber.*, **30**, 1978 (1897).
654. Flěs, D., and Markovac-Prpic, A., *Croat. Chem. Acta*, **29**, 79 (1957).
655. Akabori, S., and Kanekò, T., *Bull. Chem. Soc. Japan*, **11**, 208 (1936).
656. Werbin, H., and Palm, A., *J. Am. Chem. Soc.*, **73**, 1382 (1951).
657. Adams, E., Davis, N. C., and Smith, E. L., *J. Biol. Chem.*, **208**, 573 (1954).
658. Spies, J. R., *J. Am. Chem. Soc.*, **70**, 3717 (1948).
659. Berg, C. P., Rose, W. C., and Marvel, C. S., *J. Biol. Chem.*, **85**, 207 (1929–30).
660. Izumiya, N., and Fruton, J. S., *J. Biol. Chem.*, **218**, 59 (1956).
661. Hashizume, T., *J. Agr. Chem. Soc. Japan*, **25**, 25 (1951).
662. Sachs, H., and Brand, E., *J. Am. Chem. Soc.*, **75**, 4610 (1953).
663. Ruggli, R., Ratti, R., and Henzi, E., *Helv. Chim. Acta*, **12**, 361 (1928).
664. Ben-Ishai, D., and Berger, A., *J. Org. Chem.*, **17**, 1564 (1952).
665. Ben-Ishai, D., *J. Org. Chem.*, **19**, 62 (1954).
666. Erlanger, B. F., and Brand, E., *J. Am. Chem. Soc.*, **73**, 3508 (1951).
667. Erlanger, B. F., and Brand, E., *J. Am. Chem. Soc.*, **73**, 4025 (1951).
668. Erlanger, B. F., and Hall, R. M., *J. Am. Chem. Soc.*, **76**, 5781 (1954).
669. Miller, H. K., and Waelsch, H., *J. Am. Chem. Soc.*, **74**, 1092 (1952).
670. Cipera, J. D., and Nicholls, R. V. V., *Chem. & Ind.*, **1955**, 16.
671. Kollonitsch, J., and Vita, J., *Nature*, **178**, 1307 (1956).
672. Miller, A., Neidle, A., and Waelsch, H., *Arch. Biochem. Biophys.*, **56**, 11 (1955).
673. Velluz, L., Amiard, G., Bartos, J., Goffinet, B., and Heymes, R., *Bull. soc. chim.*, **1956**, 1464.
674. Leach, S. J., and Lindley, H., *Australian J. Chem.*, **7**, 173 (1954).
675. Amiard, G., Heymes, R., and Velluz, L., *Bull. soc. chim.*, **1956**, 97.
676. Clayton, D. W., Kenner, G. W., and Sheppard, R. C., *J. Chem. Soc.*, **1956**, 371.
677. Helferich, B., Schellenberg, P., and Ulbrich, J., *Chem. Ber.*, **90**, 700 (1957).
678. Zahn, H., and Diehl, J. F., *Angew. Chem.*, **69**, 135 (1957); *Z. Naturforsch.*, **12b**, 85 (1957).
679. Bruckner, V., Szekerke, M., and Kovacs, J., *Z. physiol. Chem.*, **309**, 25 (1957).
679a. Erlanger, B. F., Curran, W. V., and Kokowsky, N., *J. Am. Chem. Soc.*, **80**, 1128 (1958).
680. Izumiya, N., and Makisumi, S., *J. Chem. Soc. Japan*, **78**, 662 (1957).
681. North, M. B., and Young, G. T., *Chem. & Ind.*, **1955**, 1597.
682. Vaughan, J. R., *J. Am. Chem. Soc.*, **74**, 6137 (1952).
682a. Weygand, F., and Hunger, K., *Naturwiss.*, **13b**, 50 (1958).
683. Sondheimer, E., and Holley, R. W., *J. Am. Chem. Soc.*, **76**, 2467 (1954).
684. Fox, S. W., and Wax, H., *J. Am. Chem. Soc.*, **73**, 2936 (1951).
685. King, F. E., Clark-Lewis, J. W., and Smith, G. R., *J. Chem. Soc.*, **1954**, 1046.

686. Stedman, R. J., *J. Am. Chem. Soc.*, **79**, 4691 (1951).
687. Brenner, M., Sailer, E., and Rüfenacht, K., *Helv. Chim. Acta*, **34**, 2096 (1951).
688. Karrer, P., and van der Sluys Veer, F. C., *Helv. Chim. Acta*, **15**, 746 (1932).
689. Taurog, A., Abraham, S., and Chaikoff, I. L., *J. Am. Chem. Soc.*, **75**, 3473 (1953).
690. Sifferd, R. H., and du Vigneaud, V., *J. Biol. Chem.*, **108**, 753 (1935).
691. Le Quesne, W. J., and Young, G. T., *J. Chem. Soc.*, **1950**, 1959.
692. Fodor, P. J., Miller, A., Neidle, A., and Waelsch, H., *J. Biol. Chem.*, **203**, 991 (1953).
693. Le Quesne, W. J., and Young, G. T., *Nature*, **163**, 604 (1949).
694. Simmonds, S., Harris, J. I., and Fruton, J. S., *J. Biol. Chem.*, **188**, 251 (1951).
695. Holley, R. W., and Sondheimer, E., *J. Am. Chem. Soc.*, **76**, 1326 (1954).
696. Fruton, J. S., *J. Am. Chem. Soc.*, **70**, 1280 (1948).
697. Anderson, G. W., and Young, R. W., *J. Am. Chem. Soc.*, **74**, 5307 (1952).
698. Harris, J. I., and Work, T. S., *Biochem. J.*, **46**, 196 (1950).
699. Baer, E., Maurukas, J., and Clarke, D. D., *Can. J. Chem.*, **34**, 1182 (1956).
700. Bergmann, M., and Fruton, J. S., *J. Biol. Chem.*, **118**, 405 (1937).
701. Swan, J. M., *Proc. International Wool Research Textile Conf.* (*Australia*), C-175 (1955).
702. Woolley, D. W., *J. Biol. Chem.*, **172**, 71 (1948).
703. Brand, E., Erlanger, B. F., Sachs, H., and Polatnick, J., *J. Am. Chem. Soc.*, **73**, 3510 (1951).
704. Zahn, H., and Schnabel, E., *Ann.*, **604**, 62 (1957).
705. Bergmann, M., and Fruton, J. S., *J. Biol. Chem.*, **117**, 189 (1937).
706. Brand, E., Erlanger, B. F., Polatnick, J., Sachs, H., and Kirschenbaum, D., *J. Am. Chem. Soc.*, **73**, 4027 (1957).
707. Roberts, C. W., *J. Am. Chem. Soc.*, **76**, 6203 (1954).
708. Boissonnas, R. A., Guttmann, S., Jaquenoud, P. A., Waller, J. P., Konzett, H., and Berde, B., *Nature*, **178**, 260 (1956).
709. Fruton, J. S., Bergmann, M., and Anslow, W. P., *J. Biol. Chem.*, **127**, 627 (1939).
710. Bergmann, M., and Zervas, L., *J. Biol. Chem.*, **113**, 341 (1936).
711. Lautsch, W., and Kraege, H-J., *Chem. Ber.*, **89**, 737 (1956).
712. Kenner, G. W., and Stedman, R. J., *J. Chem. Soc.*, **1952**, 2069.
713. Hofmann, K., Kappeler, H., Furlenmeier, A. E., Woolner, M. E., Schwartz, E. T., and Thompson, T. A., *J. Am. Chem. Soc.*, **79**, 1641 (1957).
714. Rittel, W., Iselin, B., Kappeler, H., Riniker, B., and Schwyzer, R., *Helv. Chim. Acta*, **40**, 614 (1957).
715. Waley, S. G., and Watson, J., *J. Chem. Soc.*, **1953**, 475.
716. du Vigneaud, V., Ressler, C., Swan, J. M., Roberts, C. W., Katsoyannis, P. G., and Gordon, S., *J. Am. Chem. Soc.*, **75**, 4879 (1953).
717. Zaoral, M., and Rudinger, J., *Collection Czechoslov. Chem. Communs.*, **20**, 1183 (1955).
717a. Schnabel, E., and Zahn, H., *Ann.*, **614**, 141 (1958).
718. Merrifield, R. B., and Woolley, D. W., *J. Am. Chem. Soc.*, **78**, 4646 (1956).
718a. Schwyzer, R., Iselin, B., Kappeler, H., Riniker, B., Rittel, W., and Zuber, H., *Helv. Chim. Acta*, **41**, 1287 (1958).
719. Schwyzer, R., and Sieber, P., *Helv. Chim. Acta*, **40**, 624 (1957).
720. Smith, G. R., Ph.D. Thesis, Nottingham University, Nottingham, England, 1953.
721. Vaughan, J. R., and Osato, R. L., *J. Am. Chem. Soc.*, **74**, 676 (1952).
722. Anderson, G. W., Blodinger, J., and Welcher, A. D., *J. Am. Chem. Soc.*, **74**, 5309 (1952).
723. Goldschmidt, S., and Lautenschlager, H., *Ann.*, **580**, 68 (1953).
724. Sachs, H., and Brand, E., *J. Am. Chem. Soc.*, **76**, 1815 (1954).
725. Hofmann, K., Magee, M. Z., and Lindenmann, A., *J. Am. Chem. Soc.*, **72**, 2814 (1950).
725a. Hofmann, K., and Magee, M. Z., *J. Am. Chem. Soc.*, **71**, 1515 (1949).

725b. Sheehan, J. C., Goodman, M., and Richardson, W. L., *J. Am. Chem. Soc.*, **77**, 6391 (1955); Bamford, C. H., and Weymouth, F. J., *ibid.*, **77**, 6368 (1955).
726. Grassmann, W., and Schneider, W., *Biochem. Z.*, **273**, 452 (1934).
727. Miller, G. L., Behrens, O. K., and du Vigneaud, V., *J. Biol. Chem.*, **140**, 411 (1941).
728. Gabriel, S., *Ber.*, **40**, 2647 (1907).
729. Kraut, K., and Hartmann, F., *Ann.*, **133**, 99 (1865).
730. Curtius, T., *J. prakt. Chem.*, **24**, 239 (1881).
731. Wieland, T., and Sehring, R., *Ann.*, **569**, 122 (1950).
732. Wieland, T., Kern, W., and Sehring, R., *Ann.*, **569**, 117 (1950).
733. Emery, A. R., and Gold, V., *J. Chem. Soc.*, **1950**, 1443, 1447, 1455.
734. Vaughan, J. R., and Osato, R. L., *J. Am. Chem. Soc.*, **73**, 5553 (1951).
735. Baker, W., Ollis, W. D., and Poole, V. D., *J. Chem. Soc.*, **1950**, 1542.
736. Jackson, R. W., and Cahill, W. M., *J. Biol. Chem.*, **126**, 37 (1938).
737. Steiger, R. E., *Helv. Chim. Acta*, **17**, 555 (1934).
738. Carter, H. E., and Stevens, C. M., *J. Biol. Chem.*, **138**, 627 (1941).
739. Neuberger, A., *Advances in Protein Chem.*, **4**, 297 (1948).
740. Boissonnas, R. A., *Helv. Chim. Acta*, **34**, 874 (1951).
741. Wieland, T., and Bernhard, H., *Ann.*, **572**, 190 (1951).
742. Wieland, T., and Stimming, D., *Ann.*, **579**, 97 (1953).
742a. Kopple, K. D., and Renick, R. J., *J. Org. Chem.*, **23**, 1565 (1958).
743. Borsook, H., and Dubnoff, J. W., *J. Biol. Chem.*, **132**, 307 (1940).
744. Lipmann, F., *Advances in Enzymol.*, **1**, 99 (1941); *Federation Proc.*, **8**, 597 (1949).
745. Warburg, O., and Christian, W., *Biochem. Z.*, **303**, 40 (1939).
746. Cohen, P. P., and McGilvery, R. W., *J. Biol. Chem.*, **166**, 261 (1946); **169**, 119 (1947); **171**, 121 (1947).
747. Speck, J. F., *J. Biol. Chem.*, **168**, 403 (1947); **179**, 1405 (1949).
748. Levintow, L., and Meister, A., *J. Biol. Chem.*, **209**, 265 (1954).
749. Johnston, R. B., and Bloch, K., *J. Biol. Chem.*, **188**, 221 (1951).
750. Chantrenne, H., *Nature*, **160**, 603 (1947); *Biochim. Biophys. Acta*, **2**, 286 (1948).
751. Chantrenne, H., *Nature*, **164**, 576 (1949); *Biochim. Biophys. Acta*, **4**, 484 (1950).
752. Sheehan, J. C., and Frank, V. S., *J. Am. Chem. Soc.*, **72**, 1312 (1950).
753. Bentler, M., and Netter, H., *Z. physiol. Chem.*, **295**, 362 (1953).
754. Katchalsky, A., and Paecht, M., *Bull. Research Council Israel*, **2**, 312 (1952).
755. Katchalsky, A., and Paecht, M., *J. Am. Chem. Soc.*, **76**, 6042 (1954).
756. Atherton, F. R., Openshaw, H. T., and Todd, A. R., *J. Chem. Soc.*, **1945**, 382; Atherton, F. R., and Todd, A. R., *ibid.*, **1947**, 674.
757. Anderson, G. W., Blodinger, J., Young, R. W., and Welcher, A. D., *J. Am. Chem. Soc.*, **74**, 5304 (1952).
758. Young, R. W., Wood, K. H., Joyce, R. J., and Anderson, G. W., *J. Am. Chem. Soc.*, **78**, 2126 (1956).
759. Goldschmidt, S., and Obermeier, F., *Ann.*, **588**, 24 (1954).
759a. Maclaren, J. A., *Australian J. Chem.*, **11**, 360 (1958).
760. Maclaren, J. A., *Proc. International Wool Textile Research Conf.* (*Australia*), C-168 (1955).
761. Vaughan, J. R., *J. Am. Chem. Soc.*, **73**, 1389 (1951).
762. Kenner, G. W., *Chem. Soc. Special Publ.*, **No. 2**, 103 (1955).
763. Michaelis, A., and Schroeter, G., *Ber.*, **27**, 494 (1894).
764. Grimmel, H. W., Guenther, A., and Morgan, J. F., *J. Am. Chem. Soc.*, **68**, 539 (1946).
765. Goldschmidt, S., and Krauss, H. L., *Angew. Chem.*, **67**, 471 (1955).
766. Goldschmidt, S., *Angew. Chem.*, **62**, 538 (1950).
767. Goldschmidt, S., and Jutz, C., *Chem. Ber.*, **89**, 518 (1956).
768. Süs, O., *Ann.*, **572**, 96 (1951).

769. Wieland, T., and Heinke, B., *Ann.*, **599**, 70 (1956).
769a. Schramm, G., and Wissmann, H., *Chem. Ber.*, **91**, 1073 (1958).
770. Wurtz, A., *Ann.*, **71**, 326 (1849); **88**, 314 (1853).
771. Staudinger, H., *Helv. Chim. Acta*, **5**, 87 (1922); Dieckmann, W., and Breest, B., *Ber.*, **39**, 3052 (1906).
772. Naegeli, C., and Tyabji, A., *Helv. Chim. Acta*, **17**, 931 (1934); **18**, 142 (1935).
773. Petersen, S., *Ann.*, **562**, 205 (1949).
774. Goldschmidt, S., and Wick, M., *Ann.*, **575**, 217 (1952); *Z. Naturforsch.*, **5b**, 170 (1950).
775. Fry, A., *J. Am. Chem. Soc.*, **75**, 2686 (1953).
776. Cahours, A., and Hofmann, A. W., *Ann.*, **102**, 285 (1857).
777. Flaschenträger, B., and Halle, F., *Z. physiol. Chem.*, **192**, 253 (1930).
778. Hentschel, W., *Ber.*, **17**, 1284 (1884).
779. Gattermann, L., *Ann.*, **244**, 29 (1888).
780. Siefken, W., *Ann.*, **562**, 75 (1949).
781. Grassmann, W., and Wünsch, E., in *Fortschritte der Chemie organischer Naturstoffe*, Springer, Wien, p. 444, 1956.
782. Chancel, F., *Compt. rend.*, **116**, 330 (1893); Schmidt, E., Hitzler F., and Lahde, E., *Ber.*, **71**, 1933 (1938).
783. Khorana, H. G., *J. Chem. Soc.*, **1952**, 2081; *Chem. Revs.*, **53**, 145 (1953); *Can. J. Chem.*, **31**, 585 (1953); *J. Am. Chem. Soc.*, **76**, 3517 (1954); Khorana, H. G., and Todd, A. R., *J. Chem. Soc.*, **1953**, 2257; Dekker, C. A., and Khorana, H. G., *J. Am. Chem. Soc.*, **76**, 3522 (1954); Hall, R. H., and Khorana, H. G., *ibid.*, **76**, 5056 (1954).
784. Zetzsche, F., and Fredrich, A., *Ber.*, **72**, 1477 (1939); **73**, 1114 (1940); Zetzsche, F., and Roettger, G., *ibid.*, **73**, 465 (1940); Zetzsche, F., and Baum, G., *ibid.*, **75**, 100 (1942).
785. Sheehan, J. C., and Hess, G. P., *J. Am. Chem. Soc.*, **77**, 1067 (1955).
786. Skita, A., and Rolfes, H., *Ber.*, **53**, 1242 (1920).
787. Khorana, H. G., *Chem. & Ind.*, **1955**, 1087.
788. Sheehan, J. C., and Hlavka, J. J., *J. Org. Chem.*, **21**, 439 (1956).
789. Amiard, G., Heymes, R., and Velluz, L., *Bull. soc. chim.*, **1955**, 1464.
790. Amiard, G., and Heymes, R., *Bull. soc. chim.*, **1957**, 1373.
791. Hofmann, K., Woolner, M. E., Spühler, G., and Schwartz, E. T., *J. Am. Chem. Soc.*, **80**, 1486 (1958); Anderson, G. W., and Callahan, F. M., *ibid.*, **80**, 2902 (1958).
791a. Stevens, C. L., and Munk, M. E., *J. Am. Chem. Soc.*, **80**, 4065, 4069 (1958).
792. Walker, J. F., *Formaldehyde, Am. Chem. Soc. Monograph Series*, Rheinhold Publ. Corp., New York, Chapter 14, 1944; French, D., and Edsall, J. T., *Advances in Protein Chem.*, **2**, 278 (1945).
793. Ben-Ishai, D., *J. Am. Chem. Soc.*, **79**, 5736 (1957).
794. Micheel, F., and Thomas, S., *Chem. Ber.*, **90**, 2906, 2909 (1957).
795. Wieland, T., Schäfer, W., and Bokelmann, E., *Ann.*, **573**, 99 (1951).
796. Gordon, M., Miller, J. G., and Day, A. R., *J. Am. Chem. Soc.*, **70**, 1946 (1948).
797. Bodanszky, M., *Nature*, **175**, 685 (1955); *Acta Chim. Acad. Sci. Hung.*, **10**, 335 (1957).
798. Bodanszky, M., Szelke, M., Tömörkiny, E., and Weisz, E., *Chem. & Ind.*, **1955**, 1517; *Acta Chim. Acad. Sci. Hung.*, **11**, 179 (1957).
799. Iselin, B., Rittel, W., Sieber, P., and Schwyzer, R., *Helv. Chim. Acta*, **40**, 373 (1957).
800. Farrington, J. A., Kenner, G. W., and Turner, J. M., *Chem. & Ind.*, **1955**, 601; Farrington, J. A., Hextall, P. J., Kenner, G. W., and Turner, J. M., *J. Chem. Soc.*, **1957**, 1407.
801. Schwyzer, R., Iselin, B., and Feurer, M., *Helv. Chim. Acta*, **38**, 69 (1955).
802. Schwyzer, R., Feurer, M., Iselin, B., and Kägi, H., *Helv. Chim. Acta*, **38**, 80 (1955).

803. Schwyzer, R., Feurer, M., and Iselin, B., *Helv. Chim. Acta*, **38**, 83 (1955).
804. Iselin, B., Feurer, M., and Schwyzer, R., *Helv. Chim. Acta*, **38**, 1508 (1955).
805. Schwyzer, R., and Iselin, B., in *Biochemistry of Nitrogen* (Virtanen Commemoration), Soumalainen Tiedeakatemia, Helsinki, p. 181, 1955.
806. Schwyzer, R., Iselin, B., Rittel, W., and Sieber, P., *Helv. Chim. Acta*, **39**, 872 (1956).
807. Iselin, B., and Schwyzer, R., *Helv. Chim. Acta*, **39**, 57 (1956).
808. Arens, J. F., *Rec. trav. chim. Pays-Bas*, **74**, 769 (1955); U. S. Patent 2,793,204 (1957).
808a. Sheehan, J. C., and Hlavka, J. J., *J. Org. Chem.*, **23**, 635 (1958).
808b. Heslinga, L., and Arens, J. F., *Rec. trav. chim.*, **76**, 982 (1957).
809. Wieland, T., and Schäfer, W., *Ann.*, **576**, 104 (1952).
810. Wieland, T., and Bernhard, H., *Ann.*, **582**, 218 (1953).
811. Kenner, G. W., and Turner, J. M., *Chem. & Ind.*, **1955**, 602.
812. Schwyzer, R., *Helv. Chim. Acta*, **37**, 647 (1954).
812a. Kenner, G. W., Thomson, P. J., and Turner, J. M., *J. Chem. Soc.*, **1958**, 4148.
812b. Schwyzer, R., and Sieber, P., *Helv. Chim. Acta*, **41**, 2190 (1958).
812c. Schwyzer, R., and Gorup, B., *Helv. Chim. Acta*, **41**, 2199 (1958).
813. Bodanszky, M., *Chem. & Ind.*, **1957**, 524.
814. Weygand, F., and Swodenk, W., *Chem. Ber.*, **90**, 639 (1957).
814a. Schwyzer, R., and Sieber, P., *Helv. Chim. Acta*, **41**, 2186 (1958).
815. Wieland, T., and Köppe, H., *Ann.*, **588**, 15 (1954).
816. Pawlewski, B., *Ber.*, **31**, 661 (1898); **35**, 110 (1902).
817. Cronyn, M. W., and Jiu, J., *J. Am. Chem. Soc.*, **74**, 4726 (1952).
818. Sheehan, J. C., and Johnson, D. A., *J. Am. Chem. Soc.*, **74**, 4726 (1952).
819. Wieland, T., and Sieber, D., *Naturwiss.*, **40**, 242, 300 (1953).
820. Wieland, T., Sieber, D.. and Bartmann, W., *Chem. Ber.*, **87**, 1093 (1954).
821. Wieland, T., and Freter, K., *Chem. Ber.*, **87**, 1099 (1954).
822. Katsoyannis, P. G., and du Vigneaud, V., *J. Am. Chem. Soc.*, **78**, 4482 (1956).
823. Davis, N. C., and Smith, E. L., *J. Biol. Chem.*, **200**, 373 (1953).
824. Baddiley, J., and Mathias, A. P., *J. Chem. Soc.*, **1954**, 2803.
825. Botwinik, M. M., Awajewa, S. M., and Misstrjukow, E. A., *Zhur. Obschei Khim.*, **23**, 971, 1716 (1953).
826. Abderhalden, E., and Bahn, A., *Z. physiol. Chem.*, **219**, 72 (1933).
827. Sakami, W., and Toennies, G., *J. Biol. Chem.*, **144**, 203 (1942).
828. Okawa, K., *Bull. Chem. Soc. Japan*, **30**, 976 (1957).
829. Grassmann, W., Wünsch, E., Deufel, P., and Zwick, A., *Chem. Ber.*, **91**, 538 (1958).
830. Wünsch, E., Fries, G., and Zwick, A., *Chem. Ber.*, **91**, 542 (1958).
830a. Zahn, H., and Zürn, L., *Ann.*, **613**, 76 (1958).
831. Bergmann, M., Zervas, L., Rinke, H., and Schleich, H., *Z. physiol. Chem.*, **224**, 26 (1934).
832. Anderson, G. W., Welcher, A. D., and Young, R. W., *J. Am. Chem. Soc.*, **73**, 501 (1951).
833. Levin, Y., Berger, A., and Katchalski, E., *Biochem. J.*, **63**, 308 (1956).
834. Brenner, M., and Burckhardt, C. H., *Helv. Chim. Acta*, **34**, 1070 (1951).
835. Kurtz, A. C., *J. Biol. Chem.*, **140**, 705 (1941).
836. du Vigneaud, V., and Hunt, M., *J. Biol. Chem.*, **125**, 269 (1938).
837. Hunt, M., and du Vigneaud, V., *J. Biol. Chem.*, **127**, 43 (1939).
838. Greenstein, J. P., and Klemperer, F. W., *J. Biol. Chem.*, **128**, 245 (1939).
839. Bergmann, M., and Zervas, L., *Z. physiol. Chem.*, **175**, 145 (1928).
840. Wieland, T., and Schneider, G., *Ann.*, **580**, 159 (1953).
840a. Anderson, G. W., and Paul, R., *J. Am. Chem. Soc.*, **80**, 4423 (1958).
840b. Anderson, G. W., McGregor, A. C., and Young, R. W., *J. Org. Chem.*, **23**, 1236 (1958).

841. Akabori, S., Okawa, K., and Sakiyama, F., *Nature*, **181,** 772 (1958).
842. du Vigneaud, V., and Behrens, O. K., *J. Biol. Chem.*, **117,** 27 (1937).
843. Zervas, L., private communication.
844. Hofmann, K., Rheiner, A., and Peckham, W. D., *J. Am. Chem. Soc.*, **75,** 6083 (1953).
845. Izumiya, N., and Makisumi, S., *J. Chem. Soc. Japan*, **78,** 1768 (1957).
846. Katsoyannis, P. G., *J. Am. Chem. Soc.*, **79,** 109 (1957).
847. Boissonnas, R. A., Guttmann, S., Waller, J.-P., and Jaquenoud, P.-A., *Experientia*, **12,** 446 (1956).
848. Felix, K., and Dirr, K., *Z. physiol. Chem.*, **176,** 29 (1928).
848a. Birnbaum, S. M., and Greenstein, J. P., *Arch. Biochem. Biophys.*, **39,** 108 (1952).
849. Clarke, H. T., and Gillespie, H. B., *J. Am. Chem. Soc.*, **54,** 1964 (1932).
850. Zervas, L., Otani, T., Winitz, M., and Greenstein, J. P., *Arch. Biochem. Biophys.*, **75,** 290 (1958).
851. Baumann, E., *Ann.*, **167,** 77 (1873).
852. Schulze, E., and Winterstein, E., *Ber.*, **32,** 3191 (1899).
853. Ramsay, H., *Ber.*, **41,** 4385 (1908).
854. Greenstein, J. P., *J. Org. Chem.*, **2,** 480 (1937).
855. Kapfhammer, J., and Müller, H., *Z. physiol. Chem.* **225,** 1 (1934).
856. Schütte, E., *Z. physiol. Chem.*, **279,** 52 (1943).
857. Turba, F., and Schuster, K., *Z. physiol. Chem.*, **283,** 27 (1948).
858. Greenstein, J. P., *J. Biol. Chem.*, **109,** 541 (1935).
859. Christensen, H. N., *J. Biol. Chem.*, **160,** 75 (1945).
860. Katchalski, E., and Spitnik, P., *Nature*, **164,** 1092 (1949); *J. Am. Chem. Soc.*, **73,** 3992 (1951).
861. White, J., *J. Biol. Chem.*, **106,** 141 (1934).
862. Loring, H. S., and du Vigneaud, V., *J. Biol. Chem.*, **111,** 385 (1935).
863. Greenstein, J. P., *J. Biol. Chem.*, **124,** 255 (1938).
864. Holly, F. W., Peel, E. W., Luz, E. L., and Folkers, K., *J. Am. Chem. Soc.*, **74,** 4539 (1952).
865. Ressler, C., and du Vigneaud, V., *J. Am. Chem. Soc.*, **76,** 3107 (1954).
866. Pirie, N. W., *Biochem. J.*, **25,** 614 (1931).
867. du Vigneaud, V., Audrieth, L. F., and Loring, H. S., *J. Am. Chem. Soc.*, **52,** 4500 (1930).
868. Rudinger, J., Honzl, J., and Zaoral, M., *Collection Czechoslov. Chem. Communs.*, **21,** 202 (1956).
869. Tani, H., Yuki, H., and Sakibara, S., *Mem. Inst. Fiber Research*, **7,** 100 (1953).
870. Lecher, H., and Holschneider, F., *Ber.*, **57,** 755 (1924).
871. Sheehan, J. C., and Armstrong, W. A., *122nd Meeting of the American Chemical Society*, Abs. No. 23, p. 15M (1952).
872. King, F. E., Clark-Lewis, J. W., and Wade, R., *J. Chem. Soc.*, **1957,** 880.
873. Micheel, F., and Emde, H., *Ber.*, **72,** 1724 (1939).
874. Sheehan, J. C., and Yang, D-D. H., *J. Am. Chem. Soc.*, **80,** 1158 (1958).
875. Cook, A. H., and Heilbron, I. M., in *The Chemistry of Penicillin*, Princeton Univ. Press, p. 958, 1949.
875a. Fleš, D., Markovac-Prpic, A., and Tomašic, V., *J. Am. Chem. Soc.*, **80,** 4654 (1958).
875b. Kipnis, F., and Ornfelt, J., *J. Am. Chem. Soc.*, **73,** 822 (1951); Parham, W. E., and DeLaitsch, D. M., *J. Am. Chem. Soc.*, **76,** 4962 (1954).
875c. Holland, G. F., and Cohen, L. A., *J. Am. Chem. Soc.*, **80,** 3765 (1958).
875d. Pimlott, P. J. E., and Young, G. T., *Proc. Chem. Soc.*, **1958,** 257.
876. Zervas, L., Benoiton, L., Weiss, E., Winitz, M., and Greenstein, J. P., *J. Am. Chem. Soc.*, **81,** 1729 (1959).
877. Ryle, A. P., and Sanger, F., *Biochem. J.*, **60,** 535 (1955).

878. Bergmann, M., Zervas, L., and Fruton, J. S., *J. Biol. Chem.*, **111**, 225 (1935).
879. Semb. J., Boothe, J. H., Angier, R. B., Waller, W. C., Mowat, J. H., Hutchings, B. L., and Subba Row, Y., *J. Am. Chem. Soc.*, **71**, 2310 (1949).
880. John, W. D., and Young, G. T., *J. Chem. Soc.*, **1954**, 2870.
881. Rowlands, D. A., and Young, G. T., *Biochem. J.*, **65**, 516 (1957).
882. Melville, J., *Biochem. J.*, **29**, 179 (1935).
883. Kermack, W. O., and Matheson, N. A., *Biochem. J.*, **65**, 45 (1957).
884. Clark-Lewis, J. W., and Fruton, J. S., *J. Biol. Chem.*, **207**, 477 (1954).
885. Tanenbaum, S. W., *J. Am. Chem. Soc.*, **75**, 1754 (1953).
886. Baker, W., and Jones, P. G., *J. Chem. Soc.*, **1951**, 1143.
887. King, J. A., McMillan, F. H., and Genzer, J. D., *J. Am. Chem. Soc.*, **74**, 5202 (1952).
888. Swan, J. M., *Nature*, **169**, 826 (1952); *Australian J. Sci. Research*, **5A**, 721 (1952).
889. Berenbom, M., and White, J., *J. Am. Chem. Soc.*, **71**, 2246 (1949).
890. Rudinger, J., *Collection Czechoslov. Chem. Communs.*, **19**, 375 (1954).
891. Sachs, H., and Brand, E., *J. Am. Chem. Soc.*, **76**, 1811 (1954).
892. Sheehan, J. C., and Bolhofer, W. A., *J. Am. Chem. Soc.*, **72**, 2469 (1950).
893. Battersby, A. R., and Robinson, J. C., *J. Chem. Soc.*, **1955**, 259; Cason, J., *J. Org. Chem.*, **13**, 227 (1948).
894. Sorm, F., and Rudinger, J., *Collection Czechoslov. Chem. Communs.*, **15**, 491 (1950).
895. Liwschitz, Y., and Zilkha, A., *J. Chem. Soc.*, **1957**, 4394.
896. Stein, W. H., Moore, S., and Bergmann, M., *J. Biol. Chem.*, **154**, 191 (1944).
897. Brand, E., Erlanger, B. F., and Sachs, H., *J. Am. Chem. Soc.*, **74**, 1849 (1952).
898. Sachs, H., and Brand, E., *J. Am. Chem. Soc.*, **75**, 4608 (1953).
899. Hanson, H. T., and Smith, E. L., *J. Biol. Chem.*, **175**, 833 (1948).
900. Albertson, N. F., and Kay, F. C., *J. Am. Chem. Soc.*, **75**, 5323 (1953).
901. Brand, E., Erlanger, B. F., and Sachs, H., *J. Am. Chem. Soc.*, **74**, 1851 (1952).
902. Fruton, J. S., Hearn, W. R., Ingram, V. M., Wiggans, D. S., and Winitz, M., *J. Biol. Chem.*, **204**, 891 (1953).
903. Bergmann, M., and Fruton, J. S., *J. Biol. Chem.*, **145**, 247 (1942).
904. Zervas, L., Otani, T., Winitz, M., and Greenstein, J. P., *J. Am. Chem. Soc.*, **81**, 2878 (1959).
905. Zervas, L., Otani, T., Winitz, M., and Greenstein, J. P., unpublished data.
906. Gish, D. T., Katsoyannis, P. G., Hess, G. P., and Stedman, R. J., *J. Am. Chem. Soc.*, **78**, 5954 (1956).
907. Fischer, R. F., and Whetstone, R. R., *J. Am. Chem. Soc.*, **77**, 750 (1956).
908. Greenstein, J. P., and Price, V. E., *J. Biol. Chem.*, **178**, 695 (1949).
909. Boothe, J. H., Mowat, J. H., Hutchings, B. L., Angier, R. B., Waller, C. W., Stokstad, E. L. R., Semb, J., Gazzola, A. L., and Subba Row, Y., *J. Am. Chem. Soc.*, **70**, 1099 (1948).
910. von Brunn-Leube, I., and Schramm, G., *Chem. Ber.*, **89**, 2045 (1956).
911. Fruton, J. S., Smith, V. A., and Driscoll, P. E., *J. Biol. Chem.*, **173**, 457 (1948).
912. Smith, E. L., and Slonim, N. B., *J. Biol. Chem.*, **176**, 835 (1948).
913. Neurath, H., Elkins, K., and Kaufman, S., *J. Biol. Chem.*, **170**, 221 (1947).
913a. Fölsch, G., *Acta Chem. Scand.*, **12**, 561 (1958).
914. Zervas, L., and Katsoyannis, P. G., *J. Am. Chem. Soc.*, **77**, 5351 (1955).
914a. Sugimura, T., and Paik, W. K., unpublished data.
915. Vaughan, J. R., and Eichler, J. A., *J. Am. Chem. Soc.*, **76**, 2474 (1954).
915a. Okawa, K., *Bull. Chem. Soc. Japan*, **31**, 88 (1958).
916. Fruton, J. S., and Bergmann, M., *J. Biol. Chem.*, **145**, 253 (1942).
917. Roberts, C. W., and du Vigneaud, V., *J. Biol. Chem.*, **204**, 871 (1953).
918. Boissonnas, R. A., and Schumann, I., *Helv. Chim. Acta*, **35**, 2229 (1952).
919. Sheehan, J. C., and Richardson, W. L., *J. Am. Chem. Soc.*, **76**, 6329 (1954).

919a. Katsoyannis, P. G., and du Vigneaud, V., *J. Biol. Chem.*, **233**, 1352 (1958).
920. Work, E., Birnbaum, S. M., Winitz, M., and Greenstein, J. P., *J. Am. Chem. Soc.*, **77**, 1916 (1955).
920a. Wieland, T., and Urbach, H., *Ann.*, **613**, 84 (1958).
921. Sondheimer, E., and Holley, R. W., *J. Am. Chem. Soc.*, **79**, 3767 (1957).
922. Kraml, M., and Bouthillier, L. P., *Canadian J. Chem.*, **33**, 1630 (1955).
923. Hofmann, K., and Bergmann, M., *J. Biol. Chem.*, **134**, 225 (1940).
924. Fruton, J. S., Johnston, R. B., and Fried, M. B., *J. Biol. Chem.*, **190**, 39 (1951).
925. Hanson, H. T., and Smith, E. L., *J. Biol. Chem.*, **179**, 789 (1949).
926. Behrens, O. K., and Bergmann, M., *J. Biol. Chem.*, **129**, 587 (1939).
927. Hamer, D., and Greenstein, J. P., *J. Biol. Chem.*, **193**, 81 (1951).
928. Wiggans, D. S., Winitz, M., and Fruton, J. S., *Yale J. Biol. and Med.*, **27**, 11 (1954).
929. Milne, H. B., and Peng, C-H., *J. Am. Chem. Soc.*, **79**, 645 (1957).
930. Milne, H. B., Halver, J. E., Ho, D. S., and Mason, M. S., *J. Am. Chem. Soc.*, **79**, 637 (1957).
931. Abderhalden, E., Abderhalden, R., Weidle, H., Baertich, E., and Marneweg, W., *Fermentforsch.*, **16**, 98 (1938).
932. du Vigneaud, V., Loring, H. S., and Miller, G. L., *J. Biol. Chem.*, **118**, 391 (1937).
933. Sachs, H., and Waelsch, H., *Arch. Biochem. Biophys.*, **69**, 422 (1957).
934. Sachs, H., and Brand, E., *J. Am. Chem. Soc.*, **76**, 3601 (1954).
935. Abderhalden, E., and Neumann, A., *Fermentforsch.*, **14**, 133 (1934).
936. Greenstein, J. P., *J. Biol. Chem.*, **128**, 241 (1939).
937. Jacobsen, C. F., *Compt. rend. trav. lab. Carlsberg, Sér. Chim.*, **26**, No. 1–2 (1947).
938. Stahmann, M., Fruton, J. S., and Bergmann, M., *J. Biol. Chem.*, **164**, 753 (1946).
939. Vaughan, J. R., *J. Am. Chem. Soc.*, **73**, 3547 (1951).
940. Bergmann, M., Zervas, L., Schleich, H., and Leinert, F., *Z. physiol. Chem.*, **212**, 72 (1932).
941. Simmonds, S., and Fruton, J. S., *J. Biol. Chem.*, **174**, 705 (1948).
942. Wieland, T., and Ohly, K. W., *Ann.*, **605**, 179 (1957).
943. Dunn, F. W., and Dittmer, K., *J. Biol. Chem.*, **188**, 263 (1951).
944. Beecham, A. F., *J. Am. Chem. Soc.*, **79**, 3262 (1957).
945. Yang, P. S., and Rising, M. M., *J. Am. Chem. Soc.*, **53**, 3183 (1931).
946. Franchimont, A. P. N., and Friedmann, H., *Rec. trav. chim.*, **25**, 75 (1906).
947. Dirr, K., and Späth, H., *Z. physiol. Chem.*, **237**, 121 (1935).
948. Baugness, L. C., and Berg, C. P., *J. Biol. Chem.*, **106**, 615 (1934).
949. Brand, E., and Erlanger, B. F., *J. Am. Chem. Soc.*, **72**, 3314 (1950).
950. Abderhalden, E., and Gohdes, W., *Fermentforsch.*, **13**, 52 (1931).
951. Levene, P. A., and Pfaltz, M. H., *J. Biol. Chem.*, **70**, 219 (1926).
952. Abderhalden, E., and Köppel, W., *Fermentforsch.*, **9**, 516 (1928).
953. Thierfelder, H., and von Cramm, E., *Z. physiol. Chem.*, **105**, 58 (1919).
954. Abderhalden, E., and Fodor, A., *Z. physiol. Chem.*, **81**, 1 (1912).
955. Abderhalden, E., Hirsch, P., and Schuler, P., *Ber.*, **42**, 3394 (1909).
956. Abderhalden, E., and Hirsch, P., *Ber.*, **43**, 2435 (1910).
957. Abderhalden, E., and Sickel, H., *Fermentforsch.*, **9**, 462 (1928).
958. Abderhalden, E., and Sickel, H., *Z. physiol. Chem.*, **171**, 93 (1927).
959. Wade, R., Winitz, M., and Greenstein, J. P., *J. Am. Chem. Soc.*, **78**, 373 (1956).
960. Cavallito, C. J., *J. Biol. Chem.*, **164**, 29 (1946).
961. Kögl, F., and Akkerman, A. M., *Rec. trav. chim.*, **65**, 216 (1946).
962. Simmonds, S., Tatum, E. L., and Fruton, J. S., *J. Biol. Chem.*, **169**, 91 (1947).
963. Abderhalden, E., and Reich, F., *Fermentforsch.*, **10**, 173 (1928).
964. Miyamichi, E., *J. Pharm. Soc. Japan*, **95**, 537 (1926).
965. Grassmann, W., and Schulte-Uebbing, E., *Ber.*, **83**, 244 (1950).

966. Levene, P. A., and Pfaltz, M. H., *J. Biol. Chem.*, **68**, 277 (1926).
967. Smith, P. W. G., *J. Chem. Soc.*, **1957**, 3985.
968. Plekhan, M. I., *J. Gen. Chem.*, *U.S.S.R.*, **22**, 1675 (1952).
969. Abderhalden, E., and Schuler, J., *Ber.*, **43**, 907 (1910).
970. Abderhalden, E., and Zeisset, W., *Z. physiol. Chem.*, **200**, 179 (1931).
971. Abderhalden, E., and Vlassopoulos, V., *Fermentforsch.*, **10**, 365, (1929).
972. Abderhalden, E., and Flischmann, R., *Fermentforsch.*, **9**, 524 (1928).
972a. Theodoropoulos, D., *J. Org. Chem.*, **23**, 140 (1958).
973. Hess, W. C., and Sullivan, M. X., *J. Am. Chem. Soc.*, **63**, 881 (1941).
974. Bergmann, M., Schmitt, V., and Miekeley, A., *Z. physiol. Chem.*, **187**, 264 (1930).
975. Abderhalden, E., and Baumann, L., *Ber.*, **41**, 2857 (1908).
976. Levene, P. A., Bass, L. A., and Steiger, R. E., *J. Biol. Chem.*, **81**, 221 (1929).
977. Abderhalden, E., and Brockmann, H., *Fermentforsch.*, **9**, 446 (1928).
978. Abderhalden, E., and Zeisset, W., *Fermentforsch.*, **13**, 330 (1932).
979. Holley, R. W., *J. Chem. Soc.*, **77**, 2552 (1955).
980. Abderhalden, E., and Merkel, R., *Fermentforsch.*, **15**, 1 (1936).
981. Abderhalden, E., *Ber.*, **42**, 2331 (1909).
982. Hofmann, K., and Jöhl, A., *J. Am. Chem. Soc.*, **77**, 2914 (1955).
983. Migliardi, C., *Arch. sci. biol. Italia*, **27**, 327 (1941).
984. Okawa, K., *Bull. Chem. Soc. Japan*, **29**, 486 (1956).
985. Davis, N. C., and Adams, E., *Arch. Biochem. Biophys.*, **57**, 301 (1955).
986. Wieland, H., *Ber.*, **45**, 484 (1912); Willstätter, R., and Waldschmidt-Leitz, E., *ibid.*, **54**, 113 (1921).
987. Shriner, R. L., and Adams, R., *J. Am. Chem. Soc.*, **46**, 1683 (1924).
988. Bergmann, M., and Michalis, G., *Ber.*, **63**, 987 (1930).
989. Patterson, W. I., and du Vigneaud, V., *J. Biol. Chem.*, **111**, 393 (1935).
990. Kendall, E. C., McKenzie, B. F., and Mason, H. L., *J. Biol. Chem.*, **84**, 657 (1929).
991. Waldschmidt-Leitz, E., and Kühn, K., *Chem. Ber.*, **84**, 381 (1951).
992. Weisblat, D. I., Magerlein, B. J., and Myers, D. R., *J. Am. Chem. Soc.*, **75**, 3630 (1953).
993. Hillmann-Elies, A., and Hillmann, G., *Z. Naturforsch.*, **6B**, 340 (1951).
993a. Gawron, O., and Draus, F., *J. Org. Chem.*, **23**, 1040 (1958).
994. Schumann, I., and Boissonnas, R., *Helv. Chim. Acta*, **35**, 2235 (1952); *Nature*, **169**, 154 (1952).
995. Rosenthal, A. F., *J. Org. Chem.*, **22**, 89 (1957).
996. Shankman, S., and Schvo, Y., *J. Am. Chem. Soc.*, **80**, 1164 (1958).
997. Fling, M., and Fox, S. W., *J. Biol. Chem.*, **160**, 329 (1945).
998. Paik, W. K., Birnbaum, S. M., Winitz, M., and Greenstein, J. P., unpublished data.
999. Nienburg, H., *Ber.*, **68**, 2232 (1935).
1000. Fruton, J. S., *J. Biol. Chem.*, **165**, 333 (1946).
1001. Bovarnick, M. R., *J. Biol Chem.*, **148**, 151 (1943).
1002. Akabori, S., and Narita, K., *Proc. Acad. Sci. (Japan)*, **29**, 264 (1953).
1003. Perlmann, G. E., *Advances in Protein Chem.*, **10**, 1 (1955).
1004. Lipmann, F., and Levene, P. A., *J. Biol. Chem.*, **98**, 109 (1932).
1005. Lipmann, F., *Biochem. Z.*, **262**, 3 (1933).
1006. Levene, P. A., and Hill, D. W., *J. Biol. Chem.*, **101**, 711 (1933).
1007. de Verdier, C-H., *Acta Chem. Scand.*, **8**, 1302 (1954).
1008. Schaffer, N. K., May, S. C., Jr., and Summerson, W. H., *J. Biol. Chem.*, **202**, 67 (1953).
1009. Agren, G., de Verdier, C-H., and Glomset, J., *Acta Chem. Scand.*, **5**, 324 (1951).
1010. de Verdier, C-H., *Acta Chem. Scand.*, **7**, 196 (1953).
1011. Manake, C., *J. Biochem.*, **14**, 201 (1931–32).

1012. Plimmer, R. H. A., *Biochem. J.*, **35**, 461 (1941).
1013. Neuberg, C., and Oertel, W., *Biochem. Z.*, **60**, 491 (1914).
1014. Winnick, T., and Scott, E. M., *Arch. Biochem.*, **12**, 201 (1947).
1015. Sciarini, L. J., and Fruton, J. S., *J. Am. Chem. Soc.*, **71**, 2940 (1949).
1016. Wagner-Jauregg, T., O'Neill, J. J., and Summerson, W. H., *J. Am. Chem. Soc.*, **73**, 5202 (1951).
1017. Paplinger, R. E., and Wagner-Jauregg, T., *J. Am. Chem. Soc.*, **75**, 5757 (1953).
1018. Posternak, T., and Grafl, S., *Helv. Chim. Acta*, **28**, 1258 (1945).
1019. Black, S., and Wright, N. G., *J. Biol. Chem.*, **213**, 27 (1955).
1020. Meyerhof, O., and Lohmann, K., *Biochem. Z.*, **196**, 49 (1928).
1021. Lohmann, K., *Biochem. Z.*, **194**, 306 (1928).
1022. Ennor, A. H., Morrison, J. F., and Rosenberg, H., *Biochem. J.*, **62**, 358 (1956).
1023. Zervas, L., *Naturwiss.*, **27**, 317 (1939).
1024. Li, S-O., *J. Am. Chem. Soc.*, **74**, 5959 (1952); Li, S-O., and Eakin, R. E., *ibid.*, **77**, 1866 (1955).
1025. Zervas, L., and Dilaris, I., *J. Am. Chem. Soc.*, **77**, 5354 (1955).
1026. Baum, J., *Z. physiol. Chem.*, **9**, 465 (1885).
1027. Fischer, E., *Ber.*, **32**, 2451 (1899).
1028. Sörensen, S. P. L., Höyrup, M., and Andersen, A. C., *Z. physiol. Chem.*, **76**, 44 (1911).
1029. Felix, K., Müller, H., and Dirr, K., *Z. physiol. Chem.*, **178**, 192 (1928).
1030. Ronwin, E., *J. Org. Chem.*, **18**, 1546 (1953).
1031. Fry, E. M., *J. Org. Chem.*, **15**, 438 (1950).
1032. Voss, W., Guttmann, R., and Klemm, L., *Biochem. Z.*, **220**, 327 (1930).
1033. Reissert, A., *Ber.*, **23**, 2239 (1890); Conrad, W., *J. prakt. Chem.*, **15**, 246 (1877).
1034. Pyman, F. L., *J. Chem. Soc.*, **109**, 186 (1916).
1035. Pauly, H., *Ber.*, **43**, 2243 (1910).
1036. Gerngross, O., *Z. physiol. Chem.*, **108**, 50 (1919).
1037. Weisiger, J. R., *J. Biol. Chem.*, **186**, 591 (1950).
1038. Fones, W. S., *J. Am. Chem. Soc.*, **75**, 4865 (1953).
1039. Itschner, K. F., Drechsler, E. R., Warner, C., and Fox, S. W., *Arch. Biochem. Biophys.*, **53**, 294 (1954).
1040. Ehrlich, F., *Ber.*, **37**, 1809 (1904).
1041. Fischer, E., *Ber.*, **33**, 2370 (1900).
1042. Servigne, M., and Szarvasi, E., *Compt. rend.*, **238**, 1595 (1954).
1043. von Braun, J., *Ber.*, **42**, 839 (1909).
1044. Eck, J. C., and Marvel, C. S., *J. Biol. Chem.*, **106**, 387 (1934).
1045. Fischer, E., and Weigert, F., *Ber.*, **35**, 3772 (1902).
1046. Ross, W. F., and Green, L. S., *J. Biol. Chem.*, **137**, 105 (1941).
1047. Karrer, P., and Ehrenstein, M., *Helv. Chim. Acta*, **9**, 323 (1926).
1048. Goldschmidt, S., and Kinsky, A., *Z. physiol. Chem.*, **183**, 244 (1929).
1049. Hill, E. M., and Robson, W., *Biochem. J.*, **30**, 248 (1936).
1050. Fischer, E., and Mouneyrat, A., *Ber.*, **33**, 2383 (1900).
1051. Sörensen, S. P. L., and Andersen, A. C., *Z. physiol. Chem.*, **56**, 250 (1908).
1052. West, H. D., and Carter, H. E., *J. Biol. Chem.*, **119**, 109 (1937).
1053. Elliott, D. F., *Biochem. J.*, **45**, 429 (1949).
1054. Elks, J., Elliott, D. F., and Hems, B. A., *J. Chem. Soc.*, **1944**, 629.
1055. Fischer, E., *Ber.*, **32**, 3638 (1900).
1056. Fox, S. W., Pettinga, C. W., Halverson, J. S., and Wax, H., *Arch. Biochem.*, **25**, 21 (1950).

PART IV

General
Analytical
Procedures

chapter 11

Colorimetric Methods

1. Introduction. The qualitative and quantitative estimation of each of the α-amino acids which compose a mixture, e.g., protein hydrolysate, may be achieved through the use of chemical, physicochemical (Chapters 12, 13, 17, and 18), microbiological (Chapter 14), biochemical (Chapters 19 and 20), or chromatographic (Chapters 15 and 16) techniques. The chemical approach, which was employed virtually exclusively during the first four decades of the present century, consists in the main of the preliminary separation of each of the component amino acids and its subsequent estimation either gravimetrically or through treatment with a reagent which mediates the formation of a colored solution whose concentration may be determined from the amount of monochromatic light which it transmits at a given wavelength. Use of the latter method must, of course, be based on the premise that the intensity of coloration is proportional to the concentration. Determinations of this type are generally effected either through a comparison of the color intensity of the solution of unknown concentration with that of a standard solution with the aid of a colorimeter or, preferably, through measurement of the light absorbed by the analytical system with the aid of a photometer or spectrophotometer. It is colorimetric methods of the last-mentioned type with which the present discussion will be primarily concerned.

According to Beer's law, the intensity of incident light (I_0) at a certain wavelength transmitted through a solution is affected by a change in the concentration (c) as well as in the thickness (d) of the absorbing material such that the fraction of the light transmitted (I) at the same wavelength by a given thickness of solution undergoes an exponential decrease as the concentration of the solute increases. This relationship may be expressed mathematically as

$$\frac{I}{I_0} = e^{-kcd}$$

where c is expressed in moles per liter, d is given in centimeters, I/I_0 represents the *transmittancy* or the fraction of incident light transmitted by the medium, and k represents the *molar absorption coefficient*, a characteristic of the solute which varies with the solvent, the temperature, and the wavelength of the incident light. The equation may be written alternatively in logarithmic form to the base 10 as follows (ignoring the conversion factor):

$$\log \frac{I}{I_0} = -\epsilon cd \quad \text{or} \quad \log \frac{I_0}{I} = \epsilon cd = D$$

where ϵ represents the molar extinction coefficient at a given wavelength; the value $\log (I_0/I)$ is generally referred to as the *optical density* (D) of the

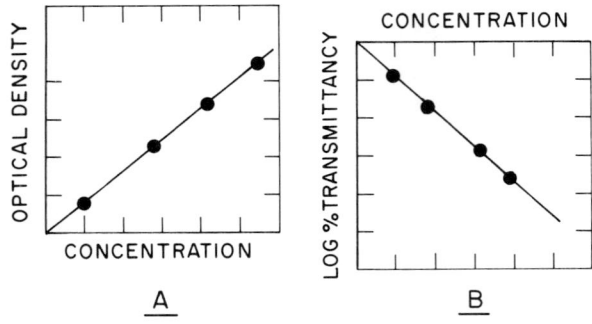

Figure 11-1. Graphical plots of optical density against concentration and log per cent transmittancy against concentration which reveal a conformity with Beer's law.

medium. Thus, for example, a medium which transmits 10% of the incident light at a given wavelength possesses an optical density of one. In any event, the validity of the above relationships is contingent upon the assumptions (a) that each molecule of the absorbing solute behaves independently of any other so that the same fraction of incident light is absorbed by each, (b) that the influence of the colorless solvent remains constant with concentration, and (c) that the light remains monochromatic. If Beer's law applies for any given system, then a graphical plot of either the optical density, $\log (I_0/I)$, or the log per cent transmittancy, $\log (I/I_0)$, against the concentration of the absorbing material (Figure 11-1) should give a straight line which passes through the origin. As the slope of this line is equal to the product ϵd, the molar extinction coefficient can be readily calculated from the known thickness of the absorbing material; hence the equation $c = D/\epsilon d$ permits the concentration of a substance of known molar extinction coefficient to be ascertained after the optical density D at thickness d has been experimentally determined. Although Beer's law is frequently followed, exceptions arise in consequence of association, dissociation, changes in solvation, or other types of molecular interaction.

COLORIMETRIC METHODS

Reagents which are utilized for the colorimetric determination of amino acids may be classified as either specific or general. Specific color reagents are those which mediate color formation by their interaction with a particular moiety in the side chain of a given amino acid, e.g., the guanidino group of arginine, the phenolic ring of tyrosine, the imidazole nucleus of histidine, or the sulfhydryl function of cysteine; further consideration of reactions of this type will be deferred to Volume 3. General color reagents, on the other hand, induce reactions which depend upon the presence of an α-amino function, an α-carboxyl group and/or an α-hydrogen atom, and hence are common to the entire class of α-amino acids. In such instances, the color which develops may be due either to the formation of a colored derivative of the amino acid or to degradation products of the color reagent per se. The end result, in any event, is the production of a hue whose intensity is sufficiently stable and reproducible, under standardized conditions, to permit its reliable measurement with a colorimeter, spectrophotometer, or other suitable instrument. Although the ideal situation would be that wherein the same color intensity arises from different amino acid solutions of identical concentration, such a situation unfortunately is not generally realized in actual practice. It therefore becomes desirable to select reagents and establish conditions such that the influence on color formation attributable to the different amino acid side chains is minimized. Since variations in color yield ordinarily do arise between solutions of different amino acids on an equimolar basis, best practice dictates that the color yield of each of the amino acids be determined relative to that of a selected standard substance. A single calibration curve of the standard substance relating optical density to concentration would then suffice to permit the calculation of the concentration of a solution of any amino acid whose color yield relative to that of the standard substance has been established.

Although innumerable studies have been concerned with the development of methods which would enable amino acids to be determined colorimetrically, the present discussion will be confined to those selected few which have gained widespread usage in routine practice. A more comprehensive treatment of this topic may be found in the lucid treatises of Block and his associates (1). The methods considered herein will be confined principally to colorimetric reactions of α-amino acids mediated by ninhydrin and by copper salts.

2. Photometric Ninhydrin Method. *Principle.* When an aqueous solution of an α-amino acid is subjected to the action of triketohydrindene hydrate (ninhydrin) (I), a violet color is produced which may be attributed primarily to the formation of the anion of diketohydrindylidenediketohydrindamine (VII) (2–5). The initial step of the reaction presumably involves the oxidative deamination of the amino acid (II), via a transitory imino acid

(IV) and α-keto acid (V), to carbon dioxide, ammonia, and an aldehyde (VIII) containing one less carbon atom than the parent amino acid; the reaction proceeds with the simultaneous reduction of the ninhydrin to hydrindantin (III). Condensation of intermediate (III) with the liberated ammonia then yields the desired colored product (VII). That this scheme may represent an oversimplification of the actual sequence arises from the facts that (a) the reaction of ammonia with hydrindantin is slower than the reaction of α-amino acids with this same reagent, and (b) the rate of carbon dioxide liberation from an amino acid-ninhydrin mixture is appreciably greater than that which would be anticipated from the decomposition of an α-keto acid under like conditions. The scheme is nevertheless consistent with the fact that diketohydrindylidenediketohydrindamine (VII) is rapidly formed by the interaction of ammonia with ninhydrin (I) in the presence of a reducing agent capable of converting the latter reagent to hydrindantin (III) (6, 7). It may therefore be presumed that the deamination and the condensation steps are coupled in some manner. In any event, violet-colored solutions are produced whose maximum absorption generally falls in the region of 570 mμ and whose optical densities, when plotted against the concentrations of the reactant α-amino acids, reveal as a rule conformity to Beer's law (6).

In contrast to the afore-mentioned behavior of α-amino acids, the interaction of aqueous solutions of the α-imino acids proline (XI; R = H) and hydroxyproline (XI; R = OH) with *excess* ninhydrin (X) leads to the formation of an adduct (XIII; R = H or OH) with the liberation of carbon dioxide but without the occurrence of concomitant deamination (8). If the reaction is effected in acetic acid media, a yellow-colored solution ensues, whereas the use of a solution at neutral pH results in the development of a purple-red color and the ultimate deposition of a purple-red condensation product. Structures (XII) and (XIII) respectively have been advanced for the yellow and the purple products, the former presumably being an intermediate in the formation of the latter when excess ninhydrin is present and the temperature is raised. Analogous reactions with ninhydrin are shown by pipecolic acid. For purposes of colorimetric estimation, it is pertinent to note that the yellow solutions possess a broad absorption spectrum with

an approximate maximum at 440 mμ; on the other hand, the purple-red solutions exhibit an intense absorption in the region of 550 to 570 mμ (7).

General Considerations. In 1862, Strecker (9) demonstrated that a mixture of alloxan (XIV) and an α-amino acid (XV) in aqueous solution, upon being warmed, reacted with the generation of carbon dioxide and the concomitant development of a deep blue color which could be attributed to the formation of murexide (acid ammonium purpurate) (XVIII). The latter product was isolated as purple-red crystals from the reaction mixture which, in addition, yielded an aldehyde (XVI) containing one less carbon atom than the parent amino acid. Hence an oxidative deamination of the amino acid was instigated by the alloxan reagent. That other reagents may behave as oxidizing agents toward amino acids with similar results was noted nearly fifty years later by Ruhemann (2), who observed that the

interaction of ninhydrin (I) with α-amino acids (II) in neutral aqueous solution was accompanied by the evolution of carbon dioxide, the formation of an aldehyde (VIII), and the development of a deep blue coloration of the reaction mixture. Subsequent studies by this same investigator (3, 4) indicated that the color development was due primarily to the production of the ammonium salt of diketohydrindylidenediketohydrindamine (VII), formed via the action of liberated ammonia on the transitory hydrindantin (III) intermediate. The preparation of the latter compound (III) by the reduction of ninhydrin with hydrogen sulfide indeed demonstrated a further resemblance between the behavior of Ruhemann's reagent and alloxan, the latter of which (XIX) previously had been converted to alloxantin (XX) (cf. 10) upon treatment with hydrogen sulfide (9). In any event, the deep blue coloration imparted to α-amino acids and related compounds by ninhydrin led Ruhemann (3) to predict early that the latter compound should ultimately prove "a most valuable reagent for proteins and their hydrolytic products, since by means of it mere traces of those substances can be recognised."

$$\text{XIX} \xrightarrow{H_2S} \text{XX}$$

The elegant investigations of Ruhemann (2–4) were followed by a succession of reports aimed at demonstrating the general utility of ninhydrin as a reagent for the qualitative detection and quantitative estimation of α-amino acids. Such reports were based on the fact that the reaction between an α-amino acid and ninhydrin proceeds with the formation of products, i.e., an aldehyde, ammonia, carbon dioxide, and a colored compound, each of which may provide a convenient measure of the initial amount of α-amino acid. In consequence, methods are presently available for the facile estimation both of volatile aldehyde and of liberated ammonia; determination of the former compound is applicable only to a limited number of α-amino acids, whereas determination of the latter compound suffers from the disadvantage that quantitative ammonia liberation is not achieved with several of the amino acids (Section 12–2). On the other hand, the carbon dioxide evolved has permitted an accurate estimation of micro amounts of virtually all available α-amino acids because the liberation of this gas is highly specific and the methods utilized for its determination are highly precise (Section 12–2). It nevertheless has been found convenient, under many circumstances, to measure amino acids in terms of the amount of colored product formed during the reaction. Toward this end, Abderhalden and Schmidt (11) in 1911 demonstrated that the color formation mediated by ninhydrin was generally applicable to a large number of α-amino acids, peptides, and proteins, and reaffirmed the remarkable sensitivity of the reaction initially observed by Ruhemann. However, early attempts (12–15) to adapt the colorimetric reaction to the quantitative estimation of α-amino acids were attended by poorly reproducible results and low color yields. Such attempts were more recently resumed with the advent of column chromatography (Chapter 15), which permitted the facile and quantitative separation of α-amino acids from protein hydrolysates and hence emphasized the urgent need for a colorimetric method which would enable a rapid and precise estimation of amino acids in the effluent fractions to be made. This need was met in 1948 by Moore and Stein (6), who devised conditions such that the color arising from the ninhydrin-amino acid interaction was of sufficient stability and reproducibility to permit its reliable measurement with a photometer. Various modifications of this procedure which have since appeared will be described in the appropriate sections below. For the present, it will suffice to note that, with most α-amino acids of the structure $RCH(NH_2)CO_2H$, the purple color induced by the ninhydrin reagent exhibits a maximum absorption at approximately 570 mμ, although slight deviations from this value may occur from one amino acid to the other; for the sake of convenience, however, this wavelength has been adopted as standard in the routine quantitative assay of α-amino acids.

That the α-imino acids proline and hydroxyproline react with aqueous solutions of ninhydrin in an entirely different fashion than do the α-amino acids was demonstrated by Grassmann and von Arnim (8) in 1934, and has already been referred to. The observation that the yellow condensation product (XII) revealed no band in the infrared spectrum corresponding to a free imino group, together with the fact that the purple condensation product (XIII) possessed ultraviolet and visible absorption spectra similar to those of analogously derived compounds of the isatin-blue series (see below), lent support to the structures assigned to these respective compounds by Johnson and McCaldin (8). The interaction of ninhydrin with pipecolic acid in aqueous solution follows a reaction course comparable to that described for proline and hydroxyproline, except that the yellow intermediate corresponding to (XII) is relatively less stable, but can nevertheless often be observed as a transient color.

Illustrative procedure 11–1 (8). Condensation of DL-proline with ninhydrin. A solution of 250 mg. of DL-proline, 850 mg. of ninhydrin, and 1.6 g. of phosphate buffer powder (*p*H 7) in 25 ml. of water is warmed over a water bath at 60°; the yellow color possessed by the solution at room temperature gradually changes to a purple-red color. During the course of the reaction, a precipitate forms whose deposition is virtually complete after 40 min. The reaction mixture, which reveals a strong odor of pyrrolidine, is permitted to stand at room temperature for several hours, after which time the purple-brown precipitate is recovered via filtration, washed copiously with hot water, and dried *in vacuo* over sulfuric acid. A 646-mg. (83%) yield of the desired compound (XIII; R = H) is so secured; it melts with decomposition over the range 176–200°. The compound may be purified, according to Johnson and McCaldin (8), by passing its chloroform solution over a column of deactivated alumina, followed by concentration of the eluate to a small volume; with L-proline as starting material there emerge crystals of (XIII) as purple needles with a metallic sheen and an m.p. at 176° (d.). A comparable procedure may be employed to secure the corresponding derivative from hydroxyproline (m.p. 132–133°), and from pipecolic acid (m.p. 238°).

At this point, it should be noted that compounds which incorporate the grouping —C(=O)—(C=C)$_n$—C(=O)—, wherein at least one of the carbonyl functions is ketonic, are capable with only a few exceptions of mediating the degradation of an α-amino acid to an aldehyde, carbon dioxide, and ammonia (cf. 16) (see Chapter 12). Compounds in this class include pyruvic acid, biacetyl, benzil, and phenylglyoxal, among others. Although ninhydrin and alloxan also fall in this category, these reagents possess the additional attribute of undergoing degradation to colored condensation products during the course of the reaction. A similar propensity is possessed by isatin (XXI), which, upon interaction with proline (XXII; R = H) or hydroxyproline (XXII; R = OH) in aqueous solution at pH 7, undergoes conversion to a blue-colored condensation product (XXIII) whose structure is analogous to that of the product (XIII) which arises from treatment of these

same imino acids with ninhydrin under comparable conditions (8). Such reaction has permitted the use of isatin as a reagent for the colorimetric estimation of proline and hydroxyproline (Sections 29–2 and 35–2); however, because of the diversity of colors which result from its interaction with different α-amino acids, isatin does not serve as a suitable reagent for the quantitative determination of these compounds.

Conditions Employed. Attempts to utilize ninhydrin for the colorimetric estimation of α-amino acids led to the early observation that the color yields obtained per microgram of α-amino acid underwent a marked diminution as the concentration of amino acid was reduced (13–15, 17–20). This phenomenon, as well as the non-reproducible nature of the reaction, was investigated in 1948 by Moore and Stein (6), who observed that such difficulties could be ascribed primarily to the presence in the reaction mixture of dissolved oxygen which oxidized the hydrindantin formed during the oxidative deamination. This oxidative side reaction could be eliminated either by the performance of the reaction in a system previously evacuated to eliminate entrapped oxygen or by the direct addition of a strong reducing agent such as stannous chloride to the reaction medium. With this in mind, Moore and Stein described a method whereby the desired color was developed by heating a solution containing an amino acid, ninhydrin, and stannous chloride in a citrate buffer-methyl Cellosolve (ethylene glycol monomethyl ether) mixture at pH 5 for 20 minutes in a boiling water bath; consistent and reproducible results were obtained upon photometric measurement at 570 mμ of the bluish purple color formed with an α-amino acid and at 440 mμ of the yellow color formed with proline and hydroxyproline. The absorption spectra indicated that all the common α-amino acids, with the single exception of cysteine, gave the blue diketohydrindylidenediketohydrindamine of Ruhemann as the major colored end product. Although reproducible results could be obtained with any given α-amino acid, an obvious, albeit minor, disadvantage was presented by the fact that the same amount of color per mole was not necessarily given by each of the different amino acids. Thus, for example, the color yields shown by leucine, phenylalanine, and glutamic acid were 93, 82, and 98%, respectively, of the amount of color given by a pure sample of diketohydrindylidenediketohydrindamine under the same conditions; however, quantitative values could be secured by the use of a factor appropriate for the amino acid under consideration. Although subsequent modifications of the afore-mentioned procedure have rendered color yields which more closely approximate the theoretically expected values, the method initially developed by Moore and Stein (6) has proved of inestimable value in that it provided, for the first time, a means whereby colorimetric measurement of the reaction between ninhydrin and an α-amino acid could be reliably placed on a quantitative basis.

In an effort to find an explanation for the apparent lack of stoichiometry revealed in the photometric ninhydrin method of Moore and Stein (6), Troll and Cannan (7) became particularly impressed by the observation of these investigators that the colors formed during the reaction faded slowly after several hours of standing at room temperature. This observation led to the inference that the exposure of the reaction system of Moore and Stein to a temperature of 100° during the color development was, at the same time, accompanied by some destruction of diketohydrindylidenediketohydrindamine. Conditions were thereupon sought which would permit the rate of formation of the latter compound to be increased relative to its rate of destruction. Toward this end, it was found that the time of heating at 100° could be materially shortened if organic solvents, such as alcohol, dioxane, methyl Cellosolve, pyridine, or phenol, were present to increase the rate of color development. A phenol-pyridine system containing 20% water was adopted as the solvent of choice while potassium cyanide was selected as the reducing agent in lieu of the less stable stannous chloride or ascorbic acid. Interaction of an α-amino acid and ninhydrin in such a system at 100° for 3 to 5 minutes, followed by measurement of the color yield at 570 mμ, revealed color values relative to diketohydrindylidenediketohydrindamine which were in most instances quantitative or very nearly quantitative (procedure 11–2); notable exceptions were lysine and tryptophan, whose color yields corresponded to 110% and 75%, respectively, of the expected values. Proline and hydroxyproline gave yellow colors which possessed a broad absorption with a maximum at 440 mμ; however, since the absorption of the ninhydrin reagent per se is quite marked in this region of the spectrum, the yellow color is not particularly well suited to photometric measurement.

Illustrative procedure 11-2 (7). Reagents: (a) *Ninhydrin solution*—500 mg. of ninhydrin is dissolved in 10 ml. of absolute ethanol; (b) *80% phenol solution*—80 g. of reagent grade phenol is dissolved in 20 ml. of absolute ethanol with gentle warming, the solution is shaken for 20 min. with 1 g. of Permutit to remove traces of ammonia, and the solid material discarded after decantation; (c) *KCN-pyridine reagent*—2 ml. of a 0.01M solution of KCN is diluted to 100 ml. with ammonia-free pyridine (prepared by shaking 100 ml. of pyridine with 1 g. of Permutit for 20 min.); (d) *60% ethanol*—mix 60 ml. of ethanol with 40 ml. of water. All reagents should be stable upon storage at room temperature for a month. The 80% phenol solution is shaken with Permutit weekly in order to eliminate possible trace contamination by ammonia vapors.

Method of analysis: A solution of 0.05 to 0.5 micromole of the amino acid in 0.5 ml. or less of water is adjusted to any pH between 1 and 8 and is then heated over a boiling water bath with a mixture of 1 ml. of the KCN-pyridine reagent and 1 ml. of the 80% phenol solution. After the reaction mixture has reached the water-bath temperature, it is treated with 0.2 ml. of the ninhydrin solution, the reaction vessel is stoppered, and the heating is continued for an additional 3–5 min. The solution is cooled to room temperature, diluted to 10 ml. with 60% ethanol, and its optical density determined at 570 mμ with a spectrophotometer. Four-tenths to 0.5 ml. of ammonia-free water, subjected to the same procedure, serves as a reagent blank.

Calculation of results: The color yield obtained with each amino acid by the afore-mentioned method is not identical but varies, relative to a molar equivalent of pure diketohydrindylidenediketohydrindamine taken as 100%, as follows: alanine, 102.0; arginine, 98.0; aspartic acid, 98.6; glutamic acid, 99.0; glycine, 98; histidine, 102.0; isoleucine, 100; leucine, 100.1; lysine, 110.5; methionine, 102.0; phenylalanine, 100.1; serine, 99.0; threonine, 102.6; tryptophan, 75.4; tyrosine, 98.8; valine, 100. Since these color yields relative to valine (or any of the other amino acids) are established at the same time, a calibration curve may be prepared from a graphical plot of optical density against micromoles of valine; for this purpose, experimental values are secured with 0.5-ml. aqueous samples of valine at six concentrations ranging from 0.05 to 0.5 micromole. Spectrophotometric readings taken at 570 mμ for a solution of any of the above amino acids are first converted to "micromoles valine" using the valine calibration curve; these values are then divided by the relative per cent color yield of that particular amino acid to obtain its concentration in micromoles.

As an alternative approach, the equation $c = D/\epsilon d$ may be employed in the determination of an amino acid of unknown concentration if both its optical density at thickness d and its extinction coefficient are known. The *millimolar extinction coefficients* have been determined at 570 mμ for several amino acids as follows: alanine, 22.0; arginine, 21.1; aspartic acid, 21.3; glutamic acid, 21.4; glycine, 21.1; histidine, 22.0; isoleucine, 21.6; leucine, 21.8; lysine, 23.8; methionine, 22.0; phenylalanine, 21.8; serine, 21.4; threonine, 22.1; tryptophan, 16.3; tyrosine, 21.3; valine, 21.6. Use of these values leads to a calculation of the concentration in terms of millimole units.

The report of Troll and Cannan (7) was followed some two years later by a study wherein Yemm and Cocking (21) were able to obviate the use of the

COLORIMETRIC METHODS

pyridine-phenol solvent but still retain the high color yields which were generally characteristic of the earlier method. Such modified procedure, which implicated aqueous methyl Cellosolve as the reaction medium, permitted the development of color yields equivalent to $100 \pm 1\%$ of pure diketohydrindylidenediketohydrindamine for all the common α-amino acids with the notable exceptions of the 89, 89, 83, and 108% yields shown respectively by tyrosine, phenylalanine, tryptophan, and lysine; proline and hydroxyproline reacted as usual with the formation of a yellow-colored condensation product. A description of this method, as further modified by Rosen (22), appears in procedure 11–3.

Illustrative procedure 11–3 (22). Reagents: (a) *Sodium cyanide solution*—dissolve 490 mg. (0.01 mole) of sodium cyanide in 1 l. of water; (b) *acetate buffer*—a mixture of 2700 g. of sodium acetate trihydrate, 2 l. of water, and 500 ml. of glacial acetic acid is diluted to 7.5 l. with water to give a solution with a pH of 5.3–5.4; (c) *cyanide-acetate solution*—20 ml. of the above sodium cyanide solution is diluted to 1 l. with the acetate buffer; (d) *3% ninhydrin solution*—3 g. of ninhydrin is dissolved in 100 ml. of methyl Cellosolve (this reagent should give a clear solution when mixed with an equal volume of water and should give a negative or very faint peroxide test with 10% aqueous potassium iodide); (e) *diluent*—mix 50 ml. of water with 50 ml. of isopropyl alcohol.

Method of analysis: To a 1-ml. sample containing 0.02–0.40 micromole of an amino acid is added 0.5 ml. of cyanide-acetate buffer and 0.5 ml. of 3% ninhydrin solution. The reaction mixture is heated in a stoppered tube for 15 min. at 100° over a steam bath; maximal color develops after 10–12 min. After its removal from the steam bath, the reaction mixture is treated with 5 ml. of the isopropyl alcohol-water diluent, shaken vigorously, and permitted to cool to room temperature. Measurement of the color density is effected at 570 mμ for all amino acids with the exception of proline and hydroxyproline, which are measured at 440 mμ. If the optical density in a given series of tubes is too high to be accurately determined (0.8 or greater), further 5-ml. portions of diluent should be added. Certain precautions to be observed with this procedure are given as follows: (a) no admixture of the cyanide-acetate and the 3% ninhydrin solutions should be effected prior to the analysis since the resulting solution is unstable; (b) the water-isopropyl alcohol diluent should be added to the reaction mixture immediately upon its removal from the steam bath, since prior cooling results in high blanks; (c) minimum blanks are secured only after the reaction mixtures have been permitted to cool to room temperature; (d) the water-methyl Cellosolve ratio must be maintained at 1 : 1 since an excess of the former solvent leads to precipitation of the ninhydrin reagent while an excess of the latter increases the blank value.

With the afore-mentioned procedure, all samples after removal from the water bath possess a deep red color which fades rapidly when the mixture is shaken and/or cooled; the resultant blank is colorless or faint blue in the isopropyl alcohol-water diluent. The final color fades by less than 2% in 24 hr. Except for proline and hydroxyproline, which incite the formation of a yellow color with the ninhydrin reagent, α-amino acids generally exhibit a purple color.

Calculation of results: The percentage color yields for several α-amino acids relative to that of leucine taken as 100% are given as follows: lysine, 103; alanine, arginine, aspartic acid, glutamic acid, glutamine, glycine, histidine, isoleucine, ornithine, taurine, and valine, 100; methionine, serine, and threonine, 97; phenylalanine and tyrosine, 96; and ammonia about 60. In each instance, a plot of optical density versus concentration of amino acid reveals a conformity to Beer's law over concentrations which range from 0 to 0.4 micromole of amino acid and 5, 10, 15 or 20 ml. of diluent per tube; such data are shown for leucine in Fig. 11–2. For purposes of calculation, a calibration curve relating optical density

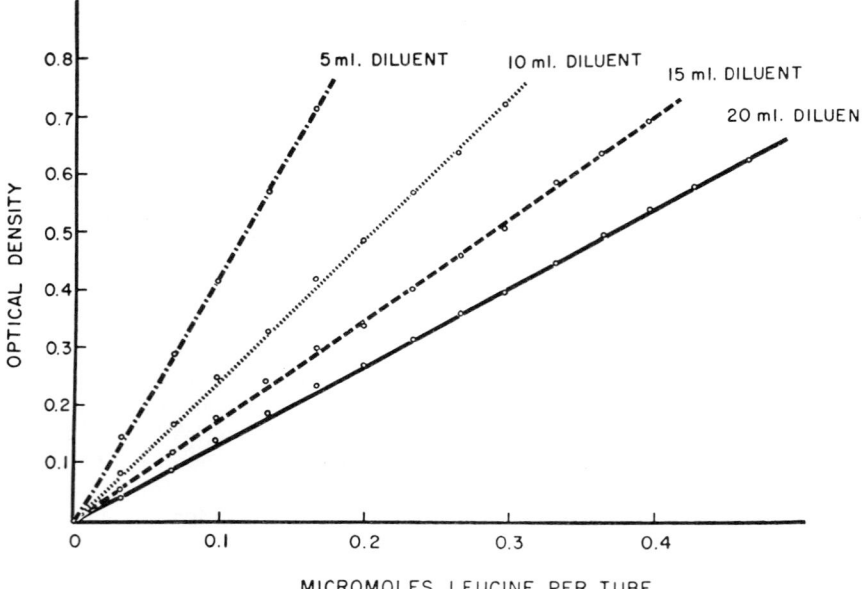

Figure 11–2. Ninhydrin-leucine color yields at 570 mμ obtained after heating for 15 minutes at 100°. Rosen, H., *Arch. Biochem. Biophys.*, **67**, 10 (1957).

to concentration may be obtained with 1.0-ml. aqueous samples of leucine at several concentrations ranging from 0.02 to 0.40 micromole with 5 ml. of diluent. If the optical density obtained with an amino acid solution of unknown concentration is 0.8 or greater, 5-ml. portions of diluent should be added until a more sensitive measurement range is reached; in such instances, the concentration ultimately calculated with the aid of the calibration curve (see calculation of results in procedure 11–2) is multiplied by $(7 + V)/7$, where V is the volume of additional diluent, in order to obtain the concentration prior to dilution.

Scope and Limitations. At the present time, the photometric ninhydrin method is the most widely utilized of all available colorimetric methods for the quantitative determination of α-amino acids. The method is sufficiently general to permit the precise estimation of most of the amino acids likely to be encountered in protein hydrolysates or other materials of biological origin and, indeed, is currently used almost exclusively in conjunction with column or paper chromatography techniques (Chapter 15). Since ninhydrin will react with other classes of compounds such as peptides, primary and secondary amines, ammonia or amino alcohols, the method cannot be considered specific for α-amino acids. Hence the estimation of the latter class of compounds requires the prior removal of interfering substances. Additionally, the use of this method with unfractionated biological materials is precluded because the color intensity is not a constant for equivalent amounts of different amino acids or other ninhydrin-reactive materials. However, no like difficulty attends the determination of individual amino acids, since a plot of the optical density versus the amino acid concentration for each yields a standard curve which is linear over a wide range of concentration and thus, with the proper precautions, leads to results which are readily reproducible. Indeed, both the marked sensitivity and the high degree of precision permitted with the method are strikingly illustrated by the fact that the readings with 0.2 micromole of an α-amino acid can be invariably reproduced to within 0.02 of an optical density unit, corresponding to an accuracy of about 2% (6).

At this point, it is worthy of note that all α-amino acids with the exception of cysteine react with ninhydrin to yield diketohydrindylidenediketohydrindamine as the major colored end product. Somewhat higher than normal color yields are given by lysine, presumably as a consequence of partial reaction of the ε-amino group, whereas low color yields are generally characteristic of tryptophan and cystine. The interaction of ninhydrin and cysteine, on the other hand, leads to the formation of a yellow-colored product whose absorption curve is similar to that revealed by proline and hydroxyproline (6). However, the quantitative or nearly quantitative formation of diketohydrindylidenediketohydrindamine arises from the use of cysteic acid in lieu of cysteine in such systems. In practice, therefore, cystine and cysteine samples are first quantitatively oxidized via the action of bromine under alkaline conditions, and the cysteic acid so derived then estimated colorimetrically after treatment with the ninhydrin reagent (23).

Although the photometric ninhydrin method can be expected to give reliable and reproducible results *under a given set of conditions*, the relative color yields shown by the different amino acids may vary with the conditions imposed (cf. 23). Such variations may arise as a consequence of the rate or time of heating, the exact temperature of the water bath, the relative proportion and quality of the reagents employed, and a host of other factors. Hence it becomes highly probable that a different order of color yields could be observed in different laboratories by investigators who to all intents and purposes employ the same procedure. On this basis, it becomes a virtual necessity that the color values given in the literature for any method be adequately verified before they may be used with any measure of reliability.

3. Copper Complex Method. *Principle.* In all but a few instances, two molecules of an α-amino acid (XXV) and one cupric ion (XXVI) interact stoichiometrically with a concomitant deepening of the blue color of the solution due to the formation of the blue-colored amino acid-copper complex (XXVII). The increase in the color intensity which so arises is not necessarily the same for each of the different amino acids. However, since Beer's law is obeyed in the case of any given amino acid, it follows that the con-

$$NH_2CHRCO_2H + Cu^{2+} \rightarrow \begin{array}{c} CO\text{——}O \quad NH_2\text{—}CHR \\ \diagdown \quad \diagup \\ Cu \\ \diagup \quad \diagdown \\ CHR\text{—}NH_2 \quad O\text{——}CO \end{array} + 2H^+$$

XXV　　　　XXVI　　　　　　　　XXVII　　　　　　　XXVIII

centration of a solution of that particular amino acid, as its complex copper salt, may be quantitatively estimated with the aid of a standard curve relating optical density to concentration.

General Considerations. During the first decade of the present century, Ley (24) demonstrated that the interaction of a hot aqueous solution of glycine with an excess of copper carbonate caused the solution to assume a deep blue color, a phenomenon which could be ascribed to the formation of a complex incorporating exactly one molecule of copper and two molecules of glycine (Chapter 6). That a like 1 : 2 ratio of copper to α-amino acid obtains where alanine, arginine·HCl, aspartic acid, glutamic acid, hydroxyproline, isoleucine, leucine, lysine·HCl, methionine, phenylalanine, proline, serine, threonine, tryptophan, tyrosine, or valine replaces glycine was subsequently reported by other investigators (25–29), all of whom observed the deep blue-colored solutions characteristically exhibited by the corresponding complex. Only the histidine-copper complex possesses a constitution which deviates from the above ratio, the amount of copper here being about 93% of that required for a composition of two molecules of the metal to three molecules of the amino acid (27, 29). Dipeptides and tripeptides, on the other hand, react with one molecule of copper per peptide molecule (25, 28); an exception is presented by dialanylcystine, which reacts with two copper molecules (29). Whereas the copper complexes of dipeptides like those of amino acids give blue solutions under slightly alkaline conditions, purple solutions are given by tripeptides under comparable circumstances (28, 29).

Several methods for the determination of α-amino acids have been developed which are based primarily on the stoichiometric 1 : 2 ratio of metal to amino acid generally found in the amino acid-copper complex. Thus an iodometric procedure is available wherein the amino acid to be determined is converted to its complex copper salt upon treatment with copper hydroxide or copper phosphate in aqueous solution, the excess copper reagent is removed by filtration or centrifugation, and the soluble copper in the supernatant liquid is determined by interaction with a solution of potassium iodide in acetic acid, followed by titration of the iodine thereupon liberated with standard sodium thiosulfate (27, 30); in such manner, the amount of copper in solution and hence the amino acid concentration become known. The copper in the soluble amino acid–copper complex may be alternatively determined either by photometric measurement of the yellow color produced after treatment of the solution with diethyldithiocarbamate (25) or via polarographic analysis (26). However, a spectrophotometric method based on the color intensity of the amino acid–copper complex undoubtedly provides the simplest and most convenient of all presently available procedures. Reliable use of such a method necessitates that proper consideration be given to the variations in the color intensity often shown by equimolar concentrations of the copper complexes of different amino acids; for example, the relative color intensities at 620 mμ produced by 0.025M solutions of the copper complexes of glycine, proline, and tryptophan, as compared to the intensity of the corresponding alanine complex taken as 100%, are 79.8, 123.7, and 108.9% respectively. That less variable values could be secured if a very large excess of alanine (XXIX) is added to the pertinent amino acid–copper complex (XXX) was shown by Spies and Chambers (29), who here exploited the principle of mass action to favor the transformation of the alanine (XXIX) reactant into its corresponding copper

```
        CH₃         CO——O   NH₂—CHR                       R           CO——O   NH₂—CHCH₃
         |              \   /                             |               \   /
   NH₂CHCO₂H +           Cu            ⇌         NH₂CHCO₂H +               Cu
                        /   \                                             /   \
                    CHR—NH₂  O——CO                                   CH₃CH—NH₂  O——CO
        XXIX             XXX                          XXXI                    XXXII
```

complex (XXXII). Application of such a reaction scheme to the copper complexes of arginine, aspartic acid, glutamic acid, glycine, hydroxyproline, isoleucine, leucine, lysine, methionine, phenylalanine, proline, serine, threonine, tryptophan, tyrosine, and valine led to the development of color intensities which ranged between 98.2 and 103.6% of that given by the alanine standard; on the other hand, a relative color intensity of 123.6% was revealed in the case of histidine, whose atypical behavior in this respect may be correlated with its apparent lack of conformity to the compositional 1 : 2 ratio of copper to amino acid. That like behavior is not evidenced for measurements carried out in the ultraviolet region of the spectrum was subsequently shown by Spies (31) who, for example, found relative color intensities of 83.5 and 144.1% for the copper complexes of histidine and tryptophan, respectively, at 230 mμ. Since absorption measurements in this region of the spectrum proved to be over 100 times as sensitive as those taken at 620 mμ, these measurements could serve as the basis of a simple, rapid, and accurate spectrophotometric micromethod for the quantitative estimation of amino acids as their copper salts. It is this method with which the following paragraphs are primarily concerned.

Conditions Employed. Estimation of α-amino acids by the method of Spies (31) involves the initial conversion of the appropriate amino acid to its copper complex by treatment of a solution of the former in sodium borate buffer, at *p*H 9.1 to 9.2, with an excess of cupric chloride; the last-mentioned reagent is preferable to the copper phosphate suspensions employed in earlier investigations (25–30) by virtue of its stability and the fact that it requires no special preparation. After storage of the reaction mixture at room temperature for exactly 10 minutes, the suspension is centrifuged for exactly 5 minutes and the transmittancy value of the clear centrifugate determined at 230 mμ. That the time intervals given for each operation should be closely adhered to for best results is indicated by the fact that the ultraviolet absorbing capacity of the alanine-copper complex undergoes an appreciable decrease with time in the presence of excess cupric chloride reagent; thus losses of 5, 7, 9, 15, and 20% in the absorbing capacity are incurred upon storage of the reaction mixture for 5, 10, 15, 30, and 60 minutes, respectively, prior to the centrifugation step, although a loss of only 1.6% ensues 60 minutes after removal of the excess cupric chloride reagent. Nevertheless, if the directions as given in procedure 11-4 are followed with moderate care, entirely reliable and reproducible results will be obtained.

Illustrative procedure 11-4 (31). Reagents: (*a*) *Copper chloride solution*—this reagent contains 8.52 g. of reagent grade cupric chloride dihydrate per liter of water solution; (*b*) *sodium borate buffer* (*p*H 9.1–9.2)—a solution of 40.3 g. of reagent grade anhydrous sodium tetraborate is brought to a total volume of 4 l. with water and filtered. For use in the procedure, 6.0 g. of reagent grade sodium chloride is dissolved in 100 ml. of the borate solution.

Method of analysis: To 5.0 ml. of sodium borate buffer-NaCl solution in a 25 ml. glass-stoppered centrifuge tube is added 5.0 ml. of an aqueous solution containing 50 to 500 micromoles of the α-amino acid. The solution is treated with 0.1 ml. of copper chloride solution, shaken, and then permitted to stand for 10 min. at a convenient room temperature, the same temperature (±1°) being used for all determinations. The suspension is centrifuged in the stoppered tube for 5 min., the clear solution carefully decanted into a clean quartz cuvette, and the transmittancy of the solution determined at 230 mμ with the aid of a spectrophotometer. Blank solutions may be prepared by the addition of 5.0 ml. of the amino acid solution to 5.0 ml. of the sodium borate buffer in order to check for slight variations in absorbancy due to distilled water or other causes.

Calculation of results: As the absorbancy is not necessarily the same at a given wavelength for equimolar solutions of different amino acid-copper complex salts,

COLORIMETRIC METHODS

it is convenient for purposes of calculation to represent the per cent absorbancy of each of these compounds relative to that of the alanine-copper complex taken as 100. Such data at 230 mμ for the copper complexes of several of the more common α-amino acids are given as follows: alanine, 100%; arginine, 103.3; aspartic acid, 96.9; cystine, 80.9; glutamic acid, 103.8; glycine, 100.2; histidine, 83.5; hydroxyproline, 91.1; isoleucine, 102.7; leucine, 103.9; lysine, 98.9; methionine, 102.6; phenylalanine, 91.1; proline, 83.5; threonine, 100.7; tryptophan, 144.1; tyrosine, 94.7; valine, 101.5. Measurement of the absorbancy of a solution of an

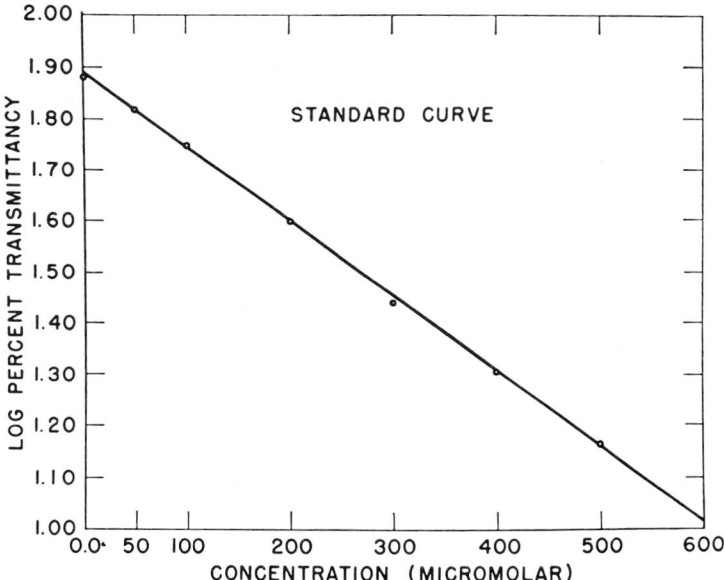

Figure 11–3. Standard curve of alanine at 230 mμ. Spies, J. R., *J. Biol. Chem.*, **195**, 65 (1952).

amino acid-copper complex then permits the concentration of the latter to be calculated with the aid of a standard curve, wherein the log per cent transmittancy is plotted against the concentration of the copper-alanine complex. As such a curve, which is depicted in Figure 11–3, is a straight line, an excellent conformity with Beer's law over the entire range of concentration is revealed; a transmittancy of only 75% is shown at zero concentration of alanine in consequence of the absorbancy of the copper solution.

Scope and Limitations. The spectrophotometric method of Spies (31) provides a convenient means for routinely estimating α-amino acids in amounts which range from 50 to 500 micromoles. That the method permits a high degree of precision is evidenced by the fact that a standard deviation from the mean of only ±1.11% was given in duplicate analyses of eight alanine solutions containing 300 micromoles of the amino acid. Since cupric ion will interact with peptides to give copper complexes which exhibit a high absorption in the ultraviolet region of the spectrum, the method cannot be considered specific for α-amino acids. However, no significant absorption is apparent with test solutions containing 500 micromoles or less of glucose, galactose, sucrose, mannitol, inositol, or ammonia; the lack of interference provided by the last-named reagent is a decided virtue of the method. On the other hand, a high absorption is shown in the case of β-alanine and presumably other β-amino acids. In any event, since the determination is an extremely sensitive one, it becomes obligatory to avoid contamination of the reagents, distilled water, or glassware with even the slightest trace of copper, amino acid or other interfering substance; test solutions which contain copper cannot be analyzed because of the extremely high absorbancy which the blank solutions would show.

REFERENCES

1. Block, R. J., and Bolling, D., *The Amino Acid Composition of Proteins and Foods*, 2nd ed., Charles C Thomas, Springfield, Ill., 1951; Block, R. J., and Weiss, K. W., *Amino Acid Handbook*, Charles C Thomas, Springfield, Ill., 1956; Block, R. J., Durrum, E. L., and Zweig, G., *Paper Chromatography and Paper Electrophoresis*, 2nd ed., Academic Press Inc., New York, 1958.
2. Ruhemann, S., *J. Chem. Soc.*, **97**, 2025 (1910).
3. Ruhemann, S., *J. Chem. Soc.*, **99**, 792 (1911).
4. Ruhemann, S., *J. Chem. Soc.*, **99**, 1486 (1911).
5. MacFadyen, D. A., *J. Biol. Chem.*, **186**, 1 (1950); MacFadyen, D. A., and Fowler, N., *ibid.*, **186**, 13 (1950).
6. Moore, S., and Stein, W. H., *J. Biol. Chem.*, **176**, 367 (1948); **211**, 907 (1954).
7. Troll, W., and Cannan, R. K., *J. Biol. Chem.*, **200**, 803 (1953).
8. Grassmann, W., and von Arnim, K., *Ann.*, **509**, 288 (1934); Johnson, A. W., and McCaldin, D. J., *J. Chem. Soc.*, **1957**, 3470; **1958**, 817.
9. Strecker, A., *Ann.*, **123**, 363 (1862).
10. Slimmer, M., and Stieglitz, J., *Am. Chem. J.*, **31**, 661 (1904).
11. Abderhalden, E., and Schmidt, H., *Z. physiol. Chem.*, **72**, 37 (1911); **85**, 143 (1913).
12. Herzfeld, E., *Biochem. Z.*, **59**, 249 (1914).
13. Harding, V. J., and MacLean, R. M., *J. Biol. Chem.*, **20**, 217 (1915); **24**, 503 (1916); **25**, 337 (1916).
14. Riffart, H., *Biochem. Z.*, **131**, 78 (1922).
15. Wieland, T., and Wirth, L., *Ber.*, **76**, 823 (1943).
16. Schönberg, A., and Moubacher, R., *Chem. Revs.*, **50**, 261 (1951).
17. Harding, V. J., and Warneford, F. H. S., *J. Biol. Chem.*, **25**, 319 (1916).
18. Cherbuliez, E., and Herzenstein, A., *Helv. Chim. Acta*, **17**, 1440 (1934).
19. Polonovski, M., and Moreno-Martin, F., *Compt. rend.*, **119**, 583 (1935).
20. Virtanen, A. I., and Laine, T., *Skand. Arch. Physiol.*, **80**, 392 (1938).
21. Yemm, E. W., and Cocking, E. C., *Analyst*, **80**, 209 (1955).
22. Rosen, H., *Arch. Biochem. Biophys.*, **67**, 10 (1957).

23. Smith, A. M., and Agiza, A. H., *Analyst*, **76,** 623 (1951).
24. Ley, H., *Z. Elektrochem.*, **10,** 954 (1904); *Ber.*, **42,** 354 (1909).
25. Woiwod, A. J., *Biochem. J.*, **45,** 412 (1949).
26. Martin, A. J. P., and Mittelman, R., *Biochem. J.*, **43,** 353 (1948).
27. Schroeder, W. A., Kay, L. M., and Mills, R. S., *Anal. Chem.*, **22,** 760 (1950).
28. Kober, P. A., and Sugiura, K., *J. Biol. Chem.*, **13,** 1 (1912–13); *J. Am. Chem. Soc.*, **35,** 1546 (1913).
29. Spies, J. R., and Chambers, D. C., *J. Biol. Chem.*, **191,** 787 (1951).
30. Pope, C. G., and Stevens, M. F., *Biochem. J.*, **33,** 1070 (1939).
31. Spies, J. R., *J. Biol. Chem.*, **195,** 65 (1952).

chapter 12
ooooooooooooooooooooo

Manometry and Titrimetry

1. Oxidative Degradation of the Amino Acids. The degradation of α-amino acids by a variety of oxidative reagents to such products as ammonia, carbon dioxide, and aldehydes has been observed by a number of investigators. Liebig in 1849 (1) utilized a mixture of lead dioxide and dilute sulfuric acid for this purpose, Strecker (2) used alloxan, and Langheld (3)

$$NH_2CHRCO_2H \xrightarrow{O} NH_3 + CO_2 + RCHO$$

employed sodium hypochlorite. In each case, the aldehyde formed was related to the amino acid degraded, and contained one carbon atom less (owing to the decarboxylation) (2). The products of the reaction were therefore both specific for the amino acid under consideration (the aldehyde), and non-specific in the sense that they could be derived by a similar process from all α-amino acids (ammonia and carbon dioxide). If the degradative reaction could be carried through to completion, the quantitative measurement of any of the products would yield knowledge of the amount of amino acid present, whilst identification of the aldehyde would furnish qualitative information about the nature of the amino acid which had undergone the oxidative degradation.

The earliest definitive work on this subject was reported in 1916–1917 by Dakin (4), who employed chloramine-T as the oxidizing agent for a variety of amino acids. This compound was prepared by combining sodium hypochlorite with *p*-toluenesulfonamide to form a neutral molecule which acted in aqueous solutions in much the same way as did the free hypochlorite, but possessed a much greater stability. Measurement of the carbon dioxide evolved by the interaction of this compound with each of several amino acids revealed that, with the exception of aspartic acid, close to one mole of the gas was liberated per mole of amino acid; aspartic acid, however, liberated two moles of carbon dioxide. Glutamic acid yielded, furthermore, the semialdehyde of succinic acid, aspartic acid glyoxal, valine isobutyraldehyde, isoleucine methylethylacetaldehyde, and alanine acetaldehyde. The yield of aldehyde was not determined, and Dakin noted that in the presence of an excess of chloramine-T the corresponding nitrile was formed at the expense of the aldehyde and of the ammonia present. An excess of the reagent acting upon the ammonia present would also be expected to convert it in part to nitrogen (cf. 5), and the quantitative measurement of ammonia was therefore not attempted.

The use of chloramine-T as a quantitative decarboxylating agent for the measurement of amino acid concentration, so promisingly begun, fell shortly into disrepute because of reports reflecting on its reliability (6). With the subsequent, very careful work of Van Slyke and his associates (7) which showed that the use of the compound at pH 2.5 or 4.7 led to an evolution of carbon dioxide which was fairly quantitative for most amino acids, quite low for tryptophan, proline, and hydroxyproline, and in all cases less sharply exact than that obtainable through the use of ninhydrin, the employment of chloramine-T in the present connection was for the most part limited to only a few quite sharply defined objectives.

It may be recalled that the decarboxylation of α-amino acids has also been effected by the reaction of these compounds with aldehydes at high temperatures. Thus in 1886 Curtius and Lederer (8) heated glycine and benzaldehyde together at 130° and obtained an evolution of carbon dioxide from the amino acid. Much more recently (9), Dose heated valine and p-dimethylaminobenzaldehyde and obtained carbon dioxide and the expected isobutylamine. The quantitative biological decarboxylation of amino acids effected by decarboxylases containing pyridoxal phosphate as the prosthetic group is alluded to in Chapter 9 and in Chapter 20. This enzymic decarboxylation provides an alternative procedure to the purely chemical for the determination of certain amino acids and, although very precise, is limited to the few L-amino acids for which specific decarboxylases are as yet available.

Ammonia, another of the oxidative degradation products of the α-amino acids, has also been obtained by the action of free radicals in X-irradiated aqueous solutions (see Section 7–2), and biologically by the action of amino acid oxidases (see Sections 20–8 and 20–9). The use of neither of these approaches leads to strictly quantitative results. Although the enzymic oxidation through the use of the oxidases goes to completion of the reaction, the reaction itself is conducted at an elevated temperature at pH 7 (L-amino acid oxidase) or at pH 8 (D-amino acid oxidase) whereby the ammonia formed is lost in part as a result of surface evaporation from the neutral or slightly alkaline mixture.

There is an obvious advantage in the quantitative assay of an amino acid or of an amino acid mixture when both ammonia and carbon dioxide can be independently determined, and this is best accomplished by the use of a variety of carbonyl compounds of which ninhydrin is probably the best known example (see Section 11–2). Although assay of total aldehydes from the oxidative degradation of amino acid mixtures has been attempted by a few investigators (10, 11), the method, involving trapping of the aldehydes with bisulfite and subsequent titration with standard iodine solution, is inferior in precision and specificity to those procedures employed for the determination of ammonia and carbon dioxide. Isolation of the aldehyde as the hydrazone (cf. 12, 13) has value in identifying the parent amino acid, and discussion of the procedure for this limited purpose is deferred to the appropriate sections in the chapters of Volume 3.

For the most part, the compounds capable of degrading an amino acid with the formation of carbon dioxide, ammonia, and an aldehyde with one less carbon atom have the following structures (12):

—CO—CO— (e.g., glyoxal, α-keto acids, isatin, ninhydrin)

—CO—[CH=CH]$_n$—CO— (e.g., benzoquinone, anthroquinone, indigo)

Many compounds in these categories produce a typical colored reaction product during the course of their degradation of the amino acids, the amount of which with suitable methodology can also serve as a measure of the amino acids present (see Chapter 11). The present chapter, however, will be confined to a description of methods involved in the determination of the non-specific degradation products of the amino acids.

2. Reaction with Ninhydrin. (a) EVOLUTION OF AMMONIA. When an amino acid is treated with ninhydrin at pH 5–7, carbon dioxide and the related aldehyde are formed, together with an intensely colored product derived from the reaction of ninhydrin and the nitrogen of the amino acid. There is no free ammonia in the mixture. At pH 2.5 or less, however, the colored product is not formed, and the nitrogen of the α-amino group of the amino acid appears as free ammonia on subsequent alkalization (14). Under carefully controlled conditions, this ammonia accounts for all the α-amino nitrogen of most of the amino acids. Before it can be measured, however, the excess ninhydrin present must be destroyed, for the alkalinization necessary to remove the ammonia from the reaction mixture will provide a condition conducive to the irreversible combination of part of the ammonia with the ninhydrin (with appearance of the characteristic color). MacFadyen (14) removed excess ninhydrin by treating the reaction mixture with H_2S gas, thereby converting the reagent to the insoluble hydrindantin which was subsequently removed by filtration. Others (15, 16) destroyed the excess ninhydrin by addition of hydrogen peroxide.

Illustrative procedure 12–1 (15). One milliliter of aqueous solution containing 20–100 μg. of amino acid is placed in an aeration tube, and 0.3 ml. of citrate buffer at pH 2.5 and 50 mg. of ninhydrin are added. The tube is placed in a boiling water bath for 10 min. and occasionally shaken during this period. Three drops of 30% hydrogen peroxide is added, and the heating continued for 3 min. longer. The contents of the tube are cooled to room temperature, 1 ml. of saturated KOH solution is added, and the ammonia aerated into a boric acid trap and measured as described in Section 20–7. It is possible to measure the carbon dioxide simultaneously by using a closed system during the first 10 min. of heating and absorbing the evolved gas in a barium hydroxide solution trap; the carbon dioxide so absorbed is subsequently estimated by titration of the remaining barium hydroxide with standard acid (17).

As noted in Table 12–1, the ammonia evolved under the above conditions is nearly quantitative for alanine, arginine (only α-amino nitrogen), aspartic acid, glutamic acid, glycine, histidine (only α-amino nitrogen), leucine, lysine (reaction conducted at pH 1 and only α-amino nitrogen involved), methionine, phenylalanine, serine, threonine, tyrosine, and valine. Proline and hydroxyproline yield no ammonia at all, and cystine, cysteine, and tryptophan much less than that expected. Although the reaction with isoleucine was not reported, there is no reason to believe that the yield of ammonia from this amino acid would not be close to the theoretical. No ammonia was released from β-alanine under the conditions stated.

Application of the method to a relatively small selection of peptides indicated that only glutathione and N-glycylpeptides yielded one mole of ammonia per mole of compound (16, 18). N-Alanyl and N-leucyl peptides evolved much less ammonia than did the glycyl peptides, whilst glycylasparagine with a C-terminal amide group yielded 1.4 moles of ammonia per mole of compound. In the study of this class of compounds, it is obviously necessary to keep the period of heating which is conducted at a quite acid pH as brief as possible in order to avoid hydrolysis and consequent erroneous results. The results given are those for a 10-minute period of heating.

(b) EVOLUTION OF CARBON DIOXIDE. This is a companion procedure to that whereby the evolution of ammonia is measured, with some added advantages. Thus, whereas proline and hydroxyproline yield no ammonia on heating with ninhydrin, and tryptophan and cystine yield less ammonia than is expected, these amino acids under conditions essentially the same as those involved in the ammonia procedure yield carbon dioxide smoothly and quantitatively (the reaction with cystine must be conducted at pH 1 in order to obtain two moles of carbon dioxide per mole of compound). With the exception noted, the reaction is conducted in a closed system at pH 2–3 for about 10 minutes in a boiling water bath, with results as given in Table 12–1 (7, 17, 19, 20).

The development of the technique of measuring carbon dioxide under these conditions has been due largely to Van Slyke and his associates, who quite early (19) had developed a manometric device for this purpose. Briefly the principle of the procedure involves (a) decarboxylation of the susceptible amino acid on heating with ninhydrin, (b) transfer of the carbon dioxide so

TABLE 12-1

Moles of Ammonia or Carbon Dioxide Evolved from α-Amino Acids and Peptides per Mole

Amino Acid or Peptide	CO$_2$ after Chloramine-T[a]	CO$_2$ after Ninhydrin[c]	NH$_3$ after Ninhydrin[e]	CO$_2$ after N-Bromosuccin-imide[f]	NH$_2$-N after Nitrous Acid[h]
α-Alanine	1	1	1	1	1
β-Alanine	0	0[d]	0	[g]	[i]
α-Aminoadipic acid	–	1	–	–	–
α-Aminotricarballylic acid	–	2	–	–	–
Arginine	1	1	1	1	1
Aspartic acid	2	2	1	2	1
Asparagine	–	1	0.9	1	1
Cystine	1[b]	2	1–2	1.25	2
α,ε-Diaminopimelic acid	–	2	–	–	–
Glutamic acid	1	1	1	1	1
Glycine	1	1	1	1	1
Histidine	1	1	1	1	1
Hydroxylysine	1	1	–	–	–
Hydroxyproline	1	1	0	–	0
Isoleucine	–	1	–	1	1
Leucine	1	1	1	1	1
tert-Leucine	–	1	–	–	–
Lysine	–	1	1 (only α)	1	2[j]
Methionine	–	1	1	1	1
Ornithine	–	1	–	–	2[j]
Phenylalanine	1	1	1	1	1
Proline	1	1	0	1	0
Serine	1	1	1	1	1
Threonine	1	1	1	–	1
Tryptophan	0.75	0.9	<1	1	1
Tyrosine	1	1	1	1.25	1
Valine	–	1	1	1	1
Isovaline	–	0	–	–	1[j]
β-Methylaspartic acid	–	2	–	–	–
β-Methyl-β-hydroxyaspartic acid	–	2	–	–	–
Sarcosine	–	0.8	–	–	–
Glycylglycine	0	0	1	–	–
Glycylglycylglycine	–	0	1	–	1
Glycylleucine	0	0	1	–	1
Leucylglycine	0	0	≪1	–	1
Glycylphenylalanine	0	0	1	1	1
Glutathione	–	1	1	1	2
Alanylglycine	–	0	≪1	–	1
Alanylglycylglycine	–	0	≪1	–	1
Glycylserine	–	0	1	1	1
Leucylglycylglycine	–	0	≪1	1	1
Glycylasparagine	–	0	1.4	1	1
Alanylasparagine	–	0	0.3	–	1
Chloroacetylasparagine	–	0	0.3	–	0
Arginylglutamic acid	–	–	–	1	1
Histidylhistidine	–	–	–	1	–
Glycylaspartic acid	–	–	–	2	–
α-Aspartylglycine	–	1	–	–	–
β-Aspartylvaline	–	1	–	–	–
Glycine amide	–	0	1	–	1
Leucine amide	–	0	0	–	1
Hippuric acid	–	0	–	–	0
Glycine ethyl ester·HCl	–	0	1	–	1
Glycyltryptophan	–	0	1	–	1
Phenylalanylglycine	–	0	0	–	1
Glycylmethionine	–	0	1	–	1
Glycyltyrosine	–	0	1	–	1

[a] Temperature 45° and heating period 10 minutes. Aspartic acid, proline, hydroxyproline, and peptide reactions at pH 4.7, all others at pH 2.5. Volume of reacting solution 1.5 ml., chloramine-T present 45 mg., amino acids or peptides 6–10 micromoles. Hydrazine present in absorbing alkali to trap chlorine evolved from reagent, and carbon dioxide removed from reagent by preliminary treatment with baryta (7).
[b] Theoretical for cystine is 2 moles of carbon dioxide per mole.
[c] Temperature 100° and heating period 10 minutes. Cystine reaction at pH 1.0 (M H$_3$PO$_4$), all others at pH 2.5. Volume of reacting solution 2.0 ml., ninhydrin present 100 mg., amino acids or peptides 6–10 micromoles.
[d] Molar ratio 0.9 in glacial acetic acid after heating for 4 minutes at 100°.
[e] Temperature 100°, heating period 10 minutes, pH 2.5.
[f] Temperature 30°, heating period for amino acids 30 minutes and for peptides 30–180 minutes, and pH 4.7.
[g] Quantitative yield of carbon dioxide only after 6 hours.
[h] After 5 minutes of reaction with nitrous acid at 20–25°.
[i] One mole of nitrogen per mole after 7 minutes.
[j] Quantitative yield of nitrogen after 30 minutes.

MANOMETRY AND TITRIMETRY

evolved to an alkaline absorbing solution, (c) liberation of the carbon dioxide from this solution with strong organic acid, (d) compression of the gas to a known volume followed by measurement of the pressure, and (e) reabsorption of the carbon dioxide in alkali and determination of the pressure at the same volume as in (d). The pressure difference between (d) and (e) at constant volume and temperature is the partial pressure of the carbon dioxide. A

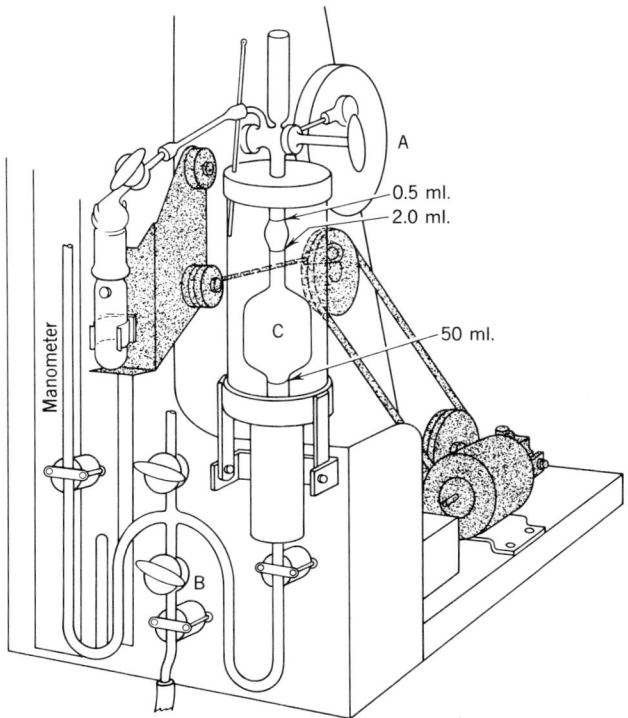

Figure 12-1. Automatic shaker for Van Slyke manometric apparatus; designed by Mrs. R. B. Kingsley.

reagent blank determination carried out in the same manner indicates the fraction of carbon dioxide arising from sources other than the amino acid sample.

Illustrative procedure 12-2 (7, with some modifications employed in this Laboratory by Dr. S. M. Birnbaum and Mrs. Rembert B. Kingsley). The Van Slyke-Neill (19) manometric assembly is readily available and is ideally suited to the procedure. In order to eliminate the tedious shaking of the reaction vessel by hand, which is necessary to release the carbon dioxide gas from the acidified reaction mixture, the apparatus has been modified by introducing a mechanical shaker, as illustrated in Figure 12-1. The shaker is powered by a 1/50-1/70 H.P. Bodine

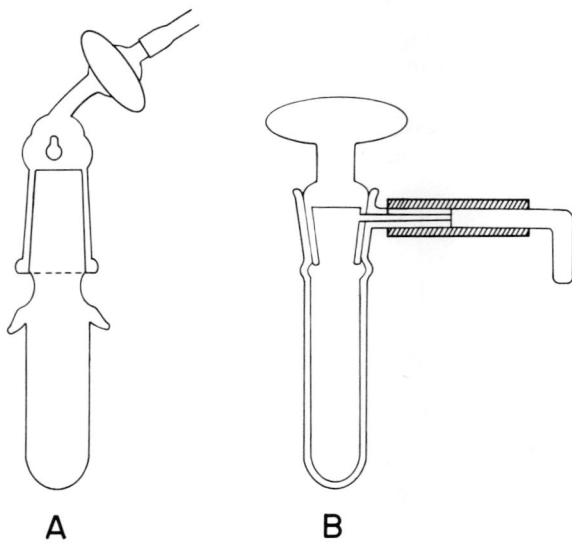

Figure 12–2. All-glass vessels for ninhydrin-CO_2 reaction.

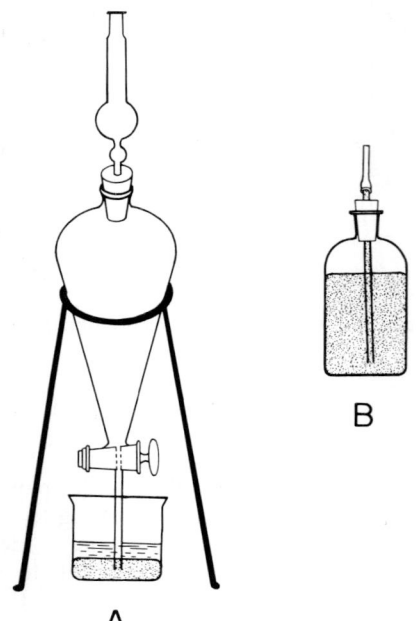

Figure 12–3. Storage vessels for CO_2-free sodium hydroxide (A) and for mercury (B).

(Chicago) Speed Reducer motor geared down so that the effective shaking speed is about 300 cycles per minute and the arc not more than 14°. The reaction vessel illustrated in Figure 12–2A is fashioned from a heavy Pyrex 20–22 mm. (OD) test tube, a standard taper 19/38 glass joint, and a 2-mm. stopcock provided with a short piece of vacuum rubber tubing. The over-all size and angle are critical when the automatic shaker is employed. Another type of all-glass reaction vessel is illustrated in Figure 12–2B. A convenient storage vessel for the nearly CO_2-free 0.5N NaOH employed (Figure 12–3A) can be prepared by drawing out slightly the tip of a 250-ml. separatory funnel and capping with a drying tube containing soda-lime. The squared-off tip of the funnel, like those of all pipettes employed, is fitted with a short rubber tubing of 7-mm. outer diameter and 2-mm. bore which is allowed to project a short distance below the glass. For refilling the side arm and inlet with mercury, the simple device illustrated in Figure 12–3B is quite satisfactory. A small glass spoon capable of measuring roughly 100 mg. of ninhydrin is also convenient.

Lubricants for the ninhydrin reaction vessels capable of withstanding boiling water temperatures are available from various sources; e.g., Nevastone, supplied by E. Machlett and Son, New York City, and Joint-Lube (yellow label), supplied by the Scientific Glass Apparatus Co., Bloomfield, N. J. An excellent high temperature lubricant can be prepared in the laboratory (21). Aluminum distearate (35 g.) is mixed to a paste in 100 ml. of heavy paraffin oil and is heated over a Bunsen burner to give a clear jelly which sets on cooling. The gel is then worked up on a glass plate at 45–50° to a smooth translucent paste.

The reagents employed are as follows (7):

Citrate buffer, 1.0M—210.1 g. of citric acid monohydrate is dissolved in water, the solution is adjusted to pH 2.5 with NaOH, and finally diluted to 1 l. A few crystals of thymol act as a preservative.

6M H_3PO_4—Syrupy phosphoric acid (specific gravity 1.72) is diluted with 1.5 volumes of water and adjusted to 6M by titration. When 0.2 ml. is added to 1.0 ml. of unknown solution there results an M H_3PO_4 solution which is sufficiently close to pH 1 for assay purposes. This solution is employed only with cystine and ninhydrin in order to get quantitative yields of carbon dioxide.

25% NaCl—250 g. of NaCl is dissolved with heating in 750 ml. of water. The solution is then cooled, acidified slightly, and deaerated with suction.

0.5N NaOH (CO_2-free)—Solid NaOH is dissolved in an equal weight of water, and the solution is allowed to stand in a paraffined bottle until the carbonate settles. The amount of the clear alkali (7–8 ml.) required to make 250 ml. of 0.5N NaOH is calculated by titration. Twenty-five per cent NaCl (240 ml.) is measured into the modified separatory funnel, the calculated amount of saturated NaOH is pipetted in, and the solution, after being brought to 250 ml. with added saline, is thoroughly mixed, covered with a soda-lime tube, and stored. Carbon dioxide is relatively insoluble in reagents nearly saturated with sodium chloride (20, 22). A solution of approximately 5N NaOH is prepared by diluting 1 volume of the 1 : 1 solution with 3 volumes of water.

2N Lactic acid—1 volume of concentrated lactic acid (specific gravity = 1.2) is mixed with 4 volumes of 25% NaCl. The addition of 2 g. of hydrazine sulfate per 100 ml. (20, 23) prevents errors arising from added pressures exerted by volatile aldehydes evolved from the presence of such amino acids as valine, leucine, and isoleucine in the reaction mixture.

The ninhydrin reaction vessel is carefully greased with the high temperature lubricant and the stopcock is cleared, if necessary, at the suction pump. One to 4 ml. of suitably buffered (pH 2.5) amino acid solution at room temperature or below and containing approximately 50 micromoles of amino acid is placed in the tube followed by 1 drop of caprylic alcohol. Ninhydrin (100 mg.) is added from the scoop, and the tube is immediately capped and evacuated at the water pump (20–30 mm. pressure) with shaking for about 30 sec. The stopcock is then closed securely and the rubber hose is pinched off from the vacuum line. The end of the short piece of rubber tubing is moistened with glycerol and is plugged with a short glass rod without admitting air. When all tubes have been brought to this stage they are immersed in a boiling water bath for 8–15 min., and then cooled to room temperature. They should not stand too long before analysis for fear of slow diffusion of the gas through the seals.

In biological mixtures it is possible that α-keto acids and urea might be present and act as sources of extra carbon dioxide. The keto acids may be removed by heating the solution at 100° in the open reaction vessel at pH 1–3 prior to adding ninhydrin, and in this way removing any carbon dioxide evolved from the acid decomposition of this type of compound; after cooling, ninhydrin is added and the capping, evacuation, and heating conducted as described. If a small amount of urea is also present it can generally be safely ignored, for in the presence of an excess of ninhydrin a relatively stable compound is formed which evolves carbon dioxide extremely slowly. In the presence of a large amount of urea, which might furnish appreciable amounts of carbon dioxide unless a proportionately large excess of ninhydrin is provided, it is best to decompose the urea before measuring through the action of carefully dialyzed urease (24); removal of the carbon dioxide so formed is accomplished by warming at pH 1–3, a pH range which is subsequently suitable for the ninhydrin reaction.

Although the period of heating of the ninhydrin reaction mixture at pH 2.5 and close to 100° is generally taken as 7 to 10 minutes, the individual amino acids themselves are decarboxylated at quite different rates within this time interval. Thus, as shown by the data in Table 12–2, hydroxyproline yields carbon dioxide very rapidly whereas valine is decarboxylated relatively slowly (23). For a mixture of amino acids, therefore, the period of 8 to 15 minutes should be sufficient to permit the degradation of all compounds present.

Prior to the transfer and measurement of the carbon dioxide formed, the tubes are warmed to 40° in a water bath. The Van Slyke-Neil apparatus is prepared for absorption of the carbon dioxide gas in the following manner. With stopcock B (Figure 12–1) open and about 2 ml. of mercury in the cup, 2 ml. of $0.5N$ CO_2-free NaOH is admitted directly from the storage funnel through stopcock A. After closing A and clearing the capillary with a little mercury from the cup, the leveling bulb is lowered, drawing the mercury about halfway down the chamber, C. Stopcock B is then closed.

TABLE 12-2

Period of Time Required to Decarboxylate Completely about 30 Micromoles of Each Amino Acid in a 5% Ninhydrin Solution at 100° and at pH 2.5 (23)

Amino Acid	Period Required for Complete Decarboxylation, min.	Amino Acid	Period Required for Complete Decarboxylation, min.
Hydroxyproline	1.2	Proline	3.2
Lysine	1.2	Norleucine	3.2
Histidine	1.4	Leucine	3.4
Tyrosine	1.9	Threonine	3.7
Asparagine	2.2	Serine	4.1
Arginine	2.5	Norvaline	4.2
Phenylalanine	2.7	Methionine	4.5
Cystine	2.9	Isoleucine	5.8
Glycine	2.9	Tryptophan	6.3
Glutamic acid	2.9	Alanine	6.6
Aspartic acid (2 moles CO_2)	3.0	Valine	8.3
		Cysteine	12.0

The warmed reaction tube is fitted onto the side arm of stopcock A as illustrated (Figure 12-1), admitting as little air as possible, and stopcock A is opened. The reaction tube stopcock is then opened and the apparatus is ready for the transfer of the carbon dioxide to the manometric system. The mercury leveling bulb held in the left hand is lowered, a partial vacuum is created in C, and stopcock B is opened. By alternately raising and lowering the bulb, the mercury level is fluctuated between the 50-ml. mark on the chamber and an estimated 10-ml. level for a total of some 10-12 times. Simultaneously, the reaction vessel is shaken rapidly by means of the motor assembly shown in Figure 12-1. At the completion of the extraction, stopcock B is closed with the mercury about halfway up the chamber and the leveling bulb is returned to its ring. Stopcock A is closed and the reaction vessel is removed. The side arm of A is refilled with mercury from the reservoir (Figure 12-3B) by attaching the two through the rubber tubing, lowering the leveling bulb to create a partial vacuum in the chamber, opening A to the side arm, sucking through sufficient mercury, and then closing A.

The unabsorbed gases above the alkali are then ejected by opening stopcock B, raising the mercury bulb, and carefully allowing the compressed gases to escape through A. Most if not all of the air should be removed in this manner before closing A and returning the leveling bulb to its carriage.

Dissolved carbon dioxide is then liberated from the 0.5N NaOH solution by the lowering of the mercury leveling bulb followed by the suction through stopcock A of 1 ml. of 2N lactic acid. An ordinary 2-ml. pipette fitted with a rubber tip fitting snugly over the capillary leading to A is quite suitable for this addition. Stopcock A is closed, the capillary sealed with mercury, and the leveling bulb lowered until the mercury meniscus reaches the 50-ml. mark. Stopcock B is then closed and the evacuated chamber is shaken for 2–3 min. to extract the carbon dioxide quantitatively. Stopcock B is reopened carefully and the liquid meniscus allowed to ascend slowly to the 2.0- or 0.5-ml. mark in the chamber. The manometer is then read to give P_1 in millimeters. (For what Van Slyke et al. (7) referred to as their "micro" method, i.e., that which involved about 30 micromoles of amino acid, the constant volume of carbon dioxide at which the pressure, P_1, was read was 2.0 ml. For much smaller quantities of amino acids, the "submicro" procedure involved a constant gas volume of 0.5 ml. In practice, when a pressure of less than 100 mm. was attained with a volume of 2.0 ml., it was considered desirable to change to the 0.5-ml. volume.)

Stopcock B is again opened, the leveling bulb lowered, 0.5 ml. of $5N$ NaOH is admitted by pipette through stopcock A to reabsorb the CO_2, and the capillary of stopcock A cleared with mercury and the stopcock closed. Two or three short excursions of the alkaline solution are accomplished by quickly raising and lowering the leveling bulb. Stopcock B is closed with the liquid meniscus below the 2-ml. mark in the chamber, and the leveling bulb is returned to the carriage. Mercury is again carefully admitted through stopcock B until the liquid meniscus is adjusted as before at the same 2.0- or 0.5-ml. mark. Pressure P_2, after B is closed, is then read from the manometer. The partial pressure of the CO_2 gas, P_{CO_2}, is therefore $P_1 - P_2$, the value of P_2 also yielding some measure of gases other than carbon dioxide which may be present. The reagent blank value, $P_1{}^c - P_2{}^c$ refers to carbon dioxide present in the reagents, and is determined by the complete procedure on a solution containing all reagents employed and lacking only in amino acid. The corrected value of the carbon dioxide pressure, P_{CO_2}, for the gas actually evolved from the amino acid, and measured at constant volume and temperature, is therefore expressed as

$$P_{CO_2} = (P_1 - P_2) - (P_1{}^c - P_2{}^c)$$

The transformation of P_{CO_2} to micromoles of carboxyl nitrogen in the sample is readily accomplished by multiplying this value by the appropriate factor in Table 12–3. Factors for converting P_{CO_2} at constant volume to milligrams of carbon by the application of the well-known gas laws were published by Van Slyke and Folch (25), and were recalculated later by MacFadyen (22) for milligrams of carboxyl nitrogen. The values given in Table 12–3 are, in turn, derived from those of MacFadyen after multiplying by 1000 and dividing by 14 in order to yield micromoles of carboxyl nitrogen.

An example of a typical analysis follows. Three milliliters of citrate buffer at pH 2.5 containing 11.5 micromoles of alanine, when analyzed for carboxyl nitrogen by the procedure described, yielded a P_1 value of 241.0 mm. at a constant volume of 2.0 ml. and a temperature of 25°. The value of P_2 at the same volume was 134.2 mm., whereby $P_1 - P_2$ representing the partial pressure, P_{CO_2}, of the carbon dioxide evolved was 106.8. The reagent blank under the same conditions, $P_1{}^c - P_2{}^c$, was found for this experiment to be 5.0 mm., although reagent blank values of 10–14 mm. have often been obtained

TABLE 12-3
Conversion Factors for Gas Pressures

	For P_{CO_2} after Ninhydrin Treatment[a]		For P_{N_2} after Nitrous Acid Treatment[b]	
Temperature, °C	At Gas Volume of 2.0 ml.	At Gas Volume of 0.5 ml.	At Gas Volume of 2.0 ml.	At Gas Volume of 0.5 ml.
15	0.1145	0.0287	0.1115	0.0278
16	0.1141	0.0286	0.1111	0.0278
17	0.1136	0.0285	0.1106	0.0276
18	0.1131	0.0284	0.1102	0.0276
19	0.1127	0.0282	0.1098	0.0275
20	0.1122	0.0281	0.1094	0.0273
21	0.1118	0.0280	0.1091	0.0273
22	0.1114	0.0279	0.1087	0.0271
23	0.1109	0.0278	0.1082	0.0271
24	0.1104	0.0277	0.1079	0.0270
25	0.1100	0.0276	0.1075	0.0268
26	0.1096	0.0275	0.1071	0.0268
27	0.1091	0.0274	0.1068	0.0267
28	0.1088	0.0273	0.1064	0.0266
29	0.1084	0.0272	0.1060	0.0265
30	0.1079	0.0271	0.1057	0.0264
31	0.0175	0.0269	0.1052	0.0263
32	0.1071	0.0268	0.1049	0.0262
33	0.1067	0.0268	0.1045	0.0261
34	0.1063	0.0267	0.1042	0.0261

[a] Multiplication of P_{CO2} by appropriate factor yields micromoles of carboxyl nitrogen.
[b] Multiplication of P_{N2} by appropriate factor yields micromoles of nitrogen.

in this Laboratory. The corrected value of P_{CO_2} was therefore 101.8 mm. The corresponding factor taken from Table 12–3 to convert this pressure to micromoles of alanine is 0.1100. Multiplication of 101.8 by the factor yields a value of 11.2 micromoles which is within 3% of the theoretical, a limit of accuracy generally satisfactory for this experimental procedure.

For all amino acids other than aspartic acid, α-aminotricarballylic acid, β-methyl-β-hydroxyaspartic acid, and β-methylaspartic acid, which readily yield with ninhydrin under the above conditions 2 moles of carbon dioxide per mole of compound (Table 12–1), the micromoles of nitrogen calculated from the product of P_{CO_2} and the factors in Table 12–3 may also be considered as micromoles of amino acid. With amino acid mixtures in which aspartic acid forms an appreciable but not precisely analyzed part of the whole, it is best to refer to the assay in terms of total carboxyl nitrogen rather than as amino acid.

With the estimation of the amino acids liberated from proteins or peptides in buffered solutions by the action of hydrolytic enzymes, it is customary to add saturated picric acid solution to the digest to a pH of about 2.5 in order to bring the reaction to a halt by denaturing and coagulating the enzyme protein (cf. 20). An aliquot of the resulting mixture is treated with ninhydrin in the prescribed manner. In order to obtain a blank value in this type of experiment, a mixture of enzyme and buffer without substrate or products is incubated simultaneously with the experimental digests. At the end of the reaction period saturated picric acid solution is added to both experimental and blank mixtures, and directly thereafter the substrate is added to the blank and equal aliquots are employed for the assay. Subtraction of the carbon dioxide at the same constant volume and temperature in the blank from that in the test run will also account for the controls, and thus permit $P_{expt.} - P_{blank}$ to be expressed directly as P_{CO_2}. As for all blank values in enzyme reactions, it is assumed that the mixture of enzyme and buffer undergoes the same changes during the experimental period as does the same mixture in the presence of the substrate.

The manometric ninhydrin-CO_2 procedure at pH 2.5 is particularly suitable for the determination of protease or peptidase activity, inasmuch as no carbon dioxide is evolved from pure peptides involving only normal α-linkages between amino and carboxyl groups (7) (cf. data in Chapter 20). Glutathione with an N-terminal, γ-linked glutamic acid residue yields one mole of carbon dioxide per mole. Aspartic acid, as noted above, yields two moles of carbon dioxide per mole, but asparagine yields only one mole of the gas under the same conditions. β-Aspartyl peptides might be expected to behave toward ninhydrin like asparagine, and actually do yield one mole of carbon dioxide per mole (26); interestingly enough, α-aspartyl peptides also yield one mole of carbon dioxide per mole. β-Alanine is little if at all decarboxylated by ninhydrin in aqueous solution at any pH from 1 to 4.7, but can yield carbon dioxide nearly quantitatively by a heating period of 4 minutes with ninhydrin in glacial acetic acid (7).

Excluding such compounds as glutathione and the α- and β-aspartyl peptides, which react quantitatively with ninhydrin to yield carbon dioxide, the commonly inert peptides may be approximately determined in the presence of free amino acids by the following differential procedure (27):

1. The free amino acids are destroyed, i.e., converted to a mixture of aldehydes, ammonia, and carbon dioxide, by reaction with excess ninhydrin at pH 2.5 for 13 minutes in a boiling water bath. The carbon dioxide evolved may be either allowed to escape or allowed to be absorbed by a standard baryta solution and thereby determined. It is assumed in this step that the greater part of the peptides present are inert, although the conditions employed will not only result in decarboxylation of glutathione and α- and β-aspartyl peptides (26), but also in complete deamination of others (15, 16). Any such deamination will result in a subsequent peptide assay (step 3 of the sequence) being lower than it should be.

2. The ninhydrin is destroyed by addition of 30% hydrogen peroxide, excess peroxide is evaporated off at 100°, and the residue containing peptide material is hydrolyzed by refluxing HCl solution for several hours.

3. The residue from the above hydrolytic step is freed by evaporation from excess HCl, brought to pH 2.5, and treated with ninhydrin as in the first step of the sequence except that here the evolved carbon dioxide must be quantitatively measured in order to have some estimate of the peptide material originally present in the mixture.

Nearly as inert to ninhydrin in so far as evolving carbon dioxide is concerned are the α-amino-α-methyl acids exemplified by α-aminoisobutyric acid and isovaline (28, 29). The decarboxylation of such compounds is apparently very slow, and in one study of this phenomenon the results obtained after heating with ninhydrin for 90 minutes required the employment of correction factors of a considerable order of magnitude in order to approach a quantitative estimate of the results (28).

The imino acids proline and hydroxyproline are quantitatively decarboxylated by ninhydrin at pH 2.5. Other types of N-alkyl amino acids, however, such as sarcosine (7) or N-methyl- and N-ethylalanine (30), yield carbon dioxide to an extent which is appreciably less than theory. Neither amino acid amides with a free α-amino group, but a blocked carboxyl group, nor N-acylated amino acids with a blocked amino group, but a free carboxyl group, yield carbon dioxide with ninhydrin. The susceptible structures for the manometric ninhydrin-CO_2 method, are therefore (Table 12-1)

NH_2CHRCO_2H
I

NH_2CHR
|
CH_2CO_2H
II

$RHC\text{------}CH_2$
| |
H_2C $CHCO_2H$
\ /
NH
III

That is to say, a free, basic α-amino or α-imino group and a free α-carboxyl group are required.

3. Reaction with N-Bromosuccinimide. In 1951, Schönberg, Moubasher, and Barakat (13) treated amino acids with N-bromosuccinimide whereby carbon dioxide and ammonia were released from the amino acids and free bromine from the reagent. In addition, aldehydes related to the amino acids so treated and containing one carbon atom less than the parent substances were also formed. The phenomenon was subsequently studied by Chappelle and Luck (31), who developed the reaction into one of the most interesting quantitative decarboxylation procedures available at the present time in this field.

The bromine evolved from the reagent can be reduced to negligible amounts by carrying on the reaction at pH 4.7 in the presence of succinimide, the last traces being removed by a potassium iodide trap (31). The reagent itself is prepared by adding 2.5 g. each of N-bromosuccinimide and succinimide to 25 ml. of M acetate buffer at pH 4.7, whereby most of the bromo compound remains in suspension. At pH 4.7 and at a temperature of about 30° the decarboxylation of most amino acids proceeds smoothly and is complete within a relatively brief period of time. Under these conditions, the action of N-bromosuccinimide resembles that of enzymic decarboxylation (except for the fact that the enzymic action leads to the production of the corresponding amine rather than of ammonia and aldehyde) or of ninhydrin (except that with this reagent a higher temperature is required). A more important difference between N-bromosuccinimide on the one hand and ninhydrin and the decarboxylases on the other arises from the behavior of these agents toward peptides. With the few exceptions noted in the previous section, most peptides are inert toward ninhydrin, and all peptides are inert to peptidase-free decarboxylase preparations. In contrast, peptides are quantitatively decarboxylated by N-bromosuccinimide; the rate of the reaction is ordinarily slower than that in which amino acids are involved, but it may be accelerated by the addition to the reaction mixture of palladium chloride at an optimal level of 5 moles of the inorganic salt to 1 of the peptide.

Illustrative procedure 12-3 (31). The reagent suspension described above (0.5 ml.) is added to one side arm of a two-arm Warburg flask, and 0.5 ml. of 40% KI solution to the other. The solution of amino acid or peptide containing 1–5 micromoles of compound in 1 ml. of acetate buffer at pH 4.7 is transferred to the main compartment of the flask, and if a peptide is under investigation 0.1 ml. of PdCl$_2$ of suitable concentration is also added. The total volume of solution in the main compartment is brought to 3 ml. by addition of 10% succinimide in the acetate buffer. After an equilibrium period of 20 min., the reaction is initiated by tipping in the N-bromosuccinimide reagent from the side arm, and the evolution of carbon dioxide is followed to its completion while shaking the assembly at 30°. The decarboxylation for most amino acids is complete within 30 min., that for most peptides may require periods of time ranging from 30 min. to 3 hr. With all α-amino acids studied, except for a few, 1 mole of carbon dioxide was released per mole of compound; aspartic acid released 2 moles per mole, and tyrosine and cystine each gave off 1.25 moles of carbon dioxide per mole. As with ninhydrin, β-alanine was decarboxylated extremely slowly. With peptides other than those involving C-terminal aspartic acid the yield of carboxyl carbon dioxide was invariably 1 mole per mole (Table 12-1). Application of the reaction to the determination of C-terminal carboxyl groups in proteins is described in Section 16-7.

4. Reaction with Nitrous Acid. In a review of the year's accomplishments, Neubauer in 1875 (32) cited the work of Sachsse and Kormann who had nearly quantitatively accounted for the amino acids present in plant extracts by the use of nitrous acid and by the subsequent measurement of the nitrogen gas evolved. The amino acids were treated with a mixture of sodium nitrite and sulfuric acid, the lower oxides of nitrogen absorbed in ferrous sulfate solution, and the nitrogen gas, after purification over alkali, determined volumetrically. In their procedure, 1 mole of leucine or asparagine yielded 28 grams of nitrogen gas. For a number of years, little or no interest was displayed in the subject. Fischer and Koelker in 1905 (33) used nitrous acid to prove that the two racemic diastereomers of leucylisoserine possessed but a single primary amino group and hence a normal peptide bond between the two amino acid residues, rather than two primary amino groups which would have, on the other hand, indicated the presence of an ester-type linkage.

In 1910 there appeared the first of a series of studies by Van Slyke (34–36) which effectively placed the reaction

$$RNH_2 + HNO_2 \rightarrow ROH + H_2O + N_2$$

and the associated manometric determination of nitrogen on a quantitative basis. Nitrous acid was prepared in excess by the reaction of acetic acid on sodium nitrite. Part of the acid decomposed spontaneously with the formation of nitric acid and gaseous nitric oxide,

$$2HNO_2 \rightarrow HNO_3 + NO$$

the latter being employed to displace all air in the apparatus. When this had occurred, the amine was introduced and the resulting nitrogen gas mixed with the nitric oxide was shaken with an alkaline permanganate solution. This solution absorbed the nitric oxide and any adventitious carbon dioxide, leaving the pure nitrogen gas to be measured in a special gas burette. A blank run, employing only the reagents, served as a control of the reaction. (This sequence of events was subsequently modified when the Van Slyke-Neil apparatus was introduced (36)). With approximately 0.5 mg. of α-amino nitrogen, and under the experimental conditions (36), all of this nitrogen appeared in the burette within 5 minutes of reaction time at 20–25°. The yield of nitrogen was quantitative for all α-amino acids studied except for glycine and cystine, which produced with nitrous acid slightly more nitrogen gas than that expected (Table 12-1). Proline and hydroxyproline yielded no nitrogen, nor did any other α-imino acid. No nitrogen appeared from the imidazole group of histidine, the indole group of tryptophan, or from the guanidino group of arginine during the 5-minute period alluded to. If, however, the reaction of the latter two amino acids was prolonged beyond this period of time, more nitrogen appeared than could be accounted for in terms of α-amino nitrogen (37, 38), and whether this extra nitrogen arose from the nitrogen-containing substituents of these amino acids, or from the reagent as in the cases of glycine and cystine, was not determined. Simple peptides with only one α-amino group yielded one molecule of nitrogen gas per mole, except for glycylglycine, which gave slightly more nitrogen than expected. Ammonia and urea reacted much more slowly than did the α-amino acids, producing with nitrous acid in 5 minutes about 0.15 to 0.25 molecule of nitrogen gas per mole. Complete conversion of ammonia to nitrogen gas required about 2 hours (35). In biological systems in which these components may be present in relatively high proportion, it is advisable to treat the biological mixture with urease at pH 6 and to drive off the ammonia from the subsequently alkalinized digest by aeration, prior to the determination of α-amino nitrogen with nitrous acid (36). The primary amino groups of the purines and pyrimidines react very slowly with nitrous acid, requiring about 2–5 hours for quantitative conversion to nitrogen gas, and nitrogen from this source during the 5-minute reaction period may be considered to be negligible (35).

The excess of nitrogen gas (6–8% above the theoretical) which was evolved from glycine and from cystine was prevented from occurring when potassium iodide to 2% concentration (or the equivalent amount of free iodine) was dissolved in the sodium nitrite solution (40). This finding was subsequently confirmed (38, 41). The presence of potassium iodide in the reaction, although beneficial for the correct analysis of glycine and cystine, was disastrous for that of tryptophan inasmuch as in the presence of the iodide this amino acid yielded only 40–60% of the theoretical α-amino nitrogen (38). The cause for the extra gas production in the reaction of glycine or cystine with nitrous acid is not yet known with certainty (it may possibly be due to a complex series of reactions leading to the formation of N_2O as well as N_2 (39)), and no less bizarre are the methods for curing the trouble. The use of iodide or iodine has been mentioned. The presence of mercury in the manometric system was also stated to be corrective (40), and later the employment of mercuric salts (40, 42).

Nitrous acid reacts more slowly with primary amino groups removed from the α-position. Thus Van Slyke (35) found that only a fraction of the ε-amino group of lysine contributed nitrogen in the 5-minute reaction period. It required about 30 minutes to deaminate lysine (43) and ornithine (44) completely. On the other hand, lysyl peptides, such as lysylglutamic acid or lysylglycine, under identical conditions, yielded their total amino nitrogen, both α and ε, in less than 7 minutes (45, 46), possibly another example of the increased reactivity of the side-chain groups of amino acids when the latter are in peptide linkage. (The greatly increased lability of the disulfide group of cystine in cystine peptides is a classic instance of this phenomenon—see Chapter 24).

With ω-monoaminomonocarboxylic acids, the rate of deamination with nitrous acid decreases with increasing distance between the amino and the carboxyl groups (43). Thus, to achieve complete deamination of α-alanine at 23° requires about 5 minutes, β-alanine 7 minutes, γ-amino-n-valeric acid 10 minutes, δ-amino-n-valeric acid 13 minutes, and ε-amino-n-caproic acid 15 minutes, for equivalent amounts of the amino acids under identical conditions. With decreasing temperature, the reaction rate also decreases, and thus with equal amounts of α-alanine complete deamination requires about 5 minutes at 23° and 15°, 10 minutes at 8.5°, and 18 minutes at 4°.

Within the 5-minute reaction period with nitrous acid at ordinary temperatures, acid amides are generally inert. Thus asparagine yields only one mole of nitrogen gas per mole. However, glutamine during this time period yields about 90% of its total nitrogen as nitrogen gas (47, 48). It is not improbable that the α-amino group of the glutamine is rapidly removed, and the resulting α-hydroxy acid γ-amide cyclizes to the lactone with liberation of ammonia susceptible to the further action of the nitrous acid (48). Pyrrolidonecarboxylic acid is completely inert toward nitrous acid, and thus little if any conversion of the glutamine under deamination conditions to this compound would therefore be expected to occur. The anomalous behavior of glutamine in the nitrous acid reaction is also reflected in a similar behavior of γ-glutamyl peptides (49). Thus, whereas α-glutamyl peptides, as might be expected, yield one molecule of nitrogen gas per mole, γ-glutamyl dipeptides react with nitrous acid to yield nearly all of their nitrogen as nitrogen gas under the usual conditions (5-minute reaction period at 20–25°). In the case of glutathione with one γ- and one α-linkage, two molecules of nitrogen per mole are evolved (49). In such cases it seems probable that deamination of the α-amino group of the N-terminal γ-glutamyl residue of the peptide is, as in the analogous case of glutamine, accompanied by hydrolysis of the N-terminal residue with formation of γ-valerolactone and the liberation of the C-terminal amino acid residue with its α-amino group susceptible to the further action of nitrous acid. In this manner, the release of two molecules of nitrogen gas per molecule of γ-glutamyl peptide may be visualized, the presence of some lactone in the reaction mixture as indicated by hydroxamic formation lending weight to the suggested mechanism (49).

α-Amino-α-alkyl acids, such as isovaline, are deaminated much more slowly by nitrous acid than are α-amino acids with a hydrogen atom on the α-carbon. Thus, for example, although α-amino-n-butyric acid, norvaline, and valine are completely deaminated within 5 minutes at 20–25°, isovaline requires about 30 minutes for the same purpose (50). Inasmuch as this type of amino acid is insusceptible to ninhydrin, its presence can be manometrically apprehended only by the nitrous acid technique, slow as the rate of this reaction may be. The enzymic resolution of N-acylated α-amino acids carried out in this Laboratory (see Volume 3) has been readily followed in all cases by determinations of ninhydrin-CO_2 except for that of isovaline which, perforce, was followed by the reaction of aliquots of the digestion mixture with nitrous acid (Chapter 47).

In most respects the ninhydrin-CO_2 procedure has supplanted the nitrous acid-N_2 method because it is more specific for α-amino acids. A considerable number of non-nitrogenous compounds will cause the liberation of nitrogen gas from nitrous acid, among them α-thiol acids (51), resorcinol and other phenols (52), α-keto acids such as pyruvic acid (53), etc. Other types of compounds acting in a similar manner have been listed (54). The absence of such compounds from a reaction mixture must therefore be assured prior to adding the nitrous acid. Extra nitrogen also appears from tyrosine or tyrosine peptides reacting with nitrous acid in bright sunlight, normal values being obtained only when darkened conditions prevail (55).

Nitrous acid has been employed in this Laboratory for the determination of α-amino acids only where the ninhydrin-CO_2 procedure is inapplicable. Because in a few instances it is invaluable, the nitrous acid method, following in the main the description by Van Slyke (35, 36), is given below.

Illustrative procedure 12-4 (cf. 36). The Van Slyke-Neil manometric apparatus (Figure 12-1) together with a Hempel pipette (Figure 12-4) serve as the equipment required. The amine solution and acetic acid are mixed and freed of air in the chamber, and the sodium nitrite is then added in saturated solution. The resulting nitrous acid is permitted to react for a certain period of time when the mixture of nitrogen and nitric oxide gases is transferred to a Hempel pipette, where the nitric oxide is absorbed by an alkaline permanganate solution. The chamber of the manometric apparatus is then washed free of nitrous acid, and the purified nitrogen gas is returned from the pipette. Finally, the partial pressure of the nitrogen gas now in the manometric assembly is measured at a constant volume at either 2.0 or 0.5 ml., and at a *constant*, known temperature, and, after suitable correction, is converted to micromoles of nitrogen by the factors given in Table 12-3 (cf. 36). The amount of dissolved atmospheric nitrogen carried into the apparatus by the amount of nitrite solution employed (2 ml.) exerts only 4 mm. pressure when the gas is measured at 0.5 ml. volume, and 1 mm. when at 2.0 ml. These corrections are small, and in any event are automatically included in the blank analysis on the reagents. The maximum amount of amino nitrogen measurable is about 0.6 mg. (about 40 micromoles), which at 2 ml. volume yields nitrogen gas giving somewhat more than 400 mm. pressure.

The analysis consists of the following sequence of events:

1. The mixed amine solution and glacial acetic acid are freed of air in the apparatus.

2. Sodium nitrite solution (from 800 g. of sodium nitrite dissolved with warming in 1 l. of water) is added, and the resulting nitrous acid allowed to act on the amine for a certain period of time.

3. The mixture of nitrogen and nitric oxide gases present as a result of the previous reaction is transferred to a Hempel pipette wherein the nitric oxide gas is absorbed by an alkaline permanganate solution (obtained from a saturated solution of 50 g. of potassium permanganate added to 1 l. of 10% sodium hydroxide, and subsequently equilibrated with air).

4. The chamber of the Van Slyke-Neil apparatus is washed free of nitrous acid, and the purified nitrogen gas in the Hempel pipette is returned to the manometric apparatus.

5. The pressure of the nitrogen gas, P_1, is determined at a constant volume of

either 2.0 ml. or 0.5 ml., depending on just how much of the gas is present. If the gas pressure at the 2.0 ml. volume is less than 100 mm., it is advisable to change to the 0.5 ml. volume instead. The gas is ejected from the chamber and the manometer reading, P_0, taken with the water meniscus in the gas-free chamber at the same volume level used for the P_1 reading. P_{N_2} will therefore be equal to $P_1 - P_0$. From this value of P_{N_2} there may be subtracted the $P_1^c - P_0^c$ value of the reagent blank in which water is substituted for the amine solution. This blank correction, in cases where at 2.0 ml. volume of gas the pressure is appreciably greater than 100 mm., may be frequently neglected. At the 0.5 ml. volume, the blank correction may be appreciable. P_{N_2} is thereupon converted to micromoles of NH_2-N by the factors given in Table 12-3. *It will be recalled that, of each millimole (28 mg.) of nitrogen gas, only half comes from the primary amine.*

Details of the procedure are as follows:

1. Removal of air from the solution of amine and acetic acid. Stopcock B (Figure 12-1) is opened, the mercury reservoir bulb lowered, stopcock B closed, and amine solution (2-5 ml.) is run carefully through opened stopcock A (Figure 12-4) into the chamber, C, of the Van Slyke-Neil apparatus, followed by 1 ml. of glacial acetic acid and a few drops of caprylic alcohol if this is necessary to reduce subsequent foaming. Stopcock A is closed and sealed with mercury in both capillaries, stopcock B (Figure 12-1) opened, and the leveling bulb lowered until the mercury in the chamber is at about the 50-ml. mark and the stopcock closed. This creates a partial vacuum, and the removal of air from the solution is facilitated by shaking the chamber C for a period of about 2 min. The air extracted thereby from the solution is ejected from the chamber in the following manner. The leveling bulb is placed in the upper ring, slightly above the chamber. Stopcock B (Figure 12-1) is opened to admit mercury from the leveling bulb into the chamber, the extracted air is compressed into a bubble at the top of the chamber and ejected through the carefully opened stopcock A by allowing the solution to rise through the capillary of A until a few drops pass into the cup. Stopcock A is then closed, the mercury leveling bulb returned to the lower position, and stopcock B closed.

2. Reaction with nitrous acid. Two milliliters of the sodium nitrite solution is added to the cup and stopcock A carefully opened to admit this solution (plus the mercury seal) into the chamber. Stopcock A is closed, mercury freshly added to the cup as a sealer, stopcock B opened, and the chamber evacuated until the mercury falls to a level just above the 50-ml. mark. The reaction mixture is allowed to stand while nitrogen and nitric oxide gases evolve until within 1 min. of the end of the reaction time. During this final minute the mixture is shaken to complete the reaction. The relatively large amount of gas evolved, due mostly to the spontaneous decomposition of the nitrous acid present, imposes a considerable pressure in the chamber, tending to lower the mercury level well below the chamber. To avoid this the mercury reservoir is occasionally raised so as to restore the mercury meniscus in the chamber at about the 50-ml. mark, and stopcock B is finally closed at the termination of the reaction.

3. Transfer of gas to the Hempel pipette. The nitrogen and nitric oxide gases accumulated in the chamber as a result of the above reaction are transferred to a Hempel pipette filled with alkaline permanganate solution. The bore of the

capillary in this instrument should be about 0.9–1.1 mm., and the stopcock perfectly ground so that the bore is continuous with the capillary. The forearm of the pipette should terminate in a rubber tip of soft material, of size which would fit snugly on the capillary over the bore of stopcock A. The permanganate, which is prepared daily, is drawn into the pipette and fills the pipette up to the three-way stopcock H. The bore of this cock, the forearm to the tip, the cup on the pipette, and the cup on the manometric apparatus are all filled with water, the last-mentioned being first cleared of the mercury seal by suction, and the forearm, with its rubber tip firmly pressed to stopcock A, is attached to the manometric apparatus. Care is taken that the Hempel pipette tip does not conceal a tiny volume of air; this may be avoided by making sure that the tip holds some excess water by capillary attraction.

Stopcock B is opened and the mercury bulb raised so as to compress the gases at the top of the chamber and under stopcock A. Stopcock H is opened to position 1 (Figure 12–4). Stopcock A is carefully opened, and the gases in the chamber are forced over into the pipette. When the aqueous solution, following the gases, has traveled up the capillary of the pipette nearly as far as stopcock H, stopcocks A and H are closed, and the pipette is removed from contact with the manometric apparatus. Stopcock H is turned to position 3 (Figure 12–4) and a little water admitted from the cup to wash down the small gas volume which collects between the stopcock and the permanganate bulb. Immediately thereafter, the stopcock is turned to position 2 (Figure 12–4) and water allowed to run from the cup through the capillary of the forearm in order to clear it of nitrous acid. The Hempel pipette is then gently shaken horizontally for about 40 sec. in order to complete the absorption of the nitric oxide gas. Only nitrogen gas now is left in the pipette, and it is found between stopcock H and the lower permanganate bulb (Figure 12–4).

4. Return of the nitrogen gas to the manometric apparatus. Before this is accomplished the nitrous acid solution must be removed from the chamber. This is done by opening stopcock B and lowering the mercury reservoir to evacuate the chamber. As the mercury level in the chamber falls, water (but no air) is admitted through stopcock A. The bulb is then raised, stopcock A opened, and the water solution pushed into the cup is removed by suction. This procedure is repeated. After this second washing, 10–15 ml. of water (careful again to exclude air) is passed through stopcock A to the chamber, stopcock A is closed, sealed with mercury, and the chamber evacuated by lowering the mercury level to the 50-ml. mark. Air is thus boiled out of the water with the assistance of a little shaking, the mercury level raised to compress the air at the top of the chamber C, stopcock A opened carefully to eject this air and subsequently to permit about 1 ml. of the water in the chamber to rise up into the cup to make sure that all the air has been ejected.

The Hempel pipette with stopcock H closed is once more attached to the manometric apparatus with the tip of its forearm firmly pressed into the bottom of the cup. When the mercury reservoir is raised and stopcock A carefully opened, (stopcock H now turned to position 2), the deaerated water in chamber C is forced up the capillary of the pipette forearm and into the cup of the pipette. Stopcock A is closed, the leveling bulb moved to a lower position, stopcock H turned to

MANOMETRY AND TITRIMETRY

position 1, stopcock A carefully opened, and the nitrogen gas from the Hempel pipette slowly drawn into chamber C. The permanganate solution which follows the gas is allowed to go as far as the capillary above stopcock A. Stopcocks A

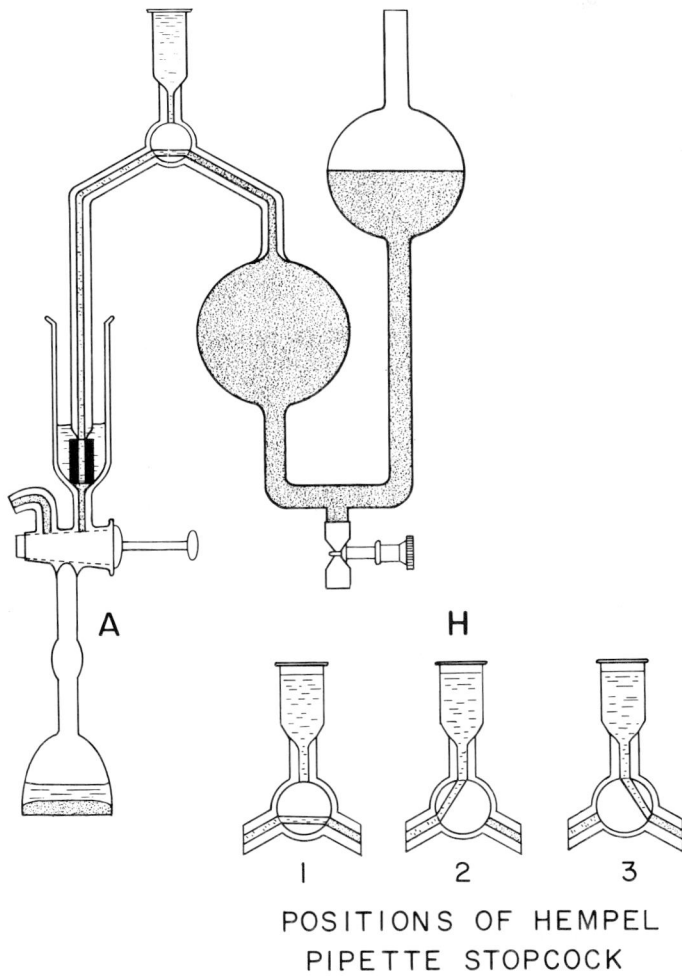

POSITIONS OF HEMPEL
PIPETTE STOPCOCK

Figure 12-4. Positions of the Hempel pipette in the determination of amino nitrogen by the nitrous acid procedure. The bore of stopcock H possesses an angle of 120°.

and H are then closed and the Hempel pipette removed. Water is added to the cup to wash out any permanganate present, the wash fluid being drawn off with suction. Mercury is added thereafter, and enough drawn through stopcock A to clear the capillary.

5. Measurement of the nitrogen gas. By lowering the mercury leveling bulb with accompanying adjustment of stopcock B, the level of the water in the chamber may be set with its meniscus at either the 2.0- or the 0.5-ml. mark according to the amount of gas present (see above). At such a level and with stopcock B open, the level of mercury in the manometer is read to give a value of P_1. The leveling bulb is raised again, stopcock A carefully opened to eject the nitrogen gas into the atmosphere, and the leveling bulb again adjusted to the same water meniscus volume level as before. The pressure now read on the manometer is P_0. As stated above, $P_{N_2} = P_1 - P_0$. The value of $P_1^c - P_0^c$ for the reagent blank run in the same manner as with the amine present is subtracted, when significant, from P_{N_2}.

An example of the data obtained follows. Five cubic milliliters of a 0.005M solution of alanine or 25 micromoles was analyzed at 22° for α-amino N by the nitrous acid procedure described above. The 2.0-ml. constant volume level was employed. P_1 was 338.0 mm., P_0 111.2 mm., and the reagent blank $P_1^c - P_0^c$, 4.0 mm. P_{N_2} was therefore 222.8 mm. The corresponding factor in Table 12–3 is 0.1087, and the number of micromoles of alanine found by analysis was 24.2. The error was thus a little over 3%. In practice, a result with this procedure which is within 5% is reasonably satisfactory.

5. Titrimetric Methods. The determination of the concentration of amino acids in aqueous solutions by means of indicator-titration procedures with strong acids or alkalis is a nearly impossible task because the dissociation constants for the amino and carboxyl groups lie at such relatively extreme pH ranges that the addition of an equivalent amount of acid or alkali would remove the pH of the solution to a point beyond that at which most standard indicators change from one color to another. This color change of the indicator is also an ionization phenomenon, and dependent upon the pK value of the indicator. Therefore, if the appropriate pK of the amino acid could be shifted in some way without disturbing the pK of the indicator, or vice versa, a practicable titration procedure for the amino acids could be developed. This has been essentially achieved by conducting the acid-base titration of the amino acids in aqueous solutions containing ethanol, acetone, or formaldehyde. The mechanisms involved in these titrations have been fully described in Chapter 4 (see particularly, Sections 4–22 and 4–23) and need not be repeated here. Titrations of amino acids under completely anhydrous conditions in glacial acetic acid are capable of reaching a state of reasonably high precision (Section 4–24), i.e., ±0.5%.

(a) TITRATIONS IN ETHANOL–WATER. This procedure may first have been described in 1920 by Foreman (56), who reported somewhat to his own surprise that leucine and valine "titrated [with alkali and phenolphthalein] in 85% alcohol behave as if they were ordinary organic acids." Similar behavior was noted for other amino acids under the same conditions. In all cases studied, however, and especially with proline and with aspartic and glutamic acids, the alkali required to bring the solution to the phenolphthalein end point was somewhat less than demanded by theory, even though the pK_2 of the α-amino group concerned was little affected by the change from water to 90% ethanol. This difficulty was met in part by Willstätter and Waldschmidt-Leitz (57), who used thymolphthalein (turning point at pH 9.6) instead of phenolphthalein (turning point at pH 8.2). Peptides with a more acid pK_2 and a more alkaline pK_1 could apparently be titrated in 40% ethanol solutions instead of the 90–95% ethanol solutions required for the titration of the amino acids (57). In the earlier studies on peptidase activities, the adaptation of this titration procedure by Grassmann and Heyde (58) provided investigators with a microtechnique which, although approximate, served usefully for some period of time.

Few amino acids are soluble in 90% ethanol, and the titration with standard alkali in a cloudy mixture which depends upon a change of the thymolphthalein indicator from colorless to pale blue has been difficult for many investigators to follow with satisfactory precision. To meet some of these objections, in part, an ammoniacal copper chloride solution as a standard end-point matching color has been employed; adding freshly precipitated barium sulfate to this standard solution to match more closely the milky appearance of the mixture being titrated has also been recommended (59). Apparently, only long experience with this procedure is capable of leading its user to valid results.

(b) TITRATIONS IN ACETONE–WATER. In contrast with alkalimetric titrations of the amino acids in ethanol–water, the titration of amino acids in acetone–water mixtures has been conducted with acid. In the latter procedure, naphthyl red is employed as an indicator (Section 4-23). This indicator undergoes an acid shift in 90% acetone as compared with its range in water, but, more importantly, the pK_1 of the carboxyl group of the amino acid undergoes a very marked shift toward the alkaline end of the pH scale. Both shifts therefore favor the titration of the carboxyl group in 90% acetone by standard acid. The procedure as developed by Linderstrom-Lang in 1928 (60) involved (a) addition of standard HCl to a solution of an amino acid in water plus indicator until the indicator changed from yellow (alkaline side) to red (acid side), (b) addition of acetone to 90%, causing a change in the indicator color from red to yellow, (c) addition of standard acid until the indicator reverted again to a red color, which was matched against that of the indicator in 90% acetone solution plus a known volume of standard acid. The concentration of amino acid could be calculated from the amount of acid employed in the titration minus that used in the standard. Here, again, the insolubility of the amino acids, even as their hydrochlorides, in 90% acetone rendered visual estimation of the progress of the titration quite difficult.

At the present time, the colorimetric titration procedures for amino acid analysis in ethanol–water and in acetone–water are mainly of historical and theoretical interest, and have been generally replaced by the more precise and specific manometric methods described earlier in this chapter. Of the aqueous titration methods still employed for amino acid analysis, the alkalimetric procedure involved with formaldehyde retains, because of its relative simplicity and ease of performance not with indicators but with the potentiometer, a certain degree of usefulness. The formaldehyde titration is essentially based upon the acid shift of the pK_2 of the amino group of the amino acid (Section 4–23).

(c) TITRATIONS IN FORMALDEHYDE–WATER. The potentiometric procedure by Dunn and Loshakoff (61) has been capable of high precision in the small-scale analysis of amino acids and peptides. In brief the method is as follows. The amino acid or peptide (0.2–0.4 g.) is dissolved in 38 ml. of water. Twelve milliliters of 37.5% reagent grade formaldehyde (previously shaken with basic magnesium carbonate and then filtered) is added. With mechanical stirring, 0.3N NaOH is added slowly, drop by drop, over a period of about 10 minutes until about 1 ml. less than the equivalent point has been supplied. The potential of the system is measured 1 minute after the last addition of alkali. From here on, approximately 0.2-ml. increments of the alkali are added, and, after waiting for about 4 minutes after each addition, the voltage is determined. The titration is continued until from 0.1 to 1.0 ml. of alkali has been added beyond the equivalence point, and the precise location of this point determined by a plot of $\Delta E/\Delta V$ (the change in voltage per unit change in volume) against the volume of standard alkali employed. A sharp point can be obtained where the two converging titration curves intersect, the accuracy of the analysis being expressed in terms of $\pm 0.1\%$ (61).

(d) TITRATIONS IN ANHYDROUS ACETIC ACID (cf. Section 4–24). The rather exact, colorimetric titration procedure developed by Toennies and Callan (62) is detailed below.

Illustrative procedure 12–5. Reagents: Glacial acetic acid with a water content of 0.2% or less; standard perchloric acid diluted to about 1N in glacial acetic acid, from which known aliquots are removed, diluted with glacial acetic acid and the exact amount of acetic anhydride required to react with the water present, and brought to a final concentration of 0.10N; crystal violet as indicator at 0.1% solution in glacial acetic acid; a standard 0.1N solution of pure glycine in glacial acetic acid which is used to determine the titer of the perchloric acid solution to both green and yellow end points; and, finally, 98–100% formic acid. The color of crystal violet in acetic acid changes with increasing acidity from blue to green to yellow. In practice, it has been found most suitable to determine both the green and the yellow end points when titrating in the acid direction, and both the green and the blue end points in those cases where a back-titration is necessary.

The titrations are conducted in 50-ml. glass-stoppered flasks. The amount of amino acid studied is usually less than 1 millimole, corresponding to less than 10 ml. of the 0.1N perchloric acid solution. Those amino acids which are soluble in glacial acetic acid (Table 2-3) are directly titrated in the dry state, using 2 drops of the crystal violet indicator (green and yellow end points). With less soluble amino acids an excess of the standard perchloric acid is added, the mixture warmed or shaken to solution, and the solution back-titrated with standard glycine solution to the green and blue end points of the crystal violet indicator. With those amino acids insoluble even in excess perchloric acid, such as aspartic and glutamic acids, 2 ml. of formic acid is added to solution followed by 20 ml. of glacial acetic acid, and a direct titration undertaken with the standard perchloric acid to only the green end point.

From each of the titration values so obtained the reagent blank value to the same colored end point is subtracted. The results for each pair of such determinations at the same end-point colors should be the same. If the reagents contain a small but appraisable amount of water, the yellow end point becomes difficult to define although the green end point still remains sharp. Water has a substantially identical effect on the end points in blank and actual titrations, so that there is little to fear in this direction unless the water content is so high (about 1%) that it is impossible to determine the yellow end point.

REFERENCES

1. Liebig, J., *Ann.*, **70**, 313 (1849).
2. Strecker, A., *Ann.*, **123**, 363 (1862).
3. Langheld, K., *Ber.*, **42**, 392, 2360 (1909).
4. Dakin, H. D., *Biochem. J.*, **10**, 319 (1916); **11**, 79 (1917).
5. Kemble, A. R., and MacPherson, H. T., *Biochem. J.*, **56**, 548 (1954).
6. Cohen, P. P., *J. Biol. Chem.*, **136**, 565 (1940); note footnote by H. A. Krebs.
7. Van Slyke, D. D., Dillon, R. T., MacFadyen, D. A., and Hamilton, P., *J. Biol. Chem.*, **141**, 627 (1941).
8. Curtius, T., and Lederer, G., *Ber.*, **19**, 2462 (1886).
9. Dose, K., *Nature*, **179**, 734 (1957).
10. Virtanen, A. I., Laine, T., and Toivonen, T., *Z. physiol. Chem.*, **266**, 193 (1940).
11. Moubasher, R., *J. Biol. Chem.*, **175**, 187 (1948).
12. Schönberg, A., Moubasher, R., and Mostofa, A., *J. Chem. Soc.*, **1948**, 176.
13. Schönberg, A., Moubasher, R., and Barakat, M. Z., *J. Chem. Soc.*, **1951**, 2504.
14. MacFadyen, D. A., *J. Biol. Chem.*, **153**, 507 (1944).
15. Sobel, A. E., Hirschman, A., and Besman, L., *J. Biol. Chem.*, **161**, 99 (1945).
16. Saidel, L. J., *J. Biol. Chem.*, **224**, 445 (1957).
17. Van Slyke, D. D., MacFadyen, D. A., and Hamilton, P., *J. Biol. Chem.*, **141**, 671 (1941); Smith, A. M., and Agiza, A. H., *Analyst*, **76**, 619 (1951).
18. Cristol, P., Benezech, C., and Gastes de Paulet, A., *Bull. soc. chim. France*, **1955**, 183.
19. Van Slyke, D. D., and Neil, J. M., *J. Biol. Chem.*, **61**, 523 (1924).
20. Hamilton, P., and Van Slyke, D. D., *J. Biol. Chem.*, **150**, 231 (1943); **164**, 249 (1946).
21. Puddington, I. E., *J. Am. Chem. Soc.*, **65**, 990 (1945).
22. MacFadyen, D. A., *J. Biol. Chem.*, **145**, 387 (1942).
23. Schott, H. F., Rockland, L. B., and Dunn, M. S., *J. Biol. Chem.*, **154**, 397 (1944).

24. Van Slyke, D. D., MacFadyen, D. A., and Hamilton, P. B., *J. Biol. Chem.*, **150**, 251 (1943).
25. Van Slyke, D. D., and Folch, J., *J. Biol. Chem.*, **136**, 509 (1940).
26. John, W. D., and Young, G. T., *J. Chem. Soc.*, **1954**, 2870.
27. Markovitz, A., and Steinberg, D., *J. Biol. Chem.*, **228**, 285 (1957).
28. Christensen, H. N., Riggs, T. R., Fischer, H., and Palatine, I. M., *J. Biol. Chem.*, **198**, 1 (1952).
29. Baker, C. G., Fu, S-C. J., Birnbaum, S. M., Sober, H. A., and Greenstein, J. P., *J. Am. Chem. Soc.*, **74**, 4701 (1952).
30. Birnbaum, S. M., personal communication.
31. Chappelle, E. W., and Luck, J. M., *J. Biol. Chem.*, **229**, 171 (1957).
32. Sachsse, R., and Kormann, W., cited in a review by Neubauer, C., *Z. anal. Chem.*, **14**, 380 (1875).
33. Fischer, E., and Koelker, W. F., *Ann.*, **340**, 177 (1905).
34. Van Slyke, D. D., *Ber.*, **43**, 3170 (1910).
35. Van Slyke, D. D., *J. Biol. Chem.*, **9**, 185 (1911); **12**, 275 (1912).
36. Van Slyke, D. D., *J. Biol. Chem.*, **83**, 425 (1929).
37. Hunter, A., *J. Biol. Chem.*, **82**, 731 (1929).
38. Van Slyke, D. D., Hiller, A., and Dillon, R. T., *J. Biol. Chem.*, **146**, 137 (1942).
39. Austin, A. T., *J. Chem. Soc.*, **1950**, 149.
40. Kendrick, A. B., and Hanke, M. E., *J. Biol. Chem.*, **117**, 161 (1937); **132**, 739 (1940).
41. Dunn, M. S., and Porush, I., *J. Biol. Chem.*, **127**, 261 (1939).
42. Sluyterman, L. A. AE., and Kooistra, M., *Rec. trav. chim.*, **70**, 1045 (1951).
43. Dunn, M. S., and Schmidt, C. L. A., *J. Biol. Chem.*, **53**, 401 (1922).
44. Gornall, A. G., and Hunter, A., *Biochem. J.*, **34**, 192 (1940).
45. Greenstein, J. P., *J. Biol. Chem.*, **101**, 603 (1932).
46. Bergmann, M., Zervas, L., Rinke, H., and Schleich, H., *Z. physiol. Chem.*, **224**, 26 (1934).
47. Vickery, H. B., Pucher, G. W., Clark, H. E., Chibnall, A. C., and Westall, R. G., *Biochem. J.*, **29**, 2710 (1935).
48. Lichtenstein, N., *J. Am. Chem. Soc.*, **64**, 1021 (1942).
49. Sachs, H., and Brand, E., *J. Am. Chem. Soc.*, **76**, 3601 (1954).
50. Leighty, J. A., and Corley, R. C., *J. Biol. Chem.*, **120**, 331 (1937).
51. Lough, S. A., and Lewis, H. B., *J. Biol. Chem.*, **104**, 601 (1934).
52. Carter, H. E., and Dickman, S. R., *J. Biol. Chem.*, **149**, 571 (1943).
53. Clarke, H. T., and Inouye, J. M., *J. Biol. Chem.*, **89**, 399 (1930).
54. Kainz, G., and Schöller, F., *Z. physiol. Chem.*, **301**, 259 (1955).
55. Fraenkel-Conrat, H., *J. Biol. Chem.*, **148**, 453 (1943).
56. Foreman, F. W., *Biochem. J.*, **14**, 451 (1920).
57. Willstätter, R., and Waldschmidt-Leitz, E., *Ber.*, **54**, 2988 (1921).
58. Grassmann, W., and Heyde, W., *Z. physiol. Chem.*, **183**, 32 (1929).
59. McLaren, A. D., *Science*, **102**, 510 (1945).
60. Linderstrom-Lang, K., *Z. physiol. Chem.*, **173**, 32 (1928).
61. Dunn, M. S., and Loshakoff, A., *J. Biol. Chem.*, **113**, 359 (1936).
62. Toennies, G., and Callan, T. P., *J. Biol. Chem.*, **125**, 259 (1938).

chapter 13

Isotope Dilution

1. The Single-Isotope Technique. This procedure, which in concept and execution is simple and powerful, was originally reported by Rittenberg and Foster (1). It is based essentially upon the following principle. If an amino acid, such as glycine, containing a heavy or radioactive isotope is added to a mixture of various amino acids, the glycine isolated from this mixture will be a representative sample of the labeled glycine and the glycine originally present. From the amount of labeled glycine added, X, and its heavy or radioactive isotope content in excess of normal, C_0, as well as the isotope excess of the isolated glycine, C, the amount Y of glycine originally present in the mixture can be calculated according to

(1) $$Y = \left(\frac{C_0}{C} - 1\right) X$$

It is only necessary in this procedure to obtain a sample large enough for isotope analysis. Quite large losses can be afforded in the isolation process. The value of C_0/C should be between 5 and 10 for most accurate results.

The procedure applied to the determination of amino acids in protein hydrolysates has been complicated by the fact that, although these various amino acids (except for glycine) are all L in configuration, the isotope-labeled synthetic amino acids added to such mixtures have often been DL. The solubilities of the L and DL varieties of the same amino acid are known to be different. The difficulties inherent in such a situation have been pointed out by Arnstein, Neuberger, and their associates (2) (see Section 9–2 for further discussion).

There are three ways in which the complications facing this situation may be met, namely, (a) the amino acids in the hydrolysate are racemized, the labeled racemic amino acid is added, and racemic amino acid is isolated, (b) the synthetic, labeled amino acid is first resolved into its optical enantiomorphs and only the L-isomer is employed, or (c) the labeled racemic amino acid is added to the hydrolysate, the sample of original L-amino acid and labeled DL-amino acid isolated, and this sample, which consists of a mixture of L-amino acid (unlabeled and in quantitative excess) plus L-amino acid (labeled) plus D-amino acid (labeled), is recrystallized several times until all the D-amino acid (labeled) is removed as a racemate with the equal amount of the sum of L (unlabeled) and L (labeled); this leaves only the L-form as a mixture of L (unlabeled) and L (labeled), the criteria being constant and correct optical rotation values, and constant isotope contents, for the products of the final two or three crystallizations. This desirable state of affairs is not always attained; and it is never attained with conspicuous ease (cf. 3).

As an illustration of the method, Rittenberg and Foster (1) refluxed 4.995 grams of fibrin with 150 ml. of 20% hydrochloric acid for 20 hours. DL-Glutamic acid amounting to 0.1266 gram and labeled with N^{15} (2.10 atom per cent excess) was added, and glutamic acid was removed as the insoluble barium salt in 80% ethanol and converted to the hydrochloride. After several crystallizations whereby the less soluble L-amino acid was readily separated from the more soluble DL-amino acid, and during which the N^{15} excess in atom per cent was found to be, in the last three crystallizations, 0.182, 0.186, and 0.185, a sample of L-glutamic acid hydrochloride with $[\alpha]_D = +25.5$ in N HCl was finally obtained. Application of equation 1, in which the value of X is now half that of the racemate added, because only one of the two optical isomers is involved, revealed the L-glutamic acid content of the fibrin molecule to be 13.2%.

The procedure can also be employed to determine the amount of D-amino acid present in a protein hydrolysate or any other biological source. Thus, instead of discarding the DL-glutamic acid in the mother liquors of the crystallizations described in the paragraph above, it may be saved and subjected to isotope analysis. From the concentration of N^{15} in the L-isomer isolated, and in the DL form isolated from the mother liquor, it is possible to calculate the concentration of N^{15} in the D-isomer, inasmuch as (2)

(2) $$C(\text{DL}) = 0.5 C(\text{D}) + 0.5 C(\text{L})$$

where $C(\text{DL})$ is the concentration of N^{15} in the racemate. The amount of the D-isomer originally present in the hydrolysate, $Y(\text{D})$, will be therefore (2)

(3) $$Y(\text{D}) = \left(\frac{C_0}{2C(\text{DL}) - C(\text{L})} - 1 \right) 0.5 X$$

This procedure was employed by Graff, Rittenberg, and Foster (4) to test the claim by Kögl and Erxleben (5) that D-glutamic acid in appreciable quantities could be found in the hydrolysates of tumor proteins. A typical example follows. A sample of 12.0 grams of dry tumor was hydrolyzed and

1.20 grams of DL-glutamic acid hydrochloride (= 0.9612 gram of DL-glutamic acid) having 1.76 atom per cent excess N^{15} was added to the hydrolysate. The L-glutamic acid hydrochloride isolated contained N^{15} in 0.511 atom per cent excess whilst the DL-glutamic acid hydrochloride contained 1.137 atom per cent excess of N^{15}. Substitution of these values in equation 3 revealed that the content of D-glutamic acid originally present in the protein hydrolysate was very close to zero.

The technical problems encountered by the addition of a labeled, racemic amino acid to a mixture of L-amino acids can be overcome simply by the use of the labeled L-amino acid provided by resolution of the racemate. It was in part for this reason that preparative methods for the isolation of pure, optically active amino acids from small amounts of the racemates was developed (6) (see Part VI).

The possibility that glycine might be formed from serine during the course of the strong acid hydrolysis of proteins was investigated by Shemin (7). To 900 mg. of serine, 500 mg. of isotopic glycine containing 1.095 atom per cent N^{15} excess was added and the mixture refluxed for 17 hours with 100 ml. of 20% hydrochloric acid. From this mixture, glycine was separated as the trioxalatochromiate and purified via the p-toluenesulfonyl derivative. The isotope value of the isolated glycine was found to be 1.091 atom per cent N^{15} excess, and, inasmuch as no isotopic dilution had occurred, it could be concluded that none of the serine had been converted to glycine.

Analyses of several proteins by the procedure of isotopic dilution were reported by Foster (8) and by Shemin (7), with results which agreed very well with those obtained by other procedures. Where the amino acid sought was also isotopically labeled, however, a new approach became necessary. Bloch and Anker (9) suggested that by the addition of different amounts of normal carrier to separate portions of the source material the isotope concentration of the required compound could be estimated. This principle was adopted by Berenbom, Sober, and White (10) who extended it further through the use of isotopically labeled carriers. After unequally labeled carriers were added to separate aliquots of the source material, two samples of the compound were isolated whose isotope concentrations could be expressed by

(4) $$C_{a+x} = \frac{aC_a + xC_x}{a + x}$$

(5) $$C_{b+x} = \frac{bC_b + xC_x}{b + x}$$

where a and b are the amount of carrier added, C_a and C_b are their isotope concentrations, while C_1 and C_2 are the isotope concentrations of the isolated products, x is the amount of unknown, and C_x is its isotope concentration. Solving the above equations simultaneously, there is obtained for x and C_x

(6) $$x = a\frac{(C_a - C_1) + b(C_2 - C_b)}{C_1 - C_2}$$

(7) $$C_x = \frac{C_1(a + x) - aC_a}{x} = \frac{C_2(b + x) - bC_b}{x}$$

By means of these equations both the amount and the isotope concentration of a compound can be determined even when it is present in amounts too small to permit direct isolation.

2. The Double-Isotope Dilution Technique. One of the most striking procedures for amino acid analysis was that originally employed by Keston, Udenfriend, and Cannan (11) in which the amino acid or acids to be determined were substituted by reaction with I^{131}-labeled p-iodobenzenesulfonyl chloride. This required the complete separation and recovery of the derivatives so formed, a result not often readily achieved. This disadvantage was overcome to a considerable extent by the subsequent device of adding a known quantity of S^{32}-labeled p-iodobenzenesulfonyl amino acid after the preparation of the I^{131}-labeled amino acid derivatives in the sample to be analyzed. By means of this double-tracer procedure, the measurement of the S^{32}/I^{131} ratio of the purified derivative gave the amount of the amino acid initially present in the mixture (12). From the point at which the known amount of labeled amino acid derivative was added, losses in the subsequent procedure had little or no effect on the analysis. The technique is described in some detail in Chapter 15.

In the hope of avoiding some of the shortcomings of this technique, among which the comparatively short half-lives of the isotopes are prominent, Whitehead introduced the use of acetic anhydride labeled with either C^{14} or H^3 (13). Each amino acid to be studied was N-acetylated with C^{14}-acetic anhydride and made up into standard solutions in water. The sample solution containing a mixture of amino acids derived from a protein or peptide hydrolysate was treated under alkaline conditions with tritiated acetic anhydride, in the usual fashion, to convert the amino acids to their N-acetyl(H^3) derivatives. Portions of the standard solutions of the N-acetyl (C^{14}) derivatives of the amino acids to be analyzed were added to the mixture just described, and the combined solution passed over a Zeo-Karb 225 (H^+) column. The acetylated amino acids passed through the column while sodium ion and unsubstituted amino acids were adsorbed. The eluate was evaporated *in vacuo* to dryness, the residue dissolved in ethanolic ammonia, and applied to Whatman No. 2 paper for chromatography. Separation of the acetylated amino acids was accomplished by employing a mixture of benzene, ethanol, and phenol (1 : 1 : 5.5) in one direction on the paper, and butanol, methanol, and NH$_4$OH (4 : 1 : 5) in the other. The completed chromatogram was dried, and the separated N-acetylated amino acids on the paper revealed as yellow spots on a blue background by dipping the paper into a solution of bromocresol green in acetone which had been converted to the blue color by a drop of morpholine. The individual areas on the chromatogram corresponding to particular N-acetylamino acids were cut out and burnt in oxygen to yield carbon dioxide and water, the C^{14} and H^3 content of which, respectively, were determined by appropriate measurement of the radioactivity. Three activity measurements were required to obtain the analytical results, namely, that of the added C^{14}-labeled acetylamino acid, and those of the C^{14} and H^3 activities of the spot removed from the paper.

REFERENCES

1. Rittenberg, D., and Foster, G. L., *J. Biol. Chem.*, **133**, 737 (1940).
2. Arnstein, H. R. V., Hunter, G. D., Muir, H. M., and Neuberger, A., *J. Chem., Soc.*, **1952**, 1329.
3. Barker, C. C., Hughes, I. W., and Young, G. T., *J. Chem. Soc.*, **1951**, 3047.
4. Graff, S., Rittenberg, D., and Foster, G. L., *J. Biol. Chem.*, **133**, 745 (1940).
5. Kögl, F., and Erxleben, H., *Z. physiol. Chem.*, **258**, 57 (1939).
6. Parikh, J., Greenstein, J. P., Birnbaum, S. M., and Winitz, M., *J. Am. Chem. Soc.*, **80**, 953 (1958).
7. Shemin, D., *J. Biol. Chem.*, **159**, 439 (1945).
8. Foster, G. L., *J. Biol. Chem.*, **159**, 431 (1945).
9. Bloch, K., and Anker, H. S., *Science*, **107**, 228 (1948).
10. Berenbom, M., Sober, H. A., and White, J., *Arch. Biochem.*, **29**, 369 (1950).
11. Keston, A. S., Udenfriend, S., and Cannan, R. K., *J. Am. Chem. Soc.*, **68**, 1390 (1946).
12. Keston, A. S., Udenfriend, S., and Levy, M., *J. Am. Chem. Soc.*, **72**, 748 (1950).
13. Whitehead, J. K., *Biochem. J.*, **68**, 662 (1958).

chapter 14

Microbiological Assay Methods

1. Introduction. Different species of bacteria, molds, yeasts, protozoa, and other unicellular organisms reveal a remarkable diversity in their nutritional needs. Thus, whereas certain microorganisms may thrive on a relatively simple medium composed of glucose, ammonia, and inorganic salts, others are more fastidious in that they require a variety of amino acids, vitamins, minerals, and other nutrilites before normal growth can be achieved. Indeed, the complexity of the nutriment which some microorganisms demand for the normal functioning of their metabolic processes may rival or even surpass that needed by the mammalian organism. A case in point is the lactobacillus *Leuconostoc mesenteroides* P-60 which requires seventeen amino acids for growth (1) in contrast to the 8 to 10 essential amino acids required by mammals (Chapter 3). Similar elucidation of the nutritional needs of a variety of microorganisms has led directly to the use of the latter for the quantitative determination of a wide range of amino acids; such application may be attributed primarily to the series of brilliant investigations which have originated in the laboratories of Snell, as well as those of Dunn, Elvehjem, Stokes, Lyman, and others (cf. 2–4). It is the practical employment of determinations involving microorganisms, generally termed *microbiological assay methods*, with which the discussion below is primarily concerned.

The use of microorganisms for the estimation of amino acids depends upon the well-established fact that the growth response elicited may be regulated by controlling the level of one or more of the essential nutrilites provided in the culture medium. In routine practice, a basal medium is prepared which, except for the amino acid to be assayed, incorporates all the known essential and stimulatory nutriments required for optimal growth of the assay organism. Graded doses of the sample to be determined are added to the basal medium which, in turn, is sterilized, inoculated with the appropriate assay organism and incubated at 37°. It is customary in practical microbiological assay work to limit the organisms employed to certain strains of bacteria which, during the course of their metabolic activities, produce lactic acid, since this substance not only is formed in an amount which is directly proportional within certain limits to the concentration of amino acid in the medium, but may be rapidly and accurately measured by direct titration with standardized alkali as well. A somewhat less satisfactory, albeit frequently used, means of estimating the amino acid concentration involves the turbidimetric measurement of the amount of bacterial growth with the aid of a nephelometer. In either event, final values are obtained after comparison with a calibration curve, wherein the response (in terms of growth or lactic acid production) is plotted against various concentrations of the pure amino acid taken as the standard.

Through the application of the microbiological assay technique, it is presently possible to analyze quantitatively for the following protein-derived amino acids: alanine, arginine, aspartic acid, cystine, glutamic acid, glycine, histidine, isoleucine, leucine, lysine, methionine, phenylalanine, proline, serine, threonine, tryptophan, tyrosine, and valine. Determination of each of these amino acids may be achieved via a number of reasonably satisfactory alternative procedures which vary in regard to the bacterial species or the composition of basal medium employed but are otherwise fundamentally similar. Most can be expected to give reliable and reproducible results. As it would prove clearly impracticable to attempt to discuss independently each of these assay procedures here, recourse has been made to the presentation of only a few procedures which can be applied to several amino acids without any change in the methodology, assay organism, or basal medium (except for the amino acid being determined). It should be borne in mind, however, that, once a microbiological assay technique has been mastered for any given amino acid with any given assay organism, it may be readily extended with little fundamental change to other amino acids, irrespective of the organism or the basal medium utilized. A compilation of many of the numerous assay procedures which have been devised appears in extensive reviews by Dunn (2) and by Barton-Wright (3).

2. Growth Conditions for Lactic Acid-Producing Bacteria. The bacteria of concern in the microbiological assay of α-amino acids generally belong to the family *Lactobacteriaceae* or, more specifically, to the genera *Lactobacillus* (*L.*), *Leuconostoc* (*Leuco.*), and *Streptococcus* (*S.*). Such organisms possess in common the ability not only to form large amounts of acid (especially lactic acid) through the fermentation of various carbohydrates but also to thrive under conditions of greater acidity than most other bacterial species are likely to endure. Thus, although many lactic acid-producing bacteria exhibit an optimal growth within the pH range 6 to 7, growth will none the less proceed until a pH of 4 or lower is attained; by virtue of this characteristic, these organisms are frequently described as *aciduric* or *acidophilic*. The organisms are non-motile, non-spore-forming, and either anaerobic or micro-aerophilic; the latter term is used to denote organisms which are not strict anaerobes but prefer rather an atmosphere which is somewhat deficient in free oxygen. Although a temperature in the vicinity of 37° to 38° is generally required for maximum growth, several species, e.g., *L. caucasicus* and *L. acidophilus*, reveal good growth at 45° whilst others, e.g., *L. thermophilus*, grow well at temperatures as high as 62°, a temperature which generally proves fatal to many non-spore-forming bacteria.

The lactic acid-producing bacteria may be classified as either *homofermentative* or *heterofermentative*, dependent upon their metabolic action on glucose. Organisms in the former category such as *L. arabinosus, L. delbrückii*, and *S. faecalis* oxidize glucose to lactic acid quantitatively according to the following scheme:

$$C_6H_{12}O_6 \rightleftharpoons 2CH_3CHOHCO_2H$$

With heterofermentative types, on the other hand, accompanying reactions may result in the formation of such co-products as ethanol and carbon dioxide in addition to lactic acid; *Leuco. mesenteroides* may be classed among the organisms of this type. Besides the need for energy provided by a utilizable source of carbon such as glucose, the lactic acid-producing bacteria require a variety of vitamins, mineral salts, and purine and pyrimidine bases, as well as nitrogen furnished by protein, protein hydrolysates or amino acid mixtures, before normal growth can be achieved. The requirement for these nutrilites, which may be either essential for or stimulatory to growth, generally varies with the individual species.

Since about 1940, studies on the nutritional needs of certain of the *Lactobacteriaceae* have led to the formulation of a wide variety of basal media which can promote maximal growth in these organisms. The composition of several of the synthetic media which have satisfactorily served in this capacity are listed in Table 14–1 (3, 5–7). It should be noted that, in addition to the required complement of amino acids, purine and pyrimidine bases, vitamins, inorganic salts, and glucose, each of these media incorporates sodium acetate, sodium citrate, or a mixture of both as a source of buffer. The use of a suitable buffer is necessitated here since the lactic acid produced during the growth and fermentation process might otherwise induce abrupt changes in the pH level of the culture medium and hence might either seriously interfere with or entirely inhibit normal growth; in practice, sufficient buffer is usually present to maintain the pH at 6.8, a condition permissive of maximal rate of growth. For the purpose at hand, the media listed in Table 14–1, when employed in conjunction with the pertinent microorganisms, serve admirably well for the microbiological assay of some eighteen different amino acids. It is the technical aspects of these assays with which the discussion below is primarily concerned.

TABLE 14-1

Composition of Various Synthetic Assay Media

Milligrams per 500 ml. of Double-Strength Medium

Constituent	A[a]	B[b]	C[c]	D[d]
Amino acids[e]				
DL-Alanine	200	1,000	200	1,000
L-Arginine·HCl	242	200	200	250
L-Asparagine	400	–	–	–
L-Aspartic acid	100	1,000[f]	200[f]	400[f]
L-Cysteine·HCl	50	–	–	–
L-Cystine	–	50	200	100
L-Glutamic acid	300	1,000	200[f]	500
Glycine	100	50	200	100
L-Histidine·HCl	62	50	200	100
DL-Isoleucine	250	100	200	200
DL-Leucine	250	100	200	100[g]
L-Lysine·HCl	250	200	100	100
DL-Methionine	100	100	200	100
DL-Phenylalanine	100	100	200	100
L-Proline	100	50	200	100
DL-Serine	50	100	200	100
DL-Threonine	200	100	200	500
DL-Tryptophan	40	100	400	200
L-Tyrosine	100	50	200	100
DL-Valine	250	100	200	200
Purine and pyrimidine bases				
Adenine sulfate·H$_2$O	10	10	10	12
Guanine·HCl·2H$_2$O	10	10	10	12
Xanthine	10	10	–	12
Uracil	10	10	10	12
Vitamins				
p-Aminobenzoic acid	0.1	0.2	0.04	0.05
Biotin	0.001	0.01	0.0002	0.005
Ca dl-pantothenate	0.5	1.0	0.2	1[h]
Folic acid	0.01	0.01	0.002	0.001
Folinic acid	–[i]	–[i]	–	–
Nicotinic acid	1.0	1.0	0.2	2
Pyridoxal·HCl	0.3	0.2	–	–
Pyridoxamine·2HCl	0.3	–	0.4	–
Pyridoxine·HCl	1.0	–	–	1.6
Riboflavin	0.5	1.0	0.2	2
Thiamine·HCl	0.5	1.0	0.2	1

TABLE 14-1 (continued)

Milligrams per 500 ml. of Double-Strength Medium

Constituent	A[a]	B[b]	C[c]	D[d]
Inorganic salts				
NH$_4$Cl	3,000	3,000	–	6,000
K$_2$HPO$_4$	600	5,000	500	500
KH$_2$PO$_4$	600	–	500	500
MgSO$_4$·7H$_2$O	200	800	200	200
MnSO$_4$·4H$_2$O	20	160	10	10
FeSO$_4$·7H$_2$O	10	40	10	2[j]
NaCl	10	40	10	5,000
Sodium citrate	–	20,000	–	–
Sodium acetate (anhydrous)	20,000	1,000	6,000	20,000[k]
Glucose	25,000	20,000	10,000	20,000

[a] Sauberlich, H. E., and Baumann, C. A., *J. Biol. Chem.*, **176**, 165 (1948).

[b] Henderson, L. M., and Snell, E. E., *J. Biol. Chem.*, **172**, 15 (1948).

[c] Stokes, J. L., Gunness, M., Dwyer, I. M., and Caswell, M. C., *J. Biol. Chem.*, **160**, 35 (1945).

[d] Barton-Wright, E. C., *Analyst*, **71**, 267 (1946); *Microbiological Assay of the Vitamin B-Complex and Amino Acids*, Pitman and Sons, London, 1952.

[e] The DL-form and L-form of an amino acid may be used interchangeably, although the concentration of the former should be twice that of the latter.

[f] Quantity as given is for DL-form.

[g] Quantity as given is for L-form.

[h] Ca d-pantothenate is here employed.

[i] When *L. citrovorum* is the assay organism, either 50 μg. of this compound or 0.08 ml. of injectable liver concentrate is added to the medium.

[j] FeCl$_3$ is here employed instead of FeSO$_4$·7H$_2$O.

[k] As trihydrate.

3. Assay Organisms. An ideal microbiological assay system would be that wherein a single test organism and a single basal medium, with the appropriate amino acid deleted, would suffice to permit the determination of each of the different amino acids. Although no such system has been hitherto devised, media are available which may be used successfully with any one of a variety of test organisms to determine as many as eighteen different amino acids. Several media of this type have been already described (Table 14–1). The assay organisms recommended in this connection include *L. arabinosus* 17–5, *Leuco. citrovorum*, *L. delbrückii* 5, *Leuco. mesenteroides* P-60, and *S. faecalis* R, although a number of other organisms would also prove satisfactory. These organisms, together with several examples of the basal media whereon they exhibit optimal growth and with the amino acids whose assay for which they are most commonly utilized, are given in Table 14-2 (3, 5-10). Note should be made that the determination of most of the amino acids listed may be alternatively effected with several different media or organisms. However, regardless of the test organism or the medium involved, excellent agreement of the assay results can be expected with any given amino acid if the assay is properly executed.

Stock cultures of the afore-mentioned assay organisms may be conveniently carried as *stab cultures* in any of a number of different media; a liver-tryptone agar medium, whose preparation is described in procedure 14-1, has proved highly satisfactory. Description of conventional manipulations involved in the preparation of a stab culture is given in what follows: A platinum inoculating needle is heated to redness in a Bunsen flame and then grasped between the thumb and the index finger of the right hand. The tubes which contain the stock culture and the liver-tryptone agar, respectively, are held in a near horizontal position in the left hand with the palm turned upward; the base of each tube is grasped lightly by the thumb, one tube being supported by the index finger and the other by the middle finger. The cotton plug of each tube is then removed, one with the aid of the little finger and palm, and the other between the little and fourth fingers of the right hand. After a few seconds are allowed for the needle to cool, the latter is quickly inserted into the stock culture tube, withdrawn, and stabbed into the liver-tryptone agar medium of the other; if any cotton fibers adhere to the lips of the tubes, these are singed by passage through a Bunsen flame. The cotton plugs are then reinserted in the proper tubes and the stab culture incubated at 37° until good growth appears in the line of the stab (generally 24 hours but not longer than 48 hours); after this time, the culture is refrigerated at about 4°. A similar transfer should be effected at intervals ranging from 1 to 4 weeks in order that the culture be maintained in a suitably active condition for purposes of assay. It is of course essential that the purity of the different cultures utilized for assay purposes be kept rigidly intact; any sudden appearance of irregular behavior therefore warrants a careful examination of the purity of that particular stock culture.

Illustrative procedure 14-1 (11). Liver-tryptone agar. The following must be made prior to the preparation of the liver-tryptone agar: (a) Salt solution A (12)—a mixture of 25 g. of K_2HPO_4 and 25 g. of KH_2PO_4 is dissolved in water and the volume diluted to 250 ml.; (b) salt solution B (12)—a mixture of 10 g. of $MgSO_4 \cdot 7H_2O$, 0.5 g. of $MnSO_4 \cdot 4H_2O$, 0.5 g. of sodium chloride, and 0.5 g. of $FeSO_4 \cdot 7H_2O$ is dissolved in water to a total of 250 ml.; (c) liver extract—1 lb. of ground fresh liver is suspended in 2 l. of water, heated for 60 min. over a steam bath, filtered through cheese-cloth, and the filtrate, after neutralization to pH 7.0, is heated again for 15 min., filtered through coarse filter paper, and stored in a dark bottle. (The above stock extract and salt solutions should be prepared with glass-distilled water and stored under sulfur-free toluene in a refrigerator.) For

TABLE 14-2

Organisms and Media Employed for the Microbiological Assay of Several Amino Acids (3, 5–10)

Amino Acid	Assay Organism[a]	Assay Medium (see Table 14–1)
Alanine	*Leuco. citrovorum* 8081	A[b]
Arginine	*Leuco. citrovorum* 8081	A
	Leuco. mesenteroides P-60	A
	S. faecalis R	B, C
Aspartic acid	*Leuco. mesenteroides* P-60	A[b], B, D
Cystine	*Leuco. citrovorum* 8081	A
	Leuco. mesenteroides P-60	A
Glutamic acid	*L. arabinosus* 17-5	B[d], D[d]
	Leuco. citrovorum 8081	A[c,d]
	Leuco. mesenteroides P-60	A[d], D[d]
Glycine	*Leuco. citrovorum* 8081	A[e]
	Leuco. mesenteroides P-60	A[e], B, D
Histidine	*Leuco. citrovorum* 8081	A
	Leuco. mesenteroides P-60	A, B, D
	S. faecalis R	B, C, D
Isoleucine	*Leuco. citrovorum* 8081	A
	Leuco. mesenteroides P-60	A, B
	S. faecalis R	C, D
Leucine	*L. arabinosus* 17-5	B
	Leuco. mesenteroides P-60	A
	S. faecalis R	C
Lysine	*Leuco. mesenteroides* P-60	A, B, D
	S. faecalis R	C
Methionine	*Leuco. citrovorum* 8081	A
	Leuco. mesenteroides P-60	A
	S. faecalis R	B, C
Phenylalanine	*L. arabinosus* 17-5	B
	Leuco. citrovorum 8081	A
	Leuco. mesenteroides P-60	A
	L. delbrückii 5	C
Proline	*Leuco. citrovorum* 8081	A
	Leuco. mesenteroides P-60	A, B, D
Serine	*Leuco. mesenteroides* P-60	A[f]
Threonine	*Leuco. citrovorum* 8081	A
	Leuco. mesenteroides P-60	A
	S. faecalis R	B, C
Tryptophan	*L. arabinosus* 17-5	B
	Leuco. mesenteroides P-60	A
	S. faecalis R	C
Tyrosine	*Leuco. citrovorum* 8081	A
	Leuco. mesenteroides P-60	A, B

TABLE 14-2 (*continued*)

Amino Acid	Assay Organism[a]	Assay Medium (see Table 14-1)
Tyrosine (*continued*)	*L. delbrückii* 5	C
Valine	*L. arabinosus* 17-5	B
	Leuco. citrovorum 8081	A
	Leuco. mesenteroides P-60	A
	S. faecalis R	C

[a] These organisms may be obtained from the American Type Culture Collection, 2112 M St., N. W., Washington, D. C. The collection serial numbers are given as follows: *L. arabinosus* 17-5, ATCC 8014; *L. delbrückii* 5, ATCC 9595; *Leuco. citrovorum*, ATCC 8081; *Leuco. mesenteroides* P-60, ATCC 8042; *S. faecalis* R, ATCC 8043.

[b] D-Isomer of the amino acid is utilized equally as well as the L-form.

[c] For this assay, L-aspartic acid is inhibitory and hence is omitted from the basal medium.

[d] In this case, 0.25 mg. of L-glutamine is added per 10 ml. of medium. Although most of the L-glutamine is subsequently converted into pyrrolidonecarboxylic acid upon sterilization of the medium under 10 lb. of pressure, a sufficient amount remains unaltered to permit initiation of growth.

[e] High blank values are revealed here, although tentative values for this amino acid can be obtained if the incubation period is decreased from 72 to 48 hr.

[f] The sensitivity of this assay is greatly increased if pyridoxal and pyridoxamine are omitted from the basal medium. These forms of vitamin B_6 may be destroyed in a test sample, without concomitant destruction of serine, by exposure to ultraviolet light for 20 to 30 min.

preparation of the medium, 1 g. of glucose, 1 g. of tryptone (tryptic digest of casein), 0.2 g. of K_2HPO_4, 0.3 g. of $CaCO_3$, 0.5 ml. of inorganic salt solution A, 0.5 ml. of inorganic salt solution B, 10 ml. of liver extract, and 1.5 g. of agar are added to glass-distilled water and the volume diluted to 100 ml. After the whole has been steamed to dissolve the agar and distributed in adequate aliquots in test tubes, the latter are plugged with cotton wool, sterilized in an autoclave at 10 lb. pressure for 10 min., and finally stored in a refrigerator until needed.

4. Assay Procedure. *Cleaning and Sterilization of Glassware.* It is essential that all glassware employed in the assay procedure be thoroughly cleaned and that aseptic conditions be maintained throughout. Cleaning of glassware is best achieved in boiling water containing a suitable detergent which may be completely removed by a thorough rinsing with tap water, followed by a final rinse with distilled water; the various available chemical cleaning mixtures such as chromic-sulfuric acid are not recommended here, not only because of their inferior action for the removal of deposited grease but also because they contain toxic ions, e.g., chromate, which form a hazard to successful assays if incompletely removed. Pipettes are generally sterilized by autoclaving at about 120° (15 lb. per sq. in.) for 30 minutes;

prior to this operation, each pipette is placed in an individual glass tube closed at the ends by either glass wool or gauze-covered cotton plugs which are not removed until the pipette is needed.

Stock Solutions. For purposes of convenience, the various related ingredients given in Table 14-1 may be combined in stock solutions which are mixed for preparation of the final medium; glass-distilled water should be used in each instance and the resulting solutions stored under sulfur-free toluene in a refrigerator at 4° to 8°. All solutions should be replaced at monthly intervals and the media derived therefrom adjusted to a pH of 6.8 prior to use. (a) Amino acid solution—the amino acids, with the exception of the one undergoing assay, are prepared in aqueous solution such that 250 ml. contains the amounts indicated; cystine and tyrosine are dissolved first in the minimum quantity of $3N$ HCl, the solution is diluted with water, and the other amino acids are added. Complete solution should be effected by heating prior to refrigeration. (b) Purine and pyrimidine base solutions—a stock solution of adenine, guanine, and uracil containing 1 mg. of each (or 1.2 mg.) per milliliter of water is prepared upon prolonged heating in the presence of a few drops of concentrated hydrochloric acid; the xanthine solution, which also possesses a concentration of 1 mg. (or 1.2 mg.) per milliliter, is effected with the aid of a few drops of concentrated ammonia. (c) Vitamin solution—the vitamins are combined in a single solution at concentrations such that 10 ml. will supply the quantities indicated in Table 14-1. This solution should be stored in the dark. (d) Salt solutions—preparation of the salt solutions is achieved either by dissolving 10 g. of $MgSO_4 \cdot 7H_2O$, 0.5 g. of $FeSO_4 \cdot 7H_2O$, 0.5 g. of NaCl, and 2 g. of $MnSO_4 \cdot 4H_2O$ or by dissolving 10 g. of $MgSO_4 \cdot 7H_2O$, 0.5 g. of $MnSO_4 \cdot 4H_2O$, 0.1 g. of $FeCl_3$ (anhydrous), and 5 drops of concentrated hydrochloric acid in sufficient water to give a total volume of 250 ml.; 40 ml. of each salt solution will give the same amount of the component ingredients as given in Table 14-1. Although salt deposition may occur as a result of exposure of the solutions to air, the solutions need not be renewed so long as a uniform suspension can be secured on shaking.

Preparation of Inocula. In routine practice, the medium employed for growing an inoculum culture varies with the particular organism involved. Table 14-3 reveals the compositions of several such media in addition to the assay organisms with which each is commonly used. For the preparation of an inoculum culture, 5- to 10-ml. aliquots of the pertinent medium are added to separate test tubes (16 x 150 mm., Pyrex) and the latter are plugged with cotton, sterilized in the autoclave at 15 pounds pressure for 15 minutes, and then permitted to cool to room temperature prior to use or stored in the refrigerator until required. Following the technique described in Section 14-3, a transfer of a portion of the appropriate agar stab culture to the inoculum medium is achieved with the aid of sterile platinum needle and the resulting subculture incubated at 37° for some 8 to 24 hours (see Table 14–3); good visible growth should be evidenced at the end of this period. The cells are centrifuged down aseptically, and the resulting deposit is suspended in distilled water (or 0.9% sodium chloride solution) after the supernatant has been removed by decantation. The cells are again centrifuged down and

TABLE 14–3
Composition of Inoculum Media and Preparation of Inocula for Various Assay Organisms

Organism	Composition of Inoculum Medium	Preparation of Inoculum
Leuco. citrovorum 8081 Leuco. mesenteroides P-60	Identical with a *single-strength* basal medium A in Table 14–1 but with all amino acids replaced with 5.0 g. of acid hydrolyzed casein except cysteine and tryptophan; in addition, the medium is supplemented with 0.1% yeast extract[a] (13).	Inoculate 10 ml. of sterilized medium, incubate for 20–24 hr. at 37°, harvest cells by centrifugation, wash cells with 10 ml. of distilled water, and finally suspend cells in 10 ml. of water.
L. arabinosus 17-5 Leuco. mesenteroides P-60 S. faecalis R	Identical with a *single-strength* basal medium B in Table 14–1 wherein the glucose and sodium citrate concentrations are reduced to one-half; in addition, the medium is supplemented with 0.5% yeast extract and 0.5% tryptone (6).	Inoculate 5 ml. of sterilized medium, incubate for 8–12 hr. at 37°, harvest cells by centrifugation, and finally suspend cells in 0.9% sodium chloride solution[b] (6).
L. delbrückii 5 S. faecalis R	Each 100 ml. of inoculum medium consists of 1 g. of glucose, 0.5 g. of peptone, 0.6 g. of anhydrous sodium acetate, and inorganic salts in one-fourth the amounts given under basal medium C of Table 14–1 (14).	Inoculate 8 ml. of sterilized medium, incubate for 16–24 hr. at 37°, harvest cells by centrifugation, wash cells with distilled water and finally suspend cells in water[c] (7, 14).

[a] An alternative inoculum medium possesses the complete composition of a *single-strength* basal medium A (Table 14–1) supplemented with 0.1% yeast extract.
[b] S. faecalis preparations are diluted approximately 5-fold and suspensions of L. arabinosus and Leuco. mesenteroides from 1- to 2-fold, dependent upon the amount of growth.
[c] Twenty milliliters of water for L. delbrückii and 100 ml. for S. faecalis.

finally resuspended in distilled water (or 0.9% sodium chloride solution) whose volume is some one to twenty times as great as that of the medium on which they were grown; one drop of this suspension is used for the inoculation of each assay tube. More specific details are given in Table 14–3.

Illustrative Assay Procedure. For the microbiological assays described herein, a total volume of 10 ml. per assay tube is employed. In routine practice, 5-ml. aliquots of a suitable double-strength (twice the concentration used in the assay) basal medium (see Table 14–2), wherefrom the amino acid to be determined has been omitted, are dispensed into rimless Pyrex test tubes (16–20 x 150–180 mm.) supported in wire racks. To permit the construction of a standard curve, aqueous solutions of the pertinent amino acid (volume not to exceed 5 ml.) are added to these tubes at about six different concentration levels ranging from zero to a concentration necessary for the organism to elicit a maximal growth response. For such purpose, the effective range over which growth is a function of concentration may be taken for each amino acid (based on the L-form) as follows (15): tryptophan

0–2 μg. per ml.; cystine, histidine, methionine, and phenylalanine 0–5 μg. per ml.; proline, serine, threonine, and tyrosine 0–10 μg. per ml.; glycine, isoleucine, leucine, and valine 0–15 μg. per ml; arginine, aspartic acid, and lysine 0–20 μg. per ml.; alanine 0–25 μg. per ml.; glutamic acid 0–30 μg. per ml. To a parallel set of tubes containing 5 ml. of basal medium, various dilutions of the test sample are added at four or five different levels estimated to provide concentrations of the amino acid under examination that fall within the range of the standard curve. All standard and test assay tubes are set up in duplicate or triplicate at each concentration level. After all additions have been made, the final volumes are adjusted to exactly 10 ml. by the addition of water, and each tube is plugged with cotton wool or capped with glass or aluminum thimbles. Sterilization is achieved at 10 to 12 pounds of pressure for a period of 10 minutes, after which time the tubes are allowed to cool slowly prior to their removal from the autoclave; higher pressures and excessive periods of autoclaving should be avoided since these can lead to caramelization and darkening of the solutions. After cooling to room temperature, each tube is inoculated with one drop of the pertinent inoculum (prepared as described in the previous section) from a sterile pipette under aseptic conditions and then incubated in a forced-air oven at 37° for some 72 hours; assay tubes which contain basal medium D (see Table 14–2) are incubated at 30° over this same period, whereas a 40-hour incubation period at 37° is used where *S. faecalis* is cultured on basal medium C. At the termination of the incubation period, the lactic acid in each tube is determined by titration with $0.1N$ sodium hydroxide either electrometrically to a pH of approximately 7.3 or in the presence of 5 drops of bromothymol blue as the indicator (prepared by dissolving 0.1 g. of bromothymol blue in 16 ml. of $0.01N$ sodium hydroxide and diluting to a volume of 250 ml. with distilled water). In the case of poor acid producers such as *S. faecalis*, the use of $0.05N$ or even more dilute alkali may be required.

Calculation of Results. The data obtained from the microbiological assay of an amino acid, when represented as a graphical plot of response (in terms of number of milliliters of standardized alkali required to neutralize the lactic acid produced) versus dose of amino acid, generally lead to a curvilinear expression in the case of both the amino acid standard (in micrograms) and the test substance (in milliliters). A method which may be utilized for the computation of assay results involves the location, directly on the standard curve, of the values which correspond to different concentration levels of the test substance. The mean average of such values may then be taken as a reliable estimate of the amount of amino acid in that particular sample, provided that the deviation between readings at three or more levels is in no instance greater than $\pm 10\%$. Representative and illustrative curves are illustrated in Figure 14–1A. For the case in point, the calculations below the figure indicate a mean average value of 22.2 µg. of amino acid per milliliter of sample and a deviation between the extreme values which is less than 5%; a reasonably reliable assay value is thereupon presumed.

Under ordinary circumstances, the coordinate points which result from a plot of the logarithm of the response (ordinate) against the logarithm of the dose (abscissa) should be fitted reasonably well by a straight line, at least over a certain range (16). When both the standard and the test response are so represented on the same graph, two parallel lines or nearly parallel lines are obtained *if the assay is a valid one;* as is revealed in Figure 14–1B, such representations may be conveniently drawn on 2 cycle × 2 cycle logarithmic paper (17). Graphs of this type provide an alternative means for estimating the amount of amino acid in the test substance (16). Thus, on the assumption that the lines are straight and parallel between approximately the same limits of response, a line is drawn which is parallel to the x-axis and crosses both the test and the standard lines; perpendiculars dropped from the two points of intersection to the x-axis will meet the latter at values which represent the milliliters of test substance and the corresponding micrograms of pure standard substance, respectively. For the data at hand (Figure 14–1B), 0.3, 0.5, and 1.0 ml. of test substance correspond, respectively, to 6.5, 11.1, and 22.0 µg. of amino acid; if all values are adjusted on the basis of 1.0 ml. of test substance, a mean average value of 22.0 µg. of amino acid and a less than 3% deviation between extreme values are indicated. Since values that fall within 5% of each other are acceptable, the estimate may be considered a reliable one. In any event, the value found here is in complete accord with the value computed from the curvilinear plot.

5. Evaluation of Method. The use of microbiological assay methods permits the quantitative determination of each of eighteen different amino acids which commonly occur in such complex mixtures as protein hydrolysates, blood, urine, and tissue extracts; only hydroxyproline among the more common protein-derived amino acids cannot yet be adequately determined in this manner. Under ideal conditions, the estimation of any given amino acid may be effected with an accuracy that is generally within ±5% of the true value. However, microbiological assays, like all analytical determinations, are subject to errors of various kinds. Such errors might arise, for example, from the presence in the test material of inhibitory or stimulatory substances which would result in either a decreased or an increased growth response of the assay organism. A case in point is presented by indole and anthranilic acid, either of which can partially fulfill the tryptophan requirement of *L. arabinosus* and hence would lead to high estimates in the assay of this amino acid (18). Since many bacteria are able to utilize peptide-bound amino acids to a greater or lesser extent (19–27), simple peptides provide another class of compounds whose presence could lead to unreliable assay values.

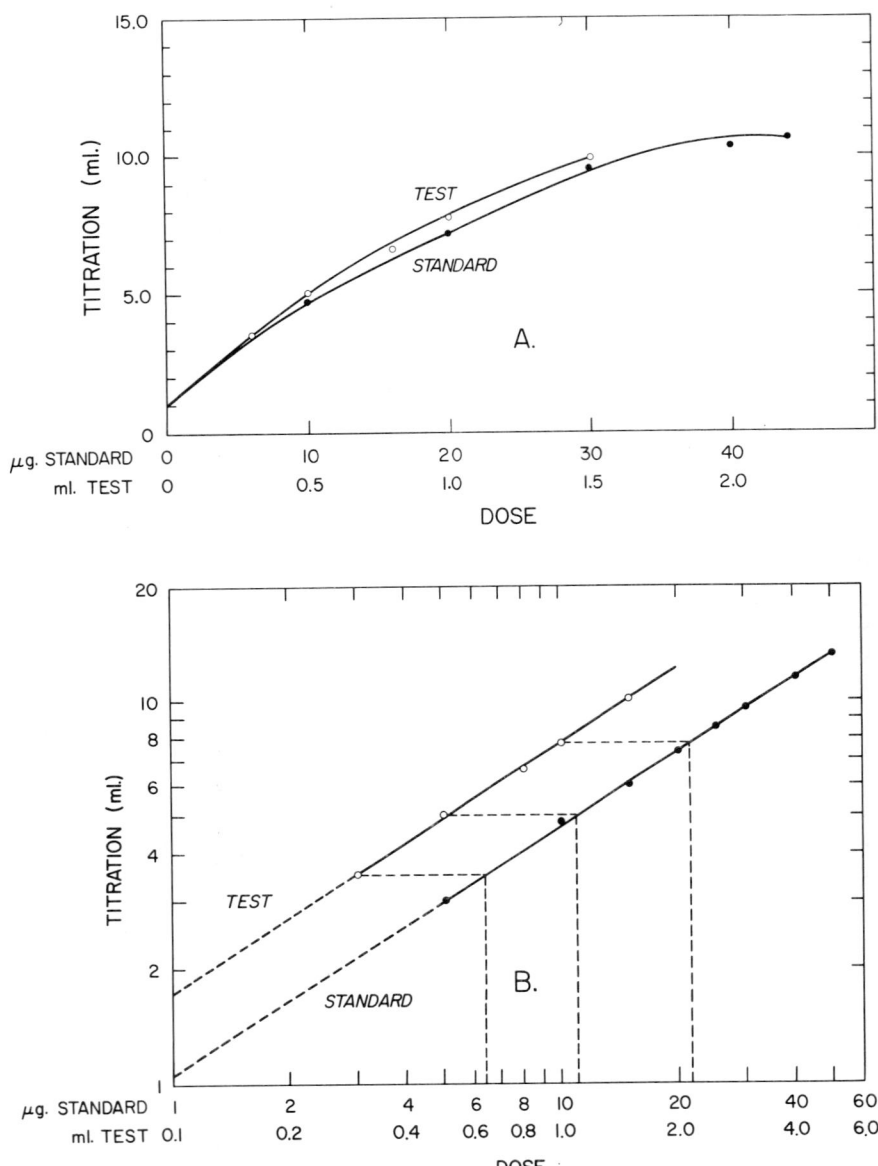

Figure 14–1. Upper curves (A) represent a plot of response versus dose, while lower curves (B) represent a plot of the logarithm of the response versus the logarithm of the dose. These illustrative curves are based on arbitrarily chosen data (see the facing page).

Added to this is the influences of certain lipoid substances (28), vitamins (29–33), closely related amino acids (34–36), oxygen (25, 37), or carbon dioxide (33) whose presence or absence may not only affect the growth of the assay organism but may even determine the extent to which a particular amino acid is essential. Hence it should be clear that the validity of any given assay depends, in good measure, upon the absence of interfering substances of the afore-mentioned type from the test material or the removal of these substances from the latter prior to the actual determination.

With the above in mind, the question might be logically posed as to what criteria are available to assure that the results of any particular assay procedure are reasonably valid and reliable. Toward this end, a test which is often employed routinely involves the addition to the test material of known amounts of the pure amino acid under consideration, followed by theoretical recovery of the latter by assay. However, although the presence of stimulatory or inhibitory substances in the test sample is demonstrable on the basis of a high or low recovery, a theoretical recovery of the added amino acid strongly implies but does not necessarily establish that the assay is a valid one. Another criterion which might be applied toward assessing the reliability of an assay depends upon whether the values calculated from the different dosage levels exhibit a regular trend or *drift* in an upward or downward direction. For example, the values calculated at the various dosage levels with the aid of Figure 14–1A are 22.0, 22.6, 21.9, 22.5, and 21.8 respectively, and hence offer no suggestion of *drift*; however, if the values obtained at these same levels were 22.6, 22.5, 22.4, 22.2, 22.1, . . . , the assay would reveal a regular shift in a given direction and would thereupon become suspect. Finally, as has already been noted, graphical plots of the logarithm of the response versus the logarithm of the dose for varying levels of both the test substance and the amino acid standard should, within a certain range, be linear and very nearly parallel (Figure 14–1B); any deviation from

---

DATA FOR FIGURE 14–1

Amino acid standard, mμg.	0.0	10.0	20.0	30.0	40.0	50.0
Mean titration, ml.	1.05	4.80	7.18	9.50	10.30	10.65
Test substance, ml.		0.3	0.5	0.8	1.0	1.5
Mean titration, ml.		3.52	5.01	6.54	7.71	10.0

Calculation of results
From curve A

Test substance, ml.	0.3	0.5	0.8	1.0	1.5
Amino acid, μg., in above	6.6	11.3	17.5	22.5	32.8
Amino acid, μg. per ml.	22.0	22.6	21.9	22.5	21.8

From curve B

Test substance, ml.	0.3		0.5	1.0
Amino acid, μg., in above	6.5		11.1	22.0
Amino acid, μg. per ml.	21.7		22.2	22.0

parallelism which is greater than 5%, as measured at the extreme limits of linearity, should be considered indicative of an unreliable assay.

It is essential that the amino acids utilized in microbiological assays be critically examined from the standpoint of both their chemical and their optical purity. Since contamination of one amino acid with another is a quite frequent occurrence in commerical preparations of both synthetic and natural origin, the direct use of such preparations without prior purification introduces the danger of high blanks and hence unreliable results. Thus, for example, since the L-leucine derived from natural sources frequently is contaminated with L-methionine to a greater or lesser extent, use of the former in a basal medium employed for the assay of the latter would lead to high blanks; another instance is presented in the case of synthetic DL-leucine preparations, which may contain DL-isoleucine as a serious contaminant. In any event, regardless of the origin of the amino acid, its chemical purity should be established by elemental analysis, chromatography, or other suitable means prior to its use for purposes of microbiological assay. Additionally, the optical purity of the amino acids employed must frequently be taken into account. Thus, although the premise is all too often made that the D-enantiomer of an amino acid possesses no biological activity, this cannot always be justified. Indeed, in many instances the D-antipode of an amino acid is an equally effective promoter of growth, whilst stimulatory or even inhibitory responses caused by the D-isomer are not uncommon (8, 38–40). In this respect, the presence of D-amino acids is of little consequence in so far as the basal medium is concerned but does become of critical importance in the construction of a standard curve. It is in fact obligatory that, in the latter instance, only the L-amino acid be used unless it has been conclusively established that the corresponding D-form of this amino acid is completely inert over the entire concentration range employed for the standard curve.

REFERENCES

1. Dunn, M. S., Shankman, S., Camien, M. N., Frankl, W., and Rockland, L. B., *J. Biol. Chem.*, **156**, 703 (1944).
2. Dunn, M. S., *Physiol. Revs.*, **29**, 219 (1949).
3. Barton-Wright, E. C., *The Microbiological Assay of the Vitamin B-Complex and Amino Acids*, Pitman and Sons, London, 1952.
4. Snell, E. E., *Physiol. Revs.*, **28**, 255 (1948); *Advances in Protein Chem.*, **2**, 85 (1945); *Ann. N. Y. Acad. Sci.*, **47**, 161 (1946); *Vitamin Methods*, Vol. 1, Academic Press, New York, p. 327, 1950.
5. Sauberlich, H. E., and Baumann, C. A., *J. Biol. Chem.*, **176**, 165 (1948).
6. Henderson, L. M., and Snell, E. E., *J. Biol. Chem.*, **172**, 15 (1948).
7. Stokes, J. L., Gunness, M., Dwyer, I. M., and Caswell, M. C., *J. Biol. Chem.*, **160**, 35 (1945).

8. Steele, B. F., Sauberlich, H. E., Reynolds, M. S., and Baumann, C. A., *J. Biol. Chem.*, **177**, 533 (1949); see also Sauberlich, H. E., and Baumann, C. A., *ibid.*, **177**, 545 (1949).
9. Gunness, M., Dwyer, I. M., and Stokes, J. L., *J. Biol. Chem.*, **163**, 159 (1946).
10. Barton-Wright, E. C., *Analyst*, **71**, 267 (1946).
11. Nymon, M. C., and Gortner, W. A., *J. Biol. Chem.*, **163**, 277 (1946).
12. Snell, E. E., and Wright, L. D., *J. Biol. Chem.*, **139**, 675 (1941).
13. Sauberlich, H. E., and Baumann, C. A., *J. Biol. Chem.*, **166**, 417 (1946).
14. Stokes, J. L., and Gunness, M., *J. Biol. Chem.*, **157**, 651 (1945).
15. Snell, E. E., *Advances in Enzymol.*, **3**, 477, (1957).
16. Wood, E. C., *Analyst*, **72**, 84 (1947).
17. Saperstein, S., in Block, R. J., and Weiss, K. W., *Amino Acid Handbook*, Charles C Thomas, Springfield, Ill., p. 50, 1956.
18. Snell, E. E., *Arch. Biochem.*, **2**, 389 (1943).
19. Krehl, W. A., and Fruton, J. S., *J. Biol. Chem.*, **173**, 479 (1948).
20. Dunn, M. S., and McClure, L. E., *J. Biol. Chem.*, **184**, 223 (1949).
21. Klungsoyr, M., Sirny, R. J., and Elvehjem, C. A., *J. Biol. Chem.*, **189**, 559 (1951).
22. Virtanen, A. I., and Nurmikko, V., *Acta Chem. Scand.*, **5**, 97, 681 (1951).
23. Kihara, H., and Snell, E. E., *J. Biol. Chem.*, **197**, 791 (1952).
24. Kihara, H., Klatt, O., and Snell, E. E., *J. Biol. Chem.*, **197**, 801 (1952).
25. Stone, D., and Hobermann, H. D., *J. Biol. Chem.*, **202**, 203 (1953).
26. Prescott, J. M., Peters, V. J., and Snell, E. E., *J. Biol. Chem.*, **202**, 533 (1953).
27. Peters, V. J., and Snell, E. E., *J. Bacteriol.*, **67**, 69 (1954).
28. Williams, V. R., *J. Biol. Chem.*, **159**, 237 (1945).
29. Stokes, J. L., and Gunness, M., *Science*, **101**, 43 (1945).
30. Lyman, C. M., and Kuiken, K. A., *Federation Proc.*, **7**, 170 (1948).
31. Holden, J. T., Wildman, R. B., and Snell, E. E., *J. Biol. Chem.*, **191**, 559 (1951).
32. Horn, M. J., Blum, A. E., Gersdorff, C. E. F., and Warren, H. W., *J. Biol. Chem.*, **203**, 907 (1953).
33. Lascelles, J., Cross, M. J., and Woods, D. D., *J. Gen. Microbiol.*, **10**, 267 (1954).
34. Lyman, C. M., Kuiken, K. A., Blotter, L., and Hale, F., *J. Biol. Chem.*, **157**, 395 (1945).
35. Brickson, W. L., Henderson, L. M., Solhjell, I., and Elvehjem, C. A., *J. Biol. Chem.*, **176**, 517 (1948).
36. Sirny, R. J., Cheng, L. T., and Elvehjem, C. A., *J. Biol. Chem.*, **190**, 547 (1951).
37. Bohonos, N., Hutchings, B. L., and Peterson, W. H., *J. Bacteriol.*, **44**, 479 (1942).
38. Rydon, H. N., *Biochem. Soc. Symposia* (*Cambridge, Eng.*), **1**, 161 (1948).
39. Prescott, J. M., Schweigert, B. S., Lyman, C. M., and Kuiken, K. A., *J. Biol. Chem.*, **178**, 727 (1949).
40. Camien, M. N., and Dunn, M. S., *J. Biol. Chem.*, **182**, 119 (1950).

chapter 15

Chromatography

1. Introduction. One of the most intricate of the chemical arts is the separation of closely related compounds, and a number of devices have been developed over many years for this purpose. Fractional distillation is probably one of the very earliest of such devices; in this procedure a separation is achieved by an unequal distribution of closely related compounds between two phases, e.g., liquid and gas. The removal of certain gases from the atmosphere by charcoal, or the removal of coloring material from solutions of sugars by charcoal, represents separations based upon unequal distribution of materials deliberately developed between solid-gas phases in the former case, and between solid-liquid phases in the latter. The possibilities of the use of the distribution of closely related solutes between immiscible or nearly immiscible liquid-liquid phases have been explored by generations of organic chemists who early learned in quite empirical fashion that compounds of the aromatic series could in general be readily extracted from aqueous solution into various organic solvents, and that, the more water-soluble such compounds were, the greater was the number of successive extractions with organic solvents required. In what may be considered a somewhat less than exact use of the term, all these procedures may be viewed as a form of chromatographic separation, i.e., a partition of one or more solutes between two relatively immiscible phases. An unequal partition results in separation, and the repeated partition is in effect a countercurrent separation.

In chromatography as it is usually practiced, one of the phases is firmly held on an inert support and is exposed in one fashion or another to the action of the second, immiscible phase. Two classic examples of this procedure are the devices of Schönbein and Goppelsroeder and of Tswett. The former device employed a combination of capillary rise and adsorption on filter paper to separate a number of substances in solution; its uses have been reviewed by Rheinboldt (1). Strips of paper were partly immersed in the solutions studied, and as the liquid was drawn up into the paper by capillary forces the solvent ran ahead of the solutes, which were adsorbed at different levels depending upon the nature of each solute. Further separation or resolution could be achieved by removal of the paper and employment of a new solvent. The adsorbed material could be removed from each zone, and tested for homogeneity by fresh treatment with filter paper, and with the same or a different system of solvents. The procedure was frequently employed as a means of distinguishing closely related dyes, and an appreciation of the value of paper as a separation medium for other kinds of compounds required many more years to attain.

The second device, derived from the observations of the botanist Tswett, was likewise simple and represented probably the first definitive experimental approach to the modern concept of column chromatography. An example of the procedure follows (cf. 2). A small volume of a petroleum ether extract of green leaves was poured onto a column of powdered calcium carbonate packed in a vertical glass tube, whereby a band of the colored material appeared at the head of the column while the solvent passed down the column. When fresh petroleum ether was added to the top of the column, the band not only began to migrate downward, but also split up into several zones or sub-bands of material of different colors. By continually washing the column with pure solvent, each zone in turn could be removed or eluted from the bottom of the column. Such a separation of components is due to a difference in the distribution of the components between liquid and solid phases. If for components 1 and 2 the distribution ratios between these phases, P_1 and P_2, are at all different, it will be possible by flowing the liquid past the solid phase to effect a separation of the two components. If P_1 is very much greater than P_2, it might be possible to accomplish the separation in bulk by simply shaking the solid phase with the solution, whereby component 2 would be largely if not wholly retained by the solid whereas component 1 would remain largely if not wholly in solution. If, however, P_1 and P_2 are not greatly different, the process of shaking would have to be conducted on each with more solvent in order to achieve separation. In a column, this equilibration process may be considered to occur in many successive stages along the column, each stage taking place over a very thin cross section, in analogy with the distilling column whose efficiency may be considered to be guided in part by the number of "theoretical plates." The method of Tswett is not greatly different from that of Schönbein and Goppelsroeder; in the former the developing solvent flows downward over the adsorbing solid, and in the latter the developing solvent flows upward through capillary forces over the adsorbed solid. Both form the basis of the modern chromatography of the amino acids.

These classic examples have been cited not only for their historic interest but also because they represent instances of what may be termed largely adsorptive phenomena or adsorption chromatography. There are two other rather broad classes of chromatographic analysis which might be described as partition chromatography (liquid-liquid extraction), and ion exchange chromatography. The dividing lines among the three classes are frequently obscure, all three are essentially distribution phenomena, and a successful separation of components in a mixture may, in the absence of a firm theoretical foundation, be tentatively ascribed to one or more of these phenomena.

Modern amino acid chromatography is the culmination of the long search for a method which would yield a physical separation and analytical rationale of the monoaminomonocarboxylic acid fraction of proteins. The work of Kossel and of Vickery led to the quantitative isolation and determination of the content of histidine, arginine, and lysine, as did that of Foreman and Chibnall for the cases of aspartic and glutamic acids (cf. 3). Until recently, a complete analysis of proteins in terms of their content of monoaminomonocarboxylic acids defied solution. The use of microbiological procedures (Chapter 14) introduced a hopeful note, and in several instances was reasonably successful. The difficulties associated ordinarily with these procedures, however, effectively limited their applicability, and when chromatographic methods were developed their use appreciably declined. The earliest systematic chemical procedure to separate the components of the neutral amino acid fraction of proteins was due to Emil Fischer (4).

Fischer hydrolyzed the protein with HCl and esterified the residue with absolute ethanol and HCl gas. The mixture of ester hydrochlorides was freed of acid, and the liberated esters were extracted into ether. Tyrosine ester and the esters of the diamino acids remained for the most part in the aqueous phase. The ether was evaporated off, and the residual mixture of esters subjected to fractional distillation *in vacuo*. At 8–15 mm. pressure, three fractions were collected between 40 and 100°, and at 0.5 mm. pressure a fraction was obtained from 100 to 160°. The esters of glycine and alanine were found in the 40–60° fraction, proline, valine, leucine, and isoleucine in the 60–90° fraction, leucine principally in the 70–90° fraction, and the esters of phenylalanine, serine, and of aspartic and glutamic acids in the fraction boiling above 100°. The ester of phenylalanine was removed from the last-mentioned fraction by dilution with water and extraction of the ester into ether. After the removal of the phenylalanine ester, the ester of serine was separated from the aqueous phase of the same fraction by addition of petroleum ether; the serine ester appeared as an oil and could be removed as such.

Fischer was under no illusion that his procedure was at all quantitative. It was, however, the first which yielded these amino acids in quantity and revealed their occurrence in a number of different proteins. With its use, Fischer discovered proline (5) in the 60–90° fraction, and hydroxyproline (6) in the residue left behind after the esters were distilled off. The butyl esters of the amino acids are more stable than the ethyl esters (7), and the N-acetyl ethyl esters still more so (8). Attempts to distill fractionally a mixture of the N-acetyl ethyl esters of amino acids derived from a protein hydrolysate led to the prepartion of chemically pure alanine, valine, leucine, and isoleucine, but these compounds were appreciably racemized (9). At pressures of 10^{-6} to 10^{-7} mm. it is possible to distill fractionally mixtures of various N-acylated amino acid and peptide esters without racemization or decomposition (10, 11). The method is now generally archaic and obsolete, but it is of interest to note that in the 1906 paper which summarized his work in this field Fischer pointed out the possible metabolic relationships which might exist among the amino acids, the carbohydrates, and the fats, and specifically designated the hydroxyamino acids and, in particular, serine, as a natural bridge between the amino acids and the carbohydrates—"denn sie bilden eine natürliche Brücke zwischen den Kohlenhydraten und den einfachen Aminosäuren . . ."[48] (4) (see Chapter 2).

The next important advance was that of Dakin, who took what was essentially a bold and far-seeing step, namely, that of extraction of the neutral amino acids themselves from water into butanol (12). In this paper, written in 1918, Dakin stated "So far as I am aware, no systematic investigation of the possibilities of extraction [of the amino acids] by partially miscible solvents has been undertaken. . . ." The hydrolyzed, neutralized, and desalted protein was subjected in a continuous extractor to the leaching action of butanol, and in this fashion alanine, valine, leucine, phenylalanine, and perhaps hydroxyproline and serine were transferred. By bringing the aqueous phase to acid reactions the dicarboxylic amino acids could be transferred, whereas at alkaline reactions the diamino acids could in turn be transferred (13, 14) to the butanol layer (cf. 15, 16).

The studies of England and Cohn in 1935 (15) were designed to investigate more exactly the distribution of individual amino acids between water and butanol. Known volumes of the two solvents were employed, and the two phases containing a definite amount of dissolved amino acid were equilibrated for 48 hours at 25°. The amino acids produced a redistribution of the butanol and the water in the two phases, and this factor had to be taken into account. Glycine, which is the most soluble in water of the amino acids studied, had the greatest influence in diminishing the solubility of the butanol (Figure 15-1). This effect generally leads to the separation into two phases of water and alcohol when the lower alcohols are in the presence of high aqueous concentrations of the amino acids, and, as will be noted later, this phenomenon sets an upper limit to the level of amino acids which can be successfully separated by liquid-liquid partition chromatography. The partition coefficients, i.e., the ratio of concentration of the amino acids in the aqueous phase to that in the butanol phase, were larger the shorter the hydrocarbon side chain of the amino acids (Table 15-1). The values given in this table are those determined at the lowest concentrations studied. At higher amino acid concentrations, the partition coefficients for glycine, alanine, and butyrine increased with descending order of magnitude of concentration,

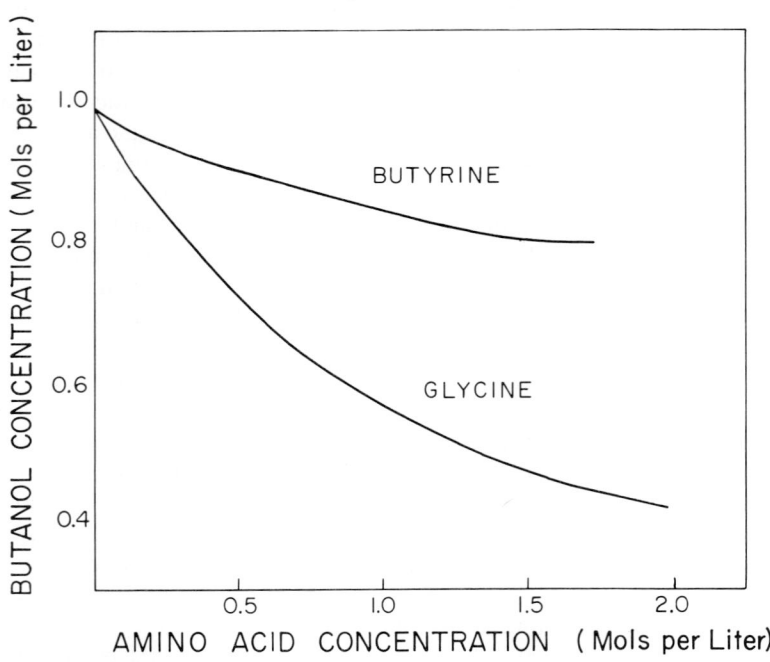

Figure 15–1. Effect of two amino acids on the solubility of butanol in water. England, A., and Cohn, E. J., *J. Am. Chem. Soc.*, **57**, 634 (1935).

TABLE 15–1

Partition Coefficients at 25° of Amino Acids in Water–Butanol (15)

Amino Acids	Partition Coefficient (water:butanol)
Glycine	70.4
DL-Alanine	42.3
DL-Butyrine	23.8
DL-Valine	13.8
DL-Norvaline	9.5
L-Leucine	5.5
DL-Norleucine	3.2

that for valine did not appear to change, whereas those for leucine and norleucine appeared to diminish. Of some interest to the later development of the subject was the observation that the partition coefficients at infinitely small amino acid concentrations stood in a definite relation to the number of CH_2 groups in the molecules (Figure 15–2). Isomers with branched chains such as valine and leucine behaved like shorter molecules, an effect which had been also noted in the solubility relations of these compounds in mixtures of water and ethanol (16) (see Chapter 5). It is no wonder, therefore, that, as will be seen below, the straight-chain amino acids move more rapidly on paper in a butanol-water solvent than do their branched-chain isomers.

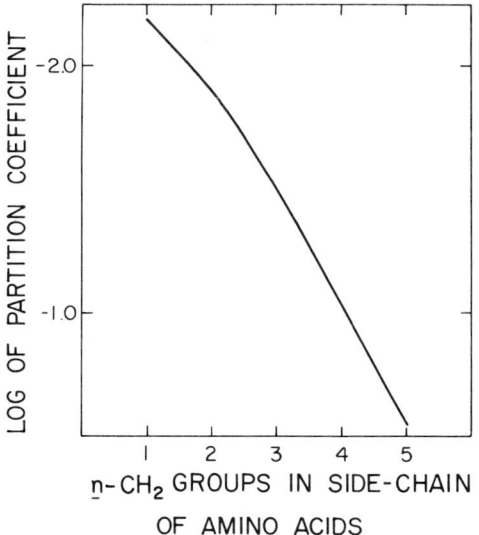

Figure 15–2. Partition coefficient between butanol-water as influenced by the number of CH_2 groups in the side chain of various amino acids. England, A., and Cohn, E. J., *J. Am. Chem. Soc.*, **57**, 634 (1935).

2. Partition Chromatography. SILICA GELS. At their isoelectric points the amino acids exist as dipolar ions, and, as such, their solubility in non-aqueous solvents is at a minimum. When this dipolar ion character is removed, as for example by esterification of the carboxyl group or acylation of the amino group, the amino acid derivatives generally become more readily soluble in non-aqueous solvents. Certain exceptions occur, as in the case of N-α-acetylhistidine, which maintains its dipolar ion character and hence is more soluble in water than in non-aqueous solvents; histidine ester, however, with no internal salt character, is readily soluble in non-aqueous, organic solvents. The esterification procedure, to transfer most of the amino acids of a protein hydrolysate into a relatively non-polar liquid phase (ether), was employed by Emil Fischer as described above. The N-acetylation of amino acids in an egg albumin hydrolysate with the object of transferring such derivatives into a non-aqueous liquid phase, in this case chloroform, was employed by Neuberger (17) in the course of a study designed, not to determine amino acid composition, but to isolate the carbohydrate of this protein. It was noted, however, that only a fraction of the total nitrogen was extractable from aqueous solution into the chloroform layer, and this was considered by Synge (18) to be due in part, at least, to differences in the partition coefficients of the various N-acetylated amino acids between water and chloroform. If this were correct it might form the basis

TABLE 15–2

Approximate Partition Coefficients of N-Acetylamino Acids between Organic Solvents and Water (18)

Compound	Organic Solvent	P^a	C^b	T^c
Acetyl-L-phenylalanine	Chloroform	5	1	37
Acetyl-L-isoleucine	Chloroform	6	1	37
Acetyl-L-leucine	Chloroform	7	1	37
Acetyl-L-proline	Chloroform	15	2	37
Acetyl-L-methionine	Chloroform	22	2	37
Acetyl-L-valine	Chloroform	30	2	37
Acetylglycine	Chloroform	600	7	18
Acetyl-L-tyrosine	Chloroform	600	4	37
Acetyl-L-glutamic acid	Chloroform	>1000	6	20
Acetyl-L-hydroxyproline	Chloroform	>1000	–	20
Acetyl-L-tyrosine	Ethyl acetate	1.4	8	37
Acetyl-L-glutamic acid	Ethyl acetate	23	10	37
Acetylglycine	Ethyl acetate	36	3	18

$^a P = \dfrac{\text{concentration of solute in aqueous phase}}{\text{concentration of solute in organic solvent phase}}$.

$^b C$ = concentration of solute in aqueous phase in mg. per ml.

$^c T$ = temperature.

of a method for the isolation and estimation of amino acids in protein hydrolysates. In theory, this concept was no more than a variation of the Fischer esterification procedure, and in practice proved to be not very much more reliable. Its consequences, however, were considerably more far-reaching.

Synge prepared a number of N-acetylated amino acids and demonstrated that their partition between chloroform or ethyl acetate and water varied for each amino acid (18) (Table 15–2). Each partition was accomplished in an individual separatory tube in much the same fashion as England and Cohn had employed for the partition of the neutral amino acids between butanol and water. The data in Table 15–2 were admittedly approximate, and some were subsequently corrected (19), but it can be seen that the partition coefficients among the first six compounds in the table, namely those of the monoaminomonocarboxylic acids, were not greatly different. Separation, however, of one from the other could conceivably be accomplished if, in analogy with the concept of continuous fractional distillation, the distribution of the solutes between the two phases were sufficiently repeated. Martin and Synge (19) developed for this purpose a countercurrent liquid-liquid extractor consisting of forty tubes, each of which was, in effect, a single separatory funnel, and in which partition between the two phases occurred. The funnels were automatically agitated, and at the expiration of a given time one liquid phase was automatically transferred to the next funnel in the series. The cycle of operations led in the case of the acetylated amino acids to the separation of methionine, valine, proline, the leucines, and phenylalanine from each other and from the other acetylated amino acids in the protein digest. Such countercurrent fractionation devices were extensively developed independently by Craig, and the results therefrom will be discussed below.

Martin and Synge, however, shortly abandoned such an approach in favor of the use of an inert support for the aqueous phase (20; cf. 21). This support at first was a silica gel mixed with methyl orange as an indicator; in it a theoretically large number of "plates," assuming the analogy to a distilling column, was possible. The immiscible phase consisted of chloroform to which a small amount of butanol was added, and in which the acetylated amino acids were contained. It was allowed to run down the silica gel column. The position of the solutes was revealed by the indicator which turned from yellow through orange to a typically acid pink color, the bands moving down the column at characteristic rates as fresh chloroform was added for resolution. Three groups of acetylated amino acids emerged in this way, namely, (a) phenylalanine, (b) leucine-isoleucine, and (c) proline-valine-methionine. The acetyl derivatives of glycine and alanine remained near the head of the column, and only very slowly descended. The procedure resembled superficially the method of Tswett. The latter, however, was an example of adsorption chromatography, separation being achieved by differences in distribution between solid and liquid phases. The method of Martin and Synge achieved separation by differences in distribution between two liquid phases, chloroform and the water held by the gel—an example of partition chromatography. Both kinds of chromatographic techniques, however, yielded their results by a form of elution analysis, to be discussed in more detail below.

On the basis of a theoretical treatment of a chromatographic column as if it consisted of a number of "theoretical plates" within each of which perfect equilibrium between the two liquid phases occurred, and with the further assumptions that the diffusion of solute from one "plate" to another was negligible and that at equilibrium the distribution ratio of one solute between the two phases was independent of the concentration and the presence of other solutes, Martin and Synge (20) calculated the value of the partition coefficient at equilibrium, P, i.e., the ratio of grams of solute per milliliter of non-mobile phase to grams of solute per milliliter of mobile phase. The value of P, in turn, was related to A (the area of cross section of the column), A_s (the area of cross section of the non-mobile phase), A_L (the area of cross section of the mobile phase), and R (the ratio of movement of position of maximum concentration of solute to the simultaneous movement of the surface of the developing fluid in the empty part of the tube above the chromatogram column, i.e., ratio of movement of the zone to the movement of the surface of the liquid) as

$$P = \frac{A}{RA_s} - \frac{A_L}{A_s}$$

A test of this relationship between rate of movement of the band and the partition coefficient was made as follows (20). A solution of 2 mg. each of

TABLE 15–3

Determination of Partition Coefficient P (20)

N-Acetylamino Acid	R	P (from band rate)	P (determined directly)[a]	C (determined directly)[b]
Acetyl-L-proline	0.37	9.4	9.5	10
Acetyl-DL-phenylalanine	1.07	1.4	1.3	2

[a] By shaking in separatory funnel, followed by titration.
[b] Mg. solute per ml. aqueous phase after shaking in separatory funnel.

acetyl-L-proline and acetyl-DL-phenylalanine in water was poured on a silica gel column 1 cm. in diameter and 20 cm. in length. The column was developed with a chloroform-butanol mixture until the bands were separated, and the movement of the center of each band for a given movement of the liquid surface above the column was measured. The column contained 5 grams of dry silica gel, 3.5 ml. of water, and 10 ml. of chloroform. The density of silica gel being assumed to be 2.3, the area of cross section of inert solid was 0.11 cm.^{2} (i.e., $A - A_s - A_L$), $A_s = 0.175$ sq. cm., and $A_L = 0.5$ sq. cm. From the above equation,

$$P = \frac{4.5}{R} - 2.8$$

R was measured experimentally from the rate of the band movement, and P was determined both from the above equation and from independent measurements of the partition of the solutes between the two phases by direct titration after shaking together in a separatory funnel. The agreement in the values of P determined by the two procedures is indicated in Table 15–3.

The good agreement noted between theory and experiment in Table 15–3.

together with recovery experiments on more complicated mixtures of acetylated amino acids, lent support to the general theory of chromatography suggested by Martin and Synge and, based as it was on a "theoretical plate" concept, related chromatography to such well-known physical processes as fractional distillation and multistage extraction. Further studies with the technique of the silica gel columns were concerned with improvements in procedure (21–23), with determinations of the values of R with different solvent systems (20), and with the use of amino acid derivatives already colored through the use of substituent groups such as dinitrobenzene, thus dispensing with the need for an outside indicator to locate the bands (24). A good deal of attention was actually paid such dinitrophenyl derivatives in view of their importance in the sequential analysis of proteins and large peptides, and variations which embraced not merely different solvents but the additional use of buffers of different pH (25, 26) were introduced for improved separations. The pH of such buffers varied from 3.72 to 6.61 (25), and, since the band rate of movement for a given amino acid decreased as the pH increased, it was possible to effect separations at will. Columns of buffered Celite (27) were also employed for the separation of the dinitrophenylated amino acids at pH values which ranged from 4 to 7. In this case ether was the non-polar solvent employed, and the order of rates of band movements on either silica gel or Celite columns was for the dinitrophenyl derivatives of the various amino acids as follows (in order of descending rates): tryptophan, isoleucine, leucine, phenylalanine, lysine, valine, methionine, alanine, proline, tyrosine, glycine, threonine, glutamic acid, serine, and aspartic acid. On the other hand, an interesting instance of "reversed phase" chromatography was employed by Partridge and Swain (28), who used chlorinated rubber as the supporting material for the column; the rubber held the non-polar solvent, in this case n-butanol, the mobile phase being an aqueous buffer at pH 3, and the order of band rates for the dinitrophenyl amino acids was quite the converse of that noted above for silica or Celite.

On the whole, however, the resolution of the bands on the silica gel columns was not quite satisfactory, presumably because of adsorption by the silica of some of the substances to be separated. This was particularly noticeable in the case of the complex mixtures arising from protein hydrolysates, and was only partly alleviated by the presence in varying low concentrations of butanol in the chloroform. Moreover, it was not possible to separate the members of such groups as the leucines, and the presence of other solutes in the hydrolysates was not without influence on the distribution of the bands for the few groups of monoaminomonocarboxylic acids studied.

More important from the viewpoint of the theoretical basis of the chromatographic procedure is the fact that the partition coefficient P is for most compounds a function of the concentration (cf. Table 15-4). As the compounds pass down the column, their concentration changes in part through diffusion. If the partition coefficient is independent of the concentration for any given component, it will travel down the column as a symmetrical zone and diffusion does not affect its separation. If, however, the partition coefficient for a given compound varies with concentration, the front and back of the band will travel at a rate different from that of the point of maximum concentration. Overlapping of bands frequently ensues, and separation by elution may on occasion be extremely difficult. On the other hand, a sharpening of the bands may occur as one solute displaces

TABLE 15-4

Partition of Acetylamino Acids between Chloroform and H_2O at 37° (19)

Compound	Conc. in H_2O, mg./ml.	Conc. in Chloroform, mg./ml.	P
Acetyl-L-phenylalanine	1.44	0.37	3.9
	0.76	0.18	4.2
Acetyl-D-norleucine	1.74	0.27	6.45
	0.94	0.13	7.2
Acetyl-D-isoleucine	1.86	0.25	7.4
	0.98	0.11	9.0
Acetyl-D-leucine	2.28	0.22	10.5
	1.20	0.12	10.0
Acetyl-L-valine	3.3	0.22	15
Acetyl-L-proline	3.03	0.16	18.9
	1.55	0.09	17.2
Acetyl-L-methionine	3.04	0.11	27.6
	1.46	0.045	32.4
Acetyl-DL-butyrine	3.42	0.05	68
Acetyl-DL-alanine	4.74	0.022	216

another on the column. This phase of chromatography, referred to as displacement analysis, was subsequently developed by Tiselius and his co-workers and will be referred to below. The use of silica gels played its part in the development of the chromatography story, and it has never been completely abandoned (cf. 29). The use of acetylated amino acids, however, like that of amino acid esters, was totally abandoned for quantitative purposes and a return to attempts to isolate and separate the free, neutral amino acids themselves from a protein hydrolysate was resorted to. The combination of Dakin's butanol extraction with silica gels failed because of the tight adsorption of various amino acids by the gel (30). Good separation, however, was achieved when the fixed support turned out to be filter paper, and the clock turned back not only to Dakin but also to Schönbein and Goeppelsroeder.

3. Paper Chromatography. The method of paper chromatography as developed by Consden, Gordon, and Martin (31) was viewed as a special case of partition chromatography, i.e., the separation of compounds with different partition coefficients between two liquid phases, and in concept was based on the same principles which governed the partition of solutes on silica gel columns. The "stationary phase" in paper chromatography was water saturated with an organic liquid, and it was considered to be held stationary within the fixed paper support up to the saturation point of the paper (some 20%), whereas the "mobile phase" or development solvent was usually an organic solvent saturated with water. Theoretically, the solutes were partitioned as they moved along the fixed, paper support, according to their distribution between the solvent systems. The equation above can be rearranged as

$$R = A/(A_L + PA_s)$$

where, now, A is the cross-sectional area of paper plus water plus solvent, A_L is the cross-sectional area of the solvent phase, A_s is the cross-sectional area of the water phase, and P, the partition coefficient, retains its usual designation. Inasmuch as R is not conveniently measured on paper chromatograms, a new symbol, R_F, was introduced and defined as

$$R_F = \frac{\text{movement of band}}{\text{movement of the advancing front of the liquid}}$$

The resemblance of R_F to the independently conceived symbol R (by LeRosen) (32), which was defined as the ratio of the rate of movement of the adsorbate zone to the rate of flow of the developing solvent, is of interest.

From these relations,

$$R_F = \frac{RA_L}{A} = \frac{A_L}{A_L + PA_s}$$

or

$$P = \frac{A_L}{A_s}\left[\left(\frac{1}{R_F}\right) - 1\right]$$

A_L/A_s is the ratio of the volumes of solvent and water phases in the chromatogram, and with a given water content of the paper this ratio may be calculated from the ratio of the weight of dry paper to that of the developed chromatogram.

The partition coefficients P were calculated from the observed R_F and A_L/A_s values for four separate experiments on the assumption that the ratio of the weight of solvent (n-butanol) to paper was constant in all parts of the paper (31). The values so calculated were compared with those found by England and Cohn for the same amino acids by direct distribution between water and butanol in a separatory funnel. The water content of the paper in each experiment was that adopted value which would yield a partition coefficient for glycine identical with that reported by England and Cohn. The data are given in Table 15–5.

The general agreement between the values of the partition coefficients found by partition paper chromatography and those derived by direct distribution (Table 15–5) suggests that specific adsorptive forces exerted by the paper may not (for the compounds studied) be an appreciable factor, and that the paper plays the role of an inert support. This is, however, a limited interpretation, undoubtedly valid for the homologous series of aliphatic amino acids studied under the conditions selected, but in the present stage of know-

TABLE 15–5

Partition Coefficients Calculated from R_F Values (31)

					Direct Partition Experiments of
Assumed % water in paper	28.7	18.0	22.6	17.7	England and
A_L/A_s	3.25	4.56	3.70	2.93	Cohn (15)
Partition coefficients					
Glycine	70.4	70.4	70.4	70.4	70.4
Alanine	35.9	39.9	43.7	36.6	42.3
Valine	12.2	14.1	14.8	12.5	13.8
Norvaline	8.7	10.8	10.5	9.2	9.5
Leucine	4.5	5.4	5.6	6.0	5.5
Norleucine	3.5	4.2	4.4	4.6	3.2

ledge inapplicable to such instances wherein optical isomers are separated on paper (Chapter 9) or completely miscible solvents are employed (33; see below). Cellulose is not entirely inert, the presence of an indefinite number of free carboxyl groups cannot be excluded, and the separation of the amino acids on this support may depend to some degree on adsorptive and solution forces, as well as upon ion exchange.

Regardless of the exact nature of the partition mechanisms on paper chromatograms, the method developed by Consden, Gordon, and Martin ranks as one of those epoch-making technical discoveries which open new fields of investigation and make the pursuit of older ones considerably lighter. The techniques described by these authors in their first paper on the subject, "Qualitative Analysis of Proteins: A Partition Chromatographic Method Using Paper" (31), laid the groundwork in all essentials for the future development of the subject. Among the advantages of the method were the need for only very small quantities of the amino acids, the ready availability of the required reagents and equipment, the facility and flexibility whereby the experimental conditions could be altered to suit the requirements for the separation, whether by changing the nature of the solvent, by changing the direction of solvent flow, or by addition of specific retaining agents, and, finally, the considerable (and sometimes deceptive) ease with which the entire procedures could be conducted and controlled.

In the first report, it was suggested that the most satisfactory solvents to use were those partially miscible with water (31), which recalls Dakin's statement much earlier (12) that "the passage of a certain proportion of water from the fluid undergoing extraction to the butyl alcohol medium was essential." A variety of solvent systems were employed, including n-butanol, phenol, t-amyl alcohol, benzyl alcohol, collidine, o-, m-, and p-cresol, and

TABLE 15-6
Effect of Temperature Resulting in Changes in Phase Composition on R_F Values in Collidine (31)[a]

Temperature	Aspartic Acid	Glutamic Acid	Glycine	Alanine	Valine
10–15°	0.22	0.25	0.25	0.32	0.45
20°	0.04	0.04	0.06	0.10	0.27
25°	–	0.04	0.05	0.10	0.18

Per Cent Collidine in

Temperature	Leucine	Serine	Proline	Collidine Phase	Water Phase
10–15°	0.58	0.28	0.35	41.7(10°)	7.8(10°)
				49.0(15°)	5.0(15°)
20°	0.37	0.10	0.12	54.9	3.4
25°	–	0.07	0.08	59.3	3.0

[a] Little or no changes of R_F with temperature in phenol–water mixtures, and very little relative changes in phase composition.

isobutyric acid. Since changes of temperature affect the mutual solubility of the liquid phases, control of this factor was recommended (Table 15–6). Addition of ammonia or of selected acids to the solvents was found to affect the relative movement of such solutes as possessed an extra carboxyl or amino group, and thus assisted in their separation.

The choice of a suitable solvent for chromatography is generally governed by many factors, and is usually arrived at empirically. There are, at present, a few very general rules for guidance in the choice of a solvent which may be summarized as follows (34): (a) for a homologous series of solvents, the R_F value of a solute will vary inversely as the molecular weight of the solvent; (b) the R_F value of a solute tends to increase with increase in water content of the solvent system (this effect can be achieved by mixing a solvent with a polar liquid prior to saturation with water, i.e., lutidine with collidine);

and (c) if the substance is a weak acid or base, depression of ionization will tend to increase its R_F, and vice-versa. Thus, addition of ammonia to a phenol system retards the dicarboxylic amino acids and accelerates the movement of the basic amino acids.

Consden, Gordon, and Martin (31) employed a strip of Whatman No. 1 filter paper the upper end of which was immersed in a trough containing the water-saturated solvent, the entire system being contained in an air-tight chamber whose atmosphere was saturated with water and solvent. For a one-dimensional chromatogram, a solution containing 5 to 15 μg. of an

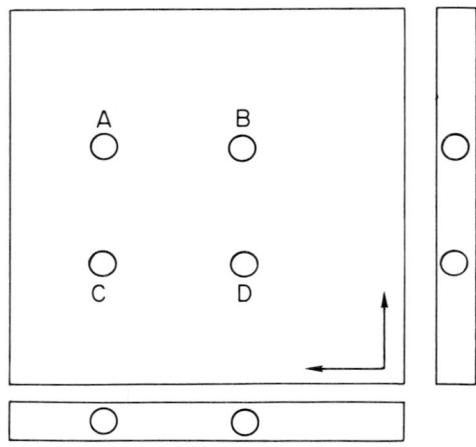

Figure 15–3. Diagram of paper chromatograms drawn to illustrate the phenomenon of double overlapping. Dent, C. E., *Biochem. J.*, **43**, 168 (1948).

amino acid was applied to one end of the paper, which was placed in the chamber as described. When the solvent had run a convenient distance, the paper was removed and the position of the solvent front noted. The paper strip was dried and then sprayed with ninhydrin. The color developed marked the position of the amino acid, and, from this distance from the point of origin and that of the solvent front, the R_F values were calculated. For a single solvent, many amino acids possessed R_F values not greatly different from each other, and the problem of separating mixtures of them presented an almost insoluble problem. An obvious method of resolving this problem was to employ several solvents in which the R_F values would differ. Another was by the introduction of the method of two-dimensional analysis. The aqueous solution of the mixture of amino acids was applied as a drop to one corner of the paper sheet and developed in a single direction by a particular solvent system. The paper was then removed from the chamber, dried, turned through an angle of 90°, and returned to a chamber prepared with a trough containing a second solvent system. Development of this chromatogram resulted in a marked separation of most of the amino acids in the mixture.

Dent (35) has given a clear illustration of the separation of a mixture of compounds A, B, C, and D by this procedure (Figure 15-3). The four circles in the figure represent four hypothetical amino acids after a two-dimensional analysis. One-dimensional chromatograms developed with solvents in the same directions as on the square sheet are shown below and to the side, respectively. The two one-dimensional analyses would show no resolution between A, D; B, C; A, C, B; A, B, D; C, B, D; or A, B, C, D. All would show only two spots on either of the one-dimensional runs. On the other hand, the two-dimensional analysis would readily resolve a mixture containing some or all of A, B, C, and D. Assuming that there is relatively little interaction among the amino acids when present in a mixture, the choice of solvents to be employed in a two-dimensional analysis may be approximately gaged by the results obtained on the R_F values for each of the amino acids in these solvents by one-directional analysis. Table 15-7 gives some R_F values for amino acids in various solvents as determined by Consden, Gordon, and Martin (31).

The R_F values are numerical expressions whose reproducibility depends on the constancy of the paper, temperature, quantity of amino acid, extraneous substances, degree of saturation with water, supply of solvent, and distance between starting point and source of solvent (31). Papers of different densities yield quite different R_F values. Resolution of two amino acids is often difficult unless the R_F values differ by more than 10%. Identification of an amino acid on a paper chromatogram can be suggested by its R_F value (but never by this alone); by its relative position to other amino acids on the same chromatogram; in some cases by the unusual color which it yields with ninhydrin, e.g., glycine, proline, hydroxyproline, etc., or with other more or less specific chemical reagents; in some cases by its reaction, after elution, with specific enzymes or microbiological agents; and best of all by comparison with the behavior of known standards run simultaneously, either in parallel positions on the paper, or as a mixture to see if a single spot ensues. The reference compounds may contain a radioactive isotope, and the techniques of autoradiography may be drawn on for purposes of accurate identification (36). A color reaction with ninhydrin is not necessarily specific for α-amino acids, but may be given by ammonia, and by many amino compounds, e.g., peptides, amines, amino alcohols, amino acid amides or esters, and ω-amino acids.

On a two-dimensional chromatogram, regardless of the nature of the solvent, glycine and its higher homologs lie on a smooth curve (37). A branched side chain results in a deviation from this line, and a slowing of the rate of movement. Since the presence of a hydroxyl group results in a decrease of R_F in phenol and has little effect in collidine, serine, threonine, tyrosine, and hydroxyproline occur almost vertically above the corresponding unsubstituted amino acids. Conversely, the bases are relatively slower in collidine than in phenol. Proline moves as fast as does leucine in phenol

TABLE 15-7

R_F Values of Amino Acids in Various Solvents on Whatman No. 1 Paper (31)[a]

Amino Acid	Phenol-HCN	Phenol-NH_3	Collidine	n-Butanol–Benzyl Alcohol–HCN	Isobutyric Acid
Glycine	0.40 RP	0.40 RP	0.25 P	0.03 P	0.36
Alanine	0.54 P	0.54 P	0.32 P	0.05 P	0.44
Norvaline	0.81 P	0.79 P	0.48 P	0.19 P	0.71
Valine	0.77 P	0.76 P	0.45 P	0.15 P	0.65
Norleucine	0.88 P	0.85 P	0.60 P	0.36 P	0.79
Isoleucine	0.86 P	0.81 P	0.54 P	0.27 P	0.76
Leucine	0.85 P	0.83 P	0.58 P	0.31 P	0.78
Phenylalanine	0.89 BP	0.87 P	0.59 G	0.38 BG	0.80
Tyrosine	0.64 GP	0.63 B	0.64 G	0.19 G	0.58
Serine	0.36 P	0.33 P	0.28 G	0.02 P	0.34
Threonine	0.50 P	0.41 P	0.32 P	0.04 P	0.43
Hydroxyproline	0.67 O	0.50 O	0.34 OY	0.05 O	0.42
Proline	0.91 Y	0.85 Y	0.35 Y	0.12 Y	0.57
Tryptophan	0.83 B	–	0.62 P	0.30 B	–
Histidine	0.69 RP	0.68 B	0.28 G	0.03 RG	0.45
Arginine	0.59 P	0.89 P	0.16 P	0.01 P	0.40
Ornithine	0.33 P	0.73 P	0.13 BG	0.00 P	0.24
Lysine	0.46 P	0.82 P	0.14 BG	0.01 P	0.27
Aspartic Acid	0.15 BP	0.12 B	0.22 B	0.00 P	0.31
Glutamic Acid	0.25 P	0.13 P	0.25 P	0.01 P	0.38
Lanthionine	0.20 RP	0.19 G	0.12 G	0.00 P	0.21
Cystine	0.30 RP	0.24 YG	0.14 G	0.00 P	0.25
Methionine	0.80 P	0.76 P	0.57 GP	0.21 P	0.69

[a] Color given by ninhydrin = B, blue; G, gray; O, orange; P, purple; R, red; Y, yellow. Basic amino acids applied to paper as hydrochlorides and neutralized with NH_3 prior to development.

and little faster than alanine in collidine. The positions of the spots for isoleucine, leucine, methionine, and phenylalanine overlap on a phenol-NH_3 and collidine chromatogram, but are readily separated by substituting an n-butanol–benzyl alcohol mixture for the phenol. The most frequently employed solvent systems are the following (38): (a) water-saturated phenol preferably in a carbon monoxide atmosphere, with HCN and NH_3 vapor, which may be used for the separation of alanine, threonine, glycine, serine, cystine, and aspartic and glutamic acids on one-dimensional chromatograms; (b) lutidine-ethanol-water in the ratios of 55 : 20 : 25, with diethylamine, which may yield a considerably different distribution of the amino acids than with the phenol system, and thus these two systems may profitably be employed on two-dimensional chromatograms for the separation of nearly all the commonly occurring amino acids except the leucine group; (c) butanol–glacial acetic acid (10 : 1) in an atmosphere of NH_3 which provides a specific separation of the faster-moving amino acids; (d) *sec*-butanol–*tert*-butanol–water (4 : 1 : 3), in $6N$ HCl or 0.3% NH_3 atmosphere, which possesses the advantage of separating the slowest-moving amino acids from those of intermediate rates; (e) 77% ethanol, whose use results in a good separation of histidine, hydroxyproline, and proline on two-dimensional chromatograms; and (f) *n*-butanol–benzyl alcohol (1 : 1) in an atmosphere of diethylamine which effects a separation of the so-called leucine group of overlapping spots, e.g., leucine, isoleucine, valine, methionine, and phenylalanine. A mixture of isobutyric and isovaleric acids (1 : 1) has been reported to be an effective medium for the purpose of separating leucine from isoleucine (39). A clear-cut separation of butyrine, valine, norvaline, *t*-leucine, leucine, isoleucine, and norleucine, has been achieved on two-dimensional chromatograms using butanol–acetic acid in one direction and pyridine–amyl alcohol in the other (40). An interesting separation of leucine, isoleucine, and phenylalanine is accomplished in *t*-amyl alcohol (water and diethylamine) (cf. 41); it is followed by the formation of colored cadmium complexes (42). Other solvent systems for the separation of leucine and isoleucine have included *t*-amyl alcohol : benzyl alcohol (saturated with water) (43), as well as *n*-butanol–methyl ethyl ketone–$17N$ NH_4OH–water (5 : 3 : 1 : 1) for the first solvent, and *n*-butanol–acetic acid–water (4 : 1 : 5) for the second (the system also separates lysine, arginine, and histidine) (44).

Many other solvent mixtures have been applied to specific problems of separation to suit the predilections both of the amino acids to be separated and of the individual investigator, but those cited above have received the most widespread and general use.

Figure 15–4, after Dent (35), represents a map of many of the known amino acids on a characteristic two-dimensional chromatogram using first phenol-NH_3 and secondly, collidine. Figures 15–5 to 15–7, taken from Block and Sober (45), illustrate the use of judiciously chosen combinations of solvents for the separation of the commonly occurring amino acids. Figure 15–5 shows the expected location of 20 amino acids using the phenol-HCN-NH_3 and lutidine-diethylamine systems. Figure 15–6 with 80% pyridine in place of the lutidine mixture indicates better separation of all the amino acids except for the leucine group, whereas in Figure 15–7 this group is separated through the use of an *n*-butanol–benzyl alcohol–diethylamine mixture. The presence of HCN, and in some cases of Cupron, in connection with phenol merely retards oxidative decomposition of the phenol.

The use of water-miscible solvents in the separation of amino acids by paper chromatography was investigated by Bentley and Whitehead (33), who

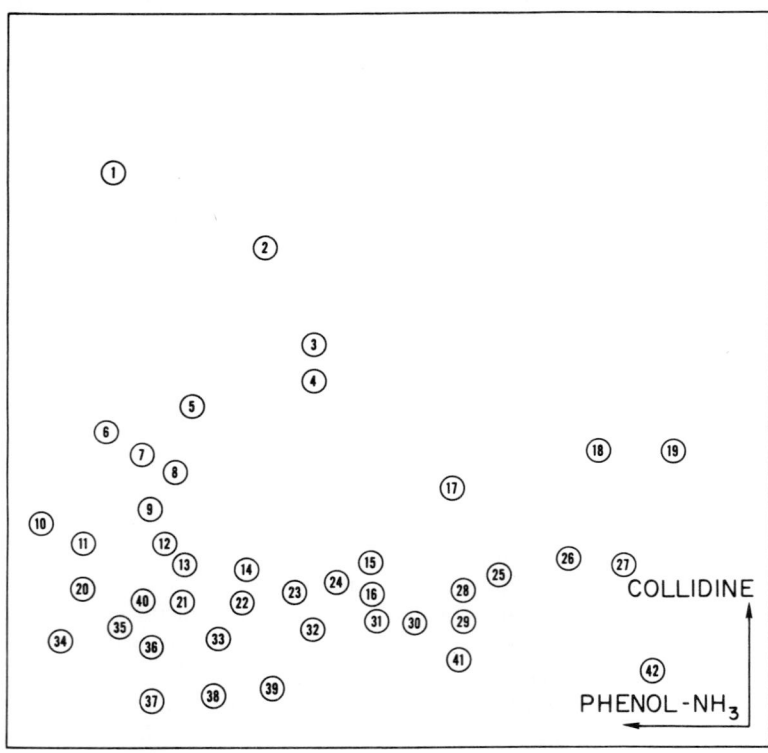

Figure 15-4. Two-dimensional chromatogram on paper, phenol-NH$_3$ as the first solvent, collidine the second. Dent, C. E., *Biochem. J.*, **43**, 169 (1948).

used the lower alcohols together with urea as a stabilizer. As in the experiments of Consden, Gordon, and Martin (31), a descending form of chromatographic analysis was employed and the amino acid positions were made visible through the use of a ninhydrin spray. The data given by Bentley and Whitehead in Figure 15-8 indicate that the actual magnitude of the R_F values but not the sequence varies with the amount of water present in the system, increasing with increasing water content whilst the range of values decreases. Figure 15-9 in which the amino acids are arranged in ascending order of R_F values in water-saturated *n*-butanol gives a comparison between this solvent and the three lower water-miscible alcohols. Whereas the general pattern is broadly similar for each solvent, the amino acids are observed

CHROMATOGRAPHY

to move more slowly with increasing molecular weight of the alcohols, and the variations in R_F values for different amino acids become less (cf. 46, 47). The results of these studies would suggest a broader interpretation of the phenomena of paper chromatography than that afforded by the principle of

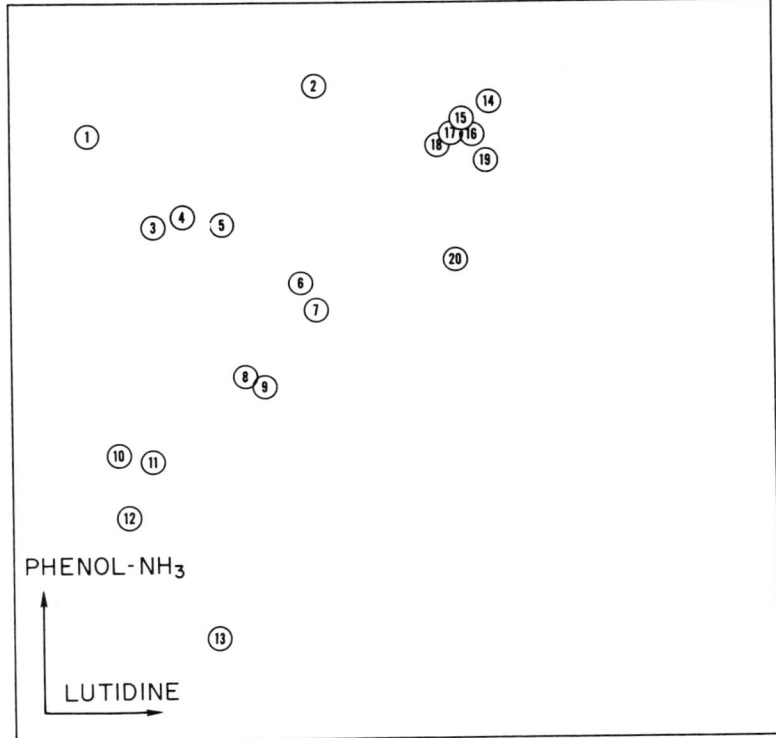

Figure 15-5. Two-dimensional amino acid distribution. 1, Arginine; 2, proline; 3, lysine; 4, histidine; 5, hydroxyproline; 6, alanine; 7, threonine; 8, glycine; 9, serine; 10, cystine; 11, glutamic acid; 12, aspartic acid; 13, cysteic acid; 14, phenylalanine; 15, isoleucine; 16, leucine; 17, methionine; 18, valine; 19, tryptophan; 20, tyrosine. Block, R. J., and Sober, H. A., *Colloid Chem.*, **7**, 181 (1950).

simple liquid-liquid partition (cf. 48), and they also suggest that the water held in filter paper is not truly free liquid water but is bound to the hydrophilic hydroxyl groups of the cellulose. The solutes which contain hydrophilic groups may compete with water and solvent molecules in the mobile phase for incorporation in the cellulose-water complex. Thus, for a given solvent, an increase in water content would result in the solute moving more quickly down the paper, and the rates of several solutes would tend to become more nearly equal. The use of the water-soluble alcohols would be expected to result in a competition by alcohol with amino acids for incorporation into the cellulose-water complex, whereby the amino acids so excluded would tend to move more and more with the mobile phase and thus demonstrate higher R_F values. With immiscible solvents, the movement may approach that due to a true partition, but in any event some overlapping must inevitably

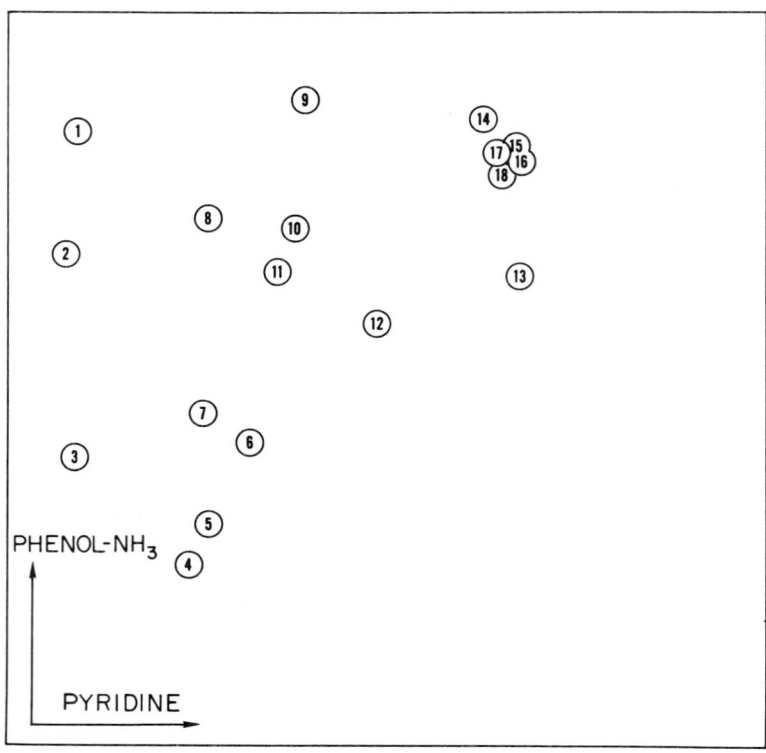

Figure 15-6. Two-dimensional amino acid distribution. 1, Arginine; 2, lysine; 3, cystine; 4, aspartic acid; 5, glutamic acid; 6, serine; 7, glycine; 8, histidine; 9, proline; 10, hydroxyproline; 11, alanine; 12, threonine; 13, tyrosine; 14, phenylalanine; 15, isoleucine; 16, leucine; 17, methionine; 18, valine. Block, R. J., and Sober, H. A., *Colloid Chem.*, **7**, 181 (1950).

occur. The similarity in distribution of amino acids between ethanol-water and *n*-butanol–water found by Cohn and his associates (15, 16) would in any event have led to the expectation that both groups of solvents would yield comparable results in any separation scheme based on their use under like conditions.

The method first employed by Consden, Gordon, and Martin (31) was that of so-called descending chromatography, whereby the solvent front

CHROMATOGRAPHY

advanced in a downward direction along the paper. Other workers have employed ascending techniques (49) which are not unlike those constructed by Schönbein and Goppelsroeder, and still others have used a combination of ascending and descending procedures (50). The results obtained with all three techniques have not been substantially different. In most cases flat

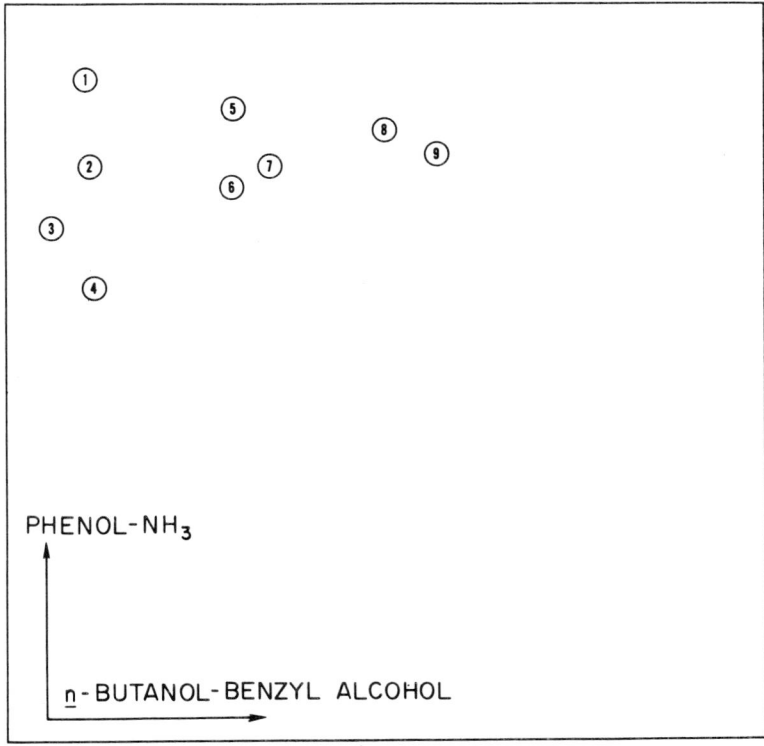

Figure 15-7. Two-dimensional amino acid distribution. 1, Proline; 2, methionine; 3, hydroxyproline; 4, tyrosine; 5, phenylalanine; 6, tryptophan; 7, valine; 8, isoleucine; 9, leucine. Block, R. J., and Sober, H. A., *Colloid Chem.*, **7**, 181 (1950).

strips or sheets of paper were employed. A variation of this method consisted of the use of circular or horizontal filter paper procedures, whereby the solutes to be analyzed are resolved into circular zones instead of spots (51-53). In this general procedure a wick of paper is immersed in the developing solvent and inserted through a small, tight aperture in the center of the horizontal sheet or disk of paper, the solvent rising by capillarity and flowing past the solute which had been deposited at the joint. With a mixture of amino acids, as in a protein hydrolysate, a continuous developing technique has been suggested (54), whereby the advancing front of solvent, most often *n*-butanol–acetic acid–water (4 : 1 : 5), is soaked up by a thick pad of absorbing material. Under such circumstances, the movement of the various amino acids from the faster at first to the slowest at the end progressively unfolds with time, and a clear separation of each is effected. Only one-dimensional

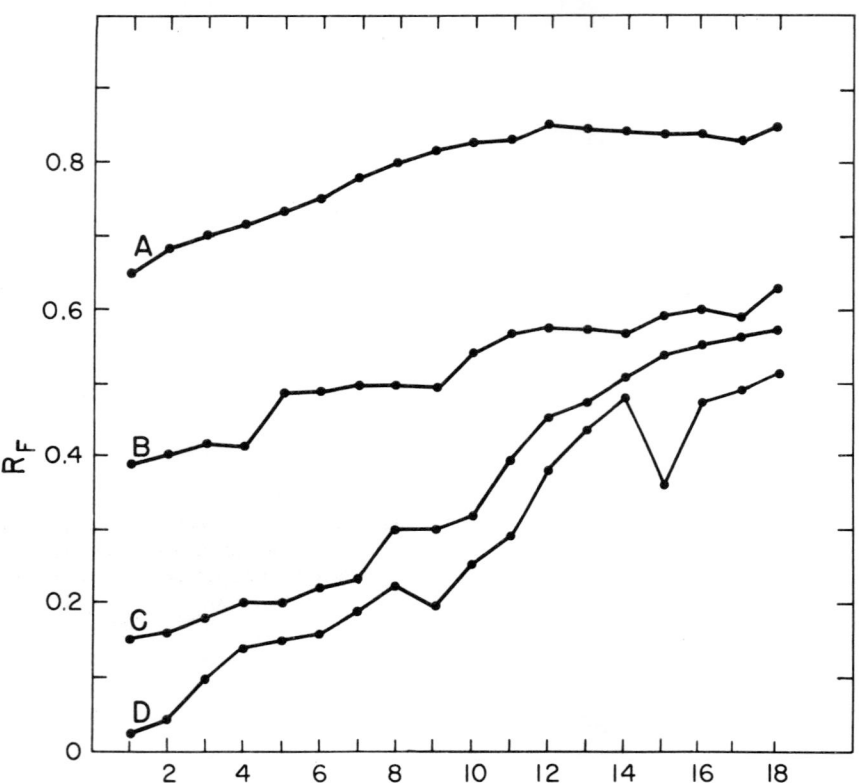

Figure 15–8. Effect of water content of furfuryl alcohol on the R_F values of amino acids on Whatman No. 4 paper. Water content (v/v): A, 60%; B, 40%; C, 30%; D, 10%. 1, Aspartic acid; 2, glutamic acid; 3, serine; 4, glycine; 5, ornithine; 6, arginine; 7, histidine; 8, alanine; 9, threonine; 10, hydroxyproline; 11, tyrosine; 12, valine; 13, methionine; 14, proline; 15, tryptophan; 16, leucine; 17, isoleucine; 18, phenylalanine. Bentley, H. R., and Whitehead, J. K., *Biochem. J.*, **46,** 341 (1953).

chromatography is possible with this technique, and the use of several solvent systems with multiple sheets employing ninhydrin as well as isatin as coloring agents has been recommended in order to encompass all the amino acids studied (cf. 53, 54*a*).

The filter papers which have been most often employed for the chromatography of the amino acids have been Whatman Nos. 1, 3, 4, and 54, as well

CHROMATOGRAPHY

as Schleicher and Schull Nos. 507, 596, 598, 602, and 604. It is not possible predict which paper will be most satisfactory for a given separation, and each problem must usually be solved empirically (cf. 38). For elution of relatively large amounts of amino acids a comparatively heavy paper is frequently desirable. When buffered solvents are employed, it is usual to buffer the paper similarly, before using the developing solvent.

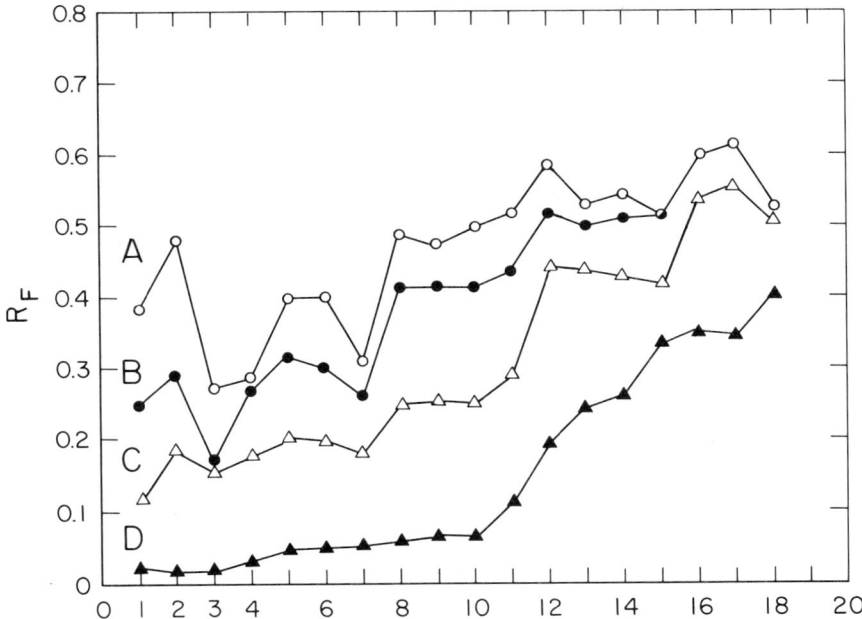

Figure 15-9. Comparison of the R_F values of amino acids in aqueous lower alcohols on Whatman No. 4 paper. A, 70% (v/v) methanol; B, 70% (v/v) ethanol; C, 70% (v/v) n-propanol; and D, n-butanol saturated with water. 1, Aspartic acid; 2, glutamic acid; 3, ornithine; 4, arginine; 5, serine; 6, glycine; 7, histidine; 8, threonine; 9, hydroxyproline; 10, alanine; 11, proline; 12, valine; 13, methionine; 14, tyrosine; 15, tryptophan; 16, leucine; 17, isoleucine; 18, phenylalanine. Bentley, H. R., and Whitehead, J. K., *Biochem. J.*, **46**, 341 (1950).

The studies of McFarren (55) were quite important in respect to the last-mentioned procedure, for the R_F of an amino acid is in some ranges of pH a function of pH (Figure 15-10) (cf. Haugaard and Kroner (56), and Levy and Chung (56a)). By the use of several solvents buffered at a selected pH, the paper (Whatman No. 1) being also buffered at the same pH, it is possible by using only one-dimensional chromatography to separate a large number of the amino acids. The paper chromatograms are buffered by dipping the paper into a buffer of desired pH and molarity, followed by drying in air, whilst the solvent is equilibrated with the same buffer. Before spotting with ninhydrin, the pH is brought to the range 5.5–7.5. An illustrative separation by this procedure with R_F values under the conditions stated follows. (It must be recalled from Chapter 4 that trivalent amino acids such as lysine or aspartic acid can exist at a certain pH in two ionic forms of different charge; paper chromatography at that pH will then yield two distinct spots for such compounds, corresponding to the two ionic forms involved).

Solvent 1. Phenol (24-hour development) saturated with buffer at pH 12.0
    Aspartic acid (0.10)   Glycine (0.32)
    Glutamic acid (0.17)   Threonine (0.41)
    Serine (0.27)   Alanine (0.48)

Solvent 2. m-Cresol (40-hour development) saturated with buffer at pH 8.4
    Alanine (0.14)   Histidine (0.33)
    Arginine (0.19)   Valine (0.42)
    Hydroxyproline (0.23)   Methionine (0.55)
    Tyrosine (0.27)

Solvent 3. Benzyl and butyl alcohol (1 : 1) (40-hour development) saturated with buffer at pH 8.4
    Isoleucine (0.24)   Leucine (0.28)

Solvent 4. o-Cresol (24-hour development) saturated with buffer at pH 6.2
    Phenylalanine (0.74)

Solvent 5. Collidine (24-hour development) saturated with buffer at pH 9.0
    Tryptophan (0.58)

Solvent 6. Benzyl and butyl alcohol (1 : 1) (12-hour development) saturated with buffer at pH 1.0
    Proline (0.26)

Solvent 7. Water-lutidine (24-hour development) unbuffered
    Lysine (0.15)

Special pretreatment before developing the paper chromatogram occurs in at least two important cases, (a) for the determination of methionine and cystine-cysteine, and (b) when it is necessary to distinguish α-amino acids from ω-amino acids. The spot for methionine overlaps that for leucine, whilst that for cystine-cysteine is frequently invisible owing to decomposition. Both may be readily demonstrated with ninhydrin after they are converted to the corresponding oxidized forms and chromatographed. Hydrogen peroxide is applied to the paper itself (35), and methionine is converted to the sulfone at a position considerably removed from that of the parent compound (Figure 15-4). The ordinary chromatographic procedure converts methionine in part to the sulfoxide, which is revealed in a position different from that either of the parent substance or of the sulfone. Confirmation of the presence of the sulfoxide can be achieved by its conversion in the presence of both hydrogen peroxide and ammonium molybdate to the sulfone (57). Cystine-cysteine is converted by the prior peroxide treatment to cysteic acid which forms a readily apparent spot with ninhydrin. The same principle is applicable to the homocysteine-homocystine system (57). Other amino acids present are not immune to this treatment, for, in the presence of chloride ions, 3-chloro- and 3 : 5-dichlorotyrosine (58) and other ninhydrin-reactive

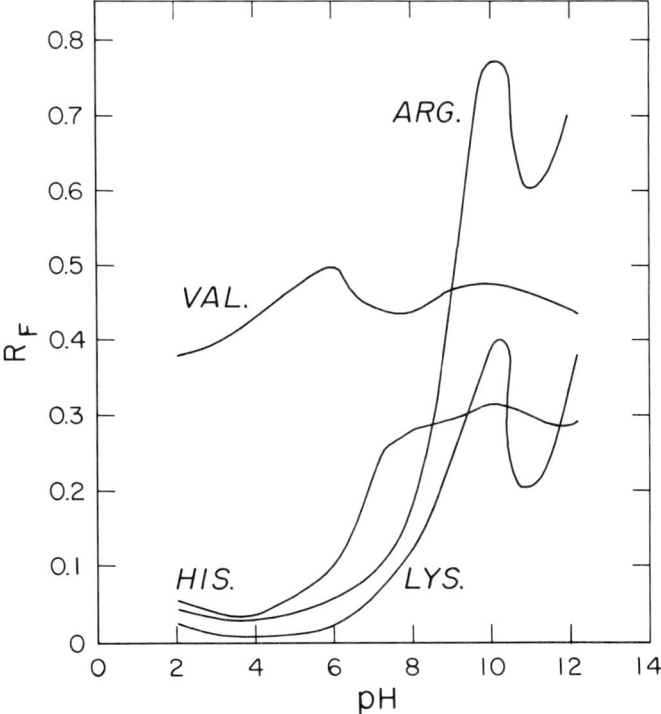

Figure 15–10. Values of R_F on paper (solvent m-cresol) as a function of the buffer pH. McFarren, E. F., *Anal. Chem.*, **23,** 168 (1951).

artifacts (59) may be formed as a result of the oxidative environment. To avoid this problem chromatography of cysteine and of homocysteine can be conducted in the presence of formaldehyde (60) or of N-ethylmaleimide (61) whereby the —SH groups are protected.

The separation of α-amino acids from ω-amino acids was accomplished by Crumpler and Dent (62), who employed the phenomenon of chelate formation with copper salts which the former compounds, in contrast with the latter, demonstrate (Chapter 6). In this procedure the paper is lightly dusted with basic copper carbonate to form a streak along the path of future movement which the amino acids would travel in phenol, the first solvent. The subsequent developing solvent is lutidine or lutidine-collidine. The α-amino acids as chelates with copper do not move appreciably, whereas some β- and all γ-amino acids, as well as various amines, move in their usual positions. The complete absence of ammonia and cyanide in the first solvent, and of diethylamine in the second, is required. α-Amino acid complexes with metals have, however, been chromatographed using dioxane-water (80 : 20) as solvent with Whatman No. 1 paper (63). Thus the amino acid is shaken with an excess of metal carbonate, filtered, and an aliquot of the filtrate placed on the paper. After development, the complexes are decomposed by treatment with 8-hydroxyquinoline and the residual amino acids spotted by dipping the paper into a solution of ninhydrin. The R_F values for some amino acid complexes of copper are: proline, 0.41; alanine, 0.36; glycine, 0.22, whilst the values for some of the metal complexes of glycine are: copper, 0.22; nickel, 0.19; and cobalt, 0.18.

Further distinctions of α-amino acids from ω-amino acids are (a) the susceptibility of the former to amino acid oxidases (Chapter 20), and (b) the fact that only the α-amino acids undergo transamination with pyridoxal in aqueous solutions (64). The pyridoxamine formed thereby gives a characteristic deep orange color with ninhydrin, and thus the sequential treatment of an amino acid with pyridoxal and ninhydrin yields, on paper, orange spots only where α-amino acids are concerned. The mixture to be analyzed is applied to duplicate papers and chromatograms are developed with n-butanol–acetic acid–water (4 : 1 : 5) as solvent. After drying in air, one chromatogram is sprayed with a solution of pyridoxal in ethanolic alkali, and dried again; compounds with a primary amino group appear as yellow spots, presumably due to Schiff base formation for no such color was revealed at the spot for proline (64). On heating the chromatogram at 90° for 10 minutes, transamination is effected. This and the control sheets are then sprayed with ninhydrin in acetone and subsequently warmed to bring out the colors. An orange color appears rapidly at spots due to α-amino acids, the color arising much earlier than that of ninhydrin, so that in the first few minutes of the reaction the color due to the former is not mixed with that due to the latter, which arises from residual α-amino acid due to incomplete transamination. α-Alkylamino acids which cannot transaminate as such nevertheless form pyridoxamine from pyridoxal as a result of some decarboxylation accompanied by partial transamination. ω-Amino acids, amines, and O-phosphoserine, and O-phosphothreonine in the presence of pyridoxal and ninhydrin yield only purple-colored spots (64), which, for the phosphorylated derivatives, is understandable in view of the α,β-elimination reactions characteristic of these compounds.

4. Desalting. An excess of inorganic ions interferes with the development of paper chromatograms, especially with those amino acids with low R_F

values in phenol. The problem of the distortion of the chromatograms due to salt is particularly acute when such fluids as urine are to be studied. The older procedures for desalting solutions of amino acids employed (a) electrolysis between a carbon anode and a circulating mercury cathode (65, 66), (b) separation of the amino acids as the camphorsulfonates (67), and (c) precipitation of the amino acids with organic solvents (68). More modern techniques employ ion exchange resins for this purpose (69–73). Thus, in the studies of Carsten (70), urine was perfused through the acid form of a cation exchange resin whereby all the amino acids as cations, except the strongly acid taurine, were retained whilst the anions were lost in the effluent. Elution of the column with ammonia (more properly displacement) resulted in recovery of the amino acids and of the weaker bases, whereas the cations of the stronger bases (Na^+, and a fraction of the arginine, etc.) were retained on the column. The eluate was then passed through an anion exchange column in the basic form which retained the amino acids as anions and rejected the weaker bases in the effluent. The amino acids were recovered from this column by elution with N HCl. Some arginine was lost by the second column chromatography by being washed through and not retained. Piez and his colleagues (72) began their desalting procedure with the anionic exchanger, thereby losing all cations except hydrogen (as well as some arginine), the HCl eluate containing Cl^-, amino acids, and the anions originally present; the eluate, on passage through an anion exchange resin in the bicarbonate form, exchanged its anions for bicarbonate, the reaction being driven to completion by the loss of bicarbonate as carbon dioxide. The amino acids were not taken up from the acid solution because of their cationic character under these conditions, and emerged from the column free of both anions and cations.

Subsequent studies of desalting by Dreze, Moore, and Bigwood (73) were concerned with the use of Dowex 2 resin in the Na^+ form applied to neutral and acidic amino acids, and of Dowex 50 in the H^+ form applied to the basic amino acids as well as tryptophan. Thus Dowex 2 was cycled with NaOH, HCl, and NaOH ($2N$ NaOH warmed to 45°), and finally water until the effluent was neutral. The amino acid solution, diluted to $0.2N$ Na^+ if necessary, was added, and washed through with water. In this way Na^+ and other inorganic cations were lost in the effluent, and the anionic amino acids and other anions could be subsequently eluted with N acetic acid. When Dowex 50 was used, the resin was cycled with HCl, NaOH, HCl, and finally water to neutrality of the effluent, and the tryptophan or basic amino acid solution added. Subsequent washing with water removed all the inorganic anions in the effluent. Washing the resin with $0.5N$ HCl removed Na^+; this was followed by elution with $4N$ HCl, which removed the tryptophan or basic amino acids from the resin as the hydrochlorides. For the neutral amino acids, either the Dowex 2 treatment, or the Dowex 50 procedure in which the amino acids are displaced from the column with ammonia, gives good results and reduces the salt content to manageable proportions.

5. **Color Reactions.** In addition to purely movement analysis, various qualitative identifications of the amino acids on paper can be undertaken in the few cases wherein the ninhydrin color is characteristic (see Chapter 11). Most amino acids yield a blue or reddish-purple color with this reagent, but asparagine gives an orange-brown color (which distinguishes it from the nearby glycine spot (26)), tyrosine a dull greenish purple, proline a yellow color, hydroxyproline a brown-yellow color (which distinguishes it from the nearby alanine spot (35)), glycine a rather grayish-purple color, and aspartic acid a rather bright blue. Treatment of the paper chromatogram with weak alkali intensifies the blue color of the ninhydrin spot of phenylalanine (74), whilst treatment of the paper (Whatman No. 1) with cyclohexylamine *prior* to spraying with ninhydrin brings about the following colors of the ninhydrin-developed spots: aspartic acid blue, cystine orange, alanine purple, histidine gray-green, serine purple, phenylalanine blue-gray, proline yellow, hydroxyproline carmine, threonine gray-purple, tyrosine gray, glycine red-brown, while all the other amino acids yield the more usual purple color (75). In addition, there is a variety of other staining reagents which are more or less specific for certain amino acids (see also Part VI). Thus the following amino acids may be qualitatively identified: (a) arginine by the Sakaguchi reaction, whereby the paper is sprayed with α-naphthol in NaOH solution, followed by NaOCl or NaOBr solution (red color, the spot for histidine becoming yellow, and that for tryptophan brown) (76); (b) histidine and tyrosine by the Pauly reaction, whereby the paper is treated with freshly diazotized sulfanilamide followed by sodium carbonate solution (histidine yielding a red color, tyrosine a reddish brown, and other amino acids a yellow color) (67, 77); (c) tryptophan and citrulline by reaction with *p*-dimethylaminobenzaldehyde in HCl (yellow color) (71), the reaction with citrulline serving to distinguish it from the neighboring purple glutamine spot (35); (d) proline and hydroxyproline by reaction with isatin in butanol–acetic acid followed by heating (blue color, all other common amino acids yielding a weak rose) (78), subsequent treatment with N HCl causing the blue spot of proline to deepen in color whilst the spots due to the other amino acids fade away (79); (e) sulfur-containing amino acids by their bleaching action when the paper is sprayed with a solution of platinic iodide (76, 80); (f) serine and threonine by the ammonia liberated (paper must be ammonia-free) when they are treated with periodate (red-brown color after Nessler reaction) (71, 76), as well as by a violet color produced by reaction first with alkaline hypochlorite and then with 1:2-dinitrobenzene (81); and (g) glycine by the green color with *o*-phthalaldehyde (82), whereas histidine gives a blue-green color and tryptophan a gray color. Various related guanidine

compounds may be distinguished by a single reagent. Thus, with alkaline ferricyanide-nitroprusside, canavanine and canavaninosuccinate give bluish violet spots, arginine, argininosuccinate, and guanidinosuccinate give red spots, the cyclized forms of the latter two compounds give blue spots, and guanidine yields a red spot (83, 84). An interesting color reagent is 1:2-naphthoquinone-4-sulfonate which in sodium carbonate solutions produces reddish spots with proline and hydroxyproline, a green spot with glycine, and blue-gray to violet colors with all other common amino acids (85).

Serine can be distinguished from threonine on paper chromatograms by the following reactions (85a). After chromatography on Whatman No. 1 paper in the solvent system methanol-water-pyridine (80 : 20 : 4), and drying at 50°, the paper is sprayed with dilute periodic acid. Formaldehyde is evolved from the serine spot. It is made visible by spraying the paper with a methanol solution containing ammonium acetate, acetic acid, and acetylacetone, whereby a yellow, highly fluorescent spot, indicating the position of serine (and a second similar spot due to δ-hydroxylysine if present), emerges in one to four hours at 25°. Threonine, which evolves acetaldehyde on oxidation with periodate, is not revealed by this procedure. It is, instead, made visible by a specific reaction for this aldehyde, consisting of a spray of a freshly prepared solution of sodium nitroprusside and piperidine in methanol. The threonine spot is indicated by a blue zone within a few minutes.

These represent only a few of the available, more or less specific, color reactions for individual amino acids, which are described in greater detail elsewhere (Part VI). The color development need not necessarily be performed on the paper, but can be ascertained on the material after it has been eluted, although the sensitivity of the reaction is greater on paper than on the eluate. An alternative procedure with such eluates would be to employ specific enzyme preparations, i.e., lysine, arginine, ornithine, glutamic acid decarboxylases, etc. (Chapter 20). Both color reactions and enzymic reactions can also form the basis of quantitative assay (see below).

Such colored derivatives of amino acids as the dinitrobenzenes can be employed to distinguish amino acids in a mixture (24). The amino acids are readily converted to yellow-colored DNP derivatives by reaction with dinitrofluorobenzene in the presence of bicarbonate or triethylamine (86, 87), which are then chromatographed on paper (86, 88, 89). The paper may also be sprayed with the reagent (90), and the resulting yellow spots eluted. The paper-DNP method of amino acid analysis of proteins has been successfully applied to insulin (89), α-corticotropin (91), and the hypophyseal growth hormone (92). The R_F values for such derivatives in several solvents are given in Table 15-8. For added confirmation, certain of the DNP-amino acids may be treated individually with hot alkali to remove the derivative

TABLE 15-8
R_F Values of DNP-Amino Acids on Whatman No. 1 Paper (88)

Compound	n-Butanol–H$_2$O	n-Butanol–Butyl Acetate–NH$_3$	Benzene–Glacial Acetic Acid
Di-DNP-tyrosine	0.78	0.90	0.33
DNP-leucine	0.74	0.71	0.70
DNP-isoleucine	0.73	0.70	0.70
Di-DNP-lysine	0.72	0.81	0.11
DNP-phenylalanine	0.71	0.70	0.55
DNP-tryptophan	0.70	0.68	0.28
DNP-valine	0.68	0.47	0.63
DNP-methionine	0.65	0.48	0.47
DNP-alanine	0.50	0.18	0.28
DNP-proline	0.48	0.17	0.44
DNP-threonine	0.43	0.12	0.00
DNP-glycine	0.36	0.08	0.07
DNP-serine	0.32	0.06	0.00
DNP-glutamic acid	0.14	0.00	0.00
DNP-aspartic acid	0.12	0.00	0.00
Di-DNP-histidine	0.35	0.50	0.00
DNP-arginine	0.37	0.00	0.00
DNP-ε-lysine	0.32	0.05	0.00
DNP-α-lysine	0.33	0.00	0.00

TABLE 15-9
R_F Values of Aminoalcohols on Whatman No. 1 Paper (98)

Compound	n-Butanol–Acetic Acid–H$_2$O	n-Butanol–NH$_3$	Phenol–NH$_3$
Alaninol	0.25	0.23	0.83
Serinol	0.16	0.15	0.69
Threoninol	0.17	0.31	–
Valinol	0.40	0.49	1
Leucinol	0.53	0.63	1
Isoleucinol	0.50	0.63	1
Prolinol	0.28	0.26	1
Phenylalaninol	0.54	0.70	1
Tyrosinol	0.40	0.54	0.81
Aspartidiol	0.19	0.23	0.82
Glutamidiol	0.21	0.23	0.85
Lysinol	0.08	0.07	0.78
Argininol	0.08	0.07	–
Histidinol	0.08	0.12	–

group, and the free amino acid rechromatographed for identification (93). Paper previously buffered with phthalate at pH 6.0 has been recommended for effective separation of the DNP-amino acids (94; cf. 95), although a pH range of 9–11 with butanol–isoamyl alcohol–ethanol–buffer (20 : 20 : 6.5 : 30) has also been employed (96). The very considerable use of the DNP-amino acids for the determination of the sequence of amino acids in peptides and in proteins is described elsewhere (Chapter 16).

If staining is to be avoided altogether, the dried paper after development may be treated with Nujol and scanned with infrared radiation, and the various peaks corresponding to each amino acid determined quantitatively at 6.2 μ (97).

A colorless series of derivatives of the amino acids which have been employed for end-group analysis of proteins are the aminoalcohols, studied by Fromageot, Jutisz, Meyer, and Penasse (98). The carboxyl groups are readily reduced to the alcohols by the action of lithium aluminum hydride in N-ethylmorpholine. The R_F values for the aminoalcohols in several solvents are given in Table 15-9 (98). Ninhydrin was employed to reveal the spots.

The amines are another interesting category of compounds related to the amino acids by the conceivable process of decarboxylation. They may be readily isolated from biological media by extraction from alkalinized aqueous solution into an immiscible organic solvent. The R_F values for a series of these compounds, employing ninhydrin as the developing agent, are given in Table 15-10 (99). The color reaction possesses about the same sensitivity as with the corresponding amino acids. Butanol–acetic acid–water is the most effective solvent for the separation of the primary n-alkylamines, whereas phenol alone is the best solvent for separating the polymethylenediamines (Table 15-10). With phenol-NH_3-HCN, however, the R_F values of nearly all the amines approaches unity. It is not inconceivable that in the ordinary course of analyzing unknown mixtures of extractives from plant and animal tissues by two-dimensional chromatography those amino acids with high R_F values might be confused with amines. Histamine may be distinguished from histidine on paper developed with butanol-NH_4OH, the red color of the well-separated spots being developed with a mixture of p-bromoaniline in HCl plus nitrite and carbonate (100). Histidine is the faster-moving compound.

Reference to Table 15-10 indicates that the R_F values for the homologous series of n-alkylamines and of the polymethylenediamines stand in a nearly linear relation to the increasing number of CH_2 groups in the molecules. This is in accord with the views of Martin (101) on the relationship between chemical constitution and partition coefficient, which in turn was compatible with the fundamental distribution studies of England and Cohn on amino acids partitioned between n-butanol and water (see above).

TABLE 15-10
R_F Values of Amines on Whatman No. 4 Paper (99)

Compound	n-Butanol–Acetic Acid–H$_2$O[a]	Phenol
Methylamine	0.37	0.72
Ethylamine	0.45	0.80
n-Propylamine	0.58	0.86
n-Butylamine	0.70	0.91
n-Amylamine	0.77	0.92
n-Heptylamine	0.85	0.94
Isopropylamine	0.57	–
Isoamylamine	0.77	–
1:2-Diaminoethane	0.14	0.18
1:3-Diaminopropane	0.15	0.25
1:4-Diaminobutane (putrescine)	0.16	0.45
1:5-Diaminopentane (cadaverine)	0.17	0.59
1:6-Diaminohexane	0.20	0.67
Benzylamine	0.68	0.91
β-Phenylethylamine	0.72	0.91
β-Phenyl-β-hydroxyethylamine	0.65	0.86
Histidine	0.19	0.68
Tryptamine	0.67	0.91
Tyramine	0.62	0.85
Glucosamine	0.24	0.30

[a] Ninhydrin colors were all purple except for benzylamine which at first was yellow and then reddish purple, β-phenylethylamine which was blue, histamine which was grayish brown, and tyramine which was grayish purple.

Illustrative Examples of the Scope of Qualitative Paper Chromatography

6. The Problem of the Natural Occurrence of Norleucine. The occurrence of this amino acid in nerve tissue proteins has been described by several investigators (cf. 102, 103). A sample of the alleged amino acid isolated from this source was examined by Consden, Gordon, Martin, Rosenheim, and Synge (104) with the aid of paper chromatograms. A small volume of solution was applied to a strip of Whatman No. 1 paper which was hung from a trough containing benzyl alcohol placed in a closed chamber whose atmosphere was saturated with water and benzyl alcohol. Hydrocyanic acid was also present. After 48 hours, the strip was dried, sprayed with a 0.1% solution of ninhydrin in n-butanol, dried again, and heated to 105° for 5 minutes. A single, purple spot was obtained. The R_F value was identical with that for leucine. In a second run, the sample was applied to the paper simultaneously with a sample of authentic norleucine. Two separate spots were obtained, with R_F values which identified them as arising from leucine and from norleucine (Figure 15–11). The alleged sample of norleucine from nerve tissue was actually DL-leucine, and this was confirmed by studies of the acetyl derivative and of the optically active isomer produced by the action of amino acid oxidase on the racemic amino acid (104).

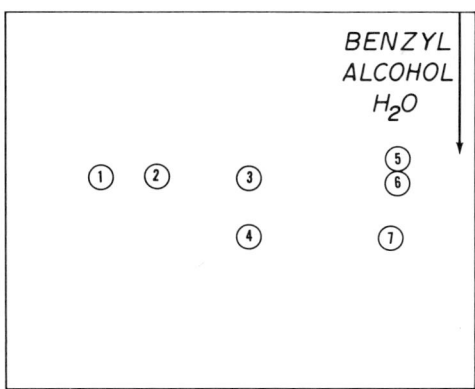

Figure 15–11. The norleucine problem. 1, Alleged norleucine isolated from brain; 2, authentic leucine; 3, 4, mixture of alleged brain norleucine and authentic norleucine; 5, 6, 7, mixture of authentic isoleucine, leucine, and norleucine. Consden, R., Gordon, A. H., Martin, A. J. P., Rosenheim, O., and Synge, R. L. M., *Biochem. J.*, **39**, 251 (1945).

7. The Problem of the Natural Occurrence of β-Hydroxyglutamic Acid. The isolation of this amino acid from protein hydrolysates was twice claimed by Dakin (12, 105). Samples of the original preparation were compared on paper chromatograms with authentic examples by Dent and Fowler (106). The analyses were performed on 0.1% solutions of the amino acids in 10% aqueous isopropanol. All the chromatograms were run by the descending technique. Unidirectional strip chromatograms were first studied with phenol-water in the presence of ammonia and hydrogen cyanide (Figure 15–12). The cyanide vapor was, as customary, intended to hinder oxidation of the phenol. Two-way chromatograms were run with this system first, followed by a mixture of collidine-lutidine-H_2O in the presence of diethylamine vapor. After drying, the paper was sprayed with ninhydrin solution and dried for 24 hours at 23°. The authentic samples of β-hydroxyglutamic acid gave brownish-purple spots which could be readily distinguished from the purple spots yielded by the other amino acids. Although the alleged samples of β-hydroxyglutamic acid yielded a variety of ninhydrin-reactive spots which could be identified as due to certain commonly occurring amino acids, no spot was present which could be identified as arising from β-hydroxyglutamic acid. These findings were in accord with the analytical data of Bailey, Chibnall, et al. (107) and of Nicolet and Shinn (108). The latter estimated the β-hydroxyamino acids in proteins and demonstrated that the total figure for this class of compounds could be accounted for completely in terms of serine and threonine. The former group repeated the Dakin isolation procedure exactly and concluded that the preparation was essentially a mixture of glutamic acid, serine, and several other amino acids (see Section 1–4 for further discussion of the ill-fated history of β-hydroxyglutamic acid in proteins).

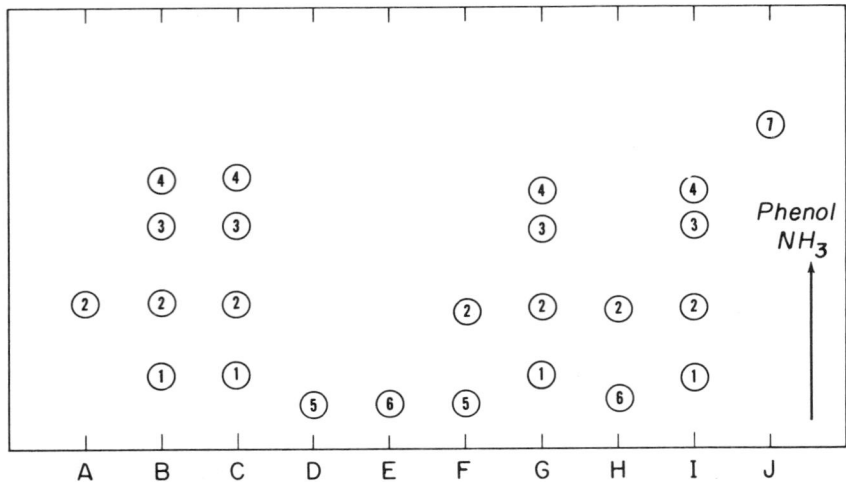

Figure 15–12. The β-hydroxyglutamic acid problem. A, authentic glutamic acid; B, alleged sample of β-hydroxyglutamic acid; C, a second alleged sample of β-hydroxyglutamic acid; D, authentic β-hydroxyglutamic acid; E, authentic allo-β-hydroxyglutamic acid; F, mixture of glutamic acid and authentic β-hydroxyglutamic acid; G, alleged sample of β-hydroxyglutamic acid; H, mixture of glutamic acid and authentic allo-β-hydroxyglutamic acid; I, second alleged sample of β-hydroxyglutamic acid; and J, taurine. Spots 3 and 4 are due, respectively, to glycine and serine, and spot 1 to aspartic acid. Dent, C. E., and Fowler, D. I., *Biochem. J.*, **56**, 54 (1954).

8. Discovery of Butyrine, β-Aminoisobutyric Acid, Methylhistidine, and Felinine. BIOLOGICAL FLUIDS. It has long been known that small amounts of many amino acids are normally excreted in the urine, but that their excretion in large amounts occurs only in rare pathological conditions (amino aciduria) (cf. 109, 110). This excessive excretion was first noted in cases of acute yellow atrophy of the liver, which is accompanied as well by a considerable increase in blood amino nitrogen. A study of amino acid excretion in patients with Franconi syndrome (associated often with bone disease), and in which there is little or no rise in amino nitrogen blood levels, was carried out by Dent (57). In the course of this study, two-dimensional chromatograms revealed the presence of butyrine (Figure 15–13). The positions of the amino acids in the urine chromatogram were checked with standard preparations of the amino acids, and the identification of methionine and of cystine by position was assured by pretreatment of the urine on the chromatogram with hydrogen peroxide prior to development, in order to convert the former to the sulfone and the latter to cysteic acid. The butyrine in the urine increased after methionine feeding. Butyrine often occurs in normal urine and plasma, and in extracts of a number of animal and plant

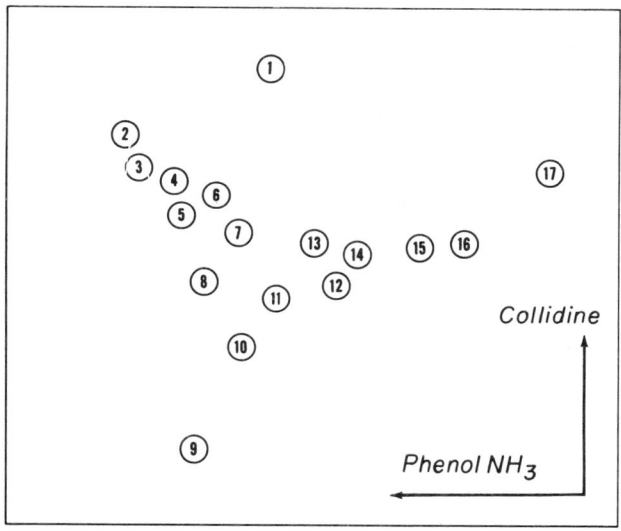

Figure 15–13. Urine in Franconi syndrome. 1, Tyrosine; 2, phenylalanine; 3, leucine, isoleucine; 4, methionine; 5, valine; 6, methionine sulfone (after H_2O_2 treatment of paper); 7, butyrine; 8, histidine; 9, arginine; 10, citrulline; 11, alanine; 12, glycine; 13, threonine; 14, serine; 15, glutamic acid; 16, aspartic acid; 17, cysteic acid (after H_2O_2 treatment of paper). Dent, C. E., *Biochem. J.*, **41**, 240 (1947).

tissues (35). Inasmuch as some peptides may possess the same mobility as some amino acids, it is necessary in working with materials from biological sources to detect the former by hydrolysis in HCl, and by rechromatography after neutralization (cf. 111).

Among the unidentified substances detected in a paper chromatographic survey of urinary amino acid excretion of normal subjects and hospitalized individuals, one appeared to occur fairly regularly (112, 113). On two-dimensional chromatograms with phenol and collidine-lutidine it appeared in about the same position as methionine sulfoxide. It was, however, not this compound for it was not oxidizable to the sulfone, and it was not an α-amino acid for it could not form an immobile copper complex after the previous dusting of the paper with copper carbonate. The compound was identified as β-aminoisobutyric acid (α-methyl-β-alanine) after isolation on a cation exchange resin followed by comparison with an authentic sample on one-dimensional chromatograms with three different solvents. The isolated compound, as might be expected, was optically active. Its metabolic source appeared to be thymine (114). The position of this β-amino acid on the chromatogram is shown in Figure 15-14.

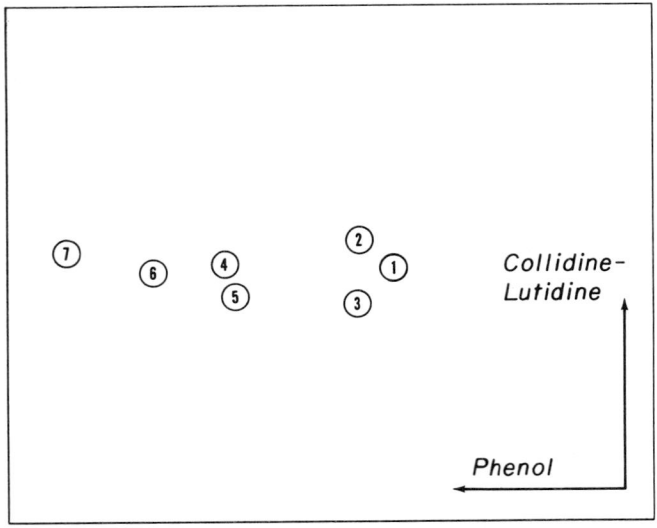

Figure 15-14. Observation of β-aminoisobutyric acid and of 1-methylhistidine in urine. 1, Serine; 2, taurine; 3, glycine; 4, alanine; 5, glutamine; 6, β-aminoisobutyric acid; 7, "green spot" (1-methylhistidine). Crumpler, H. R., Dent, C. E., Harris, H., and Westall, R. G., *Nature*, **167**, 307 (1951).

In Figure 15-14, according to Crumpler et al. (113), there occurred a fast-moving spot close to proline which was referred to as "green spot." This urinary component behaved oddly with ninhydrin for at temperatures below 100° it gave a brown color, and at temperatures above 110° it gave a green color. It was isolated from cat urine by displacement fractionation on Zeo Karb 215 (cf. 115) with the help of the specific ninhydrin color on paper, and was finally obtained in crystalline form (116). The material turned out to be 1-methylhistidine, a moiety of the anserine molecule, and a usual component of the urine of carnivorous animals (117). Methylhistidine does not give a Pauly reaction.

Further studies by Westall on cat urine revealed on two-dimensional chromatograms (phenol-NH$_3$ and collidine-lutidine) the presence of a new ninhydrin-reactive spot between that of phenylalanine and leucine-isoleucine (118). After peroxide treatment the spot disappeared and a new one appeared near valine. It was therefore suspected that the component yielding this spot contained oxidizable sulfur. For ready recognition, the compound was found to be separable on one-directional chromatograms if run in *t*-amyl alcohol. It appears to be cysteine whose sulfur atom is linked to isoamyl alcohol, i.e., an S-hydroxyalkylcysteine, and in view of its source has tentatively been designated as felinine (118) (see Chapter 50).

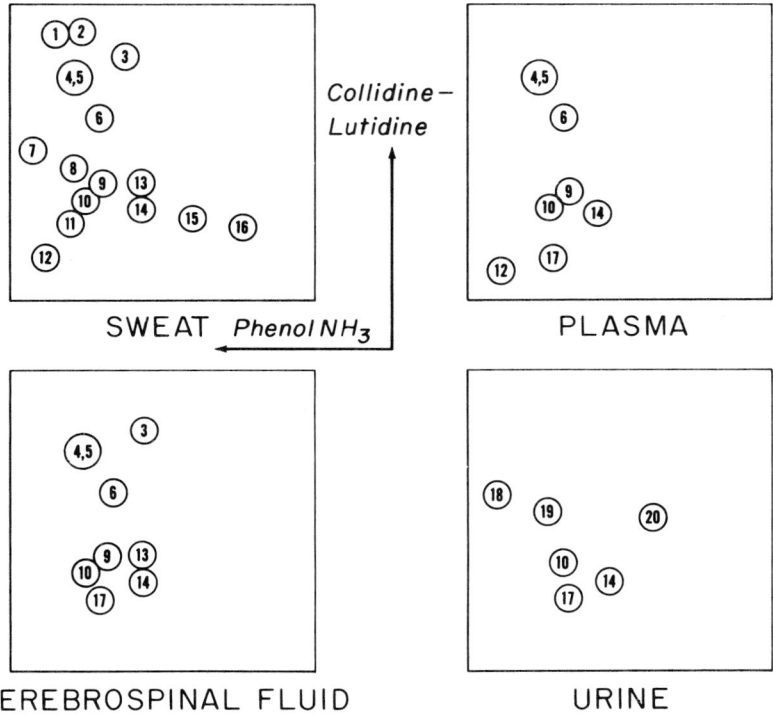

Figure 15-15. Chromatograms of normal human fluids. 1, Phenylalanine; 2, tryptophan; 3, tyrosine; 4, 5, leucine, isoleucine; 6, valine; 7, proline; 8, histidine; 9, threonine; 10, alanine; 11, citrulline (very high in sweat); 12, lysine; 13, serine; 14, glycine; 15, glutamic acid; 16, aspartic acid; 17, glutamine; 18, 1-methylhistidine; 19, β-aminoisobutyric acid; 20, taurine. Dent, C. E., and Walshe, J. M., *Brit. Med. Bull.*, **10,** No. 3 (1954).

For comparative purposes, the paper chromatograms of Dent and Walshe (109) for normal human urine, plasma, cerebrospinal fluid, and sweat are portrayed in Figure 15-15 for the principal components. Glycine is apparently the predominant amino acid in the urine, and glutamine in cerebrospinal fluid. The relatively high level of citrulline in sweat is curious.

Two-dimensional paper chromatograms of human plasma reported by

Agren and Nilsson (119) revealed the presence of all the common amino acids and, in addition, butyrine, citrulline, ornithine, and taurine. The relative proportion of those amino acids of protein derivation was not unlike that to be expected of a tissue protein, except for distinctly lower concentrations of aspartic and glutamic acids (109). An interesting study by Dent and Schilling (120) on the content of plasma amino acids in the dog fed heterologous and homologous proteins revealed that, after the former were fed, the amino acid levels of the plasma rose markedly and fell subsequently at about the same rate. Each of the protein-bound type of amino acids, except for glutamic acid, participated in this phenomenon, whereas butyrine rose very slightly in level, and taurine and citrulline did not alter in level at all. No peptides were detected. After the feeding of dog plasma proteins (homologous) there was no change in the level of any of the plasma amino acids of the fed animals.

Both plasma and urine have been intensively studied in pathologic conditions. In some cases, the amino acidurias may serve for partial diagnosis. Thus, in the presence of normal levels of plasma amino acids, cystinuria is accompanied by the excretion of unusually high amounts of cystine, lysine, arginine, and ornithine (109). The Franconi syndrome has been mentioned above (cf. 121). Other renal disorders accompanied by amino aciduria are Wilson's disease (109) and that involving galactosemia (122). Where plasma amino acid levels increase greatly in one or more components and spill over into the urine without evidence of renal damage, the cause may well be some hepatic dysfunction. Those components found to be particularly sensitive to even minor liver damage were cystine, taurine, β-aminoisobutyric acid, methylhistidine, phenylalanine, tyrosine, methionine, and ethanolamine. Of these, cystine, taurine, β-aminoisobutyric acid, and ethanolamine, with relatively high renal clearances, gave, as might be expected, striking changes on the urine chromatograms and less on the plasma chromatograms. On the other hand, those compounds with lower clearances, e.g., methionine, phenylalanine, and tyrosine, showed greater changes in the plasma. In one condition, phenylketonuria, one amino acid appears in the urine in high amount, namely phenylalanine, together with a phenylacetic acid derivative of glutamine (123). Patients with secondary neoplastic involvement of the liver, or obstructive jaundice, generally show no abnormal amino acid patterns (100). Renal damage due to exposure to heavy metals such as cadmium and uranium results in an enhanced urinary excretion of serine and threonine (124).

The amino acid levels in the plasma of dogs from which the liver had been completely removed showed a normal distribution on the chromatograms of all fifteen components observed, but each spot was greatly intensified, indicating an increase in concentration (125). This suggests that the liver ordinarily removes all these amino acids more or less uniformly, except possibly

CHROMATOGRAPHY

glutamine, the most abundant amino acid of plasma. Furthermore, chromatographic patterns of the muscle of these animals showed relatively little change from normal after hepatectomy, and it appeared likely that the liberation of amino acids from this major source occurred in about the same proportion after removal of the liver as before. The free amino acid pattern of the lymph is generally much the same as that of the serum (126).

9. Discovery of α-Aminoheptylic Acid. In the amino acids belonging to a homologous series, the partition coefficients change in a regular way with composition and polarity of the molecules. The presence of OH and COOH

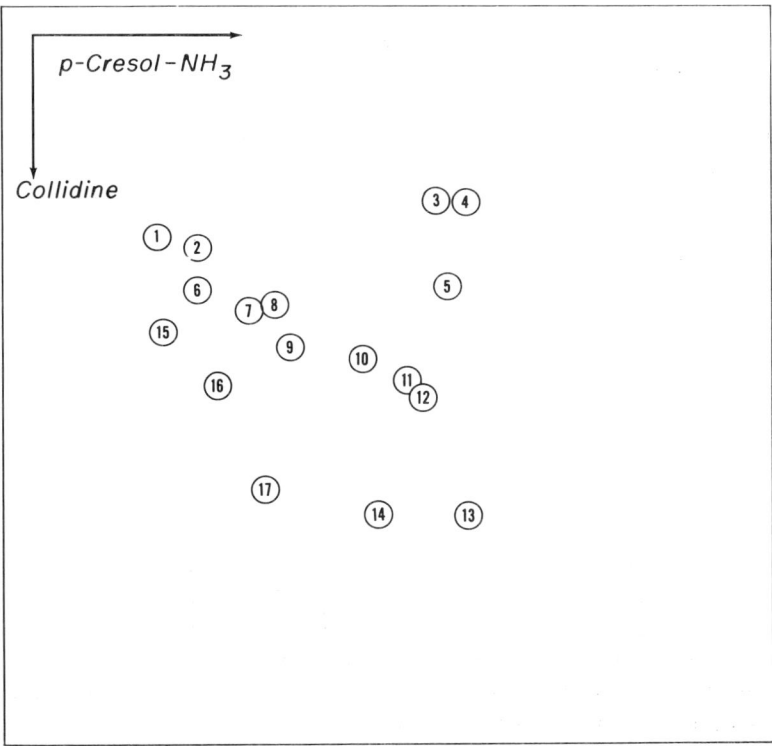

Figure 15-16. Hydrolysate of *E. coli.* 1, Aspartic acid; 2, glutamic acid; 3, lysine; 4, arginine; 5, proline; 6, glycine; 7, alanine; 8, histidine; 9, butyrine; 10, valine; 11, isoleucine; 12, leucine; 13, α-aminoheptylic acid; 14, phenylalanine; 15, serine; 16, threonine; 17, tyrosine. Polson, A., *Biochem. et Biophys. Acta*, **3**, 205 (1949).

groups would be expected to increase polarity and consequent solubility in the water phase, whereas addition of a CH_2 group would be expected to decrease polarity and hence solubility in water. Polson (37) employed these phenomena to indicate how the positions of amino acid spots which depend upon partition coefficients vary with composition in a homologous series, and through this type of analysis to observe the presence of a new amino acid. On the basis of two-dimensional chromatograms using phenol-water-ammonia and collidine-water, a known mixture of amino acids yielded data similar to those given in Figure 15-16. For comparison, and using *p*-cresol in place of phenol, a mixture of amino acids obtained by hydrolysis of *Escherichia coli* is portrayed in Figure 15-16. Spot 9 in the figure for the hydrolysate falls exactly on that characteristic of butyrine, whilst spot 13 occupies the position to be expected for a branched-chain isomer of α-aminoheptylic acid.

10. Discovery of α,ε-Diaminopimelic Acid. E. Work showed that, when hydrolysates of *Corynebacterium diphtheriae* were chromatographed on paper, the presence of a ninhydrin-reactive spot in a position ordinarily occupied by either cystine or ethanolamine-O-phosphoric acid made its appearance (127). Figure 15-17 shows its position in relation to the commonly occurring amino acids on a phenol and collidine two-dimensional chromatogram. The substance could be distinguished from cystine by its stability toward hydrogen peroxide (lack of cysteic acid formation) and from ethanolamine phosphoric acid by its neutral behavior during electrodialysis. The amino acid was isolated with the help of alumina columns, and proved to be the *meso*-form of α,ε-diaminopimelic acid. The curious behavior of the three available isomers of this amino acid on paper chromatograms, whereby the L-form on the one hand and the D, together with the L-D (*meso*) forms on the other, migrate separately and thus produce two spots on paper (128), is described elsewhere (Chapter 45). This property was of value in the subsequent isolation and separation of the L- and *meso*-forms from an *Escherichia coli* mutant (129).

The occurrence of α,ε-diaminopimelic acid in a large number of microorganisms was indicated by Work and Dewey (130) by paper chromatography of hydrolysates, using Whatman No. 4 paper, and phenol-water (NH_3 + HCN atmosphere) and collidine-lutidine-water. The hydrolysate was electrodialyzed, and the neutral fraction chromatographed. The electrodialysis procedure was essential in order to remove any ethanolamine phosphoric acid, and its completeness was assured by the absence of glutamic and aspartic acids from the paper chromatograms. A further test employed was to treat the electrodialyzed neutral fractions with H_2O_2 and molybdate to convert any cystine to cysteic acid. The final test was to match exactly the position of any enduring spot with a sample of authentic α,ε-diaminopimelic acid. The amino acid appears to be widely distributed among many bacteria (130, 131), but this distribution at the present time does not appear to be correlated with any obvious characteristics of the various organisms studied (130).

CHROMATOGRAPHY

A related compound which probably contains a single β-substituted OH group in the α,ε-diaminopimelic acid molecule was isolated by Wooley, Schaffner, and Braun (132) from the phytopathogenic toxin of *Pseudomonas tabaci*, the causative agent of the wildfire disease of tobacco. On paper chromatograms in phenol, this compound moved more slowly than did the

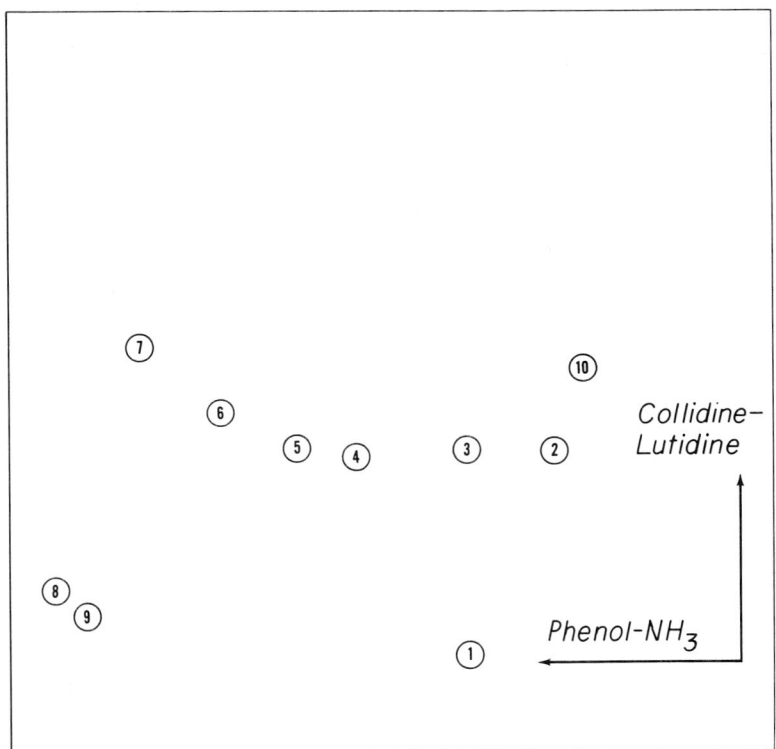

Figure 15-17. Position of α,ε-diaminopimelic acid. 1, Diaminopimelic acid; 2, aspartic acid; 3, glutamic acid; 4, glycine; 5, alanine; 6, leucine; 7, valine; 8, arginine; 9, lysine; 10 cysteic acid (on treatment of paper with H_2O_2). Work, E., *Biochem. J.*, **49**, 17 (1951).

unsubstituted α,ε-diaminopimelic acid; this behavior was suggestive of the presence of the hydroxyl group. The probable β-configuration of this hydroxyl group was revealed by the use of periodate, which caused the production of ammonia from the compound.

11. Discovery of γ-Methyleneglutamine and Related Compounds. Done and Fowden (133) chromatographed the sap of the groundnut plant and noted that, with phenol-NH$_3$, a strong, hitherto undescribed spot with $R_F = 0.66$ was produced, which yielded a uniquely colored orange-brown reaction with ninhydrin. On acid hydrolysis, a spot with $R_F = 0.30$ giving an intense yellow-brown color with ninhydrin appeared, and at the same time ammonia was liberated. Asparagine gives an orange-brown color with ninhydrin, and glutamine a purple color (35). The ratio of R_F values of asparagine to aspartic acid is 2.5, and that of glutamine to glutamic acid is 2.0 (35). Inasmuch as the ratio of the $R_{F'}$ values for the substance from the groundnut

TABLE 15-11

R_F Values of Amino Acids and Differences between Values of $\log_{10} [(1/R_F) - 1]$ for Various Pairs of Amino Acids (136)

Amino Acid	In Phenol–NH$_3$ R_F	$\log_{10}[(1/R_F)-1]$		In n-Butanol–Acetic Acid R_F	$\log_{10}[(1/R_F)-1]$	
Asparagine	0.44	0.11		0.07	1.09	
			0.61			0.26
Aspartic acid	0.16	0.72		0.13	0.83	
			0.93			0.42
β-Alanine	0.62	−0.21		0.28	0.41	
Glutamine	0.60	−0.17		0.10	0.95	
			0.58			0.26
Glutamic acid	0.28	0.41		0.17	0.69	
			0.93			0.44
γ-Aminobutyric acid	0.77	−0.52		0.36	0.25	
γ-Methyleneglutamine	0.67	−0.32		0.11	0.86	
			0.60			0.26
γ-Methyleneglutamic acid	0.34	0.28		0.20	0.60	
			0.96			0.46
γ-Amino-α-methylenebutyric acid	0.83	−0.68		0.42	0.14	

plant and for its derivative was 2.2, together with the fact that ammonia was liberated on acid hydrolysis, it was not inconceivable that these two substances stood in the relationship of amino acid amide to aminodicarboxylic acid. Isolation of the compound showed it to be γ-methyleneglutamine. The corresponding γ-methyleneglutamic acid was also shown to occur in the free state in the sap of this plant. Among the favorable circumstances for the discovery of the amino acid amide, the first since asparagine was found in 1806 (134) and glutamine in 1883 (135), was the high concentration in exudates of the plant, and the distinctive ninhydrin reaction.

The α-decarboxylated γ-methyleneglutamic acid, or γ-amino-α-methylenebutyric acid was also noted on paper chromatograms by Fowden and Done (136). On two-dimensional chromatography it could not be completely resolved from valine, but the distinctive color which it gave with ninhydrin,

CHROMATOGRAPHY

namely a yellow or orange brown, served to distinguish its position. That the spot was due to an unsaturated compound followed from the unusual color with ninhydrin, and that it was not an α-amino acid followed from its inability to complex with copper carbonate. The relationship of the compound to the dicarboxylic acid and to the corresponding γ-amide was deduced by an interesting series of calculations based on the theoretical considerations of Martin (101). Thus it may be predicted that for a particular solvent system a similar structural change brought about in any of the following three dicarboxylic acids, aspartic acid, glutamic acid, and γ-methyleneglutamic acid, would result in products such that the change in the function $\log_{10} [(1/R_F) - 1]$ calculated for the original and final molecules would be identical. Thus, when any of these compounds were converted to their ω-amide forms, $\log_{10} [(1/R_F) - 1]$ was altered by about 0.60 for phenol-NH$_3$ and by about 0.26 for the system butanol-acetic acid (Table 15-11).

12. Discovery of α-Aminopimelic Acid. Virtanen and Berg (137) noted

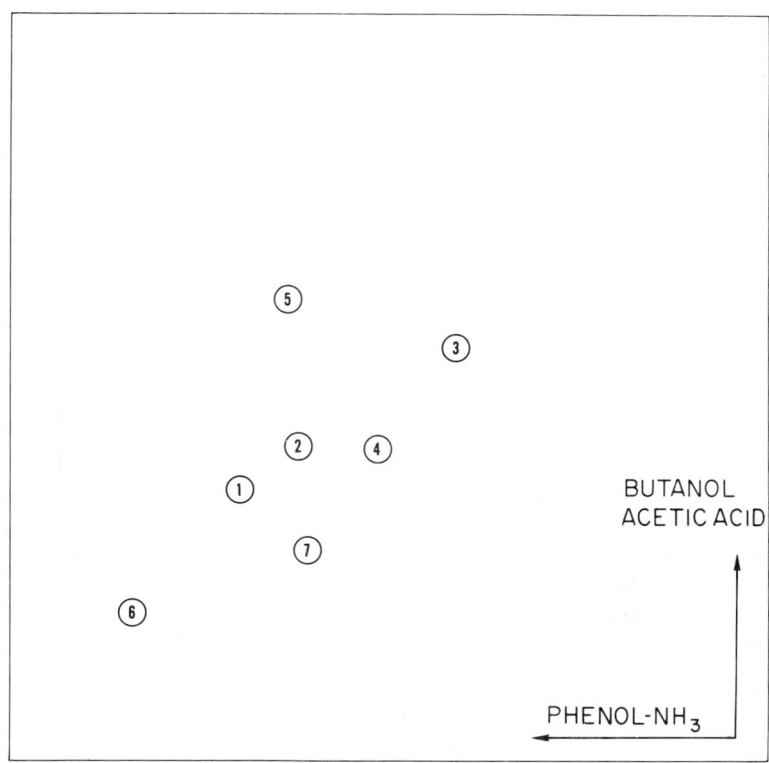

Figure 15–18. Position of α-aminopimelic acid in plant extract. 1, Alanine; 2, threonine; 3, aspartic acid; 4, glutamic acid; 5, ornithine, 6, γ-aminobutyric acid; 7, α-aminopimelic acid. Virtanen, A. I., and Berg, A.-M., *Acta Chem. Scand.*, **8**, 1085, 1725 (1954).

the presence of an unusual spot in two-dimensional paper chromatograms (phenol-ammonia and butanol–acetic acid) (Figure 15–18) of alcoholic extracts of the fern *Asplenium septentrionale*. This turned out to be due to α-aminopimelic acid, confirmed both by comparison with an authentic sample and by isolation and analysis (138). Still another, and related, amino acid was found in the extract of this plant, namely α-amino-γ-hydroxypimelic acid, which was isolated in crystalline form and identified (139).

13. Discovery of γ-Hydroxyglutamic Acid. Two-dimensional chromatograms with butanol-acetic acid and phenol-NH$_3$ of a 70% ethanolic extract

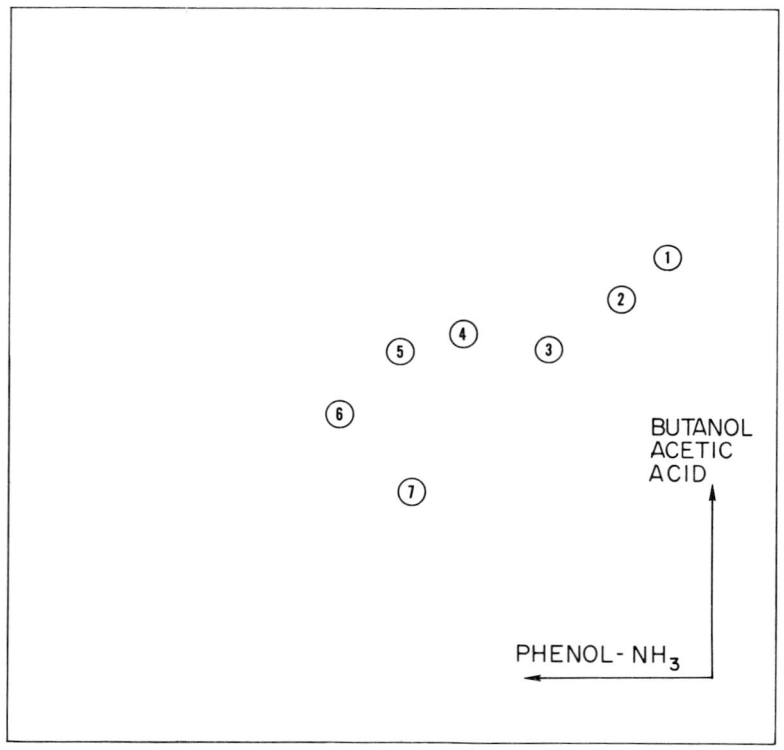

Figure 15–19. Position of γ-hydroxyglutamic acid in plant extract. 1, γ-Hydroxyglutamic acid; 2, aspartic acid; 3, glutamic acid; 4, serine; 5, glycine; 6, alanine; 7, tyrosine. Virtanen, A. I., and Hietala, P. K., *Acta Chem. Scand.*, **9**, 175 (1955).

of fresh *Phlox* showed a hitherto unknown ninhydrin-reactive spot just above that of aspartic acid (Figure 15–19) (140). Isolation of the compound by column chromatography, first on Amberlite IR-120 and then on Amberlite IR-4B, followed by reduction with HI-red phosphorus to glutamic acid indicated that the new compound was a hydroxyglutamic acid. Oxidation with $KMnO_4$-H_2SO_4 yielded aspartic acid. Comparison of the R_F value of the new compound in butanol–acetic acid with that of authentic β-hydroxyglutamic acid (0.06 and 0.09, respectively) indicated that these compounds were not identical. It appeared, therefore, quite probable that the new acidic compound must be γ-hydroxyglutamic acid.

14. Discovery of Pipecolic Acid. Steward and Thompson detected in plant materials some twenty ninhydrin-reactive substances which could not be identified with any of the known naturally occurring amino acids. Several

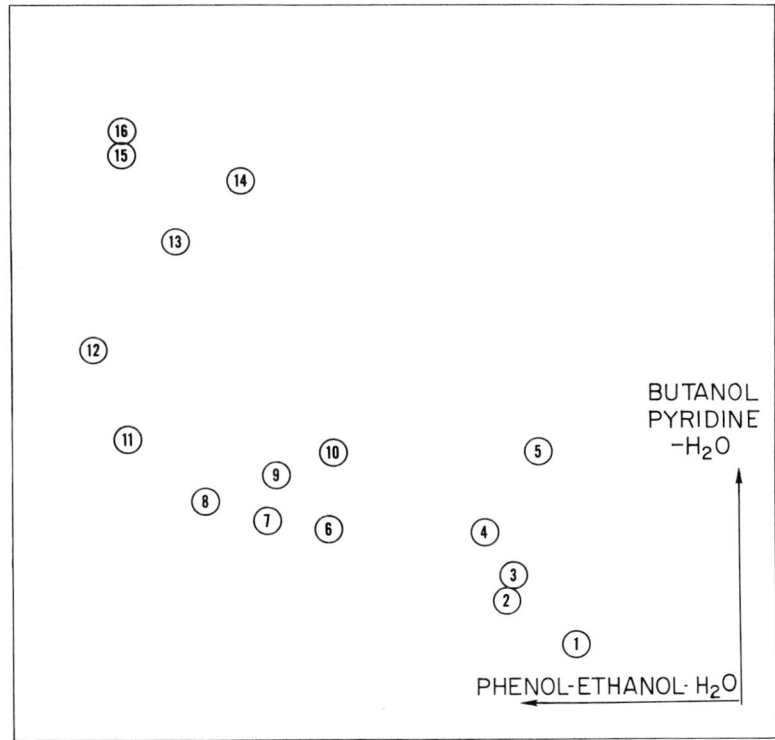

Figure 15–20. Position of pipecolic acid in clover extract. 1, Aspartic acid; 2, glutamic acid; 3, asparagine; 4, glycine, 5, serine; 6, glutamine; 7, β-alanine; 8, γ-aminobutyric acid; 9, alanine; 10, threonine; 11, proline; 12, pipecolic acid; 13, valine; 14, tyrosine; 15, phenylalanine; 16, leucine. Morrison, R. I., *Biochem. J.*, **53**, 474 (1953).

of these substances were found to be stable to acid hydrolysis and were, therefore, probably not peptides (141). Two groups of workers, namely, Zacharius, Thompson, and Steward (142) and Hulme and Arthington (143), observed the presence of a ninhydrin-reactive spot (purple color) on chromatograms of the alcohol-soluble nitrogen-containing fraction of plants, particularly that of the bean. The R_F values in phenol, collidine-lutidine, and butanol–acetic acid were, respectively, 0.90, 0.38, and 0.21 (142). A blue reaction with isatin on the chromatogram suggested that the substance was a piperidine or a pyrrolidine derivative. The substance was finally isolated by the use of an ion exchange resin (Zeo-Rex) and shown to be indistinguishable on the chromatogram in several solvents from authentic pipecolic acid. This compound is also present in the potato tuber and edible mushroom (142). On two-dimensional chromatograms using phenol-ethanol-water and *n*-butanol–pyridine–water, the spot for pipecolic acid appears between proline and phenylalanine (144).

Morrison (144) detected L-pipecolic acid in extracts of white clover leaves (*Trifolium repens*) (Figure 15–20), in which it occurs together with several other amino acids, on Whatman No. 1 paper, with the solvents phenol-ethanol-water (3 : 1 : 1) and *n*-butanol–pyridine–water (1 : 1 : 1). Fractionation of the extract by partition chromatography on columns of powdered cellulose, using a mixture of *n*-butanol with aqueous acetic or formic acid, led to isolation of the compound in crystalline form.

Another source of pipecolic acid has been noted in ethanol extracts of the pea plant (*Pisum sativum*) (145). Also found in such extracts was homoserine, which moved on Whatman No. 4 paper with phenol-NH_3 and *n*-butanol between glycine and alanine. The compound was isolated as the butyrolactone hydrochloride from Dowex 50 columns. Homoserine had previously been observed by Fling and Horowitz in extracts of a homoserineless mutant of *Neurospora* 51504 by paper chromatography in three different solvents (146).

15. Discovery of γ-Aminobutyric Acid. The presence of this amino acid in extracts of potato (147) and of yeast (148) has been reported (Figure 15–21). Almost simultaneously, three groups of workers independently observed the presence of this compound in extracts of brain (149–151). Awapara et al. (149) extracted the minced brain tissue of several species with ethanol and fractionated the extracts on starch columns. The elution was accomplished with *n*-butanol–acetic acid–water and was checked on paper chromatograms. The material isolated gave a single spot in several solvents and was compared with the behavior of various isomeric compounds (Figure 15–22). Roberts and Frankel (150) showed that an alcoholic brain extract yielded intense spots for aspartic acid, glutamic acid, glycine, taurine, glutamine, alanine, and for an unknown material which subsequently was demonstrated to be γ-aminobutyric acid. Proof of identity was afforded by comparison on paper with an authentic sample using three different water-saturated solvent systems, namely, *n*-butanol, phenol, and collidine-lutidine. The origin of this compound from glutamic acid was shown by using C^{14}-labeled glutamic acid, the mechanism most probably being an enzymic decarboxylation of the α-carboxyl group.

Udenfriend (151) employed the so-called "pipsyl" procedure (36) to identify γ-aminobutyric acid in extracts of brain tissue. The amino acids in the extraction mixture were converted to isotopic derivatives by reaction with I^{131}-labeled p-iodophenylsulfonyl chloride (pipsyl chloride). A measured

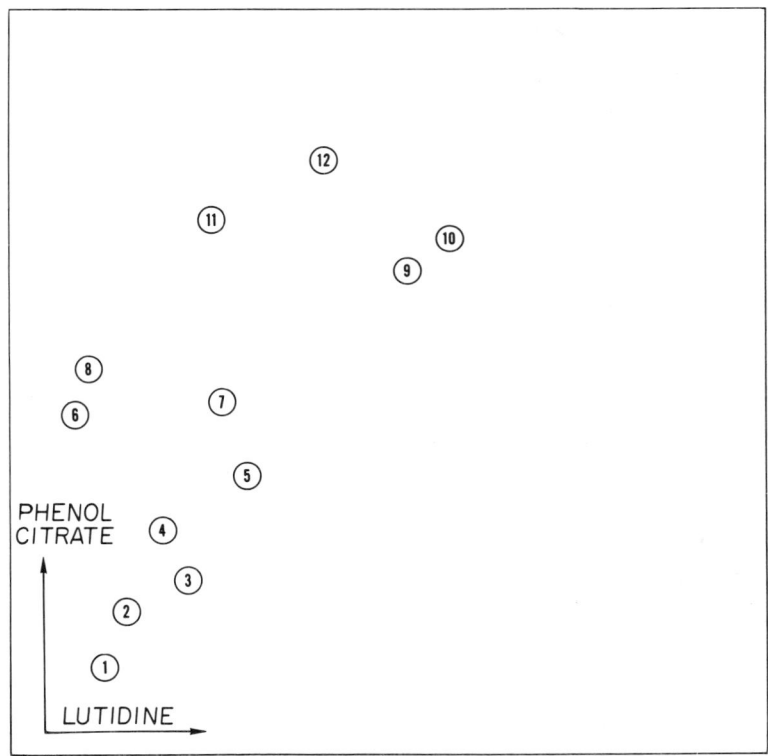

Figure 15–21. Extract of yeast. 1, Aspartic acid; 2, glutamic acid; 3, serine; 4, glycine; 5, threonine; 6, lysine; 7, alanine; 8, arginine; 9, valine; 10, leucine, isoleucine; 11, γ-aminobutyric acid; 12, proline. Reed, L. J., *J. Biol. Chem.*, **183**, 450 (1950).

amount of the S^{35}-labeled pipsyl derivative of an authentic sample of the suspected amino acid was added to the mixture and the sample purified and chromatographed on paper. The band of the suspected substance was located by S^{35} activity and cut into several thin transverse strips. The ratio of I^{131} to S^{35} in each strip was measured with a counter. An aluminum absorber was then employed to remove the greater part of the radiation from one of the two sources, e.g., about 60% of I^{131} radiation and nearly all the S^{35} radiation. The contribution of the radiation from each source was calculated from these data. A constant ratio of radiation from the two sources throughout the band indicated homogeneity, and the I^{131}-labeled compound could be identified as involving γ-aminobutyric acid. The pipsyl derivatives of the amino acids may be separated as a group on buffered Celite columns, those of the leucines, valine, phenylalanine, methionine, and proline leaving the column rapidly at pH 7.2, and those of glycine, alanine,

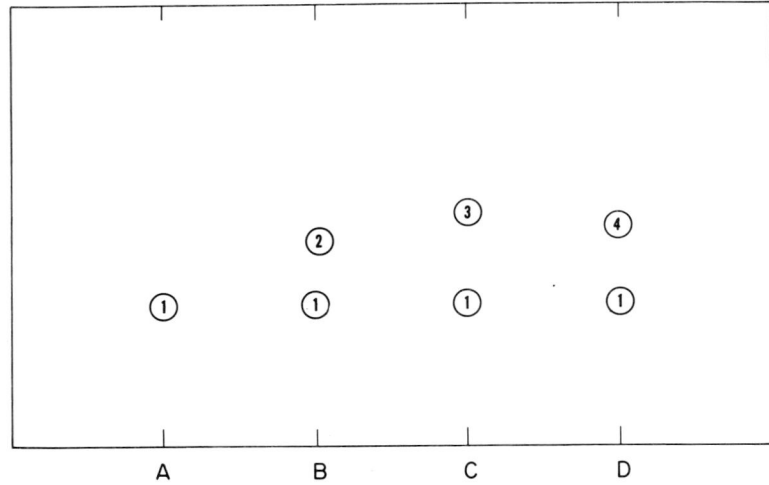

Figure 15–22. Mixtures of isolated γ-aminobutyric acid with various related amino acids. A, authentic γ-aminobutyric acid (1); B, with β-aminoisobutyric acid (2); C, with butyrine (3); and D, with α-aminoisobutyric acid. Solvent employed, 2:4-lutidine. Awapara, J., Landua, A. J., Fuerst, R., and Seale, B., *J. Biol. Chem.*, **187**, 35 (1950).

serine, and aspartic and glutamic acids running slowly at pH 5.2; in all cases the mobile phase was methyl ethyl ketone and chloroform saturated with buffer, whilst the stationary phase was buffer alone (152).

γ-Aminobutyric has been reported to occur at high levels, together with equally high levels of L-citrulline in extracts of the leaves and roots of the alder (*Alnus*) (153). Extracts of the roots contain (57), in addition, a good deal of arginine and ornithine.

16. Discovery of N-Methyl-α-amino Acids. Plattner and Nager (154, 155) obtained two peptide antibiotics from *Fusaria* which they named enniatin A and B. On acid hydrolysis, both forms yielded D-hydroxyisovaleric acid, but in addition the A form yielded N-methyl-L-isoleucine, whereas the B form yielded N-methyl-L-valine. The N-methylamino acids yielded a purple ninhydrin color on paper chromatograms which was much weaker than that observed with the same amount of the parent amino acids. When heated alone with ninhydrin *in vitro*, no color at all was produced with N-methyl-α-amino acids, and therefore the weak and variable color given on the paper chromatograms could have been attributed to some measure of hydrolysis of the N-methyl group under the conditions of chromatography. A more specific color reaction for N-methylated α-amino acids was based on the use of a mixture of *p*-nitrobenzoyl chloride and pyridine, whereby a red color

TABLE 15–12

R_F Values of N-Methyl-α-amino Acids (155)[a]

	Collidine	*s*-Collidine	*Tert*-Amyl Alcohol	*Sec*-Butanol	Benzyl Alcohol
Sarcosine	0.21	0.25	0.06	0.20	0.10
N-Methylvaline	0.40	0.36	0.17	0.37	0.39
N-Methylisoleucine	0.49	0.47	0.29	0.50	0.53
N-Methylleucine	0.51	0.48	0.35	0.54	0.59

[a] No essential difference in the use of Whatman No. 1 or No. 4 paper.

was obtained. Of all the α-amino acids tested, only glycine yielded some color with this mixture, namely an orange-brown. A third distinctive difference between the N-alkyl- and their parent α-amino acids lay in the fact that under ultraviolet illumination on paper the α-amino acids fluoresce, and may be discerned as faint, blue spots, whereas the N-substituted amino acids appear as absorbing, non-emitting dark spots. Gal and Greenberg (156) employed these phenomena to study the chromatographic behavior of the higher N-alkyl substituents of the α-amino acids, and noted that the R_F values in phenol and in collidine increased with the length of the substituent.

The R_F values of a few N-methylamino acids in several solvents were reported by Plattner and Nager (155) (Table 15–12). The L-configuration of the N-methylamino acids isolated from the antibiotics was deduced from the successful application of the Clough-Lutz-Jirgensons rule (Section 2–11).

The presence of N-methylamino acids in another antibiotic, actinomycin, was revealed independently by Brockmann and Grubhofer (157) and by Dalgliesh, Johnson, Todd, and Vining (158) who isolated N-methyl-L-valine and N-methylglycine (sarcosine) from hydrolysates of the polypeptide. Paper chromatograms run with standard solutions of amino acids agreed with those run on such hydrolysates (158).

17. Discovery of L-Allohydroxyproline. Extracts of the leaves of the sandal yielded a band on circular chromatograms which appeared to be derived from hydroxyproline (159) (Figure 15–23). Whatman No. 1 filter paper disks (25 cm. diameter) were employed, and the chromatograms developed with n-butanol-acetic acid-water solvent. The dried paper was sprayed with a solution of ninhydrin in aqueous acetone, and the amino acid bands, in which the characteristic yellowish colors of proline and hydroxyproline were prominent, made their appearance. Confirmatory tests included the isatin (blue with proline, lighter blue with hydroxyproline) (160),

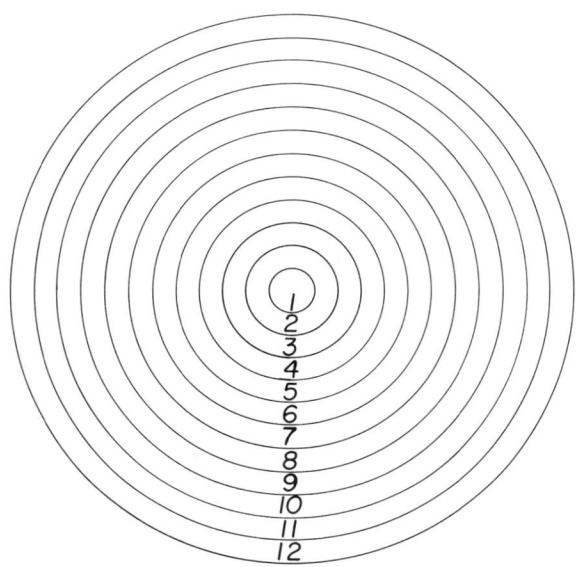

Figure 15–23. Position of L-allohydroxyproline in extract of *Sandal*. 1, Unidentified peptide; 2, lysine, ornithine; 3, histidine; 4, arginine; 5, allohydroxyproline; 6, glutamic acid; 7, alanine; 8, proline; 9, tyrosine; 10, valine, methionine; 11, phenylalanine; 12, leucine, isoleucine. Solvent employed, n-butanol-acetic acid-water (4:1:5 v/v). Radhakrishnan, A. N., and Giri, K. V., *Biochem. J.*, **58**, 57 (1954).

and isatin-*p*-dimethylaminobenzaldehyde (161) reactions. Fractionation of the extract on Zeo Karb by displacement chromatography, then on a column of basic copper carbonate and alumina, and finally over cellulose powder led to isolation of the hydroxyproline fraction which turned out to be the L-allo diastereomer (159).

18. Discovery of Lanthionine. This amino acid was isolated in 1942 from alkali-treated hair and from several other proteins after alkaline treatment (162), and its presence in small amounts in the tips of virgin wool has also been reported (163). It is not known to be a native constituent of proteins. However, it is present in the polypeptide antibiotic subtilin from *Bacillus subtilis* as the *meso* variety (164), together with a new type of sulfur-containing amino acid with apparently three asymmetric centers, and to

CHROMATOGRAPHY

which the designation of isocystathionine may tentatively be given. The structure of this compound was ascertained by Raney nickel desulfurization,

$$\text{HOOC}\underset{L}{\text{CH(NH}_2)}\text{CH}_2\text{SCH(CH}_3)\underset{D}{\text{CH(NH}_2)}\text{COOH}$$

followed by isolation of the products as the DNP derivatives of L-alanine and D-butyrine (165). Two separate bands, relating to these two compounds, were obtained on silica gel columns, the DNP-butyrine being the faster-moving.

A year later, Berridge, Newton, and Abraham (166) reported paper chromatographic studies on the hydrolysates of purified fractions of the polypeptide antibiotic nisin produced by *Streptococcus lactis*. The fractions were all high in sulfur, and the presence of methionine, lanthionine, and what appeared to be cystathionine was revealed on the chromatograms. Whether cystathionine or the iso-form which occurs in subtilin was present in the hydrolysate of nisin is not yet clear. A mixture of the eluates from the lanthionine and "cystathionine" spots when treated with Raney nickel and then chromatographed revealed the presence of alanine and butyrine (166). After lanthionine and authentic cystathionine were added to the nisin hydrolysate no new spots appeared on paper. If, as seems probable, both nisin and subtilin contain lanthionine and isocystathionine, the chief difference between the two polypeptides as far as the sulfur-containing amino acids is concerned lies in the presence of methionine in nisin and its absence in subtilin. The presence of methionine which overlaps valine on the paper chromatogram of nisin (Figure 15–24) was revealed by converting it to the sulfone (166).

19. Cyclic Imino Acids. Among the compounds of this category known in nature are proline, pipecolic acid, baikiain, hydroxyproline, and 5-hydroxypipecolic acid (Chapters 29, 35, and 46). The latter two compounds may each exist in two diastereomeric modifications. Dates are a particularly rich source of these imino acids (167, 168). Methods of separating these compounds on paper chromatograms were developed by Piez, Irreverre, and Wolff (168), employing two-dimensional chromatography (Schleicher and Schull No. 598) with *t*-butanol–formic acid (88%)–water (70 : 15 : 15) as the first solvent, and *t*-amyl alcohol–2:4-lutidine–water (178 : 178 : 114) as the second solvent. Color was developed by a solution of ninhydrin in glacial acetic acid, whereby in natural light the hydroxyprolines appeared pinkish yellow fading to brown, proline and baikiain yellow (the former fading to brown), and pipecolic acid and 5-hydroxypipecolic acid purple fading to brown. In ultraviolet light, proline, baikiain, and hydroxyproline fluoresced brick-red, the others a brighter red. All the cyclic imino acids of course gave a blue to green-blue color with isatin. Of particular interest was the fact that the diastereomers of hydroxyproline and of 5-hydroxypipecolic acid could be

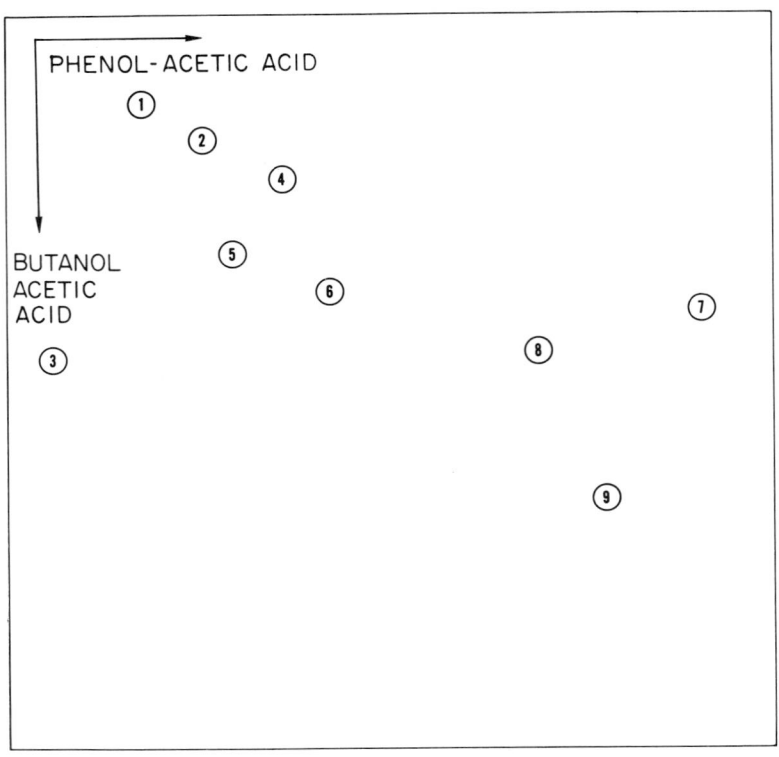

Figure 15–24. Hydrolyzed nisin. 1, Lanthionine; 2, "cystathionine"; 3, aspartic acid; 4, lysine, histidine; 5, glycine; 6, alanine; 7, proline; 8, valine, methionine; 9, leucine, isoleucine. Berridge, N. J., Newton, G. G. F., and Abraham, E. P., *Biochem. J.*, **52**, 529 (1952).

clearly separated, in both cases the allo form moving more slowly in the basic solvent. A tracing of a paper chromatogram of the cyclic imino acids in the presence of a number of the common amino acids is given in Figure 15–25 (168). A separation of the diastereomers of 5-hydroxypipecolic acid has also been achieved by Hegarty (168), who employed a collidine-lutidine solvent with Whatman No. 3 paper; the slower-moving, ninhydrin-reactive spot was that of the allo form. Elution of the spots with 30% ethanol resulted in the isolation of the two diastereomers in the pure, crystalline state.

20. Tissue Extractives. Through the use of the newly perfected nitrous acid procedure for amino nitrogen, Van Slyke in 1913 was able to demonstrate the presence of free amino acids in various tissues of the dog (169). He extracted the freshly minced tissue with boiling water and precipitated the

CHROMATOGRAPHY

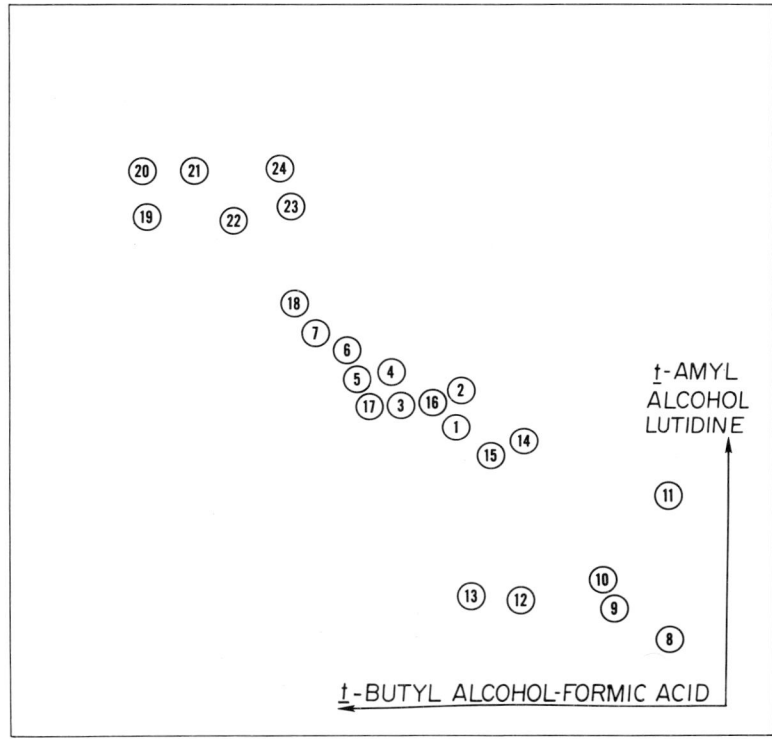

Figure 15-25. Cyclic imino acids together with the common amino acids, on S. and S. No. 598 paper. 1, Allohydroxyproline; 2, hydroxyproline; 3, allo-5-hydroxypipecolic acid; 4, 5-hydroxypipecolic acid; 5, proline; 6, baikiain; 7, pipecolic acid; 8, cystine; 9, lysine; 10, arginine; 11, histidine; 12, aspartic acid; 13, glutamic acid; 14, serine; 15, glycine; 16, threonine; 17, alanine; 18, valine; 19, isoleucine; 20, leucine; 21, phenylalanine; 22, methionine; 23, tyrosine; and 24, tryptophan. First dimension with t-butyl alcohol-formic acid(88%)-water (70:15:15 v/v) was employed over 18 hours; second dimension with t-amyl alcohol-lutidine-water (178:178:114 v/v) was employed over 24 hr. Piez, K. A., Irreverre, F., and Wolff, H. L., *J. Biol. Chem.*, **223**, 687 (1956).

protein and higher polypeptides in the extract by addition of ethanol. The final filtrate was subjected to volumetric nitrous acid analysis before and after hydrolysis with HCl (Table 15-13). The data in the table are comparable only when each tissue extractive was studied before and after refluxing HCl treatment, and they reveal that the greater part of the amino nitrogen in such extractives arises from the amino acids present. In the fasting animal, this amino acid level tended to increase. Van Slyke made the further interesting observation that the intravenous administration of amino acids was followed by a greater increase in the free amino acid content of the liver than in that of any other tissue, and that this rise in turn was followed shortly by a decrease to the normal level characteristic of the tissue. It was believed that the amino acids so administered were not incorporated into the protein, but formed during the period of their residence within the tissue a more or less loose form of molecular association. The four consecutive papers written by Van Slyke in this early issue of the *Journal of Biological Chemistry* (169) are models of scientific insight and technical skill.

TABLE 15-13

Amino Nitrogen in Aqueous and Alcohol-Cleared Extracts of Various Tissues of the Dog (169)

Mg. N per 100 g. of Fresh Tissue

Tissue	Free NH_2^-	NH_2^- after Hydrolysis with HCl
Muscle	38	61
Heart	37	61
Liver	61	89
Spleen	53	68
Kidney	65	77

The presence of glycine and glutamine was noted later in the aqueous extracts of muscle (170), but it was not until paper chromatographic methods were well developed that an identification of the free amino acid patterns in tissue fluids began to emerge. There appeared to be a burst of activity in these investigations at about 1948–1949 with studies of extractives of plant and of animal tissues by several groups of workers, during the course of which many new amino acids and related compounds were discovered (see above). Not only did each plant and animal tissue yield a different pattern for the free amino acids, but in the particular case of the plant tissues the patterns appeared to change at different seasons of the year (cf. 153).

The pattern of the free amino acids in the alcohol-soluble fraction apparently bears no relation to that of the nearly exclusively protein-bound amino acids in the alcohol-insoluble or protein fraction (147). Moreover, amino acids that are never found as constituents of proteins, i.e., β-alanine, α-aminopimelic acid, etc., occur in such extracts. An analysis of the amino acid composition of the alcohol-soluble and alcohol-insoluble fractions of the potato tuber is given in Table 15-14. It is likely that the free amino acids found in animal and in plant tissue extractives are not derived from the proteins of these tissues but represent metabolic intermediates. They are not transient phenomena, for the free amino acid pattern in animal tissues, at least, is quite constant and unique for each tissue; they are, rather, participants in a metabolic steady state.

Aqueous or ethanolic extractives of liver yielded paper chromatographic evidence for the presence of glutathione, aspartic acid, glutamic acid, ethanolamine, serine, glycine, glutamine, alanine, β-alanine, lysine, proline, valine, leucine, phenylalanine, and tyrosine (171, 172). In addition, taurine and glycerylphosphoryl ethanolamine were found in such extractives, and, in

TABLE 15–14

Composition of the Alcohol-Soluble and Alcohol-Insoluble Fractions of the Potato Tuber as Determined by Paper Chromatographic Methods (147)

Amino Compound	Alcohol-Soluble, μg. per g.	Alcohol-Insoluble after Hydrolysis, μg. per g.
Aspartic acid	106.6	708
Glutamic acid	178.2	837
Serine	66.2	213
Glycine	27.6	319
Asparagine	1374.0	–
Threonine	100.7	176
Alanine	132.0	353
Glutamine	3020.0	–
Lysine	63.2	458
Arginine	356.2	341
Methionine	82.8	95.4
Proline	Trace	201
Valine	243.4	450
Leucine plus isoleucine	104.4	1005
Phenylalanine	138.0	726
Tyrosine	121.4	230
γ-Aminobutyric acid	299.8	0.0
Ammonia	63.2	155.3

adult pig liver, these compounds formed the major part of the soluble nitrogen. Where glutamine might interfere with the identification of citrulline, the extract can be either briefly refluxed with HCl to convert the glutamine to the far-removed glutamic acid, or heated at 100° for several hours to convert the glutamine to pyrrolidonecarboxylic acid which does not react with ninhydrin (cf. 173).

A careful and skilful survey of the free amino acid patterns of a number of normal tissues and tumors of mice has been performed by Roberts and his co-workers (172, 174). Figure 15–26 represents a model of the two-dimensional chromatograms for the mixture of amino acids found in varying proportions in all the tissue extracts studied. Each of the normal tissues was found to possess a unique free amino acid pattern, but the pattern of all of the tumors studied was practically identical for each tumor, regardless of

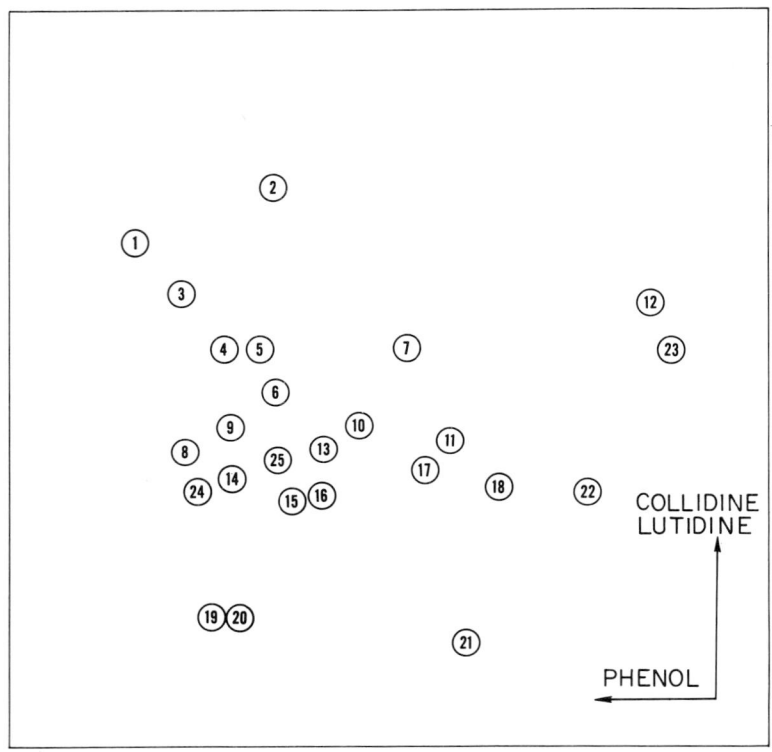

Figure 15–26. Model chromatogram. 1, Phenylalanine; 2, tyrosine; 3, leucine, isoleucine; 4, valine; 5, ethanolamine; 6, methionine sulfone; 7, taurine; 8, proline; 9, butyrine; 10, threonine; 11, serine; 12, cysteic acid; 13, alanine; 14, histidine; 15, β-alanine, glycerylphosphoryl ethanolamine; 16, glutamine; 17, glycine; 18, glutamic acid; 19, arginine; 20, lysine; 21, ethanolamine phosphate; 22, aspartic acid; 23, oxidized glutathione; 24, γ-aminobutyric acid; 25, hydroxyproline. Roberts, E., and Borges, P. R. F., *Cancer Research*, **15**, 697 (1955).

etiology or histogenesis. These findings are in accord with one of the fundamental generalizations of biochemical cancer research, namely, that tumors of all sorts converge to a common type of tissue, whereas normal tissues are highly differentiated (175).

Table 15–15 consists of data on the major free amino acid components of various mouse tissues according to the chromatograms of Roberts and co-workers (172, 174). Skin contains a high proportion of free amino acids,

TABLE 15-15

Major Amino Acids in Ethanolic Peroxide-Treated Extracts of Various Mouse Tissues as Revealed on Paper Chromatograms[a]

(From data of Roberts et al. (172, 174).)

Amino Acid	Skin	Muscle	Brain	Lymph Nodes	Liver	Testes	Growing Tumors	Regressing Tumors
Taurine	++	++	++	++	++	−	++	++
Serine	++	−	+	−	−	−	+	−
Glycine	++	−	++	+	+	−	++	+
Glutamic acid	++	−	++	−	++	+	++	+++
Alanine	++	+	++	+	++	−	++	++
Glutamine	++	−	++	−	+	−	−	+
Arginine	++	−	−	−	−	−	−	−
Lysine	++	−	−	−	−	−	−	−
Leucine-isoleucine	++	−	−	−	−	−	+	+
Valine	++	−	−	−	−	−	++	++
Aspartic acid	+	−	++	++	−	+	+	++
γ-Aminobutyric acid	−	−	++	−	−	−	−	−
Cystine	−	−	+	−	−	−	−	−

[a] Doubly crossed amino acids present in highest amount, except for triply crossed (i.e., glutamic acid in regressing tumors); singly crossed amino acids in lesser but still very appreciable amounts.

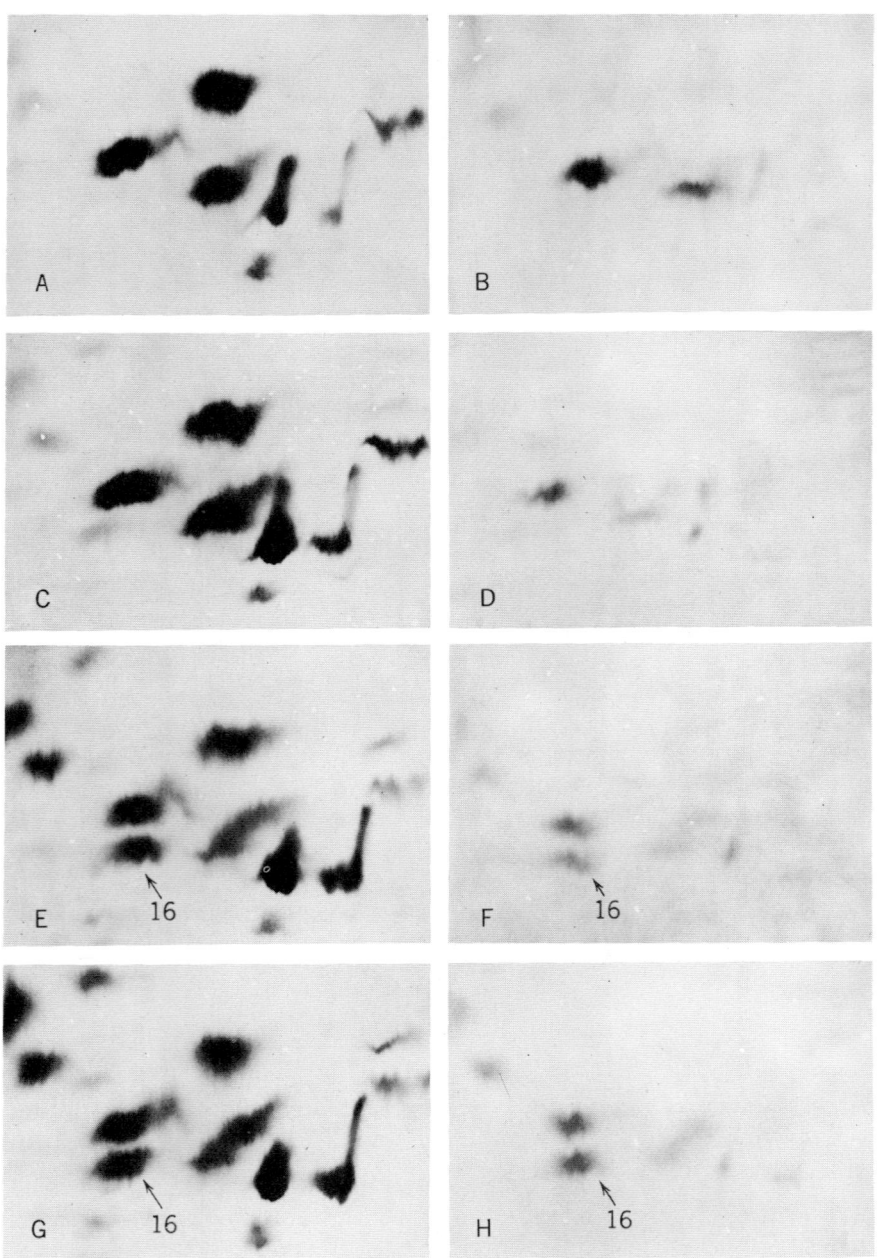

Figure 15-27. Position of glutamine [16] in extracts of cells and fluid of ascites form of tumor C1498 in mice. Figures A and B based on cells and fluid in susceptible mice at 7 days after transplantation; figures C, E, and G based on extracts of cells, and figures D, F, and H based on fluid, in resistant mice at 6, 8, and 9 days, respectively, after transplantation. Roberts, E., and Borges, P. R. F., *Cancer Research*, **15,** 697 (1955).

of which glutamine and γ-aminobutyric acid are worthy of note. There are fewer free amino acids in the cells of muscle, lymph nodes, liver, and testes. The growing tumors included those derived originally from the normal tissues studied, e.g., squamous cell carcinoma, lymphoma, hepatoma, interstitial cell tumor, as well as various sarcomas, and a spontaneous mammary tumor; all but the last were transplants, and all grew readily in the hosts.

An interesting application of this type of study to the problem of the regressing tumor was undertaken by Roberts and Borges (174). The C1498 leukemia implanted subcutaneously grows progressively in the C57BL/10-H-2(b) strain of mouse, with fatal termination. In a resistant subline of this strain of mouse, C57BL/10-H-2(d), the tumor grows at first and then regresses. The solid tumor may be converted to an ascites form by intraperitoneal injection, and the biological characteristics of the ascites cells follow the same sequence of events in the susceptible and resistant sublines as does the solid tumor.

The free amino acid patterns of the solid and ascites forms of the C1498 tumor were similar and practically identical with those of all other kinds of tumors, and in the susceptible mice were essentially constant until shortly before the death of the animals when the glutamic acid content appreciably diminished (174). For the first eight days after implantation of the solid tumor into the resistant mice, while the tumor grew progressively, the free amino acid pattern was identical with that noted for the same tumor growing in the susceptible subline. After this period, however, as the tumor progressively regressed, the glutamic and aspartic acid content increased, and glutamine, a component ordinarily undetectable in the extracts of any tumor, made its appearance. The ascitic fluid of the mice contained only alanine in appreciable amounts, with some detectable glycine, whilst glutamine was completely absent. In the resistant mice, the ascites cells showed increasing concentrations of glutamic and aspartic acids, whereas glutamine, hitherto undetectable in both cells and ascitic fluid, made its appearance at increasingly higher levels in both media.

Figure 15-27 delineates the chromatograms of extracts of cells and fluid of the ascites form of tumor C1498.

21. Thyroid Hormone Intermediates and Autoradiography. The thyroid gland contains a number of iodinated derivatives of tyrosine in addition to inorganic iodide. Until the advent of paper chromatography, the presence only of thyroxine (176) and of diiodotyrosine (177) had been well-established. The use of paper chromatograms, and the greatly increased sensitivity brought about by the employment of I^{131} labeling, resulted in the discovery of a number of iodinated intermediates in thyroid hydrolysates. Some of these intermediates occur in very low amounts, and, although they may be demonstrated by autoradiographic observation, their identification on paper is best accomplished by the addition of known carriers. The general procedures are as follows. Experimental animals are injected with iodide containing I^{131} and at a selected time are sacrificed and the thyroid or other tissues removed and hydrolyzed in alkali. Chemically detectable amounts of carrier iodinated tyrosine derivatives are added to the mixture, and the latter is chromatographed on Whatman No. 1 paper by either ascending or descending techniques. Either ninhydrin or diazotized sulfanilic acid may be used to locate the spots. The advantage of the latter reagent over the former lies in its relative specificity for phenolic substances, of which the greater number of the thyroid hormone derivatives are comprised. A recent variant of this procedure is the use of diazotized N'N'-diethylsulfanilamide (178); the colors obtained by the use of this reagent are purple for the diphenolic ethers such as thyroxine, and orange for such simpler phenols as tyrosine. Inorganic iodide spots may be stained with aqueous palladium chloride (179). The paper chromatogram is applied to a sheet of X-ray film and inserted into a cassette for exposure. Comparison of the blackened spots on the film with the colored spots on the paper leads to identification. Certain of the iodinated compounds occur in very low amounts, and the exposure of the film may necessarily be so prolonged in order to see them that other areas, arising from more abundant constituents, became overexposed. Under such conditions, a series of autoradiographs at varying periods of exposure is employed to distinguish clearly those areas requiring longer or shorter periods of exposure.

A relatively specific and sensitive locator of spots of the iodinated tyrosines is that recently developed by Bowden, Maclagan, and Wilkinson (180) in the form of a mixture of ceric sulfate and arsenious acid (see Chapter 38). The minimum detectable quantities on Whatman No. 1 paper are: for diiodo, 0.1 μg.; for triiodo, 0.025 μg.; and for tetraiodo, 0.01 μg. Solvent mixtures employed for the separation of the iodinated tyrosines have included butanol-dioxane-ammonia (181), and isopentanol–6N NH$_4$OH (182).

The early chromatographic studies by Fink, Dent, and Fink (183) led to the detection in thyroid hydrolysates of thyroxine, diiodotyrosine, inorganic iodide, and several unidentified iodine-containing compounds. One of the latter was subsequently identified as the abundant monoiodotyrosine (184–186), another as diiodothyronine (187), and still another as triiodothyronine (188, 189). A chromatogram after Gross and Pitt-Rivers (188)—of a butanol extract of a hydrolysate of the rat thyroid glands—is described in Figure 15–28. The non-thyroglobulin fraction of the thyroid apparently also contains some thyroxine (179, 190), monoiodotyrosine, and diiodotyrosine (179, 190, 191). The predominant carrier of blood iodine is thyroxine (192, 193), although some triiodothyronine has also been observed (194). A fuller description of thyroxine and related compounds is deferred to Chapter 38.

Synthetic procedures for I^{131}-labeled monoiodotyrosine and diiodotyrosine

CHROMATOGRAPHY

have been carried out in which the separation of the reactants was accomplished on S. and S. No. 589 paper chromatograms (195). *n*-Butanol–acetic acid–water was used in one direction, and water-saturated phenol in the other. A semiquantitative estimation of the products was performed by eluting the spots in basic ethanol and measuring the extinction coefficient

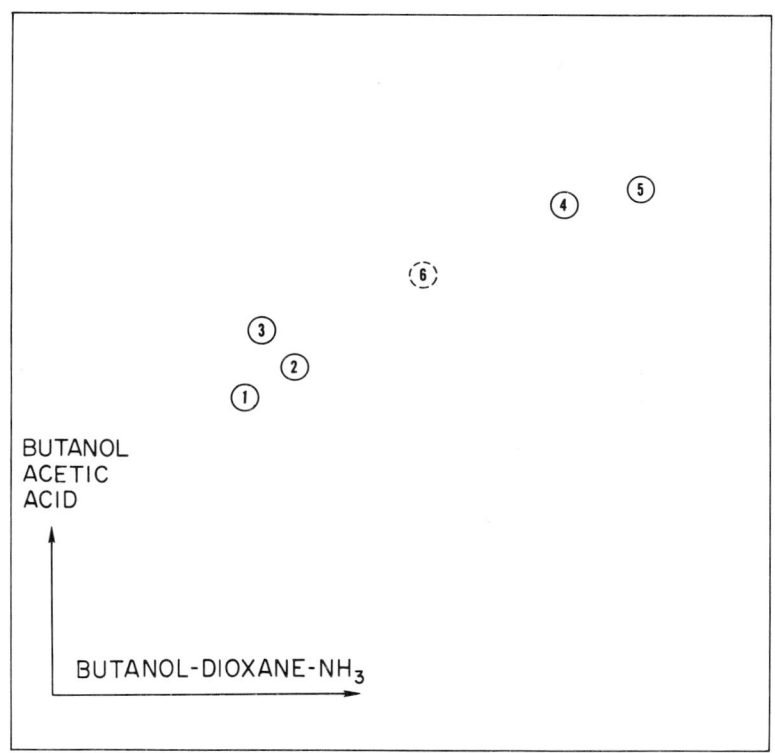

Figure 15–28. Thyroid tryptic hydrolysate. 1, Tyrosine; 2, monoiodotyrosine; 3, diiodotyrosine; 4, thyroxine; 5, triiodothyronine; 6, iodide (visualized on autoradiograph). Gross, J., and Pitt-Rivers, R., *Biochem. J.*, **53**, 645 (1953).

spectrophotometrically at 315 mμ. The possible occurrence in acid solution of exchange reactions between radioactive inorganic iodide and the organic iodine compounds due to release of iodine from the iodide (179, 196) has been partially prevented by the use of thiosulfate (196) and of alkaline solvents.

22. Procedures for Paper Chromatography. QUANTITATIVE ASPECTS OF CHROMATOGRAPHY. Up to this point, the qualitative, or at best semiquantitative (e.g., rough visual estimation of intensity of the ninhydrin color), aspects of paper chromatography have been portrayed. Many attempts have been made to estimate quantitatively the separated amino acids on paper chromatograms with some degree of success, although it seems probable since the introduction of quantitative column chromatography by Stein and Moore that these methods may diminish in use. However, although the paper chromatogram lacks high precision, it does possess the advantages of speed, economy, and ease of operation.

There are two general procedures whereby the amount of an amino acid on a given spot on the chromatogram may be determined, and these involve (a) measurements on the paper, and (b) measurements on the eluate of the spot after the latter has been cut out from the paper. Losses of amino acid due to drying of the paper chromatograms at higher temperatures have frequently been noted (cf. 197), and the part played by the interaction of reducing agents in the cellulose with the amino acids in contributing both to such losses and to the fluorescent behavior of amino acids on paper has been commented upon by several investigators (cf. 198). Procedure (b) is the simplest and most direct. The spots on the paper may be located by fluorescence under an ultraviolet lamp, or lightly or heavily developed with ninhydrin or other coloring agents, and then cut out from the paper with a pair of scissors and eluted with aqueous alcohol or acetone. The color may then be developed and matched in a photometer against any number of standards (199–204) to yield the amount in the eluate or fraction thereof (Section 11-4). A ready check on the identity of the material eluted, provided no color has been developed previously on the paper, is possible by refluxing with HCl to exclude the presence of hydrolyzable peptide, by quantitative CO_2 manometry with ninhydrin to exclude the presence of ω-amino acids or peptides (205, cf. 206), or by specific enzymic (207) or colorimetric reactions unique to the compound under investigation (cf. 38 and Part VI) (50). Inasmuch as the paper is not entirely inert, nor free of extractable, interfering substances (50), a suitable control or series of controls is necessary.

One of the earliest elution procedures involved treatment of the eluate with a mixture of secondary phosphate and copper phosphate, whereby the amino acid went into solution as the copper complex. This reaction was based essentially on the Pope and Stevens analytical procedure (208). After filtration, copper was determined in the filtrate polarographically (209), colorimetrically by the use of diethyldithiocarbamate (210), or radiometrically by the use of Cu^{64} (211), and the amino acid calculated therefrom. An accuracy of $\pm 2\%$ for 2 μg. of α-amino nitrogen was claimed for the radiometric procedure (211). Impurities in the paper which inhibit copper complex formation have been noted (212). It is not uncommon to encounter difficulties in obtaining reproducible measurements with ninhydrin (cf. 212). The ninhydrin reagent was therefore modified in a number of ways, e.g., by adding methyl Cellosolve, stannous chloride, and citrate buffer at pH 5 (213), by adding hydrindantin and acetate buffer (214), and by the use of cupric ions (215, 216), which ultimately resulted in fairly satisfactory measurements. A careful study of the ninhydrin reaction with amino acids on paper was made by Steward and co-workers (203), who recommended the following. The paper was washed successively with HCl, NaOH, water, and phosphate buffer at pH 7.0 and finally dried. The developed chromatogram was air-dried and sprayed with 2% ninhydrin in 95% ethanol containing collidine and lutidine. The color was developed in a CO_2 atmosphere, the spots cut out, the color extracted with 50% ethanol, and read with a 570-mμ filter. One of the most complete descriptions of the ninhydrin procedure is that by Giri and co-workers (52). Their procedure measures amounts of amino acids in the range 2–12 μg., and an accuracy of ± 5% is claimed. The method is based on the development of color of the amino acid bands by spraying the chromatogram with ninhydrin reagent, cutting out the colored bands individually, eluting with 75% ethanol containing copper sulfate, and measuring the intensity against known standards. The circular chromatographic technique was employed in these studies, but the analytical method could be applied to the strip technique as well. The color of the amino acids with ninhydrin and copper was red, except for proline and hydroxyproline, which yielded a yellow-colored complex. A method which does not depend upon the vagaries of color development is that by Slotta and Primosigh (205) in which the amino acid streaks (some 2 cm. in length) on Whatman No. 3 paper are eluted with dilute HCl, which serves the purpose of complete elution and reduction of the paper carbonate blank. The eluate is treated with ninhydrin to liberate quantitatively carbon dioxide which is then measured exactly by manometry (Chapter 12). The error was found to be less than ± 5%, and amino acid mixtures based on hydrolysates of 12–15 mg. of proteins could readily be employed. Still another method which does not use direct colorimetry is that by Klatzkin (217) which consisted simply in digesting the amino acid spot, after removal of ammonia from the paper, with hot sulfuric acid, then measuring the liberated ammonia from the amino acid by the Conway microdiffusion method.

Procedure (a) above, which involves various techniques of measuring the amino acid spot without removing it from the paper, has the general virtues of speed of operation and suitability for large numbers of routine analyses (50). Visual approximations have been made by comparing the color of the ninhydrin-stained spots on the paper with that of standard amounts of amino acids chromatographed simultaneously with the unknowns (218–220). A dilution method has been suggested which is based on the estimation of amino acid needed to give a barely detectable ninhydrin reaction which is then compared with that aliquot of a descending series of concentrations of test solution of the same amino acid (221). These techniques because of subjective and other hazards (e.g., background color) are certainly no better than ±10%. When a series of dilutions of an amino acid is employed on a unidimensional paper chromatogram, the size of each spot generally diminishes in a regular fashion with the dilution. By determining the size of the spot, a measure of the amino acid level may be attained (cf. 222). Thus, when the extension of the spot in the direction of solvent flow is measured, there appears to be a linear relation between the length of the (ovoid-shaped) spots and the logarithm of the amino acid concentration (223, 224). Again, the area of the spot as measured by means of a planimeter, or by actual weighing of the cut-out spot, appears to be linearly related to the logarithm of the amino acid concentration.

Other techniques involve measurement of the total color of the spot by light-transmission measurements through the paper (225–228). The usual procedure is to run one-dimensional chromatograms with a variety of alcoholic solvents, each alcoholic mixture separating a particular group of amino acids, and subsequently develop the ninhydrin color. In some cases proline and hydroxyproline are developed with isatin (cf. 227). The paper is cut into strips along the line of solvent flow, and each strip is scanned along this length with a transmission densitometer. The average color densities, corrected for the average absorption by the paper, are plotted and the areas representative of each amino acid determined. Standard curves for each amino acid provide the basis of comparison and determination of concentration. The transparency of the paper can be improved by various devices (229, 230). A high order of accuracy has been claimed for this technique (some 3–4%); a comparison of the results obtained with those derived from the use of starch columns is given in Table 15-16 (cf. 231, 232).

Block (50) and others (233–235) noted that the maximum color density of each amino acid spot was proportional to the concentration of material in the entire spot when aliquots of equal size were applied to the paper. The concentration of the amino acid in the spot could therefore be ascertained by comparison with the maximum color density of the standard amino acid solutions. This formed the basis of a rapid method for amino acid analysis of proteins (cf. 38, 71) which employed two-dimensional chromatograms.

Wieland and co-workers introduced still another quantitative procedure (236, 237) which was designated retention analysis, and which was based on the principle that, when strips of filter paper containing amino acids already developed with some solvent are exposed to a solution containing copper acetate, the latter will rise in the paper, react with the amino acid, and pass beyond it, leaving behind a triangular-shaped area above the spot. The area was located by spraying the paper with dithiodicarbamic acid; this step revealed that the triangular area was copper-free, i.e., the amino acid by complexing with the copper retained a part thereof whilst the rest moved on. The size of this area was proportional to the concentration of the amino acid.

TABLE 15-16
Amino Acid Composition of Bovine Serum Albumin
Grams Amino Acid Residue per 100 g. Protein

Amino Acid	Direct Paper Chromatography (227)	Starch Column (231)
Glycine	1.42	1.38
Serine	3.67	3.51
Threonine	5.04	4.95
Alanine	5.41	4.99
Phenylalanine	5.69	5.87
Leucine	10.25	10.58
Isoleucine	2.24	2.25
Aspartic acid	9.15	9.44
Glutamic acid	15.25	14.49
Valine	4.68	5.01
Methionine	0.74	0.71
Tyrosine	4.64	4.56
Histidine	3.63	3.54
Proline	3.68	4.00
Arginine	5.38	5.29
Lysine	11.25	11.25
Cysteine	5.5	5.54
Tryptophan	0.53[a]	0.53[a]
Total	98.1	97.9

[a] Brand (232).

The method is obviously applicable only to amino acids which form copper complexes, and is inapplicable in the presence of such polyvalent ions as phosphate or citrate, which would also complex with copper. A procedure employing Cu^{64}-containing copper acetonylacetate and measurement of radioactivity by Geiger counter scanning at the sites of complex formation was reported somewhat earlier by Wieland et al. (238).

A highly accurate procedure employing the "pipsyl" derivatives of amino acids suitable both for identification and quantitative determination (36, 151) has been described above. The procedure has been further refined for quantitative analysis of protein hydrolysates, corresponding to 1 mg. of protein or less: from the measured value of I^{131} to S^{35} ratio in the chromatographic band and the known specific activities and amounts of indicator (S^{35}-labeled) used, the content of each amino acid may be calculated on the basis of the dilution principle (239). A comparison of this procedure with microbiological assays of a protein hydrolysate revealed good agreement for glycine, threonine, and glutamic acid, whereas for serine and aspartic acid the bioassay assays were some 20% too high (240). This isotope derivative method is powerful and precise, but it has only been used in limited cases. The same may be said of the conversion of amino acids in mixtures to the corresponding dinitrophenyl derivatives followed by direct measurement of the yellow color of the derivatives after separation on the paper chromatogram (see above).

Quantitative autoradiographic determinations, as in the numerous studies of I^{131} metabolism of the thyroid (cf. 178), are usually carried out on one-dimensional chromatograms either by cutting out the area corresponding to a particular substance and determining its radioactivity, or by counting successive segments of the paper from origin to solvent front under a Geiger counter. Another procedure is to measure the densities of the spots on the exposed film with a densitometer, the density being assumed to be linearly related to the amount of incident β-radiation, and to compare the results so obtained with similar densitometric scanning of the identical, colored spots on the paper chromatogram.

An extensive study of the free amino acid levels in 80% ethanolic extracts of various rat tissues involved two-dimensional paper chromatography with Whatman No. 1 paper (241). The first solvent was phenol saturated with 10% sodium citrate, and with concentrated NH_4OH maintained in the chromatography tank. The second solvent consisted of sec-butanol–88–90% formic acid–water in the volume ratio 70 : 15 : 15. A typical run was as follows. Chromatograms 1–3: A volume of 0.01 ml. of the homogenate supernatant corresponding to 1 mg. of original wet weight of tissue was deposited 0.002 ml. at a time in the lower left corner of the paper. Chromatograms 4–6: A volume of 0.01 ml. of the homogenate supernatant with 0.004 ml. of a standard amino acid solution containing fifteen of the most common of the amino acids each present at 1–3 μg. per 0.004 ml. Chromatograms 7–9: Only the 0.004-ml. volume of the standard amino acid solution. Chromatograms 10–12: A volume of 0.05 ml. of the homogenate supernatant. Chromatograms 13–15: A volume of 0.05 ml. of the homogenate supernatant with 0.004 ml. of the standard amino acid solution. Chromatogram 16: A volume of 0.05 ml. of the homogenate supernatant with 0.002 ml. of another standard amino acid solution containing six amino acids less often encountered. Chromatograms 17 and 18: A volume of 0.002 ml. of the latter standard amino acid solution. The composition of the former standard amino acid solution in micrograms per 0.004 ml. was aspartic acid 2, glutamic acid 1, glycine 2, serine 2, α-alanine 1, glutamine 2, threonine 2, histidine·HCl 2 plus lysine·HCl 1 = 3, valine 1, leucine 1, taurine 3, tyrosine 2, butyrine 2, and glutathione 2. The composition of the latter standard amino acid solution under the same conditions was arginine·HCl 2, butyrine 2, phenylalanine 2, tryptophan 2, methionine 2, and proline 2.

The eighteen chromatograms were rolled into cylinders, run with the phenol phase for 5 to 6 hours, and dried overnight. On the next day they were unrolled, turned at an angle of 90°, recylindered, developed in the second phase for about 4 hours, and dried. After 3 hours of drying, they were dipped into a 0.25 % solution of ninhydrin in acetone, suspended on a rack, and dried for 7 minutes at 85°. The spots were then read with an Ansco densitometer using a blue filter. The background was always taken to the left of the taurine spot and subtracted from the individual results. Aspartic and glutamic acids and glutathione were calculated on the basis of the differences obtained by the readings of the homogenate supernatant plus standard minus that of the homogenate supernatant; this was done in order to apprehend the extent of the interference by the salts present. All the other amino acids were calculated by reference only to their standards. No more than the equivalent of 5 mg. of tissue was studied in order to keep the salt concentration as low as possible. Lack of representation of certain amino acids may be due to the use of this low quantity of tissue.

The measurement of the levels of glutathione, aspartic and glutamic acids, glycine, serine, α-alanine, threonine, valine, the leucines, taurine, tyrosine, γ-aminobutyric acid, butyrine, and proline presented no difficulty. Glutamine in tissues other than the liver could be measured with ease, whilst in liver homogenates the presence of citrulline caused some interference. The lack of appreciable amounts of tryptophan or phenylalanine in the tissue extracts permitted the ready measurement of valine and the leucines. Histidine and lysine were determined together, while methionine was estimated as the sulfoxide. The data, good to ±10%, are given in Table 3-53. When the rats were injected with a lethal level of ammonium acetate, the aspartic acid level in the liver increased over ten-fold (241). Glutamine levels rose four- to ten-fold in brain extracts of animals protected against this ammonia toxicity through prior administration of L-arginine.

23. Determination of Optical Configuration of Amino Acids. The possibility that D-amino acids might be more widespread in nature than was hitherto suspected probably had its origin in two reports, namely, that of Kögl and Erxleben on the occurrences of D-glutamic acid in tumor proteins (242), and those of Hotchkiss (243, 244) and of Christensen (245) on the occurrence of D-leucine and D-valine in gramicidin. Lipmann et al. studied this general problem by incubating preparations of D-amino acid oxidase with hydrolysates of various proteins, and followed the reaction in terms of oxygen consumption and ammonia evolution (246, 247). The results were essentially negative. A greater specificity as far as the individual amino acids were concerned was attained by the procedure of Synge (248), which consisted in spraying a solution of D-amino acid oxidase directly on the paper chromatograms. The spots which had reacted with ninhydrin prior to the enzyme treatment, but which did not react afterward, were presumably those due to susceptible D-amino acids. A further refinement was that of Auclair and Patton (249) which consisted in spraying a duplicate chromatogram with 2:4-dinitrophenylhydrazine to detect the keto acids produced in the reaction.

Bonetti and Dent (250) introduced the more general procedure of incubating part of an amino acid mixture with kidney D-amino acid oxidase and part with an L-amino acid oxidase derived from snake venom. The digests were then chromatographed and developed with ninhydrin on paper, phenol-NH_3-HCN being the first solvent, and collidine-lutidine (diethylamine) the second. The chromatograms were compared with those of the amino acid mixture prior to the enzyme treatment, and the lost spots were attributable to either L- or D-amino acids, depending on which of the specific oxidases had been employed. No D-amino acids of any sort were observed in hydrolysates of casein, ultrafiltrates of human plasma, cerebrospinal fluid, or urine (250; cf. 251) (Table 15-17). The same procedure was used by Dalgliesh et al. to prove the presence of D-valine in hydrolysates of of actinomycin (158).

The method is obviously useful only for amino acid isomers which are quite susceptible to the action of the respective L- and D-oxidases (see Chapter 20).

TABLE 15-17

D-Amino Acids Susceptible to Oxidation by Renal
D-Amino Acid Oxidase (250)

Oxidizable D-Isomers	Presence in Human Biological Fluids[a,b]
Alanine, histidine, isoleucine, leucine, methionine, phenylalanine, proline, tryptophan, tyrosine, and valine	Undetectable

[a] Measured in cerebrospinal fluid (cases of phenylpyruvic oligophrenia), and in urine (cases of Franconi syndrome and of renal amino aciduria) by incubating with D-amino acid oxidase followed by paper chromatography, the presence of D-amino acids leading to loss or diminution of ninhydrin-reactive spots characteristic of the chromatograms of the fluids prior to enzymatic treatment.

[b] D-Phenylalanine was shown to be absent (251) from the plasma of cases of phenylpyruvic oligophrenia by, first, determining the levels of L-phenylalanine in the plasma through the effect on the growth of *Lactobacillus*, second, converting all phenylalanine present to phenyllactic acid by treatment with nitrous acid, and, third, subjecting the phenyllactic acid so formed to *L. arabinosus*. Inasmuch as the microorganism grows equally well on L-phenylalanine, L-phenyllactic acid, and D-phenyllactic acid, but not at all on D-phenylalanine, any increase in growth after the nitrous acid procedure would have indicated the presence of D-phenylalanine in the original plasma sample. Such increase did not occur.

24. Starch Columns. The studies by Synge on the partial acid hydrolysates of gramicidin in attempts to elucidate the structure of this polypeptide were generally conducted by acetylating the products and subjecting them to partition chromatography on columns of silica gel (22, 252). The free peptide split-products could also be separated on paper chromatograms, n-butanol–water being used as solvent (31, 253). Paper in the form of large piles of disks (chromatopile) (254), or in the form of columns of cellulose powder (255), has been employed for the isolation of amino acids in modest quantity. Inasmuch as columns were evidently superior to paper sheets for larger-scale separations, the employment of raw potato starch in columns was attempted and found to be effective (253). It was observed that amino acids, as well as peptides, traveled on starch as sharply defined bands when developed with n-butanol saturated with water and located by the passage of an ethereal solution of ninhydrin through the column after development. Comparison of the partition coefficients of amino acids as calculated from the rate of movement of their bands and the column constants showed agreement with the direct measurements of England and Cohn (15), and the sequence of bands agreed essentially with that shown on paper chromatograms when the same solvent was used (Table 15–18). The color reaction

TABLE 15–18

Partition Coefficients of Amino Acids between n-Butanol–Water Phases from Band Rates on Starch (253)

Amino Acid	Band Movement	R	P (band rate)	P (England and Cohn (15))
DL-Alanine	1.0	0.10	44.0	42.2
DL-Valine	3.2	0.29	13.7	13.9
DL-Leucine	7.0	0.55	6.4	5.5

of ninhydrin on the starch was useful for distinguishing free amino acids from peptides which gave no color until heated. Fractions were collected from the effluent of the column at random but were not analyzed quantitatively.

The development of the starch column as a quantitative instrument for the analysis of the amino acid composition of proteins is due to Stein and Moore (256–258). Their columns were mounted over an automatic fraction collector designed to collect continuously small fractions of specified volume. The solution containing the amino acid mixture was added to the top of the column, allowed to drain down the column, and fresh solvent added under slight pressure to resolve the individual amino acid bands. Each effluent fraction was determined by a photometric ninhydrin procedure sensitive to one part per million of amino acid. The chromatogram development was begun with an n-butanol–n-propanol–0.1N HCl mixture and subsequently was shifted to an n-propanol–0.5N HCl mixture in order to hasten the rate of travel of the remaining zones on the column (256) (Figure 15–29). This led to a satisfactory separation of proline, threonine, aspartic acid, serine, glycine, ammonium chloride, arginine, lysine, histidine, and cystine, but not of leucine, isoleucine, phenylalanine, valine, methionine, tyrosine, glutamic acid, and alanine. The overlapping of glutamic acid and alanine

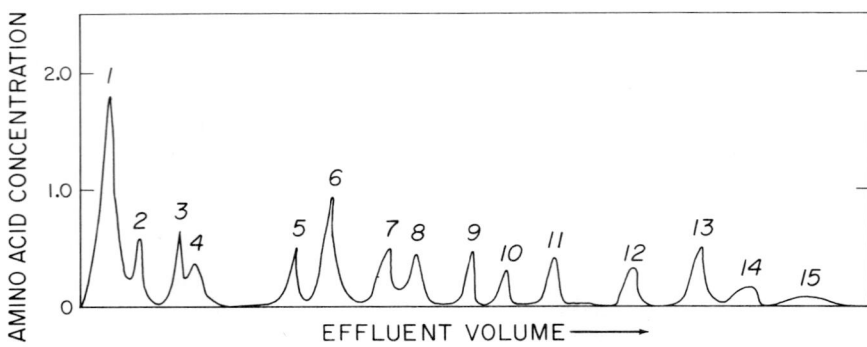

Figure 15-29. Separation of amino acids on starch columns. Solvent, 1:2:1 *n*-butanol–*n*-propanol–0.1*N* HCl, followed by 2:1 *n*-propanol–0.5*N* HCl. 1, Leucine, isoleucine; 2, phenylalanine; 3, valine; 4, methionine, tyrosine; 5, proline; 6, alanine, glutamic acid; 7, threonine; 8, aspartic acid; 9, serine; 10, glycine; 11, ammonia; 12, arginine; 13, lysine; 14, histidine; 15, cystine. Moore, S., and Stein, W. H., *J. Biol. Chem.*, **178**, 53 (1949).

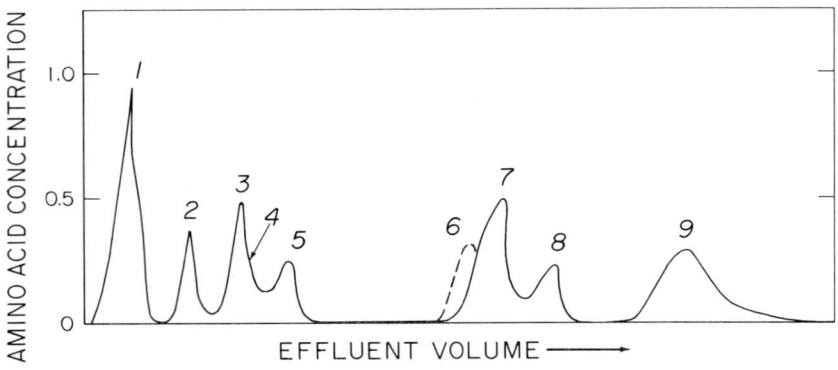

Figure 15-30. Separation of amino acids on starch columns. Solvent, 2:1:1 *t*-butanol–*sec*-butanol–0.1*N* HCl. 1, Leucine, isoleucine; 2, phenylalanine; 3, valine; 4, methionine; 5, tyrosine; 6, proline; 7, glutamic acid; 8, alanine; 9, threonine, aspartic acid. Moore, S., and Stein, W. H., *J. Biol. Chem.*, **178**, 53 (1949).

was avoided, and a clear separation of phenylalanine was effected by employing a solvent mixture of *t*-butanol–*sec*-butanol–0.1*N* HCl (256) (Figure 15-30). The use of *n*-butanol–benzyl alcohol–water containing thiodiglycol (to protect methionine) as a solvent mixture produced a separation of leucine, isoleucine, and methionine on the starch column (Figure 15–31).

Thus, by the use of the three solvent mixtures, it was possible for Stein and Moore to obtain quantitative values for nearly all the components of an amino acid mixture likely to be encountered in protein hydrolysates. Table 15–19 describes the order of emergence of amino acids of various kinds from

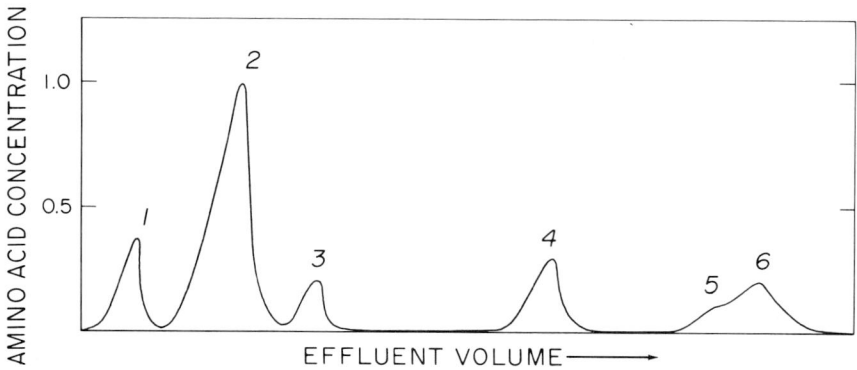

Figure 15–31. Separation of amino acids on starch columns. Solvent, 1:1:0.288 *n*-butanol–benzyl alcohol–water, containing 0.5% thiodiglycol. 1, Phenylalanine; 2, leucine; 3, isoleucine; 4, methionine; 5, tyrosine; 6, valine. Moore, S., and Stein, W. H., *J. Biol. Chem.*, **178**, 53 (1949).

the starch column under specified conditions (258). Tryptophan emerges later than phenylalanine with HCl as solvent (258). Hydroxyproline travels at about the same rate as does threonine, but can be distinguished by its ninhydrin (orange) color. Ornithine and hydroxylysine both coincide with cystine. The individual fractions can be related to the amino acids which they contain by the several specific color reactions, and by the fact that the position of each amino acid is independent of the presence of other amino acids. Thus the position of each amino acid can be determined singly, and in cases of doubt a specific amino acid may be added to a mixture with the result of merely increasing the size of the related peak without affecting its symmetry (256). A quantitative analysis of a purified protein by this procedure has been given in Table 15–16 (231). Studies on urine revealed the commonly noted relative abundance of glycine (256). Chromatography on starch was employed to separate the α-aminoadipic acid formed from L-lysine in liver homogenates (259).

The separation of N^{15}-labeled amino acids in mixtures derived from the hydrolysis of different tissue proteins was studied with starch columns by Aqvist (260). Inasmuch as the individual amino acids were to be isolated and the isotopic content determined, some 200 to 400 mg. of protein was employed, yielding 1 to 2 mg. of amino acid nitrogen. The experimental design for this operation followed that of Stein and Moore closely, but was some 80 times larger. Identification of the amino acids in the effluent fractions was effected by paper chromatography, and the quantitative aspects by the ninhydrin procedure of Moore and Stein (213) and by manometric-CO_2 measurements with ninhydrin.

TABLE 15-19

Order of Emergence of Amino Acids and Related Compounds from Starch Columns[a] (258)

Amino Acids	Position of Peak, ml.	Amino Acids and Related Compounds	Position of Peak, ml.
Leucine-isoleucine	13.5	3:5-Diiodotyrosine	12.5
Phenylalanine	16.5	Tryptophan	18
Valine	24	Butyrine	38
Methionine	26	α-Aminoadipic acid	41
Tyrosine	28	Cysteic acid	64
Proline	52	Taurine	74
Glutamic acid-alanine	59	Hydroxyproline	80
Threonine	75	Sarcosine	84
Aspartic acid	82	Citrulline	98.5
Serine	100	Ethanolamine	102
Glycine	106	Asparagine	121
Ammonia	117	Glucosamine	126
Arginine	136	Histamine	160
Lysine	149	Ornithine	176
Histidine	163	Hydroxylysine	180
Cystine	179		

[a] Columns 0.9 x 30 cm. prepared from 13.4 g. anhydrous starch, and developed with *n*-butanol–*n*-propanol–0.1N HCl, shifted to *n*-propanol–0.5N HCl at 83 ml., or directly after emergence of aspartic acid.

In connection with the studies on the recovery of amino acids from starch columns, Moore and Stein (213) made a careful study of the ninhydrin reaction with this class of compounds. Their first contribution to effect a stable and reproducible color with this reagent was to employ hydrindantin, the reduced form of ninhydrin. The addition of stannous chloride to the reaction mixture provided in many cases a suitable alternative to this procedure. Although reproducible results were obtained for a given amino acid, the different amino acids did not yield the same amount of color per mole.

The α-amino acids, except cysteine, yield the same major blue-colored end product, namely, diketohydrindylidenediketohydrindamine (261) (Section

CHROMATOGRAPHY

11–2). With proline and hydroxyproline the reaction follows a different course, yielding products with a maximum absorption at 440 mμ (262). With α-amino acids, the ninhydrin reaction color is read at 570 mμ (213).

In practice, the color yields of the various amino acids are expressed relative to the leucine value as 1.00. Table 15–20 describes the color yields per mole on this basis (213).

TABLE 15–20
Color Yields with Ninhydrin on Molar Basis Relative to Leucine (214)[a]

Compound	Color Yield	Compound	Color Yield
Aspartic acid	0.94	Carnosine	0.93
Threonine	0.94	Citrulline	1.04
Serine	0.95	Creatinine	0.027
Proline (440 mμ)	0.225	Cysteic acid	0.99
Glutamic acid	0.99	α,ε-Diaminopimelic acid (per 2NH$_2$)	1.24
Glycine	0.95	Ethanolamine	0.91
Alanine	0.97	Felinine	0.95
Valine	0.97	Glutamine	0.99
Half-cystine	0.55	Glucosamine	1.03
Methionine	1.02	Glutathionine (oxidized, half)	0.93
Isoleucine	1.00	Glycerophosphoethanolamine	0.50
Leucine	1.00	Hydroxylysine	1.12
Tyrosine	1.00	Hydroxyproline (440 mμ)	0.077
Phenylalanine	1.00	Methionine sulfone	1.02
Ammonia	0.97	Methionine sulfoxide	0.98
Lysine	1.10	1-Methylhistidine	0.88
Histidine	1.02	3-Methylhistidine	0.86
Tryptophan	0.94	Ornithine	1.12
Arginine	1.01	Phosphoethanolamine	0.43
α-Aminoadipic acid	0.96	Sarcosine	0.28
β-Alanine	0.50	Taurine	0.88
Anserine	0.78	Urea	0.0314
Asparagine	0.95	Butyrine	1.02
β-Aminoisobutyric acid	0.44	γ-Aminobutyric acid	1.01

[a] Heating time 15 min. at 100°, read at 570 mμ.

The analysis on a starch column of a hydrolysate of rabbit thyroglobulin labeled with I^{131} is pictured in Figure 15–32. Although iodide and mono- and diiodotyrosine could be well separated, both thyroxine and triiodothyronine appeared together in the front peak (196). The use of ion exchange resins to separate this class of compounds is taken up in Chapter 38.

One of the limitations on the use of starch columns is the need to greatly reduce the electrolyte concentration of the solutions used, for if this is high a generally poor resolution of the amino acids results. Stein and Moore (263) studied the electrolytic desalting method of Consden, Gordon, and Martin (65) with a mixture of amino acids followed by quantitative starch chromatography. Appreciable losses of histidine, proline, and methionine or tyrosine, and very considerable losses of arginine were noted as a result of the desalting procedure. The greater part of the loss of arginine could be attributed to deguanidination and conversion to ornithine.

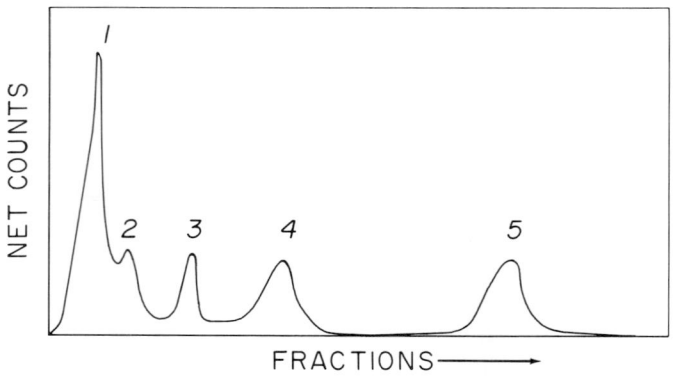

Figure 15-32. Separation on starch column of iodinated amino acids from hydrolysates of rabbit thyroid. 1, Thyroxine; 2, triiodothyronine; 3, iodide; 4, monoiodotyrosine; 5, diiodotyrosine. Solvent employed up to and including monoiodotyrosine was n-butanol–propanol–0.05N Na$_2$CO$_3$ (1:2:1) and thereafter, n-butanol–propanol–0.1N HCl (1:2:1). Dobyns, B. M., and Barry, S. R., *J. Biol. Chem.*, **204**, 517 (1953).

25. Countercurrent Distribution. The elegant procedure of extraction, fractionation, and identification of biological compounds which goes under this title has been extensively developed by Craig and his co-workers (264). It possesses the great advantage of a firm theoretical basis and, as a corollary, provides a nearly unequivocal test for chemical homogeneity and purity. The interchange of a solute between two immiscible or nearly immiscible liquid phases is one of the classic separation methods in organic chemistry, and in its simplest form is described by the equation of Nernst: $K = C_1/C_2$, where C_1 and C_2 are the concentrations of the solute in each phase at equilibrium, and K is the partition coefficient which is assumed to be independent of the total amount of solute present. Equilibrium between the phases is attained, in the absence of emulsification, after a certain period of physical agitation which may vary for each system studied. Analysis of each phase for concentration of solute is necessary during this period in order to determine when equilibrium is reached. The following treatment of the subject is taken largely from Craig (264).

The fraction, U, of the total solute found in the upper layer is

$$U = \frac{KVu}{KVu + Vl} = \frac{Kr}{Kr + 1}$$

where Vu and Vl are the volumes of the upper and lower phases, respectively, and $r = Vu/Vl$.

The fraction L remaining in the lower phase is

$$L = 1 - \frac{KVu}{KVu + Vl} = \frac{1}{Kr + 1}$$

When the lower layer is re-extracted with n successive equal volumes of the upper layer, each nth extract will contain the fraction Xn of the solute:

$$Xn = \left(\frac{1}{Kr + 1}\right)^n Kr$$

and Yn of the solute will remain in the lower layer:

$$Yn = \left(\frac{1}{Kr + 1}\right)^n$$

If the partition coefficient is not known, a reasonably accurate estimate may be obtained by several successive extractions using equal volumes of the extractant. Thus

$$U = \frac{Kr}{Kr + 1} = 1 - \frac{W_2}{W_1}$$

where W_1 and W_2 are the analytical figures for the solute in the first and second extraction. If the value of K agrees with that obtained from

$$\frac{Kr}{Kr + 1} = 1 - \frac{W_3}{W_2}$$

where W_3 is now the analytical figure for the third extraction, it may be assumed to be a close approximation to the true value. If more than one solute is present, the value of K so estimated may turn out to be the mean of the partition ratios of two or more solutes of nearly similar partition coefficients (see below).

The efficiency of the extraction of solutes as ordinarily carried out in separatory funnels in the organic chemical laboratory is not very high. This often involves the shaking of a solution phase with extracting solvent one or more times. Thus, if in 100 ml. of a solution containing 1 gram of solute it is desired to transfer as much as possible of the solute to 100 ml. of an immiscible solvent, K being 1, a single extraction would yield 0.5 gram in the solvent, four successive extractions each with 25 ml. of solvent would yield $0.20 + 0.16 + 0.128 + 0.1024 = 0.5904$ gram in the combined extracts (265–267).

The use of multiple-contact extraction leads to a higher efficiency. Thus the above solution may be divided into two portions of 50 ml. each, and one is equilibrated with 50 ml. of extracting solvent. The solvent is then removed, equilibrated with the second 50-ml. portion of solution, and removed.

TUBE NUMBER

TRANSFER NUMBER	0	1	2	3	----	p
0	1.0					
1	.50	.50				
2	.25	.50	.25			
3	.125	.375	.375	.125		
4	.0625	.25	.375	.25	.0625	
n						

Figure 15–33. Countercurrent distribution. Craig, L. C., and Craig, D., in Weissberger, A., *Technique of Organic Chemistry*, Vol. III, Interscience Publishers, New York, p. 171, 1950.

This extract should contain 0.375 gram. A fresh portion of 50 ml. of extracting solvent is then equilibrated with the first solution, removed, equilibrated with the second solution, and removed. It should contain 0.25 gram. The combined extracts should contain therefore 0.625 gram. If the solution is divided into four equal volumes and equilibrated in the same successive manner with four equal portions of extracting solvent, the total recovery will be 0.7265 gram, although the number of operations will have been substantially increased. It is obvious that, by further subdividing the volumes of solution and extraction solvent, a more complete removal of the solute will have been approached. This is the basis of the countercurrent principle.

The concept of countercurrent distribution is experimentally and theoretically refined as described in Figure 15–33 (264), where $K = 1$, 1.000 gram of

CHROMATOGRAPHY

solute is dissolved in L_0, and the two phases are of equal volume. The formula for calculating the fraction Tn,p of substance present in the pth tube for n transfers is

$$Tn,p = \frac{n!}{p!(n-p)!} \left(\frac{1}{K+1}\right)^n K^p$$

which is represented graphically in Figure 15–34 (curve 1) for a partition coefficient of 1 and for eight transfers. When this partition coefficient is 0.333 curve 2 is obtained, and when it is 3.0 curve 3 is obtained (267).

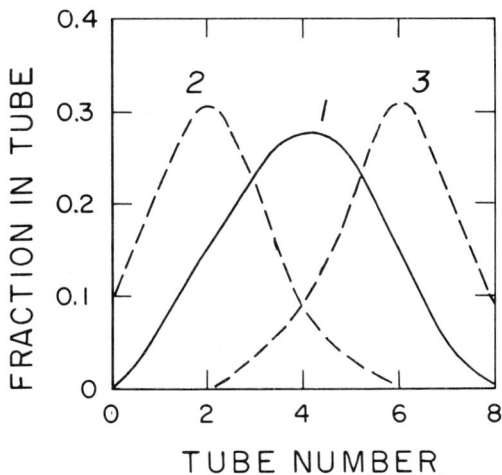

Figure 15–34. Countercurrent distribution curves (curve 1, partition ratio of 1; curve 2, partition ratio of 0.333; curve 3, partition ratio of 3.0). Craig, L. C., and Craig, D., in Weissberger, A., *Technique of Organic Chemistry*, Vol. III, Interscience Publishers, New York, p. 171, 1950.

In order to obtain the curves in Figure 15–34, $(n+1)n/2$ or 36 individual extractions are required. With complex mixtures, a still higher number of transfers would in all probability be needed, and machines for this purpose have been developed by Craig and his co-workers.

When two substances are present as solutes, each will tend to distribute itself in the phases independently of each other. If the partition coefficients are not very far apart, two overlapping curves will be obtained as shown in Figure 15–35. The total solute in each tube is given by curve 1, and is the sum of curves 2 and 3, i.e., those of the individual solutes.

The position of the maximum on the abscissa can be calculated from $N = nKr/(Kr+1)$, where N is the tube number at the maximum. From an experimental curve, N can be determined and substituted in this equation in order to derive a value of K. For purposes of plotting a curve, any units which are directly proportional to the amount of solute may be used as subdivisions of the ordinate. An agreement between calculated and experimental values for the distribution curve of any substance suggests that within limits the substance is pure and homogeneous. However, this cannot exclude the possibility of an impurity being present with a nearly identical partition coefficient. Either an increase in the number of transfers

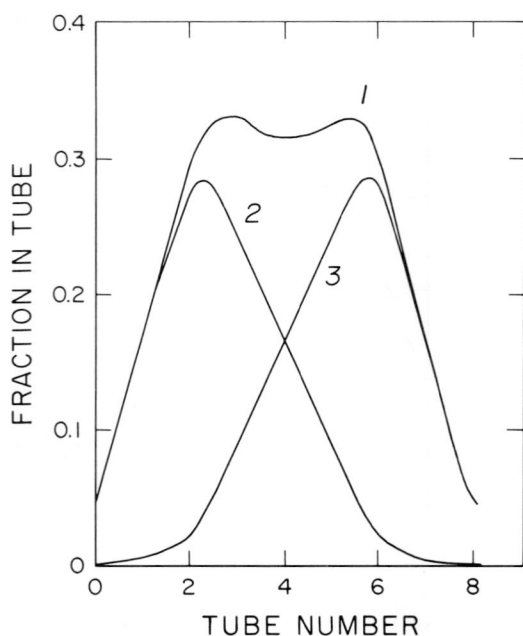

Figure 15-35. Countercurrent distribution curves (curve 1, total solute in each tube, which is the sum of curves 2 and 3 for the individual components). Craig, L. C., and Craig, D., in Weissberger, A., *Technique of Organic Chemistry*, Vol. III, Interscience Publishers, New York, p. 171, 1950.

or application of new solvent systems, or both, can reveal or discard the possibility of the presence of such impurity. The separation factor β may be taken as a measure of the ease with which the two substances can be separated, and it is used to estimate the number of transfers necessary to obtain separation, where

$$\beta = \frac{X/Y}{(1-X)/(1-Y)} = \frac{K_1}{K_2}$$

the ratio of the partition coefficients. The β values are generally different for different solvent systems. For an adequate determination of purity, therefore, there must be a sufficient number of transfers between phases, together with a choice of solvents such that the ratio of β for test substance and impurity is large. A higher number of transfers gives increasingly narrower bands with respect to the total solvent used, and thus an increased separation of the solutes in solution. A recycling procedure may be employed to effect this aim, in which the apparatus employed contains two parallel rows of tubes, and which is so arranged that the upper phases move in opposite directions. The resemblance of recycling under these conditions to the result of refluxing in a fractional distillation column has been alluded to (264).

The movement of the band from the origin is proportional to the fraction of the solute in each tube in the upper layer which is moved forward with each step. In terms of the partition coefficient, this is $Kr/(Kr + 1)$. For the same number of transfers, n, and with constant r, N_1 and N_2, which are the positions of the maxima on the abscissa for solutes 1 and 2, will be governed by K_1 and K_2, the respective partition coefficients. The resemblance of the expression $Kr/(Kr + 1)$ to the R_F of chromatography is apparent, and, as solute 1 moves from the origin toward higher tube numbers and thence to a collector at a greater rate than does solute 2, the picture of an effluent emerging from a chromatographic column or a spot moving on paper comes strongly to mind. In so far as chromatography under limited conditions may be considered to be a liquid–liquid partition, the analogy is exact, but, as noted in the previous section, the solid supporting phase is rarely if ever completely inert. Only the choice of solvents in both chromatographic and distribution methods is still empirical.

An illustration of the method of countercurrent distribution to determine the amino acids in an HCl hydrolysate of polymyxin B_1 by Hausmann and Craig (268) follows. One gram of peptide hydrochloride was refluxed with $6N$ HCl and evaporated to dryness *in vacuo*. The residue was distributed in the system n-butanol–2-butanol–5% HCl (1 : 1 : 2) and placed in the countercurrent machine. After 211 transfers, the curve shown in Figure 15–36 was obtained. The band in tubes 80–130 contained leucine and phenylalanine (as the hydrochlorides), which could be confirmed by paper chromatography. Similarly, the slow-moving peak contained threonine and γ-aminobutyrine as the hydrochlorides. The former band was removed from the apparatus, and the latter band recycled until 726 transfers had been accomplished. Figure 15–37 shows complete separation of threonine from γ-aminobutyrine, and the near concordance of experimental and theoretical curves.

The band containing leucine and phenylalanine hydrochlorides was evaporated to dryness *in vacuo*, dissolved in water, and treated with an excess of ammonia. After evaporation again to dryness, the residue was distributed in the system n-butanol–H_2O. Figure 15–38 shows almost complete separation of the two amino acids after 657 transfers.

The separate amino acids were withdrawn from the machine in a fashion analogous to elution from a chromatographic column, i.e., phenylalanine first from the faster band, threonine first from the slower band, and their respective solutions were evaporated to dryness. After purification and recrystallization, the amino acids were subjected to elemental and polarimetric analysis. The number of mole residues per mole of polypeptide was

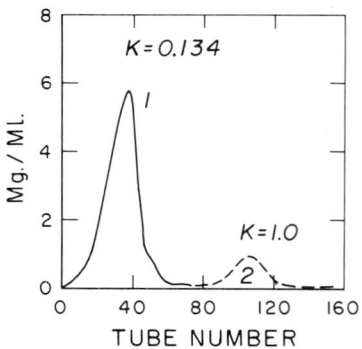

Figure 15–36. Distribution curves of amino acids from hydrolysate of polymyxin B; solvent system, *n*-butanol–2-butanol–5% HCl (1:1:2). 1, Lower phase, containing γ-aminobutyrine and threonine; 2, upper phase, containing leucine and phenylalanine. Number of transfers, 211. Hausmann, W., and Craig, L. C., *J. Am. Chem. Soc.*, **76**, 4892 (1954).

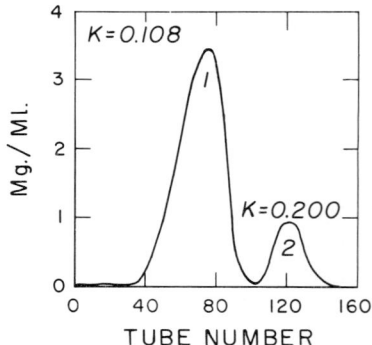

Figure 15–37. Resolution of peak 1 in Figure 15–36 using same solvent system. 1, γ-Aminobutyrine; 2, threonine. Actual and theoretical curves nearly identical. Number of transfers, 726. Hausmann, W., and Craig, L. C., *J. Am. Chem. Soc.*, **76**, 4892 (1954).

deduced from the leucine and phenylalanine bands (Figure 15–38), and yielded values of 1 mole each. Total N and ninhydrin determinations on the γ-aminobutyrine and threonine band yielded values of 6 and 2 moles, respectively, for these amino acids. Optical rotation studies revealed that the leucine was L-, the phenylalanine was D-, and both threonine residues were

L- in configuration. The rotation of the γ-aminobutyrine·HCl was some 84% that of the L-form, which may have implied some degree of racemization. An example of a separation of isomeric compounds was afforded by the use of countercurrent partition in the synthesis of γ-methyleneglutamine (269). Treatment of phthalyl-γ-methyleneglutamic anhydride with

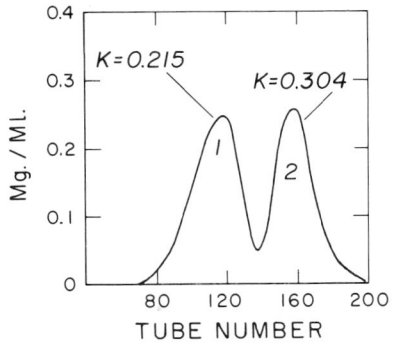

Figure 15-38. Resolution of peak 2 in Figure 15-36, after neutralization with NH₄OH, and employing the solvent system n-butanol–H₂O. 1, Leucine; 2, phenylalanine. Actual and theoretical curves nearly identical. Number of transfers, 657. Hausmann, W., and Craig, L. C., *J. Am. Chem. Soc.*, **76**, 4892 (1954).

ammonia led to a mixture of the half-amides, namely, that corresponding to glutamine and that to isoglutamine. The mixture was dissolved in butanol and equilibrated with M phosphate buffer solution at pH 6.2. The slower-moving component corresponded to the former compound, and after removal of the phthalimido group the racemic form of the material found in the ground nut plant (cf. 133) was isolated.

The very exact pipsyl (p-iodobenzenesulfonyl) procedure to estimate the concentration of glutamic acid, aspartic acid, hydroxyproline, serine, and threonine in hydrolysates of as little as 0.2 to 1.0 mg. of protein has been greatly facilitated by using a preliminary countercurrent extraction (ether–0.2N HCl) in mixtures of the hydrolysate with S^{35}-labeled derivatives of the five amino acids (36). This removed excess of reagent, and a subsequent chloroform-acid distribution was employed to remove the chloroform-soluble pipsyl derivatives of the remaining amino acids.

Adsorption Chromatography

26. Charcoal Column Chromatography. This subject may have had its inception in 1919 in the studies by Abderhalden and Fodor (270) on the possibility that adsorptive forces played an important role in the substrate–enzyme interaction. As an example of a surface-active agent, and as a model of an enzyme surface, they chose charcoal and studied the adsorption by this material of a number of amino acids and peptides. A considerable difference in the ability of charcoal to adsorb various amino acids became evident; thus glycine was adsorbed little if at all, alanine to an extent barely more than glycine, whereas leucine was adsorbed to a considerable degree. These phenomena were confirmed subsequently by several investigators (271–273), but the use of charcoal as a possible analytical tool to separate and identify amino acids was probably overlooked or even rejected when it was discovered that amino acids could be oxidized (274) or hydrolyzed with loss of the amino group (275) on prolonged exposure to crude, iron-containing charcoal. It was not until the early 1940's, and as part of the great development of chromatographic studies general at that time, that charcoal was seriously used as a means of separating the amino acids.

Cheldelin and Williams (276) showed that the aliphatic amino acids were adsorbed to a much lesser extent than were the aromatic amino acids. When charcoal columns were washed with 5% acetic acid in water, poisoned with cyanide to reduce oxidative effects, and treated with an aqueous solution containing glycine, alanine, serine, proline, methionine, valine, leucine, isoleucine, tyrosine, tryptophan, and phenylalanine, the aliphatic amino acids could be eluted with a subsequent wash of 5% acetic acid, but the three aromatic amino acids remained firmly on the column; the tyrosine, tryptophan, and phenylalanine could, however, be subsequently removed as a group by the use of 5% phenol in 20% acetic acid (277). Glycine, leucine, phenylalanine, and tyrosine in aqueous solution were separated on a Darco G-60 charcoal column by developing with water and removing the effluent fraction (leucine and glycine) (278). This fraction was placed on a larger column and yielded first glycine in the effluent and then leucine. The first column was developed with 5% aqueous acetone until the appearance of phenylalanine in the effluent, the contents of the column extruded, and the tyrosine extracted with 5% aqueous ethyl acetate. A separation of methionine from valine, and of valine from leucine, by elution from charcoal columns with relatively large water volumes, was reported by Turba, Richter, and Kuchar (279).

Many of the important developments in this technique have been due to the efforts of Tiselius and his co-workers (280–287). On a practical level, these investigators devised an apparatus suitable for continuous and quantitative observation of adsorption and elution processes in solutions passing through an adsorption column, using refractometric (*schlieren*) optical methods (cf. 283). Three general aspects of adsorption chromatography were considered under the headings of frontal analysis, elution analysis, and displacement analysis, which had significant implications in the later development of the subject and wider connotations than were apparent from their immediate application to charcoal columns.

CHROMATOGRAPHY

In frontal analysis, the adsorbent is washed with pure solvent, then the solution to be analyzed is continually added to the column. The solutes are adsorbed and move forward as the adsorbent becomes saturated. At first only pure solvent leaves the column, but as the least adsorbed solute appears the concentration in the effluent increases to a certain value and remains appreciably constant over a volume of effluent until a new increase in concentration heralds the appearance in the effluent of the next solute to emerge. That volume which emerges before the appearance of a particular

TABLE 15–21

Retention Volumes in the Adsorption of Certain Amino Acids and Peptides on Active Carbon from Aqueous (0.5%) Solutions (282)

Substance	Retention Volumes, ml. per g. carbon	Substance	Retention Volumes, ml. per g. carbon
Alanine	0.3	Phenylalanine	62.5
Hydroxyproline	2.0	Glycylglycine	3.5
Proline	2.5	Leucylglycine	18.2
Valine	3.2	Leucylglycylglycine	29.8
Leucine	7.7	Glycylalanine	4.0
Isoleucine	9.2	Valylglycine	22.0
Methionine	12.4	Alanylleucylglycine	34.4
Histidine	15.0	Glycylleucylalanine	42.5
Arginine	40.4	Glycylleucylglycine	38.0
Tryptophan	76.5		

solute is designated the retention volume for that compound, and is larger the greater the degree of adsorption (Table 15–21). The retention volume may also increase with dilution. Figure 15–39 describes an example of frontal analysis of an aqueous mixture of alanine and leucine on charcoal (282), wherein only water appears up to 4 ml., then alanine, and finally alanine and leucine. It is possible to use this method of frontal analysis to determine the components of a mixture, but a quantitative analysis is not always possible because of the mutual displacement of the solutes on the adsorbant, e.g., only in the ideal case do the components of a mixture possess mutually independent adsorptions. Often only the weakest adsorbed material can be obtained in a pure state, and thus glycine and alanine may be separated together in a fair degree of purity from other amino acids (cf. 282).

In elution analysis, the mixture in solution is poured on the column and the pure solvent employed to develop and separate the components in more or less pure bands or zones which then individually emerge in the effluent. In any event the components travel more slowly than does the developer front, with a frequently exhibited marked retardation of the more strongly adsorbed compounds. A further modification (cf. 284) is to employ an additional developer which can be adjusted in concentration, and which can effect a change in solubility or adsorption of one or more components of the mixture.

Displacement analysis is not often distinguishable from frontal or elution analysis, but essentially it involves the employment of a developing solvent

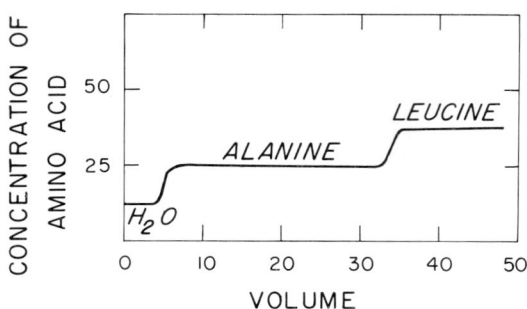

Figure 15–39. Frontal analysis on charcoal column. Tiselius, A., in *The Svedberg*, Almqvist and Wiksells, Uppsala, p. 370, 1944.

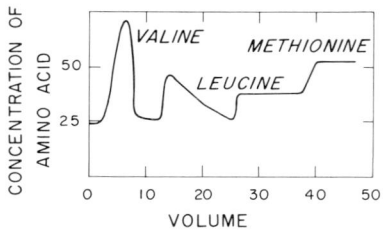

Figure 15–40. Displacement analysis on charcoal column, with 0.5% ethyl acetate as displacing agent. Tiselius, A., in *The Svedberg*, Almqvist and Wiksells, Uppsala, p. 370, 1944.

which is more strongly adsorbed and moves more slowly down the column than any of the components of the mixture (or more strongly adsorbed than some and less strongly than others) which it displaces. Figure 15–40 demonstrates an instance of displacement analysis of a mixture of valine, leucine, and methionine, the displacement developer being a 0.5 percent solution of ethyl acetate. Valine and leucine appear as peaks, whereas methionine which is most strongly adsorbed has reached a stationary state. The remaining, adsorbed methionine could, however, be washed out of the column with 5% ethyl acetate. A solution of 0.5% ethyl acetate does not displace the methionine completely, but the methionine does displace the leucine, making Figure 15–40 a representation of a combination of elution (valine) and displacement (282).

In displacement analysis the components travel down the column in adjacent fashion, and, although the method has certain advantages, complete separation of the components is not always possible. Thus it is possible completely to adsorb phenylalanine, tyrosine, and tryptophan on carbon, and to displace them with a compound with even greater tenacity for carbon such as benzyl alcohol (285), but the individual components of this mixture are difficult to separate because of the narrow contiguous zones in which they appear in the effluent. Tiselius and Hagdahl (288) attempted to overcome this difficulty by a process which they called carrier displacement, and which consisted of the interposition of zones of inert substances of intermediate affinity between pairs of amino acids to enable the cutting of fractions to be more readily accomplished. Thus, if A_1 and A_2 are the amino acids to be separated, substances S_1 and S_2 are added. S_1 is chosen to displace A_1 but not A_2, whereas S_2 displaces A_1, A_2, and S_1. The displacement diagram should therefore consist of steps A_1, S_1, A_2, and S_2 in that order, and A_1 and A_2 should be well separated as they move down the column. The separation of a mixture of methionine, tyrosine, phenylalanine, and tryptophan on an alkaline-buffered carbon-Super Cel column was effected as follows (285): methionine was displaced by *n*-butanol, tyrosine appeared at the interface where 2-methyl-2-butanol appeared, phenylalanine was displaced by 3-methyl-1-butanol, and tryptophan by benzyl alcohol. Recovery of the amino acids was reported to be close to 96%, but application of the technique to the analysis of more complex mixtures of amino acids as in a protein hydrolysate was not quite feasible.

An ingenious application by Robson and Selim (289) of charcoal column chromatography to the separation of the basic amino acids as their picrate salts depended primarily on the fact that these picrates are strongly adsorbed on such columns in the following (descending) order: arginine monopicrate > histidine dipicrate > lysine picrate, and hydroxylysine picrate > picric acid. Treatment with dilute HCl of the charcoal column on which all the picrates were adsorbed resulted in an exchange reaction whereby the basic amino acids appeared in the percolate as the hydrochlorides, whereas the picric acid still remained on the column. Lysine and hydroxylysine appeared early in the percolate, with histidine next, and arginine (N HCl required in this case) last. The procedure is in general an excellent means of removing picric acid from any amino acid picrate, and it has been frequently employed for this purpose in the writers' Laboratory. When charcoal is used to purify amino acids (Part VI), the losses involved through adsorption must be taken into consideration.

Analysis on charcoal columns permits many basic studies of purely adsorptive phenomena (cf. 284, 287). It has, however, been superseded as an analytical tool by the use of the more flexible and more powerful ion exchange resins. It is interesting to note the stages of compromise in which the use of the exchangers and of carbon were intermingled in analytical procedures for amino acid mixtures (cf. 277, 279) before the full adoption of ion exchange resins. Where, however, it is simply desired to remove the aromatic amino acids as a class from an amino acid mixture, the use of carbon is still an effective procedure (cf. 290), especially when the carbon is pretreated with some "deactivating" agent such as stearic acid (286, 291).

27. Earlier Work on Ion Exchange Resins. As in the use of charcoal, which permitted the separation of the aromatic ring-substituted amino acids as a group from a mixture, the early work on the use of ion exchangers was also based on group separation. Thus in 1923 Whitehorn (292) showed that arginine, histidine, and lysine were exchanged for Na^+ on the synthetic zeolite, Permutit, a procedure subsequently employed by Dubnoff (293) for the quantitative separation of arginine from protein hydrolysates. Strong solutions of neutral salts, such as NaCl or KCl, were required to elute the basic amino acids from the zeolite. The various Amberlite ion exchangers were developed by Adams and Holmes in 1935 (294), and employed seven years later by Block (295) to isolate quantitatively the three basic amino acids from a blood fibrin hydroylsate, and by Cannan (296) to isolate quantitatively the two acidic amino acids, aspartic acid and glutamic acid.

At about the same time, a remarkable series of studies was undertaken by Wieland, Turba, and others, on the separation of the individual amino acids by means of charcoal and of various ion exchangers. Schwab and Jochers had noted in 1937 that heavy metal cations exchanged in aqueous solutions with Na^+ in basic alumina (Al_2O_3) gels (297). The basic amino acids are in the cationic form at neutral reactions, and Wieland observed that alumina at pH 7 held arginine and lysine firmly and quantitatively (298); both amino acids were readily eluted, together with NaCl, when the gel was washed with dilute HCl. The acidic alumina now held tenaciously to aspartic and glutamic acids, and these amino acids could be eluted with dilute NaOH as the monosodium salts. Acid or basic alumina did not adsorb histidine completely. Alumina pretreated with dilute HCl was employed by Wieland (299) to isolate glutamic acid quantitatively from neutralized hydrochloric acid hydrolysates of tumors. Fifty grams of alumina was used per gram of hydrolyzed protein. Elution from the alumina with baryta, followed by removal of Ba^{2+} and saturation of the condensed filtrate with HCl at 0° led to the crystallization of glutamic acid hydrochloride in pure form whereas aspartic acid hydrochloride remained in solution. Although not pertinent here, it may be mentioned that no evidence for the presence of D-glutamic acid was observed in the preparations so isolated. In the course of this study Wieland noted that the cystine in the protein hydrolysates was, like the dicarboxylic amino acids, also adsorbed on the acid alumina column (cf. 279). Wash water containing hydrogen sulfide converted the cystine to cysteine which was readily eluted off the column by this fluid, and thus separated from the dicarboxylic amino acids. Instead of eluting the latter with dilute alkali, Wieland and Wirth (300) found that $0.5N$ HCl would strip both dicarboxylic amino acids from the alumina. A separation, however, could be achieved on the column by the use of $0.5N$ acetic acid, which resulted in the quantitative elution of the glutamic acid portion. Turba and Richter (301) made essentially the same observation, using alumina previously treated with an N acetate buffer at pH 3.3. Aspartic acid could then be subsequently eluted with either $0.5N$ HCl or with dilute alkali.

It was therefore possible by 1943 to separate completely the three basic amino acids (on a silica gel, Filtrol-Neutral (302)), and the two dicarboxylic amino acids on acidic alumina, whereas all the monoaminomonocarboxylic acids remained in solution (cystine as cysteine only in the presence of H_2S). Furthermore, the three basic amino acids could be separated as a mixture of arginine and lysine on the one hand, and histidine on the other, by elution with HCl, neutralization, and adsorption only of the former pair on basic alumina, or basic Wofatit C (cf. 303), which held little if any of the histidine. Arginine and lysine could in turn be separated by adsorption of the former on Floridin XXF Extra in the presence of $M/6$ KH_2PO_4 (304). A variation in the procedure of separating a mixture of the three basic amino acids was essentially as follows. The mixture was adsorbed on Floridin XXF Extra, and subsequent elution with water removed histidine and any monoaminomonocarboxylic acid present. Subsequent elution with $M/6$ KH_2PO_4 removed lysine. The arginine was finally eluted with a pyridine-H_2SO_4 mixture.

Aspartic acid could be separated from glutamic acid by elution of the latter from acid alumina by means of acetate at pH 3.3. Apart from the already known ready separation of the phenylalanine, tyrosine, and tryptophan on charcoal, no method was available for the most difficult task of all, namely, the separation of the individual monoaminomonocarboxylic acids. This was successfully accomplished in a few cases by Schramm and Primosigh (302), who used 10% formaldehyde as a solvent, and through the well-known reaction of this agent with the simpler amino acids effectively sharpened the differences among them. Their scheme of operation was essentially as follows. The protein hydrolysate was neutralized and poured through a column of Filtrol-Neutral (silica gel) which removed arginine, lysine, and histidine. The eluate was then passed through a column of acid alumina, which removed glutamic acid, aspartic acid, and cystine. The eluate from this operation was passed through a charcoal column pretreated with HCN whereby tyrosine, phenylalanine, and tryptophan were removed. This eluate was treated with formaldehyde to 10% and poured on a column of acid alumina, which removed serine, glycine, threonine, and cysteine, leaving proline, hydroxyproline, alanine, valine, leucine, isoleucine, and methionine in the final eluate.

In the presence of formaldehyde the neutral amino acids and peptides acquire acidic properties to a degree which depends upon their structure. The approximate pK'_2 of glycine, serine, threonine, and cysteine in 10% formaldehyde is 5.8, whilst that of glycyl peptides is 4.2; both groups of compounds are adsorbed on acid alumina, whereas the remaining neutral amino acids whose pK'_2 under the same conditions is nearer 7.0 are not adsorbed (305). In the presence of 1% formaldehyde, however, only the glycyl peptides, of the three groups of compounds, are adsorbed on acid alumina. It is not improbable that seryl, threonyl, and cysteinyl peptides would follow the same pattern of behavior as the glycyl peptides.

An analogous scheme was devised by Turba, Richter, and Kuchar (279) in which the amino acids in the final eluate mentioned above were treated in an alcohol-water mixture with a fuller's earth which adsorbed alanine and proline, and with charcoal which partially separated valine and the leucines. From an alcohol-water mixture, alanine could be adsorbed on alumina, whereas proline passed into the eluate. Filtrol-Neutrol pretreated at pH 5.5 adsorbed from an alcohol-water mixture proline, glycine, and alanine, whereas valine and the leucines passed into the eluate. The use of alcohol in these chromatographic operations probably played the same role as did that of formaldehyde in the Schramm and Primosigh procedure, namely, in producing unequal changes in the dissociation constants of the ionizing groups of the amino acids and thereby accentuating the differences among these compounds. Phenylalanine, tyrosine, and tryptophan, which were quantitatively adsorbed on charcoal pretreated with acetic acid and HCN, were removed by an acetic acid–phenol mixture, and subsequently run on a column of Wofatit M (279). Only tryptophan was adsorbed, whereas tyrosine and phenylalanine appeared in the eluate. These could be adsorbed on the usual charcoal column. Tryptophan was removed from the Wofatit M resin with aqueous pyridine or even alcohol-water.

A most interesting and unexploited type of adsorbent, bearing considerable resemblance in behavior to that of acid alumina, is the silver sulfide–silver nitrate system (306). Silver salts of the amino acids with predictable properties are formed and separated.

From these early experiments with ion exchangers a good deal of valuable information accrued. The cationic exchangers were found to function optimally in neutral or almost neutral solutions after treatment with HCl and washing out with water. The strongly acid resins with —SO$_3$H groups bound all amino acids as cations, whereas those resins with carboxyl groups bound only the basic amino acids. Elution in all cases was brought about by suitably concentrated HCl solutions. If slow enough this should be a typical displacement reaction, but if conducted rapidly the acid would overrun the other ions, yielding typical elution phenomena. A careful study of the role of several cation exchangers in the separation of the basic amino acids was reported by Block (307). In analogous fashion, the anion exchangers such

CHROMATOGRAPHY

as Amberlite IR-4 bound the dicarboxylic amino acids in a mixture of the resin with the amino acids at a final pH of 6 to 7. Again, here the amino acids could be eluted with suitably concentrated HCl (296). A compilation of all these procedures is that devised by Winters and Kunin which may be represented as in the accompanying sequence (308). Here the amino acid mixture is passed over a strong-base anion exchanger which adsorbs all the

Sequence of Separation of Amino Acids on Ion Exchangers (308)

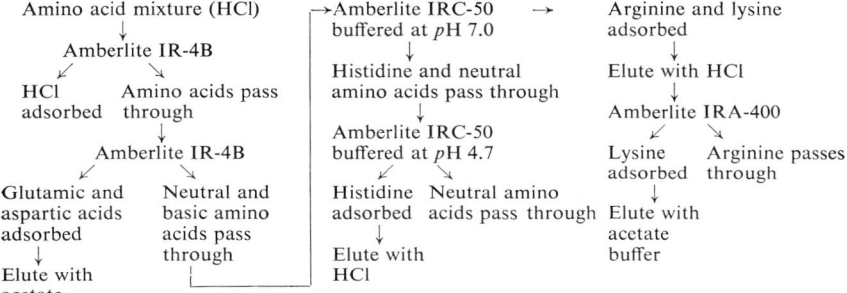

amino acids except arginine. The adsorbed amino acids are desorbed with dilute HCl and passed over IR-4B, which adsorbs the dicarboxylic amino acids. The resulting solution contains the neutral and residual basic amino acids, which may be separated by passing the solution over a carboxylic cation exchange resin, the first at pH 7.0, and the second at pH 4.7. Lysine is adsorbed on the first, and histidine on the second.

The various cation and anion exchange resins may be considered insoluble high molecular weight polymeric electrolytes. The cation resins contain polar anionic groups such as sulfonic, carboxylic, and phenolic, which are non-diffusible, and which are balanced with simple, diffusible cations. The apparent ionization constants as calculated from titration curves are approximately 2, 5 to 6, and 10 for the sulfonic, carboxylic, and phenolic resins, respectively. The nature of the cation exchanger polar group is therefore important in regard to the equilibria involving the hydrogen ion, but this is not the only factor which comes into play, for the physical structure of the resin is also decisive where large ions are to be accommodated (see below).

The anion exchange resins are frequently weakly basic polyamines which function either by an acid adsorption, or by an exchange, i.e., $RNH_3^+ + OH^- + X^- \rightleftharpoons RNH_3X + OH^-$, and $OH^- + H^+ \rightarrow H_2O$. Thus, when acid is added to this system, the hydroxyl ions are replaced by the anion of the acid whilst the hydroxyl combines with the hydrogen ion of the acid. Stronger basic resins may contain $(CH_3)_3N^+$ (Dowex 1) or $[(CH_3)_2CH_2OH]N^+$ groups.

Table 15-22 describes some of the ion exchange resins which have been employed in the separation of the amino acids and peptides. A more complete discussion on the various resins is to be found in such monographs as that by Kunin and Myers (309).

TABLE 15-22

Ion Exchange Resins

Cation Exchangers

Name	Manufacturer	Type	Capacity, meq. per g.
Amberlite IR-100	Rohm & Haas	Phenolic methylene sulfonic	1.75
Amberlite IR-105	Rohm & Haas	As above	2.70
Dowex 30	Dow	As above	4.00
Wofatit K	I. G. Farben	As above	2.50
Zeo-Karb	Permutit	Sulfonated coal	1.62
Zeo-Rex	Permutit	Phenolic methylene sulfonic	2.70
Amberlite IR-120	Rohm & Haas	Nuclear sulfonic	4.20
Dowex 50	Dow	Nuclear sulfonic	4.25
Amberlite IRC-50 (XE-64)	Rohm & Haas	Carboxylic	10.0
Wofatit C	I. G. Farben	Carboxylic	7.00
Permutit	Permutit	Aluminum silicate	1-3
Silica gel	–	Silicic acid	0.01-0.04

Anion Exchangers

Name	Manufacturer	Type	Capacity, meq. per g.
Amberlite IR-4B	Rohm & Haas	Weak base	10.0
Amberlite IR-45	Rohm & Haas	Weak base	6.0
Amberlite IRA-410	Rohm & Haas	Strong base	2.5
Amberlite IRA-400	Rohm & Haas	Strong base	2.3
Wofatit M	I. G. Farben	Weak base	–
Alumina	–	Amphoteric	0.01
Dowex 2	Dow	Strong base	2.3
Dowex 1	Dow	Stong base	2.4

28. Displacement Chromatography with Ion Exchange Resins. As alluded to above, the techniques of displacement chromatography were first developed on charcoal columns by Tiselius (282) and Claesson (283), and were based on the progressive displacement of compounds adsorbed on the column by compounds still more strongly adsorbed. The compounds so displaced formed a progressive series of contiguous bands which implied a certain degree of mixing at the boundaries, but in all cases the maximum use was made of the adsorption capacity of the column. The application of these procedures on a relatively large scale to the separation of amino acids on ion exchange resins is attributable to Partridge and his co-workers (115, 310–314), and was accomplished and described in a notable series of publications between 1948 and 1953.

The great virtue of the displacement method is the ease of separation and of preparation of the amino acids in quantity. Thus Partridge and Brimley (314) reported the hydrolysis and separation of the amino acids from 280 g. of egg albumin, and Westall (315) could isolate 3 g. of γ-aminobutyric acid from beet roots. Of equal importance is the generally sound theoretical basis of the procedure, which is largely due to Davies (316), and which is developed from the ionic equilibria of both exchanger and amino acid.

If the resin is a strong acid, it will be fully ionized and will react stoichiometrically with a solution of a strong base, the cation of the base exchanging for the H^+ of the resin. With weak bases, the reaction with the resin will be quite different in character and will depend in large measure upon the dissociation constant of the base. For a cation exchange column, an order of displacement would be expected for a series of amino acids which would run parallel with the order of dissociation constants for the process $A^+ \rightleftharpoons A^\pm + H^+$, i.e., with the order of pK_1 for monoaminomonocarboxylic acids; diamino acids because of their bivalent charge should be retarded. Similarly, the order of displacement on an anion exchange column should be directly related to the dissociation constant for the reactions $A^\pm \rightleftharpoons H^+ + A^-$, i.e., the values of pK_2, and again amino acids forming bivalent anions should be strongly retarded. Thus conditions during the separation of a mixture of monoaminomonocarboxylic acids with a strongly acidic cation exchange resin may be represented as follows (314, cf. 316):

$$\text{Resin} \begin{array}{c} SO_3^- \cdots A_1^+ \\ \updownarrow \\ A_1^\pm + H^+ \\ \\ SO_3^- \cdots A_2^+ \\ \updownarrow \\ A_2^\pm + H^+ \end{array} \rightleftharpoons \begin{array}{c} A_1^+ \rightleftharpoons A_1^\pm + H^+ \\ \\ A_2^+ \rightleftharpoons A_2^\pm + H^+ \end{array}$$

The resin adsorbs the amino acid only in the form of the cation, and this form will be in reversible equilibrium with H^+ in the surface layer. The displacement of the weaker base, A_2, will depend in effect upon the partial suppression of the cationic form of A_2 by the presence of the stronger base, A_1. In the same way, with anion exchange resins, the principle of displace-

TABLE 15–23

Sequence of Displacement of Amino Acids (314)

Sulfonated Cross-Linked Polystyrene (4.5% divinylbenzene)		Dowex 2	
Sequence (Cation)	Relevant pK	Sequence (Anion)	Relevant pK
Aspartic acid	$pK_1 = 1.88$	Lysine	$pK_3 = 10.53$
Hydroxyproline	$pK_1 = 1.92$	Proline	$pK_2 = 10.60*$
Threonine	$pK_1 = 2.15^a$	β-Alanine	$pK_2 = 10.19$
Serine	$pK_1 = 2.21$	β-Aminoisobutyric acid	–
Glutamic acid	$pK_1 = 2.19$	Alanine	$pK_2 = 9.69$
Proline	$pK_1 = 1.99*$	Butyrine	$pK_2 = 9.60$
Glycine	$pK_1 = 2.34$	Valine	$pK_2 = 9.62$
Alanine	$pK_1 = 2.34$	Leucine	$pK_2 = 9.60$
Valine	$pK_1 = 2.32$	Glycine	$pK_2 = 9.60$
Methionine	$pK_1 = 2.28*$	Carnosine	$pK_2 = 9.51$
Leucine	$pK_1 = 2.36$	Glutamine	$pK_2 = 9.73*$
Cystine	$pK_2 = 2.26*$	Threonine	$pK_2 = 9.12^a$
Creatine	$pK_1 = 3.0\ (ca.)$	Serine	$pK_2 = 9.15$
Phenylalanine	$pK_1 = 1.83*$	Histidine	$pK_3 = 9.17*$
β-Alanine	$pK_1 = 3.60$	Methionine	$pK_2 = 9.21*$
Histidine	$pK_2 = 6.0$	Asparagine	$pK_2 = 8.80$
Methylhistidine	$pK_2 = 6.48$	Methylhistidine	$pK_3 = 8.85$
Carnosine	$pK_2 = 6.83$	Cystine	$pK_3 = 7.85$
Anserine	$pK_2 = 7.04$	Phenylalanine	$pK_2 = 9.13*$
Hydroxylysine	$pK_2 = 8.62^a$	Tyrosine	$pK_2 = 9.11*$
Lysine	$pK_2 = 8.95$	Glutamic acid	$pK_2 = 4.25$
Ammonia	$pK = 9.27$	Aspartic acid	$pK_2 = 3.65$
Arginine	$pK_2 = 9.04$	Hydrochloric acid	–
Methylamine	$pK = 10.64$		

^{a} Data from this Laboratory, taken from Table 4–11.

ment depends upon the depression of the dissociation of the weakly acid ampholytes by those with more strongly acid properties. The experimental proof for these relations is shown in Table 15–23 (314), which lists the experimentally determined order of displacement of a number of solutes from a strongly acidic cation exchange resin and a strongly basic anion exchange resin, together with the relevant pK values taken from Cohn and Edsall (317). The order of displacement is substantially that of the order of pK values, but in several cases (those marked with an asterisk in Table 15–23), the amino acid is more strongly retarded than would be expected, e.g., the aromatic amino acids, proline, and methionine (cf. 318). It is not inconceivable in these anomalous cases that what occurs may be due either to solubility effects or to short-range adsorption forces associated in the main with ring structures. Amino acids which form mixed bands in the displacement procedure are bracketed together in Table 15–3. Where such mixed bands occur in the use of one resin, resolution may be accomplished by the use of another resin over a different range of pH, or by employing heated columns.

Partridge and Brimley (314) used three ion exchange resins in the course of their work, namely, Zeo Karb 215, a sulfonated polystyrene resin of their own preparation, and Dowex 2. Their columns ranged in size from 61 x 7.6 cm. to 4.8 x 0.8 cm. The difficulty due to distortion in the use of the larger columns was removed by what they called the "multiple column" principle, which was in effect a series of connected columns of diminishing diameter. The procedure of separating the amino acids in a mixture was first to carry out a primary fractionation in which the components were separated as a series of groups. The members of each group could then be separated on another resin with quite different properties. The following sequence of events was employed in the separation of amino acids from a protein hydrolysate.

Step 1. The aromatic amino acids were adsorbed on charcoal.

Step 2. The effluent (amino acids as the hydrochlorides) was poured on a column of sulfonated polystyrene resin as cation exchange, and displaced with a solution of sodium hydroxide. This stage separated arginine, lysine, and histidine on the column. The ammonia band fell between those of arginine and lysine, the ammonia thus acting as a carrier displacer (284; see above).

Step 3. The eluate containing the acidic and neutral amino acids was passed through a column of the cation exchanger Zeo Karb 215, which was subsequently displaced with dilute ammonia solution. This resulted in a series of bands, overlapping at the edges, and including, in the order of their emergence, aspartic acid, threonine-serine-glutamic acid, alanine-glycine, valine-proline, and leucine-isoleucine-methionine. The aspartic acid was thus obtained pure at this stage.

Step 4. Each of these bands was passed through a column of the anion exchanger Dowex 2 and displaced with dilute hydrochloric acid to yield the individual amino acids.

Thus the threonine-serine-glutamic acid band separated into three sharp bands; the first was the alanine-glycine overlap which was discarded, the second was the serine-threonine mixture, and the third was pure glutamic acid. The alanine-glycine band separated first into pure alanine and then into pure glycine. The valine-proline band which badly overlapped the neighboring two bands was recycled with Zeo Karb and then separated on Dowex 2 into pure valine and proline. The leucine-isoleucine-methionine band was readily resolved into leucine-isoleucine and methionine.

The identity of each amino acid in the effluent was checked by paper chromatograms, and the overlap region between contiguous zones was frequently discarded. All the amino acids were readily obtained in a relatively pure state, except leucine, which emerged with isoleucine, and threonine, which emerged with serine. The latter pair were separated by displacement on a sulfonated polystyrene resin, using sodium hydroxide dissolved in 50% aqueous acetone as the displacement developer. The isomeric leucines were not separated. A separation of amino acids such as occurs in the proline-valine-methionine band which emerges from Zeo Karb at 20° could be achieved when the temperature was raised to 60° and presumably the non-ionic adsorption effects were diminished (314). The use of the Tiselius and Hagdahl principle of carrier displacement (288), originally applied to charcoal columns (see above), was successfully employed with ion exchange resins by Buchanan (319); such substances as pyrazole, nicotinamide, piperidine, acetic acid, and hydrazine were useful in assuming positions in the displacement order of amino acids ordinarily separated with difficulty.

Displacement chromatography has found intensive application in the isolation of amino acids and related compounds, many of a rare sort, from biological sources. A general procedure for such isolations from urine has been described by Westall (320), and the separation and identification of β-aminoisobutyric acid (113), methylhistidine (116), and felinine (118) have been accomplished. From various biological sources γ-aminobutyric acid (315, 321), sarcosine (158), L-pipecolic acid (144), and γ-methyleneglutamine (136) have been isolated. With one exception, these amino acids occurred in the free and uncombined state. Sarcosine, however, together with N-methyl-L-valine, was isolated from a hydrolysate of actinomycin (158), first by a crude separation on Zeo Karb 215, and then on a column of cellulose. The last-mentioned adsorbent has not received much attention as a separation medium for amino acids, partly because of its small capacity, but it is nevertheless highly efficient where relatively small amounts of material are concerned. After treatment of a hog liver homogenate with Zeo Karb 225, a sulfonated phenol-formaldehyde resin, which removed 48% of the water-soluble dialyzable nitrogen, Campbell and Work (322, 323) could isolate from the effluent glycerylphosphorylethanolamine, ethanolaminephosphate, and taurine. The presence of salts in biological fluids has little effect on displacement reactions, for on passing the mixture through a column of a

CHROMATOGRAPHY

strongly acidic cation exchange resin in the hydrogen form the inorganic cations remain at the top of the column whereas the organic and inorganic anions pass through. The column containing only cations and ampholytes is then washed with water. Inasmuch as the inorganic cations do not interfere with the subsequent displacement when sodium hydroxide or ammonia is used as developer, the isolation of the amino acids can be accomplished by the usual procedures.

29. Elution Analysis with Ion Exchange Resins. The most elegant and precise of modern analytical devices for the separation and identification of the amino acids in a mixture are those developed by Moore and Stein. Starting with the use of starch columns for this purpose, they shortly added synthetic ion exchange resins as a further analytical tool. These resins possess one great advantage over starch in that salts do not interfere as much with the separation of the amino acids; others are the greater capacity and the greater speed of operation. In the first report on the subject, Moore and Stein (324) employed the nuclear sulfonic acid polymer Dowex 50 in the hydrogen form and separated the amino acids in a mixture by employing 1.5N HCl for the early peaks, followed by 2.5N and lastly by 4.0N HCl. The order of emergence of the amino acids from the column was quite different from that which occurred with starch, and was, as might be expected, more like that in the displacement chromatogram (cf. Table 15–23). Moreover, in the aliphatic series of amino acids, namely, glycine, alanine, valine, isoleucine, and leucine, the order of emergence on Dowex 50 was completely reversed from that on starch; thus, whereas on starch glycine was last to emerge, on Dowex 50 it was first. The use of strong HCl as a developer possessed definite limitations (as well as advantages), and Moore and Stein (324) subsequently employed Dowex 50 in the sodium form and developed the column with a series of buffers of progressively increasing pH, starting from 3.4 and ending at pH 11. With a column of 0.9 × 100 cm. dimensions, and with 3 to 6 mg. of amino acid mixture simulating that resulting from a protein hydrolysate, an effluent curve was obtained in which every component emerged as a discrete peak. Quantitative recoveries were obtained for all but the basic amino acids; these were determined with the aid of a second and much shorter column, with buffers in the range of pH 5 to 6.8. The separations were dependent in part on temperature. Thus methionine and isoleucine emerged together at 25°, but at 60° the former preceded the latter. Tyrosine and phenylalanine were completely resolved at 60°, whereas at 25° and 37° they emerged as one peak. When, however, the column was operated at 60°, isoleucine and leucine were poorly separated. Consideration of all the factors involved led to the sequence portrayed in Figure 15–41. With the use of buffers, the pH of the ambient fluid in these elution procedures was predetermined. In contrast, in the displacement chromatograms of Partridge, the pH of the ambient fluid was controlled only by the presence of the amino acids themselves. During the fractionation of the amino acids by this method the pH of the first fractions, beginning with aspartic acid, was about 3.6, the pH then gradually rising as the other amino

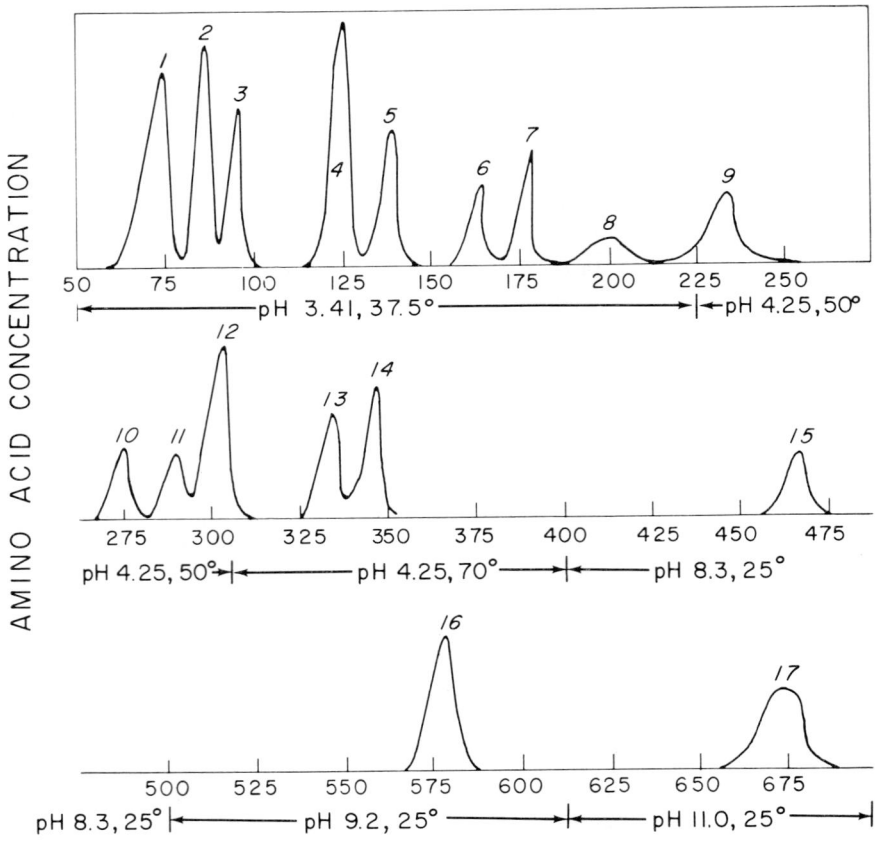

Figure 15-41. Separation of amino acids on Dowex 50 (Na+) with buffers indicated as eluents. 1, Aspartic acid; 2, threonine; 3, serine; 4, glutamic acid; 5, proline; 6, glycine; 7, alanine; 8, cystine; 9, valine; 10, methionine; 11, isoleucine; 12, leucine; 13, tyrosine; 14, phenylalanine; 15, histidine; 16, lysine; and 17, arginine. Moore, S., and Stein, W. H., *J. Biol. Chem.*, **192**, 663 (1951).

acids emerged in order of their pK_1 values, finally reaching a value of pH of about 10 in the region of lysine. The formation of elution peaks in the procedures of Moore and Stein depended to some degree on the presence in the developing solutions of cations capable of competing with the cationic form of the amino acids. Where acids were the developers the competing cations were hydrogen ions, and where sodium buffers were used for this purpose the competing ions were sodium ions. In either case, the peak of a given amino acid would be likely to be accelerated by an increase in ionic strength. Thus an acceleration of the arginine peak was accomplished by increasing the concentration of the sodium citrate buffer (324). Quantitative recovery of the basic amino acids was accomplished by employing a shorter column, and by eluting with buffers below pH 7, e.g., histidine and lysine with phosphate buffer at pH 6.5, and arginine with a citrate buffer at pH 6.5.

Of some interest was the finding that the properties of the eluant could be changed by the addition of an organic solvent (324). The presence of benzyl alcohol sharpened the peaks of the aromatic amino acids and accelerated their rates of travel. In general, the use of organic solvents mixed with the buffers produced a preferential accelerated rate of travel of the amino acids with longer non-polar side chains, e.g., alanine moved ahead of glycine, etc.

A chromatographic analysis of thirty-two ninhydrin-positive substances was studied on the Dowex 50 resin, and thirty recognizable peaks were obtained. The order of emergence of the peaks (buffer at pH 3.41, $T = 37.5°$) was cysteic acid, taurine, urea, hydroxyproline (buffer at pH 3.2), aspartic acid, threonine, serine plus asparagine, sarcosine, glutamic acid, citrulline (poorly defined), proline, glycine, alanine plus α-aminoadipic acid, cystine, butyrine (buffer at pH 4.25, $T = 50°$), valine, methionine, isoleucine, leucine (pH 4.25, $T = 75°$), glucosamine, tyrosine, phenylalanine (pH 8.3, $T = 25°$), β-alanine, histidine (pH 9.2, $T = 25°$), hydroxylysine, tryptophan (poorly resolved), ornithine, lysine (pH 11.0, $T = 25°$), ethanolamine, and arginine. The concentration of amino acids in each fraction of effluent was brought to pH 5 and determined by the ninhydrin procedure (214), proline and hydroxyproline being measured at 440 mμ, and the rest at 570 mμ (cf. Table 15–20).

A study of the effect of the nature of the resin revealed marked differences according to the particle size and degree of cross-linking of the polystyrene polymers. The standard Dowex 50 resin used in the early experiments of Moore and Stein had been prepared from styrene copolymerized with about 8% divinylbenzene (324). The product was considered to have a molecular structure characteristic of 8% cross-linking. When amino acids were chromatographed on a 16% cross-linked resin, of the same mesh (250–500) as the 8%, and at a similar rate of solvent flow, very poorly resolved zones were obtained. When a 2% cross-linked resin was employed, poor resolution was also obtained. It would appear therefore that the efficiency of the resin would be held within limits set by the molecular weight and characteristics of the compounds to be chromatographed. Inasmuch as resins of high resolving power with 4% cross-linking were subsequently studied, and given the designation Dowex 50-X4, the earlier resin was distinguished from this by the appellation Dowex 50-X8 (324). Particle sizes of 20–40 microns were quite effective (324a), when uniformly employed.

Dowex 50-X8 was employed by Stein for the characterization of the amino acids in normal human urine (325). A phosphate buffer at pH 7.5 was interposed between the pH 6.7 and 8.3 buffers (cf. Figure 15–41) to permit the separation of creatine, histidine, and methylhistidine. The ninhydrin color value for taurine was 0.97, for methylhistidine 0.85, and for α-aminoadipic acid 0.95. Table 15–24 lists the daily excretion of the various amino acids

TABLE 15-24

Amino Acid Content of Normal Human (Male) Urine in Milligrams per 24 Hours (325)

Amino Acid	Average Value, mg.	Amino Acid	Average Value, mg.
Taurine	156	Valine	<10
Aspartic acid	<10	Methionine	<10
Threonine	28	Isoleucine	18
Serine	43	Leucine	14
Asparagine	54	Tyrosine	35
Glutamic acid	<10	Phenylalanine	18
Proline	<10	Histidine	216
Glycine	132	Methylhistidine	180
Alanine	46	Lysine	19
α-Aminoadipic acid	10 ca.	Arginine	<10
Cystine	10 ca.		

in milligrams. On acid hydrolysis of the urine, relatively large amounts of glycine, glutamic acid, and aspartic acid were liberated. Only a small proportion of the conjugated forms of these amino acids could be accounted for in terms of hippuric acid, glutamine, and asparagine. Other amino acids which were present in appreciable amounts in conjugated forms were proline, cystine, threonine, serine, valine, tyrosine, and lysine. However, little or no increase after hydrolysis was noted for taurine, isoleucine, leucine, methylhistidine, or arginine. Approximately twice the amount of amino acids was excreted in the bound as in the free form. Four amino acids, taurine, glycine, histidine, and methylhistidine, comprised about 70% of all the amino acids excreted in the free form. The results in Table 15–24 were obtained without any attempt to control the diet of the subjects studied. Essentially compatible data were later obtained by Evered (326).

A similar study was instituted by Stein (327) on the urine of patients with cystinuria; he used the same separation procedures with Dowex 50-X8 as with the urine of normal subjects. Five patients were studied, with no attention to dietary control, and the remarkable amino acid pattern which was divulged was common to all five (Table 15-25). There was an unusually high excretion of ornithine, cystine, arginine, and lysine, a moderately increased excretion of isoleucine, and a greatly decreased excretion of taurine, as compared with the normal. None of these values appreciably increased on boiling the urine with strong HCl. All the other amino acids in the urine of the cystinuric patients were present at normal levels. The elution analysis data were in complete agreement with the results obtained by Dent, who used paper chromatography (109).

TABLE 15-25

Amino Acids in Unusual Concentration in the Urine of Cystinuric Patients (327)

	Excretion, mg. per day					Normal range, mg.
Ornithine	420,	180,	360,	500,	420	None
Cystine	970,	420,	820,	740,	700	10-30
Arginine	1240,	550,	920,	770,	670	0-20
Lysine	2300,	1000,	1980,	2380,	1350	10-50
Isoleucine	57,	38,	43,	65,	64	15-30
Taurine	50,	8,	62,	86,	52	100-300

Up to this point a quite satisfactory resolution of mixtures of a large number of amino acids in protein hydrolysates had been achieved by the Moore and Stein technique, employing Dowex 50-X8 screened through a 200-mesh sieve (74-μ openings) (213, 324). With such screened resins the leucine-isoleucine and tyrosine-phenylalanine separations were essentially complete, and the cystine peak was sharp. An increased resolving power for more complex mixtures was found in the use of 4% cross-linked sulfonated polystyrene resin, Dowex 50-X4, in conjunction with an eluent of continuously changing pH and ionic strength, and a temperature-controlled column 150 x 0.9 cm. This resin yielded sharp peaks with small peptides as well as with amino acids, and permitted mixtures of the two to be fractionated on the same column. For peptides containing more than 8 or 10 amino acid residues, Dowex 50-X2 was considered preferable (213). The resin was prepared in the sodium phase through successive washing with 4N HCl, water, and 2N NaOH to alkalinity, then suspending in three times the volume of N NaOH and heating with stirring on the steam bath for 3 hours, repeating this heating procedure with fresh N NaOH five times, filtering, and washing free of alkali with water, sieving through a 120-mesh screen with much water, and finally equilibrating with a sodium citrate buffer at pH 3.1. In order to analyze mixtures containing taurine and urea, an initial equilibration with a sodium citrate buffer at pH 2.2 was performed. The solution to be chromatographed was adjusted to pH 2.0 to 2.5 and poured onto the column. The buffer at pH 3.1 was added, the column mounted over a fraction collector, and the temperature of the column adjusted to 30°. Effluent fractions of 2 ml. were collected at a maximal rate of 8 ml. per hour, and occasionally 0.5-ml. effluent fractions were collected where sharp resolutions of complex mixtures were desired. Cysteic acid plus phosphoserine, glycerophosphoethanolamine, phosphoethanolamine, taurine, urea, hydroxyproline, methionine sulfoxide, aspartic acid, threonine, and serine emerged in the order named. After the emergence of serine the temperature was raised to 50°, and a gradual increase in the pH and ionic strength of the influent was begun. For the latter purpose a mixing chamber was employed, the ionic strength being increased thereby from $0.2N$ Na$^+$ to $1.4N$, and the pH from 3.1 to 5.1. There emerged, in the order named, glutamine plus asparagine plus sarcosine, proline, glutamic acid, lanthionine, citrulline plus felinine, glycine, alanine, α-aminoadipic acid, butyrine, valine, cystine, cystathionine, diaminopimelic acid, isoleucine, leucine, β-alanine, β-aminoisobutyric acid, homocystine, tyrosine, phenylalanine, γ-aminobutyric acid, hydroxylysine, ethanolamine, ammonia, ornithine, lysine, creatinine, and histidine. The temperature was increased to 75°, and there emerged 1-methylhistidine plus anserine plus carnosine, 3-methylhistidine, tryptophan, and, lastly, arginine. When a 2.5-mg. mixture of the common 18 amino acids in proteins was analyzed, corresponding to some 0.1 to 0.2 mg. of each component amino acid, recoveries within 3% of theory were achieved, except for methionine. The recovery of methionine to only 90% may have been due to some measure of oxidation despite the invariable presence of thiodiglycol as an antioxidant agent. Tryptophan was recovered to only 40 to 60% (213), although this amino acid can be nearly quantitatively recovered from starch columns operated with dilute HCl (258), or, even with less selectivity, from columns of Dowex 50-X8 (324). The losses of tryptophan in boiling acid solvents, as in protein hydrolysates, are of course nonrecoverable. The low recoveries of glutamine under the acidic conditions were not unexpected. The glutamine-asparagine combined peak could be analyzed after HCl hydrolysis to glutamic and aspartic acids, respectively, by chromatography of the resulting amino acids on Dowex 50-X4 at 30° and with a buffer at pH 3.1 as eluent. Anserine and carnosine could also be distinguished by the different peaks of methylhistidine and of histidine resulting after HCl hydrolysis of the combined peptide effluent. To resolve the citrulline-felinine-glycine overlap, the fractions were concentrated, brought to pH 2, and rechromatographed on Dowex 50-X8 at pH 3.42 and 37° (213). Citrulline could be determined directly on Dowex 50-X4 at pH 3.1 if the column were operated at 50° from the beginning of the run, the amino acid emerging just before glycine. The separation of all the amino acids required about one week's duration and was accomplished generally on a single chromatogram. (The recent development of automatic devices and the use of a different resin have reduced this period of time to 24 hours (see below)). The use of eluents of continuously changing composition possessed the advantage in that it eliminated the loss of resolving power which ordinarily occurred after stepwise changes in the composition of the eluent (cf. 324, 328). Various experimental devices for gradient elution in column chromatography have been described by Bock and Ling (329) and by Peterson and Sober in this Laboratory. The separation of histidine from hydroxylysine and of ornithine from lysine requires some care; the latter three amino acids are best resolved at pH 5.0 (330).

The first application of this new chromatographic procedure was the determination of the free amino acids of human protein-free blood plasma (331). The qualitative results obtained were not unanticipated in view of the many prior studies by the use of microbiological assays, chemical determinations, and paper chromatography (332, 333). Thus the presence of taurine (35), butyrine (35), asparagine (119, 334), citrulline (335), and glutamine (336) had previously been observed. The power of the ion exchange resin chromatography as developed by Stein and Moore, however, lent more confidence to the quantitative results obtained. A typical chromatogram of the ninhydrin-positive components of protein-free human blood plasma (adult males) is given in Figure 15–42. The greater part of the ammonia found was probably due to breakdown of glutamine.

The plasma pattern is very different from that of urine (331). In urine, taurine is a major component, glycine is present to a much greater extent than is alanine, proline and valine are low in amount, whilst histidine, 1-methylhistidine, and 3-methylhistidine are present to a much greater extent than is lysine. In plasma, the situation is quite the converse. Aspartic and glutamic acids are low or nearly absent in both plasma and urine, but are found in relatively high concentrations in deproteinized extracts of most tissues. Table 15–26 gives a picture of the free amino acids of post-absorptive plasma from normal adult males. The urea values range from 27 to 42 mg. per cent.

Major quantities of conjugated amino acids are apparently absent in plasma (331, 337). In fasting subjects, hydrolysis of the protein-free plasma produces no appreciable changes in the concentration of most of the amino acids, except for aspartic and glutamic acids whose rise could conceivably originate by hydrolysis of asparagine and glutamine, respectively (331). After a protein-containing meal, the free amino acid concentration increases (338), but on HCl hydrolysis there is no appreciable increase in the concentration of any of the amino acids except the two already mentioned.

The red blood cells of the normal adult human being are characterized by a high content of glutathione (about 50 mg. per 100 ml. of cells), which is comparable with that found in many tissues (331). In relation to plasma, the red cells contain more free taurine, aspartic and glutamic acids, glycine, and ornithine, whereas the amounts of cystine and valine are less. The concentration of the other amino acids are about the same in plasma and red cells (331). In the cystinuric patient, the concentrations of cystine (0.54 mg. per cent), arginine (0.89 mg. per cent), and alanine (2.58 mg. per

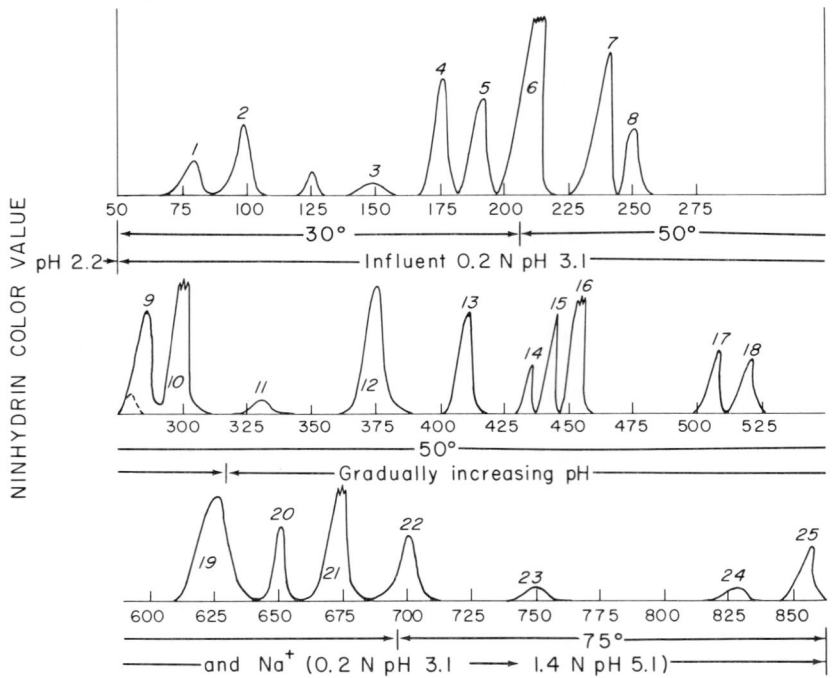

Figure 15-42. Ninhydrin-positive components of protein-free human blood plasma obtained from adult males in the post-absorptive state, separated on Dowex 50-X4 (Na+). 1, Taurine; 2, urea; 3, aspartic acid; 4, threonine; 5, serine; 6, glutamine, asparagine; 7, proline; 8, glutamic acid; 9, glycine (dashed curve represents citrulline); 10, alanine; 11, butyrine; 12, valine; 13, cystine; 14, methionine; 15, isoleucine; 16, leucine; 17, tyrosine; 18, phenylalanine; 19, ammonia; 20, ornithine; 21, lysine; 22, histidine; 23, 1-methylhistidine, 3-methylhistidine; 24, tryptophan; 25, arginine. Stein, W. H., and Moore, S., *J. Biol. Chem.*, **211**, 915 (1954).

cent) are slightly below normal, the concentration of glycine (2.56 mg. per cent) is elevated, while the levels of all other amino acids, including lysine, ornithine, and citrulline, are in the normal range. The increased excretion of cystine, lysine, arginine, and ornithine in such a patient (327, 339) is therefore not a reflection of high plasma levels of these amino acids.

The concentration of phenylalanine in the plasma of a patient with phenylpyruvic oligophrenia was 23.5 mg. per cent, and the urinary excretion 334 mg. per day (331; cf. 251, 332, 333), whereas all the other amino acids in blood and in urine were within the normal ranges. Phenacetylglutamine is a component of normal human urine (250 to 500 mg. per day), and it accounts for about 50% of the conjugated glutamic acid of urine (340); in a case of phenylpyruvic oligophrenia the excretion of this compound rose to 2.4 g. per day (cf. 123). Changes in the amino acid patterns in other pathologic states such as Wilson's disease have been reported (338).

TABLE 15-26

Free Amino Acids of Normal Human Blood Plasma (331)

Amino Acid	Milligrams Amino Acid per 100 ml. Plasma (average of 5 subjects)	Amino Acid	Milligrams Amino Acid per 100 ml. Plasma (average of 5 subjects)
Aspartic acid	0.03	Methionine	0.38
Asparagine	0.58	Taurine	0.55
Glutamic acid	0.70	Proline	2.36
Glutamine	8.30	Phenylalanine	0.84
Glycine	1.54	Tyrosine	1.03
Alanine	3.41	Tryptophan	1.11
Butyrine	0.30	Histidine	1.15
Valine	2.88	1-Methylhistidine	0.11
Leucine	1.69	3-Methylhistidine	0.08
Isoleucine	0.89	Ornithine	0.72
Serine	1.12	Lysine	2.72
Threonine	1.39	Arginine	1.51
Cysteine-cystine	1.18	Citrulline	0.50

Tallan, Moore, and Stein (341) investigated the free amino acid patterns of the deproteinized extracts of the cat with the aid of chromatograms on Dowex 50-X4. Table 15-27 lists the compounds identified. In general, the data are qualitatively comparable with those obtained by Roberts et al. (172, 174) and by Astrup et al. (342), who used techniques of paper chromatography with tissue extracts from other species. Glycerophosphoethanolamine (171) is high not only in liver but also in kidney; phosphoethanolamine (149, 342, 343) is highest in pancreas; glutamine noted in tissues by Hamilton (336) and Krebs et al. (344) is generally high throughout, whereas asparagine, first noted in tissues by Krebs (345), is found in all tissues at about one-tenth the level of glutamine; felinine (118) is remarkably high in cat urine, but low or absent in other tissues and in plasma, and probably arises by a normal metabolic factor in the kidney from which it is directly excreted; taurine (35, 172, 346) is present in high concentration in all tissues; 3-methylhistidine (347) is chiefly a urinary component, whereas 1-methylhistidine is a major component of gastrocnemius muscle; 1-methylhistidine

TABLE 15-27
Free Amino Acids and Related Compounds in the Protein-Free Tissue Extracts of the Cat in Milligrams per 100 Grams of Fresh Weight (341)

Compound	Liver	Brain	Pancreas	Muscle	Kidney	Urine	Plasma
Aspartic acid	11.6	29.7	18.4	3.9	7.3	0.1	0.1
Asparagine	2.5	1.4	4.8	—	2.3	1.4	0.9
Glutamic acid	66	128	140	36.2	137	0.9	1.8
Glutamine (ca.)	>50	>50	>50	>50	>20	>5	>5
α-Aminoadipic acid	—	—	—	—	—	<0.1	—
Glycine	9.1	10.1	17.5	6.7	14.4	1.8	2.3
Alanine	16.5	8.4	34.0	24.7	20.7	2.8	7.0
β-Alanine	1.7	0.6	<0.2	6.9	1.3	<3	<0.03
β-Aminoisobutyric acid	0.3	0.1	<0.2	<0.2	0.4	<1	<0.04
Butyrine	—	—	—	—	—	<0.1	—
γ-Aminobutyric acid	1.0	23.4	0.7	<0.1	0.5	0.3	<0.02
Valine	4.3	2.1	5.3	2.3	6.2	0.8	2.4
Leucine	3.6	1.8	3.3	2.3	3.2	1.3	1.6
Isoleucine	1.7	1.2	1.9	1.7	2.3	4.8	0.8
Serine	3.4	7.6	9.0	5.4	3.9	2.4	2.1
Threonine	3.1	2.6	3.3	3.9	3.6	1.6	1.4
Methionine	<0.9	1.5	0.3	0.4	1.1	1.1	0.4
Cystine	<0.2	1.0	0.6	<0.2	1.1	<0.2	0.4
Taurine	172	24.0	61.8	78.6	44.3	3.2	0.7
Felinine	<1.2	<0.6	—	<0.3	<1.0	185	0.4
Glutathione	118	27.1	59.9	28.7	61.6	<0.2	—
Proline	2.6	<1.6	4.3	3.2	4.6	<1.5	2.3
Phenylalanine	1.8	1.2	1.8	1.0	1.6	0.9	0.9

Tyrosine	2.1	1.2	1.7	0.8	1.8	0.9	0.7
Tryptophan	<1.0	<0.7	<0.8	<1.5	<0.7	<0.7	<0.2
Histidine	9.1	0.9	2.7	3.6	2.7	2.0	1.4
1-Methylhistidine	–	<0.3	<0.5	106	–	–	–
3-Methylhistidine	<0.4	<0.3	<0.4	3.2	1.1	9.4	0.1
Carnosine	–	–	–	150	–	–	–
Anserine	–	–	–	200	–	–	–
Ornithine	2.0	0.6	1.7	0.4	0.6	0.1	0.2
Lysine	3.6	2.0	5.2	5.5	3.7	4.2	2.8
Arginine	0.2	1.4	2.5	2.7	1.2	6.5	1.4
Creatinine	–	57	–	24	–	370	–
Citrulline	<0.9	<0.4	–	<0.2	<0.9	<0.4	<0.1
Urea	40	25	60	35	100	–	40
Ethanolamine	2.0	20.7	–	0.5	3.3	2.3	<0.04
Phosphoethanolamine	19.1	41.9	186	1.8	21.7	<0.5	0.2
Glycerophosphoethanolamine	271	<2.9	12.7	3.6	77.8	<3.3	0.1

had been isolated from cat urine by Searle and Westall (116) (origin anserine?), and 3-methylhistidine from human urine by Tallan, Stein, and Moore (347); 3-methylhistidine together with some of the 1-methyl isomer was synthesized by treating L-histidine with methyl iodide and with sodium in liquid ammonia solution (347) (Figure 15–43); γ-aminobutyric acid is found to the greatest extent in brain tissue extracts (cf. 149, 150, 342); the most common components of the tissue extracts are glycine, alanine, glutamic acid, and aspartic acid; ornithine is wide-spread throughout the tissues, and ethanolamine is a principal brain tissue component (cf. 331).

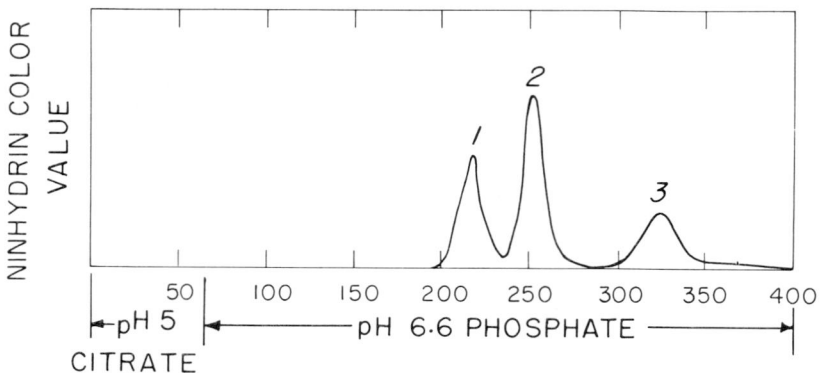

Figure 15–43. Separation on Dowex 50 (Na⁺) of the products of the methylation of histidine. 1, 3-Methylhistidine; 2, histidine; and 3, 1-methylhistidine. Tallan, H. H., Stein W. H., and Moore, S., *J. Biol. Chem.*, **206**, 825 (1954).

The separation on a Dowex 50-X12 column of a mixture of cyclic imino acids, such as is found in extracts of dates, is described in Figure 15–44 (168). The resin was washed prior to the separation with 0.25N NaOH containing detergent, and then with a citrate buffer at pH 3.1. A pH gradient, as indicated in the figure, was employed to elute the imino acids. The eluate fractions were treated with ninhydrin and read at the following wavelengths: hydroxyproline, allohydroxyproline, and 5-hydroxypipecolic acid at 350 mμ, proline at 510 mμ, baikiain at 395 mμ, and pipecolic acid at 565 mμ—all against a water blank.

Hydrolysis of the various tissue extracts with HCl revealed that glutamine and glutathione are the sources of the major proportion of the increase in amino acids in liver extracts, anserine and carnosine in muscle (cf. 331, 348), and asparagine in brain. There also seem to be small but definite quantities of conjugated serine, threonine, proline, and lysine in the extracts of several tissues (347). Acetyl-L-aspartic acid is a component of the brain of several species (341), 100 mg., approximately, being present per 100 g. of fresh brain tissue of the cat or the rat.

Taken into consideration in the hydrolysis of the extracts was the possibility that under the conditions of prolonged refluxing with HCl some decomposition of such amino acids as cystine, serine, and threonine to yield ammonia and other products (i.e., glycine, alanine, and butyrine (349)) might conceivably occur (350–353), resulting not only in apparently low values for these amino acids, but also in correspondingly high values for what would otherwise be true amide nitrogen. The well-known loss of tryptophan can be minimized under certain conditions (350). Alkaline hydrolysis may yield satisfactory results for tryptophan, but serine breaks down in part to glycine

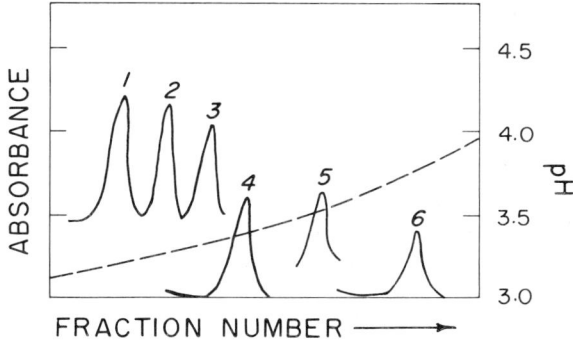

Figure 15–44. Separation of cyclic imino acids on Dowex 50-X12 (Na+). The dashed line indicates pH gradient. 1, Hydroxyproline; 2, allohydroxyproline; 3, 5-hydroxypipecolic acid; 4, proline; 5, baikiain; and 6, pipecolic acid. Piez, K. A., Irreverre, F., and Wolff, H. L., *J. Biol. Chem.*, **223**, 687 (1956).

and alanine, threonine to glycine and butyrine, cystine to alanine (351), and, of course, arginine to ornithine. When the question of balancing amino acid recoveries from protein hydrolysates arose, the situation was rendered particularly poignant, inasmuch as a prolonged period of hydrolysis might very well destroy certain amino acids, but too short a period of hydrolysis might leave such resistant linkages as valylvaline (354) or isoleucylvaline (353) untouched. Harfenist (353) employed several different periods of hydrolysis in the study of the amino acid composition of insulin (24, 48, and 96 hours), and corrected for the resulting decomposition of threonine and serine by the method of Rees (352). In connection with this chromatographic study, proline was determined in the effluent by the useful method of Chinard (355), which consists of the determination of the ninhydrin color at 490 mμ and at a pH of 1 to 2. The use of at least two periods of hydrolysis was adopted by Smith and his co-workers (356) in their studies on papain, by Hirs, Stein, and Moore (357) in their studies on ribonuclease (22 and 70 hours), by Crampton, Moore, and Stein (358) in their investigations on the composition of various histones, and by Li and Chung (92) in their studies on growth hormone. The prolonged refluxing with acid necessary to hydrolyze resistant linkages is accompanied by an increased destruction of sensitive amino acids with the formation of artifacts the possibility of whose presence on the chromatograms must be carefully considered. The decomposition of aspartic and glutamic acids during hydrolysis of the protein was noted by Smith et al. (356), and confirmed by Hirs et al. (357). Corrections were made by extrapolation of the analytical results to zero time, assuming first-order kinetics for the decomposition. The marked decomposition of serine, threonine, tyrosine, and cystine, and the somewhat appreciable decomposition of glutamic acid, aspartic acid, proline, and arginine, were corrected for in this manner (358). No such decomposition of the dicarboxylic amino acids was noted in the HCl hydrolysis of insulin (353), nor in simply boiling these amino acids with HCl (358). The perennial problem of the sensitivity of amino acids when bound in peptide linkage in unusual positions thus arises in this connection. Table 15–28 describes the number of amino acid residues found in the biologically interesting and well-characterized proteins insulin, papain, and ribonuclease, determined by hydrolysis with appropriate corrections for the sensitive amino acids and by employing chromatograhy on Dowex 50 resin.

The use of a Dowex 50 resin of 12% cross-linking and 200–400 mesh has been reported to be effective in the separation of the amino acids in collagen hydrolysates when the elution was begun with a citrate buffer at pH 3.42 and a temperature of 37.5° (359); at the beginning of the emergence of valine, the buffer was changed to one of pH 4.25 and the temperature raised to 60°, where it was maintained until after emergence of phenylalanine. The resin Zeo Karb 225 W.R. 2.3 at 200–400 mesh (328) has also been suggested as a means to separate a mixture of amino acids. This resin is capable of separating 2 micromoles of each of the following amino acids, on a 150 × 0.9 cm. column held at 40°, in the order of their respective elution: aspartic acid, threonine, serine, proline, glutamic acid, glycine, valine, methionine, leucine, tyrosine, phenylalanine, lysine, histidine, and arginine, using a 0.2M sodium citrate buffer at pH 3.15 and 40° at the beginning, and subsequently changing to a 2.0M citrate buffer at pH 5.0 added to a mixing reservoir with the buffer at pH 3.15. The resin presumably was 5% cross-linked, but the suggestion was made that the water-regain (W.R.) value constituted a better characterization of the efficiency of the resin than the degree of possible cross-linking by an agent added at the polymerization stage (328, 360).

In the presence of extraneous carbohydrate as in foods, the ordinary destruction of cystine and methionine during HCl hydrolysis is enhanced (361). To circumvent this effect with cystine, the Sanger procedure (362), whereby the protein-bound cystine is oxidized with performic acid to cysteic acid residues, may be adopted (363), and after hydrolysis the liberated cysteic acid is estimated quantitatively on the Dowex 50 column. The partial

CHROMATOGRAPHY 1475

conversion of methionine to sulfoxide (cf. 324) is no barrier to the accurate determination of this amino acid provided that both forms are taken into quantitative consideration. A diminished rate of destruction of most of the amino acids, even in the presence of carbohydrate, can be noted if the hydrolysis with HCl is conducted at high dilutions (5 to 10 mg. of protein per 200 ml. of 6N HCl) (363). If nucleic acids as well as carbohydrates are

TABLE 15-28
Amino Acid Residues in Certain Proteins of Biological Interest

Amino Acid	Ribonuclease (357)	Papain (356)	Sheep Insulin (353)[a]
Tryptophan	0	5	0
Aspartic acid	16	17	3
Threonine	10	7	1
Serine	15	11	2
Glutamic acid	12	17	7
Proline	5	9	1
Glycine	3	23	5
Alanine	12	13	3
Cystine	8	4	3
Valine	9	15	5
Isoleucine	3	9	1
Leucine	2	9	6
Tyrosine	6	17	4
Phenylalanine	3	4	3
Histidine	4	1	2
Lysine	10	8	1
Arginine	4	9	1
Ammonia	17	19	6
Methionine	4	0	0

[a] Pork insulin has 2 residues of threonine, 3 of serine, 4 of glycine, 2 of alanine, 4 of valine, and 2 of isoleucine; otherwise it is like sheep insulin. Beef insulin has 3 residues of serine and 4 of glycine. Otherwise, the composition of beef insulin resembles that of sheep insulin (353). These residues are based on a molecular weight of 6000.

present in the foods to be analyzed, the purines, pyrimidines, and amino acids may be separated and identified on the same Dowex 50 column (364).

The actual isolation of amino acids from protein hydrolysates or other biological sources possesses many desirable features, particularly where compounds labeled with stable or radioactive isotopes have been employed. Dowex 50-X8 operated with 1N to 4N HCl has frequently been employed for this purpose (260, 364–367). Where buffers have been employed, separation of the amino acids from the salts has frequently been accomplished by cycling the effluent over cationic or anionic resins (cf. 325); 3-methylhistidine was isolated from urine in this way (347). A simpler system employing volatile ammonium formate and acetate buffers which were removable by sublimation at 40° was introduced by Hirs, Moore, and Stein (368). A further improvement was suggested (369) in the use of volatile acids for elution in the separation of amino acids, but for purposes of isolation and preparation the resolution of the four most rapidly moving compounds (aspartic acid, glutamic acid, serine, and threonine) on the acid form of Dowex 50-X8 or 50-X4 is not entirely satisfactory. A first isolation of aspartic acid, glutamic acid, and tyrosine was therefore accomplished by running the amino acid mixture over a basic resin, Dowex 1-X8, followed by elution with 0.5N acetic acid. The remaining amino acids were then separated on a 150-cm. column of Dowex 50-X4 resin with an eluent of HCl increasing from 1.0N to 4.0N, and at temperatures increasing from 25° to 50°. For the separation of the basic amino acids, Amberlite IRC-50 (XE-64) with citrate-phosphate buffer at pH 6.0 has been recommended (370); the elution sequence at 30° is lysine, ammonia, histidine, and arginine.

More recently, the chromatography of amino acids on sulfonated polystyrene resins has been simplified and improved by Moore, Spackman, and Stein, and by Spackman, Stein, and Moore (370a). The finely ground sodium salt of Amberlite IR-120 was employed as the resin (finer than 200 mesh), and was washed successively with 4N HCl and then water, suspended in 2N NaOH, the mixture heated on the steam bath for 1 hour, filtered and washed with water until the washings were neutral; it was finally fractionated by flotation in water so as to yield particles of an approximately uniform size of 56 ± 9 microns. The subsequent resolution procedure was much the same as that described when the Dowex 50 resins were employed, except that only a single temperature of 50° was used, and only two buffers, at pH 3.25 and pH 4.25, were used for the elution of the larger column, and a single buffer, at pH 5.28, for elution of the smaller column yielding the basic amino acids. With resin particles of smaller size, which permit faster flow rates through the columns, an automatic recording apparatus for the ninhydrin color values of the effluents was developed (370a). In this device, the effluent, removed at a steady rate, was met by a capillary stream of ninhydrin reagent also served at a steady rate, and the color brought out by passing the mixture through a boiling water bath; the absorbance of the resulting solution was then measured continuously at 570 and 440 mμ as it continued to flow through a cylindrical glass cell.

SEPARATION OF DIASTEREOMERS. The separation of threonine from allothreonine (371), and of isoleucine from alloisoleucine, of hydroxylysine from allohydroxylysine, and of hydroxyproline from allohydroxyproline (372) on ion exchange resins is one of the most important and intriguing developments in this area. The individual phenomena are more fully described elsewhere (Chapter 9 and Part VI under headings of the separate amino acids). As pointed out by Piez (372), alloisoleucine and methionine occupy the same position on the Dowex 50 chromatogram, and, in the event of the appearance of this peak and the known presence of isoleucine under possibly racemizing (epimerizing) conditions, it is necessary to check for the possible presence of methionine by some independent method, such as by the use of platinic iodide. Indeed, it is necessary to scrutinize with care the presence of unidentified peaks on chromatograms when previous racemizing (epimerizing) conditions in the preparation of mixtures which included amino acids with two centers of optical asymmetry, i.e., hydroxyproline, threonine, isoleucine, and hydroxylysine, might have conceivably resulted in the appearance both of the normal and of the allo diastereoisomers of these compounds. Thus alloisoleucine is known to be formed from part of the pre-existing isoleucine in the course of the hydrolysis of bacitracin A (see below), and allohydroxylysine from the normal form as a result of the prolonged hydrolysis of collagen (373; cf. 372). Some conversion of L-cystine to the DL and *meso*-forms occurs during refluxing with strong acid. The problem of recognizing the presence of such artifacts in protein hydrolysates is important.

On a Dowex 50-X4 column, the HCl effluent yields *meso*-cystine earlier than L- or DL-cystine (369). The attempted separation of L- from *meso*-diaminopimelic acid on Zeo Karb 225 X-8 (129) was not complete and depended in part on the temperature; thus at 20° the *meso*-form emerged (1.5N HCl as developer) slightly ahead of the L-isomer, whereas at 2° the reverse was true.

30. Use of Ion Exchange Chromatography in the Resolution of Amino Acids.

The enzymic hydrolysis procedures developed for the separation of the optical isomers of racemic amino acids have embraced two approaches: one, the asymmetric hydrolysis of N-acyl-DL-amino acids to the L-amino acid and the acyl-D-amino acid; and, two, the asymmetric hydrolysis of DL-amino acid amides to the L-amino acid and the D-amino acid amide (cf. 374 and Chapter 9). The free L-amino acid in either case could be separated from the acyl-D-amino acid or the D-amino acid amide by differential solubility in aqueous and non-aqueous solvents. The separations could also be readily effected on a chromatographic column (375–378). Thus L-isovaline was separated from chloroacetyl-D-isovaline by pouring the deproteinized resolution mixture onto the top of a column containing Dowex 50 resin in the acid phase (375). On elution with water, chloroacetyl-D-isovaline appeared in the effluent as shown by the acid reaction to Congo red paper and by the positive ninhydrin color *after* hydrolysis, and its complete emergence was determined when these reactions terminated. The L-isovaline remaining on the column was eluted by the use of 2.5N HCl, and the termination of the elution was heralded when the ninhydrin reaction became negative. L-*t*-Leucine and D-*t*-leucinamide were separated in a resolution mixture by reaction with the acid form of Amberlite XE-64 (376). In this case, the amino acid amide was adsorbed by the resin, and the free amino acid emerged in the effluent on washing the resin with water. The amide was first eluted from the resin with $0.1N$ HCl and then with $0.05N$ HCl.

A more complicated situation arose in the separation of the products of the resolution of α,ε-diaminopimelic acid amide (377). The starting material had been a mixture of racemic and *meso*-forms of diaminopimelic acid, so that at the termination of the enzymic hydrolysis of the mixed amides the following three compounds were present: The free L-diaminopimelic acid, the L-diaminopimelic acid–D-monoamide, and the D-diaminopimelic acid diamide. The mixture of these products was freed of protein, brought to pH 9.2 with LiOH, and run onto a column of Amberlite XE-64 cation exchange resin which had been converted to the lithium form. Water was added to develop the chromatogram, and this addition was continued until the ninhydrin reaction was negative and all the free L-diaminopimelic acid had emerged ($R_F = 0.27$ in phenol-NH$_3$). On passing to 1% acetic acid as eluent, the monoamide emerged ($R_F = 0.69$) as a broad band overlapping somewhat with the subsequently emerging diamide ($R_F = 0.92$). The overlapping portion could be rejected, and each component worked up separately.

The procedure was generalized by Baker and Sober (378) and made applicable to the separation of the resolution products of initial racemic substrates equivalent to 0.3 to 1.0 g. of the amino acid enantiomorph. The substrates used were the acyl derivatives of aspartic acid, histidine, arginine, serine, phenylalanine, ornithine, alanine, methionine, valine, and the amide of proline. The acid phase of Dowex 50 was employed, and the normality of eluting HCl for the free L-amino acids given in brackets as follows: aspartic acid [1], serine [2.5], phenylalanine [5], ornithine [5], alanine [2.5], methionine [5], and valine [5]. Prior to this development, the acyl-D-amino acids had emerged from the column on washing with water. The acid phase of Amberlite XE-64 was employed with histidine and arginine, the acetyl-D-derivatives were first eluted with water, and then the free L-amino acids removed by the use of N HCl for histidine and "weak acid" for arginine. The pouring of the mixture of proline and proline amide onto acid Amberlite XE-64 resulted in complete elution first of the proline by means of water, and subsequently of the amide by means of $0.1N$ HCl.

The amount of resin employed in each case was derived on the basis of an ion exchange of 2 meq. per ml. of wet packed Dowex 50-X8 resin (5 meq. per g.) and of 3.5 meq. per ml. of wet packed XE-64 resin. Thus 1 kg. of alanine (mol. wt. = 89) is 11.2 equivalents and will require some 2440 g. or 5600 ml. of packed Dowex 50 resin in the hydrogen form. Usually a three- to fivefold excess is used, and from the volume required the dimensions of the glass column to be employed are determined.

The use of the hydrogen form of Dowex 50 is also of advantage in bringing the acylation of amino acids via the Schotten-Baumann reaction to a successful conclusion. The principle is the same as that employed in the resolution procedure above except that, inasmuch as less free amino acid is present at the end of the reaction, less resin is required. Thus an amino acid is treated in alkaline solution with a slight excess of an acylating agent in alkaline solution at about pH 8, and the reaction mixture poured onto a column of Dowex 50 (H^+). Any unchanged amino acid, together with the cation of the alkali, is retained on the column, sufficient resin being allowed for this purpose, whereas the pure acylated amino acid is washed through the column by means of water. A typical example of this procedure applied to the preparation of pure N-acetyl-DL-serine is portrayed in the chapter on serine (Chapter 36).

31. Isotope Effects in Ion Exchange Chromatography. It has been an axiom in the study of amino acids and related compounds labeled with radioactive isotopes that coincidence of radioactivity and ninhydrin or other specific color reactions constituted a criterion of identity. This may be valid for paper chromatography, but it is not likely to be valid when ion exchange resins with their very high resolving power are used. Thus the separation factor for the exchange of N^{15} and N^{14} between a solution of dilute ammonium hydroxide and the ammonium form of Dowex 50-X12 was found to be 1.0257 (379), and the conditions favorable for a nearly complete separation of the nitrogen isotopes in the pure form have been determined. When amino acids labeled with C^{14} were fractionated on a Dowex 50 column, the peaks of radioactivity in the effluent did not precisely coincide with amino acid peaks located by the ninhydrin color reaction (380). The curves (radioactivity and ninhydrin color) were shaped identically, but the presence of C^{14} in the molecule apparently caused it to move slightly slower on the column. It seemed quite probable that a partial resolution of labeled from unlabeled amino acid had occurred. In studies with such systems, the possibility of error if a single fraction rather than an entire peak is used for the determination of specific activity is worthy of consideration. For the relatively large-scale separation of N^{15}-labeled amino acids on Dowex 50 as employed by Aqvist (260), the error is negligible. Figure 15–45 is that of Piez and Eagle (380) which reveals the resolution of ninhydrin color and radioactivity in the case of two amino acids labeled with C^{14}.

32. Peptides. Chromatographic methods for the separation, purification, and identification of peptides have been applied to three general categories of these substances: (a) to the peptides which occur as such in nature, i.e., glutathione, carnosine, various antibiotics, etc.; (b) to the polypeptides and proteins; and (c) to the peptides which arise in the course of enzymic transformations *in vitro*. The methods employed have been essentially similar to those already described for the amino acids. Indeed, in their first paper on the subject of paper chromatography, Consden, Gordon, and Martin (31) stated that their purpose in developing this subject was to employ it as a basis for the study of the peptide fragments resulting from the partial hydrolysis of proteins.

In the course of their early studies on the peptides resulting from the partial hydrolysis of gelatin, Gordon, Martin, and Synge (252) first separated the

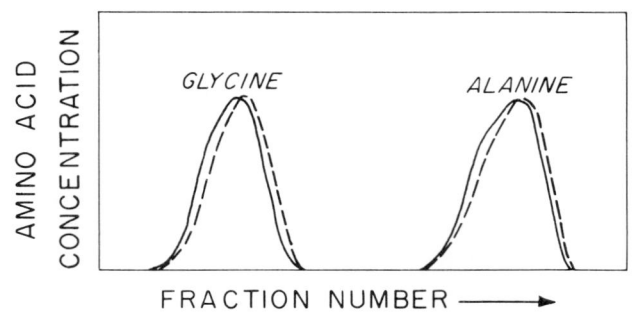

Figure 15-45. Portion of effluent curve of C^{14}-"uniformly" labeled amino acids on Dowex 50 (Na^+) at 50°. Elution begun with $0.37M$ citrate buffer at pH 3.1, employing thereafter a continuous pH gradient by addition to reservoir of $0.25N$ NaOH. Continuous lines represent amino acid concentration by ninhydrin color; dash lines represent amino acid concentration by C^{14} count, assuming 100% recovery. Piez, K. A., and Eagle, H., *Science*, 122, 968 (1955).

products by electrodialysis into basic and neutral fractions, acetylated the mixture of peptides in the neutral fraction, and subsequently fractionated the resulting N-acetylated peptides on silica gel columns with ethyl acetate–water. Indicators were employed to locate the bands. The report by Synge (253) which first described the use of starch columns for the separation of the peptides resulting from the partial hydrolysis of gramicidin also described the first application of paper chromatography to the identification of peptides. Mixtures of *n*-butanol and water were employed, and the need of a higher temperature for the interaction of ninhydrin with the amino group of peptides than that adequate with amino acids was emphasized. A more systematic approach was adopted sometime later by Consden, Gordon, and Martin (65), who noted that the R_F values of peptides appeared to be more sensitive to pH and other factors than those of amino acids. They considered it desirable in most analyses of peptide mixtures to run mixed chromatograms with authentic samples to confirm the results obtained. Table 15–29 describes the R_F values of various synthetic peptides in several solvents (65). Butanol-acetic acid mixtures (381) have also been employed with a number of peptides. The curious sequence of color reactions in the reaction of ninhydrin with peptides in which glycine is the N-terminal residue, whereby at first a yellow color occurs, then a gray, and finally a purple, has been observed by a number of investigators (65, 248, 382, 383). This phenomenon was

TABLE 15-29

R_F Values of Peptides in Various Solvents on Whatman No. 4 Paper (65)

Peptide	Phenol-NH$_3$ (coal gas)	s-Collidine	n-Butanol (Cupron)	m-Cresol (Cupron-NH$_3$)
Glycylglycine	0.57	0.28	0.01	0.18
Glycyl-DL-alanine	0.63	0.32	0.03	0.29
Glycyl-DL-valine	0.74	0.47	0.09	0.51
Glycyl-DL-leucine	0.79	0.53	0.24	0.66
Glycyl-L-proline	0.69	0.34	0.05	0.69
Glycyl-L-hydroxyproline	0.59	0.28	0.02	0.25
Glycyl-L-phenylalanine	0.70	0.79	0.18	0.72
Glycyl-L-tryptophan	0.66	0.85	0.29	0.63
Triglycine	0.59	0.32	0.01	0.19
Diglycyl-L-leucylglycine	0.75	0.71	0.11	0.67
DL-Alanylglycine	0.65	0.32	0.03	0.29
L-Alanylglycylglycine	0.63	0.46	0.01	0.29
DL-Valylglycine	0.73	0.53	0.11	0.48
DL-Leucylglycine	0.78	0.61	0.23	0.62
DL-Leucyl-DL-leucine	0.84	0.89	0.65	0.85
L-Leucyl-L-tryptophan	0.83	0.95	0.60	0.83
L-Leucylglycylglycine	0.75	0.55	0.11	0.60
L-Prolylglycine	0.68	0.49	0.03	0.55
L-Tyrosylglycine	0.59	0.95	0.09	0.33

particularly revealed in the studies by Heyns and Anders (383) as well as by Grassmann and Deffner (384) on homologous peptides of glycine (Table 15-30). As noted from Table 15-30, the R_F values increased in a homologous series with phenol and decreased with butanol. With increase in molecular weight, the ninhydrin reaction appeared to become feebler. On the whole, the R_F value of peptides appears to be somewhere between those of the component amino acids, and is most influenced by the amino acid in the N-terminal position (383). A similar increase of R_F in phenol for the homologous series of glycine peptides was observed by Grassmann and Deffner (384). Peptides in which proline is the N-terminal residue yield, like the free amino acid itself, a yellow color with ninhydrin (382). Asparagine yields a permanent yellow color with ninhydrin, but peptides of asparagine, whether N-terminal or C-terminal, although yielding initially a yellow color, soon take on a final purple tint (385). α-Aspartyl peptides give purple colors with ninyhdrin, whilst β-aspartyl peptides under the same condition give blue (386); both α- and γ-glutamyl peptides yield purple colors with ninhydrin. It is of interest, and not unexpected, that the ω-peptides of aspartic acid and of glutamic acid migrate faster in phenol:NH_3 than do the corresponding α-peptides (386), the latter being more acidic.

TABLE 15-30

R_F Values of Homologous Types of Peptides (383)

Peptide	Phenol	n-Butanol	Peptide	Phenol	n-Butanol
Diglycine	0.32	0.02	Tetraalanine	0.79	0.03
Triglycine	0.35	0.01	Glycylleucine	0.65	0.09
Tetraglycine	0.42	0.01	Leucylglycine	0.73	0.11
Pentaglycine	0.58	0.00	Leucyldiglycine	0.75	0.05
Hexaglycine	No color	No color	Leucyltriglycine	0.80	0.03
Nonaglycine	No color	No color	Leucyltetraglycine	0.88	0.02
Dialanine	0.53	0.06	Leucylglycylleucine	0.88	0.31
Trialanine	0.66	0.05	Dileucylglycine	0.83	0.26
			Alanyldiglycine	0.47	0.01

The R_F values of a number of synthetic peptides were reported by Cook and Levy (387) and by Knight (382). These values, together with those of Consden, Gordon, and Martin (65) and of Consden, Gordon, Martin, and Synge (388), were employed by Pardee (389) to test the concept advanced by Martin (101) that R_F depends essentially on the partition coefficient P of the solute between water and the solvent and the ratio of the volumes of solvent and water phases, A_L/A_s, whereby

$$P = \frac{A_L}{A_s}\left[\frac{1}{R_F} - 1\right]$$

This concept had its basis in the studies of England and Cohn (15) which showed that the partition coefficients of a homologous series of amino acids changed regularly with each additional carbon atom in the chain; this would imply that the R_F values should also change with a corresponding degree of regularity, and indeed, in selected cases of homologous compounds when $\ln\left[(1/R_F) - 1\right]$ was plotted against the number of substituted groups of any one kind, a linear relation was observed (cf. 390 and Tables 15-10 and 15-11).

The relation between the peptide and its constituent amino acids emerges as

$$RT \ln (1/R_F - 1)_{\text{Peptide}} = (n - 1)A + B + \Sigma RT \ln (1/R_F - 1)_{\text{Amino acid}}$$

where $(n - 1)$ is the number of peptide bonds, A a constant which includes the $\Delta F°$ of the amino, carboxyl, and peptide groups as well as the terms in A_L/A_s, and B is a correction term for the difference between the terminal amino and carboxyl groups of a peptide and the corresponding amino acids. A and B will therefore be constants for a given pair of phases.

A plot of $RT \ln [(1/R_F) - 1]_{\text{Peptide}} - \Sigma RT \ln [(1/R_F) - 1]_{\text{Amino acid}}$ against the number of peptide bonds should yield a straight line with slope A and intercept B. Such a relationship was observed by Pardee (389). With the system phenol-water (HCN), A was found to be -460 calories per mole and $B +460$ calories per mole. Similarly, the values of A for the system pyridine–isoamyl alcohol was -1200, and for B $+300$. Values of R_F of various peptides calculated from these and similar data were found to be in quite good agreement with observed values. These observations are explicable on the basis of the concept of a nearly predominant liquid-liquid distribution of the amino acids and peptides on the paper chromatograms, although as pointed out by Pardee (389) the data were derived on peptides composed for the most part of relatively simple glycine and leucine residues. That more complicated types of peptides with polyvalent and aromatic-ringed amino acid constituents also follow the above relationship is revealed by the later work of Moore and Baker (391). Part of their data is given in Table 15-31. It would be expected from the relationship that isomers containing the same functional groups should have identical partition coefficients. However, glycylleucine has a somewhat different R_F than leucylglycine (Table 15-30), and isomeric peptides of cysteic acid have been separated on paper by Consden and Gordon (392).

An example of the use of paper chromatography to follow the action of an enzyme *in vitro* is the very careful study by Hanes, Hird, and Isherwood (393) on γ-glutamyl transpeptidase. In this reaction a new peptide is formed, and the criteria selected by these authors for the appearance of the new compound are worthy of repetition: (a) the spot (for the new compound) must be initially absent, and should increase in amount as the reaction proceeds; (b) the spot is not formed unless both donor and acceptor substances are present; (c) the spot is distinct and separable not only from the donor and acceptor but also from possible breakdown products of these; and (d) the position of the spot is consistent with that expected for a peptide of the type in question, this expectation being based on the observation that many peptides travel on the chromatogram at rates intermediate between those of the constituent amino acids (cf. 383). Hanes et al. employed *n*-propanol and Whatman No. 1 paper, whilst phenol was employed in the presence of the basic amino acids. In several cases the new peptide was isolated by elution with 50% ethanol from the chromatogram, and for this purpose the thicker Whatman No. 3 paper was used. An improved elution and standardization procedure has been reported by Connell, Dixon, and Hanes (394) in which an accuracy to within 0.01 of a micromole of amino acid or peptide is claimed. Paper chromatography has also been employed by Fruton and his co-workers

TABLE 15-31

Observed and Calculated R_F Values of Peptides (391) in
Water–88% Formic Acid–t-Butanol (15 : 15 : 70) on Whatman No. 4 Paper

Peptide	R_F(obs.)	R_F(calc.)	Peptide	R_F(obs.)	R_F(calc.)
Glycylglycine	0.32	0.37	Sarcosylphenylalanine	0.66	0.78
Glycylsarcosine	0.42	0.43	Alanylphenylalanine	0.76	0.80
Alanylglycine	0.47	0.47	Glycylmethionine	0.64	0.66
Leucylglycine	0.75	0.75	Glycyltryptophan	0.59	0.55
Glycylalanine	0.47	0.47	α-Aspartylhistidine	0.12	0.10
Sarcosylalanine	0.53	0.53	Glycylaspartic acid	0.16	0.28
Alanylalanine	0.58	0.57	Glycylglutamic acid	0.34	0.38
Glycylserine	0.27	0.34	Glycyltyrosine	0.50	0.55
Glycylbutyrine	0.59	0.66	Triglycine	0.24	0.30
Alanylbutyrine	0.70	0.74	Alanyldiglycine	0.39	0.39
Glycylthreonine	0.35	0.40	Glycylalanylglycine	0.35	0.39
Glycylvaline	0.63	0.70	Glycylleucylglycine	0.65	0.69
Glycylnorvaline	0.64	0.77	Glycylphenylalanylglycine	0.38	0.39
Alanylnorvaline	0.78	0.84	Diglycylalanine	0.38	0.39
Glycylleucine	0.73	0.75	Diglycylleucine	0.65	0.69
α-Glutamylalanine	0.53	0.48	Diglycylphenylalanine	0.65	0.66
α-Glutamylleucine	0.70	0.76	Diglycylcystine	0.07	0.04
α-Glutamylphenylalanine	0.73	0.74	Dialanylcystine	0.16	0.09
α-Glutamylglutamic acid	0.41	0.39	Tetraglycine	0.18	0.23
Glycylisoleucine	0.74	0.80	Pentaglycine	0.12	0.18
Glycylnorleucine	0.72	0.85	α-Glycyllysine	0.12	0.20
Glycylcapryline	0.86	0.93			

(395, 396) to follow the formation of peptides in enzyme-catalyzed reactions, by Walker (83, 84) to follow the course of transamidination reactions, and by Snoke and Bloch in the course of their studies on intermediates in the synthesis of glutathione (397).

Pipsyl-labeled peptides were employed by Velick and Udenfriend (398) to determine the internal peptide structure of the glyceraldehyde-3-phosphate dehydrogenase from yeast and from muscle. Samples of the S^{35}-labeled pipsyl derivative of the yeast enzyme and of the I^{131}-labeled derivative of the muscle enzyme were mixed and subjected to partial hydrolysis by concentrated HCl at 37°. A series of six pipsyl-labeled peptides, purified by countercurrent distribution, was obtained. The ratios of I^{131} : S^{35} along the direction of migration of the bands on paper strips were constant and the same in all bands. This indicated that the same peptides were obtained from the two proteins in the same relative amounts, and the portion of the amino acid sequence in the peptide chain of the two proteins was therefore considered to be essentially the same.

Peptides generally react more slowly with ninhydrin than do amino acids, and, although some peptides may readily be detected with the usual 0.1% ninhydrin reagent, the larger neutral or acidic peptides may react so feebly as to be overlooked. For such larger peptides a more concentrated ninhydrin solution at 0.4% in a mixture of water, isopropanol, and collidine has been proposed (399). For cyclic peptides, pyrrolidonecarboxylic acid, the pyrrolidonyl peptides formed by cyclyzing glutamine peptides (cf. 400), or N-acylated amino acids, ninhydrin is completely ineffective. Rydon and Smith suggested that such compounds could be detected by chlorination on the paper, followed by spraying with starch-KI (401). The resulting color would be due to the liberation of elemental iodine by the N-chloropeptide formed in the chlorination stage:

$$-\text{CONH}- \xrightarrow{Cl_2} -\text{CONCl}- \xrightarrow{KI} -\text{CONH}- + KCl + \tfrac{1}{2}I_2$$

The reaction is of value in the absence of ninhydrin-positive compounds, for amino acids will also give positive results on chlorination due to the formation of N-chloroamino acids, e.g., ClNHCHRCOOH. An improvement of this procedure proposed by Reindel and Hoppe (402) consisted of the following steps: the compound was placed on paper, treated successively with acetic acid and an atmosphere of chlorine and chlorine oxides, then placed in a benzidine solution with acetic acid, and finally washed with ethanol. The virtue of this procedure is that most interfering substances are removed. A careful survey of the methods for detecting and determining pyrrolidonecarboxylic acid in natural sources, with emphasis on the Rydon and Smith procedure, has been made by Ellfolk and Synge (403).

Although paper chromatography has chiefly been used for the separation of the smaller peptides, the method has been found useful for some of the larger peptides. Thus the polymyxin antibiotics were first separated on paper (404). Three components were found in the antibiotic peptide fraction licheniformin by Callow and Work (405) and designated A, B, and C in order of increasing R_F values. Brockmann and Gröne (406) separated the various actinomycins on paper. Peptide fractions from deproteinized alcoholic extracts of the posterior pituitary gland were adsorbed on charcoal, together with the small amount of aromatic amino acids present (407), and were then eluted and chromatographed on paper with butanol–formic acid (408). The peptide material remained as a single component near the origin, whereas the mobile components moved outward. A biuret reaction (409) was employed to determine whole peptides, and the Troll and Cannan (410) ninhydrin colorimetric procedure (Section 11-2) to determine the conjugated amino acids before and after acid hydrolysis. With these methods, a considerable concentration of peptide material, over and above that due to oxytocin and vasopressin, was noted in the posterior pituitary gland; the hypothalamus, on the other hand, possessed no appreciable peptide pool. Paper, however, has not generally been a good medium for the separation of the larger peptides because of the tendency of such compounds to be irreversibly adsorbed with resulting "tailing," and as a rule countercurrent distribution and ion exchange techniques have been found to yield more satisfactory results.

Chromatography on paper of the mixture of peptides resulting from the partial hydrolysis of proteins or large polypeptides has frequently been preceded by some attempt at group fractionation. Thus Synge (253) used a development of gramicidin hydrolysates first on starch columns, and then on paper. Consden, Gordon, and Martin (411) partially degraded wool and transferred the hydrolysate onto an Amberlite IR-4 column. This resulted in a separation of the mixture into a fraction of acidic peptides (and amino acids) which remained on the column, and a fraction of neutral plus basic peptides. The acidic fraction was eluted with acid and purified by desalting and ionophoresis before being analyzed on two-dimensional paper chromatograms. These studies on wool were further extended by Consden and Gordon (392), who oxidized the disulfide linkages of the protein to sulfonic acids. Fractionation on Amberlite IR-4 at pH 3–4 led to the usual acidic fraction and neutral plus basic fraction. The latter was oxidized with bromine and refractionated on Amberlite IR-4 at pH 3–4, yielding now an acidic fraction composed almost entirely of cysteic acid and cysteic acid peptides. The various fractions were then purified by desalting and ionophoresis and analyzed on paper. A somewhat more elaborate procedure was employed by Sanger and Tuppy (412) in their group separations from the partial hydrolysates of the B chain (phenylalanyl) of insulin. The disulfide bonds were already converted to sulfonic acid derivatives. The accompanying diagram shows the scheme employed.

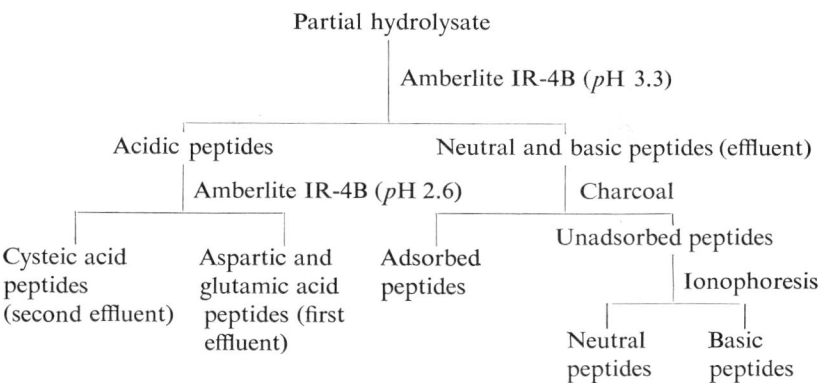

Each of the fractions was analyzed on two dimensional paper chromatograms, cresol generally being used first, and butanol–acetic acid thereafter. Ninhydrin in water-saturated butanol was sprayed on the paper to give sufficient color without destroying an appreciable amount of the peptide, so that subsequent elution could be used to identify the amino acids produced on hydrolysis. Where the peptide was to be deaminated or treated with dinitrofluorobenzene, the use of ninhydrin was avoided, and eluates from spots cut from untreated sheets were used. The purpose of using the charcoal column in the preliminary group separation was to remove peptides containing the aromatic amino acids (cf. 413). These were removed from the charcoal with phenol–acetic acid. An essentially similar approach was employed by Sanger and Thompson (86) in subsequent studies of the peptide sequences in the A chain (glycyl) of insulin. Sanger (414) had earlier separated the DNP-peptides resulting from the partial hydrolysis of DNP-insulin on columns of silica gel using chloroform–n-butanol as developer. A further purification of the DNP-peptides was effected on columns of talc which adsorbed these compounds and allowed simple peptides and amino acids to pass through. Some twenty peptides could be conveniently handled and analyzed on each paper chromatogram (86). Although the greater number of DNP derivatives were soluble only in organic solvents, those involving histidine and arginine, for example, were soluble in dilute acid, and could thereby be separated.

A partial hydrolysate of collagen (415) was separated into fractions of aromatic-ringed peptides (charcoal column), basic peptides (Amberlite XE-64 buffered at pH 6.0 with ammonium acetate), and acidic peptides (Amberlite IR-4B). The neutral fraction was converted to DNP-peptide derivatives and separated on columns of buffered Super-Cel (cf. 27). Those peptide derivatives not separated on the column were separated subsequently on paper (cf. 416). Partial hydrolysates of casein were first treated with De-Acidite-E to remove HCl, fractionated on charcoal and then on Dowex

50-12X resin in the ammonium form, and then chromatographed on paper (417); in the same study, partial hydrolysates of β-lactoglobulin were fractionated on charcoal and then on Zeo Karb 225, and finally on silica gel as DNP-peptides.

The A and B chains of insulin have been separated on silane-treated Super-Cel columns, the solvent system butanol–0.01N trichloroacetic acid being used (418). The chromatograms were developed with the aqueous phase, and the peak fractions freed of acid by neutralizing with Dowex 2 in the bicarbonate form. In paper electrophoresis experiments each peptide traveled as a single spot. This separation method has certain advantages over the conventional precipitation procedures in ammonium acetate buffer (cf. 362). The use of trichloroacetic acid in the system described stemmed from the studies by Harfenist and Craig (419) on the countercurrent distribution of insulin, in which the effect of this acid in considerably increasing the partition ratio was used with advantage. Such an increase, when applied in partition chromatography, was found to be highly desirable for good resolving power.

Mixtures of silica gel and kieselguhr have been used to fractionate DNP-peptides (29, 420). The relative adsorption affinities for the DNP-amino acids on silica gel–Celite columns, using the mixture acetic acid–acetone–ligroin as developer, range from those characteristic of the very strongly adsorbed derivatives of hydroxyproline, serine, aspartic acid, lysine, threonine, tyrosine, and glutamic acid through the moderately adsorbed derivatives of tryptophan, glycine, proline, alanine, methionine, and phenylalanine, to those characteristic of the very weakly adsorbed derivatives of valine, leucine, and isoleucine. The behavior of DNP-peptides on such columns follows roughly the order of the component amino acids (29), and adsorptive more so than partition effects appear to play the major role. Essentially similar observations and conclusions had been reached earlier by Mills (421), who employed methyl ethyl ketone–chloroform as developer with a variety of DNP-amino acids on kieselguhr.

An interesting use of orange- and red-colored derivatives of amino acids and peptides was described by Schwyzer and his associates (421a) which involved the N-acyl groups, p-(phenylazo)-carbobenzyloxy,

$$C_6H_5-N=N-C_6H_4CH_2OCO-$$

and p-(p'-methoxyphenylazo)-carbobenzyloxy,

$$CH_3OC_6H_4-N=N-C_6H_4CH_2OCO-$$

In order to introduce these groups into amino acids and peptides, the corresponding acid chlorides were employed in much the same way as the classic, colorless, carbobenzyloxy chloride (carbobenzoxy chloride) had long been used (see Section 10–14). The resulting colored derivatives possessed in methanol solution a characteristic absorption curve with a distinct maximum at 431 mμ which could be employed to determine concentration levels. A particular advantage in the use of these colored derivatives of the peptides lies not only in the possibility that their separation and identification are greatly facilitated by the possession of the color, but that, once separated, the N-acyl group can be removed and the free peptides cleanly regenerated, as in the case of carbobenzyloxy derivatives, by catalytic hydrogenolysis in the presence of palladium. This simple procedure is not possible in the case of the DNP derivatives of the peptides where the strong hydrolytic conditions necessary to remove the dinitrophenyl group also cleave the peptide linkages.

STARCH COLUMNS. Synge (248) employed starch columns for the separation of the peptides resulting from the partial hydrolysis of gramicidin, using *n*-butanol–water to develop the bands. The resolving power of starch for small peptides was shown by the separation of leucylglycine from glycylleucine by Moore and Stein (422). When the proteinase from *Bacillus subtilis* acts upon egg albumin a number of peptide fragments result, and Ottesen and Villee (423) employed starch columns to separate these peptides. The effluent fractions were analyzed by the photometric ninhydrin procedure. Ninhydrin color yields on a molar basis for various peptides relative to alanine as 100 were found to be 89 for diglycine, 93 for leucylglycine, 59 for leucyldiglycine, 56 for leucyltriglycine, 174 for dialanine, and 56 for alanyldiglycine (423). Stein and Moore (256) stated that peptides up to the four-residue stage can be efficiently handled on starch columns, but difficulties with the higher peptides were encountered, i.e., the larger peptides tended to run rapidly through the column and emerged with the solvent front, or else they scarcely moved at all. This point of view was concurred in by Fels and Tiselius (424; cf. 425).

CHARCOAL COLUMNS. The use of these columns to remove peptides containing residues with aromatic rings from mixtures of various peptides has been alluded to above. Such columns do not precisely separate aliphatic from aromatic peptides, but accomplish enough of value to warrant their use (412). Peptides with more than one tryptophan residue are retarded to a greater degree than are peptides with only one such residue, and separations can readily be achieved. Tryptophyltryptophan is more strongly adsorbed on charcoal than is tryptophan, and displacing or eluting agents such as stearic acid or phenol are of value in refining the separations obtained. From these observations it was surmised by Synge and Tiselius (286) that the adsorption of the individual peptides which occur in the mixture of tyrocidines might vary in proportion to the number of tryptophan residues per mole of these compounds (cf. 426).

COUNTERCURRENT DISTRIBUTION. The great virtue of this procedure has been revealed in the studies by Craig and his associates on the homogeneity of the polypeptide antibiotics (cf. 427). These compounds, including the gramicidins, the tyrocidines, and the bacitracins, etc., were originally isolated in states then believed to be of high purity. However, crystalline gramicidin (243) was later distributed in a methanol-water-chloroform system, and found to contain at least three if not four components (427). Crystalline tyrocidine hydrochloride was distributed in a system containing methanol–chloroform–0.1N HCl, and a minimum of five components was indicated (427). Crude bacitracin was resolved by countercurrent distribution between various solvents into at least ten polypeptides (428). A unique feature of the intact bacitracins is the lack of evidence for the presence of a free thiol group, although a thiol group appears to be liberated in all of them on mild acid hydrolysis (428). One great advantage of the distribution procedure is that the individual bands may be separated, and what may be accepted as a single chemical species can be studied and analyzed. Thus bacitracin A is the designation given the main active member of the bacitracin family of polypeptides. It was hydrolyzed into its constituent residues by Newton and Abraham (429) and found to contain cysteine, ornithine, lysine, histidine, aspartic acid, glutamic acid, phenylalanine, leucine, isoleucine, and one amide group, all arranged in a cyclic form. The polypeptide antibiotic was partially hydrolyzed before (430) and after conversion to the DNP-bacitracin A (431), and the peptide fragments distributed in a countercurrent apparatus. The free peptides in the former study were further characterized by conversion to the respective DNP derivatives (430). Prolonged hydrolysis of bacitracin A was necessary to split peptides involving isoleucine, as in the comparable case of insulin (353), but in this case the isolecuine fraction also contained some alloisoleucine, presumably as a result of racemization (epimerization) (432, 433). Tyrocidine A was isolated from a distribution by Battersby and Craig (434), and hydrolyzed to a mixture of phenylalanine, tyrosine, valine, leucine, proline, ornithine, glutamic acid, and aspartic acid. Like bacitracin A which at pH 7 was converted to another polypeptide, namely, bacitracin F (430), tyrocidine A was transformed in part to another product by recrystallization (434). The structure of tyrocidine A was subsequently arrived at by distributing the mixture of peptides produced after partial hydrolysis (435), by a further fractionating by ion exchange chromatography on Dowex 2 in the HCl form to separate the acidic peptides, and on Dowex 50 in the Na$^+$ form to separate the neutral and basic compounds. The eluted fractions were converted to DNP derivatives and further characterized by paper chromatography. The fractionation (436) of polymyxin B into several polypeptides by countercurrent distribution has been accomplished, and one of these fractions, polymyxin B$_1$, was found to yield on hydrolysis γ-aminobutyrine, threonine, phenylalanine, leucine, and isopelargonic acid.

The purification of the polypeptide hormones oxytocin and vasopressin from the posterior lobe of the pituitary was accomplished by countercurrent distribution, the former with the system 0.05% acetic acid–2-butanol, and the latter by means of aqueous p-toluenesulfonic acid–n-butanol (437–439). Hydrolysis of oxytocin and analysis on starch columns indicated a nearly equimolar content of leucine, isoleucine, tyrosine, proline, glutamic acid, aspartic acid, glycine, and cystine, together with three moles of ammonia, and thus a polypeptide with a molecular weight close to 1000. Vasopressin treated in the same way yielded equivalent amounts of phenylalanine, tyrosine, proline, glutamic acid, aspartic acid, glycine, arginine, and cystine, plus three equivalents of ammonia; these components were characteristic of vasopressin obtained from posterior pituitary glands of bovine origin. The vasopressin obtained from swine glands possessed the same analytical composition except that lysine was present in place of arginine (439).

A simple and convenient procedure for the separation of the oxytocic and pressor hormones in aqueous extracts of the gland was based on adsorption of the latter on Permutit "according to Folin," thus taking advantage of the more basic nature of this compound, whereas the more acidic oxytocic factor was not adsorbed (440). Elution of the pressor factor was accomplished by the use of sodium chloride solution. Acid silica has been used as an adsorbent for both peptides, acetic acid selectively eluting only the oxytocic factor (441).

It may be fairly said that the method of countercurrent distribution is a relatively laborious enterprise, and that hundreds of successive extractions may be required to arrive at a pure fraction from a mixture, but there is as yet no procedure comparable to it in either power or theoretical support.

Ion Exchange Columns. The use of Amberlite ion exchange resins for the preliminary separation into groups of the peptides arising from partial hydrolysates of proteins has been alluded to above. Moore and Stein (324) mentioned that, although dipeptides might readily yield sharp elution peaks with Dowex 50-X8 resin, the chromatography of the higher peptides might require resins of 4 or 2% cross-linking. Partial hydrolysates of gelatin were chromatographed on columns of Dowex 50 (442; cf. 443); separation of the various peptide zones from each other and from the accompanying buffer salts was effected by converting the peptides into the corresponding DNP-peptides, which were then separated further on columns of silicic acid–Celite (cf. 420).

The formation of peptides as products of enzyme-catalyzed transamidation reactions has been qualitatively demonstrated by paper chromatography (395, 396). The use of ion exchange resins to follow such reactions quantitatively was described by Dowmont and Fruton (444), who employed Dowex 50-X4 and Dowex 50-X8 for this purpose according to the procedures developed by Moore and Stein for amino acids. Both resins were used in the sodium form, the solvents employed for elution were sodium citrate buffers varying in pH from 4.0 to 5.5, and ninhydrin colors were based on leucine as standard. Peptides in which alanine was N-terminal possessed a color value considerably in excess of that of the molar equivalent of leucine (cf. 423); this has since been shown to be true also of N-terminal leucyl

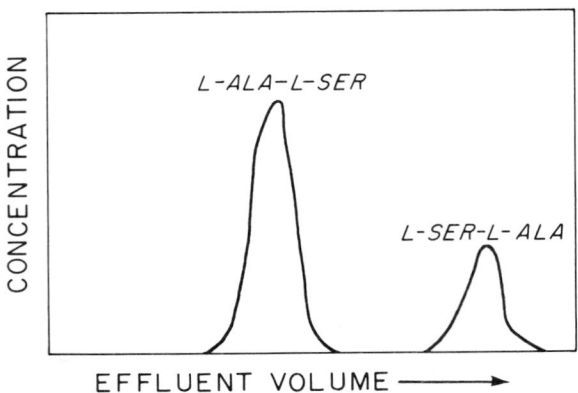

Figure 15–46. Separation of peptides on Dowex 50-X8 (Na+). Eluent buffer, pH 4.05. Dowmont, Y. P., and Fruton, J. S., *J. Biol. Chem.*, **197**, 271 (1952).

peptides (445). A further complication lies in the fact that diastereomeric peptides at equal concentration may possess quite different color yields with ninhydrin. Thus the intensity of the ninhydrin-reactive spot for L-leucyl-L-tyrosine on paper is considerably greater than that for D-leucyl-L-tyrosine (445), the ratio being about 3 : 1.

In all instances studied, peptides composed of a single type of amino acid residue emerged after the free amino acid. Also, dipeptides composed of two different neutral amino acid residues emerged after both constituent free amino acids. Figures 15–46 and 15–47 illustrate the separation of various peptides on Dowex 50 resins.

The diastereomeric peptides L-leucyl-L-tyrosine and D-leucyl-L-tyrosine, like many of the diastereomeric amino acids, are separable on Dowex 50 (Na+) (446). The column is washed with 0.2N NaOH and the peptides separated in citrate buffer at pH 4.84 in the presence of added benzyl alcohol as a detergent and disodium versenate. An illustration of this means of separation is given in Figure 15–48, which suggests a general procedure whereby the optical purity of synthetic peptides, prepared from optically active amino acids, may be ascertained.

NATURAL PEPTIDES IN BODY FLUIDS. In animal tissues three major peptide components appear, namely, glutathione which is found in relatively high concentration in nearly all tissues, and carnosine and anserine which are found almost exclusively in muscle (cf. Table 15–27). Neither plasma nor urine in normal states contains appreciable amounts of any peptides, and the increase in such amino acids as glutamic acid or aspartic acid on refluxing deproteinized homogenates of tissues with HCl is to be attributed largely to

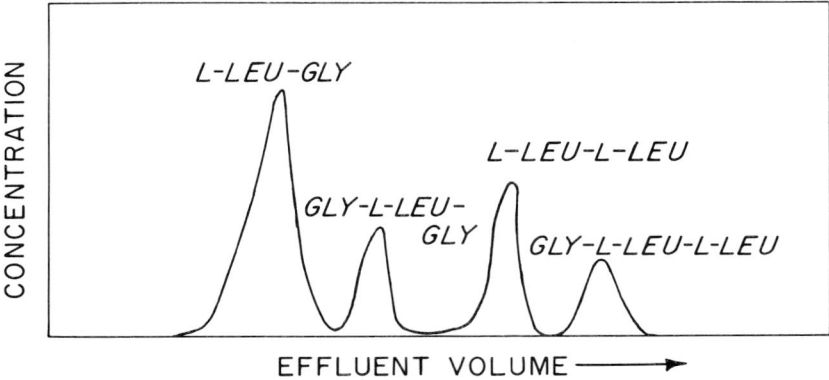

Figure 15–47. Separation of peptides on Dowex 50-X4 (Na+). Eluent buffer, pH 4.72. Dowmont, Y. P., and Fruton, J. S., *J. Biol. Chem.*, **197,** 271 (1952).

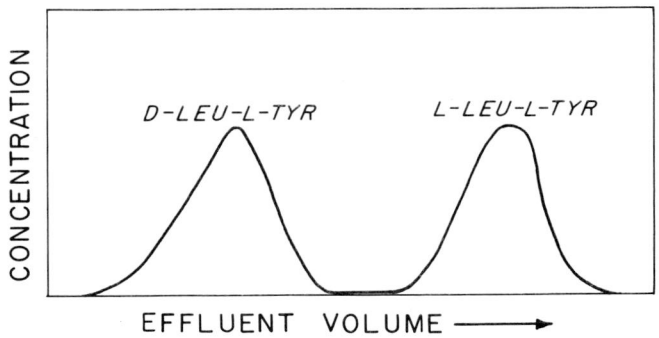

Figure 15–48. Separation of diastereomeric peptides on Dowex 50-X4 (Na+) at 37.5°. Eluent buffer at pH 4.84, containing benzyl alcohol and disodium versenate. Blackburn, S., and Tetley, P., *Biochim. et Biophys. Acta*, **20,** 423 (1956).

hydrolysis of glutamine and asparagine respectively, as is the increase of glycine, glutamic acid, and cystine to hydrolysis of glutathione. Carnosine can be distinguished from anserine by noting the presence of histidine after hydrolysis of the former, and methylhistidine after hydroylsis of the latter.

Borsook and co-workers (447) used starch to separate a peptide fraction from the protein-free portion of the livers of several species and from various protein sources such as Witte peptone from a peptic hydrolysate of fibrin. This peptide "A" when developed on the starch column with butanol–propanol–0.1 N HCl emerged from the column before any amino acid, and simultaneously with or directly after the advancing front of the solvent. It may be said to have not been chromatographed at all, but what appeared to be of considerable interest was that the quantitative amino acid composition of various preparations of peptide A, isolated from different sources, and by different methods, was essentially similar for all the preparations. Peptide A may very probably be a mixture of similar large peptides (cf. 424).

The larger ions may not be adsorbed on ion exchange resins, and a "molecular sieve" effect may be advantageously employed to separate the smaller from the larger ions, e.g., amino acids from proteins (cf. 314). This procedure may be illustrated by the isolation of ophthalmic acid, a tripeptide, from macerated calf lenses by Waley (448). Amberlite IR-4B, an anion exchange resin, was converted to the acetate form by washing first with 5% acetic acid, and then with water. Calf lenses were macerated with water, and the mixture stirred with the resin to adsorb only the acidic amino acids and the smaller peptides, and to reject the higher peptides and protein fragments. After the supernatant was discarded and the resin washed with water, the resin was transferred to a tube and eluted with 2N HCl until the eluate became ninhydrin-negative. Excess HCl was removed from the eluate by shaking with N-methyldioctylamine in chloroform solution, followed by chloroform to remove the excess of base. The eluate now had a pH of about 5, and contained chiefly glutathione, glutamic acid, ophthalmic acid, and some other acidic species. It was passed through a column of Dowex 50-X12 (H$^+$) (200–400 mesh) which adsorbed the former, amino compounds, and rejected the latter, chiefly phosphorus-containing compounds. After washing with water, the column was eluted with 3% NH$_4$OH, and the ninhydrin-reactive fraction was chromatographed on paper with phenol as solvent. The fraction which was neither glutathione nor glutamic acid, and possessed the same R_F as alanine, was cut out and eluted with water, the solute transformed to the crystalline copper salt by shaking with copper acetate, the copper removed by shaking with 8-hydroxyquinoline in chloroform, and the ophthalmic acid separated in crystalline form by the cautious addition of acetone to the aqueous layer. The tripeptide on analysis appeared to be γ-glutamylbutyrinylglycine; accompanying it was a second tripeptide, moving just behind ophthalmic acid (with R_F like that of glycine) which Waley designated as norophthalmic acid, and which appeared to be γ-glutamylalanylglycine.

These are, however, relatively small peptides, and if higher peptides are to be fractionated, i.e., those roughly between amino acids and proteins in molecular size, it is necessary to find conditions under which interference by either of these extremes would occur to a minimal extent. Conventional ion exchange resins are unsuitable, for the larger peptides would diffuse only very slowly within the gel-like structure of the resin particles. Resins with a very low degree of cross-linking may be used with advantage, but these resins tend to swell and shrink considerably as the pH or ionic strength of the ambient solution is altered. A satisfactory approach to the solution of this problem was achieved by Feitelson and Partridge (449) by preparing a resin with a very low degree of cross-linkage spread as a thin film on the surface of an inert extender. A composite resin was prepared by coating diatomaceous earth (Celite) with a sulfonatated polystyrene in the following manner. Styrene, divinylbenzene, and chloroform were mixed together and treated with benzoyl peroxide. Celite 545 was made water-repellent by treatment with dichlorodimethylsilane, and shaken with the above mixture. A rough estimate was made of the degree of coating of the Celite by weighing a filtered amount of known volume. After removal of the chloroform, polymerization was allowed to take place at 60° for 24 hours, and then continued at 80° for 6 days. The resin-coated Celite was then sulfonated with H_2SO_4, and Ag_2SO_4 as catalyst, the acid removed by washing with water, and the material stored under 1% Na_2CO_3 until required. With packed column in the wet state, 1 ml. of the resin exchanged 0.11 meq. of Na^+. The peptides themselves were spotted, not with ninhydrin which reacts too weakly with the larger compounds, but by means of the biuret reaction. The recent development of cellulose ion exchange adsorbents by Peterson and Sober (449a) holds considerable promise for the separation of the larger peptides.

33. Ionophoresis. The basis of this procedure rests upon the influence of pH on the dissociation of the amino acids, as illustrated in Figure 15–49 (450). When a mixture of amino acids maintained at pH 5.5 is placed in the middle compartment of a three-compartment cell and a direct current is passed through the solution, the amino acids are separated into three fractions: (a) aspartic and glutamic acids which are predominantly acidic, and which as anions migrate toward the anode; (b) arginine, histidine, and lysine which are basic and as cations migrate toward the cathode; and (c) the monoamino-monocarboxylic acids, which are close to their isoelectric point at this pH and hence electrically neutral, and which remain in the center compartment. On adjusting the pH of the solution of the basic amino acids to pH 7.5 and again using electrical transport, arginine and lysine migrate to the cathode, whereas histidine remains in the center compartment. The procedure was used early for the preparation of large quantities of histidine from an erythrocyte hydrolysate (451). Probably the first employment of electrical transport for the isolation of an amino acid was that relating to the separation of glutamic acid from a protein hydrolysate (cf. 452).

Gordon, Martin, and Synge (252) applied the three-compartment electrodialytic fractionation method to isolate the basic peptides resulting from the partial hydrolysis of gelatin. The apparatus employed was that developed by Albanese (453) in which carbon served as anode and platinum gauze as cathode (Chapter 28). In a subsequent study, Gordon, Martin, and Synge (252) isolated the neutral (middle-compartment) fraction of the electrodialysate of partially hydrolyzed gelatin, the initial pH of the mixture having

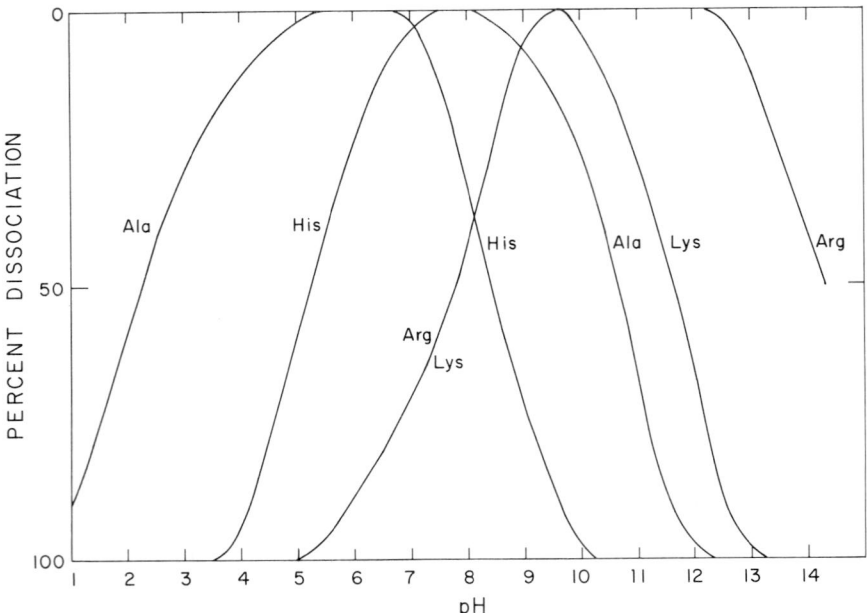

Figure 15–49. Dissociation at various pH ranges of amino acids. Foster, G. L., and Schmidt, C. L. A., *J. Biol. Chem.*, **56**, 545 (1923).

been set at 6. At an alkaline pH, Sanger and Tuppy (412) could obtain a fraction from a partial hydrolysate of insulin which contained only arginine peptides.

A series of beakers connected by inverted U-tubes was employed by du Vigneaud and his associates (454, 455) for the fairly large-scale electrical separation of the posterior pituitary hormones vasopressin and oxytocin from each other and from various impurities; the former has an isoelectric point near pH 10.8, and the latter near pH 8.5 (456).

The use of more solid supports emerged in the reports of Consden, Gordon, and Martin (65, 76; cf. 392), who employed slabs of silica jelly strengthened with paper pulp. The jelly embodied buffers ranging in pH from 2 to 9, and the electrodes (brass cathode and carbon anode) were

CHROMATOGRAPHY

continuously washed with a stream of buffer solution to prevent pH changes and to carry away electrode reaction products. The solution to be investigated was inlaid in the slab of jelly. The essential function of the jelly was to prevent convection of the electrolyte, obviating the need for diaphragms and consequent compartmentalization, and permitting each amino acid or group of amino acids (or peptides) to move along the jelly as discrete bands. The progress of the separation was followed by a "printing off" process of

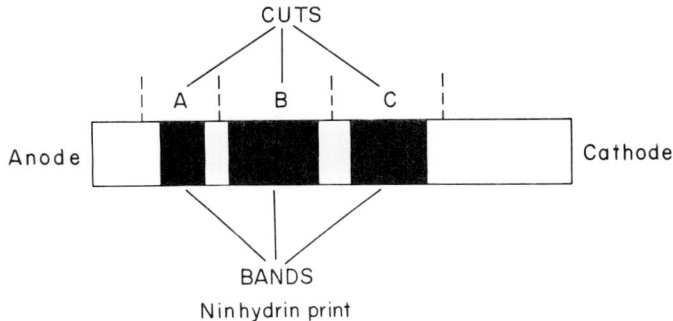

Figure 15–50. Fractions resulting from ionophoresis of partial hydrolysate of gramicidin S. Cut A contains neutral amino acids and peptides, cut B peptides of ornithine, and cut C ornithine. Consden, R., Gordon, A. H., Martin, A. J. P., and Synge, R. L. M., *Biochem. J.*, **41**, 596 (1947).

portions of the jelly onto filter paper which was treated with ninhydrin, the prints showing bands corresponding in position to those of the amino acids or peptides in the gel. Figure 15–50 (388) illustrates various fractions cut from the electrodialysate on silica jelly of a partial hydrolysate of gramicidin S. Cut C contained only free ornithine, cut B contained peptides of ornithine but no free ornithine, whereas cut A contained only neutral amino acids and their peptides. Each cut was hydrolyzed and analyzed by paper chromatography before and after treatment with dinitrofluorobenzene. In addition to free ornithine (457), ethanolamine (458) was also isolated in this fashion, the latter from gramicidin RM hydrolysates. Further aids to electrical fractionation (65) were employed to sharpen the separation of various components of partial hydrolysates, such as the oxidative conversion of cystine or cysteine residues to those of cysteic acid which resulted in an augmented mobility of these components. Asbestos fibers soaked in buffer and divided into sections by filter paper barriers were employed as a support for electrodialysis by Butler and Stephen (459), and, with the use of silver–silver chloride electrodes in NaCl solutions and at a pH of 9.3, a good separation of glycine and glycylglycine was achieved, the latter wandering to the anode.

The use of filter paper electrophoresis for the separation of amino acids and peptides most probably owes its origin to the success which attended paper chromatography, and was, like paper chromatography, the sequel to silica gel ionophoresis. Wieland and Fischer (460) separated glutamic acid (anode), histidine (cathode), and alanine (no movement) on S. and S. No. 575 paper at pH 5.0, whereas at pH 7.5 lysine could be separated from the stationary histidine by migration to the cathode. At pH 3.7, aspartic acid which migrated to the anode could be separated from the relatively unmoving glutamic acid. On filter paper buffered at pH 6.2 and treated with an electric current, the aminodicarboxylic acids migrated to the anode, the diamino acids to the cathode, whilst histidine and the neutral amino acids migrated little if at all (56; cf. 461). Durrum (462) described two-dimensional ionophoresis of amino acids in analogy with two-dimensional paper chromatography, and further suggested the use of ordinary paper chromatography followed by ionophoresis in the second dimension as providing a good separation of such closely migrating components as threonine and methionine. Table 15–32 indicates the relative order of migration of amino acids on paper in an electrical field (462) using platinum foil electrodes.

A particularly interesting separation of closely related amino acids which depends upon relatively small differences in ionization strength of the hydroxyl group is that described by Lissitzky (463). Thus, when thyroxine, triiodothyronine, and diiodothyronine were subjected to electrophoresis on paper impregnated with NaOH (0.4 ma. per cm. and 300 v.) the migration toward the anode was in the order diiodotyrosine > triiodothyronine > thyroxine. Under the same conditions except that the pH of the paper was held at 8.6, the order of migration toward the anode was, for the following amino acids, tyrosine > monoiodotyrosine > diiodotyrosine.

Peptides originally containing cystine and prepared from insulin by enzymic digestion were oxidized to convert the cystine to cysteic acid residues, and were separated by paper ionophoresis by Sanger and his associates (400, 464, 465), the separation being facilitated by making use of their high mobilities as acids in acetic acid media. In this way, all cysteic acid peptides, except those containing basic amino acids, could be completely separated from other peptides (86). The peptides obtained from ordinary paper chromatograms were applied to a sheet of Whatman No. 1 paper and electrically transported under 220 volts at pH 6.8 with ammonium acetate as electrolyte. Several peptides of cystine, without prior conversion to cysteic acid residues, and resulting from the partial degradation of insulin, were separated at high potential gradients in pyridine-acetate buffers on filter paper completely immersed in toluene (464), and the disulfide bands located by the cyanide-nitroprusside reaction (cf. 466). This run was carried on at pH 3.6. A cut containing the cystine peptides was again subjected to ionophoresis in a second dimension at pH 6.5. Owing to the unusually low

pK values of the amino groups of cystine residues in peptides, a good fractionation of neutral cystine peptides was achieved at this stage. At the end of the run a fresh sheet of paper was pressed upon that investigated and a print "taken," the position of the cystine peptides on the print noted by the cyanide-nitroprusside reagent, and thereby the original positions apprehended. The

TABLE 15–32

Relative Order of Electrical Transport of Amino Acids on
Schleicher and Schull No. 413 Paper (462)[a]

Toward Cathode in N Acetic Acid (pH 2.3)	Toward Anode in 0.2N Ammonia (pH 11.3)
Lysine	Aspartic acid
Histidine	Glutamic acid
Arginine	Cystine
Glycine	Glycine
Alanine	Serine
	Threonine
Valine	Hydroxyproline
Isoleucine	Tyrosine
Leucine	Methionine
Serine	Histidine
Threonine	Phenylalanine
Methionine	Alanine
Tryptophan	Valine
	Isoleucine
Phenylalanine	Leucine
Glutamic acid	Tryptophan
Tyrosine	Proline
Proline	Lysine
Cystine	Arginine
Aspartic acid	
Hydroxyproline	

[a] Fastest at top of columns.

zones relating to these positions were eluted, the cystine peptides converted to cysteic acid peptides by oxidation, and subjected to ionophoresis at pH 3.6 which permitted some further fractionation of the individual cysteic acid peptides and thus simplified their subsequent identification. The bands of these peptides were of course located with ninhydrin. In some cases the partial hydrolysate of insulin was fractionated in preliminary fashion on Amberlite IR-4B at pH 3–4, yielding two fractions, namely, that adsorbed on the column which contained acidic and some neutral cystine peptides, and that which came through the column and was composed of neutral and basic peptides (464). The combination of these and analogous procedures resulted in the complete description of the structure of insulin (464).

34. Ion Exchange Paper Chromatography. Attempts to combine ion exchange and paper chromatography have resulted so far in phenomena of limited interest. Two general approaches have been followed; (a) chemical alteration of the paper, and (b) incorporation or impregnation of the paper before the sheet is formed. As an example of the former procedure, Whatman No. 1 paper was immersed in a mixture of glacial acetic acid and benzenesulfonic acid, dried, and treated with succinic anhydride and pyridine for several hours at 80°. One of the carboxyl groups of the succinic acid was thereby esterified with the paper, the amount of succinic residues being dependent on the concentration of anhydride employed for the reaction, as well as on the time of the reaction. Using $0.05M$ ammonium formate brought to pH 9 as a solvent, and with paper of 3% succinyl content, the three basic amino acids were readily separated, the R_F values being as follows: arginine 0.45, lysine 0.53, and histidine 0.76 (467). Ninhydrin was used to determine the locations of these amino acids.

Examples of the latter procedure (b) have involved paper incorporating about 28% by weight of Amberlite IR-120 (Na$^+$) type cation exchange resin (468), and paper impregnated with Amberlite IRC-50 (H$^+$) cation exchange resin (469). With a $0.2M$ acetate buffer at pH 5.2 and at 25°, a clear-cut separation of the basic amino acids on the Amberlite IR-120 paper was achieved, the R_F values being: arginine 0.08, histidine 0.16, and lysine 0.24. No separation of the classic valine-leucine-isoleucine mixture could, however, be accomplished in this system. The weakly acid Amberlite IRC-50 paper, with 1-butanol–ethanol–water (4 : 1 : 5), was fairly efficient in separating the simpler amino acids, but could not be overloaded because of the ease of streaking.

REFERENCES

1. Rheinboldt, H., in *Methoden der organischen Chemie* (Houben-Weyl), Vol. I, Thieme, Leipzig, p. 272, 1921.
2. Kuhn, R., Winterstein, A., and Lederer, E., *Z. physiol. Chem.*, **197**, 141 (1931).
3. Tristram, G. R., *Advances in Protein Chem.*, **5**, 83 (1949).
4. Fischer, E., *Ber.*, **39**, 530 (1906).
5. Fischer, E., *Z. physiol. Chem.*, **33**, 151 (1901).
6. Fischer, E., *Ber.*, **35**, 2660 (1902).
7. Morgan, W. T. J., *J. Chem. Soc.*, **1926**, 79.
8. Cherbuliez, E., and Plattner, P., *Helv. Chim. Acta*, **12**, 317 (1929).
9. Mellon, E. F., Korn, A. H., Viola, S. J., Miller, N., and Hoover, S. R., *J. Am. Chem. Soc.*, **75**, 5524 (1953).

10. Gurin, S., *J. Am. Chem. Soc.*, **58**, 2104 (1936).
11. Weygand, F., Geiger, H., and Swodenk, W., *Angew. Chem.*, **68**, 307 (1956).
12. Dakin, H. D., *Biochem. J.*, **12**, 290 (1918).
13. Cohn, E. J., *Ergeb. Physiol.*, **33**, 781 (1931).
14. Calvery, H. O., *J. Biol. Chem.*, **94**, 613 (1932).
15. England, A., Jr., and Cohn, E. J., *J. Am. Chem. Soc.*, **57**, 634 (1935).
16. Cohn, E. J., McMeekin, T. L., Edsall, J. T., and Weare, J. H., *J. Am. Chem. Soc.*, **56**, 2270 (1934).
17. Neuberger, A., *Biochem. J.*, **32**, 1435 (1938).
18. Synge, R. L. M., *Biochem. J.*, **33**, 1913, 1918, 1924, 1931 (1939).
19. Martin, A. J. P., and Synge, R. L. M., *Biochem. J.*, **35**, 91 (1941).
20. Martin, A. J. P., and Synge, R. L. M., *Biochem. J.*, **35**, 1358 (1941).
21. Tristram, G. R., *Biochem. J.*, **40**, 721 (1946).
22. Gordon, A. H., Martin, A. J. P., and Synge, R. L. M., *Biochem. J.*, **38**, 65 (1944).
23. Liddell, H. F., and Rydon, H. N., *Biochem. J.*, **38**, 68 (1944).
24. Sanger, F., *Biochem. J.*, **39**, 507 (1945).
25. Blackburn, S., *Biochem. J.*, **45**, 579 (1949).
26. Middlebrook, W. R., *Biochim. Biophys. Acta*, **7**, 547 (1951).
27. Perrone, J. C., *Nature*, **167**, 513 (1951).
28. Partridge, S. M., and Swain, T., *Nature*, **166**, 272 (1950).
29. Schroeder, W. A., and Honnen, L. R., *J. Am. Chem. Soc.*, **75**, 4615 (1953).
30. Gordon, A. H., Martin, A. J. P., and Synge, R. L. M., *Biochem. J.*, **37**, xiii (1943).
31. Consden, R., Gordon, A. H., and Martin, A. J. P., *Biochem. J.*, **38**, 224 (1944).
32. LeRosen, A. L., *J. Am. Chem. Soc.*, **64**, 1905 (1942).
33. Bentley, H. R., and Whitehead, J. K., *Biochem. J.*, **46**, 341 (1950).
34. Consden, R., *Brit. Med. Bull.*, **10**, No. 3, 177 (1954).
35. Dent, C. E., *Biochem. J.*, **43**, 169 (1948).
36. Keston, A. S., Udenfriend, S., and Levy, M., *J. Am. Chem. Soc.*, **72**, 748 (1950).
37. Polson, A., *Biochim. Biophys. Acta*, **3**, 205 (1949).
38. Block, R. J., Durrum, E. L., and Zweig, G., *A Manual of Paper Chromatography and Paper Electrophoresis*, Academic Press, New York, 2nd ed., 1958. See also, Smith, I., *Chromatographic Techniques*, Interscience Publishers, New York, 1958.
39. Edman, P., *Arkiv. Kemi Mineral. Geol.*, **22**, 1 (1945).
40. Heyns, K., and Anders, G., *Z. physiol. Chem.*, **287**, 15 (1951).
41. Work, E., *Biochim. Biophys. Acta*, **3**, 400 (1949).
42. Lissitzky, S., and Laurent, G., *Bull. soc. chim. biol.*, **37**, 1177 (1955).
43. Krishnamurthy, K., and Swaminathan, M., *Anal. Chem.*, **27**, 1396 (1955).
44. Wolfe, M., *Biochim. Biophys. Acta*, **23**, 186 (1957).
45. Block, R. J., and Sober, H. A., *Colloid Chem.*, **7**, 181 (1950).
46. Müller, R. H., and Clegg, D. L., *Anal. Chem.*, **23**, 396 (1951).
47. Jirgensons, B., *Univ. Texas Publ.*, **No. 5109**, 56 (1951).
48. Hanes, C. S., and Isherwood, F. A., *Nature*, **164**, 1107 (1949).
49. Williams, R. J., and Kirby, H., *Science*, **107**, 481 (1948).
50. Block, R. J., *Anal. Chem.*, **22**, 1327 (1950).
51. Rutter, L., *Nature*, **161**, 435 (1948).
52. Giri, K. V., Radhakrishnan, A. N., and Vaidyanathan, C. S., *J. Indian Inst. Sci.*, **35**, 145 (1953).
53. Oreskes, I., and Saifer, A., *Anal. Chem.*, **27**, 854 (1955).
54. Miettinen, J. K., and Virtanen, A. I., *Acta Chem. Scand.*, **3**, 459 (1949).
54a. Chartier, J., Van Klaveren, F. W., and Vaillancourt, G., *J. Chromatography*, **1**, 317 (1958).
55. McFarren, E. F., *Anal. Chem.*, **23**, 168 (1951).

56. Haugaard, G., and Kroner, T. B., *J. Am. Chem. Soc.*, **70**, 2135 (1948).
56a. Levy, A. L., and Chung, D., *Anal. Chem.*, **25**, 396 (1953).
57. Dent, C. E., *Biochem. J.*, **41**, 240 (1947).
58. Thompson, E. O. P., *Biochim. Biophys. Acta*, **15**, 440 (1954).
59. Van Halteren, M. B., *Nature*, **168**, 1090 (1951).
60. Strack, E., Friedel, W., and Hambsch, K., *Z. physiol. Chem.*, **305**, 166 (1956).
61. Smith, E. L., and Tuller, E. F., *Arch. Biochem. Biophys.*, **54**, 114 (1955).
62. Crumpler, H. R., and Dent, C. E., *Nature*, **164**, 441 (1949).
63. Beck, M. T., and Csaszar, J., *Acta Chim. Acad. Sci. Hung.*, **7**, 465 (1955).
64. Kalyankar, G. D., and Snell, E. E., *Nature*, **180**, 1069 (1957).
65. Consden, R., Gordon, A. H., and Martin, A. J. P., *Biochem. J.*, **41**, 590 (1947).
66. Astrup, T., Stage, A., and Olsen, E., *Acta Chem. Scand.*, **5**, 1343 (1951).
67. McCollum, E. V., and Rider, A. A., *Arch. Biochem. Biophys.*, **40**, 20 (1952).
68. Boulanger, P., and Biserte, G., *Bull. soc. chim. biol.*, **33**, 1930 (1951).
69. Redfield, R. R., *Biochim. Biophys. Acta*, **10**, 344 (1953).
70. Carsten, M. E., *J. Am. Chem. Soc.*, **74**, 5954 (1952).
71. Block, R. J., and Bolling, D., *The Amino Acid Composition of Proteins and Foods*, Charles C Thomas, Springfield, Ill., 1951.
72. Piez, K. A., Tooper, E. B., and Fosdick, L. S., *J. Biol. Chem.*, **194**, 669 (1952).
73. Dreze, A., Moore, S., and Bigwood, E. J., *Anal. chim. Acta*, **11**, 554 (1954).
74. Pasieka, A. E., and Morgan, J. F., *Biochim. Biophys. Acta*, **19**, 366 (1956).
75. Hardy, T. L., Holland, D. O., and Naylor, J. H. C., *Anal. Chem.*, **27**, 971 (1955).
76. Consden, R., Gordon, A. H., and Martin, A. J. P., *Biochem. J.*, **40**, 33 (1946); Acker, R., and Crocker, C., *Biochim. Biophys. Acta*, **9**, 704 (1952).
77. Frank, H., and Petersen, H., *Z. physiol. Chem.*, **299**, 1 (1955).
78. Fromageot, C., *Cold Spring Harbor Symposia Quant. Biol.*, **14**, 49 (1950); Saifer, A., and Oreskes, J., *Science*, **119**, 124 (1954); Barrollier, J., Heilman, J., and Watzke, E., *Z. physiol. Chem.*, **304**, 21 (1956).
79. Pasieka, A. E., and Morgan, J. F., *Proc. Soc. Exptl. Biol. Med.*, **93**, 54 (1956).
80. Winegard, H. M., Toennies, G., and Block, R. J., *Science*, **108**, 506 (1948).
81. Fearon, W. R., and Boggust, W. A., *Analyst*, **79**, 101 (1954).
82. Patton, A. K., and Foreman, E. M., *Science*, **109**, 339 (1949).
83. Walker, J. B., *Arch. Biochem. Biophys.*, **59**, 233 (1955).
84. Walker, J. B., *J. Biol. Chem.*, **218**, 549 (1956).
85. Müting, D., *Naturwiss.*, **39**, 303 (1952); Giri, K. V., and Nagabhashanam, A., *ibid.*, **39**, 548 (1952).
85a. Schwartz, D. P., *Anal. Chem.*, **30**, 1855 (1958).
86. Sanger, F., and Thompson, E. O. P., *Biochem. J.*, **53**, 353, 366 (1953).
87. Rao, K. R., and Sober, H. A., *J. Am. Chem. Soc.*, **76**, 1328 (1954).
88. Mellon, E. F., Korn, A. H., and Hoover, S. R., *J. Am. Chem. Soc.*, **75**, 1675 (1953).
89. Levy, A. L., *Nature*, **174**, 126 (1954).
90. Isherwood, F. A., and Cruickshank, D. H., *Nature*, **174**, 123 (1954).
91. Levy, A. L., Geschwind, I. I., and Li, C. H., *J. Biol. Chem.*, **213**, 187 (1955).
92. Li, C. H., and Chung, D., *J. Biol. Chem.*, **218**, 33 (1956).
93. Lowther, A. G., *Nature*, **167**, 767 (1951).
94. Blackburn, S., and Lowther, A. G., *Biochem. J.*, **48**, 126 (1951).
95. Felix, K., and Krekels, A., *Z. physiol. Chem.*, **290**, 78 (1952).
96. Iwainsky, H., *Z. physiol. Chem.*, **297**, 194 (1954).
97. Goulden, J. D. S., *Nature*, **173**, 646 (1954).
98. Fromageot, C., Jutisz, M., Mayer, D., and Penasse, L., *Compt. rend.*, **230**, 1905 (1950); *Biochim. Biophys. Acta*, **6**, 283 (1950).
99. Bremner, J. M., and Kenten, R. H., *Biochem. J.*, **49**, 651 (1951).

100. Urbach, K. F., *Proc. Soc. Exptl. Biol. Med.*, **70**, 146 (1949).
101. Martin, A. J. P., *Biochem. Soc. Symposia (Cambridge, Eng.)*, **3**, 4 (1949).
102. Abderhalden, E., and Weil, A., *Z. physiol. Chem.*, **81**, 207 (1912); **84**, 39 (1913); **88**, 272 (1913).
103. Abderhalden, E., Froehlich, C., and Fuchs, D., *Z. physiol. Chem.*, **86**, 454 (1913).
104. Consden, R., Gordon, A. H., Martin, A. J. P., Rosenheim, O., and Synge, R. L. M., *Biochem. J.*, **39**, 251 (1945).
105. Dakin, H. D., *Biochem. J.*, **13**, 398 (1919).
106. Dent, C. E., and Fowler, D. I., *Biochem. J.*, **56**, 54 (1954).
107. Bailey, K., Chibnall, A. C., Ries, M. W., and Williams, E. F., *Biochem. J.*, **37**, 360 (1943).
108. Nicolet, B. H., and Shinn, L. A., *J. Biol. Chem.*, **142**, 139 (1942).
109. Dent, C. E., and Walshe, J. M., *Brit. Med. Bull.*, **10**, No. 3, 247 (1954).
110. Boulanger, P., Biserte, G., and Courtot, F., *Bull. soc. chim. biol.*, **34**, 366 (1952).
111. Deane, K. R., and Truter, E. V., *Biochim. Biophys. Acta*, **18**, 435 (1955).
112. Fink, K., Henderson, R. B., and Fink, R. M., *Proc. Soc. Exptl. Biol. Med.*, **78**, 135 (1951).
113. Crumpler, H. R., Dent, C. E., Harris, H., and Westall, R. G., *Nature*, **167**, 307 (1951).
114. Fink, K., Henderson, R. B., and Fink, R. M., *J. Biol. Chem.*, **197**, 441 (1952).
115. Partridge, S. M., *Biochem. J.*, **44**, 521 (1949).
116. Searle, J. M., and Westall, R. G., *Biochem. J.*, **48**, Proc. i (1951).
117. Datta, S. P., and Harris, H., *Nature*, **168**, 296 (1951).
118. Westall, R. G., *Biochem. J.*, **55**, 244 (1953).
119. Agren, G., and Nilsson, T., *Acta Chem. Scand.*, **3**, 525 (1949).
120. Dent, C. E., and Schilling, J. A., *Biochem. J.*, **44**, 318 (1949).
121. Bickel, H., and Smellie, J. M., *Lancet*, **1**, 1093 (1952).
122. Holzel, A., Komrower, G. M., and Wilson, V. K., *Brit. Med. J.*, **1**, 194 (1952).
123. Woolf, L. I., *Biochem. J.*, **49**, Proc. ix (1951); cf. Jervis, G. A., *Proc. Soc. Exptl. Biol. Med.*, **75**, 83 (1950).
124. Clarkson, T. W., and Kench, J. E., *Biochem. J.*, **62**, 361 (1956).
125. Flock, E. V., Mann, F. C., and Bollman, J. L., *J. Biol. Chem.*, **192**, 293 (1951).
126. Braun, P., Foldi, M., Kisfaludy, S., and Szabo, G., *Nature*, **177**, 1133 (1956).
127. Work, E., *Biochem. J.*, **49**, 17 (1951).
128. Rhuland, L. E., Work, E., Denman, R. F., and Hoare, D. S., *J. Am. Chem. Soc.*, **77**, 4844 (1955).
129. Hoare, D. S., and Work, E., *Biochem. J.*, **61**, 562 (1955).
130. Work, E., and Dewey, D. L., *J. Gen. Microbiol.*, **9**, 394 (1953).
131. Gendre, T., and Lederer, E., *Biochim. Biophys. Acta*, **9**, 19 (1952).
132. Wooley, D. W., Schaffner, G., and Braun, A. C., *J. Biol. Chem.*, **198**, 807 (1952).
133. Done, J., and Fowden, L., *Biochem. J.*, **51**, 451 (1952).
134. Vauquelin, L. N., and Robiquet, P. J., *Ann. chim. phys.*, **57**, 88 (1806).
135. Schulze, E., and Bosshardt, E., *Ber.*, **16**, 312 (1883).
136. Fowden, L., and Done, J., *Biochem. J.*, **55**, 548 (1953).
137. Virtanen, A. I., and Berg, A-M., *Acta Chem. Scand.*, **8**, 1085 (1954).
138. Berg, A-M., and Virtanen, A. I., *Acta Chem. Scand.*, **8**, 1725 (1954).
139. Virtanen, A. I., Uksila, E., and Matikkala, E. J., *Acta Chem. Scand.*, **8**, 1091 (1954).
140. Virtanen, A. I., and Hietala, P. K., *Acta Chem. Scand.*, **9**, 175 (1955).
141. Steward, F. C., and Thompson, J. F., *Ann. Rev. Plant Physiol.*, **1**, 233 (1950).
142. Zacharius, R. M., Thompson, J. F., and Steward, F. C., *J. Am. Chem. Soc.*, **74**, 2949 (1952).
143. Hulme, A. C., and Arthington, W., *Nature*, **170**, 659 (1952).
144. Morrison, R. I., *Biochem. J.*, **53**, 474 (1953).

145. Miettinen, J. K., Kari, S., Moisio, T., Alfthan, M., and Virtanen, A. I., *Suomen Kemistilehti*, **B2**, 26 (1933).
146. Fling, M., and Horowitz, N. H., *J. Biol. Chem.*, **190**, 277 (1951).
147. Thompson, J. F., and Steward, F. C., *J. Exptl. Botany*, **3**, 170 (1952).
148. Reed, L. J., *J. Biol. Chem.*, **183**, 450 (1950).
149. Awapara, J., Landua, A. J., Fuerst, R., and Seale, B., *J. Biol. Chem.*, **187**, 35 (1950).
150. Roberts, E., and Frankel, S., *J. Biol. Chem.*, **187**, 55 (1950).
151. Udenfriend, S., *J. Biol. Chem.*, **187**, 65 (1950).
152. Corfield, M. C., Fletcher, J. C., and Robson, A., *Chem. & Ind. (London)*, **1956**, 661.
153. Miettinen, J. K., and Virtanen, A. I., *Physiol. Plantarum*, **5**, 540 (1952).
154. Plattner, P. A., and Nager, U., *Helv. Chim. Acta*, **31**, 665 (1948).
155. Plattner, P. A., and Nager, U., *Helv. Chim. Acta*, **31**, 2192, 2203 (1948).
156. Gal, E. M., and Greenberg, D. M., *Proc. Soc. Exptl. Biol. Med.*, **71**, 88 (1949).
157. Brockmann, H., and Grubhofer, K., *Naturwiss.*, **36**, 376 (1949).
158. Dalgliesh, C. E., Johnson, A. W., Todd, A. R., and Vining, L. C., *J. Chem. Soc.*, **1950**, 2946.
159. Radhakrishnan, A. N., and Giri, K. V., *Biochem. J.*, **58**, 57 (1954).
160. Acher, R., Fromageot, C., and Jutisz, M., *Biochim. Biophys. Acta*, **5**, 81 (1950).
161. Jepson, J. B., and Smith, J., *Nature*, **172**, 1100 (1953).
162. Horn, M. J., and Jones, D. B., *J. Biol. Chem.*, **139**, 473 (1941).
163. Consden, R., Gordon, A. H., and Martin, A. J. P., *Biochem. J.*, **40**, 580 (1946).
164. Alderton, G., and Fevold, H. L., *J. Am. Chem. Soc.*, **73**, 463 (1951).
165. Alderton, G., *J. Am. Chem. Soc.*, **75**, 2391 (1953).
166. Berridge, N. J., Newton, G. G. F., and Abraham, E. P., *Biochem. J.*, **52**, 529 (1952).
167. Grobbelaar, N., Pollard, J. K., and Steward, F. C., *Nature*, **175**, 703 (1955).
168. Piez, K. A., Irreverre, F., and Wolff, H. L., *J. Biol. Chem.*, **223**, 687 (1956); also, Hegarty, M. P., *Australian J. Chem.*, **10**, 484 (1957).
169. Van Slyke, D. D., *J. Biol. Chem.*, **16**, 187 (1913).
170. Christensen, H. N., and Lynch, E. L., *J. Biol. Chem.*, **172**, 107 (1948).
171. Campbell, P. N., and Work, T. S., *Biochem. J.*, **50**, 449 (1952).
172. Roberts, E., and Frankel, S., *Cancer Research*, **9**, 645 (1949).
173. Morris, C. J., and Thompson, J. F., *J. Am. Chem. Soc.*, **78**, 1605 (1956).
174. Roberts, E., and Borges, P. R. F., *Cancer Research*, **15**, 697 (1955).
175. Greenstein, J. P., *Biochemistry of Cancer*, Academic Press, New York, 2nd ed., 1954.
176. Harington, C. R., and Barger, G., *Biochem. J.*, **21**, 169 (1927).
177. Harington, C. R., and Randall, S. S., *Biochem. J.*, **23**, 373 (1929).
178. Gross, J., *Brit. Med. Bull.*, **10**, No. 3, 218 (1954).
179. Gross, J., and Leblond, C. P., *Endocrinology*, **48**, 714 (1951).
180. Bowden, C. H., Maclagan, N. F., and Wilkinson, J. H., *Biochem. J.*, **59**, 93 (1955).
181. Wilkinson, J. H., *Biochem. J.*, **63**, 601 (1956).
182. Roche, J., Deltour, G. H., Michel, R., and Velez, E., *Compt. rend.*, **147**, 270 (1953).
183. Fink, R. M., Dent, C. E., and Fink, K., *Nature*, **160**, 801 (1947).
184. Fink, K., and Fink, R. M., *Science*, **108**, 358 (1948).
185. Tishkoff, G. H., Bennett, R., Bennett, V., and Miller, L. L., *Science*, **110**, 452 (1949).
186. Taurog, A., Tong, W., and Chaikoff, I. L., *J. Biol. Chem.*, **184**, 83 (1950).
187. Roche, J., Lissitzky, S., and Michel, R., *Compt. rend.*, **232**, 2047 (1951).
188. Gross, J., and Pitt-Rivers, R., *Biochem. J.*, **53**, 645 (1953).
189. Roche, J., Lissitzky, S., and Michel, R., *Biochim. Biophys. Acta*, **11**, 220 (1953).
190. Tong, W., Taurog, A., and Chaikoff, I. L., *J. Biol. Chem.*, **191**, 665 (1951).
191. Roche, J., Deltour, G. H., Lissitzky, S., and Michel, R., *Compt. rend.*, **144**, 1321 (1950).
192. Taurog, A., Chaikoff, I. L., and Tong, W., *J. Biol. Chem.*, **184**, 99 (1950).
193. Gross, J., and Pitt-Rivers, R., *Lancet*, **2**, 766 (1951).

194. Gross, J., and Pitt-Rivers, R., *Lancet*, **1**, 439 (1952).
195. Lemmon, R. M., Tarpey, W., and Scott, K. G., *J. Am. Chem. Soc.*, **72**, 578 (1950).
196. Dobyns, B. M., and Barry, S. R., *J. Biol. Chem.*, **204**, 517 (1953).
197. Fowden, L., and Penney, J. R., *Nature*, **165**, 846 (1950).
198. Woiwod, A. J., *Nature*, **166**, 272 (1950).
199. Naftalin, L., *Nature*, **161**, 763 (1948).
200. Awapara, J., *J. Biol. Chem.*, **178**, 113 (1949); cf. Landua, A. J., and Awapara, J., *Science*, **109**, 385 (1949).
201. Pereira, A., and Serra, J. A., *Science*, **113**, 387 (1951).
202. Porath, J., and Flodin, P., *Nature*, **168**, 202 (1951).
203. Thompson, J. F., Zacharius, R. M., and Steward, F. C., *Plant Physiol.*, **26**, 375, 421 (1951).
204. Boissonnas, R. A., *Helv. Chim. Acta*, **33**, 1966, 1972, 1975 (1950).
205. Slotta, K., and Primosigh, J., *Mem. inst. Butantan (São Paulo)*, **24**, 85 (1952).
206. Kemble, A. R., and Macpherson, H. T., *Biochem. J.*, **56**, 548 (1954).
207. Gale, E. F., *Advances in Enzymol.*, **6**, 1 (1946).
208. Pope, C. G., and Stevens, M. F., *Biochem. J.*, **33**, 1070 (1939).
209. Martin, A. J. P., and Mittelmann, R., *Biochem. J.*, **43**, 353 (1948).
210. Woiwod, A. J., *Biochem. J.*, **45**, 412 (1949).
211. Blackburn, S., and Robson, A., *Biochem. J.*, **54**, 295 (1953).
212. Fowden, L., *Biochem. J.*, **48**, 327 (1951).
213. Moore, S., and Stein, W. H., *J. Biol. Chem.*, **176**, 367 (1948); **211**, 893 (1954).
214. Moore, S., and Stein, W. H., *J. Biol. Chem.*, **211**, 907 (1954).
215. Bode, F., Hübner, H. J., Bruckner, H., and Hoeres, K., *Naturwiss.*, **39**, 221, 524 (1952).
216. Kawerau, E., and Wieland, T., *Nature*, **168**, 77 (1951).
217. Klatzkin, C., *Nature*, **169**, 421 (1952).
218. Polson, A., *Biochim. Biophys. Acta*, **2**, 575 (1948).
219. Berry, H. K., and Cain, L., *Arch. Biochem.*, **24**, 179 (1949).
220. Roland, J. F., and Gross, A. M., *Anal. Chem.*, **26**, 502 (1954).
221. Auclair, J. L., and Durreuil, R., *Can. J. Zool.*, **30**, 109 (1952).
222. Bita, Y., *J. Biochem.*, **43**, 523 (1956).
223. Fisher, R. B., Parsons, D. S., and Morrison, G. A., *Nature*, **161**, 764 (1948).
224. Fisher, R. B., Parsons, D. S., and Holmes, R., *Nature*, **164**, 183 (1949).
225. Bull, H. B., Hahn, J. W., and Baptist, V. H., *J. Am. Chem. Soc.*, **71**, 550 (1949).
226. Rockland, L. B., and Dunn, M. S., *J. Am. Chem. Soc.*, **71**, 4121 (1949).
227. Redfield, R. R., and Barron, E. S. G., *Arch. Biochem. Biophys.*, **35**, 443 (1952).
228. Hackman, R. H., and Lazarus, M., *Australian J. Biol. Sci.*, **9**, 281 (1956).
229. Grassmann, W., *Naturwiss.*, **38**, 200 (1951).
230. Rosenberg, I. N., *Proc. Soc. Exptl. Biol. Med.*, **80**, 751 (1952).
231. Stein, W. H., and Moore, S., *J. Biol. Chem.*, **178**, 79 (1949).
232. Brand, E., *Ann. N. Y. Acad. Sci.*, **47**, 187 (1946).
233. Roland, J. F., and Gross, S. M., *Anal. Chem.*, **26**, 502 (1954).
234. Miettinen, J. K., and Moisio, T., *Acta Chem. Scand.*, **7**, 1225 (1953).
235. McFarren, E. F., and Mills, J. A., *Anal. Chem.*, **24**, 650 (1952).
236. Wieland, T., and Bauer, L., *Angew. Chem.*, **63**, 511 (1951).
237. Wieland, T., and Wirth, L., *Angew. Chem.*, **63**, 171 (1951).
238. Wieland, T., Schmeiser, K., Fischer, E., and Maier-Liebnitz, H., *Naturwiss.*, **36**, 280 (1949).
239. Velick, S. F., and Undenfriend, S., *J. Biol. Chem.*, **190**, 721 (1951).
240. Velick, S. F., and Wicks, L. F., *J. Biol. Chem.*, **190**, 741 (1951).
241. Du Ruisseau, J. P., Greenstein, J. P., Winitz, M., and Birnbaum, S. M., *Arch. Biochem. Biophys.*, **68**, 161 (1957).

242. Kögl, F., and Erxleben, H., *Z. physiol. Chem.*, **258**, 57 (1939).
243. Hotchkiss, R. D., *J. Biol. Chem.*, **141**, 171 (1941).
244. Hotchkiss, R. D., and Dubos, R. J., *J. Biol. Chem.*, **141**, 155 (1941).
245. Christensen, H. N., Edwards, R. R., and Piersena, H. D., *J. Biol. Chem.*, **141**, 187 (1941).
246. Lipmann, F., Behrens, O. K., Kabat, E. A., and Burk, D., *Science*, **91**, 21 (1940).
247. Lipmann, F., Hotchkiss, R. D., and Dubos, R. J., *J. Biol. Chem.*, **141**, 163 (1941).
248. Synge, R. L. M., *Biochem. J.*, **44**, 542 (1949).
249. Auclair, J. L., and Patton, R. L., *Rev. canad. biol.*, **9**, 3 (1950).
250. Bonetti, E., and Dent, C. E., *Biochem. J.*, **57**, 77 (1954).
251. Prescott, B. A., Borek, E., Brecker, A., and Waelsch, H., *J. Biol. Chem.*, **181**, 273 (1949).
252. Gordon, A. H., Martin, A. J. P., and Synge, R. L. M., *Biochem. J.*, **35**, 1369 (1941); **37**, 79, 86, 92, 313, 538 (1943).
253. Synge, R. L. M., *Biochem. J.*, **38**, 285 (1944).
254. Mitchell, H. K., and Haskins, F. A., *Science*, **110**, 278 (1949).
255. Blackburn, S., *Chem. & Ind. (London)*, **1951**, 294.
256. Stein, W. H., and Moore, S., *Cold Spring Harbor Symposia Quant. Biol.*, **14**, 179 (1950).
257. Stein, W. H., and Moore, S., *J. Biol. Chem.*, **176**, 337 (1948).
258. Moore, S., and Stein, W. H., *J. Biol. Chem.*, **178**, 53 (1949).
259. Borsook, H., Deasy, C. L., Haagen-Smit, A. J., Keighley, G., and Lowy, P. H., *J. Biol. Chem.*, **176**, 1383 (1948).
260. Aqvist, S. E. G., *Acta Chem. Scand.*, **5**, 1031 (1951).
261. Ruhemann, S., *J. Chem. Soc.*, **99**, 792, 1306, 1486 (1911).
262. Grassmann, W., and von Arnim, K., *Ann.*, **509**, 288 (1934).
263. Stein, W. H., and Moore, S., *J. Biol. Chem.*, **190**, 103 (1951).
264. Craig, L. C., and Craig, D., in Weissberger, A., *Technique of Organic Chemistry*, Vol. III, Interscience Publishers, New York, p. 171, 1950.
265. Craig, L. C., *J. Biol. Chem.*, **155**, 519 (1944).
266. Craig, L. C., Golumbic, C., Mighton, H., and Titus, E., *J. Biol. Chem.*, **161**, 321 (1945); *Science*, **103**, 587 (1946).
267. Williamson, B., and Craig, L. C., *J. Biol. Chem.*, **168**, 687 (1947).
268. Hausmann, W., and Craig, L. C., *J. Am. Chem. Soc.*, **76**, 4892 (1954).
269. Wailes, P. C., and Whiting, M. C., *J. Chem. Soc.*, **1955**, 3636.
270. Abderhalden, E., and Fodor, A., *Fermentforschung*, **2**, 74, 151 (1919).
271. Negelein, E., *Biochem. Z.*, **142**, 493 (1923).
272. Ito, T., *Bull. Agr. Chem. Soc. Japan*, **12**, 204 (1936).
273. Wunderly, K., *Helv. Chim. Acta*, **17**, 523 (1934).
274. Warburg, O., and Negelein, E., *Biochem. Z.*, **113**, 257 (1921).
275. Baur, E., and Wunderly, K., *Biochem. Z.*, **262**, 300 (1933).
276. Cheldelin, V. H., and Williams, R. J., *J. Am. Chem. Soc.*, **64**, 1513 (1942).
277. Schramm, G., and Primosigh, J., *Ber.*, **76**, 373 (1943).
278. Wachtell, J. L., and Cassidy, H. G., *J. Am. Chem. Soc.*, **65**, 605 (1943).
279. Turba, F., Richter, M., and Kuchar, F., *Naturwiss.*, **31**, 508 (1943).
280. Tiselius, A., *Arkiv Kemi Mineral. Geol.*, **15B**, No. 6 (1941); **16A**, No. 18 (1943).
281. Tiselius, A., *Kolloid Z.*, **105**, 101 (1943).
282. Tiselius, A., in *The Svedberg*, edited by A. Tiselius, Almgvist and Wiksells boktryckeriab, Uppsala, p. 370, 1944.
283. Claesson, S., *Arkiv Kemi Mineral. Geol.*, **23A**, No. 1 (1946).
284. Hagdahl, L., Williams, R. J. P., and Tiselius, A., *Arkiv Kemi*, **4**, 193 (1952).
285. Hall, D. A., and Tiselius, A., *Acta Chem. Scand.*, **5**, 854 (1951).
286. Synge, R. L. M., and Tiselius, A., *Acta Chem. Scand.*, **3**, 231 (1949).

287. Williams, R. J. P., Hagdahl, L., and Tiselius, A., *Arkiv Kemi*, **7**, 1 (1954).
288. Tiselius, A., and Hagdahl, L., *Acta Chem. Scand.*, **4**, 394 (1950).
289. Robson, W., and Selim, A. S. M., *Biochem. J.*, **53**, 431 (1953).
290. Fromageot, C., Jutisz, M., and Lederer, E., *Biochim. Biophys. Acta*, **2**, 487 (1948).
291. Asatoor, A., and Dalgliesh, C. E., *J. Chem. Soc.*, **1956**, 2291.
292. Whitehorn, J. C., *J. Biol. Chem.*, **56**, 751 (1923).
293. Dubnoff, J. W., *J. Biol. Chem.*, **141**, 711 (1941).
294. Adams, B. A., and Holmes, E. L., *J. Soc. Chem. Ind. (London)*, **54**, 1 (1935).
295. Block, R. J., *Proc. Soc. Exptl. Biol. Med.*, **51**, 252 (1942).
296. Cannan, R. K., *J. Biol. Chem.*, **152**, 401 (1944).
297. Schwab, G. M., and Jockers, K., *Angew. Chem.*, **50**, 546 (1937).
298. Wieland, T., *Z. physiol. Chem.*, **273**, 24 (1942).
299. Wieland, T., *Ber.*, **75**, 1001 (1942).
300. Wieland, T., and Wirth, L., *Ber.*, **76**, 823 (1943).
301. Turba, F., and Richter, M., *Ber.*, **75**, 340 (1942).
302. Schramm, G., and Primosigh, J., *Ber.*, **77**, 417 (1944).
303. Wieland, T., *Ber.*, **77**, 539 (1944).
304. Turba, F., *Ber.*, **74**, 1829 (1941).
305. Jutisz, M., and Lederer, E., *Nature*, **159**, 445 (1947).
306. Hamoir, G. C. M., *Biochem. J.*, **39**, 485 (1945).
307. Block, R. J., *Arch. Biochem.*, **11**, 235 (1946).
308. Winters, J. C., and Kunin, R., *Ind. Eng. Chem.*, **41**, 460 (1949).
309. Kunin, R., and Myers, R. J., *Ion Exchange Resins*, John Wiley and Sons, New York, 1950.
310. Partridge, S. M., *Chem. & Ind. (London)*, **20**, 383 (1950).
311. Partridge, S. M., and Brimley, R. C., *Biochem. J.*, **44**, 513 (1949).
312. Partridge, S. M., Brimley, R. C., and Pepper, K. W., *Biochem. J.*, **46**, 334 (1950).
313. Partridge, S. M., and Westall, R. G., *Biochem. J.*, **44**, 418 (1949).
314. Partridge, S. M., and Brimley, R. G., *Biochem. J.*, **49**, 153 (1951); **51**, 628 (1952); Partridge, S. M., *Nature*, **169**, 496 (1952).
315. Westall, R. G., *Nature*, **165**, 717 (1950).
316. Davies, C. W., *Biochem. J.*, **45**, 38 (1949).
317. Cohn, E. J., and Edsall, J. T., *Proteins, Amino Acids, and Peptides*, Reinhold, New York, 1943.
318. Carsten, M. E., and Cannan, R. K., *J. Am. Chem. Soc.*, **74**, 5950 (1952).
319. Buchanan, D. L., *J. Biol. Chem.*, **229**, 211 (1957).
320. Westall, R. G., *Biochem. J.*, **52**, 638 (1952).
321. Hulme, A. C., and Arthington, W., *Nature*, **165**, 716 (1950).
322. Campbell, P. N., Simmonds, D., and Work, T. S., *Biochem. J.*, **49**, xvi (1951).
323. Campbell, P. N., and Work, T. S., *Biochem. J.*, **50**, 449 (1952).
324. Moore, S., and Stein, W. H., *J. Biol. Chem.*, **192**, 663 (1951).
324a. Hamilton, P. B., *Anal. Chem.*, **30**, 914 (1958).
325. Stein, W. H., *J. Biol. Chem.*, **201**, 45 (1953).
326. Evered, D. F., *Biochem. J.*, **62**, 416 (1956).
327. Stein, W. H., *Proc. Soc. Exptl. Biol. Med.*, **78**, 705 (1951).
328. Campbell, P. N., Jacobs, S., Work, T. S., and Kressman, T. K., *Chem. & Ind. (London)*, **1955**, 117.
329. Bock, R. M., and Ling, N-S., *Anal. Chem.*, **26**, 1543 (1954).
330. Hamilton, P. B., and Anderson, R. A., *J. Biol. Chem.*, **211**, 95 (1954).
331. Stein, W. H., and Moore, S., *J. Biol. Chem.*, **211**, 915 (1954).
332. Jervis, G. A., Block, R. J., Bolling, D., and Kanze, E., *J. Biol. Chem.*, **134**, 105 (1940).

333. Armstrong, M. D., and Tyler, F. H., *J. Clin. Invest.*, **34**, 565 (1955).
334. Barry, J. M., *Nature*, **171**, 1123 (1953).
335. Archibald, R. M., *J. Biol. Chem.*, **156**, 121 (1944).
336. Hamilton, P. B., *J. Biol. Chem.*, **158**, 397 (1945).
337. Christensen, H. N., *Biochem. J.*, **44**, 333 (1949).
338. Stein, W. H., Bearn, A. G., and Moore, S., *J. Clin. Invest.*, **33**, 410 (1954).
339. Dent, C. E., and Rose, G. A., *Quart. J. Med.*, **20**, 205 (1951).
340. Stein, W. H., Paladini, A. C., Hirs, C. H. W., and Moore, S., *J. Am. Chem. Soc.*, **76**, 2848 (1954).
341. Tallan, H. H., Moore, S., and Stein, W. H., *J. Biol. Chem.*, **211**, 927 (1954); Tallan, H. H., *ibid.*, **224**, 41 (1957).
342. Astrup, T., Carlstrom, G., and Stage, A., *Acta Physiol. Scand.*, **24**, 202 (1951).
343. Gordon, A. H., *Biochem. J.*, **45**, 99 (1949).
344. Krebs, H. A., Eggleston, L. V., and Hems, R., *Biochem. J.*, **44**, 159 (1949).
345. Krebs, H. A., *Biochem. J.*, **47**, 605 (1950).
346. Awapara, J., Landua, A. J., and Fuerst, R., *Biochim. Biophys. Acta*, **5**, 457 (1950).
347. Tallan, H. H., Stein, W. H., and Moore, S., *J. Biol. Chem.*, **206**, 825 (1954).
348. Christensen, H. N., Rothwell, J. T., Sears, R. A., and Streicher, J. A., *J. Biol. Chem.*, **175**, 101 (1948).
349. Heyns, K., and Walter, W., *Naturwiss.*, **39**, 507 (1952).
350. Monier, R., and Jutisz, M., *Bull. soc. chim. biol.*, **32**, 288 (1950).
351. Wieland, T., and Wirth, L., *Chem. Ber.*, **82**, 468 (1949).
352. Rees, M. W., *Biochem. J.*, **40**, 632 (1946).
353. Harfenist, E. J., *J. Am. Chem. Soc.*, **75**, 5528 (1953).
354. Synge, R. L. M., *Biochem. J.*, **39**, 351 (1945).
355. Chinard, F. P., *J. Biol. Chem.*, **199**, 91 (1952).
356. Smith, E. L., Stockell, A., and Kimmel, J. R., *J. Biol. Chem.*, **207**, 551 (1954).
357. Hirs, C. H. W., Stein, W. H., and Moore, S., *J. Biol. Chem.*, **211**, 941 (1954).
358. Crampton, C. F., Moore, S., and Stein, W. H., *J. Biol. Chem.*, **215**, 787 (1955).
359. Eastoe, J. E., *Biochem. J.*, **61**, 589 (1955).
360. Pepper, K. W., *J. Appl. Chem.*, **1**, 124 (1951).
361. Chibnall, A. C., *Brit. Med. Bull.*, **10**, No. 3, 183 (1954).
362. Sanger, F., *Biochem. J.*, **44**, 126 (1949).
363. Dustin, J. P., Schram, E., Moore, S., and Bigwood, E. F., *Bull. soc. chim. biol.*, **35**, 1137 (1953).
364. Wall, J. S., *Anal. Chem.*, **25**, 950 (1953).
365. Ehrensvärd, G., Reio, L., Saluste, E., and Stjernholme, R., *J. Biol. Chem.*, **189**, 93 (1951).
366. Lien, O. G., Peterson, E. A., and Greenberg, D. M., *Anal. Chem.*, **24**, 920 (1952).
367. Simpson, M. V., and Velick, S. F., *J. Biol. Chem.*, **208**, 61 (1954).
368. Hirs, C. H. W., Moore, S., and Stein, W. H., *J. Biol. Chem.*, **195**, 669 (1952).
369. Hirs, C. H. W., Moore, S., and Stein, W. H., *J. Am. Chem. Soc.*, **76**, 6063 (1954).
370. Ishii, S-I., *J. Biochem.*, **43**, 531 (1956).
370a. Moore, S., Spackman, D. H., and Stein, W. H., *Anal. Chem.*, **30**, 1185 (1958); Spackman, D. H., Stein, W. H., and Moore, S., *Anal. Chem.*, **30**, 1190 (1958).
371. Shulgin, A. T., Lein, O. G., Jr., Gal, E. M., and Greenberg, D. M., *J. Am. Chem. Soc.*, **74**, 2427 (1952).
372. Piez, K. A., *J. Biol. Chem.*, **207**, 77 (1954).
373. Hamilton, P. B., and Anderson, R. A., *J. Biol. Chem.*, **213**, 249 (1955).
374. Greenstein, J. P., *Advances in Protein Chem.*, **9**, 121 (1954).
375. Baker, C. G., Fu, S-C. J., Birnbaum, S. M., Sober, H. A., and Greenstein, J. P., *J. Am. Chem. Soc.*, **74**, 4701 (1952).

376. Izumiya, N., Fu, S-C. J., Birnbaum, S. M., and Greenstein, J. P., *J. Biol. Chem.*, **205**, 221 (1953).
377. Work, E., Birnbaum, S. M., Winitz, M., and Greenstein, J. P., *J. Am. Chem. Soc.*, **77**, 1916 (1955).
378. Baker, C. G., and Sober, H. A., *J. Am. Chem. Soc.*, **75**, 4058 (1953).
379. Spedding, F. H., Powell, J. E., and Svec, H. J., *J. Am. Chem. Soc.*, **77**, 6125 (1955).
380. Piez, K. A., and Eagle, H., *Science*, **122**, 968 (1955).
381. Phillips, D. M. P., *Biochim. Biophys. Acta*, **3**, 341 (1949).
382. Knight, C. A., *J. Biol. Chem.*, **190**, 753 (1951).
383. Heyns, K., and Anders, G., *Z. physiol. Chem.*, **287**, 8 (1951).
384. Grassmann, W., and Deffner, G., *Z. physiol. Chem.*, **293**, 89 (1951).
385. Miller, H. K., and Waelsch, H., *Arch. Biochem. Biophys.*, **35**, 176 (1952).
386. Le Quesne, W. J., and Young, G. T., *J. Chem. Soc.*, **1950**, 1959; **1952**, 24.
387. Cook, A. H., and Levy, A. L., *J. Chem. Soc.*, **1950**, 651.
388. Consden, R., Gordon, A. H., Martin, A. J. P., and Synge, R. L. M., *Biochem. J.*, **41**, 596 (1947).
389. Pardee, A. B., *J. Biol. Chem.*, **190**, 757 (1951).
390. Bate-Smith, E. C., and Westall, R. G., *Biochim. Biophys. Acta*, **4**, 427 (1950).
391. Moore, T. B., and Baker, C. G., *J. Chromatography*, **1**, 513 (1958).
392. Consden, R., and Gordon, A. H., *Biochem. J.*, **46**, 8 (1950).
393. Hanes, C. S., Hird, F. J. R., and Isherwood, F. A., *Biochem. J.*, **51**, 25 (1952).
394. Connell, G. E., Dixon, G. H., and Hanes, C. S., *Can. J. Biochem. Physiol.*, **33**, 416 (1955).
395. Fruton, J. S., Johnston, R. B., and Fried, M., *J. Biol. Chem.*, **190**, 39 (1951).
396. Jones, M. E., Hearn, W. R., Fried, M., and Fruton, J. S., *J. Biol. Chem.*, **195**, 645 (1952).
397. Snoke, J. E., and Bloch, K., *J. Biol. Chem.*, **199**, 407 (1952).
398. Velick, S. F., and Udenfriend, S., *J. Biol. Chem.*, **203**, 575 (1953).
399. Lewis, P. R., *Biochem. J.*, **52**, 330 (1952).
400. Sanger, F., Thompson, E. O. P., and Kitai, R., *Biochem. J.*, **59**, 509 (1955).
401. Rydon, H. N., and Smith, P. W. G., *Nature*, **169**, 922 (1952).
402. Reindel, F., and Hoppe, W., *Naturwiss.*, **40**, 221 (1953).
403. Ellfolk, N., and Synge, R. L. M., *Biochem. J.*, **59**, 523 (1955).
404. Jones, T. S. G., *Biochem. J.*, **42**, Proc. xxxv (1948).
405. Callow, R. K., and Work, T. S., *Biochem. J.*, **51**, 558 (1952).
406. Brockmann, H., and Gröne, H., *Naturwiss.*, **40**, 222 (1953).
407. Acker, R., Chanvet, J., Crocker, C., Laurila, U. R., Thaureaux, J., and Fromageot, C., *Bull. soc. chim. biol.*, **36**, 167 (1954).
408. Winnick, T., Winnick, R. E., and Fromageot, C., *Biochim. Biophys. Acta*, **18**, 488 (1955).
409. Gornall, A. G., Bardawell, C. J., and David, M. M., *J. Biol. Chem.*, **177**, 751 (1949).
410. Troll, W., and Cannan, R. K., *J. Biol. Chem.*, **200**, 803 (1953).
411. Consden, R., Gordon, A. H., and Martin, A. J. P., *Biochem. J.*, **44**, 548 (1949).
412. Sanger, F., and Tuppy, H., *Biochem. J.*, **49**, 463, 481 (1951).
413. Tiselius, A., Drake, B., and Hagdahl, L., *Experientia*, **3**, 651 (1947).
414. Sanger, F., *Biochem. J.*, **45**, 563 (1949).
415. Kroner, T. D., Tabroff, W., and McGarr, J. J., *J. Am. Chem. Soc.*, **75**, 4084 (1953).
416. Williamson, M. B., and Passmann, J. M., *J. Biol. Chem.*, **199**, 121 (1952).
417. Askonas, B. A., Campbell, P. N., Godin, C., and Work, T. S., *Biochem. J.*, **61**, 105 (1954).
418. Andersen, W., *Acta Chem. Scand.*, **8**, 359 (1954).
419. Harfenist, E. J., and Craig, L. C., *J. Am. Chem. Soc.*, **74**, 3083 (1952).

420. Green, F. C., and Kay, L. M., *Anal. Chem.*, **24,** 726 (1952).
421. Mills, G. L., *Biochem. J.*, **50,** 707 (1952).
421a. Schwyzer, R., Sieber, P., and Zatsko, K., *Helv. Chim. Acta*, **41,** 491 (1958).
422. Moore, S., and Stein, W. H., *Ann. N. Y. Acad. Sci.*, **49,** 265 (1948).
423. Ottesen, M., and Villee, C., *Compt. rend. trav. lab. Carlsberg*, **27,** 421 (1951).
424. Fels, I. G., and Tiselius, A., *Arkiv Kemi*, **3,** 369 (1952).
425. Li, C. H., and Pedersen, K. O., *Arkiv Kemi*, **1,** 533 (1950).
426. Synge, R. L. M., and Tiselius, A., *Acta Chem. Scand.*, **1,** 749 (1947).
427. Craig, L. C., Gregory, J. D., and Barry, G. T., *Cold Spring Harbor Symposia Quant. Biol.*, **14,** 24 (1950).
428. Newton, G. G. F., and Abraham, E. P., *Biochem. J.*, **53,** 597 (1953).
429. Newton, G. G. F., and Abraham, E. P., *Biochem. J.* **53,** 604 (1953).
430. Hausmann, W., Weisiger, J. R., and Craig, L. C., *J. Am. Chem. Soc.*, **77,** 723 (1955).
431. Weisiger, J. R., Hausmann, W., and Craig, L. C., *J. Am. Chem. Soc.*, **77,** 731, 3123 (1955).
432. Hausmann, W., Weisiger, J. R., and Craig, L. C., *J. Am. Chem. Soc.*, **77,** 721 (1955).
433. Lockhart, I. M., Abraham, E. P., and Newton, G. G. F., *Biochem. J.*, **61,** 534 (1955).
434. Battersby, A. R., and Craig, L. C., *J. Am. Chem. Soc.*, **74,** 4019, 4023 (1952).
435. Paladini, A., and Craig, L. C., *J. Am. Chem. Soc.*, **76,** 688 (1954).
436. Hausmann, W., and Craig, L. C., *J. Am. Chem. Soc.*, **76,** 4892 (1954).
437. Pierce, J. G., and du Vigneaud, V., *J. Biol. Chem.*, **186,** 77 (1950).
438. Turner, R. A., Pierce, J. G., and du Vigneaud, V., *J. Biol. Chem.*, **191,** 21 (1951).
439. Popenoe, E. A., Lawler, H. C., and du Vigneaud, V., *J. Am. Chem. Soc.*, **74,** 3713 (1952).
440. Potts, A. M., and Gallagher, T. F., *J. Biol. Chem.*, **154,** 349 (1944).
441. Maier-Hüser, H., Clauser, H., Fromageot, P., and Plongeron, R., *Biochim. Biophys. Acta*, **11,** 252 (1953).
442. Schroeder, W. A., Honnen, L., and Green, F. C., *Proc. Natl. Acad. Sci., Washington*, **39,** 23 (1953).
443. Godin, C., and Work, T. S., *Biochem. J.*, **63,** 69 (1956).
444. Dowmont, Y. P., and Fruton, J. S., *J. Biol. Chem.*, **197,** 271 (1952).
445. Yanari, S., *J. Biol. Chem.*, **220,** 683 (1956).
446. Blackburn, S., and Tetley, P., *Biochim. Biophys. Acta*, **20,** 423 (1956).
447. Borsook, H., Deasy, C. L., Haagen-Smit, A. J., Keighly, G., and Lowy, P. H., *J. Biol. Chem.*, **179,** 705 (1949).
448. Waley, S. G., *Biochem. J.*, **67,** 172 (1957).
449. Feitelson, J., and Partridge, S. M., *Biochem. J.*, **64,** 607 (1956).
449a. Peterson, E. A., and Sober, H. A., *J. Am. Chem. Soc.*, **78,** 751 (1956); Sober, H. A., Gutter, F. J., Wyckoff, M. M., and Peterson, H. A., *ibid.*, **78,** 756 (1956).
450. Foster, G. L., and Schmidt, C. L. A., *J. Biol. Chem.*, **56,** 545 (1923).
451. Cox, G. J., and Berg, C. P., *J. Biol. Chem.*, **81,** 755 (1929).
452. Ikeda, K., and Suzuki, S., U. S. Patent No. 1,015,891 (1912).
453. Albanese, A. A., *J. Biol. Chem.*, **134,** 467 (1940).
454. du Vigneaud, V., Irving, G. W., Jr., Dyer, H. M., and Sealock, R. R., *J. Biol. Chem.*, **123,** 45 (1938).
455. Irving, G. W., Jr., and du Vigneaud, V., *J. Biol. Chem.*, **123,** 485 (1938).
456. Cohn, M., Irving, G. W., Jr., and du Vigneaud, V., *J. Biol. Chem.*, **137,** 635 (1941).
457. Synge, R. L. M., *Biochem. J.*, **39,** 363 (1945).
458. Synge, R. L. M., *Biochem. J.*, **39,** 355 (1945).
459. Butler, J. A. V., and Stephen, J. M. L., *Nature*, **160,** 468 (1947).
460. Wieland, T., and Fischer, E., *Naturwiss.*, **35,** 29 (1948).
461. Schneider, F., Reinefeld, E., and Müller, H., *Biochem. Z.*, **327,** 189 (1955).

462. Durrum, E. L., *J. Colloid Sci.*, **6,** 274 (1951).
463. Lissitzky, S., *Compt. rend.*, **238,** 1167 (1954).
464. Ryle, A. P., Sanger, F., Smith, L. F., and Kitai, R., *Biochem. J.*, **60,** 541 (1955).
465. Brown, H., Sanger, F., and Kitai, R., *Biochem. J.*, **60,** 556 (1955).
466. Toennies, G., and Kolb, J. J., *Anal. Chem.*, **23,** 823 (1951).
467. Micheel, F., and Liefels, W., *Chem. Ber.*, **91,** 1212 (1958).
468. Tuckerman, M. M., *Anal. Chem.*, **30,** 231 (1958).
469. Myhre, D. V., and Smith, F., *J. Org. Chem.*, **23,** 1229 (1958).

chapter 16

Sequential Analysis of Peptides

1. Early Studies on Partial Hydrolysates of Proteins. The anatomical dissection of proteins requires three attributes: courage, a faith in the concept that proteins are basically constructed in the form of polypeptide chains, and a mastery of chromatography and related techniques. The first of these was well expressed by Emil Fischer in the opening remarks of his vigorous and colorful lecture before the German Chemical Society in 1906 (1):

Während vorsichtige Fachgenossen befürchten, dass eine rationale Bearbeitung dieser Körperklasse [proteins] durch ihre verwickelte Zusammensetzung und ihre höchst unbequemen physikalischen Eigenschaften heute noch auf unüberwindliche Schwierigkeiten stossen werde, neigen andere, optimistisch veranlagte Beobachter, zu denen ich mich zählen will, zu der Ansicht, dass man wenigstens den Versuch machen soll, mit allen Hilfsmitteln der Gegenwart die jungfräuliche Feste zu belagern; denn nur durch das Wagnis selbst kann die Grenze für die Leistungsfähigkeit unserer Methoden ermittelt werden.[49]

Support for the polypeptide concept has rested upon many lines of evidence (cf. 2), most of them of an indirect nature. Fischer himself developed two aspects of this evidence, still among the most powerful, namely, the synthesis through organic chemical procedures of polypeptides which in several respects possessed properties resembling those of the natural proteins or their degradation products, and secondly the physical isolation of amino acids bound in peptide linkage as partial degradation products of protein hydrolysates. Both aspects as Fischer employed them were interrelated, for most if not all of the peptides which he and his colleagues isolated from protein digests were identified not only by the nature of their hydrolytic products but also by comparison with peptides provided by organic chemical synthesis. Both aspects have been intensively developed and extended since Fischer's time. The immeasurable aid which the modern techniques of chromatography have rendered in the isolation and characterization of peptide fragments, and the rapidity and ease with which such techniques may be carried out, cannot be overestimated, but they can in some cases lead to the temptation to overlook the value to be derived from a comparison of these fragments with synthetic peptides. Fischer of course had no such chromatographic aids to guide him, but it is instructive to follow his experimental approaches, not merely as an exercise in filial piety and historical perspective, but as an illustration of problems in this intricate and often vexatious field which still confront the investigator.

The action of strong acid at refluxing temperature led to complete hydrolysis of the proteins with the formation of a mixture of amino acids. For the separation of the individual amino acids Fischer developed his classic ester procedure. But for the preparation of peptides and for their isolation in pure form from partial digests of proteins Fischer was faced with still more difficult problems. His first choice of a protein to serve as a source of peptides was silk fibroin whose analysis for constituent amino acids had suggested a relatively simple structure composed largely of glycine, alanine, and tyrosine. As a means of partial hydrolysis Fischer and Abderhalden first used strong sulfuric acid, followed by the action of pancreatin (3), later concentrated HCl alone (4), the temperature varying from 16° to 36°, and the period of digestion varying over several days. Recognizing that such a digest would contain a variety of products, Fischer developed two procedures which might serve to isolate peptide fragments; one of these involved the use of β-naphthalenesulfonyl chloride, which could react with the free amino group of the peptide to form the corresponding, highly insoluble naphthalenesulfonyl peptide (5), and the second involved the conversion of the partial hydrolytic products to their esters followed by the subsequent conversion through the use of ammonia at low temperatures only of the *dipeptide* esters to rapidly formed and readily crystallizable diketopiperazines (6). The possibility that the partial hydrolysis of proteins might, for the greater part, stop short at the dipeptide stage occurred to Fischer as a result of the rather surprising resistance offered by L-alanyl-L-alanine to hydrolysis by 10% HCl at 100° (7), and because of the isolation of glycylglycine in good yield after triglycine and hexaglycine were each exposed to concentrated HCl under the same conditions of temperature and length of standing undergone by proteins (4).

That diketopiperazines might be found among the products of the action of acid or of enzymes on proteins had already been indicated by the isolation of the so-called leucinimide, or leucylleucine anhydride, by Ritthausen (8) and by Salaskin (9). Such a compound would be of little value in the present connection, for it could have arisen as well from leucine as from leucylleucine. Of more crucial importance would be diketopiperazines composed of two different amino acids for, deliberately prepared by procedures (esterification and condensation) under conditions (low temperature) specific for dipeptides, and controlled in order to exclude the possible participation of free amino acids and higher peptides, they could only have arisen from a preformed dipeptide. The chief disadvantage in the characterization of these ring compounds lay, of course, in not knowing a priori the sequence of the amino acids in the original dipeptide from which the diketopiperazine was derived. Of some concern could be the relative rates of formation of the same diketopiperazine from isomeric dipeptide ester precursors; thus glycylalanine ester and alanylglycine ester were each converted by ring closure to the same diketopiperazine, but the rate of this conversion was found to be much greater for the former ester than for the latter (10). Not only dipeptide esters but also dipeptide primary amides are readily converted by ring closure into the corresponding diketopiperazines (11).

From a partial hydrolysate of silk fibroin a crystalline diketopiperazine was isolated which corresponded in all properties with synthetic glycyl-L-alanine anhydride (3). This compound could have been derived from either glycyl-L-alanine or L-alanylglycine. Fischer and Abderhalden held the view that the former peptide was the more likely precursor, inasmuch as, when the partial hydrolysate was subjected to the action of pancreatic juice which attacks L-alanylglycine much more rapidly than glycyl-L-alanine, the subsequent yield of diketopiperazine was not diminished (3). Careful control experiments suggested that the peptide was not the result of secondary reactions in the course of isolation. In the final paragraph of this paper, Fischer and Abderhalden reported that another diketopiperazine could be isolated from the partial hydrolysate of silk fibroin, namely, glycyl-L-tyrosine anhydride; this observation was later established by identification of the isolated material with synthetic glycyl-L-tyrosine anhydride (12). In the meantime, elastin was subjected to partial hydrolysis in 70% sulfuric acid, and from the resulting mixture a new diketopiperazine, namely, glycyl-L-leucine anhydride, was isolated and identified by comparison with the synthetic compound (12; cf. 4). Many years later, like an echo from the past, Abderhalden again reported the isolation of the anhydrides of glycylalanine and glycyltyrosine from partial hydrolysates of silk (13), and to these he added the anhydride of alanylserine. In these papers he reiterated the control experiments upon which much of the validity of the isolation of the diketopiperazines from partial hydrolysates of proteins depended, namely: (a) when a mixture of glycine and L-alanine was esterified and subsequently treated with ammonia under conditions suitable for diketopiperazine formation, only the anhydride of glycylglycine and of L-alanyl-L-alanine but not of glycyl-L-alanine was formed; (b) mixtures of glycine and L-alanine in concentrated acid yielded no evidence of the presence of diketopiperazines; and (c) mixtures of glycyl-L-alanine, glycylglycine, glycyl-L-tyrosine, and DL-leucylglycine in concentrated acid yielded no evidence for the presence of diketopiperazines.

Silks other than that from *Bombyx mori* gave, on partial hydrolysis and after the usual esterification and condensation reactions, diketopiperazines similar to those already described, and in addition one of considerable interest from Indian tussore (wild) silk, namely, the anhydride of L-alanyl-L-alanine (14). A short time before, Abderhalden and Funk (15) had isolated the anhydride of L-leucyl-L-leucine from a partial hydrolysate of casein, and thus these two observations were the first to suggest the possibility that somewhere in the peptide chains of certain proteins two residues of the same amino acid might occur in adjacent positions.

Inasmuch as the order of the amino acids in the original dipeptide could not be inferred from the diketopiperazine which was isolated, Fischer and Abderhalden (4) subjected part of the condensed filtrate from the phosphotungstic acid precipitate of a partial hydrolysate in cold concentrated HCl to the action of β-naphthalenesulfonyl chloride and succeeded in isolating a derivative which closely resembled synthetic naphthalenesulfonylglycyl-L-alanine. Proof of the structure was obtained by hydrolysis of this derivative in refluxing 10% HCl, which resulted in the subsequent isolation of pure naphthalenesulfonylglycine. The remainder of the condensed filtrate yielded through the esterification procedure a considerable proportion of glycyl-L-alanine anhydride and a small amount of glycyl-L-tyrosine anhydride. The phosphotungstic acid precipitate itself, after removal of the precipitant and repeated purification by alcohol treatment, yielded what appeared to be a tetrapeptide composed of two molecules of glycine, one of alanine, and one of tyrosine. A partial hydrolysate (with concentrated HCl at 16° for 7 days) of this compound yielded after the usual esterification and condensation procedures the anhydrides of glycyl-L-alanine and of glycyl-L-tyrosine. Fischer (16) subsequently synthesized glycyl-L-alanylglycyl-L-tyrosine to compare with the material isolated from the partial hydrolysate of silk fibroin, and because the synthetic product was so little precipitable by ammonium sulfate, in comparison with the isolated material, he believed that they were not at all identical. As he pointed out, the number of isomers possible for such a tetrapeptide was 12, and, even when limited by the observation, from the nature of the diketopiperazines, that glycine was combined with L-alanine and with L-tyrosine, the number of possible isomers was decreased only to 8.

From a partial hydrolysate of elastin, Fischer and Abderhalden (4), without the use of either esterification or naphthalenesulfonation, succeeded in isolating the first free dipeptide, namely, L-alanyl-L-leucine, which yielded the two amino acids after hydrolysis, and which was identified by comparison with the synthetic product. Abderhalden (17) reported the isolation of L-leucyl-L-alanine from the mother liquor of the above compound and identified it by unequivocal means. Through the esterification procedure, the anhydrides of glycyl-L-leucine, L-alanyl-L-leucine, and, probably, of glycyl-L-valine and of alanylproline, were also isolated (4).

Still another free dipeptide was obtained, namely, L-leucyl-L-glutamic acid, when gliadin was subjected to partial hydrolysis in 70% sulfuric acid (4); the peptide was isolated as its insoluble silver salt, was found to be identical with the synthetic variety, and yielded L-leucine and L-glutamic acid in nearly quantitative amounts on hydrolysis. Yet another free dipeptide was isolated from gliadin when Osborne and Clapp (18) partially hydrolyzed this protein in sulfuric acid; the compound obtained yielded proline and phenylalanine on hydrolysis, and Fischer and Luniak (19) subsequently showed by synthesis that the compound was L-prolyl-L-phenylalanine.

Several reports of the presence of free dipeptides and tetrapeptides in partial hydrolysates followed. Thus Abderhalden described the isolation of glycyl-L-tyrosine and L-alanylglycine from silk fibroin (20) and of L-alanyl-L-tyrosine from tussore silk (21). The constitution of these dipeptides was confirmed by comparison with the synthetic compounds; in addition, that of the last-mentioned dipeptide was further established by the preparation from it of the N,O-dibenzoyl derivative which on hydrolysis in 20% H_2SO_4 at 100° yielded a mixture of benzoic acid, tyrosine, and benzoylalanine. The order of amino acids in the dipeptide could therefore only be that characteristic of alanyltyrosine. The tussore silk is more difficult to hydrolyze partially than that of *Bombyx mori*, and several fractions insoluble in 70% H_2SO_4 were obtained by Abderhalden and Heyns (21). One of the fractions appeared to be a tetrapeptide in which the ratio of amino N to total N was close to 1 : 4. On total hydrolysis in $2N$ NaOH followed by complete benzoylation, a mixture containing benzoylalanine and hippuric acid in a ratio of 3 : 1 was obtained. Benzoylation of the presumed tetrapeptide yielded a monobenzoyl derivative which on refluxing in 10% H_2SO_4 for 4 hours resulted in the isolation of benzoylalanine. From these results it appeared that alanine was the N-terminal residue, and there remained only the problem of determining the position of the glycine residue. For this purpose, the procedure developed earlier by Abderhalden and Brockmann (22) was employed. The tetrapeptide was esterified at low temperature and the hydrochloric acid salt of the ester allowed to stand in the presence of excess benzylamine. The C-terminal residue was thereby converted to the very stable benzylamide, and on subsequent total hydrolysis of the whole tetrapeptide-benzylamide in boiling HCl remained in the mixture as glycine benzylamide. Treatment of the hydrolysate with excess phenylisocyanate resulted in the isolation of the very insoluble phenylureido derivative of glycine benzylamide, and the structure of the tetrapeptide was therefore determined to be alanylalanylalanylglycine. (It is curious to note that accompanying this quite elegant sequential analysis of the tetrapeptide was the casual and almost completely unsubstantiated claim for the presence of norvaline in tussore silk hydrolysates.) It appears probable that some adjacent residues of alanine are present in tussore silk protein, an observation in accord with that made by Abderhalden and Suwa some 21 years earlier when they isolated the anhydride of alanylalanine from the same type of silk (14). No such sequence of alanine residues in the silk of *Bombyx mori* was noted until recent times when more sensitive procedures suggested the presence of very small amounts of alanylalanine in this silk (see below).

The isolation of peptides with no alanine residues at all from partial hydrolysates of *Bombyx mori* silk fibrin was accomplished after digestion with N NaOH at 37° (23), when the following peptides were reportedly obtained: glycylserylprolyltyrosylproline, serylprolyltyrosylproline, and tyrosylserylprolyltyrosine. These compounds were isolated from the digestion mixtures as the benzoyl derivatives. Inasmuch as the conditions of the hydrolysis must have led to considerable racemization of the amino acid residues, the peptide fragments were very probably present in a multitude of optically isomeric forms with different solubilities and chemical characteristics. What emerges of value from these studies was more of a side issue in the experimental procedures involved, namely, the observation of the considerable lability toward dilute acid of N-acylated serine.

Meanwhile, Levene and Beatty (24) had isolated from a prolonged tryptic digest of gelatin a compound which appeared to be the anhydride of glycyl-L-proline. The synthesis of this compound by Fischer and Reif (25) followed, and its properties suggested a considerable degree of similarity with those of the material isolated from the gelatin digest (cf. 26). There is little doubt that the material of Levene and Beatty was partially if not wholly racemized by the prolonged standing at elevated temperature in an alkaline medium. As a diketopiperazine it was an artifact for no esterification procedure was used, but that it was probably derived from a peptide moiety in which glycine and proline were linked together seems likely from its subsequent isolation by Gawrilow and Lawrowsky (27), by Konuma (28), and by Gordon, Martin, and Synge (29) from acidic partial hydrolysates of gelatin. The last-mentioned authors (29) isolated a number of peptides as the acetyl derivatives, among them sequences of glycine and leucine, proline and alanine, proline and glycine, and proline, alanine, and glycine. Of some interest was the isolation of the tripeptide lysylprolylglycine by Grassmann and Riederle (30) from the so-called kyrine fraction of gelatin.

The kyrine concept was a curious development in the protein chemistry of the early years of this century. Influenced by the fascinating studies of the translocation of the simple nuclear proteins, the protamines, by Miescher and later by Kossel (cf. 31), Siegfried (32, 33) conceived of the larger tissue proteins as built around a protamine-like nucleus which he designated *Kyrin*, and which he isolated as the sulfate salt from the phosphotungstic acid precipitates of a variety of partially hydrolyzed proteins. The kyrine fraction could be further subdivided by the Kossel silver nitrate–baryta method into arginine and lysine peptide fractions (cf. 33 and 34). Inasmuch as both partial hydrolysis and phosphotungstic acid precipitations are not always reproducible, it is little wonder that many contradictory reports emerged. There is little doubt that the kyrine story provided a confused picture (cf. 2); however, it is of interest to follow the skilful procedure whereby Grassmann and Riederle arrived at the nature of their tripeptide. From 30 grams of a phosphotungstic acid precipitate (e.g., kyrine fraction) of partially hydrolyzed gelatin, there was obtained by means of the silver nitrate-baryta procedure 4.2 grams of an insoluble arginine-containing peptide fraction, and 6 grams of a soluble lysine-containing peptide fraction, both fractions as the sulfates. The arginine fraction represented a probable dipeptide of arginine with an unidentified monoaminomonocarboxylic acid and was not further studied. On acid hydrolysis, the lysine fraction yielded glycine, proline, and lysine in a 1 : 1 : 1 relation, and six possible isomers of the tripeptide could be conceived of as existing. Since nitrous acid treatment revealed the presence of two free amino groups, an N-terminal prolyl residue was excluded. The action of a kidney enzyme preparation (which today would be termed an aminopeptidase) incubated with the tripeptide resulted in the appearance of one carboxyl but no amino group, and hence a peptide bond in which the nitrogen of proline participated was opened. The digest of this enzyme preparation was precipitated with phosphotungstic acid, and after removal of the precipitant each fraction was subjected to amino group analysis before and after HCl hydrolysis. The basic fraction showed no increase in nitrous acid titer and turned out to be free lysine. The neutral, soluble fraction revealed a positive isatin reaction which would be characteristic either of free proline or of a prolyl peptide, and an increase of one amino group after hydrolysis which indicated that it was a dipeptide. The structure of the tripeptide was therefore that of lysylprolylglycine, and together with Levene's results established the presence of a linkage between proline and glycine in gelatin.

While Siegfried and his followers were degrading large proteins to what they hoped were protamine-like cores, Kossel and his colleagues were breaking down the true protamines by means of partial hydrolysis to what they referred to as "protones" (31). Of the protamines, clupeine and salmine were most actively studied. Their amino acid composition is rather simple, for complete hydrolysis appeared to yield a ratio of close to two molecules of arginine to one of a monoaminomonocarboxylic acid. In addition to arginine, hydrolysis revealed serine, valine, alanine, and either proline or hydroxyproline or both. Degradation by partial hydrolysis to protones yielded products with the same proportion of arginine, and Kossel assumed that the protamines might consist of a regular arrangement of the amino acids along the peptide chain:

AAMAAMAAM or AMAAMAAMA

where A represented arginine and M a monoaminomonocarboxylic acid.

It would have appeared that such compounds should lend themselves readily to sequential analysis and the isolation of one or more peptides of unequivocal constitution. At least two factors interfered with the realization of this hope, and these involved the considerable heterogeneity of the protamines and the difficulty in synthesizing peptides of arginine. The former had been no bar to the isolation of a few peptide fragments from the more complex proteins described above even though it militated against an adequate analysis of the whole peptide chain. But the second difficulty persisted to the present day, and only now has an unequivocal synthesis of the dipeptide most crucial for these studies, namely, arginylarginine, been described (35). Felix, Waldschmidt-Leitz, and their respective co-workers, in their studies of the partial degradation products of clupein or clupeone, worked under the handicap of having no synthetic peptides of arginine available at all for purposes of comparison, and may even have been deceived in part by results alleged to have been obtained on the erroneous sample described as arginylarginine by Edlbacher and Bonem (36). For the greater part, the peptide fragments were isolated as flavianates which are salts, not derivatives, and unsuited for purposes of determining amino acid sequences. Optical rotation measurements were rarely if ever reported, and the possibility of racemization was generally disregarded. Evaluation of the report by Felix and Schuberth (37) on the isolation of 12.5 grams of what was described as the diflavianate of arginylarginine from 50 grams of clupein methyl ester HCl is difficult in view of these considerations; the remarkably slow action described for a purified dipeptidase on this compound may have been characteristic of peptides of arginine but has never been proven.

Waldschmidt-Leitz (38) considered that clupein consisted of 15 residues, of which 10 were arginine. Protaminase split off 2 terminal arginine residues to yield clupeone. Trypsin protease then hydrolyzed the latter at linkages between arginylarginine residues to yield two dipeptides and three tripeptides. The constitution of the clupein chain therefore was envisaged as

MAAMAAMAAPAAMAA

where M was a monoaminomonocarboxylic acid, P a proline residue, and A an arginine residue.

Felix and Mager (39) fractionated the methyl ester hydrochlorides of clupein, and analyzed that fraction which they considered purest. They stated that no free amino group was observed in this fraction, and that it was probable that the N-terminal residue was that of either proline or hydroxyproline. Analysis led to the conclusion that the compounds contained 33 residues of which 22 were arginine, the remaining 11 being composed of 2 serines, 2 alanines, 4 prolines or hydroxyprolines, and 3 valines. The formula of clupein as they conceived it was

PAAAAMMAAAAMMAAAAMMAAAAMMAAAAMMAA

where P was a proline or hydroxyproline residue, M a monoaminomonocarboxylic acid inclusive of proline or hydroxyproline, and A was an arginine residue. Which of these two representations is correct, or whether neither is completely correct, remains for future investigation. That proline may be the N-terminal residue seems probable from the pioneer work of Porter and Sanger (40). The presence of arginine as a C-terminal residue was established enzymically by Waldschmidt-Leitz by hydrolysis with pancreatic protaminase, which is essentially a carboxypeptidase (38), and resulted in the splitting off of free arginine from the carboxyl end of the chain, and chemically by Dirr and Felix (41). Bergmann and Köster had shown (42) that treatment of arginine with an excess of acetic anhydride led to the formation of triacetylanhydroarginine which on treatment with water yielded diacetyl urea and β-acetylaminopiperidone. Hydrolysis of the piperidone with HCl yielded ornithine. When clupein was treated with an excess of benzoyl chloride and acetic anhydride, subsequent hydrolysis yielded ornithine, a reaction which could only have occurred if the arginine residue existed with a free α-carboxyl group and hence at the C-terminal position in the chain (41).

It is clear that the basic problem which Fischer set out to solve, and in which he was aided by many able contemporaries, namely, whether there existed peptide linkages preformed in the molecules of many proteins, was reasonably satisfactorily settled. It is nevertheless interesting to note that Fischer was careful not to claim that such amide linkages were the sole possible types of binding in proteins, and in his 1906 lecture alluded to above (1) he stated "die zahlreichen Hydroxyle der Oxyaminosäuren keineswegs indifferente Gruppen in Proteinmolekül sind—die könnten durch intramolekulare Anhydridbildung in Ester—oder Äthergruppen übergehen . . ."[50] Only one other aspect was added to this early work, and this lay in the nature of the linkage between phosphoric acid and the so-called phosphoproteins; this problem was solved by the isolation of serine phosphoric ester from several of such proteins (43, 44). A full account of the studies in the field of partial hydrolysates up to 1943 is given in the excellent review by Synge (2). Much of this work, it must be confessed, was essentially a series of fishing expeditions, in which proteins of varying degrees of purity and heterogeneity were partially hydrolyzed under conditions which were rarely controlled or standardized, and which resulted in the capture of a very small number of well-characterized minnows. The importance of these expeditions was, however, greater than the magnitude of the catch. The method of partial hydrolysis revealed that some peptide bonds were weaker than others, and thereby offered points of vulnerability which later and more powerful techniques would profitably exploit. The concept that peptide fragments could be separated by combining them with radicals whose stability to hydrolysis exceeded that of the peptide bond was destined to make possible the triumphs of a later day. Then as now, to quote Synge (2), "... it would be clearly desirable to apply the same criteria [with regard to the authenticity of partial hydrolysis products of proteins] as those applied to the naturally-occurring amino acids by Vickery and Schmidt ..."; and few would deny the essential truth of the statement which followed, "If these criteria are adopted, remarkably few of the partial hydrolysis products of proteins ... could be called authentic, since of the minority the constitution of which has been established by synthesis, few would conform to criteria 1 [that of independent confirmation]." It is with these reservations in mind that many of the observations described in this chapter must be read.

It has been frequently mentioned that the identity of the peptides isolated from partial hydrolysates of the proteins was established by comparison with peptides synthetically prepared. The former were of course optically active, their amino acid residues possessing full optical activity inasmuch as racemizing conditions for the partial hydrolysis were carefully avoided. To match these "natural" peptides in all particulars, Fischer had to develop (a) methods of resolution suitable for the acquisition of pure optically active amino acids in quantity for subsequent synthesis of the peptides, and (b) methods of bringing such optically active amino acids into peptide linkage in any desired sequence. In both of these aims Fischer was only partially successful, and therefore the extent of the comparisons he was able to make possessed severe limitations, but his awareness of these problems and the ingenious methods employed toward their solution stand as models of experimentation [cf. Chapters 9 and 10].

2. Carnosine, Anserine, and Glutathione. The discovery that certain smaller peptides exist as such in nature was of considerable influence in the establishment and acceptance of the polypeptide structure of proteins, and the study of such well-defined and crystalline materials, available long before methods of synthesizing them had been developed, led to the adoption of procedures of value when complex peptide mixtures of undefined constitution were encountered in partial protein hydrolysates.

Carnosine was first isolated in 1900 from beef extract (45, 46), and its constitution established by Barger and Tutin (47) in 1918 (cf. 48). They condensed the peptide with trinitrotoluol to form the corresponding dinitrotolylcarnosine; hydrolysis of the condensation product with HCl led to the formation of N-dinitrotolyl-β-alanine and free histidine, and therefore carnosine was considered to be the dipeptide β-alanylhistidine. This structure was established by synthesis by Barger and Tutin (47), Baumann and Ingvaldsen (48), and Siffered and du Vigneaud (49; cf. 50). Anserine, isolated in 1928 from fowl muscle extract (51), was similarly found to be a peptide of β-alanine and methylhistidine; condensation of the compound with trinitrotoluol followed by HCl hydrolysis led to the isolation of N-dinitrotolyl-β-alanine (52–54), and hence anserine was β-alanyl-l-methylhistidine. The unequivocal synthesis of anserine from β-alanine and 1-methyl-L-histidine by Behrens and du Vigneaud (55) clearly established its structure.

The determination of the structure of the tripeptide glutathione, first isolated by Hopkins in 1921 from yeast (56) offered many classic problems in analysis. The earliest clues to this structure evolved from the studies of Quastel, Stewart, and Tunnicliffe in 1923 (57) on material not yet completely purified and on the assumption held at the time that the material was a dipeptide of glutamic acid and cysteine. These investigators, however, clearly showed that this dipeptide structure was very probably γ-glutamylcysteine by the following reactions. (a) Treatment of the compound with nitrous acid followed by hydrolysis with acid yielded free α-hydroxyglutaric acid, and thus indicated that the N-terminal residue was glutamic acid. (b) The reaction discovered by Dakin (58) whereby treatment of an α-amino acid with hydrogen peroxide in the presence of a trace of iron leads to the formation of ammonia, carbon dioxide, and a fatty acid with one carbon atom less than that of the amino acid was applied to glutathione; no succinic acid was found before, but a great deal was found after, hydrolysis of the peroxide-treated glutathione, thus not only confirming the N-terminal position of the glutamic acid residue, but also strongly implying that this residue occurred in the form of an α-amino acid, i.e., the glutamyl residue was bound in a γ-linkage through its distal carboxyl group with the adjacent amino acid in the chain. (c) Treatment of glutathione with trinitrotoluol followed by hydrolysis led to the formation of an oil from which no crystalline derivative of glutamic acid could be derived (trinitrotoluation of free glutamic acid gave no clear-cut derivative either), but did result in the separation of crystals of cystine. On the basis of the dipeptide structure accepted at the time, it therefore appeared that the amino group of cysteine was combined with glutamic acid in the form of a γ-glutamylcysteine. The analytical studies of Hunter and Eagles (59; cf. 60) were suggestive of a third component in the glutathione molecule, and, impelled by a characteristic high scientific probity, Hopkins reopened the problem. With an improved preparation of glutathione, and by an unusual and unexpected reaction, he discovered that glycine was an integral component, and that, in fact, glutathione was a tripeptide (61). On boiling the oxidized form of a pure preparation of glutathione in water for several hours, a crystalline precipitate appeared which was shown to be the diketopiperazine anhydrodiglycylcystine (61). When the reduced form of the tripeptide was so treated, the corresponding anhydroglycylcysteine was formed to the same extent, but it was more soluble than the oxidized form. In either case, the glutamic acid moiety appeared in the mother liquors chiefly in the form of pyrrolidonecarboxylic acid, and in any event the glycine and cysteine residues were seemingly linked together. The equivalent weight of reduced glutathione, determined by titration by L. J. Harris (cf. 61), turned out to be 307 ± 0.8, as compared with the theoretical value of 307 for a tripeptide composed of glutamic acid, cysteine, and glycine. At this stage, therefore, it appeared that glutathione could be either γ-glutamylcysteinylglycine or γ-glutamylglycylcysteine. It is of interest to quote the tribute with which Hopkins concluded his paper, "It is sure that but for Hunter and Eagles' researches the present correction of the ... error would never have come from myself. It is right that I should freely acknowledge this circumstance."

Pirie and Pinhey in a communication (62) following that of Hopkins reported the titration constants for reduced glutathione as follows: pK' 9.62 for the —SH group because of its absence in the oxidized form, pK' 8.66 for the —NH$_2$ group because of its marked diminution as a result of formaldehyde treatment, and pK' 3.53 and pK' 2.12 for the two carboxyl groups. The pK' at 2.12 the authors suggested was that characteristic of an α-carboxyl group next to a free α-amino group as in α-amino acids, and thus might be related to the free α-carboxyl group in the glutamyl moiety of the tripeptide. The pK' at 3.53 seemed more probable for a terminal carboxyl group. The authors recorded their slight preference for the formula γ-glutamylcysteinylglycine, which ultimately turned out to be the correct one. The C-terminal position of glycine was finally established in 1930 by three independent groups of investigators at nearly the same time. Kendall, Mason, and McKenzie (63) treated the ethyl ester of glutathione with phenylmagnesium bromide, and the peptide alcohol which formed was hydrolyzed; diphenylacetaldehyde was isolated from the mixture as its azine—an indication that the carboxyl group of the glycine residue had been in the free state. Following Schlack and Kumpf (64), Nicolet (65) condensed glutathione directly with ammonium thiocyanate in the presence of acetic anhydride to yield the corresponding bis-thiohydantoin. The latter was condensed with benzaldehyde, and the product, after treatment with alkali and re-acidification, gave benzalthiohydantoin, a result which could only have been achieved if in the original glutathione molecule the carboxyl group of the glycine residue had been free; the existence of two thiohydantoin rings in the glutathione condensation product was further evidence of the attachment of glutamic acid in the molecule through its γ-carboxyl group. Finally, the observation of Grassmann, Dyckerhoff, and Eibeler (66) that pancreatic carboxypeptidase cleaved glycine to the extent of 80% from glutathione was compatible only with the C-terminal position of this amino acid in the tripeptide chain. Exact proof that glutamic acid was N-terminal was achieved when Gurin and Clarke converted oxidized glutathione to the N,N-dibenzenesulfonyl derivative; hydrolysis of this derivative followed by butyl esterification resulted in the isolation of the dibutyl ester of benzenesulfonyl-L-glutamic acid (67). The synthesis of glutathione in

1935 by Harington and Mead (68) provided the conclusive step in the structural determination of this compound.

3. More Exact Studies on Partial Hydrolysates of Proteins by the Use of Chromatographic and Other Techniques (Silk, Wool, and Lysozyme).

The studies by Gordon, Martin, and Synge (29) on the partial hydrolytic products of gelatin in 10N HCl at 37° were conducted at a time when these authors were developing the chromatographic techniques subsequently to be found so useful. For many reasons, among them the lack of quantitative results, the incomplete acetylation of the hydrolytic products, the difficulty in separating the acetylated derivatives on the silica gel columns, and the imperfect identification of those derivatives so separated as chemical individuals, the results of these studies on gelatin were rather limited in value. However, the introduction of the technique of group separation, i.e., the separation in this case of the basic and neutral peptide fractions of the partial hydrolytic products, by electrical transport at pH 6, was of considerable importance in simplifying many of the problems associated with the subsequent identification of these products. By these means, a combination of the use of ionophoresis and anionic and cationic exchangers, peptides of predominantly basic character and of predominantly acid character could later be separated from each other and from those peptides essentially electrically neutral at pH 5 to 7.

The use of ion exchangers proved of considerable value in the studies by Schroeder, Kay, LeGette, Honnen, and Green (69) on the separation of peptides in partial acid and alkaline hydrolysates of gelatin. First Dowex 50 was used to effect a separation of the peptide fragments, then these were converted to their dinitrophenyl derivatives and chromatographed on silicic acid and Celite, and finally the individual dinitrophenylpeptides were hydrolyzed and the products characterized in the usual way. The acidic hydrolysis was conducted by dissolving gelatin in 12 times the amount of 3.6N HCl and maintaining the solution at 37° for 7 days; for the basic hydrolysis the gelatin was dissolved in 10 times the amount of 0.5N NaOH and the solution kept at 37° for 7 days. Nearly all of the peptides found under either conditions were dipeptides. From the acid hydrolysate, and in descending order of amounts, the following major peptide sequences were noted: hydroxyprolylglycine, threonylglycine, serylglycine, alanylglycine, glycylproline, glycylalanine, glycylglutamic acid, alanylalanine, glutamylalanine, valylglycine, glycylprolylalanine, and alanylarginine. Similarly, there were encountered, in alkaline digests, glycylproline, hydroxyprolylglycine, glycylalanine, alanylglycine, and alanylproline. Heyns, Anders, and Becker (70) with an alkaline digest of gelatin had noted the sequences alanylglycine, glutamylglycine, and glycylaspartic acid, whilst Kroner, Tabroff, and McGarr (71) with an acid digest of steer hide collagen had noted the sequences alanylglycylalanine, glycylalanine, glycylglycine, glycylproline, hydroxyprolylglycine, leucylalanine, serylglycine, threonylglycine, and valylglycine. The principal lack of agreement in the three analytical studies was in the glycylglycine and leucylalanine sequences, which may be more nearly related to collagen than to gelatin.

In gelatin and collagen, about one-third of the residues are glycine, and about another third is composed of nearly equal amounts of proline, hydroxyproline, and alanine. In all, Schroeder et al. (69) isolated some 40 peptides from the partial hydrolysates of gelatin; and, as they point out, of these 40 compounds 23 contained glycine, 7 proline, 2 hydroxyproline, 17 alanine, 8 neither glycine nor alanine, and 5 none of the four. Both glycine and alanine were nearly equally distributed among the peptides and might have been widely distributed throughout the protein, whereas proline and hydroxyproline might have been more restricted in their combination to a single amino acid, namely glycine. The glycylproline sequence was of course familiar from many previous studies on gelatin, beginning with Levene and Beatty (24). The high proportion of hydroxyprolylglycine, together with the fact that proline and hydroxyproline are present in gelatin in nearly equal amounts, suggested the possibility of the sequence

$$\text{-glycylprolylhydroxyprolylglycyl-}$$

(69). The probability that the prolylhydroxyprolyl bond would be found to be rather labile in acid and lead to the dipeptides actually found in gelatin hydrolysates in high proportion tended to support this speculative arrangement.

The products of the partial hydrolysis of proteins include free amino acids as well as peptides, and both increase with time of standing in the hydrolytic medium (cf. 29). A method of distinguishing peptides and free amino acids in digests of protein was developed by Van Slyke, Dillon, MacFadyen, and Hamilton (72) which was based on the simultaneous measurements of total amino groups with nitrous acid and of free amino acids with ninhydrin. The application of this method to the partial hydrolysis of silk fibroin by Stein, Moore, and Bergmann (73) was considerably facilitated by the fact that such amino acid residues as lysine, proline, and hydroxyproline, which would necessitate corrections with the nitrous acid procedure, and such as aspartic acid, which yields an extra mole of CO_2 with the ninhydrin procedure, either do not occur in silk fibroin or are present only in very small amounts. However, a small, but on the whole insignificant, error could have been introduced as the result of the abnormally high results obtained in the nitrous acid procedure in the presence of glycine or of glycyl peptides which abound in the silk protein molecule. It was therefore possible by the use of these combined procedures to calculate not only the quantity of peptides present at any particular time, but also the average peptide chain length. Implicit in such calculations was the condition that the amounts of NH_2—N (by nitrous acid) and of COOH—N (by ninhydrin) obtained after *complete* hydrolysis of the silk fibroin were each closely equivalent to the total N of the protein. The small discrepancy observed, about 4%, could be attributed to the presence of minor quantities of ammonia and of arginine.

TABLE 16-1

Hydrolysis of Silk Fibroin by Concentrated HCl at 40°, Measured by Nitrous Acid and by Ninhydrin (73)[a]

Period of Hydrolysis, hr.	Total N of Hydrolysate, millimoles	NH_2—N, millimoles	CO_2H—N, millimoles	NH_2—N in Peptides, millimoles	N in Peptides, millimoles	Average Peptide Length
0.5	2.17	0.07	0.004	0.07	2.08	29.7
1.5	2.42	0.26	0.020	0.24	2.30	9.6
3.0	2.48	0.47	0.063	0.41	2.32	5.7
6.0	2.52	0.69	0.109	0.58	2.31	4.0
10.0	2.47	0.92	0.187	0.73	2.18	3.0
17.2	2.47	1.17	0.278	0.89	2.09	2.3
24.0	2.47	1.26	0.408	0.85	1.96	2.3
33.0	2.47	1.37	0.507	0.86	1.86	2.2
42.7	2.47	1.50	0.666	0.83	1.70	2.05
48.0	2.47	1.48	0.641	0.84	1.73	2.06
96.0	2.47	1.71	1.005	0.70	1.36	1.95

[a] Samples of 200 mg. silk fibroin maintained at 40° in 0.40 ml. concentrated HCl.

Table 16-1 portrays the course of the hydrolysis of silk fibroin in concentrated HCl at 40° as described by Stein, Moore, and Bergmann (73). The data on NH_2—N measure the amount of free amino groups in the amino acids and peptides present. On the other hand, the data on COOH—N measure the amount only of the free amino acids. The values on the nitrogen in peptides were calculated from 96% of the total minus the COOH—N. At any given time during the hydrolysis, therefore, the average peptide chain length in terms of amino acid residue is calculated from the ratio of the values of NH_2—N in peptides to N in peptides.

The data in Table 16-1 indicate that the average peptide length rapidly diminished shortly after the hydrolysis began, and between 40 and 48 hours leveled off at the dipeptide stage. After 40 hours of hydrolysis, the silk fibroin hydrolysate contained roughly 75% peptides and 25% free amino acids. There was little or none of the free amino acids at the beginning of the hydrolysis, but the production of these compounds continued at a steady rate well after the peptide chain length had settled down to a value of 2.

Inasmuch as the greater part of the amino acid residues in silk protein are comprised of glycine and alanine, dipeptides composed of these two amino acids should predominate in the partial hydrolysate, and indeed, as mentioned above, L-alanylglycine (20) and β-naphthalenesulfonylglycylalanine (4) had already been isolated from this protein. The use of arylsulfonic acids for the isolation of peptides from partial digests of proteins was suggested by Bergmann and Stein (74), and was applied to the specific case of silk fibroin by Stein, Moore, and Bergmann (73). From 40-hour digests of this protein in concentrated HCl at 40°, glycyl-L-alanine was precipitated as the relatively impure salt of 2:5-dibromobenzenesulfonic acid; for purification, the salt was decomposed with barium acetate, and, after removal of the barium dibromobenzenesulfonate, the freed glycyl-L-alanine was reprecipitated as the salt of 2:6-diiodophenol-4-sulfonic acid. The yield of glycyl-L-alanine obtained in this way was 5.5% of the silk employed. To the first filtrate after the dibromobenzenesulfonic acid salt of glycyl-L-alanine had been removed, 2:6-diiodophenol-4-sulfonic acid was added, and the pure salt with L-alanylglycine was separated; the yield was about 6% of the silk employed.

An interesting analysis of some of the components in a partial hydrolysate of silk fibroin was conducted by Levy and Slobodian (75), who used the powerful isotope derivative technique described by Kesten, Udenfriend, and Cannan (76). The "carriers" for the p-iodobenzenesulfonyl (pipsyl) derivatives of glycine, alanine, glycylglycine, alanylglycine, glycylalanine, etc., were prepared. Silk fibroin was first totally hydrolyzed at 105° in 6N HCl for 16 to 24 hours; the results at 24 hours were little different from those after 16 hours of hydrolysis. In terms of amino acid N as per cent of total N, the partial composition of silk turned out to be: glycine, 42.5, alanine 28.2, serine 9.4, aspartic acid 1.54, glutamic acid 1.07, threonine 0.70, hydroxyproline 0.05, and the remainder, including tyrosine, etc., about 17. Data on partial hydrolysates of silk in 12N HCl at 39° after certain time intervals are described in Table 16–2 (75). The significant aspects of these data include: (a) the much greater amount of alanylglycine than of glycylalanine, (b) the increase in both of these peptides up to about 48 hours of hydrolysis, (c) the decrease in the amount of these peptides after 48 hours as the free amino acids glycine and alanine continued to increase, and (d) the very small amount of glycylglycine present. In series III of Table 16–2 at the 48-hour hydrolysis mark, practically all the alanine of the protein could be accounted for in terms of free alanine and the two peptides of alanine, whilst half of the alanine alone was accounted for by the single dipeptide alanylglycine.

The finding that nearly twice as much alanylglycine as glycylalanine was found in the partial hydrolysates of silk suggested to Levy and Slobodian (75) that the basic unit of the protein chain might be the sequence

-alanylglycylalanylglycylinasmuch as the partial hydrolysis of such a combination to dipeptides could lead to two molecules of alanylglycine but only to one of glycylalanine. The analysis of completely hydrolyzed silk fibroin indicated that, of every seven residues, three would probably be glycyl and two would be alanyl, and a repeating sequence of residue along the chain could be conceived of as follows (where X refers to any residue other than glycyl or alanyl):

-X-alanylglycylalanylglycyl-X-glycyl-

Synge had shown that the linkages between alanylglycine and glycylalanine were hydrolyzed by acid at nearly identical rates (77). It would be expected

TABLE 16–2

Analyses of Partial Hydrolysates of Silk Fibroin in Terms of Per Cent of Total Nitrogen (75)

Series	Period of Hydrolysis, hrs.	Glycine	Alanine	Alanyl- glycine	Glycyl- alanine	Glycyl- glycine
I[a]	8	2.5	2.1	10.8	3.1	2.4
	24	7.8	6.1	11.9	6.0	0.5
	48	13.0	9.6	17.4	5.0	<0.3
	72	17.4	13.7	13.7	1.9	1.6
II[b]	24	6.0	4.6	17.6	5.8	0.65
	48	11.0	9.2	19.6	4.7	<0.17
III[b]	16	4.4	3.1	16.9	5.4	<0.1
	24	7.1	6.3	23.3	9.0	–
	48	12.9	10.5	27.0	8.3	<1.8

[a] 1 g. silk in 5 ml. 12N HCl at 39°.
[b] 1 g. silk in 2 ml. 12N HCl at 39°.

from the sequence above that the presence of the tripeptide glycylalanylglycine might occur in the partial hydrolysates, and, acting on this belief, Slobodian and Levy (78) prepared carrier p-iodobenzenesulfonylglycylalanylglycine and determined the presence of the tripeptide to about 5% after 8 hours at 37° in concentrated HCl hydrolysates and to about 6% after 24 hours (on the basis of total N). Control mixtures composed of alanylglycine, glycylalanine, glycylglycine, alanine, and glycine, treated in the same way, yielded no evidence for the presence of the tripeptide.

The problem of the nature of the peptides present in partial acid hydrolysates of *Bombyx mori* silk was subsequently undertaken by Kay and Schroeder (79), who employed the following sequence of reactions: (a) the protein was dissolved in five times the amount of concentrated HCl and maintained at 37° for 48 hours, (b) the hydrolysate was diluted with

SEQUENTIAL ANALYSIS OF PEPTIDES

buffer, adjusted to pH 2 and poured onto a column of Dowex 50, (c) the eluted peptides in the separate peaks were converted by treatment with dinitrofluorobenzene to the corresponding dinitrophenylpeptides, and the latter chromatographed and separated on columns of silicic acid–Celite, (d) the individual dinitrophenylpeptides were hydrolyzed to yield the N-terminal dinitrophenylamino acid and residual free amino acids, and (e) these residual free amino acids were in turn dinitrophenylated and characterized. The dipeptides found, in descending order of amount, were alanylglycine, serylglycine, glycylalanine, tyrosylglycine, glycyltyrosine, alanylalanine, threonylglycine, and phenylalanylglycine (79). Appreciable amounts of tripeptides were also present. Altogether, some 60% of the alanine, 50% of the glycine, 47% of the serine, and 35% of the tyrosine of the protein were isolated in peptide form. The quantities of alanylglycine, glycylalanine, glycine, and alanine found in these studies agreed well with those of Levy and Slobodian under the same experimental conditions; the value for glycylalanine reported by Stein, Moore, and Bergmann was in agreement with these, but that for alanylglycine was only about one-third as much. The finding of an alanylalanine sequence is at variance with the arrangement proposed by Levy and Slobodian above. Moreover, as Sanger pointed out (80), this arrangement makes no allowance for the alanine-free peptides isolated by Abderhalden and Bahn (23) from an alkaline digest of silk fibroin. All such sequences are proposed in tentative fashion, and in view of the known inhomogeneity of silk fibroin (cf. 81, 82), are usually regarded with some reserve.

A study essentially similar to that on *Bombyx mori* silk was undertaken by Kay, Schroeder, Munger, and Burt (83) on tussah silk fibroin. This silk was partially hydrolyzed in concentrated HCl, and the products separated on columns of Dowex 50-X4. The N-terminal sequences of the isolated peptides were determined with DNFB, the C-terminal sequences by the hydrazine procedure. In accord with the earlier observations of Abderhalden and his co-workers (14, 21), the most striking feature of the amino acid sequences in tussah silk is the repetition of alanine residues. Kay et al. (83) observed that some 35% of the alanine in this protein is in the form of alanine dipeptide, alanine tripeptide, alanine tetrapeptide, serylalanylalanine, and serylalanylalanylalanine, and these authors added "Apparently ... some portions of the tussah silk fibroin are virtually polyalanine." Thus, in contrast with *Bombyx mori* silk fibroin in which there is a regular pattern of alternating glycine residues, as in the important hexapeptide sequence serylglycylalanylglycylalanylglycyl-, the tussah silk fibroin possesses little regularity of structure aside from the repetition of adjacent alanine residues.

Protein material as inhomogeneous as, if not more so than, silk is the mixture called wool. The study of wool by the method of partial hydrolysis, however, was illuminating, not so much from the standpoint of the peptide sequences revealed by this study, but because of its position in the development of experimental techniques suitable for its undertaking. Wool was dissolved in 10N HCl and the solution kept at 37° for 3 days (84). The partial hydrolysate, after desalting, was run onto a column of Amberlite IR-4 which adsorbed the acidic peptides and allowed the neutral and basic peptides to pass through. The acidic peptides were eluted from the resin with acid, desalted, and subjected to ionophoresis in a silica gel. The results of the electrical separation at pH 7 into zones determined by ninhydrin color and controlled by a separate experiment with synthetic standard materials appeared to be as shown in the accompanying scheme (84).

Control		Ninhydrin Bands
	Anode end	
Glutamylglutamic acid	A	Dipeptides of aspartic and glutamic acids
	B	Glutamylglutamic acid
	C	Aspartic acid
Glutamic acid	D	Glutamic acid
	E	Tripeptides with two dicarboxylic residues
	F	E plus dipeptides with 1 dicarboxylic residue
Alanylglutamic acid	G	Dipeptides with 1 dicarboxylic residue
Leucylglutamic acid	H	Like G
	I	Dipeptides and tripeptides with 1 dicarboxylic residue
	J	Tripeptides with 1 dicarboxylic residue
	Cathode end	

The separate bands were subjected to two-dimensional paper chromatography using phenol and collidine. The individual markers were then studied in duplicate, one part being hydrolyzed with HCl, and the products identified by paper chromatography, the other part subjected to treatment with nitrous acid to destroy the ninhydrin reactivity of the N-acyl residue, then to hydrolysis with acid, and finally to paper chromatography. Comparison of the results in the two hydrolyzed parts revealed by difference which residues had probably been N-acyl, and hence the composition of the original peptide could be inferred. Only one of the ionophoretic fractions as shown above (84) revealed the presence of a pure peptide, namely, glutamylglutamic acid, and this sequence was by far the highest noted in concentration of any of those identified. Indeed, the glutamic acid in this dipeptide accounted for nearly 10% of the total glutamic acid of wool. Some 19 dipeptides of aspartic and glutamic acids were tentatively identified in the partial hydrolysate of wool, and of these it is probable that only glutamylglutamic acid, alanylglutamic acid, glutamylalanine, and aspartylleucine were clearly proven to be present. A number of tripeptides were separated, but the order of sequence of the residues in these compounds was, for the most part, undetermined. The presence of glutamylglutamic acid residues in a peptide chain had important implications, for, like the analogous cases of leucylleucyl residues in casein (15) and alanylalanyl residues in silk (14, 79), it underscored the fact that two residues of the same amino acid could exist in adjacent positions in the chain of a protein.

Consden, Gordon, and Martin (84) had adsorbed the acidic peptides from the partial wool hydrolysate on Amberlite IR-4. The neutral and basic peptide fraction which ran through the column contained most of the residues of cystine. Consden and Gordon (85) treated this fraction with bromine which converted the cystine residues by oxidation to those of cysteic acid, and thereby conferred highly acid qualities on peptides containing such residues bound together with those of neutral amino acids. Combination of such cysteic acid residues with basic amino acid residues, on the other hand, yielded peptides with net electrically neutral characteristics. These could be separated on the anion exchanger Amberlite IR-4, and the acidic peptides eluted with acid, desalted, and subjected to ionophoresis on a silica gel. The separation obtained at pH 7 in the form of zones outlined by intensity of color with ninhydrin, and controlled by a separate experiment with synthetic standard materials, was as shown in the accompanying scheme

Control	Ninhydrin Bands
Anode end	
	A Di- or tripeptides containing one cysteic acid with one aspartic or glutamic acid residue
	B As A and free cysteic acid
Cysteic acid	C Free cysteic acid
Cysteylglycine	D Cysteylglycine, cysteylalanine, and other cysteyl peptides with lower neutral amino acids
Glycylcysteic acid and cysteylleucine	E Glycylcysteic acid, alanylcysteic acid, cysteylvaline, cysteylleucine
Leucylcysteic acid	F As E, and leucylcysteic acid, phenylalanylcysteic acid
	G Tripeptides of cysteic acid with neutral amino acids
	H Higher peptides and dibromotyrosine
Cathode end	

(85). The various fractions were treated in the same way as were the normally acidic peptide components of wool described above (cf. 84).

Inasmuch as the disulfide bonds of the cystine residues in the wool had been broken by the oxidation with bromine, the results obtained by Consden and Gordon yielded no information concerning the residues in combination on both sides of the disulfide bonds. The following dipeptides were definitely noted: aspartylcysteic acid and glutamylcysteic acid (both in very small amounts), serylcysteic acid (in highest relative amount), glycylcysteic acid, threonylcysteic acid, alanylcysteic acid, leucylcysteic acid, cysteylglycine, cysteylthreonine, cysteylalanine, cysteylvaline, cysteylleucine, and cysteylphenylalanine. Thus cystine appeared to be linked in wool with many of the neutral amino acids, through both the amino and the carboxyl groups of the cystine residues.

The relative ease of separation of some of the peptides of cysteic acid from cysteyl peptides was found to be related to the strength of the respective ionizing group in the two types of compounds (85). Thus the pK'_2 (of the amino group) of glycylcysteic acid is about the expected value of 8.9, but that of cysteylglycine is about 6.9. At the pH of ionophoresis, therefore, the amino group of the latter compound would be approximately half-ionized, and the peptide would carry a higher net negative charge than would its isomer, glycylcysteic acid. As a consequence, the cysteyl peptides generally had a higher R_F in collidine (0.48 for cysteylglycine) and moved faster toward the anode (rate = 0.86 on the basis of cysteic acid = 1) than the peptides of cysteic acid (R_F = 0.34 for glycylcysteic acid in collidine, and rate toward anode = 0.60 on the basis of cysteic acid = 1) (85).

Ninhydrin Bands

Anode end

A Free cysteic acid
B High levels of cysteic acid residues in peptides
C Very small amounts of cysteic acid residues
D Peptides with no cysteic acid residues
E As D

Cathode end

The oxidation of crystalline papain in performic acid led to conversion of the cystine residues to those of cysteic acid (86). On complete hydrolysis of the oxidized protein an average figure of 2.48 half-cystine residue weight per cent was obtained. On partial hydrolysis for 7 days in 12N HCl at 37° a yield of peptides containing cysteic acid, as well as free cysteic acid, resulted (86). The partial hydrolysate was subjected to ionophoresis on paper at pH 2.3, and yielded the zones shown in the accompanying tabulation.

The individual zones after elution were completely hydrolyzed and chromatographed on paper to determine which were richest in peptides containing cysteic acid residues. An alternative procedure to ionophoresis was to pour the partial hydrolysate onto a Dowex 50-X4 (50–100 mesh) column in the acid phase; under these conditions cysteic acid and some of the peptides containing cysteic acid emerged unretarded, whereas the rest of the partial hydrolysate remained on the column and required more alkaline conditions for elution. The cysteic acid fractions were fractioned further by two-dimensional paper chromatography, the spots located with ninhydrin, eluted, and a portion of the eluate completely hydrolyzed and spotted again on paper. The remainder of the eluate was treated with dinitrofluorobenzene, hydrolyzed, and spotted on paper. The following peptides containing cysteic acid were isolated and identified: aspartylcysteic acid, cysteylaspartic acid, serylcysteic acid (in highest relative amount), cysteylglycine, cysteylglycylaspartic acid, valylcysteic acid, and a tripeptide containing glycine in the N-acyl position together with residues of proline and cysteic acid whose order was undetermined.

The sequence cysteinylglycine occurs in glutathione; acting on the possibility that this tripeptide may be related to the synthesis of the larger proteins, Flavin and Anfinsen (87) examined partial hydrolysates of ovalbumin for this and other sequences in which cystine might participate. The crystalline protein was oxidized with preformed performic acid (formic acid plus hydrogen peroxide) and the oxidized protein maintained in a solution of $11N$ HCl for 7 days at $37°$. Eleven acidic dipeptides were isolated and identified from the partial hydrolysate, namely, cysteylalanine, cysteylvaline, cysteylglycine, cysteylglutamic acid, cysteylphenylalanine, threonylcysteic acid, serylcysteic acid, glutamylcysteic acid, phenylalanylcysteic acid, aspartylcysteic acid, and valylcysteic acid. The separation procedure involved a preliminary isolation of all the highly acidic peptides in the watery eluate from a Dowex 50-X8 column in the acid phase, followed by a fractionation of this eluate on a Dowex 2 column, and finally by the usual treatment of the individual fractions with dinitrofluorobenzene and paper chromatography. Although one of the dipeptides isolated was indeed derived from cysteinylglycine, it was not of sufficient magnitude to appear to be of significance in the structure of the ovalbumin molecule.

In an admirably thorough and lucidly presented study, Thompson (88) examined the amino acid sequences in lysozyme through the medium of partial hydrolysates. The molecule of this protein in all probability consists of a single polypeptide chain internally cross-linked by disulfide bridges (89), and hence is well suited to such structural investigations. A tripeptide sequence, namely, arginylhistidyllysyl, and two dipeptides containing tyrosine (90) had already been identified, whilst a tetrapeptide sequence at the N-terminal end of the chain, consisting of lysylvalylphenylalanylglycyl, had also been reported (91). Thompson hydrolyzed lysozyme partially by allowing the protein to stand in 12N HCl for 7 days at 37° (88). The solution was then treated with performic acid to break the disulfide bonds and convert the cystine to cysteic acid residues. A first attempt was made to separate the mixture of peptides in the hydrolysate by methods of displacement chromatography on ion exchange resins which had been found so useful by Partridge and his co-workers (cf. 92), and which depended essentially on differences in the pK values of the ionizing groups of the various compounds to be separated. The hydrolysate was added to a column of sulfonated polystyrene with a small amount of ammonia to act as a carrier to increase the separation of lysine and arginine, whilst dilute NaOH was used as displacement developer. An alternative procedure was to employ finely powdered Zeo-Karb 215, which among its many advantages possesses the disadvantage of not permitting the ready displacement of arginine and of lysine and thus, presumably, of their peptides. The various fractions were identified by paper chromatography after hydrolysis, while N-terminal groups were determined with dinitrofluorobenzene and C-terminal groups with the aid of carboxypeptidase where applicable. The use of displacement chromatography to separate the peptides in the partial hydrolysate was found to be somewhat unsuitable because, unlike the amino acids, which, with the notable exception of the aromatic amino acids, are displaced in the order of the pK values of their ionizing groups, the behavior of the peptides appeared to be governed to a considerable extent by van der Waals adsorption forces. It was nevertheless possible to determine several peptide sequences by virtue of the structure of smaller peptide sequences which could be more readily identified. An example of this follows (88):

Probable sequence: Threonylaspartylvalylglutamylalanyl
Peptides identified: Threonyl (N-terminal) with aspartic acid, valine, glutamic acid, and alanine
Threonyl (N-terminal) with aspartic acid, valine, and glutamic acid
Aspartyl (N-terminal) with valine, glutamic acid, and alanine
Threonyl (N-terminal) with aspartic acid and valine
Aspartyl (N-terminal) with valine and glutamic acid
Threonyl (N-terminal) with aspartic acid
Glutamyl (N-terminal) and alanine
Valyl (N-terminal) and glutamic acid

These studies (88) were continued, elution chromatography on Dowex 50-X4 columns and gradient elution through employment of ammonium formate and acetate buffers being used (cf. 93). A much higher resolving power for the separation of the peptides of lysozyme was thereby achieved. Some 130 peptides were identified, although none was isolated in the pure state. Those sequences considered most probable by Thompson are collected in Table 16-3 (88). To these must be added the N-terminal lysylvalylphenylalanylglycyl (91), arginylhistidyllysyl (90), tyrosylglycyl, and glycyltyrosyl (90). There are some 125 to 130 peptide bonds in lysozyme (molecular weight approximately 14,900), and of these bonds 79 were deduced from the data presented in Table 16-3 (88). Fourteen additional bonds were

TABLE 16-3

Twenty-five Probable Peptide Sequences in Lysozyme (88)

Threonylaspartylvalylglutamylalanyl
Isoleucylglutamylleucylalanylleucyl
Aspartylglutamylalanyl
Leucylthreonylalanyl
Glutamylaspartylisoleucyl
Threonylglutamylalanylglycyl
Serylaspartylglycylmethionylaspartyl
Aspartylalanylmethionyllysylcysteylarginyl
Valylthreonylprolylglycylalanyl
Serylaspartylarginyl
Lysylphenylalanylglutamylglycyl
Arginylcysteylglutamylalanyl
Serylphenylalanylaspartylglutamyl
Threonylaspartylarginylarginyl
Threonylglycylaspartylvalyl
Serylvalylcysteylalanyllysylglycyl
Glycylcysteylaspartyl
Leucylglycylalanylvalyl
Aspartylisoleucylprolylcysteyl
Arginylcysteyllysylglycyl
Serylvalylaspartylcysteylalanyl
Aspartylleucylcysteylaspartyl
Arginylaspartylcysteylisoleucyl
Serylarginylleucyl
Serylaspartylcysteylarginylleucyl

established by the presence of various dipeptides reported by Thompson (88), and still another 6 by the work of other investigators, making a total of 99 peptide bonds allocated. There are some 16 bonds involving tryptophan which could not be determined because of destruction of this compound in the warm acid solution, and another 14 involving the amino groups of serine and threonine which might not have been noted for the same reason. These 30 inaccessible bonds added to the 99 represent the limits to which the study on lysozyme had been extended, and which come close to representing a complete accounting as far as this protein is concerned.

As Thompson pointed out (88), the results indicated that under conditions of partial acid hydrolysis a fairly random cleavage of the protein occurs, yielding a mixture of considerable complexity. The possibility that the use of a less highly cross-linked resin, such as the 2% cross-linked Dowex 50, would be more suitable for the separation of the larger peptides, was tentatively proposed.

Consideration of the sequences reported reveals two aspects of the problem. The first is concerned with the relative absence of linkages involving identical amino acids adjacent to each other; in only one of the sequences given in Table 16–3 does such a linkage occur, namely, the arginylarginyl sequence in threonylaspartylarginylarginyl, although alanylalanine and leucylleucine residues as dipeptides were isolated by Thompson but not used in compiling the sequences reported. The second aspect, as stated by Thompson (88), is the apparent lack of regularity of the structure of lysozyme as revealed by the peptide sequences, and what seems to be very much of a random distribution of the amino acids.

The lysozyme molecule contains 2 residues of proline, 2 of methionine, 3 of phenylalanine, and 3 of tyrosine, and with so limited a number of residues it was considered by Acher, Laurila, and Fromageot (94) that a more precise pinpointing of the amino acid sequences involving these components could be accomplished. Lysozyme was subjected to partial hydrolysis in three ways, (a) in 11.2N HCl at 37° for 4 days, (b) by the action of chymotrypsin, and (c) by the action of pepsin. The enzymic hydrolysates were fractionated with alcohol, and the soluble fractions containing the smaller peptides chromatographed on a charcoal column to which the peptides containing aromatic residues preferentially adhered. Elution of these peptides was accomplished by a mixture of acetic acid, ethyl acetate, and water, and the contents separated into basic, neutral, and acidic fractions by ionophoresis. Each of the fractions was chromatographed on paper, and the individual bonds identified after elution by total hydrolysis, baryta being used for this purpose where tryptophan was involved. End-group analysis was conducted at the N-terminal residue by means of nitrous acid, of dinitrofluorobenzene, and of phenylisocyanate, and at the C-terminal residue by the use of carboxypeptidase. The ensuing sequences involving the three phenylalanyl residues were lysylvalylphenylalanylglycylarginyl, glutamylserylphenylalanylaspartyl, and alanyllysylphenylalanylglutamyl. The first of these sequences is that characteristic of the N-terminus of this protein. The sequences aspartyltyrosylarginylglycyl, arginylglycyltyrosylisoleucylleucyl, and asparaginylalanyltyrosylglycylserylleucylasparaginyl corresponded to the three tyrosine residues. The two proline residues apparently took part in threonylprolyl and leucylprolyl bonds, whilst one of the two methionine residues seemed to participate in an alanylalanylmethionyl linkage. Both Thompson (88) and Acher et al. (94) were in agreement on the presence of phenylalanylglutamyl, phenylalanylaspartyl, threonylprolyl, and alanylmethionyl bonds in lysozyme. The sequence or sequences responsible for the enzymic activity of the lysozyme molecule are not yet known.

4. Procedures for Terminal Amino Acid Analysis. The peptide chain in its general form may be represented as follows:

$$NH_2CHR^0CONHCHR^1CONHCHR^2CONHCHR^3CONHCHR^4 \cdots CONHCHR^nCO_2H$$

N-terminal residue   C-terminal residue

In accordance with the suggestion of Sanger (80), the amino acid residue bearing the free α-amino (or imino, if proline) group is called N-terminal, whereas that residue at the end of the chain bearing the free α-carboxyl group is referred to as C-terminal. As described in the previous section, methods were devised for the determination of the terminal amino acids in the relatively small and simple peptide fragments resulting from the partial hydrolysates of proteins, as well as in the small peptides of natural origin such as glutathione, carnosine, and anserine. That a few of these methods could be applicable to a determination of the terminal residues of proteins was a kind of "Wagnis" which perhaps even Fischer did not altogether have in mind. In the case of the peptides, knowledge of the terminal residues contributed to the determination of the purity and identity of these compounds. In the case of proteins, the capacity to detect and estimate quantitatively the terminal residues is at once a measure (a) of purity, inasmuch as a finding of non-stoichiometric amounts of such residues would be suggestive of the presence of adventitiously adsorbed amino acids or of contaminating proteins, and (b) of structure, inasmuch as a failure to detect one or the other terminal residue or both would be suggestive of a cyclic configuration involving these residues, an inaccessible steric arrangement, or an attachment to some prosthetic group if present; of equal importance, as Chibnall stated in 1942 (95), a knowledge of the number of free amino groups over and above the ε-amino groups of lysine residues in the protein would yield a measure of the number of peptide chains likely to be present.

N-Terminal Sequences (Peptides)

Many of the procedures employed have depended upon a reaction in which an acylating agent combines with the N-terminal group through a linkage which is more stable to subsequent hydrolysis of the peptide chain than are the other linkages in the chain. The derivative so formed must be separable and capable of identification. Separation is facilitated when the dipolar ion character of the terminal amino acid is removed, and the derivative formed, unlike all the other components in the hydrolysate, is soluble in non-polar solvents. Methods of identification were at first of the classic variety, i.e., melting point, optical rotation, etc., but, for modern work on a micro scale, they have relied more frequently on chromatographic devices.

The very first of such procedures was that reported in 1907 by Fischer and Abderhalden (4), who coupled β-naphthalenesulfonyl chloride with a peptide which they suspected of being glycylalanine. On hydrolysis of the β-naphthalenesulfonylglycylalanine, a good yield of β-naphthalenesulfonylglycine was obtained, proving the N-terminal position of glycine in the peptide.

$$\text{[naphthalene]}-SO_2Cl + NH_2CH_2CONHCH(CH_3)CO_2H \xrightarrow{\text{NaOH}}$$
Glycylalanine

β-Naphthalenesulfonyl chloride

$$\text{[naphthalene]}-SO_2 \cdot NHCH_2CONHCH(CH_3)CO_2H \xrightarrow[\Delta]{\text{HCl}}$$

β-Naphthalenesulfonylglycylalanine

$$\text{[naphthalene]}-SO_2 \cdot NHCH_2CO_2H + NH_2CH(CH_3)CO_2H$$
Alanine

β-Naphthalenesulfonylglycine

In 1910 Abderhalden and Blumberg (96) tried a new N-terminal reagent, 1-chloro-2:4-dinitrobenzene, with which in a sodium bicarbonate medium they prepared a number of amino acid derivatives. Initial attempts to employ this reagent for the determination of N-terminal amino acid residues

$$NO_2-\text{[benzene]}-Cl + NH_2CHRCO_2H \rightarrow NO_2-\text{[benzene]}-NHCHRCO_2H + HCl$$
$\qquad\quad$ | $\qquad\qquad$ Amino acid $\qquad\qquad\qquad\quad$ |
$\qquad\;\, NO_2 \qquad\qquad\qquad\qquad\qquad\qquad\qquad\qquad NO_2$
Dinitrochlorobenzene $\qquad\qquad\qquad\qquad\quad$ Dinitrophenylamino acid

were unsuccessful (97). Not until many years later did it attain the position in end-group analysis which it presently holds. A description of this modern position is deferred to a later account. In the meantime, an analogous reaction involving nitro groups in *ortho* position was developed in 1918 by Barger and Tutin (47), who condensed trinitrotoluene with carnosine; hydrolysis of the product yielded the N-terminal residues as the dinitrotolyl derivative. (See the reaction at the top of the facing page.)

The failure of this reagent to yield information about the N-terminal residue of glutathione (cf. 57), perhaps an unfair trial in view of the lability of this tripeptide and its unusual N-terminal structure, led to its abandonment.

Bergmann, Miekeley, and Kann (98) in 1927 proposed a determination,

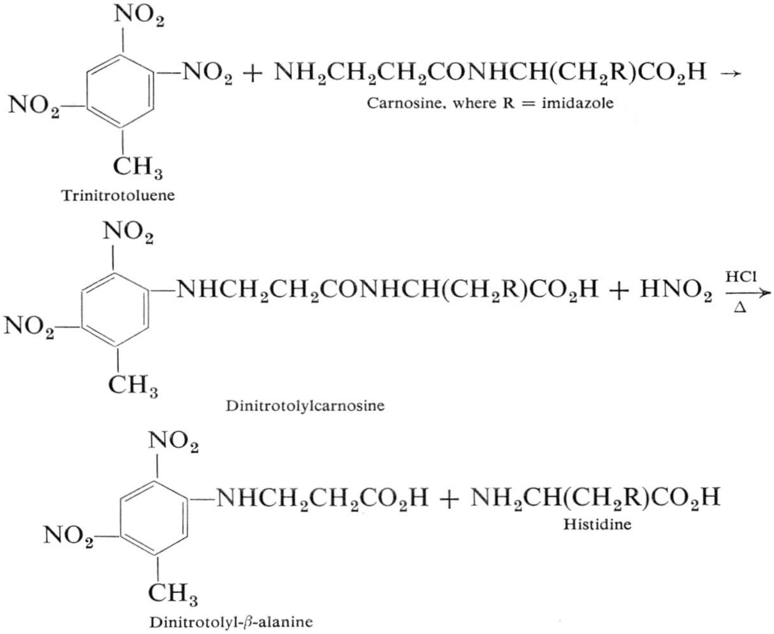

SEQUENTIAL ANALYSIS OF PEPTIDES

$$\text{Trinitrotoluene} + NH_2CH_2CH_2CONHCH(CH_2R)CO_2H \rightarrow$$

Carnosine, where R = imidazole

$$\text{Dinitrotolylcarnosine} + HNO_2 \xrightarrow{HCl, \Delta}$$

$$\text{Dinitrotolyl-}\beta\text{-alanine} + NH_2CH(CH_2R)CO_2H$$

Histidine

somewhat obscured in a long communication devoted to something else, of the N-terminal residue of peptides by condensing the latter with phenylisocyanate and then hydrolyzing the product to yield a highly insoluble hydantoin derived from the residue. The method was first illustrated with glycylserine.

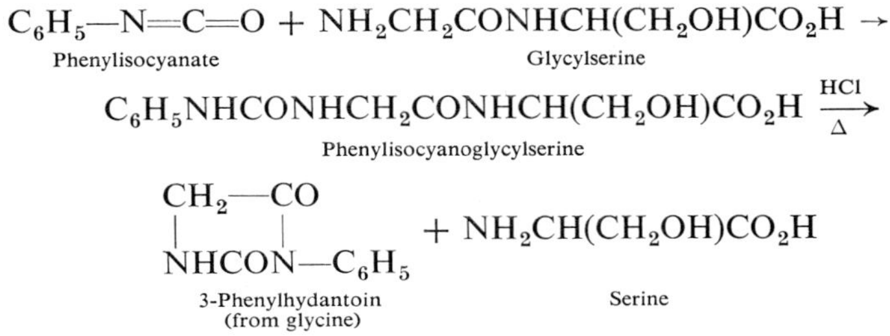

$$C_6H_5-N=C=O + NH_2CH_2CONHCH(CH_2OH)CO_2H \rightarrow$$
Phenylisocyanate   Glycylserine

$$C_6H_5NHCONHCH_2CONHCH(CH_2OH)CO_2H \xrightarrow{HCl, \Delta}$$
Phenylisocyanoglycylserine

3-Phenylhydantoin (from glycine) + $NH_2CH(CH_2OH)CO_2H$

Serine

The procedure was subsequently extended in 1930 by Abderhalden and Brockmann (22), who demonstrated how it could be applied *step by step* to the determination of amino acid residues starting from the N-terminal, and illustrated it with the tripeptide alanylglycylleucine. The feature of this procedure was in the use of methanol-HCl at 60–65° which hydrolyzed the phenylisocyano-substituted N-terminal residue from the peptide chain without appreciably affecting the remaining peptide bonds. Combined with this procedure was the use of benzylamine to form the difficultly hydrolyzable and readily identifiable benzylamide of the C-terminal residue.

Alanylglycylleucine + phenylisocyanate →

N-phenylisocyanoalanylglycylleucine $\xrightarrow[60-65°]{CH_3OH-HCl}$

3-phenyl-5-methylhydantoin (from alanine) + glycylleucine

Glycylleucine + methanol·HCl → glycylleucine ester·HCl

Glycylleucine ester·HCl + (excess) benzylamine →

glycylleucine benzylamide $\xrightarrow{C_6H_5-N=C=O}$

phenylisocyanoglycylleucine benzylamide $\xrightarrow[\Delta]{HCl}$

3-phenylhydantoin (from glycine) + leucine benzylamide

Leucine benzylamide + C_6H_5—N=C=O →

phenylisocyanoleucine benzylamide

The first successful end-group analysis of a protein was accomplished by Jensen and Evans in 1935 (99) when they condensed insulin in an $0.066M$ disodium phosphate solution with phenylisocyanate; on hydrolysis of the condensation product in $5N$ HCl for 15 hours in a boiling water bath there was isolated the phenylhydantoin of phenylalanine. About 25 mg. of this compound was obtained from 1 gram of phenylisocyanoinsulin. Some two years prior to these studies, Hopkins and Wormall (100) had condensed phenylisocyanate with various proteins, not for the purpose of end-group analysis, but in order to observe the alteration in the immunological characteristics of such substituted proteins. Modern techniques of end-group analysis, employing not phenylisocyanate but the related phenylisothiocyanate, will be described below.

The use of the very common reagent benzoyl chloride for purposes of N-terminal residue determination was introduced relatively late and was abandoned at practically the moment of its inception in favor of the use of benzenesulfonyl chloride for this purpose. Abderhalden and Heyns (21) treated alanyltyrosine with benzoyl chloride to yield N-benzoylalanyl-O-benzoyltyrosine, and on hydrolysis with sulfuric acid obtained benzoylalanine, benzoic acid, and tyrosine. N-Benzoylglycyl-O-benzoylserine required only warming with acid to yield benzoylglycine, benzoic acid, and serine, and it was further noted by Abderhalden and Bahn (23) that N-benzoylserine was very readily hydrolyzed to benzoic acid and serine under quite mild conditions. On the other hand, N-benzenesulfonylserine was very stable to hot acid, and the substituted peptide N-benzenesulfonylseryl-proline could be refluxed with dilute H_2SO_4 to yield N-benzenesulfonyl-serine and proline. Again, the reaction of benzenesulfonyl chloride with glycyltyrosine yielded N-benzenesulfonylglycyl-O-benzenesulfonyltyrosine, and this substituted dipeptide on refluxing with 25% H_2SO_4 gave N-benzenesulfonylglycine and O-benzenesulfonyltyrosine (23). On either nitrogen or oxygen atoms the benzenesulfonyl group, $C_6H_5SO_2$—, was very much more stable than the benzoyl group, C_6H_5CO—, and was therefore considered preferable for end-group analysis.

These observations on the relative stability of the two groups were substantiated when they were introduced into proteins. The free amino groups of a protein may be expected to belong to the N-terminal amino acid residue (which would be α in position for a neutral amino acid or α and ε if lysine) and to the internal lysine residues (ε in position). In the event of a limited number of polypeptide chains in the protein together with a good many internal lysine residues, the overwhelming proportion of free amino groups would be derived from the latter. Indeed, Van Slyke and Birchard (101) found many years ago that in most proteins the free amino-N values found by the nitrous acid technique could be closely accounted for in terms of one half of the total lysine N. Therefore, when a protein was N-acylated, it would be expected that the N-terminal α-amino and internal lysine ε-amino groups would be acylated, the latter by far predominating. On complete hydrolysis of the ordinary peptide linkages in the protein, it would be highly desirable that all linkages involved with the newly introduced acyl group be unaffected, i.e., the latter should be much more stable than the former.

$$NH_2CHR^0CONHCH[(CH_2)_4NH_2]CO \cdots NHCH[(CH_2)_4NH_2]CONHCHR^n CO_2H + R^x COCl \xrightarrow{\text{acylating agent}}$$

$$R^x CONHCHR^0 CONHCH[(CH_2)_4 NHCOR^x]CO \cdots NHCH[(CH_2)_4 NHCOR^x]CONHCHR^n CO_2H \xrightarrow[\Delta]{HCl}$$

$$R^x CONHCHR^0 CO_2H + \Sigma NH_2CH[(CH_2)_4 NHCOR^x]CO_2H$$

N-Terminal-N-acylated residue | Sum of ε-N-acylated internal lysine residues + $(n - Z)NH_2CHRCO_2H$ where $(n - Z)$ is the total number of amino acid residues in the protein minus the sum of the N-terminal and the internal lysine residues

Under these conditions, the N-terminal residue appears as an acylated derivative with a free α-carboxyl but no free α-amino group, and the lysine residues as ε-N-acylated derivatives with both a free α-amino and a free α-carboxyl group. These conditions imply of course the ideal arrangement of a single open polypeptide chain in the protein, with free amino groups accessible to reagents, and lacking such groups as imidazole and phenol groups which might also combine with the reagents employed.

Goldschmidt and Kinsky (102) benzoylated ovalbumin and subsequently hydrolyzed the benzoylated protein in strong acid. Considerable loss of benzoyl groups which appeared as benzoic acid occurred, but it was possible nevertheless to isolate an appreciable amount of ε-benzoyllysine from the hydrolysate (cf. 103). It is now known that ovalbumin possesses no reactive N-terminal amino group, so that no N-α-benzoyl amino acid was present in the products of the hydrolysis of benzoylated ovalbumin, but otherwise, and viewed in retrospect, ovalbumin was a poor choice for an exhaustive benzoylation because of probable Bamberger fission of the imidazole moieties in the protein. A more suitable choice of protein and of reagent was involved in the study of the reaction between gelatin and benzenesulfonyl chloride by Gurin and Clarke (104). The benzenesulfonation was maintained at pH 10–11 in order to avoid reaction with the guanidino groups of arginine which would occur at more alkaline ranges, and the benzenesulfonated gelatin was hydrolyzed for 4 days at 90–100° in a mixture of formic and sulfuric acids. A high yield of ε-benzenesulfonyl-L-lysine was obtained on isolation as the copper salt; identity of the product was confirmed by conversion to the α-phenylhydantoin and comparison with a synthetic preparation. Gelatin is another protein in which the presence of a reactive N-terminal α-amino group is doubtful, and no such benzenesulfonated residue was observed in the hydrolytic products of gelatin. Gurin and Clarke (104) did, however, show that the reagent could be employed to determine N-terminal residues when they treated glutathione with benzenesulfonyl chloride, hydrolyzed the product, and isolated N-α-benzenesulfonyl-L-glutamic acid as the identifiable dibutyl ester. This constituted the first direct proof of the presence of glutamic acid in the N-terminal position of the tripeptide.

$$C_6H_5SO_2Cl + \underset{\underset{\text{Glutathione (where R is the cysteinylglycine residue)}}{CH_2CH_2COR}}{NH_2CHCO_2H} \rightarrow \underset{CH_2CH_2COR}{C_6H_5SO_2NHCHCO_2H}$$

Benzenesulfonyl chloride

$$\xrightarrow[\Delta]{HCl} \underset{\underset{\text{N-Benzenesulfonylglutamic acid}}{CH_2CH_2CO_2H}}{C_6H_5SO_2NHCHCO_2H} + \text{cysteine} + \text{glycine}$$

The experiments of Gurin and Clarke illustrated one of two important and frequently interrelated aspects of terminal residue analysis. The first of these is concerned with the fact that the protein surface contains many kinds of reactive residues other than possible α-amino and α-carboxyl, which may combine with a variety of reagents. The ease with which the ε-amino groups of the probably internal lysine residues are acylated has been demonstrated. Other reactive groups are the phenolic of tyrosine, the imidazole of histidine, the guanidino of arginine, the β-carboxyl and γ-carboxyl of aspartic and glutamic acids, respectively, and of their amides, the indole of tryptophan, the sulfhydryl and disulfide of cysteine and cystine, respectively, the methyl mercaptan of methionine, the aliphatic hydroxyls of serine and of threonine, the phenyl of phenylalanine, and even the peptide linkage itself. The second of the aspects mentioned above relates to the fact that many of these groups are not available to all reagents when certain proteins are in what is called the "native" state, and only become available when these proteins are denatured. The latter aspect will be referred to again briefly in a later connection. The former has been considered in part in Chapter 1; more complete accounts of this subject are to be found in the reviews by Herriott (105) and by Putnam (106). Assuming that all the groups are equally available to the reagents, only those newly formed bonds which survive acid hydrolysis, or extremes of pH at moderate temperature, are important from the standpoint of terminal residue analysis. This immediately eliminates nearly all the residual active groups mentioned above except the α-amino, the α-imino (of proline and hydroxyproline), the ε-amino of lysine and δ-amino of ornithine, the carboxylic groups, and on occasion the phenolic group of tyrosine and the imidazole of histidine. By controlling the pH it is sometimes possible to evade implicating unwanted groups. Thus Clutton, Harington, and Mead (107) treated the azide of glucosido-carbobenzoxytyrosine with protein at pH 8 in the expectation of avoiding reaction with the ε-amino groups of the lysine residues, whilst Gurin and Clarke set their conditions at pH 10–11 to avoid reaction with the highly basic guanidino group. However, if a pH not far removed from neutrality is employed for the reaction, the protein may remain in a native, folded configuration, and the reagents may not reach not only undesired but also desired groups. The conditions for a successful terminal group analysis will therefore depend to a considerable extent upon the nature of the protein as well as upon the nature of the reagent.

A number of more or less indirect procedures for the detection of terminal residues have been reported from time to time. Among the earliest of these was that of Skraup and Kaas (108), who in 1906 treated casein, gelatin, and serum albumin with nitrous acid, hydrolyzed the deaminized proteins, and noted the absence of lysine in the hydrolysates. These experiments not only demonstrated the presence of free amino groups derived from lysine residues in the protein, but also furnished an example of what is now referred to as *subtractive analysis*. The deaminized lysine residues in casein, as α-amino-ε-hydroxy-*n*-caproic acid (ε-hydroxynorleucine), have been shown to be anemia-producing factors and lysine metabolic antagonists (109; cf. 110). The method of deamination proved useful in the first studies on glutathione (57) whereby the reaction of this natural compound with nitrous acid followed by hydrolysis led to the isolation of α-hydroxyglutaric acid and thus suggested the N-terminal position of glutamic acid.

$$\text{HNO}_2 + \begin{array}{c} \text{NH}_2\text{CHCO}_2\text{H} \\ | \\ \text{CH}_2\text{CH}_2\text{COR} \end{array} \rightarrow \begin{array}{c} \text{HOCHCO}_2\text{H} \\ | \\ \text{CH}_2\text{CH}_2\text{COR} \end{array} \xrightarrow{\text{HCl}}_{\Delta}$$

Glutathione (where R is the cysteinylglycine residue)

$$\begin{array}{c} \text{HOCHCO}_2\text{H} \\ | \\ \text{CH}_2\text{CH}_2\text{CO}_2\text{H} \end{array} + \text{cysteine} + \text{glycine}$$

α-Hydroxyglutaric acid

A nitrous acid procedure was also found useful as a check on end-group assay by an independent method. Thus N-terminal aspartic acid, methionine, histidine, and alanine were noted for bovine plasma albumin (111). When the protein was deaminized by nitrous acid and subsequently hydrolyzed, these amino acids, determined by microbiological assay, were found to be greatly reduced in amount, together with arginine, lysine, and tyrosine. The latter three amino acids are not N-terminal, but their reactive ω-residues are affected by nitrous acid to the extent that the growth of the microorganisms which require the unchanged amino acid is reduced. Such subtractive procedures using nitrous acid have been frequently employed to determine the N-terminal residues in the peptides resulting from the partial hydrolysis of proteins and natural peptides, the general assumption being made that the amino acid which apparently disappeared in the hydrolyzed, treated peptide as a result of this deamination reaction, and failed to appear on the chromatogram, must have possessed an α-amino group and hence was originally N-terminal in the chain (84, 85, 90, 94, 112–115). When the results are clear-cut and definitive, there is no problem. When, however, the N-terminal amino acid is also present elsewhere in the chain, and the result is only a fairly appreciable decrease in intensity of the ninhydrin color on a paper chromatogram, a decision is difficult to reach. When the N-terminal residue is proline, or even if free proline is present, a complication with nitrous acid arises (116). As the peptide is treated with nitrous acid, the N-terminal proline residue is converted to the stable nitrosoproline. On hydrolysis of the peptide in acid, the nitroso group is released as nitrous acid, free proline is regenerated, and the nitrous acid then attacks the freed amino acids and converts them to hydroxy acids. On subsequent paper chromatography amino acids will therefore disappear which never were N-terminal. This situation can be avoided by treating the nitroso derivative with alkali prior to acid hydrolysis.

$$\begin{array}{c} \text{CH}_2\!\!-\!\!\text{CH}_2 \\ |\qquad\quad | \\ \text{CH}_2\quad \text{CHCOR} \\ \diagdown\ \ \diagup \\ \text{N(NO)} \end{array}$$

Nitrosoproline as N-terminal residue

A curious, interesting, and obscure phenomenon was revealed in the racemization experiments described by Dakin. Kossel and Weiss (117) had noted that certain amino acids such as arginine were more readily racemized by alkali when bound in peptide linkage than when free. Dakin (118) digested gelatin with dilute alkali and then hydrolyzed the protein, separated several of the amino acids, and determined the values of their optical rotations. Completely racemic leucine, aspartic acid, arginine, histidine, and phenylalanine were obtained, but proline, glutamic acid, alanine, and lysine were isolated in a state of complete or nearly complete optical activity. Dakin interpreted these findings on the basis of a shift in the keto-enol tautomerism of the linkages in the alkali-treated protein, whereby only those amino acids in the interior of the molecule would undergo racemization. A study of this sort was extended by Dakin and Dale (119) to the crystalline ovalbumins of the hen and of the duck, two antigenically distinct proteins. The proteins were separately maintained for 23 days at 37° in 0.5N NaOH, and then hydrolyzed. The same optical rotation values were noted for the alanine, valine, proline, phenylalanine, tyrosine, glutamic acid, arginine, and lysine components which were isolated, but marked differences were noted for leucine and histidine which were racemic (hen) and fully active (duck), and for aspartic acid which was fully active (hen) and racemic (duck). It is difficult to take these findings seriously, especially in the absence of full experimental details. As Dakin himself pointed out, the prolonged period of digestion could have resulted in a cleavage of free amino acids from the protein, while comparable results on the racemization of amino acids in a wide variety of synthetic peptides were then and even now not adequately known.

An indirect, yet quite exact, procedure for determining not only the N-terminal amino acid residue in a peptide chain but also the residue adjacent to it was developed by Goldschmidt and co-workers. In alkaline hypobromite solution, dipeptides are attacked at the free amino group with simultaneous cleavage of the peptide bond to yield the nitrile corresponding to the N-terminal amino acid with one less carbon atom, together with the free C-terminal amino acid as the corresponding N-carbamic acid (120).

$$RCH(NH_2)CONHCH_2CO_2H \xrightarrow{2HOBr} RCH(NBr_2)CONHCH_2CO_2H \xrightarrow[H_2O]{-HBr}$$

Valylglycine (where R is $CH(CH_3)_2$)

$$RCH{=}NBr \; + \; HO_2C{\cdot}NHCH_2CO_2H$$

$\downarrow$ −HBr $\qquad\qquad$ $\downarrow$ Acid

$$RC{\equiv}N \qquad\qquad NH_2CH_2CO_2H + CO_2$$

Isobutyronitrile (from valine) $\qquad\qquad$ Glycine

With tripeptides and higher peptides a more complex reaction is revealed

(121, 122). The products of the reaction of alkaline hypobromite with these compounds are again a nitrile corresponding to the N-terminal amino acid with one carbon atom less, and in addition a dehydrohydantoin. The latter on alkaline hydrolysis yields an α-keto acid derived from the amino acid residue adjacent to the N-terminal residue, and in addition the free

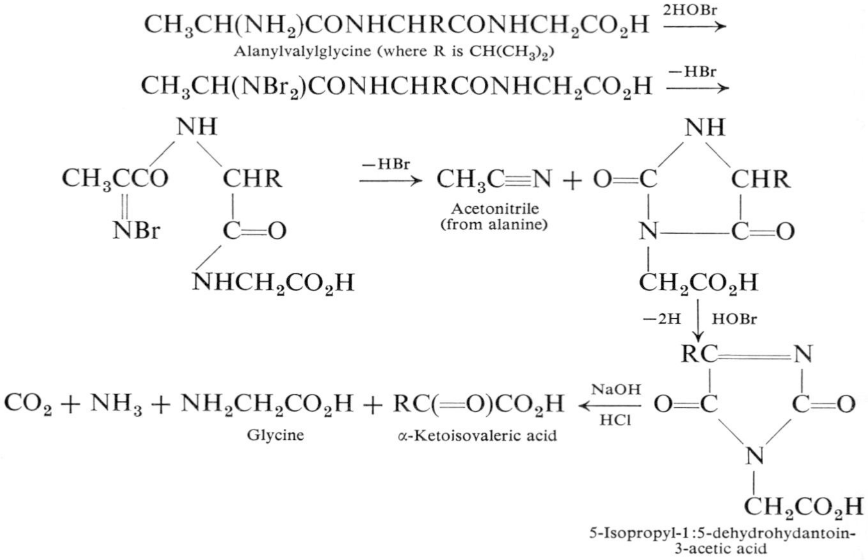

$$CH_3CH(NH_2)CONHCHRCONHCH_2CO_2H \xrightarrow{2HOBr}$$
Alanylvalylglycine (where R is $CH(CH_3)_2$)

$$CH_3CH(NBr_2)CONHCHRCONHCH_2CO_2H \xrightarrow{-HBr}$$

$$\underset{\underset{NBr}{|}}{CH_3CCO}\diagdown\underset{\underset{\underset{NHCH_2CO_2H}{|}}{C=O}}{CHR} \xrightarrow{-HBr} CH_3C{\equiv}N + O{=}\underset{\underset{\underset{CH_2CO_2H}{|}}{N\text{———}C=O}}{C}\diagdown\underset{}{CHR}$$

Acetonitrile (from alanine)

$$\downarrow -2H \mid HOBr$$

$$CO_2 + NH_3 + NH_2CH_2CO_2H + RC({=}O)CO_2H \xleftarrow[HCl]{NaOH} O{=}\underset{\underset{CH_2CO_2H}{|}}{C}\diagup\underset{N}{\overset{RC\text{———}N}{|}}\diagdown C{=}O$$

Glycine   α-Ketoisovaleric acid

5-Isopropyl-1:5-dehydrohydantoin-3-acetic acid

amino acid or acids in the original peptide. Thus alanylvalylglycine yields acetonitrile, α-ketoisovaleric acid, and glycine.

In a similar fashion, with alkaline hypobromite and the tetrapeptide

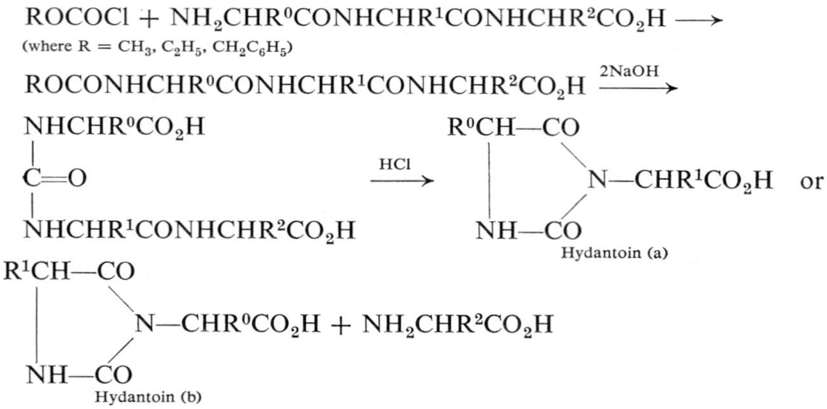

$$ROCOCl + NH_2CHR^0CONHCHR^1CONHCHR^2CO_2H \longrightarrow$$
(where $R = CH_3, C_2H_5, CH_2C_6H_5$)

$$ROCONHCHR^0CONHCHR^1CONHCHR^2CO_2H \xrightarrow{2NaOH}$$

$$\underset{\underset{\underset{\underset{R^1CH\text{—}CO}{NHCHR^1CONHCHR^2CO_2H}}{C=O}}{|}}{NHCHR^0CO_2H} \xrightarrow{HCl} \underset{\underset{NH\text{—}CO}{|}}{\overset{R^0CH\text{—}CO}{|}}\diagdown N\text{—}CHR^1CO_2H \quad \text{or}$$

Hydantoin (a)

$$\underset{\underset{NH\text{—}CO}{}}{\overset{R^1CH\text{—}CO}{|}}\diagdown N\text{—}CHR^0CO_2H + NH_2CHR^2CO_2H$$

Hydantoin (b)

Hydantoin (either a or b) + HCl $\xrightarrow{\Delta}$ $NH_2CHR^0CO_2H + NH_2CHR^1CO_2H$

SEQUENTIAL ANALYSIS OF PEPTIDES 1547

leucylalanylvalylglycine there was produced isovaleronitrile (from the N-terminal leucine) and 5-methyl-1:5-dehydrohydantoin-3-valerylglycine. Treatment of the latter with boiling NaOH followed by neutralization resulted in the separation of pyruvic acid (from alanine), valine, glycine, ammonia, and carbon dioxide.

Another procedure whereby the N-terminal residue and the one adjacent to it are determined was developed by Wessely and his co-workers, who used as a basis the reaction between alkali and N-carboalkyloxy derivatives of peptides to form the hydantoins of the two amino acids with simultaneous cleavage of the peptide bond. The scheme outlined by Wessely, Schlögl, and Körger (123) is as shown at foot of facing page.

Thus the reaction of leucylglycylphenylalanine with carboethoxy chloride followed by treatment with alkali led to the carbonyl compound

$$\begin{array}{c} CH_2C_6H_5 \\ | \\ NHCH_2CONHCHCO_2H \\ | \\ C=O \\ | \\ NHCHCO_2H \\ | \\ CH_2CH(CH_3)_2 \end{array}$$

which on heating with HCl yielded

$(CH_3)_2CHCH_2CH-CO$ $\quad\quad$ CH_2-CO
$\quad\quad\quad\quad\quad\quad\quad\diagdown$ $\quad\quad\quad\quad\quad\quad\quad\quad\diagdown$
$\quad\quad\quad\quad\quad\quad\quad\quad NCH_2CO_2H$ or $\quad\quad\quad\quad\quad\quad NCHCO_2H \quad$ + phenylalanine
$\quad\quad\quad\quad\quad\quad\quad\diagup$ $\quad\quad\quad\quad\quad\quad\quad\quad\quad |$
$\quad NH-CO$ $\quad\quad\quad\quad\quad\quad\quad$ $NH-CO \quad CH_2CH(CH_3)_2$

The hydantoin formed may be either of the two isomeric forms, and since both forms on hydrolysis yield leucine and glycine it is impossible to determine which of the two amino acids was actually the N-terminal one. The problem was solved by treating the hydantoin with thionyl chloride to form the acid chloride followed by reduction with sodium borohydride to yield the alcohol. Hydrolysis of the compound yielded the N-terminal residue as the free amino acid, and its adjacent residue as the corresponding amino alcohol (cf. 124).

The procedure was extended to peptides in which lysine occupied the N-terminal position (125). Under these circumstances, the hydantoin which appears possesses a free ε-amino group. To facilitate isolation of the compound, the reaction mixture was treated with phenylisocyanate which combined not only with the free ε-amino group of the hydantoin and thereby facilitated its separation, but also with the α-amino group of the third residue in the chain. As an illustration of its usefulness for protein end-group analysis, lysozyme was treated with carbobenzoxy chloride, and the carbobenzoxylated protein treated first with alkali and then with acid. The resulting hydantoin yielded lysine and valine, which are, respectively, the N-terminal and adjacent amino acids in lysozyme.

Wessely, Schlögl, and Wawersich (126) suggested that this hydantoin procedure could be employed to distinguish between γ- and α-glutamyl peptides. Thus only the α- but not the γ-glutamyl peptide could react as follows:

$$HO_2CCH_2CH_2CHCONHCHR^1CO \cdots \xrightarrow[2NaOH]{-ROH} HO_2CCH_2CH_2CHCO$$
$$\qquad\qquad |\qquad\qquad\qquad\qquad\qquad\qquad\qquad\qquad\qquad |\quad\diagdown NCHR^1CO \cdots$$
$$\quad NHOCOR \qquad\qquad\qquad\qquad\qquad\qquad\qquad\qquad NHCO$$
(where R = CH_3, C_2H_5, or $CH_2C_6H_5$)

Other procedures suggested for this purpose have been the reaction with ninhydrin which yields carbon dioxide only with γ- and not with α-glutamyl peptides (127, 128), and the reduction with lithium aluminum hydride followed by hydrolysis, which yields γ-amino-δ-hydroxy-n-valeric acid from γ-glutamyl peptides, and α-amino-δ-hydroxy-n-valeric acid from α-glutamyl peptides (129). Analogous reactions would be expected to distinguish β- from α-aspartyl peptides.

Reactions whereby the N-terminal amino acid residue is removed alone, and in cyclic form, simultaneously with hydrolysis of the adjacent peptide bond have been described by several investigators. Levy (130) mixed alanylglycine with carbon disulfide and baryta, then treated the mixture with hydrochloric acid to obtain the thio-thiazolidone corresponding to alanine together with free glycine (cf. 131):

$$NH_2CH(CH_3)CONHCH_2CO_2H + CS_2 \xrightarrow{OH^-} HS_2CNHCH(CH_3)CONHCH_2CO_2H \xrightarrow[pH\ 3-4]{HCl}$$
Alanylglycine

$$CH_3-CH\!-\!\!-\!\!-CO$$
$$\quad |\qquad\qquad | \quad + NH_2CH_2CO_2H$$
$$\ NH\qquad\ S\qquad\quad\ Glycine$$
$$\quad\diagdown\ \diagup$$
$$\quad\ CS$$
2-Thio-4-methylthiazolid-5-one

A method of developing this reaction on paper strips has been attempted (132).

Analogous reactions have been employed by Kenner and Khorana (133) and by Elmore and Toseland (134) who used, respectively, diethylxanthates and methylacyldithiocarbamates to couple with the free α-amino group in the N-terminal amino acid residue of a peptide; subsequent treatment resulted in cyclization of this treated residue with simultaneous hydrolysis of the linkage from the remainder of the peptide. Thus Kenner and Khorana combined dialkyl xanthate with alanylglycine to yield N-thioncarboethoxy-alanylglycine:

$$C_2H_5OC(=S)-SCH_3 + NH_2CH(CH_3)CONHCH_2CO_2H \xrightarrow[-CH_3SH]{pH\ 8}$$

$$C_2H_5OC(=S)NHCH(CH_3)CONHCH_2CO_2H \xrightarrow[\text{nitromethane}]{HCl\ in}$$

NH——CH(CH$_3$)
| | + NH$_2$CH$_2$COOH
CO   CO   Glycine
  \\   /
    S
Thiazolid-2:5-dione

↓ NaOH

$$(S)(O)CNHCH(CH_3)CO_2H \xrightarrow{HCl} NH_2CH(CH_3)CO_2H$$
                                                                Alanine

In similar fashion leucylglycylglycine yielded leucine and glycylglycine (133).

Elmore and Toseland observed that the most effective of their substituted dithiocarbamates was the methylacetyldithiocarbamate and the most appropriate medium for cyclization and peptide bond cleavage was glacial acetic acid saturated with HCl gas (cf. 134). Their generalized reaction is

$$R^1CONHCSSCH_3 + NH_2CHR^2CONHCHR^3CONHCHR^4CO_2H \xrightarrow[-CH_3SH]{pH\ 8}$$
(where R^1 = CH_3, C_2H_5, or C_6H_5)

$$R^1CONHCSNHCHR^2CONHCHR^3CONHCHR^4CO_2H \xrightarrow[HCl]{\text{Acetic acid}}$$

NH——CO
| |
CS   CHR^2 + R^{1}CO$_2$H + NH$_2$CHR^{3}CONHCHR^{4}CO$_2$H
  \\   /
    NH
5-Substituted hydantoin

N-Methylation reactions with proteins and peptides have been employed with some degree of success. The earliest reagents were dimethyl sulfate, methyl halides, and diazomethane. In a protein, such reagents would affect amino, hydroxyl, carboxyl, and phenolic groups. The methyl esters would be unstable at extremes of pH, and the phenolic ether would be largely hydrolyzed in hot strong acid. Only the N-methyl groups would be expected to possess a reasonable stability, and Edlbacher (136) was able to isolate ε-N-methyllysine from an acid hydrolysate of casein which had previously been treated with dimethyl sulfate. The betaine of glycine hydrochloride is very insoluble in ethanol, and Zimmermann (137) attempted to convert the N-terminal glycine residue of peptides into its betaine by exhaustive methylation; when applied to insulin the test turned out to be unaccountably negative. The o-phthalaldehyde reagent is relatively specific for glycine or N-glycyl residues (138), and it was shown to be effective in distinguishing such residues from those of other amino acids in various synthetic peptides (139); alloxan and ninhydrin were subsequently employed for the same purpose, albeit in very dilute solution (140).

The use of N-methylation as a means of end-group analysis was first demonstrated in the work of Bowman. Amino acids could be converted to their N,N-dimethyl derivatives by reductive condensation with formaldehyde and hydrogen in the presence of palladized charcoal (141). Only the monomethyl derivative occurs in the case of proline. As the dimethyl derivatives, many of the amino acids were more soluble in non-aqueous solvents then were the parent amino acids. An interesting side-light on these derivatives from a configurational viewpoint was the fact that the specific optical rotations of all L-amino acids tested was shifted in a positive direction as compared with the values for the corresponding parent amino acids, and the suggestion was indeed made that the conversion to the N,N-dimethyl derivative, which is accomplished without racemization, could serve as a means of optical configurational analysis (141) (Chapters 2 and 52). Higher N,N-dialkyl derivatives could be prepared only with glycine and alanine by the procedure, for with amino acids with larger side chains only such mono-N-alkyl substituents as N-butyl would result (142). With polypeptides, a method of N-terminal residue analysis was developed (143) as follows:

$$(CH_3)_2CHCH_2CH(NH_2)CONHCH_2CO_2H + 2HCHO \xrightarrow{H_2}$$
Leucylglycine

$$(CH_3)_2CHCH_2CH[N(CH_3)_2]CONHCH_2CO_2H \xrightarrow[\Delta]{HCl}$$
N,N-Dimethylleucylglycine

$$(CH_3)_2CHCH_2CH[N(CH_3)_2]CO_2H + NH_2CH_2CO_2H$$
N,N-Dimethylleucine   Glycine

or

Leucylglycine + butyraldehyde $\xrightarrow{H_2}$ N-butylleucylglycine $\xrightarrow[\Delta]{HCl}$
N-butylleucine + glycine

The dimethylamino residues are not entirely stable to acid hydrolysis, and a small percentage of the free amino acid may form in the event (144). Nevertheless, the dimethyl derivative of glycine and the monomethyl derivative of proline are much more stable toward acid then are the more frequently employed dinitrophenyl derivatives of these amino acids. A procedure employing paper chromatography for the detection of the dimethylamino acids was developed by Ingram (144). Either of two reagents was employed for this purpose, the one consisting of a solution of thymol blue whereby the dimethylamino acids appear as yellow spots on a red background, and the other consisting of a solution of orcinol whereby the dimethylamino acids appear in ultraviolet light as dark spots against a fluorescent background. Successful application of this procedure to the determination of the N-terminal amino acid residues of several synthetic peptides could be demonstrated (144).

Bromoacetate reacts with the amino group of peptides at pH 9 to form carboxymethylamino acids. With most amino acids a disubstituted derivative is formed, but with phenylalanine and aspartic and glutamic acids it is also possible to obtain a monosubstituted derivative (145). The hydroxyl group of tyrosine, the imidazole of histidine, and, of course, the ε-amino

$$\underset{\text{Peptide}}{-N\begin{smallmatrix}H\\[2pt]H\end{smallmatrix}} + \begin{smallmatrix}BrCH_2CO_2H\\[2pt]BrCH_2CO_2H\end{smallmatrix} \rightarrow \underset{\text{N-Dicarboxymethyl peptide}}{-N\begin{smallmatrix}CH_2CO_2H\\[2pt]CH_2CO_2H\end{smallmatrix}}$$

group of lysine react with the agent, the last-mentioned group as a disubstituted derivative, but the guanidino group of arginine is not reactive under the conditions used. After the N-terminal derivative is formed, the peptide is hydrolyzed and the N-terminal carboxymethylamino acid separated as the insoluble mercuric salt after mercuric nitrate is introduced into the hydrolysis mixture. In this way, glutathione yielded an amount of the mercury salt of the dicarboxymethyl derivative of glutamic acid which was 74% of the theoretical (145).

Azobenzenesulfonyl chloride has also been suggested as a reagent for the detection of N-terminal residues (146). The pertinent peptide derivative, after preparation in bicarbonate solution, is hydrolyzed with baryta solution, the azobenzenesulfonyl-N-terminal amino acid extracted into N HCl–amyl acetate, isolated, and hydrolyzed in $6N$ HCl at 140° to yield the free amino acid.

A rather specialized observation was made almost simultaneously by Cristol and his associates (147) and by Saidel (148) which involved the reaction of ninhydrin at pH 2.5 and at elevated temperature with a variety of peptides. Only N-terminal glycyl peptides yielded one mole of ammonia per mole of peptide, and thereby could be distinguished from peptides with other N-terminal residues which without exception yielded less than this value. It seems rather obvious that steric considerations are strongly involved in this and similar reactions with peptides and ninhydrin (Chapter 12).

N-Terminal Sequences (Proteins)

The description of the various procedures for N-terminal amino acid residues up to this point have dealt with those so far applied almost exclusively to peptides. It is not that these procedures are not applicable to proteins, but that, in view of the great popularity of two current methods, most of them have not yet been tried. The two current methods whose description has been deferred to this point are those developed by Sanger and by Edman.

THE SANGER PROCEDURE. It may be properly stated that the modern aspects of this field began with the studies of Sanger in 1945 (149). The reagent of choice to interact with the terminal residue bearing the free amino group was 1-fluoro-2:4-dinitrobenzene, which was found to react smoothly at room temperature in alcohol-bicarbonate mixtures. The earlier procedure by Abderhalden and Blumberg (96), in which the corresponding 1-chloro derivative was used, required heating in order to effect the required condensation. With amino acids alone, the reagent combined not only with the free amino groups, but also with the imino group of proline, the phenolic group of tyrosine, the sulfhydryl group of cysteine, and, under certain circumstances, with the imidazole group of histidine. In view of the production of hydrofluoric acid during the course of the reaction, care had always to be taken to maintain an alkaline environment. The condensation product of the reagent (usually referred to as DNFB) and protein (called DNP-protein) was refluxed in strong acid, and the products subjected at first to fractionation on silica gel columns. Only the combinations of the reagent with nitrogen, DNP-N, were yellow colored, and no indicator was needed to reveal the presence of the bands. The O-DNP derivative of tyrosine was colorless. With insulin of 6000 molecular weight, three kinds of DNP-N compounds were found, namely, one derived from glycine, one from phenylalanine, and one from the ε-amino group of lysine. It was therefore concluded that from the N-terminal position of insulin there were apparently two peptide chains, one with N-terminal glycine and one with N-terminal phenylalanine. In the earlier reports by Sanger, residue numbers based on a molecular weight of 12,000 for insulin (subsequently revised to 6,000) are twice the currently accepted values.

Illustrative procedure (cf. 149). Crystalline insulin (0.5 g.) and 0.5 g. of sodium bicarbonate are dissolved together in 5 ml. of water. To the solution are added 10 ml. of ethanol and 0.5 ml. of a solution of dinitrofluorobenzene (0.4 g. of DNFB in 10 ml. of ethanol). The mixture is shaken mechanically for 2 hr. at room temperature, and the DNP-insulin precipitates as an insoluble yellow granular mass. The product is centrifuged, washed with water, ethanol, and ether, and finally dried in air.

One hundred milligrams of the DNP-insulin is suspended in 10 ml. of 20% HCl, and the mixture refluxed for 8 hr. After cooling, the mixture is extracted three times with ether. This separates the hydrolysate into two fractions, each colored yellow. The ether extract contains the N-terminal DNP-amino acid(s), whilst the aqueous solution contains the free amino acids obtained by hydrolysis of the protein, together with any *im*-DNP-histidine and ε-DNP-lysine (and if arginine were

N-terminal there would also be some α-DNP-arginine). The ether extract, which is free of salt, is taken to dryness, the residue taken up in a little acetone, and the solution subjected to paper chromatography as described in Section 15-5 and Table 15-8. Clear-cut spots are observed only for the DNP-derivatives of glycine and of phenylalanine.

In the course of these as well as later studies, four factors emerged which have created special problems. The first of these was concerned with the stability of the DNP-amino acids which were liberated during the course of the strong acid hydrolysis of the DNP-substituted proteins. With amino acids alone under hydrolytic conditions employed with proteins, the DNP derivatives of glycine, proline, cystine, and, naturally, tryptophan were especially subject to destruction (40). In the presence of free tryptophan (150, 151) and cysteine (152) derived from the protein, and destroyed wholly or in part during the acid hydrolysis, the destruction of many DNP-amino acids was particularly marked. Correction factors have therefore been introduced to take into account the instability of DNP-amino acids, and have been based on the recovery of these compounds either in the presence of protein or of DNP-protein after various periods of hydrolysis (cf. 151). The approximate nature of such corrections, which in such cases as DNP-glycine may be as great as if not greater than the experimental values, needs little emphasis.

In their studies on the hydrolysis of N-terminal valine from DNP-hemoglobin, Porter and Sanger used a destruction factor of some 20–35% for DNP-valine in boiling acid (40); more recently, Rhinesmith, Schroeder, and Pauling (153) employed a factor closer to 13%. The difference in the use of factors of this magnitude amounts to more than one residue of valine per molecule of hemoglobin of 66,000 molecular weight!

In the case of DNP-peptides and DNP derivatives of smaller proteins in which less vigorous hydrolytic methods are required, the use of nearly anhydrous acidic mixtures has been found to produce less destruction of DNP-amino acids. Thus Hanes, Hird, and Isherwood (154) reported nearly complete recovery of DNP-glycine after hydrolyzing DNP-glycyl-glycine in a 1 : 9 mixture of 60% perchloric acid and glacial acetic acid, and Monier and Jutisz (155) observed a better recovery of DNP-prolyl-arginine from DNP-salmine with a formic acid–acetic anhydride–perchloric acid mixture as a hydrolyzing medium than with strong hydrochloric acid. Still another device to reduce the extent of destruction of DNP-amino acids during hydrolysis was suggested by Dickman and Asplund (156). This depended on the combination of xanthydrol with the indole residues of tryptophan in the protein and largely prevented their destruction during hydrolysis, thereby sparing the DNP-substituted amino acids. Thus 1 mole of lysozyme is known to contain 1 mole of N-terminal lysine and 5 moles of internal lysine residues (157, 158). DNP-Lysozyme was prepared in the usual way and treated with xanthydrol in 90% acetic acid. On hydrolyzing the DNP-xanthyl-lysozyme, the recovery of di-DNP-lysine was 97% and of ε-DNP-lysine 91% of the theoretical as compared, respectively, with recoveries of 78% and of 56% from DNP-lysozyme without preliminary treatment with xanthydrol (156). Finally, it may be added that destruction of DNP-amino acids during hydrolysis of the protein results not only in an apparent deficiency of these compounds, but also in the production of artifacts; thus DNP-proline (155, 159–161) and DNP-trytophan (162) partly decompose in boiling acid to yield dinitrophenol and various unidentified compounds, some yellow colored and others colorless. Thus a test for N-terminal proline would be to find dinitrophenol as well as proline (163). A mixture of DNP-amino acid and dinitrophenol in benzene can be removed on aluminum oxide; on washing with 2% acetic acid the dinitrophenol is extracted, whilst the DNP-amino acid can be subsequently eluted with dilute bicarbonate solution. To avoid hydrolysis altogether, the unusual absorption spectra of DNP-proline and DNP-hydroxyproline and of their peptides may be used to determine whether these residues are N-terminal (164) in the intact peptide.

The second of the troublesome factors lies in the nature of the solvent to be employed in order to extract the DNP-amino acid from the remainder of the protein hydrolysate. Most of the DNP-amino acids which are N-terminal have by the N-substitution lost the dipolar ion character of the parent amino acids, and hence are soluble in non-polar solvents. Ether has proved quite satisfactory in these cases as an extraction medium (cf. 149). However, such possible N-terminal residues as DNP-arginine, di-DNP-histidine, DNP-asparagine, and DNP-cysteic acid are relatively insoluble in ether, whilst internal DNP-substituted residues, such as ε-DNP-lysine, *im*-DNP-histidine, and O-DNP-tyrosine, being essentially α-amino acids when in the freed state in the protein hydrolysate, are completely insoluble in ether and remain in the aqueous layer. Both *im*-DNP-histidine and O-DNP-tyrosine are colorless or nearly so. A continuous ether extraction will transfer di-DNP-histidine from the aqueous to the ether phase (165), and ethyl acetate as a solvent will extract several of the DNP-amino acids otherwise sparingly soluble in ether; ethyl acetate, however, will extract some of the more water-soluble DNP-amino acids also, and hence this solvent is more generally used for the extraction of DNP-peptides (166). The derivatives are thereby freed of salts. Weakly basic anion exchangers have also been employed to selectively adsorb smaller, neutral DNP-peptides (166). Identification of the DNP-amino acids in the ether and aqueous phases has been performed by column and by paper chromatography. Some of these procedures have been described elsewhere in this volume (Chapter 15). Fuller accounts are to be found in the excellent reviews by Thompson and Thompson (167) and by Schroeder (168). Only the DNP-leucines (i.e., leucine and isoleucine) cannot yet be distinguished by chromatographic criteria; and in this case it is necessary to regenerate the free amino acids by heating with baryta (169) or ammonia (170), and to chromatograph the resulting amino acid or acids; although necessary in this instance, it is often desirable in others as an independent means of confirmation, while taking into consideration the degradative side reactions involved in heating such compounds as DNP-threonine or DNP-serine with baryta. Several of the water-soluble DNP derivatives react with ninhydrin; thus O-DNP-tyrosine gives a purple color with this reagent, ε-DNP-lysine a brown color, and *im*-DNP-histidine a brown color. The yellow-colored α-N-DNP-arginine does not react with ninhydrin to yield any change in color (114).

The third of the troublesome aspects of the DNFB procedure (or, for that matter, all terminal residue analyses) consists of the problem of a quantitative reaction of the agent with all the available groups of the protein. It may be assumed that the native protein generally exists in a coiled or folded configuration, in which the free reactive groups on the α- or ω-carbon atoms may be all or only partly accessible to chemical reagents; when the protein is denatured, its unique configuration is lost, it assumes an extended configuration, and all the reactive groups become accessible. The topic in its wide ramifications has been frequently discussed (171–173) and in its broader aspects is outside of the scope of this volume. Specifically, however, it is concerned with the proper evaluation of terminal group analysis. Sanger's choice of insulin as the first protein to study with DNFB was particularly fortunate, for in this material all or nearly all of the ε-amino groups of the internal lysine residues, as well as the α-amino groups of the N-terminal residues, reacted with the agent. Two years later, Porter, working in Sanger's laboratory, reported that native β-lactoglobulin when treated under the same conditions with DNFB yielded only 12 out of a possible total of 31 ε-DNP-lysine moles per mole of protein (174); when, however, the protein was completely denatured by acid, heat, or guanidine hydrochloride prior to the reaction with DNFB, all the ε-NH$_2$ groups reacted with the agent. Similar findings were noted for horse serum pseudoglobulin and cow and pig β- and γ-globulins. A particularly interesting example of this problem is ovalbumin which in the native state apparently possesses no free N-terminal α-amino group, but does react with fluorodinitrobenzene at 3 of the 12 possible ε-amino groups of the internal lysine residues (174*a*); on complete denaturation of the protein the other 9 ε-amino groups became reactive and readily formed the DNP derivatives, but still no reactive α-amino group was revealed.

With bovine serum albumin, however, as with insulin, all the ε-NH$_2$ groups of the internal lysine residues reacted with DNFB without any special effort to denature (or further denature) the protein. Again, with the hemoglobins or globins of several species, whether specially denatured or not, all the ε-NH$_2$ groups of the internal lysine residues reacted with DNFB (40); in connection with this particular study, Porter and Sanger found several N-terminal residues to be free, namely, 6 of valine for horse and donkey hemoglobin, 5 of valine for adult human hemoglobin, and 2 of valine and 2 of methionine for cow, sheep, and goat hemoglobin, on the basis of 64,000 for the molecular weight of the protein.

The reactivity toward DNFB of another internal residue in proteins, namely, the imidazole of histidine, was studied by Porter (175). It was first thought that the imidazole ring of histidine could not form a stable compound with DNFB, but hydrolysates of globin treated previously with excess of the reagent yielded no free histidine. Acetylhistidine combined with DNFB to form a stable crystalline compound; on hydrolysis with acid, a colorless, mono-DNP compound, possibly *im*-DNP-histidine, was obtained. All the histidine residues of hemoglobin, of ovalbumin, and of bovine serum albumin were fully accessible and could be nearly quantitatively accounted for in terms of *im*-DNP-histidine; however, not all the imidazole groups of β-lactoglobulin reacted until the protein was fully denatured. These various observations are not at all unfamiliar in the field of protein denaturation, for it is well known that some proteins are more difficult to denature than are others, and not all react to the same extent with the same denaturing agent (171–173). The Sanger procedure to treat protein with DNFB involved basically an exposure for 2 hours at room temperature to a mixture of the reagent with sodium bicarbonate saturated in over 60% ethanol. These are essentially denaturing conditions for hemoglobin (cf. 173), and no further treatment was apparently necessary to convert this protein to the fully denatured and reactive state. The same situation probably held for insulin and serum albumin, but not for the milk and serum globulins studied. As will be noted below, some proteins have been reported to possess no N-terminal amino acid residues after treatment with DNFB and complete hydrolysis, and the results have been interpreted in part as suggesting the presence of a cyclic structure in which the N-terminal residue is involved. On the basis of the studies described, the possibility cannot be excluded that certain of these observations may be due to a lack of complete denaturation and unfolding of the protein. An adequate control of this possibility is illustrated by Bailey's studies on myosin (176) which revealed in the DNFB reaction no N-terminal amino acid residue, but full reactivity of the ε-amino groups of the internal lysine residues.

A particularly striking example of the effect of denaturing agents is noted with the tobacco mosaic virus protein. Attempts to determine by either Sanger or Edman procedures (cf. 161) the N-terminal residue of the native protein with DNFB had not been successful. When, however, the virus protein was first treated with 5% trichloroacetic acid and then combined with

DNFB, followed by partial hydrolysis in 12N HCl at 37° for 48 hours, there appeared in the hydrolysate DNP-proline, DNP-prolylisoleucine, and DNP-prolylisoleucylglutamic acid (177). That higher peptides could not be found prompted the supposition that serine or threonine might be the next member of the chain. When DNP-virus was treated with trypsin, a yellow-colored peptide could be isolated from the digest which was soluble in ethyl acetate, which was homogeneous by electrophoretic and chromatographic criteria, and which could be brought to crystallization from either ethyl acetate–methanol or methanol-ether solutions (178). The peptide had an N-terminal proline and a C-terminal lysine residue, and on complete hydrolysis yielded a total of 21 amino acid residues:

DNP-proline(alanine-2, aspartic acid, glutamic acid, glycine, isoleucine, leucine-2, phenylalanine, threonine-2, tryptophan, serine-4, O-DNP-tyrosine, and valine-2)-ε-DNP-lysine

Finally, the fourth aspect which has created some special problems in the DNFB (and other) procedures has involved the stability of certain peptide linkages during what might be considered the very mild reaction between protein and DNFB. The existence of this problem was noted in the cases of carboxypeptidase and of the "old yellow enzyme," and the phenomena involved are discussed later in this section. It is obvious that if the protein is not completely stable during the coupling with the DNFB reagent,and internal bonds open to yield new reactive amino groups to the reagent, the results will be ambiguous; together with the true N-terminal DNP-amino acid there will appear one or more DNP-amino acids originating from the points of breakage in the protein molecule. The stoichiometry of the results obtained is often a help in this problem, for if very close to one residue of DNP-amino acid is obtained per mole of protein, together with only traces of other DNP-amino acids, it may be assumed that few if any secondary reactions occurred; if, however, appreciable amounts of two or more DNP-amino acids are obtained per mole of protein, the problem of deciding whether the results are valid and representative of two or more N-terminal peptide chains in the molecule, or whether they may spring from secondary causes, could well be difficult to solve. Treatment of an apparently homogeneous protein with DNFB may produce a physical fractionation as in the example of crotoxin cited by Fraenkel-Conrat and Singer (179); in this case two DNP-proteins were obtained, one soluble and the other insoluble, each differing in amino acid composition; the former revealed the presence of one N-terminal serine and one C-terminal aspartic acid residue, the latter possessed only a fraction of these terminal residues. Exposure of a cystine-containing protein to the alkaline environment necessary to create the DNP derivative may well result in a disulfide interchange with a sequence about the cystine residue different from that of the original protein (see below). Of considerable importance in the interpretation of the data on end-group analysis has been the finding by Narita (179a) that chymotryptic hydrolysates of several strains of the tobacco mosaic virus protein yielded N-acetylseryltyrosine to about 1.8% of the protein sample used. This was the first time that an N-acetylated peptide sequence was isolated from a partial protein hydrolysate. The structure of the peptide derivative was proven by comparison with an authentic synthetic sample. The method of isolation, following acidification of the digest to pH 3.8 and filtration, was to pour the filtrate over a Dowex 50-X2 (H⁺) column and to collect the acidic effluent. Fractions of the effluent reactive toward the tyrosine residue were separated and chromatographed on paper using n-butanol–acetic acid–water (4 : 1 : 1) as solvent system and chlorine–starch–iodide reagent as indicator; the strongest spot with R_F 0.69 turned out to be acetylseryltyrosine. Elution of the unstained material with water followed by lyophilization of the solution yielded the peptide.

The finding of a natural N-acylated peptide sequence in a protein suggests that a failure to obtain an α-N-DNP-substituted protein does not necessarily imply that the protein is cyclic at the N-terminal portion, nor that the protein has been insufficiently unfolded. In brief, the α-amino group of the N-terminal residue may, like the serine in the tobacco mosaic virus protein, be already substituted, if not by acetyl then perhaps by carbohydrate, as in the probable instance of ovalbumin (cf. 179a).

Most of the proteins studied possess one or two N-terminal amino acid residues, suggesting a molecular structure composed of no more than one or two chains. A few proteins, however, have yielded evidence for the possession of a number of chains, or sub-units, at the N-terminal end; by definition, a full, open chain will have one C-terminal for one N-terminal residue, and in the absence of the isolated chain the participation of such open chains in the protein can only be suspected if the number of C-terminal residues equals that of the N-terminal. Few proteins have been examined by this criterion. Insulin, with two separable chains, and identified by a phenylalanyl residue at the N-terminal position of the chain which C-terminates with alanine, and by a glycyl residue at the N-terminal position of the chain which C-terminates with asparagine, constitutes a well-studied exception. It is possible in most cases to refer to chains only at one or the other terminal residue.

Of the proteins with apparently multichain structures at the N-terminal residue, equine hemoglobin with 6 (all valine) (40), edestin with 7 (6 glycine and 1 leucine) (180), wool keratin with 27 (4 valine, 2 alanine, 8 glycine, 8 threonine, 2 serine, 2 glutamic acid, and 1 aspartic acid) (181), α-casein with 10–11 arginine and 1–2 lysine N-terminal residues (182), and β-casein with 5–6 arginine and 2–3 lysine residues (182) are particularly outstanding.

No C-terminal data other than for hemoglobin (2 C-terminal histidine residues) are available to suggest whether these figures represent full chains or not. The tobacco mosaic virus protein with about 2500 N-terminal proline residues (after acid treatment) (177, 178), and, as will be noted below, about the same number of C-terminal threonine residues, is probably composed of close to 2500 peptide chains. The several chains in a multichain protein may have the same N-terminal residue but different sequences from there on. Thus equine hemoglobin may have N-terminal valylleucyl, valylglycyl, and valylglutaminyl sequences (40, 183), and dog hemoglobin, N-terminal valylleucyl, valylglycyl, and valylaspartyl (183). Porter and Sanger, Brown, and Havinga, all reported 5 N-terminal valine residues in human hemoglobin (40).

Complete hydrolysis of a DNP-protein yields the DNP-N-terminal amino acid (if present), and various DNP-substituted internal residues, as substituted or free amino acids, such as ε-DNP-lysine. Partial acid hydrolysates of proteins yield a mixture of peptides of various sizes together with free amino acids. This mixture may be fractionated in a number of ways, and each fraction treated with DNFB and further fractionated, or else the mixture may be treated directly with DNFB and the DNP-peptides and DNP-amino acids separately fractionated and identified (94). The use of trimethylamine in place of bicarbonate in the reaction of the protein fragments with DNFB saves the subsequent desalting required prior to paper chromatography (115, 88) or to separation on columns of ion exchange resins. On the other hand, the reaction of DNFB with serine or seryl residues in the presence of triethylamine (but not of bicarbonate) may lead to substitution not only on the amino but also on the hydroxyl group to yield N,O-di-DNP derivatives (184). This may introduce certain complicating factors, not yet fully evaluated. Sanger has demonstrated how the sequence of amino acids following the DNP-substituted N-terminal amino acid may be determined from partial acid hydrolysates of a DNP-protein (166). The studies of Sanger on the amino acid sequences in insulin are of so striking a nature as to warrant a separate discussion. Modifications in the procedures have been introduced by others, frequently of necessity, for the study of each new protein raises problems peculiar to that protein. Selected examples to illustrate the approaches employed are given below.

The N-terminal residue of papain was found to be isoleucine, present to the extent of one equivalent per mole (151). Partial hydrolysates of the DNP-enzyme protein in $12N$ HCl yielded the following DNP derivatives: DNP-isoleucine, DNP-isoleucylproline, and DNP-isoleucylprolylglutamic acid. The N-terminal sequence therefore appeared to be isoleucylprolylglutamyl. No DNP-peptides higher than the tripeptide were observed; this suggested that the fourth residue might be serine or threonine whose bond is labile to acid, or tryptophan which is destroyed by acid.

Schroeder (91) determined the N-terminal residue sequence of DNP-lysozyme to be lysylvalylphenylalanylglycyl, the procedure embodying the following. ˙DNP-Lysozyme was partially hydrolyzed by refluxing for 10 minutes in 6N HCl solution. Three α,ε-di-DNP-lysyl peptides were isolated and separated on silicic acid–Celite columns. The most strongly adsorbed peptide contained, in addition to the di-DNP-lysyl residue, valine, phenylalanine, and glycine; the next most strongly adsorbed di-DNP-lysyl peptide contained valine and phenylalanine, whereas the least strongly adsorbed di-DNP-lysyl peptide was composed only of lysine and valine. These results suggested the sequence proposed. Acher et al. (185) suggested that the fifth residue of this N-terminal sequence was arginine, making it lysylvalylphenylalanylglycylarginyl, and based this proposal in part on the action of trypsin which yielded the sequence valylphenylalanylglycylarginine. Papaya lysozyme, unlike the animal lysozymes which contain an N-terminal lysine residue, contains an N-terminal glycine (186). A particularly interesting and rare example of a repeating unit at the N-terminal position is that described for prolactin by Cole, Geschwind, and Li (187) which involved the N-terminal sequence threonylprolylvalylthreonylprolyl-; the C-terminus of this protein is apparently cyclic.

Ribonuclease appears to consist of a single chain arranged in a folded structure, and cross-linked by four disulfide bridges. After performic acid oxidation there is still a single chain. The N-terminal sequence appears to be lysylglutamyl(or glutaminyl)threonylalanyl. Anfinsen, Redfield, Choate, Page, and Carroll (188) proposed this sequence in part on the basis of the following evidence:

1. The partial hydrolysate of DNP-ribonuclease, after 72 hours at 37° in 11N HCl, was subjected to paper electrophoresis and showed the presence of di-DNP-lysylglutamic acid.

2. The pepsin hydrolysate of DNP-ribonuclease was subjected to paper electrophoresis and showed the presence of di-DNP-lysine and of a di-DNP-lysyl peptide which on complete hydrolysis yielded di-DNP-lysine, glutamic acid, threonine, and alanine in equivalent amounts. The same peptide was partially hydrolyzed by maintaining its solution in 11N HCl for 18 hours at 37°, and this hydrolysate showed the presence of di-DNP-lysine and di-DNP-lysylglutamic acid; the mother liquor from which these two components were removed was treated with DNFB, the mixture subjected to complete hydrolysis, and DNP-threonine and free alanine were identified. The structure of ribonuclease may therefore be represented as in the diagram on the facing page, the second member of the N-terminal sequence being either glutamic acid or glutamine.

The action of DNFB on crystalline carboxypeptidase followed by complete hydrolysis of the DNP-protein revealed the presence of DNP-aspartic acid,

DNP-serine, DNP-threonine, and ε-DNP-lysine. The molar residues were, respectively, 0.7, 0.3, only traces, and 17–18 per mole of carboxypeptidase with molecular weight 34,000 (190). When the protein was subjected to the action of pepsin and subsequently treated with DNFB, the peptide DNP-asparaginylserine was isolated in good yield. This turned out to be the

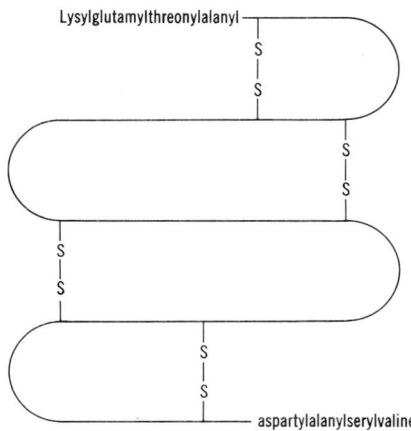

N-terminal sequence, but the linkage between asparagine carboxyl and serine amino groups, although expected to be labile because of the serine residue, was unusually so. When the protein was treated with DNFB and the mother liquor examined for DNP-amino acids, DNP-asparagine was recovered in an amount almost equivalent to the DNP-serine isolated from a complete hydrolysis of the DNP-protein, and in addition trace amounts of DNP-serine and DNP-threonine were also found in the above mother liquor. It is noteworthy that the mild conditions in bicarbonate solution employed for the coupling of DNFB with carboxypeptidase were sufficient to cause hydrolysis of certain sensitive bonds in the protein, and this phenomenon suggests that consideration be given the possibility of this occurrence with other proteins. The "old yellow enzyme" with an N-terminal aspartic acid residue loses this residue when coupled with DNFB (191), but human serum albumin with the same N-terminal residue does not (152, 192). The results themselves indicate the N-terminal sequence of carboxypeptidase to be asparaginylseryl; the next residue could be threonine, which would account for the free DNP-serine found in the mother liquor after DNFB treatment, as well as for the traces of DNP-threonine obtained in acid hydrolysates of the DNP-protein.

Williamson and Passmann (193) reported that pepsin possessed one N-terminal residue per mole of protein, and Biserte and Dautrevaux (194) that the N-terminal sequence was leucylleucylalanylvalyl. The chromatographic distinction of DNP-leucine and DNP-isoleucine is ordinarily difficult to achieve, and the more recent investigations by Van Vunakis and Herriott (195) have indicated that isoleucine is the N-terminal amino acid in pepsin, leucine that in pepsinogen, and leucine that in the pepsin inhibitor; the adjacent residue in each case is, respectively, glycine, leucine or isoleucine, and glutamic acid. By means of partial acid hydrolysis, fractionation on silicic acid–Celite, and paper electrophoresis, the N-terminal di-DNP-lysyl sequence of α-casein was found to be lysylleucylvalylalanylglutamyl-aspartyl (196).

The description of protein structure in terms of N-terminal residues has been of value not only for enzyme proteins but also for proteins involved in immune reactions. Thus one of the oldest problems in immunology is the relation of antibody to the normal γ-globulin of serum. Porter (197) demonstrated with the DNFB procedure on partial hydrolysates that normal rabbit γ-globulin and antiovalbumin were alike in possessing the N-terminal tetrapeptide sequence alanylleucylvalylaspartyl, with glutamic acid as probably the fifth residue. The subsequent studies by McFadden and Smith (198) on several different types of antipneumococcal antibodies in the rabbit confirmed the N-terminal sequence proposed by Porter and showed unequivocally that glutamic acid was the fifth residue in the chain. Some DNP-leucylvaline, DNP-leucine, DNP-valine, DNP-aspartic acid, and DNP-glutamic acid were also found; this might suggest that the bonds at the N-terminal sequence are rather labile and are hydrolyzed during treatment of the proteins with DNFB. Not merely the N-terminal residues but the entire amino acid composition of the rabbit antibodies are identical (199). Less clear-cut results were obtained on N-terminal residue analysis of equine normal globulins and antibodies for these proteins after treatment with DNFB followed by complete hydrolysis yielded a mixture of DNP-amino acids each in much less than stoichiometric amounts (198).

Another interesting phenomenon revealed in serum occurs in patients with multiple myeloma who frequently possess a marked hyperglobulinemia. The problem of whether the excess protein represents a new constituent or an increase in a normal constituent has remained unsolved. Studies by Smith, et al. (201) and by Putnam (202) on normal human γ-globulins have shown that different fractions differ in the N-terminal residues, but usually contain N-terminal aspartic and glutamic acids. Putnam described myeloma globulins with two N-terminal residues of either aspartic acid or leucine per 160,000 grams of protein. Smith, et al. studied four different myeloma globulins and found each to differ from the others; three possessed N-terminal glutamic acid (two with two residues and one with close to three) and no N-terminal aspartic acid, whilst the fourth possessed one N-terminal aspartic acid residue and no N-terminal glutamic acid. Two had the same proportion of ε-DNP-lysine residues; it was different from that of the other two which also contained the same amount of these residues. Two normal serum γ-globulins had the same proportion of ε-DNP-lysine residues, and both showed the presence of one N-terminal aspartic acid residue, but one had in addition one N-terminal glutamic acid residue and the other had close to two. The results are of considerable interest despite their apparent complexity, and further illumination of the problem is anticipated. It cannot be said at this time that the question of the identity or non-identity of the normal and myeloma globulins has been answered, although considerable progress has been made (202).

In one of the earliest reports on the DNFB procedure, Porter and Sanger (40) stated that the evidence for the N-terminal amino acid residue of salmine pointed to proline, and was thus confirmatory of the assignment made by Felix and Mager (39) some time earlier. Further evidence accrued from studies on the acid and tryptic hydrolysates of DNP-salmine by Monier and Jutisz (203) which yielded evidence for the N-terminal sequence prolyl-arginylarginyl. Proline is also the N-terminal amino acid for a fraction of another basic protein, namely, calf thymus histone (200).

A few interesting variations on the use of reactive nitrophenyl derivatives include that of 2:4-dinitrobenzenesulfonic acid which reacts with the free amino groups of proteins with the evolution of sulfonic acid (204), and the proposed reaction of 4-carbomethoxy-2-nitro-1-fluorobenzene with the amino group of peptides and proteins (205).

The ingenious procedure developed by Holley and Holley is given in the accompanying reaction (205). The procedure can be continued successively with the residual peptide as each N-terminal residue is removed as the lactam.

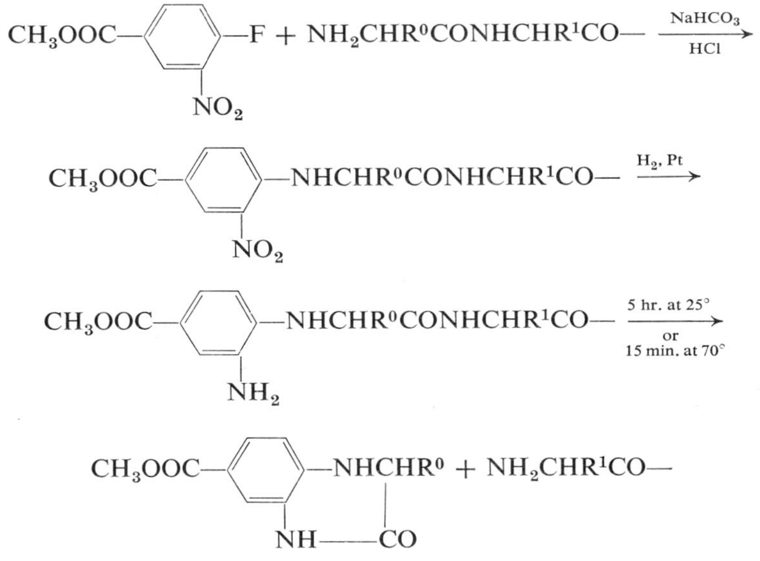

$$CH_3OOC-\underset{NO_2}{\underset{|}{\bigcirc}}-F + NH_2CHR^0CONHCHR^1CO- \xrightarrow[HCl]{NaHCO_3}$$

$$CH_3OOC-\underset{NO_2}{\underset{|}{\bigcirc}}-NHCHR^0CONHCHR^1CO- \xrightarrow{H_2, Pt}$$

$$CH_3OOC-\underset{NH_2}{\underset{|}{\bigcirc}}-NHCHR^0CONHCHR^1CO- \xrightarrow[\substack{or \\ 15 \text{ min. at } 70°}]{5 \text{ hr. at } 25°}$$

$$CH_3OOC-\underset{NH\text{------}CO}{\underset{|\quad\quad\quad|}{\bigcirc}}-NHCHR^0 + NH_2CHR^1CO-$$

TABLE 16-4
Properties of 2:4-Dinitrophenyl-L-amino Acids (208)[a]

DNP-L-Amino Acid	Mol. Wt.	M.P., °C.	$[M]_D$ in N NaOH	$[M]_D$ in NaHCO$_3$	$[M]_D$ in Glacial Acetic Acid
Alanine	255	177	+367	–	+39
Butyrine	269	133	+266	+277	−23
Norvaline	283	58	+170	–	−78
Valine	283	132	+309	–	−79
Isovaline	283	141	+114	–	–
Leucine	297	94	+177	+176	−135
Isoleucine	297	113	+252	–	−104
Alloisoleucine	297	119	+260	–	−119
Nonyline	339	69	−277	–	−118
Serine	271	173	–	+341	−65
Threonine	285	145	–	+305	−141
Allothreonine	285	152	–	+305	−84
γ-Hydroxybutyrine	285	164	–	+75	−179
ε-Hydroxynorleucine	313	141	+119	–	−134
Cystine (di)	572	109	–	−1487	−1833
S-Benzylcysteine	377	111	–	–	−669
Phenylalanine	331	189	−310	−261	−342
Tyrosine (di)	513	178	–	–	−60
Tryptophan	370	221	−1291	–	−672
Proline	281	138	−2172	–	−1978
Hydroxyproline	297	174	−3852	–	−3410
Allohydroxyproline	297	–	−2706	−1874	−1322
Aspartic acid	299	186	+275	–	−20
Glutamic acid	313	–	–	−20	−253
Asparagine	298	180	–	+190	−100
Glutamine	312	189	−177	−172	−302
γ-Aminobutyrine (di)	450	120	–	–	−360
Ornithine (di)[b]	464	156	–	–	−339
Lysine (di)[b]	478	170	–	–	−127
Histidine (di)[c]	487	232	−107	–	–
Arginine (only α)	340	260	–	–	−121
Glycine[d]	241	203	–	–	–
β-Alanine[d]	255	177	–	–	–
γ-Aminobutyric acid[d]	269	145	–	–	–

[a] Molar rotations calculated as specific rotation multiplied by the molecular weight and divided by 100.

[b] These data are of value only if these residues are N-terminal. Sanger prepared the ω-DNP derivatives which may arise from the interior of the protein chains by treating ornithine or lysine as the copper chelates in alkaline medium with DNFB, and on removal of copper with H$_2$S gas isolated the δ-DNP-ornithine and ε-DNP-lysine by acidification to about pH 7 (149). Because of the possibility that lysine (or ornithine) might participate in

2:4-Dinitrofluorobenzene has also been employed in analogous fashion, the hydrogenation step being accomplished either with Pt, H_2 or with ammonium sulfide (206). With the latter, only the "vicinal" nitro group is reduced.

The conversion to the esters of N-terminal amino acids isolated into ether after hydrolysis of the DNP-protein, using diazomethane as the esterification agent, followed by the separation of the DNP-amino acid esters by adsorption chromatography in alumina, was studied by Fletcher, Lowther, and Reith (207). With insulin two N-terminal phenylalanyl residues, two or three N-terminal glycyl residues (the uncertainty due to the great variations in magnitude of the correction factors for the decomposition of DNP-glycine as a result of refluxing in acid), and two ε-amino groups derived from internal lysine residues were observed (on the basis of a molecular weight of 12,000).

The DNFB procedure has, like all such procedures, required the use of reference standards, and the characteristics of various synthetic DNP-amino acids have been recorded since 1910 when Abderhalden and Blumberg first prepared them (40, 96, 149). Inasmuch as pure L-amino acids have not been available in quantity until recently, most of the reference standards have of necessity been based on the use of DL-amino acids. However, the DNP-amino acids isolated from acidic or neutral digests of proteins would be expected to be of the L-variety, and, although the chromatographic criteria by which the DNP-L-amino acids derived from the protein are compared with synthetic DNP-DL-amino acids may be justified as being relatively independent of optical configuration, it would nevertheless (a) remove any lingering doubts if the DNP reference standards were also L- in configuration, and (b) introduce in measurements of the specific optical rotation still another criterion of comparison. For these reasons, Rao and Sober have prepared a number of the optically active DNP-amino acids listed in Table 16–4 (208).

The bifunctional reagent 1-fluoro-5-chloro-2:4-dinitrobenzene, which reacts with amino acids to form compounds of the reagent with two molecules of the same or different amino acids, has been proposed (209). In the former case, two molecules of the amino acid are condensed with the reagent; in the latter case, one molecule of each amino acid is condensed in turn with

---

the peptide chain through their ω- rather than through their α-amino groups, and thus appear on hydrolysis of the DNP-protein as α-DNP-lysine (or α-DNP-ornithine), Sanger prepared such reference compounds by treating ε-benzoyllysine (or δ-benzoylornithine) with DNFB, and subsequently hydrolyzing the benzoyl group.

[c] *Im*-DNP-Histidine was prepared by treating α-acetylhistidine with DNFB and subsequently hydrolyzing the acetyl radical (175). The *im*-DNP group in di-DNP-histidine is readily removed by aminolysis, such as by free histidine whereby α-N-DNP-histidine is formed in good yield (175).

[d] Possesses no center of asymmetry.

one molecule of reagent. The procedure has not yet been extensively employed with peptides.

THE EDMAN PROCEDURE. The method introduced in 1950 by Edman (210) for N-terminal residue analysis is to some extent complementary to that of Sanger's DNFB procedure, and the results on the same protein by the two methods, for the greater part, have been consistent. In point of historic sequence, Aschan in 1883 (211) had synthesized thiohydantoins by heating phenylisothiocyanate with glycine, alanine, and leucine at 140°. The method of forming thiocarbamyl derivatives of amino acids in weakly alkaline solution, and subsequently converting them into thiohydantoins through the action of acid, was first employed by Marckwald, Neumark, and Stelzner (212) in 1891. Edman's procedure was based on the property first noted by Bergmann, Miekeley, and Kann (98) and extended by Abderhalden and Brockmann (22) that, when the N-terminal residue of a peptide was treated with phenylisocyanate and the resulting phenylisocyano (PTC) peptide exposed to cyclizing conditions, i.e., HCl in anhydrous media, the N-terminal residue would split off as the phenylhydantoin and leave the residual peptide intact. Edman proposed the use of phenylisothiocyanate for the condensation reaction as leading to more readily separated and characterized derivatives of the amino acids than the corresponding phenylisocyano compounds, and of HCl in nitromethane rather than the methanol-HCl mixture employed by Abderhalden and Brockmann. Theoretically the Edman procedure has some advantages over the Sanger procedure. In the latter, the N-terminal DNP derivative is removed only after complete hydrolysis of the peptide bonds. In the former, the phenylthiocarbamyl derivative of the N-terminal residue is cleaved to the free phenylthiohydantoin (PTH) without breaking the other peptide bonds of the chain so that the process can be repeated, one residue at a time, from the N-terminal end of the chain, as in the accompanying reaction. As the terminal amino group is progressively substituted by

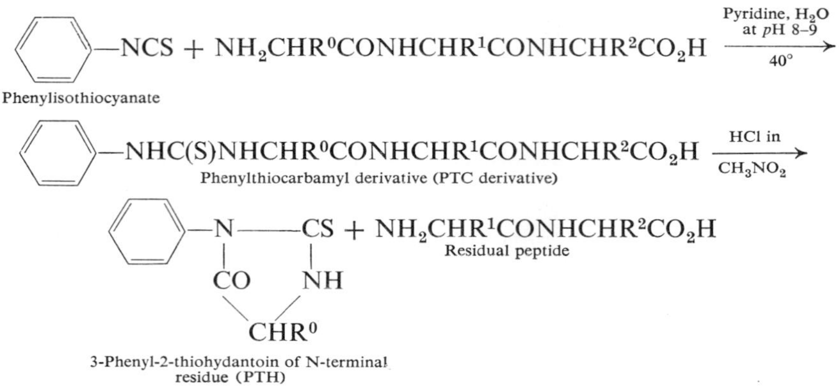

$$\text{C}_6\text{H}_5\text{—NCS} + \text{NH}_2\text{CHR}^0\text{CONHCHR}^1\text{CONHCHR}^2\text{CO}_2\text{H} \xrightarrow[40°]{\text{Pyridine, H}_2\text{O at } p\text{H 8–9}}$$

Phenylisothiocyanate

$$\text{C}_6\text{H}_5\text{—NHC(S)NHCHR}^0\text{CONHCHR}^1\text{CONHCHR}^2\text{CO}_2\text{H} \xrightarrow[\text{CH}_3\text{NO}_2]{\text{HCl in}}$$

Phenylthiocarbamyl derivative (PTC derivative)

$$\text{C}_6\text{H}_5\text{—N}\underset{\underset{\text{CHR}^0}{\diagdown\;\diagup}}{\overset{\displaystyle|\qquad|}{\underset{\text{CO}\quad\text{NH}}{}}}\text{CS} + \text{NH}_2\text{CHR}^1\text{CONHCHR}^2\text{CO}_2\text{H}$$

Residual peptide

3-Phenyl-2-thiohydantoin of N-terminal residue (PTH)

reaction with the thioisocyanate, the basicity of the reaction mixture decreases, and alkali must be added to maintain a slightly alkaline pH; by measuring the alkali consumption the end point of the reaction and its stoichiometry can be independently apprehended (213). The PTH derivatives of most of the amino acids are soluble in non-aqueous solvents, and hence may be separated by extraction into such solvents from the more water-soluble residual peptide or protein. The phenylthiohydantoin so removed is heated with baryta (214) to convert it to the free amino which is then identified by paper chromatography (210); under these conditions, arginine was found as ornithine, asparagine and glutamine as the corresponding dicarboxylic acids, serine in part as alanine, and threonine in part as butyrine and glycine (210, 215; cf. 216). 6N HCl at 150° has also been used to regenerate the amino acids from the phenylthiohydantoins, but here again serine, threonine, cysteine, cystine, and, of course, tryptophan, were destroyed or only partly regenerated (217).

As experience was gained with the PTH procedure, various problems emerged, some of which were common with the Sanger DNFB procedure, and others which were peculiar to itself alone. The cyclization and splitting procedure involving the PTC derivatives of glycine and proline is accompanied by no such losses as those encountered in the isolation of the DNP derivatives of these amino acids, but in both procedures the derivatives of serine, threonine, and cysteine are obtained in poor yield because of decomposition, and in both procedures the DNP and PTC derivatives of ε-NH$_2$-lysine, of histidine, and of arginine because of their dipolar ion nature are not extractable with non-aqueous solvents.

Edman (210) employed nitromethane·HCl as a cyclizing medium and solvent inasmuch as water was unnecessary, possibly destructive to the remaining peptide bonds, and conducive to back-reaction whereby the ring could be reopened. Frequently the PTC-amino acid and peptide or protein would form an insoluble mass from which the former was extractable with some difficulty, and Edman introduced the use of glacial acetic acid saturated with HCl gas (about 2M) at 37° as a more effective solvent and cyclizing system (135). Dioxane·HCl was subsequently employed by Fox and his collaborators (cf. 218). An aqueous medium, however, was found to yield good results when a 0.05M aqueous citrate buffer at pH 4.5–5.0 was used simultaneously with a continuous extraction of the PTH-amino acid into benzene as fast as it was formed (219). Phenylthiocarbamyl-protein has been maintained in aqueous acid solutions when sufficient guanidine hydrochloride was added both to increase the solubility and to denature the protein (220, 221). Another procedure has been to use strips of filter paper as carriers for the protein (221); the distribution of phenylthiocarbamyl-protein over the large surface renders it accessible to the phenylisothiocyanate reagent at each reaction stage without interference with the thiohydantoin which is split off at each stage and extracted from the paper. In this manner, several consecutive steps have been carried through with several phenylthiocarbamyl proteins, yielding, for protamine, the N-terminal sequence prolylarginylarginyl; for β-lactoglobulin, leucylleucylvalyl; for myoglobin, glycylleucylseryl; and, for lysozyme, lysylvalyl(missing)glycyl (221). With the A and B chains of insulin, i.e., the glycyl and phenylalanyl chains, respectively, the same sequences were found as had been observed by Sanger when he used the DNFB procedure (see below). Equine hemoglobin revealed six valine N-terminal residues per mole of protein (222), a result in agreement with that arrived at by the DNFB procedure (40), whilst the N-terminal residue sequence of equine myoglobin was found to be glycylleucyl; attempts to carry the procedure beyond these residues were not successful. More recent work (178) suggests that the N-terminal residues of bovine, human, and equine hemoglobins may be four in number, e.g., two valine and two methionine in the bovine, and four valine each in the human and equine hemoglobins. The four N-terminal residues may be representative of chains attached or related to the four heme residues in these proteins.

Illustrative procedure (cf. 210). DL-Alanylglycine (0.29 g. or 0.2 millimole) is dissolved in 10 ml. of a 1 : 1 mixture of pyridine and water. To this solution, warmed to 40°, is added N NaOH to a pH of 9. With constant stirring 0.48 ml. of phenylisothiocyanate (0.4 millimole) is added together with sufficient N NaOH to maintain the pH at 9. When no more alkali is necessary the reaction is at an end. About 2.4 ml. of the sodium hydroxide solution is consumed in the reaction. The solution is evaporated *in vacuo* nearly to dryness, and the residue is repeatedly extracted with benzene to remove any pyridine and excess reagent remaining. N HCl is added to pH 3, whereby the phenylthiocarbamyl-DL-alanylglycine separates as a rapidly hardening oil. It is filtered off and recrystallized from ethanol-water; m.p. 153°. The product (0.28 g.) is suspended in 20 ml. of anhydrous glacial acetic acid which had previously been saturated at room temperature with dry HCl gas, and the mixture is warmed at 37° for 15 min. There separates almost immediately a precipitate of glycine hydrochloride whilst the phenylthiocarbamyl-DL-alanine cyclizes to the hydantoin and passes into solution. The yield of glycine·HCl after filtration and washing with acetic acid·HCl is about 90% of the theoretical. The mother liquor is evaporated to dryness *in vacuo*, the residue taken up in hot acetic acid, filtered, and water added to crystallization. Crystals of the phenylthiohydantoin emerge and are recrystallized from absolute ethanol; m.p. 184–185°.

With alanylleucylglycine treated in the same way as the above, no precipitate appears as a result of the cyclizing reaction. The glacial acetic acid HCl solution is taken to dryness *in vacuo*, the residue extracted with water, filtered, and an aliquot of the aqueous solution subjected to paper chromatography. Only a single ninhydrin spot appears, namely, that due to leucylglycine. The insoluble residue is the phenylthiohydantoin of alanine. The aqueous solution of the leucylglycine can be treated in turn at pH 9 with phenylisothiocyanate, precipitated on acidification to pH 3 as the phenylthiocarbamyl derivative, and subjected to simultaneous cyclization and cleavage; the hydantoin obtained is that of leucine.

The reference amino acid hydantoins are made in the same way as described above for the peptide, the cyclization of the phenylthiocarbamyl derivative being effected at pH 1 or less at refluxing temperature for 2 hours. In the case of the phenylthiocarbamyl derivatives of arginine and of histidine, precipitation is carried out at pH 7 and at pH 3.5, respectively. Melting points for the phenylthiohydantoin of glycine is 245–248°, of L-leucine 178°, of L-isoleucine 173–175°, of L-proline 179°, of L-tyrosine 216°, and of L-arginine 180°.

In order to avoid the step of converting the isolated phenylthiohydantoin of the N-terminal amino acid residue into the free amino acid by the hot baryta or acid treatment with all the losses and side reactions attendant thereto, several procedures were developed almost simultaneously to characterize the hydantoin by paper chromatography. Sjöquist (223) used starch-impregnated paper with the iodine-azide reaction to spot the divalent sulfur atom of the *thiol* radical of the phenylthiohydantoin. Landmann, Drake, and Dillaha (224) cleaved the N-terminal phenylthiocarbamyl residues of several proteins in dioxane·HCl media and spotted the resulting phenylthiohydantoins on paper with the aid of Grote's reagent. This reagent consists of a mixture of sodium nitroprusside, hydroxylamine hydrochloride, and sodium bicarbonate, to which a little bromine is added, and it yields various colors with the phenylthiohydantoins of different amino acids. Thus the PTH derivative of alanine is blue, aspartic acid blue, arginine blue-violet, cystine blue, glycine red, glutamic acid blue, histidine yellow, isoleucine blue, leucine blue, lysine blue-violet, methionine blue, phenylalanine blue to yellow, proline blue to purple, serine red, threonine blue, tyrosine yellow, tryptophan yellow, and valine blue. Together with the determined R_F values in various solvents and the specific colors developed, the identification of various PTH derivatives as they were successively split off the N-terminal end of the proteins could be readily accomplished. In this manner the following N-terminal amino acid residues were observed: for salmine, proline; for β-lactoglobulin, leucine; for glutathione, glutamic acid; for insulin, glycine and phenylalanine; and, for lysozyme, lysine. The N-terminal sequence for lysozyme was reported to be lysylvalylphenylalanylglycylseryl, the first four components of which were in agreement with the results of Schroeder (91) and of Acher et al. (185), who used the DNFB procedure; the fifth residue, however, was claimed by Acher et al. (185) to be arginyl rather than seryl.

Quantitative estimation of the phenylthiohydantoins could be accomplished by absorption measurements at 267–272 mμ (178), whilst infrared measurements of these compounds have been proposed for qualitative identification and semiquantitative estimation (225). The separation of the phenylthiohydantoins in pure form has been accomplished on Hyflo Super-Cel as inert support, with heptane–amyl acetate as moving phase and aqueous formic acid as the stationary phase; the effluent from the column

TABLE 16-5

R_F Values for the Phenylthiohydantoins of Various Amino Acids in Different Solvents (227)

R_F in Solvent

Phenylthiohydantoin of	A[a]	B[b]	C[c]
Glycine	0.09	0.63	0.62
Alanine	0.18	0.77	0.78
Valine	0.53	0.87	0.89
Isoleucine	0.65	0.92	0.91
Leucine	0.67	0.92	0.92
Serine	0	0.47	0.14
Threonine	0	0.55	0.34
Proline	0.83	0.90	0.89
Hydroxyproline	–	–	0.54
Methionine	0.45	0.89	0.88
Cysteic acid	0	0	0
Phenylalanine	0.57	0.90	0.91
Tyrosine	0	0.75	0.41
Tryptophan	0.12	0.86	0.82
Aspartic acid	0	0.38	0.16
Glutamic acid	0	0.56	0.27
Asparagine	0	0.31	0.08
Glutamine	0	0.41	0.15
Histidine	0	0.22	0
Arginine	0	0.11	0
ε-Derivative of lysine	0.05	0.85	0.81

[a] o-Xylene-formamide.
[b] n-Butyl acetate–propionic acid–formamide.
[c] n-Heptane–ethylene chloride–formic acid.

is led through a spectrophotometric cell with quartz windows and the absorption measured at 269 mμ (226). Generally, however, paper chromatography has been preferred to column separations, and the most exact study of the former procedure has been described by Edman and Sjöquist (227) (Table 16-5). Whatman No. 1 paper was employed, and the solvent systems so chosen that after the paper was dried no material absorbing near 270 mμ

remained. In ultraviolet light, the phenylthiohydantoins appeared on the paper as black spots against a red background, and by this means their R_F values were determined and their positions located prior to cutting out the spots and eluting the product with ethanol. The lower limit of sensitivity on the paper is approximately 1 μg. of phenylthiohydantoin per spot; for quantitative determination at least 5 μg. per spot is needed. The yield of the extracted spot is about 75–100%, the lower extraction values being generally obtained with phenylthiohydantoins possessing the higher R_F values.

At 269 mμ, the molar extinction for most of the amino acid phenylthiohydantoins in ethanol is 14,000 to 16,000; the ε-derivative of lysine is, however, closer to 29,000, whilst the derivative of tryptophan is about 19,700. Reference solutions are prepared in ethylene chloride (0.5–1.5 mg. per ml.), except for the derivatives of arginine and of histidine which, because of their poor solubility in this solvent, are prepared in hexanol. The reference compounds themselves have been prepared by a number of investigators (210, 228, 229), inclusive of the difficult serine, threonine, cystine, and glutamine phenylthiohydantoin derivatives.

At just about this time, Reith and Waldron (230) proposed the use of colored thiohydantoins to assist in the identification of the various members of this class of substances, and introduced the use of 4-dimethylamino-3:5-dinitrophenylisothiocyanate (DDPT) for this purpose. The reagent combined readily with the N-terminal amino group of amino acids or peptides in bicarbonate-water-acetone solution at pH 8–9 and readily yielded deep orange-colored thiohydantoins in acetic acid. When optically active amino acids were employed, the process of cyclization resulted in extensive racemization. The amino acids were regenerated from the DDP-thiohydantoins by treatment with the acid mixture of Hanes, Hird, and Isherwood (154) and were chromatographed on paper. The sequence of amino acids in the tripeptide alanylglycylglycine was successfully determined in the usual manner of splitting one residue off at a time from the N-terminal position, but the reagent has not yet had extensive trials with any protein.

The yield of the phenylthiohydantoin as it is separated from the reaction mixture is frequently not quantitative. For this reason, and to avoid the steps involved in the separation and subsequent indentification, Fox and his colleagues introduced the use of subtractive methods. The method is to an extent analogous to that of the nitrous acid procedure whereby the amino acid known to be present beforehand, and subsequently lost as a result of the nitrous acid treatment, must have been in a position in which its amino group was free to react with the reagent, i.e., N-terminal. Fox, Hurst, and Itschner (218) treated the synthetic peptide valylglycylphenylalanine with phenylisothiocyanate, cyclized the derivative in dioxane HCl, and hydrolyzed part of the residual peptide in HCl. Glycine and phenylalanine were quantitatively recovered, with only 2% of valine present. The other part of the residual peptide was treated in the same way, and from the residual fraction only phenylalanine was recovered. The procedure was then applied to the determination of the N-terminal sequence of lysozyme by De Fontaine and Fox (231). Part of the protein was first hydrolyzed with 6N HCl to the constituent amino acids, which were determined by microbiological methods. The other part was treated with phenylisothiocyanate to make the PTC-lysozyme, followed by selective fission of the N-terminal PTC residue in dioxane·HCl. After extraction of the thiohydantoin, part of the residual protein was hydrolyzed to the constituent amino acids, which were again quantitatively determined by microbiological methods. The remainder of the residual protein was again treated with phenylisothiocyanate and the process repeated. A picture of what occurred is found in the data by De Fontaine and Fox (231) in Table 16–6. The N-terminal sequence as

TABLE 16–6

N-Terminal Sequence of Lysozyme by the Subtractive Procedure (231)[a]

Number of Residues per Mole of Lysozyme
(14,700 molecular weight)

Amino Acid	Before PTC	After 1st PTC	After 2nd PTC	After 3rd PTC
Alanine	9.9	9.7	9.9	–
Arginine	11.0	11.0	11.0	–
Glycine	11.3	11.5	11.3	11.3
Histidine	0.9	0.9	0.8	0.9
Isoleucine	6.7	6.7	6.7	7.2
Leucine	6.9	6.9	6.6	6.6
Lysine	6.1	*4.9*	5.0	–
Methionine	2.4	2.2	2.1	2.1
Phenylalanine	3.1	3.0	3.1	*2.1*
Proline	2.2	1.9	1.9	1.8
Serine	9.4	9.5	9.5	9.4
Threonine	7.4	7.2	7.0	7.3
Tyrosine	2.8	2.9	2.8	3.0
Valine	5.5	5.3	*4.0*	3.8

[a] PTC = phenylisothiocarbamyl. The residues lost are italicized for ready identification.

observed was lysylvalylphenylalanyl, in agreement with the findings of others by different approaches. The fact that the microbiological methods employed required that the amino acids tested be of the L-configuration provided the first evidence that the components of this N-terminal sequence were indeed L in optical configuration.

A similar type of study by McClure, Schieler, and Dunn (111) on bovine plasma albumin led to the finding of two or three N-terminal aspartic acid residues, one methionine, one histidine, and an undetermined number of N-terminal alanine residues. These observations are at variance with those of Desnuelle, Rovery, and Fabre (152), who found a single N-terminal aspartic acid residue by the DNFB procedure, and of Thompson (232), who noted by means of the Edman procedure a single N-terminal sequence in this protein consisting of aspartylthreonyl. In addition to this, Thompson (232) observed that human plasma albumin possessed a single N-terminal sequence beginning with aspartylalanyl. A single N-terminal aspartyl residue in human serum albumin was also noted by Caputo and Zito (cf. 232); in contrast with bovine serum albumin which possesses a C-terminal alanine residue (152), the corresponding human protein possesses a C-terminal leucine. As in the cases of the insulins and vasopressins of different species, analogous proteins may vary from each other in one or more residues.

A particularly interesting illustration of the solution of a problem which occurred when a protein was inert toward the Edman reagent is that involved in the finding of the N-terminal residue of chymotrypsinogen. Rovery, Fabre, and Desnuelle (233) could find no N-terminal residue in this protein, and, inasmuch as Gladner and Neurath (234) could find no C-terminal residue either, through the use of carboxypeptidase, it was tentatively considered that chymotrypsinogen was completely cyclic. When, however, the disulfide linkages were oxidized by treatment with performic acid (235), it was possible to find one N-terminal residue of cysteic acid per mole of protein. The procedure was as follows. DNP-Chymotrypsinogen was oxidized with performic acid and completely hydrolyzed with HCl. The hydrolysate was extracted with ether, the aqueous layer evaporated to dryness, and the residue taken up in water and passed through a Dowex 50 column in the acid phase to remove free amino acids and ε-DNP-lysine. The yellow-colored material still in solution was identified by paper chromatography as DNP-cysteic acid. The amount of this substance was determined after corrections were introduced through recovery experiments of DNP-cysteic acid added to unoxidized DNP-chymotrypsinogen followed by hydrolysis and the normal procedure of isolation. Although the correction appeared to be of a considerable order of magnitude, it was clear that the protein contained close to one N-terminal residue of a half-cystine per mole of protein as follows:

$$\underset{\underset{CH_2S-SCH_2CH(NH_2)CO_2H}{|}}{NH_2CHCONHCHR_1CONHCHR_2CO\ .-\ ..}$$

It would therefore be expected that the Edman procedure would fail with this structure, for no thiohydantoin extractable into ethyl acetate would be likely to form (134). Hence the oxidative rupture of the disulfide bridge by performic acid, prior to the application of the Edman procedure, is that necessarily employed. Oxidative rupture of *interchain* disulfide bonds leads to fragmentation of the protein (e.g., insulin); if no fragmentation of a cystine-containing protein occurs under these conditions, it may be assumed that the disulfide bonds are *intrachain*, i.e.,

$$\begin{array}{c} CH_2S\text{---}SCH_2 \\ | \qquad\qquad | \\ \text{---NHCHCONHCHCO---} \end{array}$$

and the protein is composed of a single chain as in prolactin (187).

Phenylisothiocyanate may on occasion produce the complication of combining not only with the N-terminal residue, but also with the nitrogen of glycine in the interior of the chain (178). The phenylthiohydantoin of glycine alone of the common amino acids yields a red color when treated with alkaline oxidizing agents, and by these means may be separately distinguished (178).

The N-terminal position of proline in trichloroacetic acid-denatured tobacco mosaic virus protein, earlier observed by the DNFB procedure, was confirmed by the Edman method (178). As a control, ovalbumin, which revealed in the native state no N-terminal residue by either Sanger or Edman procedures, was denatured with trichloroacetic acid; still no N-terminal residue was found after this treatment. Rhodopsin apparently possesses neither N-terminal nor C-terminal residues (236).

MISCELLANEOUS PROCEDURES. The use of the pipsyl procedure for end-group analysis was applied by Udenfriend and Velick (237) to insulin and to hemoglobin with somewhat limited results, for only one glycine and one phenylalanine N-terminal residue were found per mole (12,000) of the former protein where Sanger had found two each, and only two N-terminal valine residues were found per mole (66,000) of hemoglobin where Porter and Sanger had found six, and Schramm et al. had found four (178). A study of rabbit muscle aldolase with this procedure revealed the presence of at least two chains each with N-terminal proline residues. It is of interest to follow this procedure as illustrated by the subsequent study of salmine (238). The possibility that proline might be the N-terminal amino acid residue in the chain of this protamine had been suggested in 1931 when Waldschmidt-Leitz, Zeigler, Schaffner, and Weil (239) found no free α-amino groups to react with nitrous acid. Salmine was thereupon converted in pyridine solution to the N-terminal pipsyl derivative by treatment with a benzene solution of I^{131}-labeled pipsyl chloride. The derivative was dissolved in dilute HCl, treated with S^{35} labeled pipsylproline, concentrated HCl added, and the whole hydrolyzed by reflux. The ether-soluble fraction was then purified by countercurrent distribution and chromatographed on paper. The single band for pipsylproline showed a constant ratio of S^{35} to I^{131} along the direction of migration, and clearly demonstrated that the N-terminal residue of salmine was indeed proline. To test for end groups in proteins by this procedure it is necessary to have a variety of pipsyl amino acids on hand, each to be tried in turn.

The use of the very mild guanidination agents S-methylisothiourea and O-methylisourea, which function by a molecular rearrangement, appeared to be suitable for N-terminal residue analysis but the results were disappointing from this standpoint. The reaction

$$-NH_2 + CH_3OC(NH_2)(=NH) \rightarrow -NHC(=NH)NH_2 + CH_3OH$$

was found to be applicable to proteins (240), and, on treating human serum albumin with O-methylisourea, Hugues, Sarof, and Carney (241) were able to introduce a number of guanidino groups into the molecule. The amino groups converted to guanidino groups were thus freely reactive in the protein and were derived from the ε-carbon position of the presumably internal lysine residues. These residues were thereby converted from lysine to homoarginine. The procedure was extended to globin, casein, lysozyme, ovalbumin, thyroglobulin, and gelatin (242), chymotrypsinogen (243), ribonuclease (244), and various hormone proteins (245). On hydrolysis, paper chromatography revealed in each case the presence of homoarginine and little if any lysine; lysozyme which possesses an N-terminal lysine residue would have been expected to reveal the corresponding α,ε-diguanidino-*n*-caproic acid if the isourea reagent had reacted with the α- as well as with the ε-amino group, but no such compound was found. No inactivation of any of the biologically active proteins could be observed (cf. 245).

The use of highly purified aminopeptidase to degrade proteins from the N-terminal position has been proposed by Smith (246, 247), and has been applied to *β*-lactoglobulin, insulin, the oxidized B chain of insulin, and mercuripapain. In each case free amino acids were produced, but the actual sequences were not apprehended. Some 120 residues of the original 180 in papain could be removed by aminopeptidase without affecting the enzymic property of the residual protein (toward benzoyl-L-arginine amide); the active site of the enzyme is thus considerably removed from the N-terminal position. Not all proteins in the native state are susceptible to the action of the enzyme, e.g., human serum albumin must first be oxidized with performic acid (247). By the use of a less pure preparation of amino-polypeptidase, Waldschmidt-Leitz and Mindemann (248) were enabled to detect N-terminal residues of several proteins. Thus, for beef insulin, they found glycine and phenylalanine; for beef globin, valine and methionine; for horse myoglobin, glycine; for edestin, glycine and leucine; for gliadin, isoleucine; for amandin and excelsin, glycine; for arachin, arginine; and, for conarachin, isoleucine.

C-Terminal Sequences

These have been apprehended by a variety of chemical reactions and by a single enzymic reaction, namely, that involving pancreatic carboxypeptidase. Good qualitative agreement has generally been obtained where at least two different methods were employed with the same protein, although the results might quantitatively be considerably at variance. Only a few of the several chemical reactions have been successfully applied to the determination of the C-terminal amino acid residues of proteins, for reasons which will be apparent as these reactions are described.

CHEMICAL REACTIONS. The earliest of the procedures developed to determine the C-terminal residues of peptides, and one still employed with some measure of success with proteins, is that of Schlack and Kumpf (64). The method was based on the reaction of acetic anhydride and ammonium thiocyanate with the N-acylated peptide whereby a terminal hydantoin was formed and split off, leaving the residual N-acyl peptide for a subsequent reaction. The illustration given by Schlack and Kumpf was as follows:

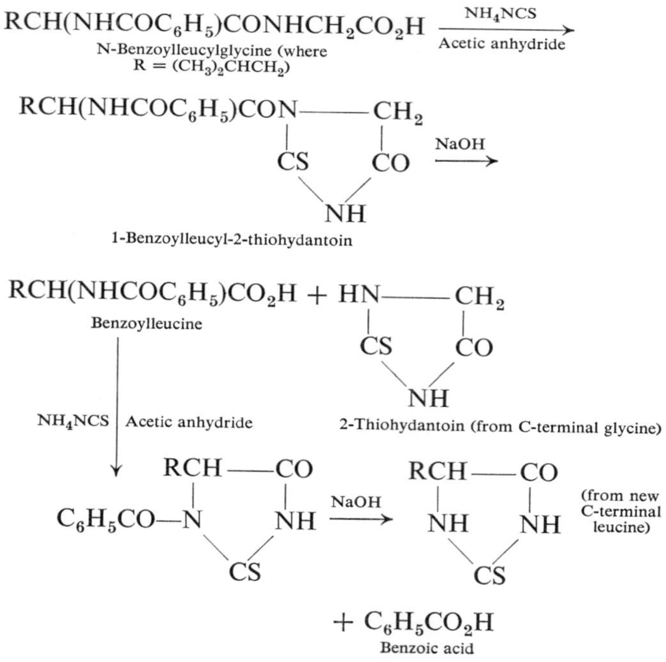

$$\text{RCH(NHCOC}_6\text{H}_5\text{)CONHCH}_2\text{CO}_2\text{H} \xrightarrow[\text{Acetic anhydride}]{\text{NH}_4\text{NCS}}$$

N-Benzoylleucylglycine (where R = (CH$_3$)$_2$CHCH$_2$)

$$\text{RCH(NHCOC}_6\text{H}_5\text{)CON}\underset{\underset{\text{CS}}{|}}{\underline{\hspace{2em}}}\underset{\underset{\text{CO}}{|}}{\text{CH}_2} \xrightarrow{\text{NaOH}}$$

$$\text{NH}$$

1-Benzoylleucyl-2-thiohydantoin

$$\text{RCH(NHCOC}_6\text{H}_5\text{)CO}_2\text{H} + \text{HN}\underset{\underset{\text{CS}}{|}}{\underline{\hspace{2em}}}\underset{\underset{\text{CO}}{|}}{\text{CH}_2}$$

Benzoylleucine

NH

2-Thiohydantoin (from C-terminal glycine)

↓ NH$_4$NCS | Acetic anhydride

$$\text{C}_6\text{H}_5\text{CO}-\text{N}\underset{\underset{\text{CS}}{\diagdown\diagup}}{\underset{|}{\overset{|}{\text{RCH}\underline{\hspace{1em}}\text{CO}}}}\text{NH} \xrightarrow{\text{NaOH}} \underset{\underset{\text{CS}}{\diagdown\diagup}}{\underset{|}{\overset{|}{\text{RCH}\underline{\hspace{1em}}\text{CO}}}}\text{NH} \quad \text{(from new C-terminal leucine)}$$

$$+ \text{C}_6\text{H}_5\text{CO}_2\text{H}$$

Benzoic acid

SEQUENTIAL ANALYSIS OF PEPTIDES

The method was successfully employed by Nicolet (65) to prove that glycine was the C-terminal residue of glutathione:

$$\text{Glutathione} + NH_4SCN + (CH_3CO)_2O \longrightarrow$$

```
         NH—CO                          NH—CO
          |   |                          |   |           C₆H₅CHO
          CS  |        CH₃COSCH₂        CS  |          ————————→
          |   |          |   |           |   |
   CH₃CON———CHCH₂CH₂CONHCHCO N———CH₂
         Bis-thiohydantoin of S-acetylglutathione
```

```
                    NH—CO
              NaOH   |   |
          ————————→  CS  |
              HCl    |   |
                    NH—C═CHC₆H₅
          Benzalthiohydantoin (could only have
          been derived from a C-terminal glycine)
```

The procedure was applied by Waley and Watson (249) to insulin which had been acetylated to protect the amino and hydroxylic groups, and a C-terminal thiohydantoin was split off which on hydrolysis to the free amino acid was identified by paper chromatography as alanine. The yield was low and the results merely qualitative. Turner and Schmertzler (250) used the method to detect a C-terminal alanine residue in ovalbumin (which was in error) and a C-terminal phenylalanine residue in ovomucoid. The latter finding was in agreement with the observation by Pénasse, Jutisz, Fromageot, and Fraenkel-Conrat (251), who used a reduction procedure (see below). Further application of the method to insulin revealed a C-terminal asparagine residue (252). By this time, a more critical view of the method was being taken. Baptist and Bull (253) studied the completeness of extraction into ethyl acetate of the thiohydantoin split off from the peptide chain, and found that it was considerably less than quantitative for the derivatives of most of the amino acids, and that correction factors of a considerable order of magnitude would be necessary in order to obtain quantitative results. The method appeared to fail completely to detect C-terminal aspartic and glutamic acids, lysine, and arginine (253, 254), as well as C-terminal serine and proline (252). C-Terminal asparagine was, however, detectable, as noted in the case of insulin (252), and C-terminal alanine was again found by this procedure in the same protein (253). The thiohydantoins had been hydrolyzed by acid and by alkali to yield the free amino acids, on occasion with considerable losses and evidence of conversions (i.e., serine to alanine, and threonine to glycine and butyrine; cf. 216, 254), and the introduction of a direct chromatographic method to distinguish the various thiohydantoins on paper promised to simplify the procedure. Edward and Nielson (255) devised such a procedure in which the thiohydantoin spots on paper were revealed by a spray of the phosphotungstic acid reagent of Folin and Denis (256) which was followed by exposure to fumes of ammonia: the thiohydantoins of tyrosine and tryptophan yielded green colors, whereas those of the other amino acids were blue. By this procedure a C-terminal leucine was revealed in lysozyme, and a C-terminal alanine residue in bovine plasma albumin (cf. 152). C-Terminal proline with its α-imino group cannot be determined by this procedure.

Part of the difficulty in using the Schlack and Kumpf procedure was due to the necessity of forming the thiohydantoin from the acylated peptide or protein and ammonium thiocyanate at an elevated temperature. In order to effect this formation at an ordinary temperature, Kenner, Khorana, and Stedman (257) replaced the ammonium thiocyanate with diphenylphosphoroisothiocyanatidate. This reagent reacted in acetonitrile or dimethylformamide solution with the triethylamine salt of N-acylated peptides to give 1-acyl-2-thiohydantoins in good yield:

$$\text{RCONHCHR}^1\text{COO}^- + (\text{C}_6\text{H}_5\text{O})_2\text{P}(=\text{O})\text{NCS} \longrightarrow \text{RCONHCHR}^1\text{CO}_2\text{P}(=\text{O})(\text{C}_6\text{H}_5\text{O})_2\text{NCS}$$

$$\text{RCOO}^- + \underset{\underset{\text{NH}}{\diagdown\diagup}}{\overset{\text{HN}\text{------}\text{CHR}^1}{\underset{\text{CS}\quad\text{CO}}{|\quad\quad|}}} \xleftarrow{\text{OH}^-} \underset{\underset{\text{NH}}{\diagdown\diagup}}{\overset{\text{RCON}\text{------}\text{CHR}^1}{\underset{\text{CS}\quad\text{CO}}{|\quad\quad|}}} \longleftarrow \text{RCONHCHR}^1\text{CONCS} + {}^-\text{OP(O)(C}_6\text{H}_5\text{O})_2$$

This variation has not yet been applied to proteins.

At the same time that Schlack and Kumpf announced their thiohydantoin procedure, Bettzieche and Manger (258) reported a method of determining the C-terminal residue of peptides which was based on the Grignard reaction. The peptide was esterified, the ester treated with phenylmagnesium bromide and subsequently treated with acid to yield the appropriate ketone. Thus, in the case of glycylalanine, the sequence of reactions was

$$\underset{\text{Glycylalanine}}{\text{NH}_2\text{CH}_2\text{CONHCH(CH}_3)\text{CO}_2\text{H}} \xrightarrow[\text{HCl}]{\text{C}_2\text{H}_5\text{OH}} \underset{\text{Glycylalanine ester}}{\text{NH}_2\text{CH}_2\text{CONHCH(CH}_3)\text{CO}_2\text{C}_2\text{H}_5} \xrightarrow{\text{C}_6\text{H}_5\text{MgBr}}$$

$$\text{NH}_2\text{CH}_2\text{CONHCH(CH}_3)\text{C(C}_6\text{H}_5)_2\text{OH} \xrightarrow{\text{HCl}} \underset{\text{Glycine}}{\text{NH}_2\text{CH}_2\text{CO}_2\text{H}} + \text{NH}_3 + \underset{\substack{\text{Diphenylacetone}\\\text{(from C-terminal}\\\text{alanine)}}}{\text{CH}_3\text{C}(=\text{O})\text{CH}(\text{C}_6\text{H}_5)_2}$$

The next contribution to the problem of determining the C-terminal residue in peptides by means of chemical procedures was the elegant one devised by Bergmann and Zervas (259) which rested essentially on the utilization of the azide method. The procedure applied to removing the C-terminal residue as the aldehyde with one less carbon atom from benzoylglycylalanylleucylglutamic acid was as follows:

SEQUENTIAL ANALYSIS OF PEPTIDES

Benzoylglycylalanylleucylglutamic acid + diazomethane ⟶

dimethyl ester $\xrightarrow{NH_2NH_2}$

dihydrazide $\xrightarrow{HNO_2}$

diazide $\xrightarrow{C_6H_5CH_2OH}$

dibenzyl urethane $\xrightarrow[H_2O(\Delta)]{H_2(Pd)}$

benzoylglycylalanylleucine amide + β-aminopropionaldehyde (from glutamic acid residue)
↓
hydrazide
↓
azide
↓
benzyl urethane $\xrightarrow[H_2O(\Delta)]{H_2(Pd)}$

benzoylglycylalanine amide + *isovaleraldehyde* (from leucine residue)
↓
hydrazide
↓
azide
↓
benzyl urethane $\xrightarrow[H_2O(\Delta)]{H_2(Pd)}$

benzoylglycine amide + *acetaldehyde* (from alanine residue)

To illustrate the procedure in greater detail, the last of these reactions is essentially given by

$C_6H_5CONHCH_2CONHCH(CH_3)CONH_2$ $\xrightarrow[HNO_2]{NH_2NH_2}$ $C_6H_5CONHCH_2CONHCH(CH_3)CON_3$ $\xrightarrow{C_6H_5CH_2OH}$
Benzoylglycylalanine amide   Benzoylglycylalanine azide

$C_6H_5CONHCH_2CONHCH(CH_3)NHCO_2CH_2C_6H_5$ $\xrightarrow{H_2(Pd)}$
Benzyl urethane

$C_6H_5CONHCH_2CONHCH(CH_3)NH_2 + (C_6H_5CH_3 + CO_2)$ $\xrightarrow{\Delta}^{H_2O}$
Benzoylglycylalanamine

$C_6H_5CONHCH_2CONH_2 + CH_3CHO + NH_3$
Benzoylglycine amide + *acetaldehyde* (from alanine residue) + ammonia

A reaction analogous to this was developed many years later by Wieland and Fritz (260), who employed the Lossen degradation (261). The method in outline is shown at the top of the next page.

An odd but interesting method of determining the C-terminal residue of tripeptides was found by Lichtenstein to consist of dissolving them directly in heated β-naphthol; the N-terminal residue and its neighbor form a diketopiperazine which is readily separated by its alcohol solubility from the C-terminal amino acid which is liberated in the free state (262). Another procedure applicable to tripeptides was developed by Schlögl and Wawersich (263) which rested in part on the hydrazine procedure of Akabori, Ohno, and Narita (264), and by which all three members of the tripeptide could be simultaneously identified. According to this procedure, if an

$$\underset{\text{Benzoyl peptide ester}}{C_6H_5CONHCHR^1CONHCHR^2CO_2CH_3} + NH_2OH \xrightarrow{\text{Na-methylate}}$$

$$\underset{\text{Benzoyl peptide hydroxamic acid}}{C_6H_5CONHCHR^1CONHCHR^2CONHOH} + \underset{\text{Benzoyl chloride}}{C_6H_5COCl} \xrightarrow{\text{NaOH}}$$

$$\underset{\text{Benzoyl peptide hydroxamic acid benzoate}}{C_6H_5CONHCHR^1CONHCHR^2CONHOCOC_6H_5} \xrightarrow{\text{NaOH}}$$

$$\underset{\text{Bis-carbonyl derivative}}{(C_6H_5CONHCHR^1CONHCHR^2NH)_2CO} + 2C_6H_5CO_2Na + CO_2 + H_2O$$

$$\downarrow 7\% \text{ HCl}$$

$$\underset{\text{Benzoylamino acid amide}}{C_6H_5CONHCHR^1CONH_2} + CO(NH_2)_2 + R^2CHO$$

$$\downarrow \text{NaOH}$$

$$\underset{\text{Benzoylamino acid}}{C_6H_5CONHCHR^1CO_2H} + NH_3$$

N-carbobenzoxy tripeptide is heated for several hours with hydrazine, the peptide bonds are broken, the C-terminal residue appears as the free amino acid, the N-terminal residue appears as the dihydrazide, and the middle residue appears as the amino acid hydrazide. Thus

$$C_6H_5CH_2OCONHCHR^1CONHCHR^2CONHCHR^3CO_2H + NH_2 \cdot NH_2 \rightarrow$$
$$NH_2NHCONHCHR^1CONHNH_2 + NH_2CHR^2CONHNH_2 + NH_2CHR^3CO_2H$$

$$\downarrow \text{HCl} \qquad\qquad \downarrow \text{HCl}$$

$$NH_2CHR^1CO_2H \qquad NH_2CHR^2CO_2H$$

The excellent method of Akabori, Ohno, and Narita (264) for the determination of C-terminal amino acids rested upon the reaction of the peptide or protein with anhydrous hydrazine to form the hydrazides of all the amino acids, except the C-terminal one which was released in the free state. Reaction of the hydrazides with benzaldehyde resulted in the separation of the very insoluble benzilidene compounds. The procedure was subsequently improved by Ohno (265), who treated the products with DNFB to form di-DNP derivatives of the amino acid hydrazides which could be readily separated from the C-terminal DNP-amino acid with free carboxyl group by extraction of the latter into aqueous sodium bicarbonate from an ethyl acetate solution of the reaction mixture. The C-terminal DNP-amino acid could then be identified by chromatography and estimated spectrophotometrically.

$$NH_2CHR^1CO \cdots NHCHR^nCO_2H \xrightarrow{NH_2NH_2}$$

$$NH_2CHR^1CONHNH_2 + \cdots + NH_2CHR^nCO_2H \xrightarrow{DNFB}$$

$$DNP \cdot NHCHR^1CONHNH \cdot DNP + \cdots + DNP \cdot NHCHR^nCO_2H$$

With this procedure, Ohno obtained a yield of leucine as the C-terminal residue of lysozyme which was very close to one mole per mole of protein.

Illustrative procedure (cf. 265). Hydrazine hydrate (commercial 60%) is distilled at normal temperature and pressure until a constant-boiling residue remains. This is about 97% hydrate with b.p. 119.5°. The residue is then distilled *in vacuo* over KOH pellets, the product collected, and redistilled over KOH pellets; bath temperature is 95–105°, pressure about 20 cm. Hg. The distillate (about 99% pure and amounting to some 17% of the starting material) is sealed in glass ampoules.

Ten milligrams of lysozyme is introduced into a tube with a partly constricted neck, and dried for several hours *in vacuo*. Anhydrous hydrazine (0.3 g.) is introduced into the tube, the neck is sealed off in the oxygen flame, and the entire tube and contents heated for 12 hr. at 100°. At the end of this period of time, the tube is cooled, opened, and the contents dried *in vacuo* in a desiccator over concentrated H_2SO_4. The residue is dissolved in 10 ml. of 5% $NaHCO_3$ and the solution shaken with an ethanolic solution of 0.1 g. of dinitrofluorobenzene in 20 ml. for 3 hr. in a dark room. At the end of this period, the mixture is evaporated *in vacuo* to dryness, and the residue taken up in 30 ml. of water. $0.1 N$ Hydrochloric acid is added to an acid reaction and the mixture is extracted several times with ethyl acetate. The combined ethyl acetate extracts are then shaken out several times with 4% $NaHCO_3$, whereby the DNP-leucine which is the C-terminal residue together with α,α-di-DNP-aspartic acid (α-hydrazide) is extracted into the aqueous layer, all other di-DNP-amino acid hydrazides being left in the ethyl acetate layer. The combined bicarbonate extracts are washed by shaking twice with ethyl acetate, the organic solvent layer being discarded each time. The aqueous layer is then acidified and extracted with ethyl acetate several times, the combined ethyl acetate extracts dried over anhydrous Na_2SO_4, filtered, and evaporated to dryness. The residue is sublimed *in vacuo* at 60° to remove dinitrophenol. The final residue is taken up in a little acetone and chromatographed on Whatman No. 1 paper (Section 15-5 and Table 15-8). Two yellow-colored spots are observed, one of which corresponds with DNP-leucine. It is eluted with ethanol and its absorption at 360 mμ determined in a spectrophotometer. From the molar extinction at the same wavelength of known samples of DNP-leucine run at the same time, the amount of the DNP-leucine extracted from the paper is determined.

Ohno extended the procedure to characterize the mode of linkage of the acidic residues in peptides (266). The various possibilities were distributed as follows, and illustrated by the use of glutamyl residues, although analogous results were obtained with aspartyl.

a. C-Terminal aspartyl or glutamyl residues (only glutamyl given as example).

$$\underset{\mid}{-\mathrm{NHCHCO_2H}} \atop \mathrm{CH_2CH_2CO_2H} \xrightarrow{NH_2 \cdot NH_2} \underset{\mid}{\mathrm{NH_2CHCO_2H}} \atop \mathrm{CH_2CH_2CO_2H} \xrightarrow{DNFB} \text{DNP-aspartic or glutamic acid}$$

b. α-Aspartyl or α-glutamyl residues.

$$\underset{\underset{CH_2CH_2CO_2H}{|}}{-NHCHCO-} \xrightarrow{NH_2 \cdot NH_2} \underset{\underset{CH_2CH_2CO_2H}{|}}{NH_2CHCONHNH_2} \xrightarrow{DNFB}$$

$$\underset{\underset{CH_2CH_2CO_2H}{|}}{DNP-NHCHCONHNH-DNP}$$

α,α-Di-DNP-aspartic or glutamic acid-α-hydrazide

c. β-Aspartyl or γ-glutamyl residues; or C-terminal asparagine or glutamine (only glutamyl or glutaminyl given as example).

$$\underset{\underset{CH_2CH_2CO-}{|}}{-NHCHCO_2H}$$
or
$$\underset{\underset{CH_2CH_2CONH_2}{|}}{-NHCHCO_2H} \xrightarrow{NH_2 \cdot NH_2} \underset{\underset{CH_2CH_2CONHNH_2}{|}}{NH_2CHCO_2H} \xrightarrow{DNFB}$$

$$\underset{\underset{CH_2CH_2CONHNH-DNP}{|}}{DNP-NHCHCO_2H}$$

α,β-Di-DNP-aspartic acid-β-hydrazide
α,γ-Di-DNP-glutamic acid-γ-hydrazide

d. Asparaginyl or glutaminyl residues (only glutaminyl given as example).

$$\underset{\underset{CH_2CH_2CONH_2}{|}}{-NHCHCO-} \xrightarrow{NH_2 \cdot NH_2} \underset{\underset{CH_2CH_2CONHNH_2}{|}}{NH_2CHCONHNH_2} \xrightarrow{DNFB}$$

$$\underset{\underset{CH_2CH_2CONHNH-DNP}{|}}{DNP-NHCHCONHNH-DNP}$$

α,α,β-Tri-DNP-aspartic acid-dihydrazide
α,α,γ-Tri-DNP-glutamic acid-dihydrazide

These approaches were used to determine the C-terminal sequence in lysozyme (267) which turned out to be aspartyl(or asparaginyl)glycylalanylasparaginylleucine. It is apparent from this procedure that the free, C-terminal amino acid is exposed to boiling, anhydrous hydrazine for several hours. Studies on the stability of the various free amino acids under these conditions indicated that good recoveries were obtained with glycine, alanine, valine, leucine, serine, proline, tyrosine, methionine, and histidine; poor recoveries (<50%) were obtained with tryptophan, cystine, and aspartic and glutamic acids, as well as with arginine which, however, was recoverable as ornithine. These recovery conditions were, of course, not quite comparable with those involved in the state of the C-terminal residue hydrazinolyzed from a protein, but the recovery in the latter case was apparently never less than in the former. An improvement in the yields of the C-terminal residues was accomplished by the use of hydrazine sulfate which allowed the reaction to be conducted at 60° instead of 100° (268). In this reaction a mixture of 10 mg. of the peptide, 26 mg. of dried hydrazine sulfate, and 0.2 ml. of 100% hydrazine (distilled into the tube) was heated in a sealed tube at 60° for 16 hours. The excess hydrazine was evaporated over concentrated H_2SO_4 *in vacuo*, the residue dissolved in 1 ml. of dilute HCl, the solution shaken with 0.4 ml. of benzaldehyde for 2 hours, and the aqueous solution, separated by centrifugation, was made alkaline with sodium carbonate solution and shaken with DNFB at 40°. After extracting with ether to remove excess DNFB, the solution was acidified and the DNP-amino acid(s) (C-terminal) extracted into ethyl acetate. Evaporation of the solvent *in vacuo* was followed by extraction of the residue into a toluene–phosphate–*t*-amyl alcohol solvent and by one-dimensional paper chromatography. The spots were qualitatively identified, and then quantitatively determined by elution with bicarbonate followed by measurement of the optical density at 360 mμ (385 mμ for DNP-proline), the extinction of known DNP-amino acids for standard comparison substances being used.

One of the most striking applications of the hydrazine procedure has been that involving the tobacco mosaic virus protein. Knight (269) had shown that each virus particle contains approximately 2900 peptide-chain subunits. When the virus was treated with carboxypeptidase, about 2900 residues of threonine (and only threonine) were liberated per mole of protein (270). When the protein prepared from the virus was subjected to hydrazinolysis for about 10 hours, and the DNP derivative of the free C-terminal amino acid identified and quantitatively determined by paper chromatography (271), one equivalent of threonine was found per 18,000 g. of the virus protein (272). The C-terminal position of about 2800 threonine residues was established. Almost simultaneously, Braunitzer (273) reported substantially the same findings, with some 2300 moles of C-terminal threonine residues present per mole of virus.

Again at about the same time, Niu and Fraenkel-Conrat (272) and Braunitzer (274) sought the C-terminal sequence of the tobacco mosaic virus, and arrived at substantially the same conclusions. After the virus protein was acted upon by carboxypeptidase and all the C-terminal threonine completely hydrolyzed off, the residual protein was treated with hydrazine to yield a single C-terminal alanine residue (2300–2500 residues per mole). With shorter periods of hydrazinolysis, evidence accrued for the presence in very small amounts of a DNP-peptide which on hydrolysis yielded DNP-proline, alanine, and the expected degradation products of DNP-proline, namely, dinitrophenol and proline (272, 274). Although rather meager on this basis alone, the evidence suggested that the C-terminal sequence might be -prolylalanylthreonine. This sequence was confirmed on more substantial grounds when the native virus was treated with hydrazine for 3-6 hours to yield one tripeptide and one dipeptide. The DNP derivatives of these compounds were shown by hydrolysis to be constituted as DNP-prolylalanylthreonine and DNP-alanylthreonine, respectively (274). The sum of the free threonine plus the two peptides was 2500 moles per mole. After 3-4 hours of hydrazinolysis the yield per mole of virus was 1000–1100 moles of threonine, 100 moles of dipeptides, and 250 moles of tripeptides; after 6 hours, there were approximately 2000 moles of threonine and 150 moles of both peptides. The reason for the lower yields of peptides may be attributed to the instability of the bond involving threonine (274).

Application of the hydrazinolysis procedure by Akabori and his associates to taka-amylase indicated the presence of three C-terminal residues, namely, serine, glycine, and alanine (275). Together with data indicating that this protein possesses one N-terminal alanine residue (275), it would appear that some branching structure must exist, involving perhaps a glutamic γ- or aspartyl β-bond, as follows:

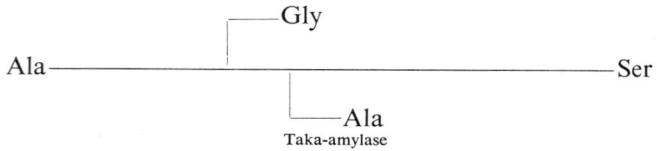
Taka-amylase

Steric factors apparently play some as yet not clearly delineated role in hydrazinolysis (268).

A method analogous to hydrazinolysis was that of ammonolysis, proposed in 1955 by Chambers and Carpenter (276). Thus, on cleavage of the bonds in a peptide sequence by strong ammonia at elevated temperature, it would be expected that amino acid amides would be derived from all residues whose carboxyl group participated in a peptide bond, whereas the C-terminal residue would appear in the free state, and indeed glycylphenylalanine on heating in liquid ammonia solution at 100° for 48 hours yielded glycine amide and free phenylalanine. Separation of NH_4^+ and the amides from the C-terminal free amino acid could be readily accomplished by passing the solution over an Amberlite XE-64 resin column (basic ion exchanger), the free amino acid, except arginine, being quantitatively retained on the column whilst everything else passed through. The method appears to be simple, but some C-terminal amino acids such as glycine are readily converted to the corresponding amide by the treatment described (276).

Khorana (277) developed a procedure for C-terminal analysis based on the use of the aromatic carbodiimides, such as $RN{=}C{=}NR$ (where R is *p*-tolyl, etc.) which react with carboxylic acids at room temperature to yield acylureas. Thus

$$\text{BzNHCH}_2\text{CONHCH}_2\text{CO}_2\text{H} + \text{RN}{=}\text{C}{=}\text{NR} \longrightarrow$$
Benzoylglycylglycine
(where R = *p*-tolyl, and Bz = C_6H_5CO)

$$\text{BzNHCH}_2\text{CONHCH}_2\text{C}({=}\text{O})\text{NRCONHR} \xrightarrow{\text{Alkali}}$$

$$\text{BzNHCH}_2\text{CO}_2\text{H} + \text{RNHCONHCH}_2\text{CONHR}$$
Benzoylglycine   N-*p*-Tolylcarbamylglycine-*p*-toluidide

The method has not been applied to proteins, and, because of the tendency of the products of the reaction to form difficultly separable mixtures with the starting material, its range of usefulness is limited.

Two subtractive methods have been suggested for C-terminal residue analysis. One of them (278), based upon the Dakin and West reaction (279), consisted in heating the peptide with acetic anhydride and pyridine; the C-terminal residue was converted as follows:

$$-\text{NHCHR}^1\text{CONHCHR}^2\text{CO}_2\text{H} \xrightarrow[\text{Acetic Anhydride}]{\text{Pyridine}} -\text{NHCHR}^1\text{CONHCHR}^2\text{COCH}_3 + \text{CO}_2$$
Peptide   Peptide ketone

Hydrolysis and analysis of the peptide before and after treatment revealed by comparison the missing residue, which must have been C-terminal. The method may be useful in cases where the C-terminal residue is serine and hence almost impossible to detect by other, more positive means. The other subtractive method was proposed by Boissonnas (280); it consisted of the successive degradation of the C-terminal residues of the peptide through the agency of anodic oxidation. The method itself was based on the findings by Linstead, Shephard, and Weedon (281) that electrolysis of N-acylglycine or N-acylalanine in methanol gave N-methoxymethyl- and N-1′-methoxyethylamides, respectively, in good yields. The C-terminal residue analysis was conducted by submitting the carbobenzoxy or DNP-peptide, whose

$$\text{RCONHCH}_2\text{COOH} \rightarrow \text{RCONHCH}_2\text{OCH}_3$$

amino acid composition was known, to anodic oxidation. A sample was hydrolyzed, and analysis revealed a missing constituent which must have been the C-terminal residue whose carboxyl group had been converted to methoxyl. The product of the first oxidation was then hydrolyzed to a limited extent and the residue submitted to another anodic oxidation; again analysis revealed the missing new C-terminal residue. An unexpected complication in the procedure occurs in the case of residues of phenylalanine and tyrosine, for these residues disappear as a result of anodic oxidation even when not C-terminal (282). This phenomenon renders the method inapplicable to peptides containing these amino acids within the chain.

One of the most straightforward of the chemical methods for C-terminal residue analysis was that developed by Fromageot and his collaborators (283). It consisted essentially of a reduction by means of lithium aluminum hydride of the free carboxyl groups of the protein suspended in N-ethylmorpholine. The protein was then hydrolyzed, the C-terminal residue as the primary β-amino alcohol separated on silica and charcoal columns, and identified by means of paper chromatography. Quantitative determination was accomplished through the use of periodic acid (284), and per mole of insulin (6000) one C-terminal alanine residue and one C-terminal glycine residue were reported.

$$RCONHCHR^nCO_2H \xrightarrow{LiAlH_4} RCO_2H + NH_2CHR^nCH_2OH$$

$$NH_2CHR^nCH_2OH + HIO_4 \longrightarrow HIO_3 + R^nCHO + HCHO + NH_3$$

Shortly after the announcement by Fromageot et al. (283) of their reduction procedure, Chibnall and Rees (285) described a reduction method based on the reaction of lithium borohydride on the protein *ester*. Earlier Karrer, Portmann, and Suter (286) had demonstrated that this reaction occurs readily with amino acid esters and leads directly to the preparation of amino alcohols. Insulin was dissolved in ethanol·HCl and treated with excess diazomethane whereby the free α-, β-, and γ-carboxyl groups were converted to the esters. After treatment with lithium borohydride, the protein was hydrolyzed, and it would be expected that internal glutamyl residues would appear as δ-hydroxynorvaline, aspartyl as the lactone of γ-hydroxybutyrine, and the C-terminal residue as the β-amino alcohol; internal asparagine and glutamine residues would not be affected, so that on acid hydrolysis they would appear in the hydrolysate as free aspartic acid and glutamic acid, respectively. In this fashion, Chibnall and Rees reported that insulin contained two asparaginyl, one aspartyl, four glutaminyl, and three glutamyl residues, and, using the periodate procedure, one C-terminal alanine and about 0.5 C-terminal glycine residues.

Shortly thereafter, Sanger and Thompson (287) found that carboxypeptidase liberated asparagine readily from acetyl insulin, and that only alanine and asparagine were the C-terminal residues of insulin. Chibnall and Rees (288) thereupon reinvestigated the reductive procedure on insulin and found that the insulin molecule should contain three glutaminyl, four glutamyl, and three asparaginyl residues. One amide group must therefore be present as a C-terminal residue. Although internal aspartic acid residues appear after reduction and hydrolysis of the protein as the lactone of γ-hydroxybutyrine (γ-hydroxy-α-amino-*n*-butyric acid), C-terminal asparagine residues would appear after the same treatment as the lactone of γ-hydroxy-β-amino-*n*-butyric acid. Consequently, insulin was reduced, the hydrolysate passed through a Dowex 2 column which would retain the lactone while permitting the β-amino alcohols to pass through, and both fractions were subsequently tested with periodate. One equivalent per mole of the hydroxyamino acid and one of alaninol were found. It would appear that the earlier observations of the apparent presence of glycinol, and to some extent of leucinol (cf. 288), arose from some splitting of the insulin chain during the reduction, perhaps at a glycylseryl bond. Appreciable fission of peptide bonds in the interior of the chain when lithium borohydride was employed with lysozyme was shown by Crawhall and Elliott (289).

A serious complication might be expected to occur if a C-terminal residue happened to be cystine or cysteine, for the corresponding alcohol is difficult to prepare by the reduction of the corresponding esters with metal hydrides (289). The necessary comparison compounds (cystinol and cysteinol) were finally prepared by treating the ester with methyl benzimidate, reducing the resulting 4-ethoxycarbonyl-2-phenylthiazoline with $LiAlH_4$, and refluxing the 4-hydroxymethyl-2-phenylthiazoline, so formed, with acid to yield— after oxidation—cystinol hydrochloride in crystalline condition (290).

Subsequent studies with the lithium aluminum hydride reagent revealed one C-terminal phenylalanine residue in ovomucoid (250, 251), and two C-terminal alanine residues in pepsin (291), as confirmed by carboxypeptidase action. One C-terminal asparagine residue (as β-amino-γ-hydroxy-n-butyric acid) was found in insulin (292). The action of lithium aluminum hydride on hemoglobin and on edestin led to γ-amino-δ-hydroxy-n-valeric acid, which is suggestive of the presence of γ-glutamyl linkages in these proteins (293, 294). The possibility of intramolecular rearrangement is, however, not excluded (see below). A very considerable aid to the separation and identification of the amino alcohols was afforded by coupling them with DNFB to form the corresponding DNP-amino alcohols (295–297). The DNP-amino alcohols can be separated on paper (297), or first fractionated on Hyflo-Supercel columns impregnated with a partially hydrolyzed polymer of chlorosiloxane (inverse phase chromatography) and then separated and identified on paper (291, 295). Quantitative assay may be effected by spectrophotometric measurement at 350 mμ (291).

An interesting stepwise determination of C-terminal residues in peptides was described by Leggett Bailey (298), who used aluminum hydride after noting that lithium aluminum hydride possessed some tendency to reduce peptide carbonyl groups. Reduction of peptide esters was carried out at $-40°$ in the medium aluminum chloride–tetrahydrofuran to yield the corresponding β-hydroxyalkylamide. Thus

$$RCONHCHR^1CONHCHR^2CO_2Et \xrightarrow{AlH_3} RCONHCHR^1CONHCHR^2CH_2OH$$
(where R is p-tosyl)

In the presence of $POCl_3$ or thionyl chloride, a rearrangement occurs to yield a β-amino ester (cf. 299) which can be further reduced with aluminum hydride to give the free amino alcohol and residual peptide in a form prepared for a further rearrangement:

$$\xrightarrow{POCl_3} RCONHCHR^1CO_2CH_2CHR^2NH_2 \cdot HCl \xrightarrow{AlH_3}$$
$$RCONHCHR^1CH_2OH + HOCH_2CHR^2NH_2$$
(from C-terminal residue of the original peptide)

In order to be quite sure that only the C-terminal esterified amino acid is reduced, with no accompanying reduction of peptide bonds, it is preferable to employ lithium borohydride. This reagent, in contrast to lithium aluminum hydride, has little effect on free carboxyl groups. Where possible, the esterification of the C-terminal residue is best carried out by the use of diazomethane, the N-terminal amino group being previously blocked by a DNP group (300).

A procedure which, although it does not reveal the nature of the C-terminal residue in peptides or proteins, can, however, reveal whether one or more C-terminal carboxyl groups are present is that developed by Chappelle and Luck through the use of N-bromosuccinimide (301). This reagent when warmed at 30° and pH 4.7 with amino acids *or peptides* produces a quantitative decarboxylation (Chapter 12), the liberated CO_2 being measured manometrically in a Warburg respirometer. All protein-bound amino acids, with the following exceptions, yield 1 mole of CO_2 per mole of compound: tyrosine and cystine, 1.25 moles, and aspartic acid 2.0 moles. Care must therefore be taken when a protein yields 2 moles of CO_2 per mole, to distinguish between a single chain ending in a C-terminal aspartic acid residue, or two chains each ending in an amino acid which yields 1 mole of CO_2. With this procedure, Chappelle and Luck determined the number of C-terminal carboxyl groups in the following proteins, the number enclosed in parentheses being the currently accepted molecular weight of each protein: insulin (6000) 2, chymotrypsinogen (25,000) 1, α-lactalbumin (15,000) 1, β-lactoglobulin (35,400) 1, papain (20,700) 2, α-chymotrypsin (21,600) 1, δ-chymotrypsin (21,600) 2, lysozyme (17,200) 1, and trypsin (23,800) 1. The reagent also possesses the capacity of rapidly cleaving tryptophan-containing peptides at the bond involving the tryptophan carboxyl group (301a).

ENZYMIC REACTIONS. Nature has provided a relatively specific enzyme elaborated by the pancreas which possesses the capacity to hydrolyze amino acids from the C-terminal position of the peptide chain. This enzyme, called carboxypeptidase, whose properties have been described in excellent reviews by Smith (302) and by Neurath and Schwert (303), has been of considerable value in the C-terminal analysis of peptides and of proteins. The use of an enzyme in this connection possesses both virtues and handicaps. Theoretically it is ideal for the most part, for among the most characteristic features of carboxypeptidase, as its name implies, is its attack exclusively on the peptide bond linking the amino group of an amino acid possessing a free α-carboxyl group. Again, the reaction is conducted as all enzymic reactions must be, under mild conditions not likely either to disrupt other bonds in the peptide chain or to degrade the amino acid which is liberated, and thus permit, without the use of the considerable correction factors associated with entirely chemical procedures, a truly quantitative analysis of the reaction. The drawbacks involved in the use of this enzyme are many. The rate at which the C-terminal residue is released will depend upon the structure of this amino acid, and to some extent upon the structure of the amino acid adjacent to it. If the C-terminal residue is proline or hydroxyproline which is bound to the chain by a peptide bond containing no hydrogen atom, the enzyme will not act. The mere presence of a proline residue is a deterrent to the action of the enzyme, for, even if the C-terminal residue is one which is ordinarily rapidly hydrolyzed, this rate will be considerably diminished if the adjacent residue is that of proline (or of cysteic acid, for that matter (115)). The enzyme is inert toward linkages involving D-amino acids, but it is not likely that such residues will be found in most proteins. However, where partial acid hydrolytic procedures have been employed over a long period in order to degrade a protein into smaller fragments, the use of carboxypeptidase to determine the sequence in these fragments is problematical if the residues have been racemized. The enzyme is also inert if the C-terminal residue is an amide, for example, the C-terminal glycine amide in oxytocin.

As the C-terminal residue is being hydrolyzed off, the enzyme does not stand politely by until this residue is completely removed before starting its hydrolytic action on the next, newly exposed C-terminal residue, but attacks the latter, and likewise the still newer C-terminal residue, until a C-terminal residue is finally reached which is resistant to the enzyme and further action ceases. This successive, and nearly simultaneous, action of carboxypeptidase along the peptide chain starting with the C-terminal residue is not too great a handicap to interpretation if the first C-terminal residue is hydrolyzed at a rate in good excess of that of the second, or third, etc., C-terminal residue. An illustration of this approach is afforded by the experiments of Locker on the action of carboxypeptidase on tropomyosin (304) (Figure 16–1). The relative rates of liberation of the residues which are related to their sequence along the chain indicate that this protein possesses a single C-terminal isoleucine residue, that serine is adjacent thereto, followed by threonine, methionine, by a second isoleucine, and by alanine, the C-terminal sequence being -alanylisoleucylmethionylthreonylserylisoleucine. Myosin was likewise found to contain a C-terminal isoleucine residue, and actin a C-terminal phenylalanine with sequence -histidylisoleucylphenylalanine (304). Hydrazinolysis of the proteins confirmed the assignment of the C-terminal residues as given. None of these muscle proteins appears to contain an N-terminal amino acid residue.

A similar study of sheep ACTH (α-corticotropin) after digestion with carboxypeptidase (305) yielded rate curves which indicated that a C-terminal phenylalanine residue was quantitatively released during the first 4 hours of digestion, glutamic acid appearing at a slower rate and leucine at a still slower rate. The C-terminal sequence in this hormone was therefore assumed

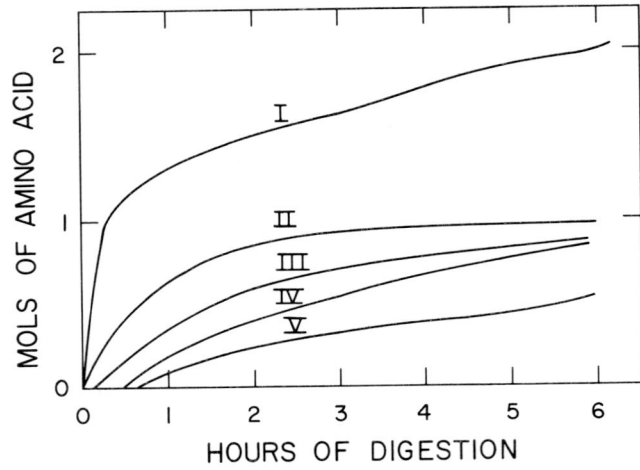

Figure 16-1. Liberation of amino acids during digestion of tropomyosin at pH 8.0 and 37° by carboxypeptidase. Unit weight of protein taken as 53,000. Aliquots of digest removed at intervals of time, shaken with a cation exchange resin, the latter eluted with $5N$ NH$_4$OH, and the eluate (after removal of ammonia) chromatographed on paper, using phenol-NH$_3$ and butanol–acetic acid as solvent pairs with subsequent resolution of leucine-isoleucine or valine-methionine with t-amyl alcohol–water. Curves: I, isoleucine; II, serine; III, threonine; IV, methionine; and V, alanine. Locker, R. H., *Biochim. et Biophys. Acta*, **14**, 533 (1954).

to be -leucylglutamylphenylalanine. When the reaction stopped short with the liberation of the three amino acid residues alluded to, it was suspected that the preceding residue might be proline; this was indeed found to be the case when a subsequent pepsin digest of the hormone yielded the tetrapeptide prolylleucylglutamylphenylalanine (306). Of some interest was the fact that the carboxypeptidase-digested hormone, from which the -leucylglutamylphenylalanine C-terminal sequence had been digested off was found to retain full adrenal-stimulating potency.

Illustrative procedure (cf. 305). Crystalline carboxypeptidase (Chapter 20) is washed with distilled water just prior to use to remove traces of adsorbed amino acids, and is brought into solution at pH 8.0 as follows. About 1 mg. of the enzyme protein is suspended in 1 ml. of distilled water containing 1% NaHCO$_3$ (0.1 ml.) at 0–4°. Addition with stirring of 0.05–0.10 ml. of 0.1N NaOH brings the enzyme into solution, whereupon the pH is quickly adjusted to about 8.0 by addition of about 0.1 ml. of 0.1N HCl. In order to inactivate any contaminating endopeptidases, the enzyme solution is treated with a solution of diisopropyl phosphofluoridate in dry propan-2-ol (15 μl. of 0.1M per mg. of enzyme).

Crystalline insulin (6 mg. or 1 micromole) is incubated with 0.15 mg. of carboxypeptidase in 2.0 ml. of solution at pH 8.0 and 40°. A constant pH is maintained at 8.0 by addition from time to time of 0.05N NaOH from a microburette. Aliquot parts of the digest equivalent to 0.2 to 0.5 micromoles of substrate are withdrawn after suitable periods of time and pipetted directly into a series of tubes containing hydrochloric acid at pH 3, resulting in termination of the enzyme reaction. Each aliquot portion is separately treated with an excess of DNFB solution with vigorous stirring, and the pH is then raised to 9.0 and maintained at this level for 90 min. at 40° with good stirring. The contents are then transferred quantitatively to a centrifuge tube and the excess of DNFB reagent removed by continuous extraction with ether. 6N Hydrochloric acid is added to a pH of 1.0, and the DNP derivatives of the amino acids released by carboxypeptidase action are extracted into ether. (The DNP derivatives of histidine and of arginine are not extracted by ether, and would remain in the aqueous acid layer. If C-terminal, however, these residues would not be hydrolyzed off by carboxypeptidase in any event and are therefore of no interest in this connection.) The combined ether extracts are dried over Na$_2$SO$_4$, evaporated to dryness, and the residue is sublimed *in vacuo* at 60° in order to remove dinitrophenol. The residual DNP-amino acids are dissolved in a small volume of acetone and chromatographed on Whatman No. 1 paper as described in Section 15-5. Spots corresponding to the DNP derivatives of the amino acids released by carboxypeptidase action are separately eluted with ethanol and estimated from readings of the molar absorption at 360 mμ. Each aliquot portion taken from the enzyme digest is subjected to this procedure, and in this way the rates of release of amino acids from protein or peptide substrates are obtained. When the rate of release reaches a constant value, it may be assumed that one equivalent of a C-terminal amino acid has been obtained. Blank values are noted by performing the various reactions in the absence of enzyme, but in the presence of protein substrate and one equivalent of each of the free amino acids shown to be C-terminal; in this way corrections are introduced for losses during extraction, subsequent chromatography, and elution of the DNP-amino acid spots. An overall recovery of 80–85% is normally obtained. Inasmuch as the dinitrophenylation reaction also results in substitution on the free N-terminal residue of the residual protein, it is possible to wash this material with ethyl acetate to remove any traces of DNP-amino acids, to hydrolyze it with 6N HCl for 16 hr. at 105° (in vacuo, 1 ml. of acid for 0.2–1.0 micromole of protein substrate), and to extract the cooled hydrolysate with ether to remove the DNP N-terminal amino acid(s) then revealed by paper chromatography as above.

The time relations for the release of the C-terminal residues from insulin indicate that release of alanine is effected completely in about 4 hours (approximately 1 mole per mole unit = 6000) of insulin, whereas asparagine is released much more slowly. This could have suggested that alanine is the C-terminal residue and asparagine the penultimate residue, but separate studies on the individual A and B chains of insulin revealed only alanine from the B chain and only asparagine from the A chain. In addition to DNP-asparagine, the paper chromatograms reveal almost invariably the presence of DNP-aspartic acid due to the loss of the amide group as a result of the commercial preparation of insulin which involves the use of hot acid.

An alternative experimental procedure which does not involve dinitrophenylation is to remove the aliquots from the enzymic digest and to pipette them directly into a tube containing 50 mg. of wet Dowex 50 resin (H^+). The enzymic reaction is thereby terminated and the free amino acids taken up by the resin. The resulting suspension is shaken mechanically for 1 hour, the supernatant fluid removed with a fine pipette, the resin washed several times by decantation with water (by which some glutamic acid, if present, may be lost), and the amino acids adsorbed on the resin eluted with $5N$ NH_4OH. The combined ammonia eluates are evaporated to dryness, and the residue taken up in a little water and chromatographed on paper (usually phenol-NH_3 as solvent system, and ninhydrin-spotting).

When less than stoichiometric amounts of the successive amino acid residues appear, as in Figure 16–1, a reasonable interpretation of the C-terminal sequence can be attempted, provided that some assurance is available that these fractional quantities do not simply represent contaminants of the protein substrate. When, however, the second residue is of such a nature that it can be hydrolyzed at a rate equal to or greater than that of the first, the two adjacent residues may appear simultaneously, and the results appear to be interpretable on the basis of two C-terminal chains when only one in fact may exist. Thus, in the case of the hypophyseal growth hormone somatropin, studied by Harris, Li, Condliffe, and Pon (307), carboxypeptidase splits off from this protein two equivalents of the very susceptible phenylalanine residues, and the question arises whether a single chain is present with a C-terminal sequence of phenylalanylphenylalanine or whether two chains are present with a single C-terminal phenylalanine residue in each. The fact that this protein reveals two N-terminal residues, namely, alanine and phenylalanine, suggests that two chains are present, but nevertheless this does not yield an answer to the question raised, for one chain may still possess the phenylalanylphenylalanine C-terminal sequence whereas the other may possess a resistant residue. (The presence of only a single N-terminal phenylalanine residue in human somatropin has recently been reported (307a).) A similar problem emerged in the study of actin (304) from which phenylalanine and isoleucine were liberated by carboxypeptidase at nearly equal rates; in this case, the problem was solved through the use of hydrazine, which showed that phenylalanine was the true C-terminal residue. The dilemma posed does suggest that terminal residue analysis is unequivocal only when applied to proteins known to possess a single chain, or else to those proteins with more than one chain in cases where the chains can be separated and studied individually, as in the case of insulin. Without these restrictions, other complications in interpretation can arise. Thus pepsin has only one N-terminal leucine residue but two C-terminal alanine residues (291), whilst β-lactoglobulin has three N-terminal leucine residues (174) but only two C-terminal residues, one being isoleucine and the other histidine (308). There may be structural differences in the same protein at its N-terminal and C-terminal extremes, but such an interpretation is as yet difficult to establish.

Carboxypeptidase action on a protein may slow down not only because a resistant residue is encountered, but also because the amino acids accumulated by the successive action of the enzyme inhibit its further activity. Addition of fresh enzyme has little effect in this respect, and, as shown by Gladner and Neurath (309), the reaction products must be removed in order for the enzymic hydrolysis to proceed further. Another factor which must be taken into account is the possibility that the carboxypeptidase employed, although recrystallized several times, may yet be contaminated by traces of other proteolytic pancreatic enzymes such as trypsin and chymotrypsin, as well as by proteases of bacterial origin due to the lack of sterilizing conditions during the preparation of the enzyme. These enzymes may hydrolyze interior-peptide linkages of the protein substrate and expose thereby new C-terminal residues to the action of the carboxypeptidase, yielding results at once confusing and deceptive. The contaminating proteases can, however, be inactivated by incubating the carboxypeptidase preparation with di-isopropylfluorophosphate (DFP) which apparently has no effect upon the activity of the carboxypeptidase itself. Steinberg had reported that the action of carboxypeptidase on ovalbumin yielded evidence of one C-terminal residue of alanine per mole of protein, but that DP-carboxypeptidase, with unaltered activity toward chloroacetyl-L-tyrosine, had no effect on ovalbumin (310); it appeared that the original carboxypeptidase preparations may have been contaminated with a DFP-sensitive protease which hydrolyzed ovalbumin somewhere in the molecule so as to expose a C-terminal alanine residue. The failure of carboxypeptidase to detect a C-terminal residue in ovalbumin now appears to be due to the presence of proline in this position (311), the peptide link involving the imino group of this compound being resistant to the action of the enzyme; the C-terminal sequence in ovalbumin determined by hydrazinolysis appears to be -valylserylproline. The C-terminal position of proline in this protein was subsequently confirmed by Akabori et al. (312). As a protein, carboxypeptidase is subject to denaturation, and as a denatured protein it is hydrolyzable not only by contaminating proteases (which can be prevented by DFP) but also by the active carboxypeptidase itself (which cannot be prevented by DFP). Thus, although native carboxypeptidase is quite stable at pH 7.5 and 25° and does not reveal appreciable autolysis (313), the presence of any denatured enzyme is occasion for attack by the active enzyme, and a mixture of amino acids will result. Prolonged digestion of a protein substrate by a carboxypeptidase preparation originally native will be accompanied by some denaturation of the enzyme, and thus to the C-terminal residues yielded by the chosen protein substrate will be added those C-terminal residues yielded by the involuntary denatured enyzme which now is also a substrate. When the protein substrate is itself a protease, such as trypsin and chymotrypsin, the situation becomes increasingly complex, and in such cases at the least the substrate itself is treated with DFP (cf. 309, 314). In some cases, the protein substrate must be denatured before carboxypeptidase will act on it (313). Fortunately, in many cases, all but the first C-terminal residue of the protein substrate appears in traces or less than stoichiometric amounts, and it is necessary to do little more than to interpret the results with caution.

One mole of diisopropylfluorophosphate combines with the hydroxyl group of one of the approximately 25 serine residues in chymotrypsin (315), and both proteolytic and esterase activities disappear in parallel fashion (316). From partial hydrolysates of the DP-chymotrypsin, Schaffer et al. (317, 318) could isolate serine and serylgylcine marked with DP. Further studies by Turba and Gundlach (319) on partial acid hydrolysates of DP^{32}-chymotrypsin revealed the presence of two peptide fragments containing serine so labeled: one was a dipeptide of serine and glycine which yielded with DNFB and subsequent hydrolysis DNP-serine, the other a tripeptide of aspartic acid, serine, and glycine which yielded with DNFB and subsequent hydrolysis DNP-aspartic acid. On the basis of these phenomena, it was concluded that the amino acid sequence in the immediate neighborhood of the reactive serine residue in chymotrypsin was -aspartyl-serylglycyl- (319). A similar study (320) resulted in the isolation of a DP^{32} peptide composed of one residue each of proline, leucine, aspartic acid or asparagine, serine, and two or three residues of glycine. No histidine residues were observed in the neighborhood of the critical serine residue, although the possibility has been proposed that the action of diisopropylfluorophosphate may actually be a two-phase process whereby the primary action is a phosphorylation of the imidazole side chain of a particular histidine residue, followed by a secondary shift of the DIP group to the hydroxyl group of the critical serine residue (321, 322). The short-range sequence Gly·Asp·(DIP)Ser·Gly seems to be common to the active sites of several esterases (cf. 322a).

The first use of carboxypeptidase as an agent for C-terminal residue analysis was made by Grassmann, Dyckerhoff, and Eibeler (66) when they found that a crude preparation of this enzyme would hydrolyze one mole of glycine from glutathione. Nineteen years later, Lens (323) incubated insulin with crystalline carboxypeptidase and reported the release of one and perhaps three mole residues of alanine. Somewhat later, Harris showed that both alanine and asparagine were simultaneously liberated by the action of carboxypeptidase on insulin, the rate of liberation of the alanine being some eight times faster than that of asparagine. After six hours of digestion at pH 7.8, the reaction was stopped by adjustment to pH 5.4, the resulting precipitate tested for insulin activity and the soluble fraction tested by paper chromatography and starch column analysis (324, 325). Alanine and asparagine were the main products in solution, with 1.9 moles of alanine and 0.4 mole of asparagine present. Hormonal activity was present in the precipitate to 80% of normal; with further incubation with carboxypeptidase and continuous loss of asparagine, the hormonal activity declined but did not vanish. Prior acetylation of insulin resulted in a much faster release of the C-terminal asparagine residue (287). The establishment of alanine and asparagine as the C-terminal residues of insulin by Sanger and Thompson (287) and by Chibnall and Rees (288) has been alluded to above. Alanine alone was released by carboxypeptidase action on the C-terminal prolyl-lysylalanine sequence of the B-chain of insulin, the reaction halting at the new, resistant prolyllysine C-terminal sequence.

The fact that some biologically active proteins through the agency of carboxypeptidase can lose their C-terminal residues without appreciable loss of biological potency was also shown in the case of the hypophyseal growth hormone (somatropin) which lost its two C-terminal phenylalanine residues (307), the tobacco mosaic virus protein which lost its C-terminal threonine (270), and crotoxin which lost its C-terminal aspartic acid (179). The retention of full hormone activity by ACTH after losing three C-terminal residues (306) has been mentioned above. It is worthy of note that the virus arising in tobacco plant leaves injected with the C-terminal threonine-less inciting virus possessed a normal C-terminal threonine residue (270). The digestion of lysozyme with carboxypeptidase led to the hydrolysis of one mole of C-terminal leucine (325, 326), with no appreciable diminution in biological activity; DNP-lysozyme yielded its C-terminal leucine residue even more readily (327). The conversion of zymogen proteins into active enzymes occurs in many cases through the loss of peptide structures (see below). Carboxypeptidase action on ribonuclease resulted in the hydrolysis of one C-terminal residue of valine, followed by a sequence of methionine, tyrosine, alanine, leucine, and phenylalanine (188). Some 15% of the total amino acids present in ribonuclease could be cleaved from the C-terminus by carboxypeptidase before any measurable inactivation occurred (328). Treatment of tobacco mosaic virus protein with chymotrypsin resulted in the splitting off of a hexapeptide from the C-terminal end which possessed the sequence threonylserylglycylprolylalanylthreonine (329);

TABLE 16-7
Terminal Residues of Various Proteins

Protein	N-Terminal Residue	Moles per Mole	Refs.	C-Terminal Residue	Moles per Mole	Refs.
Actin	None	—	(304)	Phenylalanine	1	(304)
Amylase (taka)	Alanine	1	(275)	Serine	1	(275)
				Glycine	1	(275)
				Alanine	1	(275)
Avidin	Alanine	3	(337)			
Carboxypeptidase	Asparagine	1	(190)	None	—	(313)
α-Casein	Arginine	10–11	(182)			
	Lysine	1–2	(182)			
β-Casein	Arginine	5–6	(182)			
	Lysine	2–3	(182)			
Clupein	Proline	?	(338, 163)	Arginine	?	(38)
	Alanine	?	(395)			
Collagen	None	—	(339, 340)	None	—	(340)
Conalbumin	Alanine	1	(337)			
Corticotropin	Serine	1	(509, 510)	Phenylalanine	1	(509, 510)
Crotoxin (soluble fraction)	Serine	1	(179)	Aspartic acid	1	(179)
Crystallin (lens)	Glutamic acid	1	(584)	Alanine	1	(584)
Edestin	Glycine	6	(180)			
	Leucine	1	(180)			
γ-Globulin						
Human	Aspartic acid	1	(201, 202)			
	Glutamic acid	1–2	(201, 202)			

SEQUENTIAL ANALYSIS OF PEPTIDES

Rabbit					
active	Alanine	1	(197)		
inactive	Alanine	1	(197)		
Glucagon	Histidine	1	(514)	Threonine	1	(514)
Hemoglobin					
Horse and donkey	Valine	6	(40)		
Horse	Valine	4	(178)	Histidine	2	(583)
Cow, sheep, and goat	Valine	2	(40, 178)		
	Methionine	2	(40, 178)		
Human (adult)	Valine	5	(40)	Histidine	2	(583)
Human (sickle cell)	Valine	5	(40)		
Human (adult)	Valine	4	(178)		
Human (fetal)	Valine	2–3	(40)		
Hypertensin I	Aspartic acid	1	(559)	Leucine	1	(559)
Insulin					
Ox, pig, and sheep	Phenylalanine	1	(149)	Alanine	1	(287, 288)
	Glycine	1	(149)	Asparagine	1	(287, 288, 292)
β-Lactoglobulin	Leucine	3	(174)	Isoleucine	1	(308)
				Histidine	1	(308)
α_1-Lipoprotein (human serum)	Aspartic acid	1	(192)		
β_1-Lipoprotein (human serum)	Glutamic acid	1	(192)		
Lysozyme					
Animal	Lysine	1	(157)	Leucine	1	(265)
Plant	Glycine	1	(186)		
Muscle aldolase (rabbit)	Proline	2	(237)		

TABLE 16-7 (continued)

Protein	N-Terminal Residue	Moles per Mole	Refs.	C-Terminal Residue	Moles per mole	Refs.
Myeloma serum protein No. 1	Aspartic acid	2	(202)			
Myeloma serum protein No. 2	Aspartic acid	1	(201)			
Myeloma serum protein No. 3	Glutamic acid	2	(201)			
Myeloma serum protein No. 4	Glutamic acid	2–3	(201)			
Myoglobin						
Horse	Glycine	1	(40)			
Whale	Valine	1	(341)			
Myosin	None	—	(176)	Isoleucine	1	(304)
Ovalbumin	None	—	(342)	Proline	1	(311)
Ovomucoid	Alanine	1	(337)	Phenylalanine	1	(250, 251)
"Old" yellow enzyme	Aspartic acid	?	(191)			
	Glutamic acid	?	(191)			
Oxytocin	Cystine	0.5	(520)	Glycine amide	1	(520)
Papain	Isoleucine	1	(104)			
Pepsin	Isoleucine	1	(195)	Alanine	2	(291)
Pepsinogen	Leucine	1	(195)			
Prolactin	Threonine	1	(187)			(187)
Prothrombin	Alanine	1	(558a)	Cyclic configuration	—	
Ribonuclease	Lysine	1	(178)	Valine	1	(178)
Salmine	Proline	1	(155)			

Serum albumin					
Bovine	Aspartic acid	1	(152, 232)	Alanine	1	(152)
Horse, pig	Aspartic acid	1	(152)			
Human	Aspartic acid	1	(232)	Leucine	1	(232)
Somatotropin	Alanine	1	(307)	Phenylalanine	2	(307)
Bovine	Phenylalanine	1	(307)			
Human or monkey	Phenylalanine	1	(307)	Phenylalanine	1	(307)
Subtilisin	Alanine	1	(568)			
Tobacco mosaic virus	Proline	2500	(177, 178)	Threonine	2500	(270)
Tropomyosin	None	—	(304)	Isoleucine	1	(304)
Vasopressin	Cystine	0.5	(527)	Glycine amide	1	(527)
Wool keratin	Valine	4	(181)	Glycine, alanine serine, and threonine	?	(343)
	Alanine	2	(181)			
	Glycine	8	(181)			
	Threonine	8	(181)			
	Serine	2	(181)			
	Glutamic acid	2	(181)			
	Aspartic acid	1	(181)			
Yeast triosephosphate dehydrogenase	Valine	2	(336)	Methionine	2	(335)

the threonine-less protein after carboxypeptidase treatment yielded with chymotrypsin a pentapeptide with sequence threonylserylglycylprolylalanine, thus confirming the C-terminal positions of the hexapeptide in the tobacco mosaic virus protein.

C-Terminal basic residues are hydrolyzed quite slowly by carboxypeptidase (330), and owing to this circumstance the slow attack by this enzyme on lysozyme following removal of the C-terminal leucine residue (325, 326; cf. 265, 331) suggested the presence in the intact protein of a basic amino acid next to the C-terminal leucine. This penultimate residue was finally established as arginine (332, 333).

One of the advantages of the carboxypeptidase procedure for C-terminal analysis is that the reaction can be stopped at any given time by lowering the pH of the reaction mixture analyzed. This is an important feature, for the C-terminal sequences have frequently been determined by kinetic criteria (cf. Figure 16–1). The protein present may be precipitated by trichloroacetic acid and the amino acids adsorbed onto and eluted from ion exchange resins followed by paper and column chromatography (308), or the digestion mixture may be directly stirred with a sulfonated polystyrene resin (326) which adsorbs the amino acids and does not affect the protein, thus acting in the sense of the "molecular sieve" described by Partridge (334); ammonium hydroxide is used to displace the amino acids from the resin, and the results determined by paper chromatography. The amino acids released may also be converted by the DNFB procedure to the readily identifiable DNP derivatives (305).

Carboxypeptidase has been found to be active in $6M$ urea, a solvent mixture which denatures many proteins and thereby reveals terminal residues otherwise inaccessible to the enzyme (335). Because of this fortunate circumstance, Halsey and Neurath were enabled to determine that yeast triosephosphate dehydrogenase possessed two C-terminal methionine residues (335). Some time earlier, Velick and Udenfriend (336) had noted that this protein contained two N-terminal valine residues, and it is therefore possible that two peptide chains make up the protein.

Table 16–7 describes the N-terminal and C-terminal residues of a number of proteins (337–343). Omitted from this table are data on peptides and on the zymogens and their conversion products which are collected below in a separate table.

"Carboxypeptidase-B" is a pancreatic enzyme which appears to possess the capacity of hydrolyzing C-terminal basic amino acids from peptide chains (330), and in this respect resembles the pancreatic enzyme with the older designation of protaminase. No matter what the designation may be, it is clear that this enzyme is a true exopeptidase and may be employed for C-terminal residue analysis where the residue concerned is strongly basic in nature, i.e., lysine or arginine. Another pancreatic enzyme, trypsin, is an endopeptidase whose specificity is largely concerned with the hydrolysis of linkages involving the carboxyl groups of strongly basic amino acids within the peptide chain. With the intention of bringing a hitherto resistant linkage within the scope of action of this enzyme (trypsin), Lindley (344) coupled the thiol groups of protein, or previously reduced protein, with β-bromoethylamine to form S-(β-aminoethyl)-cysteine residues. Such residues are now highly basic because of the possession of a free amino group, and are consequently hydrolyzed by trypsin at the linkages involving their carboxyl group. For the same reason, S-(β-aminoethyl)-cysteine residues, now rendered C-terminal, are hydrolyzable through the action of carboxypeptidase-B (345). This was demonstrated by the successive action of trypsin and of carboxypeptidase-B on insulin previously reduced with thioglycolic acid, the liberated S-(β-aminoethyl)-cysteine being determined by paper chromatography with Whatman No. 1 paper and n-butanol–acetic acid–water (4 : 1 : 5) as solvent; oxidation with peroxide was essential to distinguish this amino acid from lysine.

Problems of Partial Hydrolysis

CONCENTRATED ACID. The use of partial hydrolysates of proteins to prepare degradation products of proteins for sequential analysis of amino acids along the peptide chain has been alluded to above. Concentrated acid at temperatures well below the boiling has been most frequently used for this purpose. As a rule, dissolution of the protein in acid is followed in the early stages by a rapid hydrolysis of peptide bonds with a subsequent slowing down as a mixture of free amino acids and lower peptides (di- and tripeptides, mainly) is approached (346). The almost explosive character of the hydrolysis of the protein in the early stages suggests that little value can accrue from a study of the great variety of large fragments yielded in these stages, which are rarely reproducible in character or composition (347), and that more valid results are obtained from an examination of the mixture of smaller peptides which accumulate at or toward the end of the reaction. Bull and Hahn (346) have suggested that, when ovalbumin is dissolved in strong acid, about 50 bonds are rapidly split, the remainder breaking down more slowly at about one-tenth of the initial rate. The protein has approximately 400 amino acid residues, and the hydrolysate in the initial phase should contain on the average some fifty octapeptides representing 50^2 or 2500 different combinations (cf. 80). However, it is unlikely that any protein is hydrolyzed in equal segments, and, because of the unequal strength of the peptide bonds, it is more likely to be hydrolyzed in the initial stages into a mixture of larger and smaller fragments. But, even during the initial stages, the slower hydrolyses occur, and the hydrolysate is nearly completely unapproachable on an experimental level.

One of the earliest of the studies in which some quantitative knowledge of the progress of the hydrolytic reaction was sought was that of Gordon, Martin, and Synge on wool (348); the size of the peptides formed during the course of the reaction of the protein with concentrated HCl at 37° was approximated by simultaneous determinations of ninhydrin-CO_2 and amino-N on the partial and on the complete hydrolysate at various stages of the digestion. The ratio of the differences in these values, in the absence of complicating factors such as the imino group of proline, would be expected to be $2/1 = 2.0$ for a dipeptide, $3/2 = 1.5$ for a tripeptide, $4/3 = 1.33$ for a tetrapeptide, etc. Thus glycylglycine gives no ninhydrin-CO_2 and only one mole of NH_2-N; on hydrolysis, it gives 2 moles of ninhydrin-CO_2 and 2 moles of amino-N; for amino acids the ratio would be zero, and for glycylglycylproline the ratio would be 3.0. For partial hydrolysates of wool, it was found that this ratio leveled off at 1.50, for edestin at 1.48, and for gelatin (because of the high proline content) at 3.6 (348). At the termination of the reaction about one-third of the residues appeared as free amino acids, and the remainder as a mixture of lower peptides. The later study by Stein, Moore, and Bergmann (73) (cf. Table 16-1) on silk fibroin has been described above. There seems to be little doubt that the partial hydrolysates of proteins in strong acid contain an overwhelming proportion of dipeptides (cf. 69). Gordon, Martin, and Synge (348) offered an explanation of this finding based on the following: when a peptide bond has been hydrolyzed in acid medium, a free-NH_3^+ or NH_2^+ group is liberated which would repel the H^+ ion of the medium and thus stabilize the peptide bond in which the amino acid residue carrying the positively charged group is involved; in this fashion the higher peptides will have a tendency to be shortened to dipeptides. Careful studies of the rates of hydrolysis of triglycine and of diglycine under identical conditions revealed that the rate constant for the hydrolysis of the first bond to be split in the tripeptide was about eight times greater than that for the hydrolysis of the bond in the dipeptide (349). Thus the peptide bond involving the carbonyl group of an N-terminal residue may well be more stable to acid hydrolysis than is the same bond when present in the interior of the peptide chain. A further implication of this position would be that the peptide bonds noted in peptides might not themselves necessarily possess a high degree of stability, but may be preserved because of their proximity to bonds very much more labile in character. On the other hand, it was soon recognized that, just as certain amino acid residues conferred an unusual lability to the peptide bonds in which they were involved, still others conferred an unusual stability. With such extremes, it was considered that the partial hydrolysis of proteins could not be, at least entirely, a random procedure, and that a certain measure of reproducibility in the experimental procedure, with the hope of a rational approach to the problem of residue sequence, would be attained.

In a search for the most labile of the peptide bonds, Gordon, Martin, and Synge (348) followed the rate of liberation of the free amino groups of serine and threonine residues by means of the periodate reaction, and noted that these groups were liberated much more rapidly than was the average amino group as estimated by the nitrous acid procedure. Similar results were reported by Christensen and Hegstedt (350), and the frequent finding of seryl and threonyl dipeptides in various protein partial hydrolysates (69, 351) lent further confirmation. Few peptides have been found with

TABLE 16–8
Relative Hydrolysis of Dipeptides in HCl-Acetic Acid at 37° (77)

Dipeptide	Relative Hydrolysis (glycylglycine = 1)	Dipeptide	Relative Hydrolysis (glycylglycine = 1)
Glycylglycine	1	Glycylvaline	0.31
Glycylalanine	0.62	Leucylglycine	0.23
Alanylglycine	0.62	Leucylleucine	0.045
Glycylleucine	0.40	Leucyltryptophan	0.041
Glycyltryptophan	0.35	Valylglycine	0.015

intact bonds between these residues (114). The results on the protein peptide chain were therefore consistent with the earlier findings of Abderhalden and Bahn (23) on simpler peptides containing serine. Synge (77) had found that dipeptides were more stable than were higher peptides containing the same residues, and, when gramicidin S was subjected to partial hydrolysis with strong acid at 37°, a number of dipeptides were obtained containing all the possible variants of the residues present in the antibiotic molecule except for prolylvaline (113). A small amount of the tripeptides phenylalanylprolylvaline and prolylvalylornithine was present in the partial hydrolysate, and the inference was necessarily drawn that the degradation of these tripeptides would be expected to occur preferentially in both cases at the prolylvaline bond.

On the other hand, the finding of valylglycine in 10-day acid hydrolysates of gramicidin (352), and of valylvaline in refluxing acid solutions of the same antibiotic peptide (353), furnished the first clues to residues which conferred an abnormally high resistance on the peptide bond to which they adhered. Table 16–8 including data by Synge (77) describes the relative velocity of hydrolysis of several dipeptides (glycylglycine = 1) in a 50:50 mixture of equal volumes of 10N HCl and glacial acetic acid at 37°. It would appear that peptides high in valine or leucine residues, particularly when these residues are N-terminal, would be relatively resistant to hydrolysis. On the other hand, peptide bonds in which the carboxyl group of glycine is involved, tend to be rather labile (77, 114). Monier and Fromageot (354) partially hydrolyzed lysozyme and collected several of the smaller peptides.

On analysis, they revealed the following residues in descending order of occurrence: leucine, valine, alanine, glutamic acid, glycine, serine, threonine, and aspartic acid. It is possible therefore to conceive of a relatively specific and non-random hydrolysis of the protein chain whereby bonds involving the amino groups of serine and of threonine are favored by acid whereas bonds involving the amino groups of valine and of leucine are shunned. The most obvious reason for the high resistance to hydrolysis offered by such residues as valyl and leucyl lies in the steric effect induced by the branched chain on the β- and γ-carbon atom, respectively.

TABLE 16-9

Relative Hydrolysis of Dipeptides in 2N HCl at 99° (355)

Dipeptide	Relative Hydrolysis (glycylglycine = 1)	Dipeptide	Relative Hydrolysis (glycylglycine = 1)
Glycylglycine	1.00	Serylglycine	0.40
Alanylglycine	0.69	Alanylserine	>1.1
Glycylalanine	0.40	Serylalanine	0.74
Glycylserine	1.83	Serylserine	0.40

The lability of peptide bonds involving serine is considerable only when the amino group of the serine residue is concerned in these bonds. Thus Harris, Cole, and Pon (355) in studying the hydrolysis of a series of dipeptides in 2N HCl at 99° found that, although glycylserine and alanylserine were quite rapidly cleaved (as compared with glycylglycine), serylglycine and serylalanine were split more slowly. Serylserine proved to be surprisingly resistant to hydrolysis. Some of the data by Harris et al. are given in Table 16-9.

In glacial acetic acid mixtures with N HCl and at 100°, glycyl-DL-serine was reported to be hydrolyzed at a rate considerably less than that of glycylglycine (356). It may be that in the presence of a less aqueous medium the ease of hydrolysis of glycylglycine and of glycylserine may be reversed from that shown in Table 16-9. In the glacial acetic acid-HCl mixture D-leucyl-L-leucine was hydrolyzed appreciably faster than L-leucyl-L-leucine, a finding consistent with the steric effect expected when two bulky radicals are on the same side of the plane as in the latter peptide. The most resistant of the peptides was found to be valylvaline. The very resistant linkage between isoleucine and valine in insulin has been described by Harfenist (357). That these peptides, resistant because of their relative steric inaccessibility, should react weakly with ninhydrin (357) is not at all surprising.

Desnuelle and Bonjour (358) noted that N-acetylamino acids are hydrolyzed under the influence of acids at faster rates than the corresponding N-acetylamines. The introduction of a second free carboxyl group into the former type of compound resulted in a still faster rate, and this suggested that electron-attracting groups such as carboxyl tend to increase the rate of hydrolysis of the peptide bond. Indeed glycylaspartic acid is hydrolyzed nearly twice as fast as glycylglycine under the same conditions.

An ingenious explanation for the high order of susceptibility of serine and threonine residues was offered by Desnuelle and Casal (342). Bergmann, Brand, and Weinmann (359) had shown that it was possible to convert N-acyl-β-hydroxy acids to O-acylamino acids reversibly through the intermediate formation of an oxazoline:

$$\begin{array}{c} -CH-CHCO- \\ | \quad\quad | \\ OH \quad NH \\ \quad\quad / \\ \quad\quad CO \\ \quad\quad | \\ \quad\quad R \end{array} \quad \longleftarrow \quad \left[\begin{array}{c} -CH-CHCO- \\ | \quad\quad | \\ O \quad\quad NH \\ \quad\searrow\quad\swarrow \\ \quad\quad C \\ \quad /\quad\backslash \\ OH \quad\quad R \end{array}\right]$$

N-Acyl derivative

$\downarrow$ PCl$_5$ or SOCl$_2$ $\quad\quad\quad\quad\quad\quad\quad\quad\quad\quad\quad\quad\quad\quad\quad$ $\uparrow$ NaOH

$$\begin{array}{c} -CH-CHCO- \\ | \quad\quad | \\ O \quad\quad N\cdot HCl \\ \quad\searrow\quad\nearrow \\ \quad\quad C \\ \quad\quad | \\ \quad\quad R \end{array} \quad \xrightarrow[+H_2O]{HCl} \quad \begin{array}{c} -CH-CHCO- \\ | \quad\quad | \\ O \quad\quad NH_2\cdot HCl \\ | \\ C=O \\ | \\ R \end{array}$$

Oxazoline $\quad\quad\quad\quad\quad\quad\quad\quad\quad\quad\quad\quad\quad\quad\quad\quad\quad\quad$ O-Acyl derivative

Desnuelle and Casal proposed that a similar mechanism was operative in partial hydrolysates of proteins in concentrated acid and at low temperature whereby the specific bond of a residue with the amino group of a serine (or threonine) residue would be converted from a normal N- to an O-peptide structure which would be then followed by a ready hydrolysis of the ester:

$$\begin{array}{c} -RCHCONHCHCO- \\ | \quad\quad\quad | \\ NH \quad\quad CH_2 \\ \quad\quad\quad | \\ \quad\quad\quad OH \end{array} \xrightarrow{-H_2O} \begin{array}{c} -RCHC=N-CHCO- \\ | \quad\quad O----CH_2 \\ NH \end{array} \longrightarrow$$

Normal N-peptide $\quad\quad\quad\quad\quad\quad\quad\quad\quad\quad\quad\quad\quad\quad\quad$ Oxazoline

$$\begin{array}{c} \quad\quad\quad\quad NH_2 \\ -RCH-CO \quad CH-CO- \\ | \quad\quad\quad | \\ NH \quad O----CH_2 \\ | \end{array} \xrightarrow{H_2O} \begin{array}{c} RCHCOOH + NH_2CHCO- \\ | \quad\quad\quad\quad\quad\quad\quad\quad | \\ NH \quad\quad\quad\quad\quad\quad\quad CH_2 \\ \quad\quad\quad\quad\quad\quad\quad\quad\quad | \\ \quad\quad\quad\quad\quad\quad\quad\quad\quad OH \end{array}$$

O-Peptide

Desnuelle and Bonjour (360) proceeded to give quantitative data on the release of bonds involving the amino groups of serine and threonine residues during the hydroysis of proteins with 12N HCl at 20° which were in good agreement in general with those obtained before by Gordon, Martin, and Synge (348). Where the latter authors relied on the periodate method which yielded ammonia with residues of both serine and threonine and only acetaldehyde with threonine, Desnuelle and Bonjour could distinguish between the two residues themselves, and between them and all others, by

TABLE 16-10

Specificity of Serine and Threonine Bonds in Globin Hydrolyzed Partially by 12N HCl at 20° (360)

Period of Hydrolysis, hr.	Peptide Bonds Hydrolyzed	N-Terminal Bonds by DNFB Procedure, %		
		Serine	Threonine	All Others
7	59	48	35	4
20	114	85	83	12
41	151	103	86	15

the DNFB procedure of Sanger. Representative results on globin are embodied in Table 16-10. Thus at 7 hours of digestion, bonds involving serine and threonine were hydrolyzed, respectively, twelve times and nine times more rapidly than were bonds involving other amino acids.

An interestingly drastic experiment was undertaken by Desnuelle and Bonjour to test their concept further. Reitz, Ferrel, Olcott, and Fraenkel-Conrat (361) had found that proteins could be dissolved in anhydrous sulfuric acid without peptide bond fission provided that the solution was not too long maintained. Desnuelle and Bonjour dissolved dried and finely powdered edestin in sulfuric acid at −20°, maintained the solution for about a week, and recovered the protein by pouring the solution into dry ether at 0°. The protein was dissolved in 6N HCl at 18° and after 6 hours of digestion was subjected to the sort of analysis described in Table 16-10. The N-terminal serine bonds amounted to 71.5%, those of threonine to 32.5%, and those of all others to 1%.

All these results supported the idea of some unusual mechanism which might be involved in the abnormally high rate of hydrolysis of serine and threonine bonds, but constituted little if any positive evidence for the idea advanced by Desnuelle and Casal. The subsequent studies by Elliott and others (362) could be interpreted as supporting this concept. Elliott dissolved silk fibroin in concentrated sulfuric acid and maintained the solution for 3 days at 21°. Application of the DNFB procedure at this point revealed, very largely, DNP-serine. Some 62% of the serine residues were converted

SEQUENTIAL ANALYSIS OF PEPTIDES

to the O-peptide form. This figure was arrived at by the considerable increase in amino-N revealed in the protein. That this increase in amino-N was largely due to the intramolecular rearrangement of N- → O-peptide, and not to simple hydrolysis of peptide bonds, was shown by the reversible drop in the amino-N value when the protein was transferred to a buffer solution at pH 9 and maintained therein for several hours. The decrease in amino-N was due to the reverse O- → N-peptide arrangement, and thus the difference between the amino-N before and after exposure to the buffer could be taken as a measure of the serine residues involved in the original rearrangement. In order to prevent the reverse O- → N-peptide arrangement, Elliott acetylated the sulfuric acid-treated protein at pH 5 so as to block the freed amino group of the serine residue in the O-peptide combination, and thus render the protein susceptible at this bond to mild alkaline saponification. When this protein was dissolved in alkali, free acid groups were liberated, and it was concluded that saponification of ester groups had occurred. On dialysis, 86% of the total nitrogen of the protein was found to be diffusible with practically all of the serine and threonine residues present in the diffusible fraction. The reactions involved could be formulated as follows:

$$\begin{array}{c} CH_2-CHCONHCHR^2\cdots \\ | \quad | \\ OH \quad NH \\ | \\ CO \\ | \\ CHR^1 \\ | \\ NH \\ \vdots \end{array} \xrightarrow{H_2SO_4} \begin{array}{c} CH_2-CHCONHCHR^2\cdots \\ | \quad | \\ O \quad NH_2 \\ | \\ CO \\ | \\ CHR^1 \\ | \\ NH \\ \vdots \end{array} \xrightarrow[pH5]{\text{Acetic anhydride}}$$

$$\begin{array}{c} CH_2CHCONHCHR^2\cdots \\ | \quad | \\ O \quad NHCOCH_3 \\ | \\ CO \\ | \\ CHR^1 \\ | \\ NH \\ \vdots \end{array} \xrightarrow{\text{Alkali}} \begin{array}{c} CH_2CHCONHCHR^2\cdots \\ | \quad | \\ OH \quad NHCOCH_3 \end{array} + \cdots NHCHR^1CO_2H$$

Despite the plausible appearance of these formulations, it is not yet clear that they represent the entire picture of what occurs at the bonds involving serine and threonine residues in proteins dissolved in aqueous acid. The reactions originally developed by Bergmann envisaged non-aqueous media, and the fact, as pointed out by Sanger and Tuppy (114), that serine and threonine bonds are still highly labile in dilute as well as in concentrated acid solutions, would suggest that the concept of the N- → O-peptide sequence be regarded at this time with some degree of reserve.

A known ester linkage in proteins is that involved in phosphate esters of serine and threonine, for phosphoserine has been isolated from acid digests of vitellinic acid (44, 363) and casein (43, 364) as well as from chymotrypsin (317), tumor (365), and cholinesterase (366). The dipeptide sequence phosphoserylglycyl was isolated from chymotrypsin (367), and phosphoserylglutamyl from casein (368). Phosphothreonine has also been isolated from a hydrolysate of casein (369). In all the peptides isolated, phosphoserine occupied the N-terminal position. More recently, peptides with phosphoserine in positions other than the N-terminal have been isolated from partial acid hydrolysates of ovalbumin and of pepsin (370). For detection of these peptides, the partial hydrolysates after removal of excess HCl were submitted to ion exchange chromatography on Dowex 50-X8 resin and the eluates chromatographed on paper; after the ninhydrin-positive spots were marked with an ammonium molybdate reagent, ultraviolet light was employed as an aid to the identification of the presence of phosphate. Ovalbumin partial hydrolysates yielded aspartylphosphoseryl, aspartyl (glutamic acid, phosphoserine), aspartyl (glutamic acid, isoleucine, phosphoserine), phosphoseryl (alanine, glutamic acid, isoleucine), aspartyl (alanine, glutamic acid, isoleucine, phosphoserine), and phosphoserylalanyl. Partial hydrolysates of pepsin yielded threonylphosphoseryl, threonyl (glutamic acid, phosphoserine), and phosphoserylglutamyl, suggesting that the single phosphate residue of pepsin may be esterified with a serine residue present in the sequence threonylphosphoserylglutamyl (370). The possibility that phosphate might originally be attached to nitrogen and undergo an O-migration has been expressed (cf. 371), and the finding of certain phosphorylserine residues in peptides in other than the N-terminal position might suggest that phosphorylation had reduced the acid lability of the peptide bond involving the serine amino group (370). Whatever the interpretation may be, the findings constitute the first unequivocal evidence for the existence of phosphoserine ester bonds in phosphoproteins.

DILUTE ACID. Acid at concentrations of $1N$ or below has been used infrequently in partial or complete hydrolysates of proteins. Several years ago, Brigl (372) observed that the heating of glycylglycine in 0.5% HCl at 180° led to the formation of a mixture of free glycine and the diketopiperazine glycylglycine anhydride. This observation was extended by Abderhalden and Komm (373), who heated dipeptides in both water and dilute HCl at high temperatures and observed the formation of diketopiperazines in high yield (Table 16–11). When the concentration of acid was raised, the proportion of diketopiperazine formed was diminished, until in sufficiently high concentration of acid no anhydride at all was found.

Diketopiperazines may also be produced almost spontaneously from dipeptides when proline is one of the components (374, 375). The isolation of glycylproline anhydride from a hydrolysate of gelatin by Levene and Beatty (24) has been alluded to. The anhydride of L-leucyl-L-proline has been isolated from a number of sources, i.e., adrenal cortex (376, 377), culture filtrates of several bacteria (378), and the chrysalis of the silk worm (379); also isolated from the last-mentioned source were the anhydrides of

TABLE 16-11

Yield of Diketopiperazine in Per Cent after Heating Dipeptides (373)[a]

Dipeptide	In H_2O at 150–160°	In HCl at 150–160°
Glycylglycine	91	81 (0.13 mole HCl per mole)
Glycylleucine	84	92 (0.18 mole HCl per mole)
		64 (0.36 mole HCl per mole)
		11 (0.52 mole HCl per mole)
		0 (1.0 mole HCl per mole)
Leucylglycine	77	73 (0.36 mole HCl per mole)
		0 (1.0 mole HCl per mole)
		0 (2.0 moles HCl per mole)

[a] In sealed tubes.

valylproline, alanylproline, and leucylalanine. It is not improbable that the peptides corresponding to these diketopiperazines exist in the free state in the various natural sources, and that the cyclization is a result of the isolation procedures. Hydrolysis of the anhydride of L-leucyl-L-proline with 33% sulfuric acid yielded L-leucine of good, and L-proline of fair, optical purity (378).

The data in Table 16-11 are important in revealing the possibility of inversion of sequences when dilute acids are used for partial hydrolysates. Sanger and Thompson (380) made particular reference to this possibility and have actually demonstrated such an inversion. As shown in the work of Synge (77) (Table 16-8), the bond in valylglycine is more stable than is that in glycylvaline. If, therefore, glycylvaline were exposed to conditions in which diketopiperazine formation could take place, the resulting mixture should also show the presence of valylglycine. Sanger and Thompson refluxed glycylvaline in 0.1N HCl solution; on paper chromatography of the solution employing the DNFB procedure followed by hydrolysis, the presence of valylglycine in the mixture could be established. In 12N HCl at 37° no inversion could be observed.

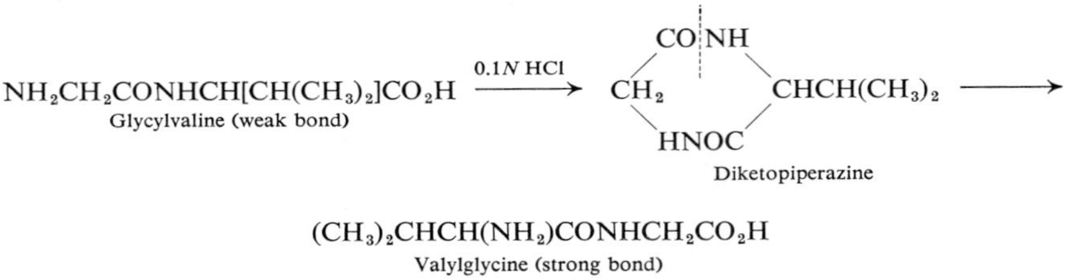

$$NH_2CH_2CONHCH[CH(CH_3)_2]CO_2H \xrightarrow{0.1N\ HCl} \underset{\text{Diketopiperazine}}{\begin{array}{c}CO-NH\\ \diagup\quad\quad\diagdown\\ CH_2\quad\quad CHCH(CH_3)_2\\ \diagdown\quad\quad\diagup\\ HNOC\end{array}} \longrightarrow$$

Glycylvaline (weak bond)

$(CH_3)_2CHCH(NH_2)CONHCH_2CO_2H$
Valylglycine (strong bond)

A very interesting example of specificity in the use of dilute acid was demonstrated by Partridge and Davis (381; cf. 382). When proteins were heated in 0.25M oxalic acid at 100°, aspartic acid was preferentially liberated before any other amino acids made their appearance (Table 16–12), and it

TABLE 16–12

Appearance of Aspartic and Glutamic Acids in Proteins
Heated at 100° with 0.25M Oxalic Acid (381)

Intensity of Ninhydrin Color after

Protein	Amino Acid	2 hours	4 hours	8 hours	16 hours
Insulin	Aspartic acid	+	+ +	+ + +	+ + + +
	Glutamic acid				Trace
	Others				Trace
Edestin	Aspartic acid	+	+ +	+ + +	+ + + +
	Glutamic acid			Trace	+
	Others				+
Ovalbumin	Aspartic acid	+	+ +	+ + +	+ + + +
	Glutamic acid			Trace	+
	Others			Trace	+
Gelatin	Aspartic acid	+	+ +	+ + +	+ + + +
	Glutamic acid			+	+ +
	Others		Trace	+ +	+ + + +
Ovomucoid	Aspartic acid	+	+ +	+ + +	+ + + +
	Glutamic acid				+
	Others				+

may be assumed that this dilute acid possesses a specificity of attack on the protein chain. A sequel to these studies was devised by Desnuelle and Bonjour (358), who used synthetic substrates as an approach to an explanation of the findings by Partridge and Davis. Thus N-acetylbenzylamine was employed as a model of a peptide internal residue of a neutral amino acid, acetyl-β-alanine as model of a β-carboxyl of an internal aspartic acid residue, acetyl-γ-aminobutyric acid as model of a γ-carboxyl of an internal glutamic acid residue, acetylglycine as model of a C-terminal neutral residue, acetylaspartic acid as model of a C-terminal aspartic acid residue, acetylglutamic acid as model of a C-terminal glutamic acid residue, and methylisoasparagine (N-methylamide) as a model of an N-terminal aspartic acid residue. The relative rates of hydrolysis in $0.25M$ oxalic acid at 105° were: acetylaspartic acid > methylisoasparagine > acetylglutamic acid > acetyl-β-alanine > acetylglycine > acetyl-γ-aminobutyric acid > acetylbenzylamine. The results were not inconsistent with those noted with proteins. Later results, in substantial agreement, revealed that the bond in glycylaspartic acid was extremely labile toward acid (355). That dilute HCl may have an effect different from that of concentrated HCl was suggested by the greater stability of glycine bonds in the former than in the latter solvent, although to all appearances the lability of serine and threonine bonds was equally high in both (114).

Aspartyl and glutamyl residues in the protein chain, so far as is known, participate in α-linkages. The possibility exists that they may be vulnerable to a specific type of fission by rearrangement to β- and γ-linkages, respectively. Thus, in model experiments, Battersby and Robinson (383) have converted the esters of α- and β-aspartyl peptides into mixtures of acidic aspartyl peptides, probably through cyclization to the related imides:

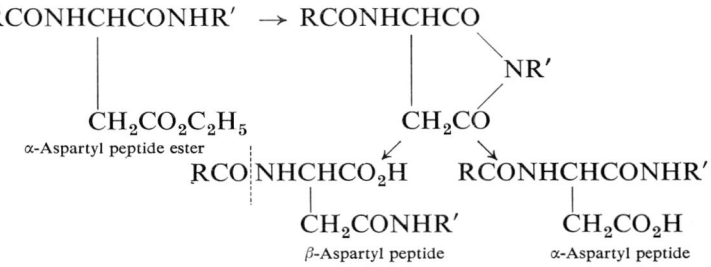

Likewise, in model experiments, Clayton, Kenner, and Sheppard (384) have converted α-glutamyl peptide derivatives into the corresponding γ-glutamyl isomers by the following series of reactions:

RCONHCHCONHR' $\xrightarrow{\text{Pyridine} \atop \text{SOCl}_2}$ RCONHCHCO
| | \
(CH₂)₂CO₂H | NR'
                                                              (CH₂)₂CO
                                                                  ↓
                                              RCO⋮NHCHCO₂H
                                                    |
                                              (CH₂)₂CONHR'

Whether such rearrangements may occur spontaneously or be induced within the peptide chain of the protein is of course not known, but the experiments of Partridge and Davis call for some sort of explanation. If the model experiments described are indeed applicable to proteins, selective fission at the bonds indicated could be accomplished by the use of several of the methods developed for removal of the C-terminal residue.

The important studies by Steinhardt and Fugitt (385) have shown that the effectiveness of an acid as a hydrolytic agent in dilute solutions of the acid is proportional to the affinity of its anion for the protein being hydrolyzed. Thus at 65° cetylsulfonic acid at 0.05M concentration hydrolyzed wool some 114 times faster than did hydrochloric acid at the same 0.05M concentration. All degrees of effectiveness between these extremes were represented by the other acids studied. Sulfuric and picric acids at 0.05M concentration, for example, were about half as effective as cetylsulfonic acid and twice as effective as hydrochloric acid, whilst dodecylsulfuric acid was barely less effective than cetylsulfonic acid. The same order of effectiveness of the anions of acids used as hydrolytic agents was also found with ovalbumin (385); cetylsulfonic acid was about 200 times more effective at 0.05M concentration than was hydrochloric acid at the same concentration. At lower concentrations of the long-chain anions, amide hydrolysis was catalyzed more strongly than peptide bond hydrolysis, and by keeping the concentration of the acid slightly below the stoichiometric equivalent of the sum of the amino plus amide groups of the protein the amide groups were rapidly hydrolyzed without extensive hydrolysis of the peptide bonds. The effect of the long-chain anions is probably exerted by their combination with the very weakly basic peptide and amide groups, by which these groups acquire a negative charge, attract hydrogen ions from the dilute solution, and become, in consequence, labile. At higher concentrations of acid, as the concentrations of hydrogen ions increase and assume greater importance in the medium, the influence of the anions declines but is never quite lost.

These anion-catalyzed reactions are dramatic. As Steinhardt and Fugitt point out, however, none of the long-chain anionic catalysts approaches weight for weight the catalytic activity of the proteolytic enzymes, crystalline pepsin at 35° being some 3000 times more active in liberating groups in ovalbumin than cetylsulfonic acid at 65°. Whether the action of anions of high molecular weight may offer a clue to the still more effective action of enzymes of even greater molecular weight remains to be determined.

ALKALI. This medium has rarely been used for the partial hydrolysis of proteins. The destruction of serine and threonine by alkali to yield, respectively, alanine and glycine plus butyrine, of cystine or cysteine to yield ammonia, pyruvic acid, hydrogen sulfide, and alanine, and of arginine to yield ornithine, citrulline, and ammonia produces in the alkaline hydrolysate a mixture difficult to disentangle. As so frequently happens, these residues are still more labile when bound in peptide linkage. Racemization furnishes a further complication not likely to be encountered, at least to the same extent, in acid solution. The only apparent advantage in the use of alkali is the preservation of residues of tryptophan otherwise so subject to destruction in acid media.

WATER. The partial and complete hydrolysis of peptide bonds in polypeptides may be accomplished by a process of exhaustive trifluoroacetylation followed by treatment of the product with water (386). The action of an excess of trifluoroacetic anhydride in trifluoroacetic acid solutions leads to acylation not only of the N-terminal amino group but also of the NH moiety of the peptide bond as well as of the carboxyl group:

$$NH_2CHRCONHCHR'CO_2H \xrightarrow{(F_3CCO)_2O} F_3CCONHCHRCON(COCF_3)CHR'CO_2COCF_3 \xrightarrow{H_2O}$$
$$F_3CCONHCHRCONHCHR'CO_2H + F_3CCONHCHRCO_2H + F_3CCONHCHR'CO_2H + F_3CCO_2H$$

Thus trifluoroacetylation of the peptide bond NH moiety makes the bond highly labile even to water, and splitting will take place at this point at a rate which depends upon the nature of the two amino acids which participate in this bond. In the case of the tetrapeptide isoleucylglycylvalylalanine, treatment with excess trifluoroacetic anhydride in trifluoroacetic acid followed by treatment with water yielded (as shown by paper electrophoresis and chromatography), in addition to the four free N-trifluoroacetylated amino acids, the N,N'-trifluoroacetylated dipeptides isoleucylglycine, glycylvaline, and valylalanine, and the N,N',N"-trifluoroacetylated tripeptides isoleucylglycylvaline and glycylvalylalanine (386).

These phenomena are essentially similar to those observed by Bergmann, du Vigneaud, and Zervas (387), who found that N,N'-diacetyldiketopiperazine would open by alcoholysis in the presence of arginine base to form the N,N'-diacetylglycylglycine ethyl ester which on treatment with one mole of sodium hydroxide splits rapidly to yield N-acetylglycine.

The employment of these methods could serve to distinguish peptide bonds involving the imino group of proline and of hydroxyproline (386). Inasmuch as these bonds possess no replaceable hydrogen they would not be acylated and hence would be completely resistant to the treatment with water which would split their neighbors involving the more usual peptide bonds. In this way, it should be possible to isolate unaltered amino acid–proline peptides from reaction mixtures of polypeptides exhaustively treated with trifluoroacetic anhydride.

ENDOPEPTIDASES (PEPSIN, TRYPSIN, AND CHYMOTRYPSIN). These enzymes appear to attack proteins somewhere in the interior of the chain, in contrast to carboxypeptidase whose action is limited to the C-terminal end and to aminopeptidase whose action is limited to the N-terminal end. On the belief that the endopeptidases act in a relatively specific fashion, it would be expected that their action on proteins would result in the production of peptides split at known linkages along the protein chain. The extraordinary efforts of Bergmann and his many co-workers were directed toward the goal of elucidating the relative specificity of these proteases by the use of a large variety of synthetic substrates. The subject has been reviewed by Bergmann and Fruton (388) and by Neurath and Schwert (303), and it appears that pepsin hydrolyzes the bonds involving the amino group of the aromatic amino acids, trypsin hydrolyzes bonds involving the carboxyl group of arginine and lysine, and chymotrypsin the bonds involving the carboxyl groups of methionine and of the aromatic amino acids. These are not the only bonds hydrolyzed by the enzymes, but, with the substrates available, they are the bonds which are hydrolyzed fastest.

When applied to proteins, the only endopeptidase which appeared in some cases to preserve the same relative specificity which it exhibited with synthetic substrates was trypsin. The other two, namely, pepsin and chymotrypsin, attacked a diversity of bonds. Thus Desnuelle, Rovery, and Bonjour (389) found that when pepsin acted upon ovalbumin no specificity could be detected, and free amino groups of nearly all the amino acids were simultaneously liberated, with globin, the initial stages of peptic action involved the liberation of the amino groups of alanine, phenylalanine, leucine, and serine, and in later stages the liberation of all amino groups without discrimination. Sanger and Tuppy (114) also found such bonds as those involving leucylvalyl and alanylleucyl in insulin to be attacked by pepsin, although the expected bonds involving residues of tyrosine, phenylalanine, and the dicarboxylic amino acids were primarily attacked (cf. also 115). On the other hand, Roche et al. (390) could definitely distinguish the action of pepsin and of trypsin on thyroglobulin and iodinated proteins in that the former enzyme but not the latter attacked bonds involving diiodotyrosine residues. The hydrolysis of globin independently by pepsin, trypsin, and chymotrypsin liberated, respectively, 1 mole of phenylalanine, 0.25 mole of lysine, and 0.1 mole of arginine (391). The action of papain, pepsin, trypsin, and chymotrypsin on gelatin, as revealed by N-terminal residue analysis by the DNFB procedure, suggested that bonds involving substantially the same amino group-bearing residues, i.e., glycine, alanine, etc., were attacked (although to different degrees) by all four enzymes (392). The limitations imposed by the paucity of aromatic amino acid residues in this mixed protein substrate and by the very large proportion of insusceptible linkages involving the imino groups of proline and hydroxyproline residues upon the number of available and normal specific points of attack by these enzymes could conceivably have compelled them to choose points of attack ordinarily quite secondary in proteins more completely endowed with amino acid residues. Deviations from the classic concepts of chymotrypsin specificity have been noted in the action of this enzyme on corticotropin-A (393). Deviations from the classic concepts of pepsin specificity have also been noted in the action of this enzyme on the C-terminal sequence of α-corticotropin; this sequence has been reported to be

-Asp·Glu·Ala·Ser·Glu·Ala·Phe·Pro·Leu·Glu·Phe

(394), and every bond in this sequence was cleaved by pepsin except the linkage between the proline and leucine residues. Free amino acids, namely, phenylalanine, glutamic acid, serine, and alanine, were found in the hydrolysate.

Trypsin, however, has acted upon clupein in fairly expected fashion. Thus DNP-clupein was treated with trypsin at pH 7 and the mixture chromatographed on a column of talc (395). The free peptides were washed off with N HCl, and the DNP-peptides subsequently with ethanol-N HCl (1 : 4). The latter were a mixture of DNP-prolyl peptides and DNP-alanyl peptides. Refluxing the former type of peptide with strong HCl yielded DNP-proline, dinitrophenol, free proline (as expected from the lability of DNP-proline), and arginine, whilst the same sort of treatment of the latter type of peptide yielded DNP-alanine and arginine (163, 395). It seems clear that trypsin hydrolyzed linkages involving the carboxyl group of the arginine residues, which are the second (and possibly the third also) members of the N-terminal sequence.

With the possible exception of trypsin, there appears to be no way in which the knowledge of specificity which has accrued as a result of the study of synthetic substrates can be employed so as to use accurately the endopeptidases to determine the site of specifically hydrolyzable linkages in the protein. Indeed, even in the case of the exopeptidase carboxypeptidase, the ready capacity of this enzyme to hydrolyze C-terminal aliphatic amino acid residues such as threonine from proteins came as something as a surprise, for this enzyme acts upon synthetic peptides with appreciable velocity only when the C-terminal residue is an aromatic amino acid. The action of carboxypeptidase on the tobacco mosaic virus protein was complete in the relatively brief period of 90 minutes when all the C-terminal threonine way hydrolyzed off. Viewed in retrospect, it is probable that the specificity limits set by the study of synthetic substrates with the endopeptidases may have been too narrow, and largely confined to synthetic peptides with only a few residues available for the enzymes to make a proper choice. The bonds more readily hydrolyzed between certain amino acid residues in simple synthetic compounds, upon which the doctrines of specificity rested, may not be so openly available within a protein chain partly folded in a configuration unique to each protein (396). But, if the endopeptidases lack some measure of specificity, their use in partial degradation of the proteins would still be of value were it not for the possible complications arising from synthetic reactions and consequent rearrangement of the residues. Bergmann and Fraenkel-Conrat (397) had shown that papain readily synthesized benzoylglycinanilide from benzoylglycinamide and aniline without prior hydrolysis of the amide, and a reaction whereby an exchange of residues occurred by concurrent lytic and synthetic steps was shown by Behrens and Bergmann (398). Direct transacylation or transpeptidation reactions (cf. 399) by immediate replacement have been demonstrated by Janssen, Winitz, and Fox (400) in such cases as benzoylphenylalanine and alaninanilide, the products being benzoylphenylalaninanilide and alanine. More recent studies of transpeptidation reactions have been described by Durell and Fruton (401), while Johnson and Herriott have noted that glycyl-L-leucine is not hydrolyzed by papain unless some other peptides (e.g., peptides of glutamic acid) are present in the reaction mixture (402). Some of the reactions involved (403) are as follows:

—CHRCONHCHR¹CONHCHR²CO ··· + NH₂CHR¹CONHCHR¹¹CO ··· ⇌
—CHRCONHCHR¹CONHCHR²CONHCHR¹CONHCHR¹¹CO ··· ⇌
—CHRCONHCHR¹CONHCHR²CONHCHR¹COOH + NH₂CHR¹¹CO ···
and
—CHRCONHCHR¹CONHCHR²CO ··· + NH₂CHR¹CONHCHR¹¹CO ··· ⇌
—CHRCONHCHR¹CONHCHR¹CONHCHR¹¹CO ··· + NH₂CHR²CO ···

As an example of an actual experimental occurrence with free peptides, Waley and Watson (404) subjected L-lysyl-L-tyrosyl-L-lysine to the action of a mixture of trypsin and chymotrypsin, and obtained as products lysine, tyrosine, lysyltyrosine, tyrosyllysine, and lysyllysine. The last-mentioned sequence did not occur in the original peptide. It might have resulted by a mechanism in which the hexapeptide, lysyltyrosyllysyllysyltyrosyllysine was first formed as an intermediate which then broke down to lysyltyrosine, lysyllysine, and tyrosyllysine. Again, an alternative mechanism might have involved the following: lysine + lysyltyrosyllysine → lysyllysine + tyrosyllysine, or lysine + lysyltyrosine → lysyllysine + tyrosine. The course of the breakdown of lysyllysine itself to free lysine is not simple, for in the presence of trypsin are formed lysine, trilysine, and some tetralysine as intermediates, the complete reactions ending with free lysine (405). Similar chymotrypsin-catalyzed transpeptidations occur with tyrosyltyrosine as the initial substrate (406), tyrosine and trityrosine being found as intermediates, and the digestion mixture yielding the theoretical amount of free tyrosine only at the end of the reaction. Thus measurement of the over-all rate of hydrolysis is not adequate to give a correct picture of the course of the reactions involved, and the attack by endopeptidases on linkages in proteins ordinarily quite resistant when found in simple peptides may not be unrelated to the mechanisms just described. Results essentially similar to those of Waley and Watson (404) were noted by Levin, Berger, and Katchalski (407);

thus L-lysylglycine amide which was slowly hydrolyzed by trypsin yielded in the digest a mixture of dilysine and lysine in addition to the starting product.

To what extent these reactions occur in digests of proteins with endopeptidases is not known. As Bergmann has warned (408): "When proteolytic enzymes have at their disposal a number of peptides, as will be the case in the course of an enzymatic hydrolysis of a protein, the possibility will frequently arise for the occurrence of a sequence of coupled reactions—synthetic as well as hydrolytic reactions—the overall result of which might give a misleading picture of the specificity of the enzymes involved." The converse might well be equally true, and a proteolytic procedure based on an assumed enzyme specificity to reveal specific linkages and sequences in a protein may likewise in some cases be misleading. The linkages so revealed, inconsistent with what is known of the relative specificity of the endopeptidases with available synthetic peptide models, may simply be secondary to a sequence of coupled reactions beginning with those linkages primarily expected from this specificity.

The sequential analysis of amino acid residues in proteins began with unimpeachable methods of end-group determinations. It was understandable that such investigations would be extended to sequences in the interior of the protein chain, and for this purpose the use of concentrated acids at low temperature to split the chain into smaller fragments was employed at first. The considerable lack of specificity and reproducibility of such reagents were soon recognized, and the use of endopeptidases of presumably known specificity for certain peptide linkages was introduced. Peptide fragments have thereby been obtained, separated, the sequences in each determined by unequivocal methods, and the sequences of amino acid residues in the entire chain assembled from the information so accrued. The results have frequently been consistent in themselves and with the results of procedures based on purely chemical approaches (cf. 114, 115). A consistent picture of amino acid sequences has been obtained when investigations on the same protein have been conducted through the use of several endopeptidases with presumably different specificities (189). There is no reason to doubt the mass of brilliant experimental evidence which has been obtained for several proteins. Yet the question must persist—has the possibility of transpeptidation been excluded, and are the peptide fragments, so laboriously separated and so exactly characterized, truly representative of the sequence of amino acids in the original protein? It is not impossible to conceive that transpeptidation may be a quite insignificant reaction in mixtures of protein substrate and proteolytic enzyme under certain conditions, or that the products of such digests may resemble each other regardless of the nature of the proteolytic agent. The difficulty in accepting evidence apparently internally consistent, and of proving or disproving the possibility of the presence of artifact, should be no barrier to the sympathetic and admiring reception of the efforts to deduce the sequential pattern of amino acids in the interior of the protein chain, but it is only proper to caution that the results of these efforts are as yet quite tentative. The proof of the pudding thus revealed lies in its final synthesis, and in identification of synthetic and natural products—in the case of the proteins an adjuration more easily stated than accomplished. Only in the case of oxytocin has this comparison been successfully performed, and in this example no enzymes were employed for structural determination.

DISULFIDE INTERCHANGE REACTIONS. This reaction may be formulated as

$$R^1SSR^1 + R^2SSR^2 \rightleftharpoons 2R^1SSR^2$$

If this reaction could occur to any appreciable extent during the partial hydrolysis of a protein rich in cystine residues, the original sequence of amino acids in peptides involving cystine which were isolated from the hydrolysate might not be known (409). Thus, if at one portion of a double chain held together by a disulfide bridge the sequence is diglycylcystine, and if at another it is dialanylcystine, the mixture of peptides in the hydrolysate may turn out

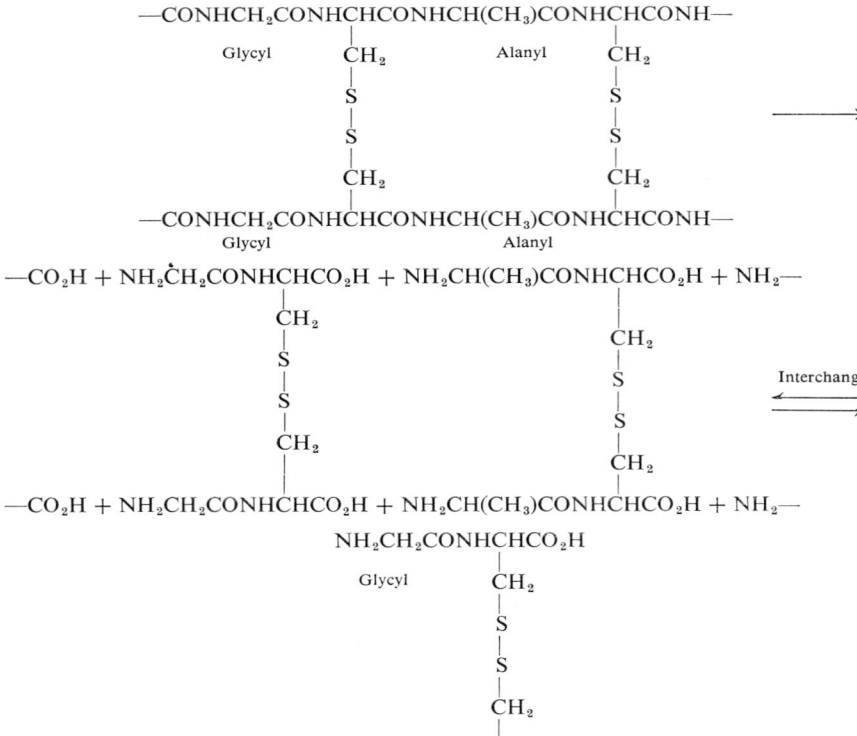

to be N-glycyl-N-alanylcystine, and an erroneous concept of the sequences in the original chains be arrived at.

This possibility was tested at first on a mixture of cystine and di-DNP-cystine in acid solutions of varying strength (409). Unmistakable evidence for a disulfide interchange reaction was obtained by the actual isolation of the relatively water-soluble, ninhydrin-reactive mono-DNP-cystine from such a mixture. This was readily accomplished by extraction of the excess di-DNP-cystine into ether, followed by adsorption of the mono-DNP-cystine on talc columns and subsequent elution and crystallization.

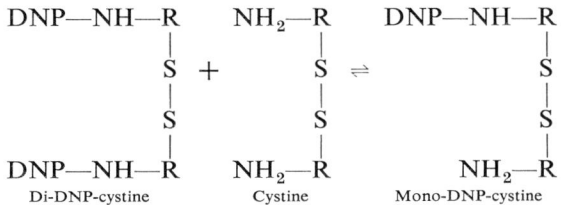

The interchange reaction was found to be very rapid in concentrated HCl but fell off as the concentration of acid diminished. The reverse appeared to be true for sulfuric acid. Higher temperatures, whether in hydrochloric or sulfuric acid solutions, appeared to favor interchange of disulfide. Quite striking was the effect of added thiol compounds on the interchange reaction, for addition of cysteine in relatively low amounts appeared to abolish the reaction almost completely. Conditions were therefore sought by Ryle and Sanger (409) which would prevent any appreciable disulfide interchange in partial hydrolysates of protein. For this purpose, a study was made of insulin dissolved in acid and digested in the presence of di-DNP-cystine. The amount of colored material remaining in the aqueous solution after ether extraction of excess di-DNP-cystine was taken as a measure of the interchange reaction, the color being due to a mixture of peptides of the type

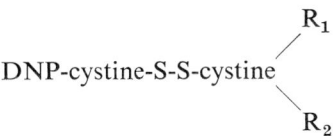

The data by Ryle and Sanger (409) are presented in Table 16–13 to give some concept of the order of magnitude of the effect. When the protein was hydrolyzed for 10 days at 37° with 10N sulfuric acid in the presence of thiol, there was very little evidence of disulfide interchange, nor even in the same solutions maintained at 100° for 2 hours. Similar results were obtained when $10^{-3}M$ cystine and $10^{-4}M$ di-DNP-cystine were dissolved in 10N sulfuric acid in 50% acetic acid at 35°; $1.1 \times 10^{-5}M$ thioglycolic acid completely inhibited any interchange reaction for five days. Therefore, to

TABLE 16-13
Disulfide Interchange during Hydrolysis of Insulin (409)[a]

Acid	Temperature	Additions	Time	Number of Disulfide Bonds Reacting per Mole of Protein[b]
12N HCl	37°	None	1 hr.	0.3
			2 hr.	0.65
			5 hr.	1.2
5.7N HCl in 50% acetic acid	37°	$10^{-3}M$ Cysteine	1 day	0.35
			4 days	1.0
			10 days	1.35
10N H_2SO_4 in 50% acetic acid	37°	$2 \times 10^{-3} M$ Cysteine	5 days	0
			10 days	0.01
10N H_2SO_4 in 30% acetic acid	100°	–	30 min.	0.35
			90 min.	0.7
10N H_2SO_4 in 30% acetic acid	100°	$5 \times 10^{-3} M$ Thioglycolic acid	35 min.	0.05
			2 hr.	0.15

[a] $0.02M$ Di-DNP-cystine; 10 mg. insulin per ml. Acetic acid used to bring the di-DNP-cystine into solution.
[b] Molecular weight 6000.

avoid such disulfide interchange reactions, the conditions set by Ryle and Sanger included the use of 10N sulfuric acid for the hydrolysis in the presence of some thiol compound.

Of some independent degree of interest was the fact that in neutral or slightly alkaline media the presence of added thiol compounds appeared to accelerate the process of disulfide interchange. When thiol was removed either by oxidation in the presence of oxygen, or by combination with such compounds as N-ethylmaleimide (410) or *p*-chloromercuribenzoate (411), the disulfide interchange reaction was considerably inhibited. In the absence of added thiol compounds, the reaction probably proceeds by virtue of the liberation of catalytically small amounts of thiol, formed from the disulfide bonds by some process of hydrolytic fission (cf. 412):

$$2RSSR + 2H_2O \rightleftharpoons 2RSH + 2RSOH$$
$$2RSOH \rightleftharpoons RSH + RSO_2H$$

To prevent interchange of disulfide groups in neutral or slightly alkaline solutions it is therefore only necessary to add thiol-binding or -oxidizing agents (409), whereas to accomplish the same purpose in acid solutions it is equally necessary to add thiol compounds. In accord with these conclusions are the findings by Wieland and Schwahn (413) that mixed disulfides,

R¹SSR, are stable in acid solution, but in alkaline solution, in the presence of catalytic amounts of thiol, they tend to disproportion to the symmetrical form RSSR, e.g., R¹SSR + RSH ⇌ RSSR + R¹SH.

The finding by Ryle and Sanger that thiol compounds promoted disulfide interchange reactions in neutral or slightly alkaline solution was consistent with the observation made by Huggins, Tapley, and Jensen (414) on the promoting role of thiol compounds in the gelation of serum albumin in urea solution. This phenomenon was interpreted as a cross-linking by chain reaction between protein disulfide and mercaptan groups throughout the protein to form a tightly knit reticulum. In the presence of agents which combined with mercaptan, the gelation did not occur, and presumably the interchange reaction was absent.

Of historical interest is the fact that in 1909 Fischer and Gerngross (cf. 414) observed for the first time the phenomenon of disulfide interchange but were apparently unaware that they had done so. These authors prepared crystalline monochloroacetylcystine, and on ammonolysis observed the formation of appreciable amounts of free cystine. The monoglycylcystine which should theoretically have alone been formed evidently produced by the interchange reaction some diglycylcystine and some cystine. Pure crystalline monoglycylcystine has since been prepared in this Laboratory (see Section 10–39), and shown to undergo disulfide interchange at pH 7.5, as revealed by the subsequent isolation of free cystine.

Oxytocin, like insulin and many other proteins, as well as like the very simple models, mono-DNP-cystine and monoglycylcystine, may be considered to be an unsymmetrically substituted cystine derivative, or mixed disulfide. Under mildly alkaline conditions (highly conducive to disulfide interchange reactions) oxytocin rather readily becomes biologically inactivated, and simultaneously many of its physical properties change (414a). Molecular weight determinations of the inactive material revealed that it was at least the dimeric form of the original peptide, arising very probably by cleavage of the intramolecular disulfide bond of oxytocin and the formation of intermolecular disulfide bonds between at least two molecules of the original peptide. In view of these findings, which occurred under conditions to which cystine-containing proteins and peptides have been subjected in the formation of DNP and other N-terminal derivatives for subsequent structural determinations, it appeared reasonable to caution that the interpretations based upon such determinations should be considered with care (414a).

ULTRAVIOLET RADIATION. That the absorption of ultraviolet light by a chromophoric group adjacent to a peptide bond would result in a splitting of the bond was first shown by Mitchell (415) in the case of stearylanilide irradiated at 248.3 and 237.5 mμ. The reaction was

$$C_{17}H_{35}CONHC_6H_5 + H_2O + h\nu \rightarrow C_{17}H_{35}CO_2H + C_6H_5NH_2$$

When films of ovalbumin were irradiated at 253.7 mμ they liquified, and Mitchell interpreted this phenomenon as involving a cleavage of peptide bonds adjacent to the highly absorbing tyrosine residues in the protein. About 8.2% of the total number of bonds were apparently split, and this figure was not very far from the proportion of tyrosine residues present.

It seemed possible that in ultraviolet radiation an agent could be employed which might be able selectively to split peptide bonds in the neighborhood of known residues of high absorbing capacity (tyrosine, tryptophan, and, to a lesser extent, phenylalanine). Carpenter (416), however, pointed out that the absorbing group in stearylanilide was attached to the peptide bond, and that this fact constituted an improper comparison with tyrosine residues which were two carbon atoms removed from the peptide bond. He therefore subjected stearylbenzylamine and stearyl-β-phenylethylamine, wherein one carbon and two carbons, respectively, separated chromophore and peptide bond, to radiation at 253.7 mμ. In both cases hydrolysis to stearic acid and the respective amine occurred, as measured by specific analytical methods. It seemed probable therefore that the energy of the absorbed light could be propagated along an aliphatic chain to break a comparatively weak bond at some distance (cf. 417).

Amino acids when irradiated in aqueous solution break down into a variety of products including free ammonia (418), and when solutions of N-acylated amino acids are so irradiated the production of ammonia may be considered to have been preceded in large measure by a prior cleavage of the peptide bond. Mandl, Levy, and McLaren (419) studied the photolysis at 253.7 mμ of a series of acylated amino acids:

$$C_6H_5(CH_2)_nCONHCH(CH_3)CO_2H$$

where $n = 0$, 1, 2, and 3. Included in this study was a pair of isomeric compounds, namely, propionylphenylalanine and phenylpropionylalanine, in which the chromophore was on opposite sides of the peptide bond. Quantum yields were determined according to the formula $\phi =$ (moles liberated per ml. per hr./einsteins absorbed per ml. per hr.). Separate values obtained for ammonia and amino acids were added to calculate the total quantum yield for the splitting of the peptide bond (Table 16–14). The quantum yield apparently rose with an increase of n from 0 to 3, which might imply an internal photosensitization in the molecule with folding over of the chromophore to the neighborhood of the peptide bond, rather than a travelling of energy along the chain. The correct interpretation is not yet at hand. Little difference in quantum yield was apparent in the photolysis of the isomeric substrates. It seems, however, that the application of sufficient light energy absorbed by the aromatic rings of the protein and passed along the chain on either side of the rings finally to split some weak peptide bond will also be sufficient to deaminate the residue so liberated,

TABLE 16-14
Quantum Yields for Photolysis of Acylated Amino Acids at 253.7 mμ (419)

Compounds	$\phi \times 10^3$ Amino Acid	$\phi \times 10^3$ Ammonia	Total $\phi \times 10^3$
Acetylalanine (in air)	None	71.5	71.5
Benzoylalanine (in air)	1.25	2.09	3.34
Phenylacetylalanine (in air)	4.77	2.27	7.04
Phenylpropionylalanine			
(in air)	0.89	5.91	6.80
(in O_2)	0.65	6.3	6.95
(in N_2)	0.12	5.0	5.12
Propionylphenylalanine			
(in O_2)	None	5.8	5.8
(in N_2)	None	4.5	4.5
Phenylbutyrylalanine (in air)	26.8	16.9	43.7

and lead to a rather complex state of affairs (420). The simultaneous splitting of the disulfide bonds of the cystine residues adds to this complexity, and tyrosine has been known to be split off in the free state from irradiated protein (420). The quantum yields for the photochemical inactivation of specifically active proteins such as enzymes and viruses have been found to be quite low, and perhaps very few bonds need be split for this purpose. The magnitude of these quantum yields has been expressed in terms of an inverse relationship to the molecular weight of the proteins involved (421), and of direct relationship to the cystine content (422). For such catalytic proteins, if both empirical relationships are nearly correct, there should be a correlation between molecular weight and cystine content, and indeed such a correlation was observed (423).

CLEAVAGE OF DISULFIDE BRIDGES. Many proteins may be considered to exist in part at least of polypeptide chains connected with each other by the disulfide bridges of their constituent cystine residues:

Chain (1 to n) —NHCHR¹CONHCHCONHCHR³CONHCHR⁴CO—
                              |
                              CH₂
                              |
                              S
                              |
                              S
                              |
                              CH₂
                              |
Chain (I to n) —NHCHR¹CONHCHCONHCHR^III CONHCHR^IV CO—

The sequence of amino acid residues in chain (1 to n) is not likely to be the same as in chain (I to n), and to apprehend the nature of the sequence in each chain it is advisable to separate them. This can be done in a number of ways, for the disulfide bridge is susceptible to attack by a host of various chemical reagents. For example, it can be reduced with sulfides (424), bisulfites (425), and thiols (425), oxidized by peroxide (426), chlorine (427), and bromine (85), split by sulfite (427a) and by biological agents such as enzymes (428, 429), and totally removed by Raney nickel catalyst (430, 431). Obviously, the method of choice should be that which would be least damaging, not only to the sulfur linkage itself, but also to the rest of the protein molecule. A great deal of work on this problem has been accomplished by the textile chemists in modifying the nature of wool (cf. 425). In many instances the protein fragments, after breaking the disulfide bonds, were more water-soluble than the original protein, and sequence studies were more readily accomplished (427a).

For the study of the amino acid sequences in the peptide chains, essentially two courses of approach have been undertaken, namely, the over-all sequence from N-terminal to C-terminal residues, and the more limited objective of the sequences in the immediate vicinity of the cystine residues. In the former sequence the chains are separated by some method of fission of the disulfide bonds, and each chain separately degraded by partial hydrolysis with acid or with enzymes to smaller fragments. In the latter, the whole protein is partially degraded, and the cystine-containing fragments subjected to the disulfide-splitting procedure and subsequently characterized.

Offhand, it might have seemed that the reduction of the disulfide bonds would have been the simplest and mildest, as well as perhaps the most specific of the procedures for splitting this kind of bond. The thiol groups so formed, however, have a tendency to reoxidize and produce polymerization of the products (432), and, if this is avoided by reaction of the reduced protein with alkylating agents so as to convert the reactive thiol groups to stable thioethers (433), groups other than thiol will also become alkylated to a greater or lesser extent and thus introduce a new complication to replace the old. Actually, an oxidizing reaction was found to be the most suitable method, not merely because it accomplished the purpose of splitting the disulfide bond, but because by converting the cystine residues to cysteic acid it endowed them with new, highly acidic properties by which their separation was facilitated.

Toennies and Homiller (434) in a study of the effect of performic acid, a mixture of hydrogen peroxide and formic acid, on a variety of amino acids found that cystine and cysteine were quantitatively converted to cysteic acid, methionine to the sulfone, and tryptophan, which consumed exactly three atoms of oxygen, to products not then characterized. The use of this agent was applied by Sanger (435) to the separation of the individual chains known to exist in insulin by virtue of their N-terminal glycyl (A) and phenylalanyl (B) residues. This protein has no tryptophan or methionine residues, so that no complications were to be expected on that score, although the conversion of the latter residue to the sulfone in other proteins has an advantage in identifying it subsequently on paper chromatograms.

The conversion by performic acid of the double chain represented above to two single chains containing cysteic acid residues,

$$-NHCHR^1CONHCHCONHCHR^3CONHCHR^4CO-$$
$$|$$
$$CH_2$$
$$|$$
$$SO_3H$$

$$SO_3H$$
$$|$$
$$CH_2$$
$$|$$
$$-NHCHR^ICONHCHCONHCHR^{III}CONHCHR^{IV}CO-$$

when applied to the insulin molecule by Sanger (435) yielded readily separable entities by virtue of the low solubility of the B chain and the high solubility of the A chain at pH 6.5. The theoretical relative quantities of the A and B chains were subsequently obtained in good yield after oxidation of insulin for 15 minutes at 50° with performic acid (436). Recently, Ryle, Sanger, Smith, and Kitai (437) subjected insulin to partial hydrolysis with pancreatic systems and with acid, and the cystine-containing peptides in the hydrolysate were separated and their structure determined after oxidation with performic acid to cysteic acid-containing peptides. Consden and Gordon (85) used bromine water to oxidize the cystine-containing fragments of the partial acid hydrolysates of wool to the corresponding cysteic acid-containing fragments.

The use of bromine water provided an unexpected clue to the sequence of amino acid residues in the peptide hormones oxytocin and vasopressin. Treatment of these compounds with performic acid yielded peptide chains in which the N-terminal residue sequence was β-sulfonylalanyltyrosyl (i.e., cysteyltyrosine) (438, 439). When these cysteic acid-containing peptides were treated at low temperature with bromine water, two fragments resulted. Those from oxytocin consisted of β-sulfonylalanyl-3:5-dibromotyrosine and the residual peptide fragment with an N-terminal isoleucine residue (440), whilst those from vasopressin consisted of β-sulfonylalanyl-3:5-dibromotyrosine and the residual peptide fragment with an N-terminal phenylalanine residue (439). The bromine water had evidently split the tyrosylisoleucine bond in the former case, and the tyrosylphenylalanyl bond in the latter, suggesting that the original N-terminal sequences were, respectively, (half) cystinyltyrosylisoleucyl and (half) cystinyltyrosylphenylalanyl in oxytocin and in vasopressin.

If a protein contains only cystine and no cysteine, the complete hydrolysate after treatment with performic acid will contain two cysteic acid residues for every cystine. This is the case, for example, with insulin (435) and with oxytocin (438). Where the protein contains only cysteine residues, the complete hydrolysate of the performic acid-treated protein will contain an equal number of cysteic acid residues, as in the case of papain (cf. 86, 247). Proteins which contain an unknown relative proportion of both cystine and cysteine residues would be expected on oxidation to yield results rather difficult to interpret. The successful uses of the procedure described have been based in part on the selection of unequivocal material at least as far as the cystine or cysteine residues are concerned.

On the other hand, performic acid may produce side effects on other residues, and if chloride ion is present and the concentration of peroxide high, chloro-substitution in the tyrosine ring is known to occur (441). The monochlorotyrosine so formed was the compound referred to by Sanger (114) in his earlier studies as tyrosine-X. Its formation can be very substantially reduced by conducting the oxidation reaction at $-10°$ (439, 442), or eliminated altogether by prior removal of chloride which permits a higher temperature of reaction to be employed. Careful studies of the amino acid composition of native and of oxidized ribonuclease revealed that no significant changes in the levels of any of the amino acids occurred as a result of the oxidation except for the quantitative conversion of cystine to cysteic acid, and of methionine to the sulfone (442).

Performic acid oxidation has been useful in the separation of disulfide-bound chains in such proteins as insulin. It has also been of use in the case of single-chain proteins like ribonuclease, whose coiled and condensed native configuration is at least partly due to the presence of disulfide bridges at various locations in the molecule (188). Such native ribonuclease is slightly susceptible to the action of trypsin, but, after oxidation with subsequent uncoiling, the molecule becomes readily susceptible to tryptic hydrolysis (442), and amenable thereby to sequential analytical studies (cf. 189).

5. Sequences in Peptides. The study of the amino acid sequences in the simpler, naturally occurring peptides such as glutathione and carnosine has been described above. The most readily available peptides of larger size have been those derived from fungi and bacteria, and in the early development of sequential analysis of proteins the parallel study of such compounds as gramicidin played an important part.

PHALLOIDIN. This peptide is a highly toxic, heat-stable substance isolated in 1940 in the crystalline state from the fungus *Amanita phalloides* (443). On hydrolysis, it yielded two compounds which had not been found in Nature up to that time, namely, L-allohydroxyproline and what appeared to be a hydroxytryptophan or oxindolylalanine. Other components produced by hydrolysis were L-cysteine and alanine. The peptide itself possessed no free amino or carboxyl group and was therefore probably cyclic in structure. Two observations suggested further unusual aspects to its structure: (a) phalloidin gave no alkaline plumbite reaction such as would be expected from the cysteine residue (444), and (b) its ultraviolet absorption spectrum revealed a maximum at 290 mμ instead of the band at 250 mμ of oxindolylalanine (445). It appeared therefore that a modification of the oxindolylalanine structure in which the cysteine residue was involved might conceivably be present in phalloidin, and Cornforth, Dalgliesh, and Neuberger (446) proposed that oxindolylalanine (447) was combined with cysteine in the peptide as follows:

Oxindolylalanine (447)
(asterisks denote centers of optical asymmetry)

Oxindolylalanine and cysteine residues
proposed for phalloidin (446)

This structure in which the mercaptan and oxindole groups are masked would be expected to yield free oxindolylalanine and cysteine on hydrolysis (446). A further consequence of the structure would be the generation after the hydrolysis of a center of asymmetry at the γ-carbon atom of the freed oxindolylalanine, whereby the compound would exist in the hydrolysate as a mixture of two diastereomers, probably in unequal amounts, with identical configurations at the α-carbon atom. Oxindolylalanine has been synthesized but not yet resolved (447).

Some time later Wieland and Schmidt (448) noted the presence of threonine in hydrolysates of phalloidin, and on the basis of their analytical results proposed that the peptide contained the following components: two moles of alanine, two of oxindolylalanine, one of cysteine, one of allohydroxyproline, and one of threonine, and was thus a heptapeptide (cyclic). These results were for the most part obtained by paper chromatographic techniques after reduction with nickel catalyst, the cysteine residue yielding thereby alanine, and the spot noted for threonine might just as well have been due to allothreonine or to a mixture of both, inasmuch as these diasteromers cannot yet be distinguished by the procedures used. Optical configurations were known only for the cysteine and allohydroxyproline components, and these were undoubtedly L (443). By sequential analysis, Wieland and Schmidt (448) arrived at the segment: -threonylcysteinylalanylallohydroxyprolyl(oxindolylalanyl)$_2$alanyl-. The likelihood that at least one of the aromatic amino acid residues was bound to the cysteine residue through a thioether combination in the way proposed by Cornforth, Dalgliesh, and Neuberger (446) was favored by Wieland and Schmidt.

More recent analysis by Meloun and Sorm (449) has suggested that phalloidin may be a cyclic hexapeptide containing only one aromatic amino acid residue, and possessing the sequence segment: -threonylcysteinylalanylallohydroxyprolyl-. Analytical values for the oxindolylalanine residue in hydrolysates of the peptide were considered questionable because of the instability of this residue under the conditions employed. The peptide was therefore first desulfurized with nickel (448) and then hydrolyzed either directly after the desulfurization or after hydrogenation of the desulfurized product with platinum. Paper chromatography of the former revealed the presence of threonine, alanine, allohydroxyproline, and tryptophan, and of the latter, threonine, alanine, allohydroxyproline, and octahydrotryptophan; in both cases cysteine (or cystine) was completely missing. Had a residue of oxindolylalanine as such been present in the original peptide, the reductive procedures might have been expected to have revealed the subsequent presence of hexahydrooxindolylalanine in the hydrolysates, but this compound was in no case observed. The ultraviolet absorption spectrum of dethiophalloidin revealed the presence of an absorption maximum at 280 mμ, with no trace of a band at 250 mμ which would be characteristic of an oxindolylalanine residue. The spectrum of dethiohydrophalloidin possessed no maxima at all. Quantitative analyses of the hydrolysate of desulfurized and reduced phalloidin were in good agreement with the following molecular combinations: threonine 1, alanine 3 (one of these residues was derived from the original cysteine residue), allohydroxyproline 1, and octahydrotryptophan 1. It would therefore appear that the presence of oxindolylalanine in hydrolysates of the native phalloidin peptide, as surmised by Cornforth, Dalgliesh, and Neuberger (446) was an artifact, due to cleavage of a thioether combination between tryptophan and cysteine residues.

With the recent isolation of 27 grams of crystalline phalloidin from 650 kg. of the toxic mushrooms, Wieland and Schön (450) were enabled to arrive at the complete structure and sequence of phalloidin. A new amino acid, hitherto confused to some extent with alanine, was isolated from an acid hydrolysate of phalloidin as a lactone (450). Its structure was determined to be that of a γ,δ-dihydroxy derivative of leucine. The cyclic peptide could

be opened at a single peptide bond by treatment with 0.2N H$_2$SO$_4$ at 100° for 30 minutes. Treatment with DNFB indicated an N-terminal residue of alanine. Previous data had shown all alanine residues to be of the L-configuration (451). The C-terminal group of the opened peptide was the δ-hydroxyleucenine lactone. Thus the partial hydrolysis opened the bond between alanine and hydroxyleucine. From the earlier data on the sequence of residues in phalloidin, the structure ·Ala·Thr·CySH·Ala·Hypro·*oxy*Try· lactone could be deduced, and the complete structure described as (450, 452)

$$\begin{array}{c}\text{Phalloidin structure}\end{array}$$

Phalloidin

THE ERGOT ALKALOIDS. These compounds, extracted from ergot of rye, have offered many interesting problems of structure and, like the example of phalloidin just described, yield phenomena which suggest that the hydrolysis of complex structures may yield products not necessarily identical with residues present in the original molecule. All the alkaloids yield on complete acid hydrolysis a complex acid, lysergic acid, whose properties are of no pertinence in the present connection, ammonia, D-proline, a second amino acid with an L-configuration, and an α-keto acid. The second amino acid may be L-valine, L-leucine, or L-phenylalanine. The nature of the α-keto acid serves to distinguish two classes of the ergot alkaloids; thus pyruvic acid (derivable from alanine) is characteristic of the ergotoxine group of the ergot alkaloids, and α-ketoisovaleric acid (derivable from valine) of the ergotamine group (453).

Jacobs and Craig, who performed much of the early work on this class of compounds, had noted the presence of D-proline in the hydrolysates, and had further observed that all four carboxyl groups, as well as the three basic groups corresponding to the ammonia, the imino group of proline, and the amino of the second amino acid, were all blocked (454). They concluded that these alkaloids possessed a cyclic structure containing two peptide bonds, and assumed that the α-keto acid and ammonia were derived on hydrolysis from an α-hydroxy-α-amino acid residue which could not exist in the free state but which would be stable within the alkaloid molecule where both hydroxy and amino groups were substituted. The following structure of an ergotamine residue was proposed (454):

α-Hydroxy-α-aminopropionic acid residue
(NH₃ and pyruvic acid precursor)

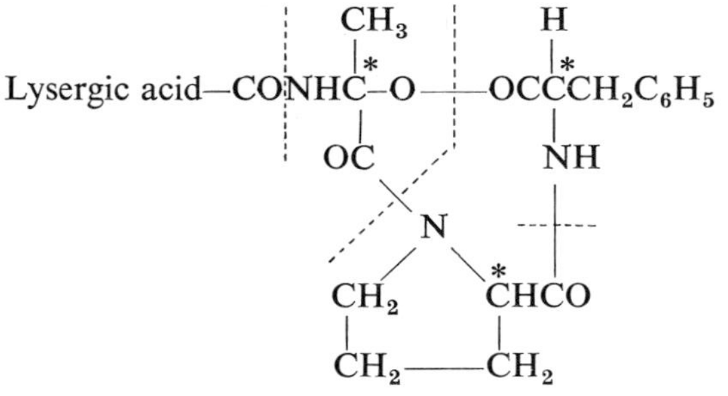

$$\text{Lysergic acid—CONHC—O—OCCCH}_2\text{C}_6\text{H}_5 \quad \text{L-Phenylalanine residue}$$

Older formulation of ergotamine (301)
(* denotes centers of asymmetry)

D-Proline residue

This nine-membered ring structure would be expected to yield, on hydrolysis, lysergic acid, ammonia, pyruvic acid, proline, and phenylalanine. It contains two peptide and one lactone linkages, and the α-hydroxyalanine structure has created an additional center of asymmetry.

The problem was subsequently taken up by Stoll and his collaborators, who found in their early experiments that merely heating aqueous solutions of the alkaloids of the ergotamine group permitted the subsequent isolation of diketopiperazines of D-proline with L-leucine, L-valine, or L-phenylalanine (453). As in similar cases, the sequence of the amino acid residues could not be apprehended from such cyclic compounds, and therefore a hydrazinolysis procedure directed toward the original alkaloids was adopted (453). By this means, the lysergic acid residue was separated as the hydrazide, leaving the peptide residue largely untouched, whilst the α-keto acid residue appeared as the fatty acid acyl radical of the peptide. From ergotamine, propionyl-L-phenylalanyl-L-proline was thereby obtained. Similarly, isovaleryl-L-valyl-L-proline, isovaleryl-L-leucyl-L-proline, and isovaleryl-L-phenylalanyl-L-proline were obtained from members of the ergotoxine group. Thus the carboxyl of the precursor of the α-keto acid is linked with the amino group of the variable L-amino acid, which in turn is linked through its carboxyl group with L-proline. On treatment of the acylated dipeptides with concentrated HCl in the cold there was obtained in every case the acylated-L-variable amino acid together with L-proline.

Analogous peptides from the ergot alkaloids were also obtained by the careful action of alcoholic KOH (455). Thus ergotamine yielded pyruvoyl-L-phenylalanyl-L-proline, and members of the ergotoxine group yielded α-ketoisovaleryl-L-phenylalanyl-L-proline, etc. The older formulation (454) in which the order of the amino acids in the peptide sequence was reversed was thus shown to be in error at least as far as this point was concerned. Of more striking importance was the observation that the proline residue in the alkaloid molecule was unquestionably L in configuration, whereas on complete hydrolysis of this molecule the proline residue was found in the D-configuration. To account for this phenomenon, and also to allow for the appearance of an α-keto acid on hydrolysis, Stoll, Hofmann, and Petrzilka (456) proposed the following formulation of ergotamine:

α-Hydroxy-α-aminopropionic acid residue
(NH₃ and pyruvic acid precursor)

$$\begin{array}{c}
\text{CH}_3 \quad \text{OH} \quad \text{CH}_2\text{---CH}_2 \\
| \quad\quad | \quad\quad | \quad\quad\quad | \\
\text{Lysergic acid---CONHC---O---C}_*\quad\quad\text{CH}\quad\text{CH}_2 \quad\text{L-Proline residue} \\
| \quad\quad\quad\quad\quad\quad\quad\quad\quad * \quad\quad\quad\swarrow \\
\text{OC---N} \quad\quad\quad \text{N} \\
\quad\quad\quad\quad\quad\quad\quad\quad\quad\quad\quad\searrow *\swarrow\text{CO} \\
\quad\quad\quad\quad\quad\quad\quad\quad\quad\quad\quad\text{CH} \quad\text{L-Phenylalanine residue} \\
\quad\quad\quad\quad\quad\quad\quad\quad\quad\quad\quad| \\
\quad\quad\quad\quad\quad\quad\quad\quad\quad\quad\quad\text{CH}_2 \\
\quad\quad\quad\quad\quad\quad\quad\quad\quad\quad\quad| \\
\quad\quad\quad\quad\quad\quad\quad\quad\quad\quad\quad\text{C}_6\text{H}_5
\end{array}$$

Newer formulation of ergotamine (456)
(* denotes centers of asymmetry)

Thus the carboxyl of the proline residue is asymmetric, through the asymmetric C-atom of the orthocarbonic acid grouping. This is conceived of as possessing an asymmetrically directing influence on the neighboring center of asymmetry, and therefore, on hydrolysis, when the carboxyl asymmetry vanishes, no racemization but only inversion of configuration of the proline residue takes place (456). The L-proline residue thereby inverts to D-proline when freed. In the newer formulation, the older concept of Jacobs and Craig (454) of an α-hydroxy-α-amino acid residue which serves as a precursor of the ammonia and α-keto acid released on hydrolysis was retained.

Lycomarasmin is a substance which has been isolated from *Fusarium*, and possesses strong leaf-wilting effects on tomato plants. On hydrolysis, ammonia, pyruvic acid, glycine, and aspartic acid were isolated (457), and some possible resemblances to the ergot alkaloids in structure have been noted (458).

BACTERIAL PEPTIDES. On passing to the peptides elaborated by bacteria, one enters into the great area of the antibiotics. The excellent review by

Hotchkiss furnishes much of the earlier data on the isolation and chemistry of the antibiotic peptides (459). As mentioned above, the structural studies of these compounds played an important role in the development of both concepts and techniques applicable to similar studies contemplated with proteins. For, as chromatographic techniques appeared in stages of development in which the study of protein fragments and degradation products could be conveniently approached, there were no models of sizes intermediate between such simple peptides as carnosine and glutathione and such highly complicated structures as the proteins, except the bacterial peptides, which might serve to test adequately the effectiveness of these techniques. Thus the development of the structural chemistry of the antibiotic peptides was for the most part totally unrelated to their enormous practical significance and was rather intimately involved in the perfection of techniques to be subsequently applied to the purification and characterization of more complicated molecules of biological origin.

Tyrocidines and Gramicidins. The mixture of peptides isolated by Dubos and Hotchkiss from *Bacillus brevis* was designated tyrothrycin (cf. 459). These compounds were early noted to be nearly or completely resistant to the action of proteolytic enzymes. Fractionation of tyrothrycin led to the separation of the neutral gramicidins from the basic tyrocidines. The gramicidin fraction appeared to yield on repeated crystallization from acetone an individual substance (460), and much of the early work was performed with this material; subsequent studies by Gregory and Craig in which countercurrent distribution techniques were employed (461) showed that this material was heterogeneous and could be resolved into at least three peptide components which were designated A, B, and C. Despite the mixed nature of this gramicidin preparation, much interesting information was obtained. It possessed no free amino or carboxyl groups, and it could be considered cyclic in nature. Unlike the proteins which are hydrolyzed almost explosively when first exposed to strong acid, the bacterial peptide mixture was attacked much more slowly (113). On complete hydrolysis it yielded glycine, L-alanine, L- and D-valine, L-tryptophan, and D-leucine, together with ethanolamine (462). On prolonged exposure to strong acid at relatively low temperature the following peptides were separated: L-valylglycine (77), D-leucylglycine (463), L-alanyl-D-valine (463), L-alanyl-D-leucine (463), L-valyl-L-valine (353), and D-valyl-D-valine (353). Although these sequences could not be fitted into any reasonable concept of structure, several points of interest emerged from the work on this preparation: (a) the cyclic nature; (b) the presence of D-amino acids in the hydrolysates, unique except for the ergot peptides, among natural products of a peptide nature; and (c) the very considerable resistance of the valylvaline linkage to acid hydrolysis. Moreover, it was in connection with these studies that D-amino acid oxidase

SEQUENTIAL ANALYSIS OF PEPTIDES

preparations were first employed to detect D-amino acids on paper chromatograms (463). The cyclic nature of the gramicidins was subsequently found to be nearly generally characteristic of the bacterial antibiotic peptides, a structure which might have been facilitated by the presence of D-amino acid residues in the cyclic chain (464). Whether some or all of these D-residues, found in the hydrolysate, actually exist preformed in the cyclic peptide has been a subject of some discussion (464) in view of the somewhat drastic hydrolytic conditions necessarily employed. That these conditions could lead to partial or complete racemization of some of the residues is unquestionably true, and the directive effect of one center of asymmetry on the configuration of a neighboring center under such conditions is already familiar from studies on diastereomers (Chapter 2), and particularly from the work of Stoll on the inversion of configuration of proline in the ergot alkaloids alluded to above. Many proteins appear to be of a cyclic nature, but, whether cyclic or extended in configuration, none of them under hydrolytic conditions approaching in vigor those employed with the antibiotic peptides, has yet given evidence of the presence of D-amino acid residues. It seems probable therefore that, in the case at least of the antibiotic peptides, the D-amino acids exist preformed in the molecule. The resistance of the valylvaline peptide bond to acid hydrolysis is very probably due to steric considerations; the same bond in benzoylvalylvaline is much more labile (353). The optically inactive valylvaline isolated from partial hydrolysates of the gramicidin mixture might have been derived from either of the following two mixtures, (a) L-valyl-L-valine plus D-valyl-D-valine, or (b) L-valyl-D-valine plus D-valyl-L-valine. Christensen (353) solved this problem by preparing the *p*-phenylphenacyl ester of the N-benzoyl derivative of the isolated valylvaline and showed that its melting point of 201° was not depressed when admixed with the same derivatives of synthetic (a), but was strongly depressed when admixed with the identical derivatives of synthetic (b), whose melting point of 144° provided a wide range from that of (a), namely 201°. Gramicidin A is the major component of the mixture of the gramicidins; as far as is known at the present time, gramicidin B contains phenylalanine in place of the tryptophan in A, whereas gramicidin C contains a tyrosine residue lacking in both A and B (465).

The basic tyrocidines also found in *B. brevis* are characterized by the lack of free α-amino and carboxyl group and hence are cyclic in structure, but uniquely possess a basic residue in L-ornithine, the δ-amino group of which is free. The member of this group whose structure was first apprehended was isolated from a Russian strain of *B. brevis* and designated, unfortunately for nomenclature, gramicidin S (466). Synge (467) found this peptide to contain one residue each of L-ornithine, L-proline, L-valine, L-leucine, and D-phenylalanine. The presence of one free amino group per minimum stoichiometric unit in the intact peptide, together with the absence of free carboxyl groups, as well as the possession of a high optical rotation ($[\alpha]_D = -295°$ in 70% ethanol), all pointed to a cyclic structure, and Synge commented that the compound could be either a cyclopentapeptide or a cyclodecapeptide. In one of the earliest uses to which the DNFB procedure was put, Sanger (468) showed by the isolation of δ-DNP-ornithine from hydrolysates of DNP-gramicidin S that the free amino group was that on the δ-carbon of the ornithine residue. This proof was accomplished by preparing α-DNP-ornithine and δ-DNP-ornithine, and showing that, whereas the former yielded no CO_2 when heated with ninhydrin, the latter gave one mole of CO_2 per mole of compound; the DNP-ornithine isolated from the acid hydrolysate of DNP-gramicidin S evolved one mole of CO_2 per mole of compound when heated with ninhydrin and hence was the δ-DNP derivative. Indeed, the failure to find any DNP-amino acid other than δ-DNP-ornithine in hydrolysates of DNP-gramicidin S constituted further confirmation of the cyclic structure of the peptide.

In an approach which could be termed a model for all later sequential analyses of proteins, Consden, Gordon, Martin, and Synge (113) subjected gramicidin S to partial hydrolysis in a 1 : 1 mixture of glacial acetic acid and 10N HCl at 37° for 58 days and succeeded in separating products which were mainly dipeptides. These authors employed two-dimensional paper chromatography at first, the spots were cut out and extracted, hydrolyzed, and rechromatographed; deamination with nitrous acid was used in parallel experiments to reveal the N-terminal residues of the peptides. Ionophoresis was also employed whereby three main bands were obtained, that nearest the anode which contained the neutral amino acids and peptides, that nearest the cathode which contained only free ornithine, and that in the center which contained principally peptides of ornithine. The DNFB procedure, well-developed by that time by Sanger, was employed to characterize the members of these fractions. The isolated peptides on which the final structure was apprehended consisted of the following: α-valylornithine, ornithinylleucine, leucylphenylalanine, phenylalanylproline, prolylvalylornithine, α-valylornithinylleucine, and phenylalanylprolylvaline (113). The structure of gramicidin S was therefore conceived of as: -L-Val·L-Orn·L-Leu·D-Phe·L-Pro-. Inasmuch as the molecular weight has been found to be in the range of 1100 (469), the gramicidin S ring described must be enlarged to twice the size, yielding a 30-membered ring, and hence a cyclodecapeptide.

The structure of gramicidin S may therefore be represented in the dimeric form as shown at the top of the facing page. Proof of this structure was furnished by the synthetic procedure worked out by Schwyzer and Sieber (470) which yielded a product indistinguishable from the natural variety of gramicidin S, and which possessed an $[\alpha]_D = -289°$ in 70% ethanol (see Section 10–38). An alternative formulation, in which a double transannulation of phenylalanine NH— with proline

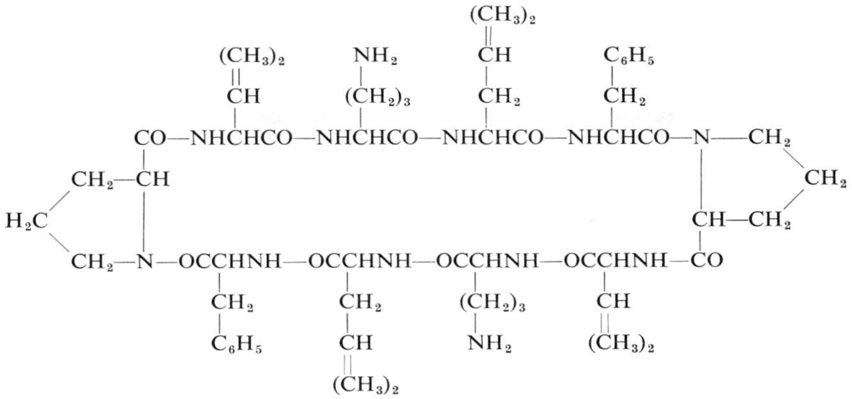

SEQUENTIAL ANALYSIS OF PEPTIDES

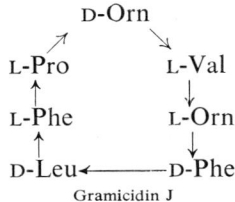

Gramicidin S

CO— occurred, was envisaged by Gavrilov and his associates (471).

A Japanese strain of *B. brevis* has recently yielded an antibiotic peptide (472), purified by countercurrent distribution, which appears to be a cyclic heptapeptide to which the designation gramicidin J has been given. From the complete hydrolysate one mole each of L- and D-phenylalanine, one mole each of L- and D-ornithine, one mole of D-leucine, one mole of L-valine, and one mole of L-proline were isolated. Studies of the sequences of amino acids in the peptides isolated from partial hydrolysates of the compound yielded the following structure:

$$
\begin{array}{ccc}
 & \text{D-Orn} & \\
\nearrow & & \searrow \\
\text{L-Pro} & & \text{L-Val} \\
\uparrow & & \downarrow \\
\text{L-Phe} & & \text{L-Orn} \\
\uparrow & & \downarrow \\
\text{D-Leu} & \leftarrow & \text{D-Phe}
\end{array}
$$

Gramicidin J

where the arrow symbol refers to the C—N bond.

Peptides with the same sequences of the same amino acids found in gramicidin S have been synthesized by Harris and Work (473) and by Boissonnas and Schumann (474). These compounds were not cyclic in structure, however, and possessed little if any antibiotic capacity.

The tyrocidine fraction of the *B. brevis* antibiotic peptides has been resolved by countercurrent distribution into individual components A, B, and C (475) which differ essentially in their amino acid content. All are cyclic, and possess a free amino group arising from the δ-carbon of an ornithine residue, as well as a free phenolic group arising from a tyrosine residue. Two amide groups are present, derived from the ω-carbons of the aspartic and glutamic acid residues. In early studies on the tyrocidine fraction,

Christensen (476) employed S-methylisothiourea. This reagent combined with the free amino group of the ornithine residue to form a guanidine group. On subsequent hydrolysis and treatment of the neutralized hydrolysate with hepatic arginase, urea was evolved, proving (a) that the free amino group of the ornithine residue is δ because this residue had obviously been converted to one of arginine, and (b) that the original residue is L in configuration. The employment as well of p-toluenesulfonyl chloride followed by hydrolysis to yield O-tosyl-L-tyrosine and δ-N-tosyl-L-ornithine was again a means of proof for the free position of the phenolic and δ-amino groups arising from the tyrosine and ornithine residues, respectively, of the intact tyrocidines. Later studies with the DNFB technique confirmed these observations.

Tyrocidine A has been purified to a stage where it probably represents a single substance (477). Molecular weight determinations by the method of partial substitution yielded values close to 1270 (478). This method arose, interestingly enough, from attempts by Battersby and Craig to purify tyrocidine A by crystallization from a mixture of methanol and dry HCl. An unexpected methanolysis of one of the two amide groups occurred whereby a methyl ester group was formed. From the methoxyl value a molecular weight close to 1300 was indicated. This finding was extended to a more general procedure in which DNFB was employed and the products of the reaction subjected to countercurrent distribution. If only one reactive group was present two bands should result, and if two reactive groups were present three bands should result. Tyrocidine A so treated yielded three bands, namely, those due to the unsubstituted material, the N-DNP derivative, and the N,O-di-DNP derivative in the order of separation within the system. Inasmuch as the molecular extinction coefficient at the 350-mμ band for any DNP-amino acid alone or in simple peptides, in which a primary amino group is involved, is in the range of 15,000 to 16,000 (166), absorption measurements of the yellow-colored, second band above, in which only the ornithine residue participates in the DNP combination, result in the calculation of a molecular weight of about 1600 for the DNP-peptide. It is possible that the extinction coefficient assumed from measurements of DNP-amino acids may be in error when applied to similar residues within larger peptides (478), and, until this is more accurately known, the molecular weights calculated by this procedure yield no more than close orders of magnitude.

Tyrocidine A yielded on complete hydrolysis three moles of phenylalanine, two of which were of the D- and one of the L-configuration, and one mole each of L-valine, L-tyrosine, L-leucine, L-proline, L-ornithine, L-glutamic acid, and L-aspartic acid; two moles of ammonia were also present in the hydrolysate, derived from the amide groups of the aspartic and glutamic acid residues (479). Studies on partial hydrolysates after treatment in glacial

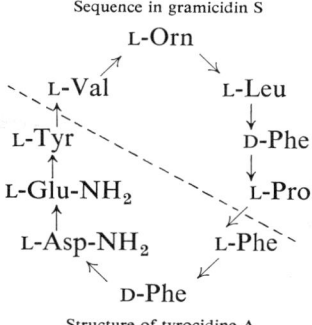

Structure of tyrocidine A

acetic acid–concentrated HCl mixtures yielded the structural formula (479). It is of interest that the gramicidin S sequence is found in tyrocidine A as half of the peptide ring; the other half of the tyrocidine ring is, however, quite different. The gramicidin S sequence is doubled in its own ring in view of its molecular weight of close to 1140.

Tyrocidine B differs from A in that an L-tryptophyl residue replaces one of the L-phenylalanyl residues (480). The molecular weights of the two components are very nearly the same, in the neighborhood of 1400, and both are cyclic decapeptides. On partial hydrolysis, twelve peptides were separated, and, as shown in the accompanying tabulation, the sequence of residues may readily be apprehended from the series of overlapping peptide fragments (480). The use of DNP derivatives revealed the N-terminal residues, and

Peptide	
1	Try·Phe
2	Phe·Asp·Glu
3	Asp·Glu
4	Glu·Tyr
5	Tyr·Val·Orn·Leu
6	Tyr·Val·Orn
7	Val·Orn
8	Orn·Leu
9	Val·Orn·Leu·Phe
10	Orn·Leu·Phe
11	Leu·Phe
12	Phe·Pro

sufficient amounts of each residue after hydrolysis were obtained by countercurrent purification to enable accurate optical rotation determinations to be performed. Some simplification in the separation of the peptide fragments was accomplished by Craig and King (481) in the use of a technique

of partial dialyses through cellophane. The sequential structure of tyrocidine
B is (480)

Sequence in gramicidin S

```
         L-Orn
        ↗    ↘
   L-Val      L-Leu
    ↑           ↓
   L-Tyr ~~~  D-Phe
    ↑           ↓
  L-Glu-NH₂ ~~ L-Pro
    ↑          ↙
  L-Asp-NH₂   L-Try ~~
    ↖        ↙
        D-Phe
```

Structure of tyrocidine B

Bacitracins. Bacitracin is the name given to an interesting group of peptides isolated from a strain of *Bacillus subtilis* (482). Separated by methods of countercurrent distribution, the most abundant of the series of related compounds, and so far the most extensively studied, is the remarkable compound designated bacitracin A (483, 484). The molecular weight of purified bacitracin A has been established as about 1500 (485, 486). Quantitative amino acid analysis and examination of the isolated products of complete hydrolysis have indicated the empirical formula (486–488)

L-Ileu₃, D-Phe, L-His, D,L-Asp₂, D-Glu, L-Cys, L-Lys, D-Orn, L-Leu

The phenylalanyl residue was isolated in a partly racemized state, whilst the isoleucine complement was isolated in the form of about two moles of L-isoleucine and about a half mole of D-alloisoleucine. Racemization of one of the residues of L-isoleucine would be expected to lead to approximately a half mole each of L-isoleucine and D-alloisoleucine (487) (488, cf. 489). It is of interest to note in this connection that Brockmann et al. had isolated D-alloisoleucine from the products of hydrolysis of actinomycin C (490); in this case, however, racemization (epimerization) was not involved inasmuch as no L-isoleucine was reported to be present.

The intact peptide was isolated as the trihydrochloride (486). There appeared to be one amide group present. Electrometric titration and reaction with DNFB indicated that bacitracin A contains the following ionizable groups: two carboxyls, one α-amino, one imidazole, and one δ-amino group belonging to the ornithine residue; the ε-amino group of the lysine residue is not free (486). When bacitracin was fully substituted with DNFB, three DNP groups were attached. On hydrolysis, good yields of δ-DNP-ornithine and *im*-DNP-histidine were obtained, together with a poor yield of DNP-isoleucine (491). It was believed that it is this seemingly N-terminal isoleucine residue which is that racemized (epimerized) in whole or in part during the hydrolysis of the peptide, and that this reaction is induced in part at least by an unusual relation between this residue and

SEQUENTIAL ANALYSIS OF PEPTIDES

others in the compound (487, 492). That three isoleucine residues were actually present in the bacitracin A structure was shown by the isolation of the following three sequences in good yield from a partial hydrolysate of the peptide: isoleucylcysteine, isoleucylphenylalanine, and isoleucyllysine (487). Furthermore, these dipeptides were found to be quite difficult to hydrolyze completely, and this resistance on the part of isoleucyl peptides was probably sufficient to account for the failure to account for more than about 2.5 moles of isoleucine of the 3 moles present, as well as for the poor yield of DNP-isoleucine on hydrolysis of tri-DNP-bacitracin A (492). Deaminated bacitracin A yielded on hydrolysis not quite 2 moles of isoleucine with no trace of alloisoleucine present, a finding which lends support to the concept that an isoleucine residue, which is unusually subject to racemization, is N-terminal in the intact peptide (492). This N-terminal residue is also that adjacent to the potential cysteine residue, inasmuch as isoleucine attached to phenylalanine and to lysine remained intact in the deaminated bacitracin A.

Other than the problem of the nature of the isolecuine residues and the unusual racemizability of one of them, two further problems in regard to the structure of bacitracin A emerged. One was concerned with the nature of the residue which gave rise to cysteine on hydrolysis, and the other with the nature of the lysine and aspartic acid residues. On complete hydrolysis, the peptide yielded one mole of cysteine and this accounted for all the sulfur present in bacitracin A (486). Partial hydrolysates readily yielded the isolated sequence isoleucylcystyl(cysteinyl)leucine (493). Yet the intact antibiotic peptide gave no reaction for free mercaptan (486), nor did the completely substituted DNP-bacitracin yield an S-DNP derivative of cysteine on hydrolysis (492). However, after mild acid hydrolysis, a clear test for mercaptan was revealed (486), suggesting that the mercaptan group was blocked in some way in the intact peptide. The possibility that the sulfur might be present in a thiazoline ring was suggested by Newton and Abraham (486) and by Weisiger, Hausmann, and Craig (492). Hydrogenolysis of bacitracin A with Raney nickel resulted in the formation of an N-terminal alanine residue and several volatile bases, among them isoleucinol, which further demonstrated the presence of the isoleucylcysteine sequence (487); all the amino acids were found in the hydrolysate of the desulfurized peptide except cysteine and alloisoleucine, another indication of the linkage of the cysteine precursor with an N-terminal, racemizable isoleucine residue.

The concept that the cysteine precursor was present as a thiazoline received support from a study of the transformation products of bacitracin A. The peptide is unstable in aqueous solution at a pH greater than 7 and is slowly transformed with loss of antibiotic activity into a product called bacitracin F (485, 486). In this transformation, ammonia is evolved and one of the α-amino groups disappears. Analysis of hydrolysates of bacitracin F revealed all the residues characteristic of A to be present except cysteine and alloisoleucine. Hydrolysis of fully DNP-substituted bacitracin F yielded only δ-DNP-ornithine and *im*-DNP-histidine with no trace of DNP-isoleucine present (492). The ammonia lost in the transformation of A to F came from the isoleucine residue, which is N-terminal and which gives rise ordinarily to the alloisoleucine found on hydrolysis of bacitracin A. Among the hydrolytic products of bacitracin F was a crystalline material containing S : N in a 1 : 1 ratio (492). Its structure was determined as (465)

$$\underset{CH_3}{\overset{C_2H_5}{\diagdown}}CHC(=O)C\underset{N=CCO_2H}{\overset{S-CH}{\diagup}}$$

The appearance of the thiazole could best be explained on the basis of a precursor thiazoline ring in bacitracin A. The structure of the N-terminal isoleucylcysteine residue in bacitracin A, as an equilibrium system, may therefore be represented as (cf. 487)

$$\underset{CH_3}{\overset{C_2H_5}{\diagdown}}CH-\bar{C}(NH_3{}^+)-C\underset{\underset{H}{N-CH-CO-}}{\overset{S-CH_2}{\diagup}} \rightleftharpoons$$

$$\underset{CH_3}{\overset{C_2H_5}{\diagdown}}CH-C(NH_3{}^+)=C\underset{\underset{H}{N-CH-CO-}}{\overset{S-CH_2}{\diagup}}$$

As suggested by Neuberger (464), racemization of an amino acid residue may be a consequence of the ionization of a hydrogen on the α-carbon atom, and this situation should be facilitated as shown under strongly acid hydrolytic conditions by the positive charges on the nitrogen atoms and by the possibility of resonance. Lockhart, Abraham, and Newton (487) made the point that the rate of such racemization (epimerization) may be sufficiently rapid to compete with those hydrolytic reactions which result in a rupture of the thiazoline ring and the formation of a normal peptide bond between isoleucyl and cysteine residues.

When bacitracin A was treated with 11N HCl at 80° for 43 hours, four relatively resistant peptides were found to be present in the hydrolysate (494), namely, isoleucylphenylalanine, isoleucyllysine, isoleucyl(aspartyl)lysine, and aspartyllysine. The DNP derivative of isoleucyllysine yielded on hydrolysis DNP-isoleucine and ε-DNP-lysine, whilst the DNP derivative of aspartyllysine yielded DNP-aspartic acid and α-DNP-lysine. Through the skilful use of D-aspartic acid oxidase, Lockhart and Abraham (494) determined that the aspartic acid combined with the lysine residue was L in configuration whereas the aspartic acid combined with the former through a labile, β-linkage was of the D-configuration:

$$\text{D-Asp} \xleftarrow{\beta} \text{L-Asp} \xrightarrow{\varepsilon} \text{L-Lys} \xleftarrow{\alpha} \text{L-Ileu}$$
$$\downarrow$$
$$\leftarrow \text{D-Orn}$$

According to presently accepted concepts therefore, the L-aspartic acid residue is combined with the L-lysine residue through the α-carboxyl group of the former and the ε-amino group of the latter, whilst the α-amino group of the latter is combined with L-isoleucine. The relatively slow hydrolysis of the aspartyl-lysine bond, believed to be characteristic of most bonds involving the ε-amino group of lysine (495), was subsequently interpreted as being due to an artifact produced as a result of the hydrolytic procedure. Thus α-aspartyl-ε-lysine on treatment with $12N$ HCl at $80°$ is apparently converted by cyclization to an aminosuccinoyllysine (496):

$$\begin{array}{c} \text{NH}_2\text{—CH—CO} \\ | \qquad\qquad\qquad \searrow \\ | \qquad\qquad\qquad\quad \text{NCH}_2\text{CH}_2\text{CH}_2\text{CH}_2\text{CH(NH}_2\text{)COOH} \\ \text{CH}_2\text{—CO} \qquad \nearrow \end{array}$$

On the basis of the evidence so far obtained, which may not be altogether complete, the structure of bacitracin may be represented as follows, *the arrows as usual pointing from a C to an N in the peptide linkage* (494):

L-Ileu
↓
L-CyS (thiazoline ring)
↓
L-Leu
↓
D-Glu
↓
L-Ileu
α ↓

D-Asp   L-Lys
  ↖ β ε ↗   ↘
    L-Asp   D-Orn
      ↑   ↓
    L-His   L-Ileu
      ↖   ↙
        D-Phe

Structure of bacitracin A

Bacitracin B has been found to possess all or nearly all the residues in A, and in addition appears to possess a valine residue (483).

Miscellaneous Peptides of Bacterial Origin. The common structure of the penicillins may be represented as follows:

$$\begin{array}{c} S \\ \text{RCONHCH}\text{---}\text{CH}\diagdown\diagup\text{C(CH}_3)_2 \\ ||| \\ \text{C}\text{------}\text{N}\text{------}\text{CHCO}_2\text{H} \\ \| \\ \text{O} \end{array}$$

Penicillin

Hydrogenolysis followed by hydrolysis results in breaking the bonds as indicated with the production of glycine, L-alanine, and D-valine. Cephalosporin N, which is a hydrophilic penicillin (497) (D-4-amino-4-carboxy-*n*-butylpenicillin) occurs together with a related compound cephalosporin C which behaves like a monoaminodicarboxylic acid, and yields after hydrogenolysis and hydrolysis the same products as the penicillins together with D-α-aminoadipic acid (498). This residue of D-α-aminoadipic acid is linked with the rest of the molecule through its δ-carboxyl group.

Tuberculin is the designation given the peptides isolated from tubercle bacilli; a representative of this group has been found to possess β-alanine as the N-terminal residue (499).

The polymyxins (500) comprise a category of basic, cyclic peptide antibiotics all of which contain γ-aminobutyrine and threonine. Polypeptin and circulin also appear to belong to this category. Studies on the structure of polymyxin B, conducted almost simultaneously by Hausmann (501) and by Biserte and Dautrevaux (502), were in substantial agreement in suggesting a cyclic octapeptide inasmuch as no free α-amino groups were detectable. Partial acid hydrolysates yielded a complicated mixture of strongly basic peptides which were either converted to their DNP derivatives and separated by countercurrent distribution in various combinations of pyridine and acetic acid (501), or fractionated directly on Dowex 50 (X4) ion exchange resin (502). One possible structure arrived at by a recombination of the peptide fragments is as shown at top of next page (where DAB is α,γ-diaminobutyric acid or γ-aminobutyrine), the optical configuration of the components being not yet known.

The actinomycins are another group of cyclic, peptide antibiotics, isolated from cultures of *Streptomyces*, which have been extensively studied (503). Like the polymyxins, various strains of the parent organism give rise to obviously related but constitutionally different peptides. All the actinomycins apparently contain L-threonine, sarcosine, L-proline, and

SEQUENTIAL ANALYSIS OF PEPTIDES

```
              DAB (γ-NH₂)
             ↗          ↘
         Leu              DAB (γ-NH₂)
          ↑                ↓
         Phe              Thr
          ↑                ↓
  (γ-NH₂) DAB             DAB (γ-NH₂)
             ↖          ↙
              DAB
               ↑
              Thr
               ↑
           DAB (γ-NH₂)
```
Polymyxin B (possible)

N-methyl-L-valine. By means of graded acid hydrolysis, the structure of actinomycin C appears to be

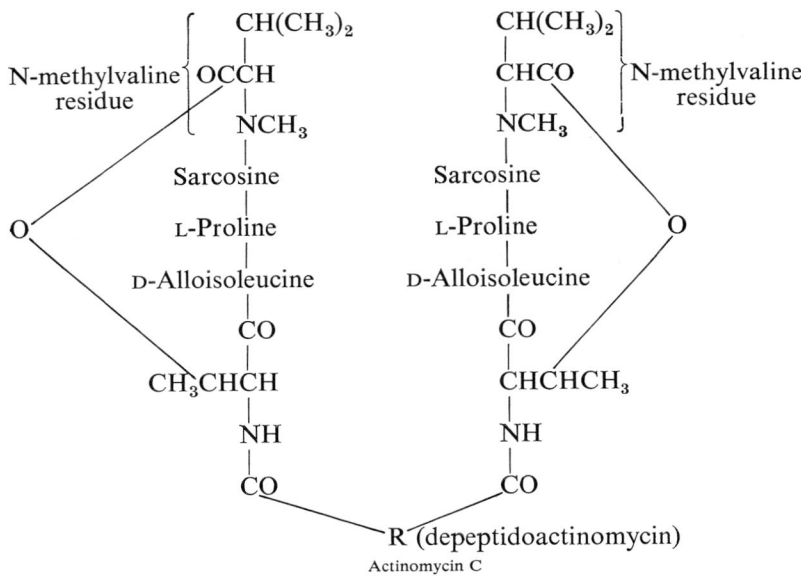

Actinomycin C

Actinomycin D, isolated from the same cultures as the C-variety, contains valine (optical configuration unknown) in place of the allosioleucine moiety (504).

Echinomycin, derived from the *Actinomycetes*, on hydrolysis with acid yielded L-alanine, D-serine, and N-methylvaline (505). N-Methylamino acids have also been isolated from hydrolysates of the enniatins produced by certain species of *Fusarium*. These enniatins have been shown by Plattner and Nager (506) to be 12-membered cyclic molecules containing two moles of D-α-hydroxyisovaleric acid and 2 moles of an N-methyl-L-amino acid. In enniatin A, the latter is N-methyl-L-isoleucine, in enniatin B it is N-methyl-L-valine, and in the possible enniatin C it is N-methyl-L-leucine. The various strains of *Fusarium* produced different mixtures of these three antibiotics.

From a taxonomically distinct organism, namely, *Streptomyces*, Vining and Taber (507) isolated an antibiotic which they designated amidomycin, and which turned out to be a 24-membered cyclic structure composed of four moles each of D-valine and D-α-hydroxyisovaleric acid linked alternately by ester and amide bonds. The basis of this formulation rested upon (a) the consumption of four moles of alkali on mild alkaline hydrolysis to form a hydroxy acid, which (b) on distillation yielded a crystalline lactone, namely, 3:6-diisopropyl-2:5-diketomorpholine, which (c) on acid hydrolysis gave one mole each of D-valine and D-α-hydroxyisovaleric acid:

$$\text{Amidomycin} \xrightarrow{OH^-} \begin{array}{c} (CH_3)_2CH-CHCO_2H \\ | \\ NH \\ | \\ CO \\ | \\ (CH_3)_2CH-CH \\ | \\ OH \end{array} \xrightarrow{\Delta}$$

Hydroxy acid

$$\begin{array}{c} (CH_3)_2CH-CH-NH-CO-CH-CH(CH_3)_2 \\ | \qquad\qquad\qquad | \\ \qquad\qquad CO-O \end{array} \xrightarrow[\Delta]{H^+}$$

3:6-Diisopropyl-2:5-diketomorpholine

$$(CH_3)_2CHCH(NH_2)CO_2H \;+\; (CH_3)_2CHCH(OH)CO_2H$$

D-Valine   D-α-Hydroxyisovaleric acid

A compound analogous to amidomycin was isolated from *Streptomyces fulvissimus* by Brockmann and Geeren (508) which was given the designation valinomycin for obviously good and sufficient reasons. Whereas in amidomycin the basic unit, D-α-hydroxyisovaleryl-D-valine, is repeated four times in the ring, valinomycin was considered to contain only two units of D-α-hydroxyisovaleryl-D-valine which were separated from each other in the ring by two units of a second type, namely, L-lactyl-L-valine.

CORTICOTROPIN (ACTH). This material, obtained from the anterior pituitary, has been separated into several fractions, α, β, etc., by adsorption on oxycellulose and by countercurrent distribution (509). Of the material employed clinically, the β-fraction constitutes the chief component. A major fraction isolated from the same source of crude corticotropin by somewhat different techniques has been designated corticotropin A (510). Both fractions appear to be nearly if not entirely identical.

Complete hydrolysis of β-corticotropin (hog) (509) yielded the formulation

$$Ala_3 Arg_3 Asp_2 Glu_5 Gly_3 His Leu_2 Lys_4 Met Phe_3 Pro_4 Ser_2 Try Tyr_2 Val_3 NH_3$$

There are apparently 39 amino acid residues in this peptide hormone with a calculated molecular weight of 4566; the molecular weight found experimentally was 4500 (509). To determine the sequences in the peptide, Bell and his colleagues employed: (a) specific cleavage by proteolytic enzymes; (b) resolution of the fragments from the enzyme digests through countercurrent distribution; and (c) characterization of the individual fragments by amino acid analysis, Edman degradations from the N-terminal end, and carboxypeptidase degradations from the C-terminal end. The results yielded the following sequence, complete except for three residues:

Ser·Tyr·Ser·Met·Glu·His·Phe·Arg·Try·Gly·Lys·Pro·Val·Gly·Lys·Lys·
Arg·Arg·Pro·Val·Lys·Val·Tyr·Pro·Ala·(Gly,Glu,Asp)·
Asp·Glu-NH$_2$·Leu·Ala·Glu·Ala·Phe·Pro·Leu·Glu·Phe

β-Corticotropin

In much the same manner, White and Landmann (510) arrived independently at the following sequence of the 39 residues in corticotropin A (porcine ACTH):

Ser·Tyr·Ser·Met·Glu·His·Phe·Arg·Try·(Gly,Lys,Pro,Val,Gly)·Lys·Lys·
Arg·Arg·(Pro,Val)·Lys·Val·Tyr·Pro·Gly·Ala·Glu·Asp·
Asp·Glu·Leu·Ala·Glu·Ala·Phe·Pro·Leu·Glu·Phe

Corticotropin A

Bovine fibrinolysin hydrolyzed the corticotropin A after arginine in position 8, and after lysine in position 15, with complete loss of physiological activity (511). Bovine liver cathepsin, on the other hand, cleaved the chain after leucine in position 31 and phenylalanine in position 35 with no loss in activity. In these types of attack, the fibrinolysin tended to resemble trypsin, and the cathepsin pepsin.

Application of the Edman degradation to α-corticotropin (sheep) by Harris and Li (306) yielded the following N-terminal sequence:

Ser·Tyr·Ser·Met·Glu·His·Phe·

(cf. also 512, 513). Acid hydrolysis of DNP-α-corticotropin resulted in a recovery of only about 10–20% of the expected DNP-serine (306). For the same peptide preparation, the following C-terminal sequence was proposed (306): ·Asp·Glu·Ala·Ser·Glu·Ala·Phe·Pro·Leu·Glu·Phe.

GLUCAGEN. This is a peptide containing 29 amino acid residues and possessing a molecular weight of approximately 3500 (514). The procedures employed by Behrens et al. to determine the sequences included: (a) partial digestion with trypsin, chymotrypsin, and subtilisin; (b) resolution of the peptides so produced on Dowex 50 resin columns; and (c) characterization of the peptides by quantitative amino acid analysis, N-dinitrophenylation followed by acid hydrolysis or carboxypeptidase-induced hydrolysis and subsequent paper chromatography. The action of N-bromosuccinimide led to cleavage at the tryptophyl residue, and to isolation of the C-terminal —Leu·Met·Asp·Thr sequence (301a). The complete sequence in this small protein was found to be as follows:

His·Ser·Glu-NH$_2$·Gly·Thr·Phe·Thr·Ser·Asp·Tyr·Ser·Lys·Tyr·
Leu·Asp·Ser·Arg·Arg·Ala·Glu-NH$_2$·Asp·Phe·Val·
Glu-NH$_2$·Try·Leu·Met·Asp-NH$_2$·Thr

Glucagen

OXYTOCIN. The determination of the amino acid sequence in the peptide hormone oxytocin consisted of a series of skilful and brilliant experiments carried out by du Vigneaud and his associates, with the quite important consideration that the sequence was ultimately confirmed by synthesis of the complete peptide (see Section 10–39). The hormone, purified by countercurrent distribution (515), yielded on complete analysis one mole residue each of leucine, isoleucine, tyrosine, proline, glutamic acid, aspartic acid, glycine, and cystine, together with three moles of ammonia (516, 517). No free carboxyl group was present (516), and it appeared probable that three of the residues might exist as amides, one of them C-terminal. On desulfurization with Raney nickel, alanine appeared in place of cystine in the hydrolysate (518). Preliminary experiments employing the DNFB procedure of Sanger for the determination of N-terminal residues were not quite decisive, although the fact that six of the eight amino acids did not react with reagent, namely, leucine, isoleucine, proline, glutamic acid, aspartic acid, and glycine, appeared to exclude each of them from the N-terminal position in the peptide (519). The problem was clarified by the discovery that oxytocin or performic acid-oxidized oxytocin preparations when treated with bromine water yielded two fragments; one gave on hydrolysis equimolar 3:5-dibromotyrosine and cysteic acid, whilst the other gave one mole residue each of cysteic acid, leucine, isoleucine, proline, glutamic acid, aspartic acid, and glycine, together with three moles of ammonia (438, 440). The N-terminal residues in performic acid-treated oxytocin, and in the two degradation fragments, were finally located by analysis on starch columns before and after treatment with DNFB (440). One of the two cysteic acid residues was found to be N-terminal in oxidized oxytocin, and also in the smaller fragment found after bromine treatment. Thus this smaller fragment was cysteyltyrosine, and was presumed to be the N-terminal sequence in oxytocin (440); the larger fragment possessed an N-terminal isoleucine residue and hence the N-terminal sequence could be considered as cysteyltyrosylisoleucyl-. The final determination of the sequence of amino acids was accomplished by du Vigneaud, Ressler, and Trippett (520) through the study of the fragments resulting from the partial acid hydrolysates of oxytocin and of desulfurized oxytocin. The peptide fragments were separated into neutral and acidic components by the use of ion exchange resins, further separated by paper chromatography, the individual peptides eluted, hydrolyzed, and rechromatographed. Sequences were determined in part by the Edman degradation.

The aspartylcysteic acid isolated was confirmed by isolation of the peptide (Asp, Ala) from a partial hydrolysate of desulfurized oxytocin. This peptide, together with three others, isolated from the acidic fraction of the heptapeptide formed after bromine treatment, namely ($CySO_3H$, Pro), ($CySO_3H$, Pro, Leu), and ($CySO_3H$, Pro, Leu, Gly), suggested the sequence

$$\begin{array}{c} \text{CyS} \\ | \\ \text{Asp·CyS·Pro·Leu·Gly} \end{array}$$

This was consistent with the peptide (Pro, Leu, Gly) isolated from several fractions of the partial hydrolysates. With another peptide fragment, (CyS, Asp, Glu), the sequence became

$$\begin{array}{c} \text{CyS} \\ | \\ \text{Glu·Asp·CyS·Pro·Leu·Gly} \end{array}$$

which was also consistent with the peptide (Ala, Asp, Glu) from desulfurized oxytocin, and with (CyS, Asp, Glu) isolated from hydrolysates of oxytocin.

Again from partial hydrolysates of desulfurized oxytocin, there was obtained the peptide (Ileu, Glu), and the sequence became

$$\begin{array}{c} \text{CyS} \\ | \\ \text{Ileu·Glu·Asp·CyS·Pro·Leu·Gly} \end{array}$$

This is the heptapeptide formed from oxytocin through treatment with bromine water, and the finding of the peptide fragment (Tyr, CyS, Asp, Glu) suggested

CyS(Tyr)
|
Ileu·Glu·Asp·CyS·Pro·Leu·Gly

Inasmuch as only one of the two cysteic acid residues in performic acid-oxidized oxytocin carried a free amino group, and thus one-half of a cystine moiety possessed a free amino group, it appeared that it was this residue which was linked through its carboxyl group to the amino group of tyrosine:

CyS·Tyr
|
Ileu·Glu·Asp·CyS·Pro·Leu·Gly

The Edman degradation applied to performic acid-oxidized oxytocin yielded one mole of cysteic acid at the first step, tyrosine at the second step together with a small amount of isoleucine, most of the isoleucine at the third step, and much of the glutamic acid at the fourth step. These observations were based on the subtractive method of measuring losses from starch column chromatograms of bands ordinarily present and derived from hydrolysates of unaltered oxytocin. In this way independent evidence of the N-terminal CyS·Tyr·Ileu·Glu· sequence was obtained, and the backbone structure of oxytocin established. There remained only the problem of allocating the residues from which the three moles of ammonia were derived on hydrolysis. Oxytocin was resistant to carboxypeptidase and did not react when treated by the Schlack and Kumpf thiohydantoin procedure. However, after treatment with N HCl at 90–100° for 1 hour, oxytocin yielded one mole of ammonia and, through the Schlack and Kumpf procedure close to one mole of glycine was revealed. The C-terminal residue was therefore glycine amide. The sites of the other two ammonia precursors were assumed to be asparagine and glutamine, but this assumption, together with that whereby all of the optically active residues were L in configuration, remained to be proved by the subsequent synthesis of oxytocin.

H·CyS·Tyr·Ileu·Glu-NH$_2$·Asp-NH$_2$·CyS·Pro·Leu·Gly·NH$_2$
Oxytocin

Tuppy (521), and Tuppy and Michl (522) arrived at the same structure of oxytocin by a study of the fragments resulting from the partial hydrolysis with acid and with *Bacillus subtilis*. The bacterial enzyme split the bond between tyrosine and isoleucine; the same specificity was employed to determine the asparaginyl—glutamine bond in oxidized insulin B (523).

The partial sequence ·Tyr·Ileu·Glu-NH₂· in oxytocin was subsequently confirmed by Fraenkel-Conrat (221) by the direct use of the Edman degradation procedure.

Vasopressin is the designation given the pressor principle of the posterior pituitary, and the purified material has been shown to be composed of residues of the eight amino acids phenylalanine, tyrosine, proline, glutamic acid, aspartic acid, glycine, arginine, and cystine, plus three moles of ammonia per mole of any one amino acid (524). This hormone, derived from beef tissue, has been termed *arginine* vasopressin to distinguish it from *lysine* vasopressin, isolated from the hog posterior pituitary, and which has a similar amino acid composition except that lysine is present in place of arginine (525). Partial acid hydrolysates of arginine vasopressin oxidized previously with performic acid, together with hydrolysates derived from the action of trypsin on intact vasopressin (526) which released the C-terminal glycine amide residue, yielded a series of peptide fragments which suggested the sequence (527)

$$\overline{\text{CyS·Tyr·Phe·Glu·Asp·CyS}}\text{·(Pro, Arg)Gly·NH}_2$$
Vasopressin

Comparison with the structure of oxytocin indicated that, within the ring, a residue of phenylalanine had been substituted in vasopressin for a residue of isoleucine. That the C-terminal sequence may be Pro·Arg·Gly·NH₂ followed from a synthetic approach to the above structure, utilizing L-amino acids, whereby a biologically active material, closely resembling natural arginine vasopressin in all respects, was successfully prepared (528).

Oxytocin is reducible by sodium and liquid ammonia, and in the presence of benzyl bromide will form the inactive dibenzyl derivative, each benzyl group being substituted on an S atom; on removal of the benzyl groups and oxidation of the regenerated mercaptan groups in air at *p*H 6.5, the original —S—S— bond within the ring is formed and the hormone molecule reconstituted (529); thus

$$\overline{\text{CyS·Tyr·Ileu·Glu-NH}_2\text{·Asp-NH}_2\text{·CyS·R}}$$
Oxytocin

H₂ ↕ O₂, *p*H 6.5

$$\text{CySH·Tyr·Ileu·Glu-NH}_2\text{·Asp-NH}_2\text{·CySH·R}$$
Reduced oxytocin

In the main, therefore, the oxidative conversion of the dithiol peptide consisted of a monomeric, intramolecular reaction, with no change in molecular weight beyond the loss of two hydrogen atoms.

PEPTIDES INVOLVING TWO CYSTINE RESIDUES. A similar study of the oxidation by aeration of the simpler compound, L-cysteinyl-L-cysteine, not at pH 6.5 but at pH 8.5, led to the isolation of a crystalline preparation of an oxidized peptide with twice the molecular weight of the reduced peptide (530), which yielded L-cystine almost quantitatively on complete hydrolysis with acid, and which gave on paper chromatography (phenol) two ninhydrin-reactive spots one of which was major with $R_F = 0.18$, and the other quite minor with $R_F = 0.49$ (531, 532). The product was evidently L-cystinyl-L-cystine, for which two cyclic dimeric structures are possible:

$$\text{CySH·CySH} \xrightarrow[pH\ 8.5]{O_2} \begin{array}{c} \text{CyS} \rightarrow \text{CyS} \\ | \quad\quad | \\ \text{CyS} \rightarrow \text{CyS} \end{array} \quad \text{or} \quad \begin{array}{c} \text{CyS} \rightarrow \text{CyS} \\ | \quad\quad | \\ \text{CyS} \leftarrow \text{CyS} \end{array}$$

L-Cysteinyl-L-cysteine "Parallel" L-cystinyl-L-cystine   "Antiparallel" L-cystinyl-L-cystine

Both "parallel" and "antiparallel" structures form di-DNP derivatives with DNFB, but it would be expected that the hydrolysis of such a derivative of the former would lead to a mixture of di-DNP-L-cystine plus L-cystine, whereas that of the latter would lead to two equivalents of mono-DNP-L-cystine (532). The DNP derivative formed in the usual manner in 50% ethanolic bicarbonate solution was a crystalline material with $R_F = 0.72$ in t-amyl phthalate with S. and S. paper No. 598. Hydrolysis in refluxing 30% ethanolic $2N$ HCl for 3 hours was followed by evaporation to dryness *in vacuo* and distribution of the residue between dilute HCl and ether. Both layers were colored yellow. Evaporation of each layer to dryness and chromatography of each residue revealed the presence of cystine in the previous aqueous layer ($R_F = 0.22$, phenol), as well as of mono-DNP-cystine ($R_F = 0.62$ in phenol-citrate-cyanide-ammonia), whilst from the previous ether layer there was clear evidence for the presence of di-DNP-cystine ($R_F = 0.81$ in phenol-citrate-cyanide-ammonia). There was, therefore, seemingly evidence in the crystalline L-cystinyl-L-cystine prepared by the oxidation of L-cysteinyl-L-cysteine *at pH 8.5* structures compatible with a mixture of both "parallel" and "antiparallel" configurations, a conclusion consistent with the presence of two ninhydrin-reactive spots on the paper chromatogram for the free dipeptide as mentioned above. That the results obtained were not due to disulfide interchange (409) during the hydrolysis of the di-DNP derivative in the acidic solvent follows from the results described below.

When the oxidation by aeration of L-cysteinyl-L-cysteine was conducted at pH 6.5, a crystalline product was isolated (531) which had the same molecular weight as the starting material (532), which yielded L-cystine almost quantitatively on complete hydrolysis with acid, and which gave on paper chromatography (phenol) only a single ninhydrin-reactive spot with

$R_F = 0.49$. This product could only be the cyclic monomer to which the designation cyclo-L-cystinyl was given (532):

$$\underset{\text{L-Cysteinyl-L-cysteine}}{\text{CySH·CySH}} \xrightleftharpoons[\text{pH 6.5}]{O_2} \underset{\text{Cyclo-L-cystinyl}}{\overset{\rceil}{\text{CyS·CyS}}}$$

The DNP derivative of cyclo-L-cystinyl was prepared and found to possess, coincidentally, the same R_F value as that observed for the di-DNP derivative of cystinylcysteine. On hydrolysis under the same conditions as undergone by the latter compound it should yield only mono-DNP-cystine, provided no disulfide interchange occurred whereby some di-DNP-cystine plus cystine could be formed. The results of the experiment were clear-cut and decisive. The only product of hydrolysis that could be detected was mono-DNP-cystine. Under the hydrolytic conditions employed there was no observable disulfide interchange. Under other hydrolytic conditions, however, such a reaction was readily detectable, for when the DNP derivative of cyclo-L-cystinyl was heated at reflux temperature in a solvent composed of 3N HCl in 25% formic acid for 3 hours, the products included not only mono-DNP-cystine but also some free cystine, and a yellow, ninhydrin-insensitive compound which was probably di-DNP-cystine.

It would appear that the character of the oxidized disulfide product depends upon the pH at which the dimercaptan compounds are oxidized (as well as upon the concentration (cf. 532)), and that the successful regeneration of active oxytocin may probably have been due to the use of pH 6.5 in conducting the oxidation of the reduced peptide.

The oxidation at pH 8.5 of L-cysteinyl-L-cysteine and of several peptides in which glycine, diglycine, triglycine, or tetraglycine was inserted between the two cysteine residues was studied by Heaton, Rydon, and Schofield (533). In these cases, the solution of each oxidized peptide was evaporated *in vacuo* to dryness, and the entire crude residue converted to the DNP derivatives. These derivatives were subsqeuently separated by paper chromatography and paper electrophoresis. In the oxidation of cysteinylcysteine, at least four DNP derivatives were present. The major component was selected for study, and it was hydrolyzed at 100° with 1:1 acetic acid–20% HCl, conditions leading readily to disulfide interchange. The earlier product of the hydrolysis was apparently mono-DNP-cystine which, by disulfide interchange, was partly converted to di-DNP-cystine and free cystine. On the basis of these findings, the authors ascribed to the cystinylcystine structure, whose DNP derivative was selected for study, an "antiparallel" configuration. A similar interpretation was given to the major components among the DNP derivatives of the oxidation products of L-cysteinylglycyl-L-cysteine. However, as the number of glycine residues between the L-cysteine end groups increased, the oxidation products appeared to contain an increasingly larger proportion of the cyclic monomer configuration. No "parallel" dimer was noted at any time, but this might have been due to the method of selecting only the more abundant DNP derivative for hydrolytic study.

ZYMOGENS AND PEPTIDES RELEASED THEREFROM. The digestive enzymes of the alimentary tract in mammals occur in an inactive form, and are activated by some proteolytic reaction whereby one or more peptides are split off from the original protein molecule.

The autocatalytic conversion of pepsinogen to pepsin may be illustrated:

$$P'g \xrightarrow{P} X \text{ peptides} + PI \underset{}{\overset{pH\ 5.4}{\rightleftharpoons}} P + I \longrightarrow P + Y \text{ peptides}$$

where P'g = pepsinogen, P = pepsin, PI is an inactive pepsin-inhibitor complex, I = the inhibitor, and X and Y are peptide products (534). Although pepsin catalyzes the initial change in pepsinogen, pepsin is not the immediate product but rather an inactive pepsin-inhibitor compound, PI. This compound dissociates below pH 5 into active pepsin P, and free inhibitor I. Nine peptide bonds are cleaved during the conversion of the precursor to the active enzyme. Applications of the DNFB procedure to pepsinogen, the pepsin inhibitor, and pepsin have yielded results not fully consistent with each other. Thus it has been reported that the N-terminal residue in pepsin is leucine (193, 194) and isoleucine (534). The N-terminal residue of pepsinogen and of the pepsin inhibitor is reported to be leucine (534). By the use of carboxypeptidase, alanine has been found to be the C-terminal residue in both pepsinogen and pepsin, the sequence in both proteins being valylleucylalanine (534), with the probability that pepsin might occupy the C-terminal segment of pepsinogen. Further clarification of the pepsinogen-pepsin problem is anticipated.

Chymotrypsinogen apparently exists in two forms, designated α (535) and B (536). The conversions considered herein will be concerned with the α variety. The autocatalytic activation of this material at ordinary temperature led to an enzyme designated α-chymotrypsin (535). If, however, the activation with trypsin was carried out rapidly at 0°, an enzyme resulted which was much more active than α-chymotrypsin, and which was designated π-chymotrypsin (537). On continued contact with trypsin, the π enzyme changed further to a product referred to as δ-chymotrypsin; autolysis of this product led finally to the α-enzyme. The δ-enzyme has been shown to be more active than the α toward synthetic substrates (538). Further autolysis of the α-enzyme led to two other forms, designated β and γ (539). In terms of milk-clotting capacity, the enzymes in order of activity are $\pi > \delta > \alpha = \beta = \gamma$ (537).

α-Chymotrypsinogen possesses a molecular weight of 25,000 (540). On treatment of the native protein with the DNFB or PTH reagent or with carboxypeptidase, no evidence for N-terminal (541) or C-terminal residues (309) was obtained, although the oxidized protein (with performic acid) did reveal an N-terminal half-cystine residue as DNP-cysteic acid (235), and a C-terminal tyrosine or leucine residue. When the protein was previously cleaved with sulfite it appeared to yield a C-terminal aspartic acid residue (427a). The presence of a single C-terminal residue in this protein was subsequently substantiated by the finding that one mole of CO_2 was evolved when the protein was warmed with N-bromosuccinimide (301). α-Chymotrypsin apparently possesses two N-terminal residues as obtained by the DNFB procedure, namely alanine and isoleucine (541), and two C-terminal residues, leucine and tyrosine, as obtained through the use of carboxypeptidase (309); whether this enzyme still possesses the N-terminal half-cystine residue of the precursor zymogen, or whether it has been split off to reveal the new N-terminal alanine residue in the α-enzyme is not clear at the present time. The rapid activation technique whereby α-chymotrypsinogen is converted to the π, δ, etc., modifications has been extensively studied by Neurath and his collaborators (542–544). This technique was conducted at 0°, trypsin being used as the activating agent. Inasmuch as the chymotrypsin products themselves possess activity, and would thus tend to obscure some of the activation phenomena, β-phenylpropionate was employed in certain stages in the activation mixtures, e.g., the π → δ conversion, to inhibit this activity (542). Similarly, when it was desired to inhibit the trypsin activator and allow the chymotrypsin activity full sway, the crystalline soybean trypsin inhibitor was employed, and the use of β-phenylpropionate was avoided (542). Again, to avoid self-digestion of either chymotrypsin employed as a substrate or carboxypeptidase as an enzyme, the endopeptidase activity of both proteins was removed by appropriate substitution with diisopropylfluorophosphate, whereby valid end-group analyses could be conducted. Under these conditions, the conversion of α-chymotrypsinogen by rapid action with trypsin to π-chymotrypsin was accomplished with no change in electrophoretic mobility at pH 4.97, and two N-terminal residues became apparent, namely, half-cystine and isoleucine, and there was still no evidence of a C-terminal residue susceptible to the action of carboxypeptidase (although if this were tyrosine it would seem unusual to be resistant to this enzyme). The next stage, δ-chymotrypsin, had a lower electrophoretic mobility at pH 4.97; it also contained N-terminal half-cystine and isoleucine and revealed definitely one C-terminal residue, namely, leucine by carboxypeptidase action, and some evidence of C-terminal tyrosine. On further degradation, when α-chymotrypsin made its appearance, a second, fully-defined C-terminal residue, namely tyrosine, was found.

Thus in the α-chymotrypsinogen → π-chymotrypsin activation a new N-terminal residue makes its appearance, and this isoleucine residue is known to be combined with valine as the next member in the sequence (543);

the DNP-isoleucine isolated is associated with some DNP-isoleucylvaline as a result of the difficulty in hydrolyzing the isoleucylvaline bond with acid. The C-terminal leucine and tyrosine residues are very probably derived from two different C-terminal chains or sequences inasmuch as the former arises as a result of one conversion, $\pi \rightarrow \delta$, and the latter as a result of a second conversion, $\delta \rightarrow \alpha$ (542). All the chymotrypsins, whether π, δ, or α, contain the N-terminal isoleucylvalyl sequence in common, but this is apparently lacking in the chymotrypsinogen. The conversion of π- to δ-chymotrypsin, which involves a decrease in electrophoretic mobility, suggested the splitting off of a basic peptide of some sort. Little change in molecular weight accompanied the α-chymotrypsinogen $\rightarrow$ π-chymotrypsin $\rightarrow$ δ chymotrypsin conversions (543).

That a loss of a small basic peptide actually occurs was shown in the experiments by Dreyer and Neurath (544). Chromatographic analysis of a solution of chymotrypsinogen undergoing activation revealed that, parallel with the appearance of δ-chymotrypsin, a peptide appeared which was identified as serylarginine. In view of the known specificity of trypsin, it is not improbable that the appearance of the N-terminal isoleucine residue in π-chymotrypsin is connected with the hydrolysis of a bond joining the carboxyl group of an arginine residue with the amino group of the isoleucine residue, and thus activation to this stage at least is associated with the cleavage of a single peptide bond. To carry the hypothesis further, Dreyer and Neurath considered that this arginine residue may be the C-terminal of the serylarginine peptide split off in the $\pi \rightarrow \delta$ conversion. The sequence of steps may well be

α-Chymotrypsinogen (N-terminal half-cystine, and possibly C-terminal tyrosine or leucine)
↓ Trypsin

π-Chymotrypsin (N-terminal half-cystine, N-terminal isoleucine, and possibly C-terminal tyrosine)
↓ Chymotrypsin

δ-Chymotrypsin (N-terminal half-cystine, N-terminal isoleucine, C-terminal leucine, C-terminal tyrosine) plus serylarginine
↓

α-Chymotrypsin (N-terminal alanine, N-terminal isoleucine, C-terminal leucine, C-terminal tyrosine)

The presence of serylarginine and, in addition, of threonylaspartic acid among the products of the activation of α-chymotrypsinogen was subsequently reported by Sakota (545). The N- and C-terminal residues of β- and γ-chymotrypsin appear to be the same as those in the α-variety (309, 545, 546).

Trypsinogen is an enzymically inert protein of molecular weight 23,800

(547), and it possesses one N-terminal valine residue (548), and no detectable C-terminal residue in the presence of added carboxypeptidase (549). When trypsinogen was converted to trypsin through the action of minute amounts of trypsin (550), there was little change in the molecular weight (547), isoleucine appeared as the N-terminal residue in place of valine (548), but there was still no detectable C-terminal residue when carboxypeptidase was used (549). Hydrazinolysis of trypsinogen before and after activation revealed no C-terminal residue (550a). The appearance of a different N-terminal residue as a result of the trypsinogen → trypsin conversion suggested that some residue or sequence of residues may have been cleaved. Davie and Neurath (549) investigated this possibility by removing aliquots of a solution containing such an activation mixture, adsorbing any free amino acids or peptides onto and subsequently eluting them from ion exchange resins, and finally chromatographing them on paper before and after complete hydrolysis. Thus a typical experiment consisted in establishing a mixture of 120 mg. of trypsinogen with 0.7 mg. of trypsin in a borate buffer, removing aliquots from time to time on a Dowex 50 resin (H$^+$), following the rate and extent of activation using benzoylarginine ester as substrate (551), eluting adsorbed material with ammonia, and subjecting the eluate to paper chromatography (butanol–acetic acid–water); the zero time control revealed no ninhydrin-reactive areas, but with time a single spot appeared with increasing intensity. Elution of the spot, followed by hydrolysis with strong HCl, neutralization, and paper chromatography, indicated the presence of lysine, valine, and aspartic acid in molar ratios close to 1 : 1 : 4 (551).

It appeared therefore that the activation of trypsinogen to form trypsin was accompanied by the splitting off of a hexapeptide from the former molecule (549). Application of the DNFB procedure to the peptide revealed one DNP-valine residue. Carboxypeptidase failed to release any detectable ninhydrin-positive material. The empirical formula of the peptide is thus Val·[(Asp)$_4$, Lys]. Its structure was considered to be Val·(Asp)$_4$·Lys by inference inasmuch as (a) the activating enzyme, trypsin, possesses a known preferential action toward hydrolyzing bonds involving the carboxyl group of basic amino acids such as arginine or lysine, and, therefore, (b) it would be expected that carboxypeptidase might be inert toward a peptide containing a basic, C-terminal amino acid residue. The hydrolysis of a lysyl-isoleucine bond in trypsinogen may therefore be the single hydrolytic event which leads to the formation of active trypsin (548, 549):

$$\underset{\text{Trypsinogen}}{\text{Val·(Asp)}_4\text{·Lys·Ileu-Protein}} \xrightarrow{\text{Trypsin}} \underset{\text{Hexapeptide}}{\text{Val·(Asp)}_4\text{·Lys}} + \underset{\text{Trypsin}}{\text{Ileu-Protein}}$$

The N-terminal sequence of trypsin is Ileu·Val·Gly·Glu·Tyr- (551a).

A crystalline protein was isolated from soybean meal by Kunitz (552) which inhibited the proteolytic activity of trypsin, possibly through a salt-like combination of the carboxyl groups of the inhibitor with the free amino groups of trypsin (553). The inhibitor protein was shown to be composed of a single polypeptide chain, containing aspartic acid or asparagine as the N-terminal residue, and leucine (through the action of carboxypeptidase) as the C-terminal residue (554). The inhibitor together with trypsin in equal amounts may be crystallized as a compound (552); carboxypeptidase liberated leucine from this compound (554). Inasmuch as trypsin alone was inert to carboxypeptidase, it was inferred (554) that the C-terminal leucine residue was not involved in the compound formation. This inference was strengthened by the fact that the inhibitor protein alone, after losing its C-terminal leucine residue through the action of carboxypeptidase, was still able to combine with trypsin with undiminished inhibitory activity. That trypsin may actually possess a single C-terminal residue follows from the reaction of the protein with N-bromosuccinimide (301); the nature of this residue, however, is unknown.

The conversion of fibrinogen to fibrin is an enzymic process catalyzed by thrombin. During the clotting process, non-protein material is split off (555), and it is probable that thrombin functions in part at least as a proteolytic enzyme. With synthetic peptides as substrates, thrombin appears to exert a preferential hydrolytic action on bonds involving the carboxyl group of arginine (556). Rovery and Desnuelle (541) found tyrosine as N-terminal residues of both fibrinogen and fibrin; this is true for several species (556a). By the use of the DNFB procedure, Bailey and Bettelheim (557) observed that bovine fibrinogen possessed two N-terminal tyrosine and one N-terminal glutamic acid residues, whereas fibrin possessed two N-terminal tyrosine and two or three N-terminal glycine residues; both proteins split off phenylalanine as C-terminal residue after treatment with carboxypeptidase. Human fibrinogen contains N-terminal alanine instead of glutamic acid (556a). The excess of N-terminal glycine residues in bovine fibrin over the single N-terminal glutamic acid residue in fibrinogen suggested that two or more peptides may be split off from the latter during its conversion to fibrin (558), and indeed two peptides were isolated and separated from the conversion mixture and from each other. One of them possessed, as might be expected, an N-terminal glutamic acid residue, the other revealed no detectable N-terminal group by the DNFB procedure; the latter possessed one lysine residue as shown by the isolation of ε-DNP-lysine, the former none. One of these peptides contains tyrosine-O-sulfate (558). It would appear from these data that the clotting process involves at least hydrolytic action of thrombin on one or more bonds concerned with the amino groups of glycine (557). Prothrombin itself, whether of human or bovine origin, possesses one mole of N-terminal alanine per mole of protein (558a).

Hypertensin I is a peptide material split off from bovine serum protein by the proteolytic action of renin, an enzyme preparation from the kidney. A purified decapeptide (559) with high physiological activity was subjected by Elliott and Peart (560) to sequential residue analysis. Complete analysis revealed two moles of histidine, two of valine, and one each of arginine, aspartic acid, proline, leucine, phenylalanine, and tyrosine. Application of the DNFB procedure showed that the N-terminal residue was aspartic acid, treatment with carboxypeptidase revealed leucine as the C-terminal residue with phenylalanine and histidine as adjacent residues, and stepwise degradation by the Edman method indicated the N-terminal sequence as Asp·Arg·Val·Tyr. Partial acid hydrolysis yielded only one identifiable peptide, namely, histidylleucine, which suggested the C-terminal sequence of Phe·His·Leu. Thus the sequence so far was

$$Asp·Arg·Val·Tyr \ldots Phe·His·Leu$$

The sequence of the remaining three residues was determined from the products of chymotrypsin digestion: these products, including a tetrapeptide (His, Pro, Val, Phe), were separated from each other by paper electrophoresis. Application of the DNFB procedure to the tetrapeptide revealed an N-terminal valine residue, the Edman procedure revealed a Val·His·Pro sequence, and the carboxypeptidase procedure revealed a C-terminal phenylalanine residue—the full sequence was therefore Val·His·Pro·Phe. The action of aminopeptidase on the hypertensin I decapeptide resulted in rapid liberation of all the amino acids present, strongly suggesting that they were all L in optical configuration. The sequence of the residues in the hypertensin I peptide is therefore (559)

$$Asp·Arg·Val·Tyr·Val·His·Pro·Phe·His·Leu$$

A similar peptide, differing only in replacement of the valine residue fifth from the N-terminus by a residue of isoleucine, was isolated from horse serum.

Hypertensin II is an octapeptide isolated from equine serum, and derived from the corresponding decapeptide by enzymic cleavage of the leucine and histidine residues from the C-terminus (561); it is highly effective *in vitro*. The octapeptide has recently been synthesized (562) (Chapter 10).

MELANOCYTE-STIMULATING HORMONES (MSH). There are apparently two polypeptides which can be isolated from the posterior lobes of the hog pituitary gland, and which possess the capacity to stimulate the growth of melanocytes. The two polypeptides have been distinguished by the designations α and β, the former being basic in character with an isoelectric point at pH 10.5–11.0, whereas the latter is slightly acidic in reaction with an isoelectric point at pH 5.5. The sequences in these compounds were largely elucidated by Harris and his associates (563, 564).

No N-terminal residue could be detected in the α-peptide with either the Sanger or Edman procedures, nor any C-terminal residue with carboxypeptidase (564), whilst the maximum whole number molar ratios of the principal constituent amino acids, as revealed by analysis, appeared to be: Arg_1 Glu_1 Gly_1 His_1 Lys_1 Met_1 Phe_1 Pro_1 Ser_2 Try_1 Tyr_1 Val_1 (and NH_3, 1). On digestion of the α-peptide with trypsin and with chymotrypsin, and submitting the resulting mixtures to ionophoresis on paper in a pyridine–acetic acid buffer at pH 6.5 and at 40 volts per cm., the various peptide fragments could be located on guide strips with ninhydrin. Peptides containing tryptophan, tyrosine, and histidine residues were separately located by specific color reactions. After elution with 5% acetic acid, the solution of each peptide component was divided essentially into two parts. One part was subjected to complete hydrolysis to the free amino acids, whilst the other part was subjected to various techniques such as the Sanger and Edman for N-terminal residues, the carboxypeptidase for C-terminal, or to further partial hydrolysis via chymotrypsin or strong HCl at 37°, the products being determined by paper chromatography.

The following peptides were isolated after trypsin (T) and chymotrypsin (C) treatment, their amino acid compositions being

T_1 (Ser_2, Tyr, Met, Glu, His, Phe, Arg)
T_2 (Try, Gly, Lys, Pro, Val)
C_1 (Ser, Tyr)
C_2 (Ser, Met, Glu, His, Phe)
C_3 (Arg, Try, Gly, Lys, Pro, Val)
C_4 (Arg, Try)
C_5 (Gly, Lys, Pro, Val)

Peptide C_1 was negative to ninhydrin but gave serine and tyrosine on acid hydrolysis, whilst tyrosine was shown to be C-terminal by being cleaved to the free state by carboxypeptidase. C_1 was therefore an amino-substituted derivative of Ser·Tyr, or R—Ser·Tyr.

Peptide T_1 must possess a C-terminal arginine in accordance with the specificity of trypsin. The action of carboxypeptidase on C_2 showed that the C-terminal residue was phenylalanine. Comparison of T_1, C_1, and C_2 suggested that C_1 and C_2 were part of the T_1 sequence, which in turn formed quite probably the N-terminal sequence R—Ser·Tyr·(Ser, Met, Glu, His)·Phe·Arg in the structure of the α-peptide hormone. Application of the Edman degradation to C_2 resulted in the successive formation of the phenylthiohydantoins of serine, methionine, and glutamic acid, which established the N-terminal sequence of the hormone as R—Ser·Tyr·Ser·Met·Glu·His·Phe·Arg.

Subjection of C_3 to digestion with chymotrypsin yielded equimolar amounts of C_4 and C_5. Peptides T_2, C_3, and C_5 were found to be unusually basic as revealed by their mobilities during ionophoresis at pH 6.5, and it could be inferred that in all three compounds the carboxyl group of the C-terminal residue did not exist in the free state. This inference was further supported by the resistance shown by all three compounds to the action of carboxypeptidase, and it appeared therefore that T_2, C_3, and C_5 formed the C-terminal sequence in the α-peptide hormone. The partial acid hydrolysis of C_5 in $12N$ HCl at 37° for 5 days yielded the peptide fragments Gly·Lys, Gly·Lys·Pro, Lys·Pro, and Pro·Val, and in addition one mole of ammonia. This established the sequence in C_5 as Gly·Lys·Pro·Val·NH$_2$.

The complete amino acid sequence of the α-peptide hormone, an N-substituted tridecapeptide amide, could be represented as (564)

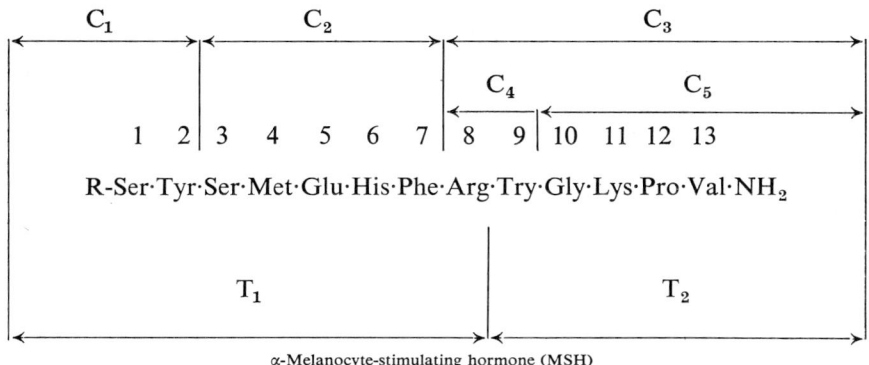

α-Melanocyte-stimulating hormone (MSH)

This sequence for the α-hormone is identical with the N-terminal tridecapeptide sequence of the corticotropins. Corticotropin, in which the N-terminal serine is free, has a low activity as a melanocyte stimulator; when this terminal serine is removed (as on alkaline treatment of the hormone or through periodate treatment), there is complete loss of the original adrenocorticotropic activity, but also a very significant increase in the melanocyte-stimulating activity (564). Thus corticotropin can be changed to a predominantly melanocyte-stimulating substance, and this phenomenon suggests that the state of the N-terminal serine residue influences which of the two biological properties of the peptide structure will be the stronger.

The β-form of the melanocyte-stimulating hormone was studied by Harris and Roos (563) and by Geschwind, Li, and Barnafi (565), and was shown to possess 18 amino acid residues, 7 of which were the same as in the corticotropins and in the α-peptide (564), as indicated by the diagram shown on page 1660.

It is probable that the essential minimal structural requirements for melanocyte-stimulating activity may adhere to the common sequence Met·Glu·His·Phe·Arg·Try·Gly, inasmuch as positions 6 and 14 in the β sequence and 3 and 11 in the α-sequence can be occupied by either lysine or serine without effect on the biological activity of the two peptides (564). Indeed, the pentapeptide sequence His·Phe·Arg·Try·Gly, synthesized in two different laboratories (565a), was found to be active. A β-type peptide hormone isolated from the ox pituitary gland possessed much the same sequence as that of swine origin except for the presence of a serine residue in position 2 in place of glutamic acid (565).

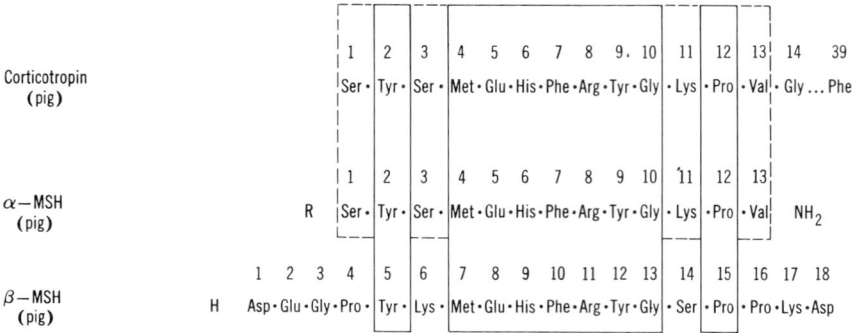

OPHTHALMIC ACID. This is a tripeptide isolated from the lens which yielded on acid hydrolysis one mole each of glutamic acid, butyrine, and glycine (566). Determination of the end groups revealed that the N-terminal residue was glutamic acid, and the C-terminal residue glycine. The tripeptide therefore was glutamylbutyrinylglycine. With the observation that the glutamyl residue was linked through the γ-carboxyl group, the analogy of ophthalmic acid to glutathione was complete. Because of the paucity of the lens peptide, the evidence on which this γ-linkage was developed was based at first on analogy. Thus the electrophoretic mobility at pH 4 in pyridine–acetic acid buffer on paper, with a potential gradient of 11.1 volts per cm., was over twice as large for known γ-glutamyl peptides as for known α-glutamyl peptides. The mobility of ophthalmic acid under these conditions was very close to that of glutathione and of other γ-glutamyl peptides, and more than twice as great as that of α-glutamylvaline or of α-glutamyltyrosine (566). Final proof of the structure of the tripeptide came about through its synthesis, L-glutamic acid and L-butyrine, as well as glycine, being employed for this purpose. The $[\alpha]_D$ value for the synthetic ophthalmic acid was $-29°$ in water at 20°; comparison with the optical value for the natural material was not possible because of its scarcity. However, comparison of the X-ray diagrams of natural and synthetic materials furnished strong presumptive evidence of their identity.

EVOLIDINE. This is a cyclic peptide isolated from the leaves of *Evodia xanthoxyloides* which on hydrolysis in refluxing acid yielded a mixture of

L-amino acids and ammonia. Analysis of the hydrolysate via column chromatography and extent of ninhydrin color of each peak versus a leucine standard (Chapter 15) revealed the following composition: $Val_1Leu_2 Pro_1Phe_1Ser_1$ and Asp_1-NH_2. No end groups could be determined on the intact peptide, and therefore a cyclic structure was assumed (566a). Partial hydrolysis with concentrated HCl at 35°, separation of the resulting smaller peptides by paper chromatography, and determination of the N-terminal residues and residue sequences for each eluted peptide with fluorodinitrobenzene or phenyl isothiocyanate led to identification of the following sequences in five well-separated peptide fragments:

$$Asp·Leu$$
$$Val·Asp$$
$$Leu·Pro·Val$$
$$Phe·Leu·Pro$$
$$Ser·Phe$$

The structure of evolidine was therefore assumed to be (566a)

$$Cyclo[Ser·Phe·Leu·Pro·Val·Asp(-\beta-NH_2)·Leu]$$

PLAKALBUMIN. Ovalbumin is susceptible to the limited action of a proteolytic enzyme from *Bacillus subtilis* whereby a peptide is split off. The residual protein can be obtained in crystalline form, generally in rectangular plates, and hence has been designated plakalbumin (567). The peptide which is cleaved from ovalbumin contains six residues, namely, three of alanine and one each of glycine, valine, and aspartic acid. Together with the hexapeptide there appears in the reaction medium two degradation products thereof, namely, a tetrapeptide with one residue each of glycine, valine, aspartic acid, and alanine, and a dipeptide, alanylalanine (213), all of which were separated from each other on starch columns. By the use of the Edman degradation, the sequence of residues in the tetrapeptide was shown to be alanylglycylvalylaspartic acid, and that in the hexapeptide, very probably, alanylglycylvalylaspartylalanylalanine (213). The *subtilis* enzyme apparently hydrolyzed the hexapeptide from the ovalbumin molecule at a bond involving the amino group of an alanine residue, and secondarily attacked the penultimate bond of the liberated hexapeptide, again involving the amino group of an alanine residue. More recent investigations by Ottesen (213) with a more purified preparation of the enzyme indicated that glutamic acid very probably preceded alanine on the amino end of the hexapeptide. Subtilisin itself possesses an alanine N-terminal residue with glutamic acid next in line (568).

CYTOCHROME c. After the pepsin digestion of cytochrome c, a brown-red colored peptide was isolated which contained the prosthetic group of the enzyme (569, 570). The yield of crude product was about 100 mg. from 0.83 g. of cytochrome c. The compound was purified by partition chromatography on Hyflo Supercel, and yielded a final product which weighed 41 mg. Complete analysis revealed three residues of glutamic acid, two of valine, and one each of threonine, alanine, histidine, and lysine; two residues of ammonia were present, suggestive of two possible residues of glutamine. Sulfur was present in this peptide, and it was presumed that the ferriporphyrin prosthetic group was combined with the peptide, as it is in the parent cytochrome c protein (570, 571), through thioether bridges involving cysteine residues. Consequently, the thioether bridges were split, and the thiol groups, set free through the action of silver salts (572), were oxidized to sulfonic acid groups by treatment with performic acid. The porphyrin-free peptide now, on complete hydrolysis, revealed, in addition to the amino acids described above, two residues of cysteic acid. The complete peptide derived by peptic digestion of cytochrome c contained, therefore, eleven amino acid residues. End-group analyses, partial digestion with trypsin, and partial acid hydrolysis of the porphyrin-free peptide provided data on which the following sequence of amino acids was based (570):

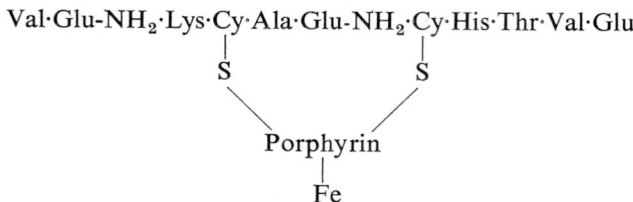

Ferriporphyrin peptide from cytochrome c (peptic action)

A tryptic digest of cytochrome c yielded a peptide also containing the ferriporphyrin prosthetic group (573), and on analysis the following sequence was obtained:

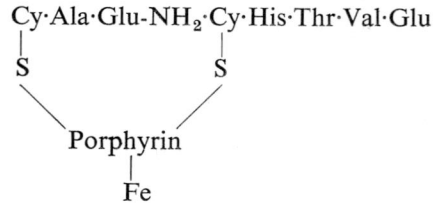

Ferriporphyrin peptide from cytochrome c (tryptic action)

Thus, in both fragments, the porphyrin is bound via thioether linkages to two cysteine residues, and the sequence of amino acids in the peptide chain is the same. The shorter fragment after tryptic digestion may be attributed to the specific action of trypsin toward bonds involving the carboxyl group of a lysine residue. The histidine residue attached to one of the cysteine residues in the peptide sequence may be linked to the iron atom of the heme in the intact cytochrome c molecule (574).

The above sequences have been found in the ferriporphyrin peptides prepared by the peptic degradation of bovine and of salmon cytochrome c (570); the corresponding peptide obtained from chicken cytochrome c, however, differed from the others by the replacement of the alanine by a serine residue.

Cytochrome c possesses a slight peroxidative activity in the presence of mesidine and hydrogen peroxide. At equimolar levels of cytochrome c, and of the ferriporphyrin peptide based on iron content, the latter possessed more than twenty times the peroxidative activity of the former (575), and thus about 1 % of the activity of peroxidase itself (576).

In Table 16–15 are collected data on the terminal residues of the peptides cleaved from various proteins.

EISENINE. In 1940, Ohira (576a) isolated an acidic tripeptide ($[\alpha]_D =$ $-54.2°$ in water at 16°) from a brown marine alga, *Eisenia bicyclis* Setchell, and named it eisenine. Complete acid hydrolysis of the compound yielded 2 moles of L-glutamic acid, 1 mole of L-alanine, and 1 mole of ammonia. The intact tripeptide possessed no free α-amino group, and thus no N-terminal residue could be determined. The compound was not cyclic, for a C-terminal alanine residue could readily be identified. On the basis of all this information, Ohira assumed that the structure of the tripeptide was L-pyrrolidonyl-L-glutaminyl-L-alanine. That this structure was correct was shown subsequently by Rudinger and Pravda (576a) by synthesis through the following sequence (Chapter 10): tosylpyrrolidonyl chloride was combined with glutamine in water at pH 8.7 and the resulting dipeptide coupled with alanine benzyl ester via the mixed anhydride procedure; the benzyl ester group was removed from the tosyl tripeptide by catalytic hydrogenation, the residue converted in refluxing ammonia water to tosylglutaminylglutaminylalanine, the tosyl group removed in a sodium–liquid NH_3 solution, and the free glutaminylglutaminylalanine cyclized to pyrrolidonylglutaminylalanine, identical in all respects with the natural product, by treatment with boiling water.

$$\begin{array}{c} CH_2\text{——}CH_2 \\ | \quad\quad | \\ CO \quad CHCONHCHCONHCH(CH_3)CO_2H \\ \diagdown \diagup \quad\quad\quad | \\ NH \quad\quad\quad CH_2 \\ \quad\quad\quad\quad | \\ \quad\quad\quad\quad CH_2CONH_2 \end{array}$$
Eisenine

TABLE 16-15
Terminal Residues of Peptides Split from Proteins and of the Residual Protein

Protein	N-Terminal Residue	Moles per Mole	Refs.	C-Terminal Residue	Moles per Mole	Refs.
Pepsinogen	Leucine	1	(534)	Alanine	2	(534)
Pepsin (pepsin)	Leucine	1	(193)	Alanine	2	(291)
α-Chymotrypsinogen	Half-cystine	1	(235)	Tyrosine or leucine	1	(309)
α-Chymotrypsin (trypsin)	Alanine	1	(541)	Leucine	1	(309)
α-Chymotrypsin (trypsin)	Isoleucine	1	(541)	Tyrosine	1	(309)
π-Chymotrypsin (trypsin)	Half-cystine	1	(544)	Tyrosine?	1	(544)
	Isoleucine	1	(544)			
δ-Chymotrypsin (chymotrypsin)	Half-cystine	1	(544)	Leucine	1	(544)
	Isoleucine	1	(544)	Tyrosine	1	(544)
Plus serylarginine	Serine	1	(544)	Arginine	1	(544)
β-Chymotrypsin γ-Chymotrypsin	Terminal residues identical with α-variety (378)					
Trypsinogen	Valine	1	(548, 549)	None	—	(549)
Trypsin (trypsin)	Isoleucine	1	(548, 549)	None	—	(549)
Plus [Val(Asp)₄Lys]	Valine	1	(549)	Lysine	1	(549)
Fibrinogen (bovine)	Tyrosine	2	(557)	Phenylalanine	1	(557)
	Glutamic acid	1	(557)			
Fibrin (thrombin)	Tyrosine	2 or 3	(557)	Phenylalanine	1	(557)
	Glycine	2 or 3	(557)			
Plus peptide	Glutamic acid	1	(558)			
Serum globulin	Aspartic acid	1	(201)			
Hypertensin (renin)	Aspartic acid	1	(559)	Leucine	1	(559)
Ovalbumin	None	—	(342)	Proline	1	(311)
Peptide (*subtilis*)	Alanine	1	(213)	Alanine	1	(213)

6. The Amino Acid Sequences in Insulin. The skilful determination of the amino acid sequences in the protein hormone insulin by Sanger and his colleagues ranks as the high point of this kind of investigation. Several aspects of this problem have been referred to in earlier pages, and the present discussion will serve in the nature of a summary.

The method of partial substitution applied to insulin by Harfenist and Craig (577) indicated that the molecular weight of this protein was in the neighborhood of 6000 (cf. 578). Amino acid analyses for beef insulin by Harfenist (357) revealed, in terms of residues per mole: glycine 4, alanine 3, valine 5, leucine 6, isoleucine 1, proline 1, phenylalanine 3, cystine 3, arginine 1, histidine 2, lysine 1, aspartic acid 3, glutamic acid 7, serine 3, threonine 1, tyrosine 4, amide—NH_3 6, methionine 0, and tryptophan 0. The molecular weight calculated from these figures emerges as 5734.

Treatment of insulin with DNFB followed by acid hydrolysis of the DNP-insulin yielded close to one residue each of DNP-glycine and DNP-phenylalanine (149); this result suggested the possible presence of two peptide chains in the insulin molecule. One residue of ε-DNP-lysine was also obtained in the hydrolysate and subsequently served as a point of reference in the determination of neighboring sequences. C-Terminal residue analyses (287, 288) had already shown the presence of one alanine and one asparagine residues (see above); if there were indeed two chains, it would be difficult from the data so far obtained to assign the proper terminal group to each particular chain. This problem was solved by the device of splitting the two chains through oxidation with performic acid, whereby the cystine residues were converted to those of cysteic acid, and the two resulting peptide fragments could be fractionated from each other (435). Thus, from the oxidized insulin mixture, an acidic fraction (A) which contained the glycyl N-terminal residue and no basic amino acid residues, and which was soluble at pH 6.5, could be separated from the more basic N-terminal phenylalanyl chain in the insoluble (B) fraction (435). The two chains could also be separated by partition in a butanol–aqueous dichloroacetic acid system after 30 to 40 transfers, the B chain collecting in the top layer (578*a*). The glycyl chain was found to terminate in asparagine, the phenylalanine chain in alanine. About twenty amino acid residues were found in the glycyl chain, which yielded a molecular weight close to 2900 (cf. 579); not only the basic amino acids were absent from this fraction, but also phenylalanine, threonine, and proline. The phenylalanyl chain contained about thirty amino acid residues, and had a molecular weight of approximately 3800. There were four residues of cysteic acid in the glycyl chain, and two residues in the phenylalanyl chain. Of the six amide groups, four were present in the glycyl chain, and two in the phenylalanyl chain.

The determination of the sequence of residues in the phenylalanyl chain was carried out by Sanger and Tuppy in 1951 (114), who utilized in full the

TABLE 16-16
Peptides Identified in Partial Hydrolysates of the Phenylalanyl Chain of Insulin (114)

Dipeptides from acid or alkaline hydrolysates	Phe·Val Glu·His CySO₃H·Gly His·Leu Glu·Ala Leu·Val CySO₃H·Gly Arg·Gly Lys·Ala Val·Asp His·Leu Leu·Val Ala·Leu Val·CySO₃H Glu·Glu Gly·Phe Asp·Glu Leu·CySO₃H Ser·His Val·Glu Glu·Arg Thr·Pro
Tripeptides from acid or alkaline hydrolysates	Phe·Val·Asp Leu·CySO₃H·Gly Val·Glu·Ala Tyr·Leu·Val Gly·Glu·Arg Pro·Lys·Ala Val·Asp·Glu Glu·His·Leu Ser·His·Leu Val·CySO₃H·Gly His·Leu·CySO₃H Leu·Val·Glu Leu·Val·CySO₃H Ala·Leu·Tyr
Higher peptides from acid or alkaline hydrolysates	Phe·Val·Asp·Glu Ser·His·Leu·Val Tyr·Leu·Val·CySO₃H Thr·Pro·Lys·Ala His·Leu·CySO₃H·Gly Leu·Val·Glu·Ala Leu·Val·CySO₃H·Gly Phe·Val·Asp·Glu·His Ser·His·Leu·Val·Glu Glu·His·Leu·CySO₃H His·Leu·Val·Glu Ser·His·Leu·Val·Ala
Sequences deduced from above	Phe·Val·Asp·Glu·His·Leu·CySO₃H·Gly Tyr·Leu·Val·CySO₃H·Gly Thr·Pro·Lys·Ala Ser·His·Leu·Val·Glu·Ala Gly·Glu·Arg·Gly
Peptides from peptic hydrolysates	Phe·Val·Asp·Glu·His·Leu·CySO₃H·Gly·Ser·His·Leu Leu·Val·CySO₃H·Gly·Glu·Arg·Gly·Phe Tyr·Thr·Pro·Lys·Ala His·Leu·CySO₃H·Gly·Ser·His·Leu Val·Glu·Ala·Leu
Peptides from chymotrypsin hydrolysates	Phe·Val·Asp·Glu·His·Leu·CySO₃H·Gly·Ser·His·Leu·Val·Glu·Ala·Leu·Tyr Tyr·Thr·Pro·Lys·Ala Leu·Val·CySO₃H·Gly·Glu·Arg·Gly·Phe·Phe
Peptides from tryptic hydrolysates	Gly·Phe·Phe·Tyr·Thr·Pro·Lys
Structure of phenylalanyl chain of insulin	Phe·Val·Asp·Glu·His·Leu·(CyS)·Gly·Ser·His·Leu·Val·Glu·Ala·Leu·Tyr·Leu·Val·(CyS-)·Gly·Glu·Arg·Gly·Phe·Phe·Tyr·Thr·Pro·Lys·Ala 1 2 3 4 5 6 7 8 9 10 11 12 13 14 15 16 17 18 19 20 21 22 23 24 25 26 27 28 29 30

SEQUENTIAL ANALYSIS OF PEPTIDES

methods developed previously by Consden, Gordon, and Martin (112) (see above and Chapter 15). In the first of their studies, Sanger and Tuppy subjected the phenylalanyl chain to partial hydrolysis in acid and in alkali, and fractionated the resulting peptides by paper chromatography; N-terminal groups were determined by the DNFB and nitrous acid methods. The large number of simple peptides were identified and several amino acid sequences deduced therefrom. It was, however, not possible to determine the complete structure of the chain, partly because of the difficulty of fractionating the less polar peptides containing the aromatic amino acids, and partly because of the lability of certain bonds such as those involving serine and threonine residues. Therefore, in the second report of Sanger and Tuppy (114) peptides produced by partial hydrolysis of the phenylalanyl chain of insulin by the action of the proteolytic enzymes pepsin, chymotrypsin, and tryspin were successfully fractionated by paper chromatography. These were larger in size than the peptides obtained by acid hydrolysis, and the total data permitted the complete sequence to be apprehended. Table 16–16 gives the peptides obtained on which Sanger and Tuppy based their determination of this sequence. Positions 3 and 4 in this sequence actually refer to asparagine and to glutamine, respectively.

Figure 16–2, taken from the report by Sanger and Tuppy (114), is representative of the approach employed by these investigators. The paper chromatogram is that of the cysteic acid peptide fraction obtained from the 11N HCl partial hydrolysate of the phenylalanine chain, itself derived from insulin oxidized by performic acid to convert the cystine residues to cysteic and thereby also to separate the two chains. After removal of excess HCl by evaporation *in vacuo*, the residue taken up in water was fractionated according to the scheme

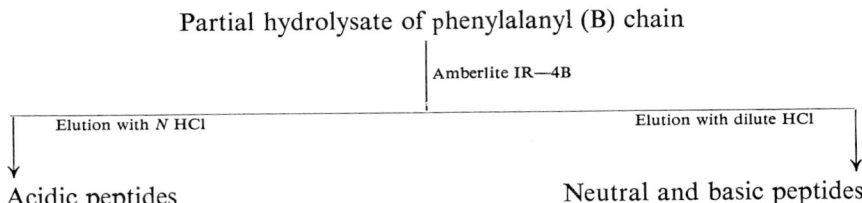

Each fraction was further subdivided, the acidic on Amberlite IR-4B at pH 2.6; this was subsequently eluted with HCl at pH 2.6 to give a first fraction of aspartic and glutamic acid peptides and a second fraction mainly of cysteic acid peptides. The neutral basic peptides were first adsorbed on charcoal to remove peptides with aromatic residues, and the effluent then subjected to ionophoresis at pH 4.5 to separate the basic peptides from the remaining neutral compounds.

Each ninhydrin-reactive peptide spot on the chromatogram portrayed in Figure 16-2 was eluted and subjected to the treatment described in Table 16-17. Spot 8, consisting of a tripeptide of equimolar amounts (as measured photometrically) of leucine, cysteic acid, and valine with leucine N-terminal but the sequence of cysteic acid and valine unknown (except as possibly revealed by spot 4) was further analyzed as follows. The eluate of this spot was further subjected to partial hydrolysis in 11N HCl at 37° for 4 days, and

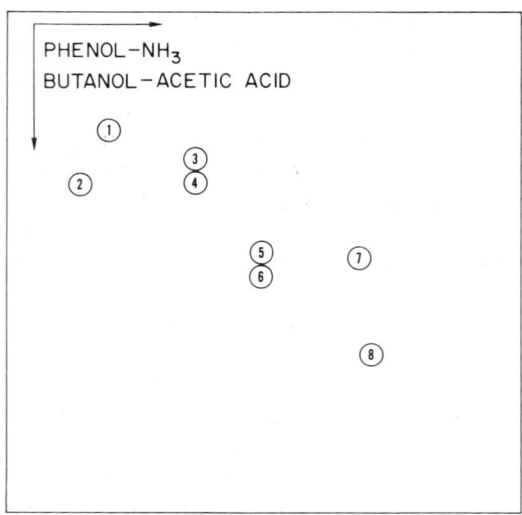

Figure 16-2. Chromatogram of fraction containing peptides of cysteic acid from partial hydrolysate of the B chain (phenylalanyl) of insulin. Spots identified in Table 16-17. Sanger, F., and Tuppy, H., *Biochem. J.*, **49**, 463 (1951).

the mixture, freed of excess HCl, chromatographed on paper as in Figure 16-2. In addition to spots derived from cysteic acid, valine, leucine, and unchanged tripeptide, there was a new spot which when hydrolyzed yielded valine and cysteic acid, and a second new spot which moved faster than leucine and contained valine. Inasmuch as valine was present in both of these dipeptides, it must be in the middle of the tripeptide (spot 8), whose structure must therefore be Leu·Val·CySO$_3$H, which is consistent with the Val·CySO$_3$H sequences found for the dipeptide in spot 4. Comparison of the full sequence of the phenylalanyl chain portrayed in Table 16-16 with the partial sequences given here indicates that the Leu·CySO$_3$H·Gly sequence (from spots 1, 5, and 6 of Figure 16-2 and Table 16-17) occupies positions 6, 7, and 8 of the chain, whilst the Leu·Val·CySO$_3$H sequence determined as described above occupies positions 17, 18, and 19 of the chain.

The glycyl chain of insulin was essentially more difficult to study than

TABLE 16-17
Characteristics of the Peptide Spots Revealed in Figure 16-2 (114)

Spot No.	Amino Acids Revealed by Complete Hydrolysis	Intensity of Ninhydrin Color after Complete Hydrolysis	Deamination and Complete Hydrolysis	Complete Hydrolysis of DNP Derivative	Sequence
1[a]	Cysteic acid Glycine	++++ ++++	? ++++	- - - ++++	}CySO$_3$H·Gly
2	Aspartic acid Glutamic acid	+ +			}[Asp·Glu]
3	Cysteic acid Glycine Valine	++ + ++		+ + - - -	}Val·[CySO$_3$H, Gly]
4	Cysteic acid Valine	+++ +++	++ ?	++ - - -	}Val·CySO$_3$H
5	Cysteic acid Glycine Leucine	+ + +	+ ? - - -	+ ? - - -	}Leu·[CySO$_3$H, Gly]
6	Cysteic acid Leucine	+++ +++	+++ ++	+++ - - -	}Leu·CySO$_3$H
7	Cysteic acid Glycine Valine Leucine	++ ++ ++ ++	+ + + ?	++ ++ ++ -	}Leu·[CySO$_3$H, Gly, Val]
8	Cysteic acid Valine Leucine	++++ ++++ ++++	+++ +++ +	+++ +++ - - -	}Leu·[CySO$_3$H, Val]

[a] This spot with ninhydrin gave first a yellow color which on further heating became gray and then violet.

the phenylalanyl chain, for, even though it possessed fewer amino acid residues, these were composed in larger proportion of cysteyl, as well as of the less easily identifiable leucyl, isoleucyl, and valyl residues. The sequence was finally determined and reported in two papers by Sanger and Thompson (115). The first report dealt with the peptides obtained by partial hydrolysis in strong acid, the second with the larger peptides obtained by peptic and chymotryptic action; trypsin was found to be ineffective toward the glycyl chain, probably because of the lack of basic amino acid residues in this fraction of the insulin molecule. Carboxypeptidase, however, was active toward this fraction, and by the use of this reagent asparagine was found to be the C-terminal residue. The peptides were separated by ionophoresis on silica jelly (115), and further identified by paper chromatography using the DNFB procedure. From the various peptides obtained by acid partial hydrolysis the following four sequences were observed for the glycyl chain:

(N-terminal)   Gly·Ileu·Val·Glu·Glu·CySO$_3$H·CySO$_3$H·Ala
Ser·Leu·Tyr·Glu·Leu·Glu·Asp·Tyr·CySO$_3$H
Ser·Val·CySO$_3$H   CySO$_3$H·Asp   (C-terminal)

Together with the peptides obtained by enzymic action, the complete sequence for the glycyl chain of insulin was deduced as follows:

Gly·Ileu·Val·Glu·Glu·CySO$_3$H·CySO$_3$H·Ala·Ser·Val·CySO$_3$H·Ser·Leu·
 1   2   3   4   5   6   7   8   9   10   11   12 13
               Tyr·Glu·Leu·Glu·Asp·Tyr·CySO$_3$H·Asp-NH$_2$
               14   15 16   17 18 19   20   21

With the determination of the sequence in each of the two chains of insulin, only two more areas of information were necessary before the complete structure of the protein could be assigned, namely, the allocation of the amide groups to particular dicarboxylic amino acid residues, and the structure of the original cystine residues from which the cysteic acid residues had been derived.

Six amide groups were found to be present in insulin (580), one of them being assigned to the C-terminal asparagine residue of the glycyl chain. The two remaining aspartic acid residues were also present as amides, as were three of the seven glutamic acid residues (288). It was therefore necessary only to locate which of the glutamic acid residues were present as glutamine. This was accomplished by Sanger, Thompson, and Kitai (581) substantially as follows: (a) the peptides obtained from enzymic digests with intact amide groups were compared ionophoretically with those obtained from acid hydrolysates in which the amide groups had been split off, and from the relative rates of migration it was possible to calculate the number of charged groups on the peptides and hence the number of carboxyl groups masked as amides; and (b) the number of amide groups present in peptides from the enzymic digests was determined directly by estimation of the ammonia produced by hydrolysis with acid. The enzymic digests were obtained after action by pepsin, chymotrypsin, cyanide-activated papain, and mold protease. As a result of these studies, the following residues were determined to be glutamine: 5 and 15 in the glycyl chain, and 4 in the phenylalanyl chain, leaving residues 4 and 17 in the former and 13 and 21 in the latter chain as glutamyl (581). When N-terminal in the peptide fragments, residues 5 and 15 appeared as pyrrolidonyl.

The identification of the peptides containing cystine, which was the last step before determining the complete structure of the intact insulin molecule, was conducted by Ryle, Sanger, Smith, and Kitai (437) by a procedure which involved the following: (a) the partial hydrolysis of insulin under conditions whereby the disulfide bonds remained intact, (b) the fractionation of the cystine peptides from one another, (c) oxidation of cystine peptides to cysteic acid peptides, (d) fractionation of the cysteic acid peptides, and (e) identification of the cysteic acid peptides from the amino acids produced on hydrolysis. From the known cysteic acid peptides the structure of the original cystine peptides could be inferred, and from this the distribution of the disulfide bonds in insulin. In stages (a) and (b) it was necessary to ensure against any rearrangement and interchange of the disulfide bonds. Ryle and Sanger (409) had demonstrated such exchange reactions in cold concentrated hydrochloric acid and in neutral media (see above).

There are three disulfide (cystine) bridges in insulin. Chymotrypsin and crude pancreatin were employed in the presence of the thiol inhibitor N-ethylmaleimide to yield peptide fragments free of disulfide rearrangement, and the position of one disulfide bridge was found in this way. However, no enzyme could be found which would cleave the bond between the two half-cystine residues located at positions 6 and 7 in the glycyl chain, and sulfuric acid hydrolysis in the presence of added thiol to avoid disulfide rearrangement was therefore employed to identify the molecular architecture about these remaining two disulfide bridges; sulfuric acid was removed from such digests by use of the basic ion exchange resin Amberlite IR-4B (44–100 mesh per in.) in the acetate form (437). The cystine peptides, detected by the KCN-nitroprusside reaction, were fractionated by ionophoresis on paper, the spots eluted, and the peptides converted to cysteic acid derivatives by oxidation with performic acid. These new peptides were again subjected to ionophoretic separation, elution, hydrolysis, and paper chromatography. From the ionophoretic rates and composition it was possible to identify the cysteic acid peptides, and the structures of the cystine peptides could thus be inferred.

As an example, an electrophoretic band contained two components, namely (CySO₃H, Glu) and CySO₃H, and probably had the structure Glu·Glu·CyS·CyS. Another band with two components, (CySO₃H, Ser, Val) and (CySO₃H, Glu), was very probably derived from

$$\begin{array}{c} \text{Glu·Glu·Cy} \\ \text{S} \\ | \\ \text{S} \\ \text{Ser·Val·Cy} \end{array}$$

Two principal cystine-containing peptides were present in the chymotryptic hydrolysate, namely, (a) (CySO₃H, Asp, Glu, Tyr, Leu) plus (CySO₃H, Glu, Gly, Val, Leu, Phe, Arg), and (b) (CySO₃H, Asp) plus (CySO₃H, Glu, Gly, Val, Leu, Phe, Arg). The probable structure of the former is

$$\begin{array}{c} \text{Glu-NH}_2\text{·Leu·Glu·Asp-NH}_2\text{·Tyr·Cy·Asp-NH}_2 \\ \text{S} \\ | \\ \text{S} \\ \text{Leu·Val·Cy·Gly·Glu·Arg·Gly·Phe·Phe} \end{array}$$

and of the latter

$$\begin{array}{c} \text{Cy·Asp-NH}_2 \\ \text{S} \\ | \\ \text{S} \\ \text{Leu·Val·Cy·Gly·Glu·Arg·Gly·Phe·Phe} \end{array}$$

Results with the crude pancreatin digests yielded (a) (CySO₃H, Gly, Val, Leu) plus (CySO₃H, Asp) and (b) (CySO₃H, Glu, Gly, Val, Leu) plus (CySO₃H, Asp) which, respectively, suggested

$$\begin{array}{c} \text{Leu·Val·Cy·Gly} \\ \text{S} \\ | \\ \text{S} \\ \text{Cy·Asp-NH}_2 \end{array}$$

and

$$\begin{array}{c} \text{Leu·Val·Cy·Gly·Glu} \\ \text{S} \\ | \\ \text{S} \\ \text{Cy·Asp-NH}_2 \end{array}$$

and, since the acid hydrolysate yielded

$$\begin{array}{c} \text{Leu·Val·Cy} \\ \text{S} \\ | \\ \text{S} \\ \text{Tyr·Cy} \end{array}$$

it was concluded that there was a disulfide bridge joining the half-cystine residues in positions 20 of the glycyl and 19 of the phenylalanyl chains.

Several of the neutral peptides from the acid hydrolysates yielded

CySO₃H·Ala on oxidation. These were

```
Cy·Gly            Leu·Cy           Leu·Cy·Gly
 S                 S                 S
 S                 S                 S
Cy·Ala            Cy·Ala            Cy·Ala
```

CySO₃H·Ala was also found linked in the basic peptide fraction with His·Leu·CySO₃H and His·Leu·CySO₃H·Gly. All these peptides strongly suggest the presence of a disulfide bond between positions 7 of the glycyl and 7 of the phenylalanyl chains.

This left only the half-cystine residues in positions 6 and 11 of the glycyl chain to be considered, and it seemed likely that they were joined together. This allocation was reinforced by isolation of the acidic peptides:

```
Ser·Val·Cy        Val·Cy           Glu·Glu·Cy        Gly·Ileu·Val·Glu·Glu·Cy
 S                 S                 S                 S
 S                 S                 S                 S
Glu·Cy            Glu·Cy           Ser·Val·Cy        Ser·Val·Cy
```

which, together with the detection of a considerable number of peptides containing the CyS·CyS sequence, indicated the presence of the glycyl 6 to 11 ring. The complete structure of beef insulin as given by Ryle, Sanger, Smith, and Kitai (437) is shown in the accompanying diagram.

Structure of Beef Insulin (437)

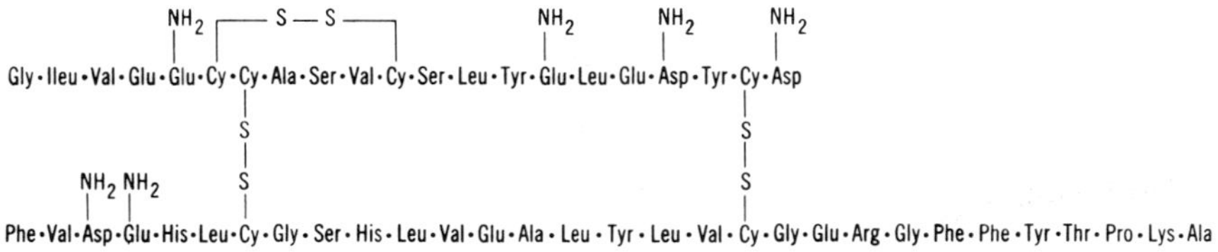

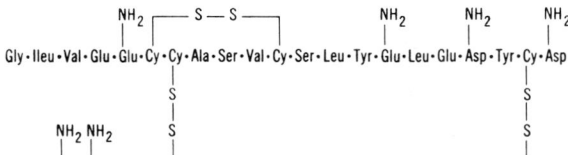

The structures of pig and sheep insulins were determined in much the same way as that of beef insulin (582), and it was found (a) that the amino acid sequence in the phenylalanine chain was identical for all three insulins, (b) the glycyl chains were the same except for three residues in positions 8 to 10 inclusive, and (c) in the beef insulin this sequence was Ala·Ser·Val, in the pig insulin Thr·Ser·Ileu, and in the sheep insulin Ala·Gly·Val.

REFERENCES

1. Fischer, E., *Ber.*, **39**, 530 (1906).
2. Synge, R. L. M., *Chem. Revs.*, **32**, 135 (1943).
3. Fischer, E., and Abderhalden, E., *Ber.*, **39**, 752 (1906).
4. Fischer, E., and Abderhalden, E., *Ber.*, **40**, 3544 (1907).

5. Fischer, E., and Bergell, P., *Ber.*, **35**, 3779 (1902); **36**, 2592 (1903).
6. Fischer, E., and Abderhalden, E., *Z. physiol. Chem.*, **46**, 52 (1905).
7. Fischer, E., *Ber.*, **39**, 453 (1906).
8. Ritthausen, H., *Ber.*, **29**, 2109 (1896).
9. Salaskin, S., *Z. physiol. Chem.*, **32**, 592 (1901).
10. Ågren, G., *Arkiv Kemi, Geol. Mineral.*, **14B**, No. 21 (1940).
11. Niemann, C., and Huang, H. T., *J. Am. Chem. Soc.*, **72**, 921 (1950).
12. Fischer, E., and Abderhalden, E., *Ber.*, **39**, 2315 (1906).
13. Abderhalden, E., *Z. physiol. Chem.*, **265**, 23 (1940); **277**, 248 (1943).
14. Abderhalden, E., and Suwa, A., *Z. physiol. Chem.*, **66**, 13 (1910).
15. Abderhalden, E., and Funk, C., *Z. physiol. Chem.*, **53**, 19 (1907).
16. Fischer, E., *Ber.*, **41**, 850 (1908).
17. Abderhalden, E., *Z. physiol. Chem.*, **58**, 373 (1908).
18. Osborne, T. B., and Clapp, S. H., *Am. J. Physiol.*, **18**, 123 (1907).
19. Fischer, E., and Luniak, A., *Ber.*, **42**, 4752 (1909).
20. Abderhalden, E., *Z. physiol. Chem.*, **63**, 401 (1909); **65**, 417 (1910).
21. Abderhalden, E., and Heyns, K., *Z. physiol. Chem.*, **202**, 37 (1931).
22. Abderhalden, E., and Brockmann, H., *Biochem. Z.*, **225**, 386 (1930).
23. Abderhalden, E., and Bahn, A., *Z. physiol. Chem.*, **210**, 246 (1932); **219**, 72 (1933).
24. Levene, P. A., and Beatty, W. S., *Ber.*, **39**, 2060 (1906); *Z. physiol. Chem.*, **49**, 247 (1906).
25. Fischer, E., and Reif, G., *Ann.*, **363**, 118 (1908).
26. Levene, P. A., *Ber.*, **43**, 3168 (1910).
27. Gawrilow, N. I., and Lawrowasky, K., *Biochem. Z.*, **190**, 278 (1927).
28. Konuma, N., *J. Biochem. (Tokyo)*, **28**, 51 (1938).
29. Gordon, A. H., Martin, A. J. P., and Synge, R. L. M., *Biochem. J.*, **37**, 92 (1943).
30. Grassmann, W., and Riederle, K., *Biochem. Z.*, **284**, 177 (1936).
31. Kossel, A., *The Protamines and Histones*, New York, 1928.
32. Siegfried, M., *Z. physiol. Chem.*, **43**, 44, 46 (1906).
33. Siegfried, M., *Z. physiol. Chem.*, **84**, 288 (1913).
34. Levene, P. A., and Van der Scheer, J., *J. Biol. Chem.*, **22**, 425 (1915).
35. Zervas, L., Otani, T., Winitz, M., and Greenstein, J. P., *Arch. Biochem. Biophys.*, **75**, 290 (1958); *J. Am. Chem. Soc.*, **81**, 2878 (1959).
36. Edlbacher, S., and Bonem, P., *Z. physiol. Chem.*, **145**, 77 (1925).
37. Felix, K., and Schuberth, H., *Z. physiol. Chem.*, **273**, 97 (1942).
38. Waldschmidt-Leitz, E., *Monatsh.*, **66**, 357 (1935); Waldschmidt-Leitz, E., and Gauss, K., *Z. physiol. Chem.*, **203**, 10 (1953).
39. Felix, K., and Mager, A., *Z. physiol. Chem.*, **249**, 111 (1937).
40. Porter, R. R., and Sanger, F., *Biochem. J.*, **42**, 287 (1948); see also Brown, H., *Arch. Biochem. Biophys.*, **61**, 241 (1956), and Havinga, E., *Proc. Natl. Acad. Sci. U.S.*, **39**, 59 (1953).
41. Dirr, K., and Felix, K., *Z. physiol. Chem.*, **205**, 83 (1932).
42. Bergmann, M., and Köster, H., *Z. physiol. Chem.*, **159**, 179 (1926).
43. Lipmann, F., *Biochem. Z.*, **262**, 3 (1933).
44. Lipmann, F., and Levene, P. A., *J. Biol. Chem.*, **98**, 109 (1932).
45. Gulewitsch, W., and Amiradzibi, S., *Z. physiol. Chem.*, **30**, 565 (1900); *Ber.*, **33**, 1902 (1900).
46. Gulewitsch, W., *Z. physiol. Chem.*, **50**, 535 (1906–1907); **73**, 434 (1911).
47. Barger, G., and Tutin, F., *Biochem. J.*, **12**, 402 (1918).
48. Baumann, L., and Ingvaldsen, T., *J. Biol. Chem.*, **35**, 263 (1918).
49. Sifferd, R. H., and du Vigneaud, V., *J. Biol. Chem.*, **108**, 753 (1935).
50. Hanson, T., and Smith, E. L., *J. Biol. Chem.*, **179**, 789 (1949).

51. Ackermann, D., Timpe, O., and Poller, K., *Z. physiol. Chem.*, **183**, 1 (1929).
52. Linneweh, W., Keil, A. W., and Hoppe-Seyler, F. A., *Z. physiol. Chem.*, **183**, 11 (1929).
53. Keil, A. W., *Z. physiol. Chem.*, **187**, 1 (1930).
54. Linneweh, W., and Linneweh, F., *Z. physiol. Chem.*, **189**, 80 (1930).
55. Behrens, O. K., and du Vigneaud, V., *J. Biol. Chem.*, **120**, 517 (1937).
56. Hopkins, F. G., *Biochem. J.*, **15**, 286 (1921).
57. Quastel, J. H., Stewart, C. P., and Tunnicliffe, H. E., *Biochem. J.*, **17**, 586 (1923).
58. Dakin, H. D., *J. Biol. Chem.*, **1**, 171 (1905).
59. Hunter, G., and Eagles, B. A., *J. Biol. Chem.*, **72**, 147 (1927).
60. Johnson, J. M., and Voegtlin, C., *J. Biol. Chem.*, **75**, 703 (1927).
61. Hopkins, F. G., *J. Biol. Chem.*, **84**, 269 (1929).
62. Pirie, N. W., and Pinhey, K. G., *J. Biol. Chem.*, **84**, 321 (1929).
63. Kendall, E. C., Mason, H. L., and McKenzie, B. F., *J. Biol. Chem.*, **87**, 55 (1930).
64. Schlack, P., and Kumpf, W., *Z. physiol. Chem.*, **154**, 125 (1926).
65. Nicolet, B. H., *J. Biol. Chem.*, **88**, 389 (1930).
66. Grassmann, W., Dyckerhoff, H., and Eibeler, H., *Z. physiol. Chem.*, **189**, 112 (1930).
67. Gurin, S., and Clarke, H. T., *J. Biol. Chem.*, **107**, 395 (1934).
68. Harington, C. R., and Mead, T. H., *Biochem. J.*, **29**, 1602 (1935).
69. Schroeder, W. A., Kay, L. M., Le Gette, J., Honnen, L., and Green, F. C., *J. Am. Chem. Soc.*, **76**, 3556 (1954).
70. Heyns, K., Anders, G., and Becker, E., *Z. physiol. Chem.*, **287**, 120 (1951).
71. Kroner, T. D., Tabroff, W., and McGarr, J. J., *J. Am. Chem. Soc.*, **75**, 4084 (1953).
72. Van Slyke, D. D., Dillon, R. T., MacFadyen, D. A., and Hamilton, P., *J. Biol. Chem.*, **141**, 627 (1941).
73. Stein, W. H., Moore, S., and Bergmann, M., *J. Biol. Chem.*, **154**, 191 (1944).
74. Bergmann, M., and Stein, W. H., *J. Biol. Chem.*, **129**, 609 (1939).
75. Levy, M., and Slobodian, E., *J. Biol. Chem.*, **199**, 563 (1952).
76. Keston, A. S., Udenfriend, S., and Cannan, R. K., *J. Am. Chem. Soc.*, **68**, 1390 (1946); **71**, 249 (1949).
77. Synge, R. L. M., *Biochem. J.*, **39**, 351 (1945).
78. Slobodian, E., and Levy, M., *J. Biol. Chem.*, **201**, 371 (1953).
79. Kay, L. M., and Schroeder, W. A., *J. Am. Chem. Soc.*, **76**, 3564 (1954).
80. Sanger, F., *Advances in Protein Chem.*, **7**, 1 (1952).
81. Drucker, B., and Smith, S. G., *Nature*, **165**, 196 (1950).
82. Meyer, K. H., Fuld, M., and Klemm, O., *Helv. Chim. Acta*, **23**, 1441 (1940).
83. Kay, L. M., Schroeder, W. A., Munger, N., and Burt, N., *J. Am. Chem. Soc.*, **78**, 2430 (1956).
84. Consden, R., Gordon, A. H., and Martin, A. J. P., *Biochem. J.*, **44**, 548 (1949).
85. Consden, R., and Gordon, A. H., *Biochem. J.*, **46**, 8 (1950).
86. Kimmel, J. R., Thompson, E. O. P., and Smith, E. L., *J. Biol. Chem.*, **217**, 151 (1955).
87. Flavin, M., and Anfinsen, C. B., *J. Biol. Chem.*, **211**, 375 (1954).
88. Thompson, A. R., *Biochem. J.*, **60**, 507; **61**, 253 (1955).
89. Fraenkel-Conrat, H., Mohammad, A., Ducay, E. D., and Mecham, D. K., *J. Am. Chem. Soc.*, **73**, 625 (1951).
90. Acher, R., Thaureaux, J., Crocker, C., and Fromageot, C., *Biochim. Biophys. Acta*, **9**, 339 (1952); cf. Acher, R., Chauvet, J., Crocker, C., Laurila, U.-R., Thaureaux, J., and Fromageot, C., *Bull. soc. chim. biol.*, **36**, 167 (1954).
91. Schroeder, W. A., *J. Am. Chem. Soc.*, **74**, 5118 (1952).
92. Partridge, S. M., and Brimley, R. C., *Biochem. J.*, **51**, 628 (1952).
93. Hirs, C. W. H., Moore, S., and Stein, W. H., *J. Biol. Chem.*, **195**, 669 (1952).
94. Acher, R., Laurila, U.-R., and Fromageot, C., *Biochim. Biophys. Acta*, **19**, 97 (1956).
95. Chibnall, A. A., *Proc. Roy. Soc. (London)*, **B131**, 136 (1942).

96. Abderhalden, E., and Blumberg, P., *Z. physiol. Chem.*, **65**, 318 (1910).
97. Abderhalden, E., and Stix, W., *Z. physiol. Chem.*, **129**, 143 (1923).
98. Bergmann, M., Miekeley, A., and Kann, E., *Ann.*, **458**, 40 (1927).
99. Jensen, H., and Evans, E. A., Jr., *J. Biol. Chem.*, **108**, 1 (1935).
100. Hopkins, S. J., and Wormall, A., *Biochem. J.*, **27**, 740 (1933); **28**, 228, 2125 (1934).
101. Van Slyke, D. D., and Birchard, F. J., *J. Biol. Chem.*, **16**, 539 (1913–14).
102. Goldschmidt, S., and Kinsky, A., *Z. physiol. Chem.*, **183**, 244 (1929).
103. Goldschmidt, S., and Füner, W., *Ann.*, **483**, 190 (1930).
104. Gurin, S., and Clarke, H. T., *J. Biol. Chem.*, **107**, 395 (1934).
105. Herriott, R. M., *Advances in Protein Chem.*, **3**, 169 (1947).
106. Putnam, F. W., in Neurath, H., and Bailey, K., *The Proteins*, Vol. 1, part B, Academic Press, New York, 1953.
107. Clutton, R. F., Harington, C. R., and Mead, T. H., *Biochem. J.*, **31**, 764 (1937).
108. Skraup, Z. H., and Kaas, K., *Ann.*, **351**, 379 (1906).
109. Hogan, A. G., Powell, E. L., and Guerrant, R. R., *J. Biol. Chem.*, **137**, 41 (1941).
110. Gaudry, R., in Begg, R. W., *Canadian Cancer Conference*, Vol. I, Academic Press, New York, p. 163, 1955.
111. McClure, L. E., Schieler, L., and Dunn, M. S., *J. Am. Chem. Soc.*, **75**, 1980 (1953).
112. Consden, R., Gordon, A. H., and Martin, A. J. P., *Biochem. J.*, **41**, 590 (1947).
113. Consden, R., Gordon, A. H., Martin, A. J. P., and Synge, R. L. M., *Biochem. J.*, **41**, 596 (1947).
114. Sanger, F., and Tuppy, H., *Biochem. J.*, **49**, 463, 481 (1951).
115. Sanger, F., and Thompson, E. O. P., *Biochem. J.*, **53**, 353, 366 (1953).
116. Heyns, K., and Königsdorf, W., *Z. physiol. Chem.*, **290**, 171 (1952).
117. Kossel, A., and Weiss, F., *Z. physiol. Chem.*, **68**, 165 (1910).
118. Dakin, H. D., *J. Biol. Chem.*, **13**, 357 (1912).
119. Dakin, H. D., and Dale, H. H., *Biochem. J.*, **13**, 248 (1919).
120. Goldschmidt, S., Wiberg, E., Nagel, F., and Martin, K., *Ann.*, **456**, 1 (1927).
121. Goldschmidt, S., and Strauss, K., *Ann.*, **471**, 1 (1929).
122. Goldschmidt, S., and Strauss, K., *Ber.*, **63**, 1218 (1930).
123. Wessely, F., Schlögl, K., and Körger, G., *Monatsh.*, **83**, 1157 (1952).
124. Wessely, F., Schlögl, K., and Wawersich, E., *Monatsh.*, **83**, 1426, 1439 (1952).
125. Schlögl, K., and Fabitschowitz, H., *Monatsh.*, **84**, 936 (1953).
126. Wessely, F., Schlögl, K., and Wawersich, E., *Monatsh.*, **84**, 263 (1953).
127. King, F. E., and Kidd, D. A. A., *J. Chem. Soc.*, **1949**, 3315.
128. Le Quesne, W. J., and Young, G. T., *J. Chem. Soc.*, **1950**, 1954, 1959.
129. Jollès, P., and Fromageot, C., *Biochim. Biophys. Acta*, **9**, 287 (1952).
130. Levy, A. L., *J. Chem. Soc.*, **1950**, 404; Leonis, J., and Levy, A. L., *Bull. soc. chim. biol.*, **33**, 779 (1951).
131. Leonis, J., *Compt. rend. trav. lab. Carlsberg*, **26**, 315 (1948).
132. Leonis, J., *Bull. soc. chim. Belges*, **61**, 524 (1952).
133. Kenner, G. W., and Khorana, H. G., *J. Chem. Soc.*, **1952**, 2076.
134. Elmore, D. T., and Toseland, P. A., *J. Chem. Soc.*, **1954**, 4533; **1956**, 188, 192.
135. Edman, P., *Acta Chem. Scand.*, **7**, 700 (1953).
136. Edlbacher, S., *Z. physiol. Chem.*, **112**, 80 (1921).
137. Zimmermann, W., *Z. physiol. Chem.*, **231**, 19, 25 (1935).
138. Zimmermann, W., *Z. physiol. Chem.*, **189**, 4 (1930).
139. Abderhalden, E., and Neumann, A., *Z. physiol. Chem.*, **238**, 177 (1936).
140. Abderhalden, R., *Z. physiol. Chem.*, **252**, 81 (1938).
141. Bowman, R. E., and Stroud, H. H., *J. Chem. Soc.*, **1950**, 1342.
142. Bowman, R. E., *J. Chem. Soc.*, **1950**, 1346.
143. Bowman, R. E., *J. Chem. Soc.*, **1950**, 1349.

144. Ingram, V. M., *J. Biol. Chem.*, **202**, 193 (1953).
145. Korman, S., and Clarke, H. T., *J. Biol. Chem.*, **221**, 113, 133 (1956).
146. Keil, B., Knesslova, V., and Sorm, F., *Collection Czechoslov. Chem. Comms.*, **18**, 310 (1953).
147. Cristol, P., Crastes de Paulet, A., and Cristol, P., *Bull. soc. chim. biol.*, **38**, 639 (1956).
148. Saidel, L. J., *J. Biol. Chem.*, **224**, 445 (1957).
149. Sanger, F., *Biochem. J.*, **39**, 507 (1945).
150. Thompson, A. R., *Nature*, **168**, 390 (1951).
151. Thompson, E. O. P., *J. Biol. Chem.*, **207**, 563 (1954).
152. Desnuelle, P., Rovery, M., and Fabre, C., *Compt. rend.*, **233**, 987 (1951).
153. Rhinesmith, H. S., Schroeder, W. A., and Pauling, L., *J. Am. Chem. Soc.*, **79**, 609 (1957).
154. Hanes, C. S., Hird, F. J. R., and Isherwood, F. A., *Biochem. J.*, **51**, 25 (1952).
155. Monier, R., and Jutisz, M., *Biochim. Biophys. Acta*, **14**, 551 (1954).
156. Dickman, S. R., and Asplund, R. O., *J. Am. Chem. Soc.*, **74**, 5208 (1952).
157. Green, F. C., and Schroeder, W. A., *J. Am. Chem. Soc.*, **73**, 1385 (1951).
158. Lewis, J. C., Snell, N. S., Hirschmann, D. J., and Fraenkel-Conrat, H., *J. Biol. Chem.*, **186**, 23 (1950).
159. Acher, R., and Laurila, U.-R., *Bull. soc. chim. biol.*, **35**, 413 (1953).
160. Schramm, G., and Braunitzer, G., *Z. Naturforsch.*, **8B**, 61 (1953).
161. Fraenkel-Conrat, H., and Singer, B., *J. Am. Chem. Soc.*, **76**, 180 (1954).
162. James, A. T., and Synge, R. L. M., *Biochem. J.*, **50**, 109 (1951).
163. Scanes, F. S., and Tozer, B. T., *Biochem. J.*, **63**, 282, 565 (1956).
164. Schroeder, W. A., Honnen, L. R., and Green, F. C., *Proc. Natl. Acad. Sci. U.S.*, **39**, 23 (1953).
165. Mills, G. L., *Biochem. J.*, **50**, 707 (1952).
166. Sanger, F., *Biochem. J.*, **45**, 563 (1949); Keil, B., *Collection Czechoslov. Chem. Communs.*, **23**, 740 (1958).
167. Thompson, E. O. P., and Thompson, A. R., *Fortschr. Chem. org. Naturstoffe*, **12**, 270 (1955).
168. Schroeder, W. A., *Fortschr. Chem. org. Naturstoffe*, **11**, 240 (1954).
169. Mills, G. L., *Nature*, **165**, 403 (1950).
170. Lowther, A. G., *Nature*, **167**, 767 (1951).
171. Neurath, H., Greenstein, J. P., Putnam, F. W., and Erickson, J. O., *Chem. Revs.*, **34**, 157 (1944).
172. Anson, M. L., *Advances in Protein Chem.*, **2**, 36 (1945).
173. Steinhardt, J., and Zaiser, E. M., *Advances in Protein Chem.*, **10**, 151 (1955).
174. Porter, R. R., *Biochim. Biophys. Acta*, **2**, 105 (1948).
174a. Steven, F. S., and Tristram, G. R., *Biochem. J.*, **70**, 179 (1958).
175. Porter, R. R., *Biochem. J.*, **46**, 304 (1950); Zahn, H., and Pfannmüller, H., *Biochem. Z.*, **330**, 97 (1958).
176. Bailey, K., *Biochem. J.*, **49**, 23 (1951).
177. Braunitzer, G., *Naturwiss.*, **42**, 371 (1955).
178. Schramm, G., and Anderer, F. A., *Naturwiss.*, **42**, 74 (1955); c.f. Schramm, G., Schneider, J. W., and Anderer, A., *Z. Naturforsch.*, **11b**, 12 (1956).
179. Fraenkel-Conrat, H., and Singer, B., *Arch. Biochem. Biophys.*, **60**, 64 (1956).
179a. Narita, K., *Biochim. Biophys. Acta*, **30**, 352 (1958).
180. Sanger, F., *Biochem. Soc. Symposia*, **No. 3**, 29 (1948).
181. Middlebrook, W. R., *Biochim. Biophys. Acta*, **7**, 547 (1951).
182. Mellon, E. F., Korn, A. H., and Hoover, S. R., *J. Am. Chem. Soc.*, **75**, 1675 (1953).
183. Ozawa, H., and Satake, K., *J. Biochem. (Tokyo)*, **42**, 641 (1955).
184. Wagner-Jauregg, T., and Short, J. H., *Chem. Ber.*, **89**, 253 (1956).

185. Acher, R., Laurila, U.-R., Thaureaux, J., and Fromageot, C., *Biochim. Biophys. Acta*, **14**, 151 (1954).
186. Smith, E. L., Kimmel, J. R., Brown, D. M., and Thompson, E. O. P., *J. Biol. Chem.*, **215**, 67 (1955); Li, C. H., *ibid.*, **229**, 157 (1957).
187. Cole, R. D., Geschwind, I. I., and Li, C. H., *J. Biol. Chem.*, **224**, 399 (1957).
188. Anfinsen, C., Redfield, R. R., Choate, W. L., Page, J., and Carroll, W. R., *J. Biol. Chem.*, **207**, 201 (1954); cf. Redfield, R. R., and Anfinsen, C. B., *ibid.*, **221**, 385 (1956).
189. Hirs, C. H. W., Moore, S., and Stein, W. H., *J. Biol. Chem.*, **219**, 623 (1956); cf. Hirs, C. H. W., Stein, W. H., and Moore, S., *J. Biol. Chem.*, **221**, 151 (1956).
190. Thompson, E. O. P., *Biochim. Biophys. Acta*, **10**, 633 (1953).
191. Weygand, F., and Junk, R., *Naturwiss.*, **38**, 433 (1951).
192. Avigan, J., Redfield, R. R., and Steinberg, D., *Biochim. Biophys. Acta*, **20**, 557 (1956).
193. Williamson, M. B., and Passmann, J. M., *J. Biol. Chem.*, **199**, 121 (1952).
194. Biserte, G., and Dautrevaux, R., *Bull. soc. chim. biol.*, **36**, 204 (1954).
195. Van Vunakis, H., and Herriott, R. M., *Biochim. Biophys. Acta*, **23**, 600 (1957).
196. Seno, N., Murai, K., and Shimura, K., *J. Biochem.* (*Tokyo*), **42**, 699 (1955).
197. Porter, R. R., *Biochem. J.*, **46**, 473 (1950).
198. McFadden, M. L., and Smith, E. L., *J. Biol. Chem.*, **214**, 185 (1955).
199. Smith, E. L., McFadden, M. L., Stockell, A., and Buettner-Janush, V., *J. Biol. Chem.*, **214**, 197 (1955).
200. Phillips, D. M. P., *Biochem. J.*, **68**, 35 (1958).
201. Smith, E. L., Brown, D. M., McFadden, M. L., Buettner-Janush, V., and Jager, B. V., *J. Biol. Chem.*, **216**, 601 (1955).
202. Putnam, F. W., *J. Am. Chem. Soc.*, **75**, 2785 (1953); *J. Biol. Chem.*, **233**, 1448 (1958).
203. Monier, R., and Jutisz, M., *Biochim. Biophys. Acta*, **14**, 551 (1954).
204. Eisen, H. N., Belman, S., and Carsten, M. E., *J. Am. Chem. Soc.*, **75**, 4583 (1953).
205. Holley, R. W., and Holley, A. D., *J. Am. Chem. Soc.*, **74**, 5445 (1952).
206. Jutisz, M., and Ritschard, W., *Biochim. Biophys. Acta*, **17**, 548 (1955); cf., Scoffone, E., Vianello, E., and Lorenzini, A., *Gazz. chim. ital.*, **87**, 354 (1957); Ingram, V. M., *Biochim. Biophys. Acta*, **20**, 577 (1956).
207. Fletcher, C. M., Lowther, A. G., and Reith, W. S., *Biochem. J.*, **56**, 106 (1954).
208. Rao, K. R., and Sober, H. A., *J. Am. Chem. Soc.*, **76**, 1328 (1954).
209. Zahn, H., and Klockläuner, R., *Biochem. Z.*, **325**, 333 (1954).
210. Edman, P., *Acta Chem. Scand.*, **4**, 277, 283 (1950).
211. Aschan, O., *Ber.*, **16**, 1544 (1883).
212. Marckwald, W., Neumark, M., and Stelzner, R., *Ber.*, **24**, 3278 (1891).
213. Ottesen, M., and Wollenberger, A., *Compt. rend. trav. lab. Carlsberg*, **28**, 463 (1953); Ottesen, M., *Compt. rend. trav. lab. Carlsberg*, **30**, 211 (1958).
214. Wheeler, H. L., and Hoffmann, C., *J. Am. Chem. Soc.*, **45**, 368 (1911).
215. Ingram, V. M., *J. Chem. Soc.*, **1953**, 3717.
216. Bremner, J., *Nature*, **168**, 518 (1951); *Biochim. Biophys. Acta*, **20**, 579 (1956).
217. Levy, A. L., *Biochim. Biophys. Acta*, **15**, 589 (1954).
218. Fox, S. W., Hurst, T. L., and Itschner, K. F., *J. Am. Chem. Soc.*, **73**, 3573 (1951).
219. Daklerup-Petersen, B., Linderstrøm-Lang, K., and Ottesen, M., *Acta Chem. Scand.*, **6**, 1135 (1952).
220. Fraenkel-Conrat, H., and Fraenkel-Conrat, J., *Acta Chem. Scand.*, **5**, 1409 (1951).
221. Fraenkel-Conrat, H., *J. Am. Chem. Soc.*, **76**, 3606 (1954).
222. Ingram, V. M., *Biochim. Biophys. Acta*, **16**, 599 (1955).
223. Sjöquist, J., *Acta Chem. Scand.*, **7**, 447 (1953).
224. Landmann, W. A., Drake, M. P., and Dillaha, J., *J. Am. Chem. Soc.*, **75**, 3638 (1953).
225. Ramachandran, L. K., Epp, A., and McConnel, W. B., *Anal. Chem.*, **27**, 1734 (1955).
226. Sjöquist, J., *Biochim. Biophys. Acta*, **16**, 283 (1955).

227. Edman, P., and Sjöquist, J., *Acta Chem. Scand.*, **10**, 1507 (1956).
228. Levy, A. L., and Chung, D., *Biochim. Biophys. Acta*, **17**, 454 (1955).
229. Edman, P., and Lauber, K., *Acta Chem. Scand.*, **10**, 466 (1956).
230. Reith, W. S., and Waldron, N. M., *Biochem. J.*, **56**, 116 (1954).
231. De Fontaine, D., and Fox, S. W., *J. Am. Chem. Soc.*, **76**, 3701 (1954); Fox, S. W., Serat, W., Hurst, T. L., Trapp, O. U., and Lutjens, D., *ibid.*, **79**, 2846 (1957).
232. Thompson, E. O. P., *J. Biol. Chem.*, **208**, 565 (1954); see also Caputo, A., and Zito, R., *Bull. soc. chim. biol.*, **37**, 1255 (1955).
233. Rovery, M., Fabre, C., and Desnuelle, P., *Biochim. Biophys. Acta*, **12**, 547 (1953).
234. Gladner, J. A., and Neurath, H., *J. Biol. Chem.*, **205**, 345 (1953).
235. Bettelheim, F. R., *J. Biol. Chem.*, **212**, 235 (1955).
236. Albrecht, G., *J. Biol. Chem.*, **229**, 477 (1957).
237. Udenfriend, S., and Velick, S. F., *J. Biol. Chem.*, **190**, 733 (1951).
238. Udenfriend, S., and Velick, S. F., *J. Biol. Chem.*, **191**, 233 (1951).
239. Waldschmidt-Leitz, E., Zeigler, F., Schaffner, A., and Weil, L., *Z. physiol. Chem.*, **197**, 219 (1931).
240. Schütte, E., *Z. physiol. Chem.*, **279**, 52, 59 (1943).
241. Hugues, W. L., Sarof, H. A., and Carney, A. L., *J. Am. Chem. Soc.*, **71**, 2476 (1949).
242. Roche, J., Mourgue, M., and Baret, R., *Bull. soc. chim. biol.*, **36**, 85 (1954).
243. Chervenka, C. H., and Wilcox, P. E., *J. Biol. Chem.*, **222**, 635 (1956).
244. Klee, W. A., and Richards, F. M., *J. Biol. Chem.*, **229**, 489 (1957).
245. Geschwind, I. I., and Li, C. H., *Biochim. Biophys. Acta*, **25**, 171 (1957).
246. Smith, E. L., and Hill, R. L., *Proc. 3rd Intern. Congr. Biochem.*, Brussels, *1955* (pub. 1956).
247. Hill, R. L., and Smith, E. L., *Biochim. Biophys. Acta*, **19**, 376 (1956); *J. Biol. Chem.*, **228**, 577 (1957).
248. Waldschmidt-Leitz, E., and Mindemann, R., *Z. physiol. Chem.*, **304**, 166 (1956).
249. Waley, S. G., and Watson, J., *J. Chem. Soc.*, **1951**, 2394.
250. Turner, R. A., and Schmertzler, G., *Biochim. Biophys. Acta*, **11**, 586 (1953).
251. Pénasse, L., Jutisz, M., Fromageot, C., and Fraenkel-Conrat, H., *Biochim. Biophys. Acta*, **9**, 551 (1952).
252. Turner, R. A., and Schmertzler, G., *Biochim. Biophys. Acta*, **13**, 553 (1954).
253. Baptist, V. H., and Bull, H. B., *J. Am. Chem. Soc.*, **75**, 1727 (1953).
254. Swan, J. M., *Australian J. Sci. Research*, **A5**, 711 (1952).
255. Edward, J. T., and Nielsen, S., *Chem. Ind.*, **1953**, 197.
256. Folin, O., and Denis, W., *J. Biol. Chem.*, **14**, 95 (1913).
257. Kenner, G. W., Khorana, H. G., and Stedman, R. J., *J. Chem. Soc.*, **1953**, 673.
258. Bettzieche, F., and Manger, R., *Z. physiol. Chem.*, **161**, 37, 178 (1926).
259. Bergmann, M., and Zervas, L., *J. Biol. Chem.*, **113**, 341 (1936).
260. Wieland, T., and Fritz, H., *Chem. Ber.*, **86**, 1186 (1953).
261. Lossen, W., *Ann.*, **175**, 313 (1875).
262. Lichtenstein, N., *J. Am. Chem. Soc.*, **60**, 560 (1938).
263. Schlögl, K., and Wawersich, E., *Naturwiss.*, **41**, 38 (1954).
264. Akabori, S., Ohno, K., and Narita, K., *Bull. Chem. Soc. Japan*, **25**, 214 (1952).
265. Ohno, K., *J. Biochem. (Tokyo)*, **40**, 621 (1953).
266. Ohno, K., *J. Biochem. (Tokyo)*, **41**, 345 (1954).
267. Ohno, K., *J. Biochem. (Tokyo)*, **42**, 615 (1955).
268. Bradbury, J. H., *Nature*, **178**, 912 (1956); *Biochem. J.*, **68**, 475 (1958).
269. Knight, C. A., *Advances in Virus Research*, **2**, 153 (1954).
270. Harris, J. I., and Knight, C. A., *Nature*, **170**, 613 (1952).
271. Levy, A. L., *Nature*, **174**, 126 (1954).
272. Niu, C-I., and Fraenkel-Conrat, H., *Biochim. Biophys. Acta*, **16**, 597 (1955).

273. Braunitzer, G., *Z. Naturforsch.*, **9b**, 675 (1954).
274. Braunitzer, G., *Chem. Ber.*, **88**, 2025 (1955).
275. Akabori, S., and Ikenaka, T., *J. Biochem.* (*Tokyo*), **42**, 603 (1955); Ikenaka, T., *ibid.*, **43**, 255 (1956).
276. Chambers, R. W., and Carpenter, F. H., *J. Am. Chem. Soc.*, **77**, 1527 (1955).
277. Khorana, H. G., *J. Chem. Soc.*, **1952**, 2081.
278. Turner, R: A., and Schmertzler, G., *J. Am. Chem. Soc.*, **76**, 949 (1954).
279. Dakin, H. D., and West, R., *J. Biol. Chem.*, **78**, 91, 745, 757 (1928).
280. Boissonnas, R. A., *Helv. Chim. Acta*, **35**, 2226 (1952).
281. Linstead, R. P., Shephard, B. R., and Weedon, B. C. L., *J. Chem. Soc.*, **1951**, 2854.
282. Thompson, A. R., *Biochim. Biophys. Acta*, **15**, 299 (1954).
283. Fromageot, C., Jutisz, M., Mayer, D., and Pénasse, L., *Biochim. Biophys. Acta*, **6**, 283 (1950).
284. Nicolet, B. H., and Shinn, L. A., *J. Am. Chem. Soc.*, **61**, 1615 (1939).
285. Chibnall, A. C., and Rees, M. W., *Biochem. J.*, **48**, xlvii (1951).
286. Karrer, P., Portmann, P., and Suter, M., *Helv. Chim. Acta*, **31**, 1617 (1948).
287. Sanger, F., and Thompson, E. O. P., *Biochem. J.*, **52**, iii (1952); **53**, 366 (1953).
288. Chibnall, A. C., and Rees, M. W., *Biochem. J.*, **52**, iii (1952); **68**, 105, 122 (1958).
289. Crawhall, J. C., and Elliott, D. F., *Nature*, **175**, 299 (1955); *Biochem. J.*, **61**, 264 (1955).
290. Crawhall, J. C., Elliott, D. F., and Hooper, K. C., *J. Chem. Soc.*, **1956**, 4066.
291. Williamson, M. B., and Passmann, J. M., *Biochim. Biophys. Acta*, **15**, 246 (1954).
292. Jollès, P., and Fromageot, C., *Biochim. Biophys. Acta*, **9**, 416 (1952).
293. Jollès, P., and Fromageot, C., *Bull. soc. chim. France*, (5) **18**, 862 (1951); cf. Fromageot, C., and Jutisz, M., *The Chemical Structure of Proteins* (Ciba Foundation Symposium), Little, Brown, Boston, Mass., 1954.
294. Haurowitz, F., and Bursa, F., *Biochem. J.*, **44**, 509 (1949).
295. Jutisz, M., Privat De Garilke, M., Suquet, M., and Fromageot, C., *Bull. soc. chim. biol.*, **36**, 117 (1954).
296. Jatzkewitz, H., and Tam, N.-D., *Z. physiol. Chem.*, **296**, 188 (1956).
297. Grassmann, W., Hörmann, H., and Endres, H., *Chem. Ber.*, **86**, 1477 (1953); **88**, 102 (1955).
298. Leggett Bailey, J., *Biochem. J.*, **60**, 170 (1955).
299. Bergmann, M., and Brand, E., *Ber.*, **56**, 1280 (1923).
300. Hörmann, H., Grassmann, W., Wünsch, E., and Preller, H., *Chem. Ber.*, **89**, 933 (1956).
301. Chappelle, E. W., and Luck, J. M., *J. Biol. Chem.*, **229**, 171 (1957).
301a. Patchornik, A., Lawson, W. B., and Witkop, B., *J. Am. Chem. Soc.*, **80**, 4747 (1958).
302. Smith, E. L., in *The Enzymes*, Vol. I, part 2, Academic Press, New York, p. 802, 1951.
303. Neurath, H., and Schwert, G. W., *Chem. Revs.*, **46**, 69 (1950).
304. Locker, R. H., *Biochim. Biophys. Acta*, **14**, 533 (1954).
305. Harris, J. I., in Glick, D., *Methods of Biochemical Analysis*, Vol. II, Interscience Publishers, New York, 1955; cf. *Symposium on Peptide Chemistry*, Chemical Society of London, p. 71, 1955.
306. Harris, J. I., and Li, C. H., *J. Am. Chem. Soc.*, **76**, 3607 (1954); also Geschwind, I. L., and Li, C. H., *Arch. Biochem. Biophys.*, **63**, 316 (1956).
307. Harris, J. I., Li, C. H., Condliffe, P. G., and Pon, N. G., *J. Biol. Chem.*, **209**, 133 (1954); also Li, C. H., and Papkoff, H., *Science*, **124**, 1293 (1956); Parcells, A. J., and Li, C. H., *J. Biol. Chem.*, **233**, 1140 (1958); Li, C. H., Parcells, A. J., and Papkoff, H., *ibid.*, **233**, 1143 (1958).
307a. Heijkenskjöld, F., *Acta Chem. Scand.*, **12**, 132 (1958).
308. Neurath, H., Gladner, J. A., and Davie, E. W., in *Mechanism of Enzyme Action*, Johns Hopkins Press, Baltimore, p. 50, 1954.
309. Gladner, J. A., and Neurath, H., *J. Biol. Chem.*, **206**, 911 (1954).

310. Steinberg, D., *J. Am. Chem. Soc.*, **75**, 4875 (1953).
311. Niu, C.-I., and Fraenkel-Conrat, H., *J. Am. Chem. Soc.*, **77**, 5882 (1955).
312. Akabori, S., Ohno, K., Ikenaka, T., Okada, Y., Hanafusa, H., Haruna, I., Tsugita, A., Sugae, K.-I., and Matsushima, T., *Bull. Chem. Soc. Japan*, **29**, 507 (1956).
313. Davie, E. W., and Neurath, H., *J. Am. Chem. Soc.*, **74**, 6305 (1952).
314. Desnuelle, P., Rovery, M., and Fabre, C., *Biochim. Biophys. Acta*, **9**, 109 (1952).
315. Jansen, E. F., Nutting, M. D. F., Jang, R., and Balls, A. K., *J. Biol. Chem.*, **185**, 209 (1950).
316. Kaufman, S., Schwert, G. W., and Neurath, H., *Arch. Biochem.*, **17**, 203 (1948).
317. Schaffer, N. K., May, S. C., and Summerson, W. H., *J. Biol. Chem.*, **202**, 67 (1953).
318. Schaffer, N. K., Harshman, S., and Engle, R. R., *J. Biol. Chem.*, **214**, 799 (1955).
319. Turba, F., and Gundlach, G., *Biochem. Z.*, **327**, 186 (1955).
320. Oosterbaan, R. A., Kunst, P., and Cohen, J. A., *Biochim. Biophys. Acta*, **16**, 299 (1955).
321. Jandorf, B. J., Michel, H. O., Schaffer, N. K., Egar, R., and Summerson, W. H., *Discussions Faraday Soc.*, No. 20, 134 (1955).
322. Wilson, I. B., *Discussions Faraday Soc.*, No. 20, 119 (1955).
322a. Dixon, G. H., Kauffman, D. L., and Neurath, H., *J. Biol. Chem.*, **233**, 1373 (1958).
323. Lens, J., *Biochim. Biophys. Acta*, **3**, 367 (1949).
324. Harris, J. I., *J. Am. Chem. Soc.*, **74**, 2944 (1952).
325. Harris, J. I., and Li, C. H., *J. Am. Chem. Soc.*, **74**, 2945 (1952).
326. Thompson, A. R., *Nature*, **169**, 495 (1952).
327. Jollès, P., and Fromageot, C., *Biochim. Biophys. Acta*, **14**, 228 (1954).
328. Kalnitsky, G., and Rogers, W. I., *Biochim. Biophys. Acta*, **20**, 378 (1956).
329. Niu, C-I., and Fraenkel-Conrat, H., *Arch. Biochem. Biophys.*, **59**, 538 (1955).
330. Folk, J. E., *J. Am. Chem. Soc.*, **78**, 3541 (1956).
331. Pénasse, L., Jutisz, M., and Fromageot, C., *Bull. soc. chim. biol.*, **35**, 376 (1953).
332. Thaureaux, J., and Jollès, P., *Compt. rend.*, **243**, 1926 (1956).
333. Thompson, E. O. P., *Biochim. Biophys. Acta*, **25**, 210 (1957).
334. Partridge, S. M., *Nature*, **169**, 496 (1952).
335. Halsey, Y. D., and Neurath, H., *J. Biol. Chem.*, **217**, 247 (1955).
336. Velick, S. F., and Udenfriend, S., *J. Biol. Chem.*, **203**, 575 (1953).
337. Fraenkel-Conrat, H., and Porter, R. R., *Biochim. Biophys. Acta*, **9**, 557 (1952).
338. Felix, K., Fischer, H., Krekels, A., and Rauen, H. M., *Z. physiol. Chem.*, **286**, 67 (1950).
339. Bowes, J. H., and Moss, J. A., *Biochem. J.*, **55**, 735 (1953).
340. Grassmann, W., and Hörmann, H., *Z. physiol. Chem.*, **292**, 24 (1953).
341. Schmid, K., *Helv. Chim. Acta*, **32**, 105 (1949).
342. Desnuelle, P., and Casal, A., *Biochim. Biophys. Acta*, **2**, 64 (1948).
343. Blackburn, S., and Lee, G. R., *J. Textile Inst.*, **45**, 487 (1954).
344. Lindley, H., *Nature*, **178**, 647 (1956).
345. Tietze, F., Gladner, J. A., and Folk, J. E., *Biochim. Biophys. Acta*, **26**, 659 (1957).
346. Bull, H. B., and Hahn, J. W., *J. Am. Chem. Soc.*, **70**, 2132 (1948).
347. Acher, R., Jutisz, M., and Fromageot, C., *Biochim. Biophys. Acta*, **8**, 442 (1952).
348. Gordon, A. H., Martin, A. J. P., and Synge, R. L. M., *Biochem. J.*, **35**, 1369 (1941).
349. Lawrence, L., and Moore, W. J., *J. Am. Chem. Soc.*, **73**, 3973 (1951).
350. Christensen, H. N., and Hegstedt, D. M., *J. Biol. Chem.*, **158**, 593 (1945).
351. Mills, G. L., *Biochem. J.*, **56**, 230 (1954).
352. Synge, R. L. M., *Biochem. J.*, **38**, 285 (1944).
353. Christensen, H. N., *J. Biol. Chem.*, **151**, 319 (1943); **154**, 427 (1944).
354. Monier, R., and Fromageot, C., *Biochim. Biophys. Acta*, **5**, 224 (1950).
355. Harris, J. I., Cole, R. D., and Pon, N. G., *Biochem. J.*, **62**, 154 (1956).

356. Hirohata, R., Kanda, Y., Nakamura, M., Izumiya, N., Nagamatsu, A., Ono, T., Fujii, S., and Kimitsuki, M., *Z. physiol. Chem.*, **295**, 368 (1953).
357. Harfenist, E. J., *J. Am. Chem. Soc.*, **75**, 5528 (1953); Harfenist, E., and Craig, L. C., *ibid.*, **75**, 5532 (1953).
358. Desnuelle, P., and Bonjour, M., *Biochim. Biophys. Acta*, **9**, 356 (1952).
359. Bergmann, M., Brand, E., and Weinmann, F., *Z. physiol. Chem.*, **131**, 1 (1923).
360. Desnuelle, P., and Bonjour, G., *Biochim. Biophys. Acta*, **7**, 451 (1951).
361. Reitz, H. G., Ferrel, R. E., Olcott, H. S., and Fraenkel-Conrat, H., *J. Am. Chem. Soc.*, **68**, 1024 (1946).
362. Elliott, D. F., *Biochem. J.*, **50**, 542 (1952); see also Wiseblatt, L., Wilson, L., and McConnell, W. B., *Can. J. Chem.*, **33**, 1295 (1955); Ramachandran, L. K., and McConnell, W. B., *ibid.*, **33**, 1638 (1955); and Josefsson, L., and Edman, P., *Biochim. Biophys. Acta*, **25**, 614 (1957).
363. Mecham, D. K., and Olcott, H. S., *J. Am. Chem. Soc.*, **71**, 3670 (1949).
364. Ågren, G., de Verdier, C. H., and Glomset, J., *Acta Chem. Scand.*, **5**, 324 (1951).
365. Kennedy, E. P., and Smith, S. W., *J. Biol. Chem.*, **207**, 153 (1954).
366. Schaffer, N. K., May, S. C., Jr., and Summerson, W. H., *J. Biol. Chem.*, **206**, 201 (1954).
367. Schaffer, N. K., Harshman, S., and Engle, R. R., *Federation Proc.*, **13**, 289 (1954).
368. Posternak, T., and Pollaczek, H., *Helv. Chim. Acta*, **24**, 921 (1941).
369. de Verdier, C. H., *Acta Chem. Scand.*, **7**, 196 (1953).
370. Flavin, M., *J. Biol. Chem.*, **210**, 771 (1954).
371. Perlmann, G. E., in *Phosphorus Metabolism*, Johns Hopkins Press, p. 167, Baltimore, 1952.
372. Brigl, P., *Ber.*, **56**, 1887 (1923).
373. Abderhalden, E., and Komm, E., *Z. physiol. Chem.*, **139**, 147 (1924).
374. Abderhalden, E., and Nienburg, H., *Fermentforsch.*, **13**, 573 (1933).
375. Smith, E., and Bergmann, M., *J. Biol. Chem.*, **153**, 627 (1944).
376. Wintersteiner, O., and Pfiffner, J. J., *J. Biol. Chem.*, **111**, 599 (1935).
377. Kuizenga, M. H., Nelson, J. W., Lyster, S. C., and Ingle, D. J., *J. Biol. Chem.*, **160**, 15 (1945).
378. Johnson, J. L., Jackson, W. C., and Eble, T. E., *J. Am. Chem. Soc.*, **73**, 2947 (1951).
379. Butenandt, A., Karlson, P., and Zilling, W., *Z. physiol. Chem.*, **288**, 279 (1951).
380. Sanger, F., and Thompson, E. O. P., *Biochim. Biophys. Acta*, **9**, 225 (1952).
381. Partridge, S. M., and Davis, H. F., *Nature*, **165**, 62 (1950).
382. Biserte, G., and Pigache, P., *Bull. soc. chim. biol.*, **33**, 1379 (1951); **34**, 51 (1952).
383. Battersby, A. R., and Robinson, J. C., *J. Chem. Soc.*, **1955**, 259.
384. Clayton, D. W., Kenner, G. W., and Sheppard, R. C., *J. Chem. Soc.*, **1956**, 371.
385. Steinhardt, J., and Fugitt, C. H., *J. Res. Natl. Bureau Standards*, **29**, 315 (1942).
386. Weygand, F., Geiger, R., and Glöckler, U., *Chem. Ber.*, **89**, 1543 (1956).
387. Bergmann, M., du Vigneaud, V., and Zervas, L., *Ber.*, **62**, 1909 (1929).
388. Bergmann, M., and Fruton, J. S., *Advances in Enzymol.*, **1**, 63 (1941).
389. Desnuelle, P., Rovery, M., and Bonjour, G., *Biochim. Biophys. Acta*, **5**, 116 (1950).
390. Roche, J., Michel, R., Lissitzky, S., and Yogi, Y., *Bull. soc. chim. biol.*, **36**, 127 (1954).
391. Rovery, M., and Desnuelle, P., *Biochim. Biophys. Acta*, **8**, 450 (1952).
392. Courts, A., *Biochem. J.*, **59**, 382 (1955).
393. White, W. F., and Landmann, W. A., *J. Am. Chem. Soc.*, **76**, 4193 (1954).
394. Cole, R. D., Li, C. H., Harris, J. I., and Pon, N. G., *J. Biol. Chem.*, **219**, 903 (1956).
395. Ando, T., Abukumagawa, E., Nagai, Y., and Yamasaki, M., *J. Biochem. (Tokyo)*, **44**, 191 (1957).
396. Linderstrøm-Lang, K., *Cold Spring Harbor Symposia Quant. Biol.*, **14**, 117 (1949).

397. Bergmann, M., and Fraenkel-Conrat, H., *J. Biol. Chem.*, **119**, 707 (1937); **124**, 1 (1938).
398. Behrens, O. K., and Bergmann, M., *J. Biol. Chem.*, **129**, 587 (1939).
399. Hanes, C. S., Hird, F. J. R., and Isherwood, F. A., *Nature*, **166**, 288 (1950).
400. Janssen, F., Winitz, M., and Fox, S. W., *J. Am. Chem. Soc.*, **75**, 704 (1953).
401. Durell, J., and Fruton, J. S., *J. Biol. Chem.*, **207**, 487 (1954).
402. Johnson, A. C., and Herriott, R. M., *J. Biol. Chem.*, **222**, 855 (1956).
403. Fruton, J. S., *Yale J. Biol. Med.*, **22**, 263 (1950).
404. Waley, S. G., and Watson, J., *Nature*, **167**, 360 (1951).
405. Waley, S. G., and Watson, J., *Biochem. J.*, **57**, 529 (1954).
406. Blau, K., and Waley, S. G., *Biochem. J.*, **57**, 538 (1954).
407. Levin, Y., Berger, A., and Katchalski, E., *Biochem. J.*, **63**, 308 (1956).
408. Bergmann, M., *Advances in Enzymol.*, **2**, 33 (1942).
409. Ryle, A. P., and Sanger, F., *Biochem. J.*, **60**, 535 (1955).
410. Friedmann, E., Mariann, D. H., and Simon-Reuss, I., *Brit. J. Pharmacol.*, **4**, 105 (1949).
411. Hellerman, L., Chinard, F. P., and Dietz, V. R., *J. Biol. Chem.*, **147**, 443 (1943).
412. Cecil, R., *Biochem. J.*, **47**, 572 (1950).
413. Wieland, T., and Schwahn, H., *Chem. Ber.*, **89**, 421 (1956).
414. Huggins, C., Tapley, D. F., and Jensen, E. V., *Nature*, **167**, 592 (1951); cf. Fischer, E., and Gerngross, O., *Ber.*, **42**, 1485 (1909).
414a. Ressler, C., *Science*, **128**, 1281 (1958).
415. Mitchell, J. S., *Proc. Roy. Soc. (London)*, **A155**, 696 (1936).
416. Carpenter, D. C., *J. Am. Chem. Soc.*, **62**, 289 (1940).
417. McLaren, A. D., *Advances in Enzymol.*, **9**, 75 (1949).
418. Allen, A. J., Steiger, R. E., Magill, M. A., and Franklin, R. G., *Biochem. J.*, **31**, 195 (1937).
419. Mandl, I., Levy, B., and McLaren, A. D., *J. Am. Chem. Soc.*, **72**, 1790 (1950).
420. Kaplan, E. H., Campbell, E. D., and McLaren, A. D., *Biochim. Biophys. Acta*, **4**, 493 (1950).
421. McLaren, A. D., Gentile, P., Kirk, D. C., and Levin, N. A., *J. Polymer Sci.*, **10**, 333 (1953).
422. Setlow, R., *Biochim. Biophys. Acta*, **16**, 444 (1955).
423. McLaren, A. D., *Biochim. Biophys. Acta*, **18**, 601 (1955).
424. Speakman, J. B., *J. Textile Inst.*, **27**, 231 (1936).
425. Brown, A. E., and Harris, M., *Ind. Eng. Chem.*, **40**, 316 (1948).
426. Smith, A. L., and Harris, M., *J. Res. Natl. Bureau Standards*, **16**, 301 (1936).
427. Alexander, P., Hudson, R. F., and Fox, M., *Biochem. J.*, **46**, 27 (1950).
427a. Swan, J. N., *Nature*, **180**, 643 (1957); Pechère, J.-F., Dixon, G. H., Maybury, R. H., and Neurath, H., *J. Biol. Chem.*, **233**, 1364 (1958).
428. Linderstrøm-Lang, K., and Duspiva, F., *Z. physiol. Chem.*, **237**, 131 (1935).
429. Geiger, W. B., Patterson, W. I., Mizell, L. R., and Harris, M., *J. Res. Natl. Bureau Standards*, **27**, 459 (1941).
430. Cooley, S. L., and Wood, J. L., *Arch. Biochem. Biophys.*, **34**, 372 (1951).
431. Turner, R. A., Pierce, J. G., and du Vigneaud, V., *J. Biol. Chem.*, **193**, 359 (1951).
432. Miller, G. L., and Andersson, K. J. I., *J. Biol. Chem.*, **144**, 465 (1942).
433. Patterson, W. I., Geiger, W. B., Mizell, L. R., and Harris, M., *J. Res. Natl. Bureau Standards*, **27**, 89 (1941).
434. Toennies, G., and Homiller, R. P., *J. Am. Chem. Soc.*, **64**, 3054 (1942).
435. Sanger, F., *Biochem. J.*, **44**, 126 (1949).
436. Pierce, J. G., *J. Am. Chem. Soc.*, **77**, 184 (1955).
437. Ryle, A. P., Sanger, F., Smith, L. F., and Kitai, R., *Biochem. J.*, **60**, 541 (1955).

438. Mueller, J. M., Pierce, J. G., and du Vigneaud, V., *J. Biol. Chem.*, **204**, 857 (1953).
439. Popenoe, E. A., and du Vigneaud, V., *J. Biol. Chem.*, **205**, 133 (1953).
440. Ressler, C., Trippett, S., and du Vigneaud, V., *J. Biol. Chem.*, **204**, 861 (1953).
441. Thompson, E. O. P., *Biochim. Biophys. Acta*, **15**, 440 (1954).
442. Hirs, C. H. W., *J. Biol. Chem.*, **219**, 611 (1956).
443. Wieland, H., and Witkop, B., *Ann.*, **543**, 171 (1940).
444. Lynen, F., and Wieland, U., *Ann.*, **533**, 93 (1937).
445. Wieland, T., *Ann.*, **564**, 152 (1949).
446. Cornforth, J. W., Dalgliesh, C. E., and Neuberger, A., *Biochem. J.*, **48**, 598 (1951).
447. Cornforth, J. W., Cornforth, R. H., Dalgliesh, C. E., and Neuberger, A., *Biochem. J.*, **48**, 591 (1951).
448. Wieland, T., and Schmidt, G., *Ann.*, **577**, 215 (1952).
449. Meloun, B., and Sorm, F., *Collection Czechoslov. Chem. Communs.*, **20**, 265 (1955).
450. Wieland, T., and Schön, W., *Ann.*, **593**, 157 (1955).
451. Wieland, T., Pfleiderer, G., and Grein, L., *Ann. Acad. Sci. Fennicae*, **A60**, 381 (1955).
452. Wieland, T., and Weiberg, O., *Ann.*, **607**, 168 (1957).
453. Stoll, A., Petrzilka, T., and Becker, B., *Helv. Chim. Acta*, **33**, 57 (1950).
454. Jacobs, W. A., and Craig, L. C., *J. Biol. Chem.*, **110**, 521 (1935); **122**, 419 (1937).
455. Stoll, A., and Hofmann, A., *Helv. Chim. Acta*, **33**, 1705 (1950).
456. Stoll, A., Hofmann, A., and Petrzilka, T., *Helv. Chim. Acta*, **34**, 1544 (1951).
457. Plattner, P. A., Clauson-Kaas, N., Boller, A., and Nager, U., *Helv. Chim. Acta*, **31**, 860 (1948).
458. Woolley, D. W., *J. Biol. Chem.*, **176**, 1291 (1948).
459. Hotchkiss, R. D., *Advances in Enzymol.*, **4**, 153 (1944).
460. Synge, R. L. M., and Tiselius, A., *Acta Chem. Scand.*, **1**, 749 (1947).
461. Gregory, J. D., and Craig, L. C., *J. Biol. Chem.*, **172**, 839 (1948).
462. Synge, R. L. M., *Biochem. J.*, **39**, 355 (1945).
463. Synge, R. L. M., *Biochem. J.*, **44**, 542 (1949).
464. Neuberger, A., *Advances in Protein Chem.*, **4**, 297 (1948).
465. Craig, L. C., *Proc. 3rd Intern. Congr. Biochem., Brussels, 1955* (pub. 1956), p. 21.
466. Gause, G. F., and Brazhnikova, M. G., *Medgiz*, 5 (1943); *Lancet*, **247**, 715 (1944).
467. Synge, R. L. M., *Biochem. J.*, **39**, 363 (1945).
468. Sanger, F., *Biochem. J.*, **40**, 261 (1946).
469. Battersby, A. R., and Craig, L. C., *J. Am. Chem. Soc.*, **73**, 1887 (1951).
470. Schwyzer, R., and Sieber, P., *Helv. Chim. Acta*, **40**, 624 (1957).
471. Gavrilov, N. I., Podduknaya, N. A., Akimova, L. N., and Grigoryava, E. M., *J. Gen. Chem. (U.S.S.R.)*, **26**, 2261 (Tr.) (1956).
472. Otani, S., and Saito, Y., *Proc. Japan Acad.*, **30**, 991 (1954).
473. Harris, J. I., and Work, T. S., *Biochem. J.*, **46**, 582 (1950).
474. Boissonnas, P. A., and Schumann, J., *Helv. Chim. Acta*, **35**, 2229, 2237 (1952).
475. Craig, L. C., Gregory, J. D., and Barry, G. T., *Cold Spring Harbor Symposia Quant. Biol.*, **14**, 24 (1950).
476. Christensen, H. N., *J. Biol. Chem.*, **160**, 75 (1945).
477. Battersby, A. R., and Craig, L. C., *J. Am. Chem. Soc.*, **74**, 4019 (1952).
478. Battersby, A. R., and Craig, L. C., *J. Am. Chem. Soc.*, **74**, 4023 (1952).
479. Paladini, A., and Craig, L. C., *J. Am. Chem. Soc.*, **76**, 688 (1954).
480. King, T. P., and Craig, L. C., *J. Am. Chem. Soc.*, **77**, 6624, 6627 (1955).
481. Craig, L. C., and King, T. P., *J. Am. Chem. Soc.*, **77**, 6620 (1955).
482. Johnson, B. A., Anker, H. S., and Meleney, F. L., *Science*, **102**, 376 (1945).
483. Newton, G. G. F., and Abraham, E. P., *Biochem. J.*, **47**, 257 (1950).
484. Craig, L. C., Weisiger, J. R., Hausmann, W., and Harfenist, E. J., *J. Biol. Chem.*, **199**, 259 (1952).

485. Craig, L. C., Hausmann, W., and Weisiger, J. R., *J. Biol. Chem.*, **200**, 765 (1953).
486. Newton, G. G. F., and Abraham, E. P., *Biochem. J.*, **53**, 604 (1953).
487. Lockhart, I. M., Abraham, E. P., and Newton, G. G. F., *Biochem. J.*, **61**, 534 (1955).
488. Hausmann, W., Weisiger, J. R., and Craig, L. C., *J. Am. Chem. Soc.*, **77**, 721 (1955).
489. Greenstein, J. P., Levintow, L., Baker, C. G., and White, J., *J. Biol. Chem.*, **188**, 647 (1951).
490. Brockmann, H., Grubhofer, N., Kass, W., and Kalbe, H., *Chem. Ber.*, **84**, 260 (1951).
491. Weisiger, J. R., Hausmann, W., and Craig, L. C., *J. Am. Chem. Soc.*, **77**, 731 (1955).
492. Weisiger, J. R., Hausmann, W., and Craig, L. C., *J. Am. Chem. Soc.*, **77**, 3123 (1955).
493. Hausmann, W., Weisiger, J. R., and Craig, L. C., *J. Am. Chem. Soc.*, **77**, 723 (1955).
494. Lockhart, I. M., and Abraham, E. P., *Biochem. J.*, **62**, 645 (1956).
495. Theodoropoulos, D., and Craig, L. C., *J. Org. Chem.*, **21**, 1376 (1956).
496. Swallow, D. L., and Abraham, E. P., *Biochem. J.*, **65**, 39P (1957).
497. Newton, G. G. F., and Abraham, E. P., *Biochem. J.*, **62**, 651 (1956).
498. Abraham, E. P., and Newton, G. G. F., *Biochem. J.*, **62**, 658 (1956).
499. Kasuya, I., and Hagitani, A., *J. Biochem.*, **42**, 805 (1955).
500. Hausmann, W., and Craig, L. C., *J. Am. Chem. Soc.*, **76**, 4892 (1954).
501. Hausmann, W., *J. Am. Chem. Soc.*, **78**, 3663 (1956).
502. Biserte, G., and Dautrevaux, M., *Bull. soc. chim. biol.*, **39**, 795 (1957).
503. Brockmann, H., *Angew. Chem.*, **66**, 1 (1954).
504. Bullock, E., and Johnson, A. W., *J. Chem. Soc.*, **1957**, 3280.
505. Keller-Schierlein, W., and Prelog, V., *Helv. Chim. Acta*, **40**, 205 (1957).
506. Plattner, P. A., and Nager, U., *Helv. Chim. Acta*, **31**, 665, 2192, 2203 (1948).
507. Vining, L. C., and Taber, W. A., *Can. J. Chem.*, **35**, 1109 (1957).
508. Brockmann, H., and Geeren, H., *Ann.*, **603**, 216 (1957).
509. Bell, P. H., *J. Am. Chem. Soc.*, **76**, 5565 (1954).
510. White, W. F., and Landmann, W. A., *J. Am. Chem. Soc.*, **77**, 1711 (1955).
511. White, W. F., and Gross, A. M., *J. Am. Chem. Soc.*, **79**, 1141 (1957).
512. Landmann, W. A., Drake, M. P., and White, W. F., *J. Am. Chem. Soc.*, **75**, 4370 (1953).
513. Fox, S. W., Hurst, T. L., and Warner, C., *J. Am. Chem. Soc.*, **76**, 1154 (1953).
514. Bromer, W. W., Sinn, L. G., Staub, A., and Behrens, O. K., *J. Am. Chem. Soc.*, **78**, 3858 (1956); Bromer, W. W., Sinn, L. G., and Behrens, O. K., *ibid.*, **79**, 2798 (1957); Bromer, W. W., Staub, A., Sinn, L. G., and Behrens, O. K., *ibid.*, **79**, 2801 (1957).
515. Livermore, A. H., and du Vigneaud, V., *J. Biol. Chem.*, **180**, 365 (1949).
516. Pierce, J. G., and du Vigneaud, V., *J. Biol. Chem.*, **186**, 77 (1950).
517. Mueller, J. M., Pierce, J. G., Davoll, H., and du Vigneaud, V., *J. Biol. Chem.*, **191**, 309 (1951).
518. Turner, R. A., Pierce, J. G., and du Vigneaud, V., *J. Biol. Chem.*, **193**, 359 (1951).
519. Davoll, H., Turner, R. A., Pierce, J. G., and du Vigneaud, V., *J. Biol. Chem.*, **193**, 363 (1951).
520. du Vigneaud, V., Ressler, C., and Trippett, S., *J. Biol. Chem.*, **205**, 949 (1953).
521. Tuppy, H., *Biochim. Biophys. Acta*, **11**, 449 (1953).
522. Tuppy, H., and Michl, H., *Monatsh.*, **84**, 1011 (1953).
523. Tuppy, H., *Monatsh.*, **84**, 996 (1953).
524. Turner, R. A., Pierce, J. G., and du Vigneaud, V., *J. Biol. Chem.*, **191**, 21 (1951).
525. Popenoe, E. A., Lawler, H. C., and du Vigneaud, V., *J. Am. Chem. Soc.*, **74**, 3713 (1952).
526. du Vigneaud, V., Lawler, H. C., and Popenoe, E. A., *J. Am. Chem. Soc.*, **75**, 4880 (1953).
527. Popenoe, E. A., and du Vigneaud, V., *J. Biol. Chem.*, **206**, 353 (1954).

528. du Vigneaud, V., Gish, D. T., and Katsoyannis, P. G., *J. Am. Chem. Soc.*, **76**, 4751 (1954).
529. du Vigneaud, V., Ressler, C., Swan, J. M., Roberts, C. W., Katsoyannis, P. G., and Gordon, S., *J. Am. Chem. Soc.*, **75**, 4879 (1953).
530. Greenstein, J. P., *J. Biol. Chem.*, **118**, 321 (1937); **121**, 9 (1937).
531. Izumiya, N., and Greenstein, J. P., *Arch. Biochem. Biophys.*, **52**, 203 (1954).
532. Wade, R., Winitz, M., and Greenstein, J. P., *J. Am. Chem. Soc.*, **78**, 373 (1956).
533. Heaton, G. S., Rydon, H. N., and Schofield, J. A., *J. Chem. Soc.*, **1956**, 3157.
534. Herriott, R. M., in *Mechanism of Enzyme Action*, Johns Hopkins Press, Baltimore, p. 24, 1954; see also ref. (195).
535. Kunitz, M., and Northrop, J. H., *J. Gen. Physiol.*, **18**, 433 (1935).
536. Keith, C. K., Kazenko, A., and Laskowski, M., *J. Biol. Chem.*, **170**, 227 (1947).
537. Jacobsen, C. F., *Compt. rend. trav. lab. Carlsberg*, **25**, 325 (1947).
538. Schwert, G. W., and Kaufman, S., *J. Biol. Chem.*, **180**, 517 (1949).
539. Kunitz. M., *J. Gen. Physiol.*, **22**, 207 (1938).
540. Schwert, G. W., *J. Biol. Chem.*, **179**, 655 (1949).
541. Rovery, M., and Desnuelle, P., *Bull. soc. chim. biol.*, **36**, 95 (1954).
542. Bettelheim, F. R., and Neurath, H., *J. Biol. Chem.*, **212**, 241 (1955).
543. Dreyer, W. J., Wade, R. D., and Neurath, H., *Arch. Biochem. Biophys.*, **59**, 145 (1955).
544. Dreyer, W. J., and Neurath, H., *J. Biol. Chem.*, **217**, 527 (1955).
545. Sakota, N., *J. Biochem.*, **42**, 69, 649 (1955); **43**, 565 (1956).
546. Rovery, C., Fabre, C., and Desnuelle, P., *Biochim. Biophys. Acta*, **10**, 481 (1953).
547. Cunningham, L. W., Jr., Tietze, F., Green, N. M., and Neurath, H., *Discussions Faraday Soc.*, **No. 20**, 58 (1955).
548. Desnuelle, P., and Fabre, C., *Bull. soc. chim. biol.*, **36**, 181 (1954).
549. Davie, E. W., and Neurath, H., *J. Biol. Chem.*, **212**, 515 (1955).
550. Northrop, J. H., Kunitz, M., and Herriott, R. M., *Crystalline Enzymes*, Columbia University Press, New York, 2nd ed., p. 126, 1948.
550a. Pecherè, J.-F., and Neurath, H., *J. Biol. Chem.*, **229**, 389 (1957).
551. Tietze, F., *J. Biol. Chem.*, **204**, 1 (1953).
551a. Gabeloteau, C., and Desnuelle, P., *Bull. soc. chim. biol.*, **40**, 35 (1958).
552. Kunitz, M., *J. Gen. Physiol.*, **30**, 291, 311 (1947).
553. Fraenkel-Conrat, H., Bean, R. S., and Lineweaver, H., *J. Biol. Chem.*, **177**, 385 (1949).
554. Davie, E. W., and Neurath, H., *J. Biol. Chem.*, **212**, 507 (1955).
555. Lorand, L., *Biochem. J.*, **52**, 200 (1952).
556. Sherry, S., and Troll, W., *J. Biol. Chem.*, **208**, 95 (1954).
556a. Blombäck, B., and Yamashina, I., *Arkiv. Kemi*, **12**, 299 (1958).
557. Bailey, K., and Bettelheim, F. R., *Biochim. Biophys. Acta*, **18**, 495 (1955).
558. Bettelheim, F. R., *Biochim. Biophys. Acta*, **19**, 121 (1956); *J. Am. Chem. Soc.*, **76**, 2838 (1954).
558a. Magnusson, S., *Acta Chem. Scand.*, **12**, 355 (1958).
559. Peart, W. S., *Biochem. J.*, **62**, 520 (1956).
560. Elliott, D. F., and Peart, W. S., *Nature*, **177**, 527 (1956); *Biochem. J.*, **65**, 246 (1957).
561. Lentz, K. E., Skeggs, L. T., Woods, K. R., Kahn, J. R., and Shumway, N. R., *J. Exptl. Med.*, **104**, 183 (1956).
562. Rittel, W., Iselin, B., Kappeler, H., Riniker, B., and Schwyzer, R., *Helv. Chim. Acta*, **40**, 614 (1957).
563. Harris, J. I., and Roos, P., *Nature*, **178**, 90 (1956).
564. Harris, J. I., and Lerner, A. B., *Nature*, **179**, 1346 (1957).
565. Geschwind, L. I., Li, C. H., and Barnafi, L., *J. Am. Chem. Soc.*, **78**, 4494 (1956); **79**, 620, 1003, 6394 (1957).

565a. Hofmann, K., Woolner, M. E., Spuhler, G., and Schwartz, E. T., *J. Am. Chem. Soc.*, **80**, 1486 (1958); Schwyzer, R., and Li, C. H., *Nature*, **182**, 1669 (1958).
566. Waley, S. G., *Biochem. J.*, **64**, 715 (1956); **67**, 172 (1957); **68**, 189 (1958).
566a. Law, H. D., Millar, I. T., Springall, H. D., and Birch, A. J., *Proc. Chem. Soc., (London)*, **1958**, 198.
567. Linderstrøm-Lang, K., and Ottesen, M., *Compt. rend. trav. lab. Carlsberg*, **26**, 403 (1949).
568. Ottesen, M., and Schellman, C. G., *Compt. rend. trav. lab. Carlsberg*, **30**, 157 (1957).
569. Tsou, C. L., *Biochem. J.*, **49**, 362, 367 (1951).
570. Tuppy, H., and Paléus, S., *Acta Chem. Scand.*, **9**, 353 (1955).
571. Theorell, H., *Biochem. Z.*, **298**, 242 (1939).
572. Paul, K. G., *Acta Chem. Scand.*, **3**, 1178 (1949); **4**, 239 (1950).
573. Tuppy, H., and Bodo, G., *Monatsh.*, **85**, 1024 (1954).
574. Theorell, H., and Åkeson, Å., *J. Am. Chem. Soc.*, **63**, 1804 (1941).
575. Paléus, S., Ehrenberg, A., and Tuppy, H., *Acta Chem. Scand.*, **9**, 365 (1955).
576. Paul, K. G., and Avi-Dor, J., *Acta Chem. Scand.*, **8**, 649 (1954).
576a. Ohira, T., *J. Agr. Chem. Soc., Japan*, **16**, 293 (1940); Rudinger, J., and Pravda, Z., *Collection Czechoslov. Chem. Communs.*, **23**, 1947 (1958).
577. Harfenist, E. J., and Craig, L. C., *J. Am. Chem. Soc.*, **74**, 3087 (1952).
578. Fredericq, E., and Neurath, H., *J. Am. Chem. Soc.*, **72**, 2684 (1950).
578a. Leach, S. J., and Scheraga, H. A., *Compt. rend. trav. lab. Carlsberg*, **30**, 271 (1958).
579. Gutfreund, H., and Ogston, A. G., *Biochem. J.*, **44**, 163 (1948).
580. Rees, M. W., *Biochem. J.*, **40**, 632 (1946).
581. Sanger, F., Thompson, E. O. P., and Kitai, R., *Biochem. J.*, **59**, 509 (1955).
582. Brown, H., Sanger, F., and Kitai, R., *Biochem. J.*, **60**, 556 (1955).
583. Kauffmann, T., and Boettcher, F.-P., *Z. Naturforsch.*, **136**, 467 (1958).
584. Firfarova, K. F., *Biokhimiya*, **21**, 122 (1956).

chapter 17

Spectrophotometry

The amino acids do not absorb light to any appreciable extent in the visible range of the spectrum, and the characterization of this class of compounds has been, perforce, restricted to the regions of longer and of shorter wavelength.

1. Ultraviolet Absorption Spectra. All amino acids absorb to a greater or lesser extent in the ultraviolet region of the spectrum, but of the twenty or so amino acids which commonly occur in proteins, only four possess a characteristic absorption in the 220–300 mμ region, namely, tyrosine, tryptophan, phenylalanine, and cystine (1). Table 17–1 (2, 3) lists the molecular absorption coefficients (*E* mol.) of these compounds at the maximum and minimum absorptions.

The absorption spectra of tryptophan and of phenylalanine are relatively little affected by ionization in solution inasmuch as the amino and carboxyl groups involved are separated from the aromatic groups by two saturated carbon atoms (Figures 17–1 and 17–2). The absorption spectrum of tyrosine is not very sensitive to changes in *p*H until alkaline conditions are reached, the spectral change then being essentially complete at *p*H 12. The marked difference in absorption of tyrosine in acid and in alkaline solutions is attributable to ionization of the phenolic group in this compound (4–6):

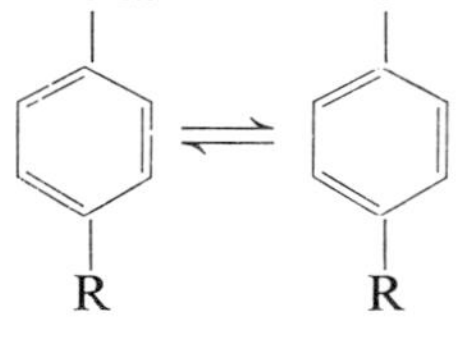

The phenoxide ion of tyrosine absorbs strongly between 290.0 and 310.0 mμ, whereas the phenolic form absorbs little in this region. By employing the absorption coefficients at 295.0, 300.0, and 305.0 mμ as a measure of the

TABLE 17-1
Molecular Absorption Coefficients (3, 4) and λ in mμ

Compound	In Acid λ max.	In Acid λ min.	In Acid E mol.	In Alkali λ max.	In Alkali λ min.	In Alkali E mol.
Tyrosine	274.5		1,340	293.5		2,330
		245.0	170		269.5	1,000
	223.0		8,200	240.0		11,050
Tryptophan	287.5		4,550	288.0		4,600
	278.0		5,550	280.5		5,430
		242.0	1,930		244.0	1,900
	218.0		33,500	221.5		34,600
Phenylalanine	267.1		92	267.6		124
	263.4		152	264.0		160
	260.3		144	261.0		176
	257.5		195	258.0		206
	251.6		154	252.2		172
	246.5		115	246.8		128
	241.5		81	241.5		84
		236.0	63		235.8	62
Cystine	248.0		345	–	–	–
		237.0	300	–	–	–

phenoxide ion concentration, and by employing partly neutralized solutions of known pH, it was possible for Crammer and Neuberger to determine the phenolic dissociation constant of tyrosine, namely $pK' = 10.15$ (5) (see Section 17-7·for further discussion of this procedure).

If it is assumed as a first approximation that the absorption curve of a protein is the sum of the absorbencies of its constituent amino acids, then the amount of those amino acids absorbing at a particular region of the spectrum can be computed (7, 8). Analysis of proteins in the region of 280.0 to 320.0 mμ, wherein only tyrosine and tryptophan absorb appreciably, led to values for these two amino acids in substantially good agreement with those secured by methods of chemical analysis (7, 8).

The maximum absorption of 3:5-diiodotyrosine occurs at 291.0 mμ in acid solution with a molecular absorption value of 2310; in alkaline solution two maxima are observed, one at 316.0 mμ (E mol. $= 5260$) and the other at 306.0 mμ (E mol. $= 5170$) (4). The dissociation constant measured for the phenolic group in this compound at the wavelengths 330.0 mμ, 325.0 mμ, and 315.0 mμ yielded a value of 6.42 (5).

The absorption of light by phenylalanine is considerably less than that by tyrosine or tryptophan, but is much more complex than that of either of these two amino acids. At its maximum, cystine absorbs considerably more than does phenylalanine at *its* maximum. The classic studies of Ley and Arends (9; cf. 10) on the hydrochloride salt and on the sodium salt of cystine revealed parallel absorption curves for these compounds, that of the latter being shifted some 10 mμ toward the red end of the spectrum. That the absorption maximum at about 250 mμ was due to the disulfide group was established by these authors in the case of diethyldisulfide, which possesses

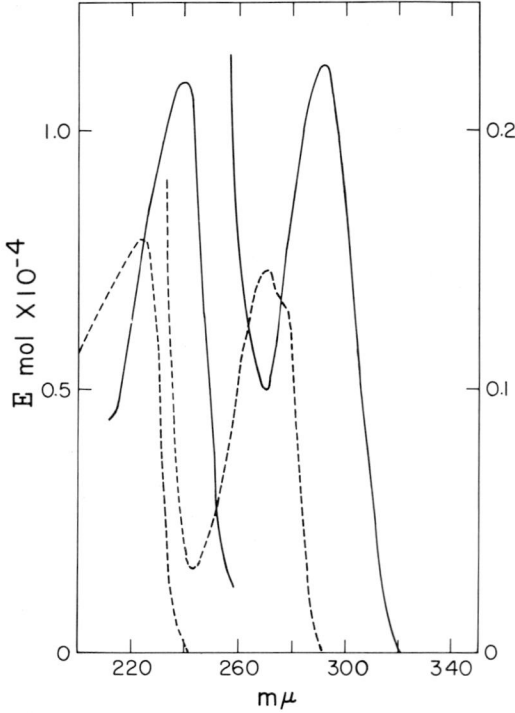

Figure 17-1. Absorption curves of tyrosine in 0.1N HCl (dash lines) and in 0.1N NaOH (continuous lines). Beaven, G. H., and Holiday, E. K., *Advances in Protein Chem.*, **7**, 319 (1952).

a relatively sharp band at this wavelength. As might be expected, the absorption characteristics of homocystine resemble those of cystine, the maximum occurring at 243 mμ (E mol = 360), and the minimum at 228 mμ (E mol. = 285) (3). In contrast with cystine, cysteine (except in alkali) absorbs very little and possesses no characteristic features (6). Methionine shows a general and steep absorption, somewhat greater than that of homocystine, from 210 to 230 mμ, and much less from 230 to 245 mμ (3).

In an ingenious study, Goldfarb, Saidel, and Mosovich (11) observed that the absorption of proteins and simple peptides rose considerably toward

205 mμ with an intensity approximately proportional to the number of peptide bonds present. This rise is due to the specific absorption by the peptide linkage which possesses a maximum at about 185 mμ (12). By dividing the difference between the molecular absorption coefficient of the protein or peptide and the sum of the coefficients of the individual amino acids by the number of peptide bonds, values were obtained as a first

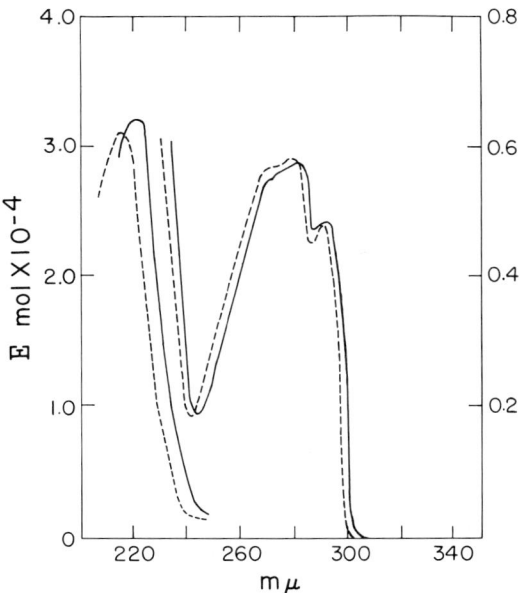

Figure 17-2. Absorption curves of tryptophan in 0.1N HCl (dash lines) and in 0.1N NaOH (continuous lines). Beaven, G. H., and Holiday, E. K., *Advances in Protein Chem.*, **7**, 319 (1952).

approximation for what was termed the peptide bond coefficient (11). These values ranged from 2500 to 2800 for several proteins and simple peptides of glycine when the absorption at 205 mμ was measured in water. As the pH was decreased by addition of acid, and the carboxylate ion shifted to the un-ionized state, the absorption at 205 mμ for the simpler peptides decreased to an ultimately constant value for each peptide (11, 13). Inasmuch as the molecular absorption coefficients of amino acids at this wavelength change relatively little between pH 1 and 6 (14), the result is that the calculated peptide bond coefficients appear to be lower at the lower pH values (13). Table 17-2 describes the molecular absorption coefficients for the various amino acids at 205 mμ (11); the relatively high values for arginine and histidine are noteworthy.

TABLE 17-2
Molecular Absorption Coefficients of Amino Acids at 205 mμ (11)

Amino Acid	E mol. (205 mμ)	Amino Acid	E mol. (205 mμ)
Glycine	54	Arginine·HCl	1,350
Alanine	79	Lysine·HCl	98
Leucine	104	Cysteine·HCl	690
Isoleucine	104	Cystine	2,200
Proline	72	Methionine	1,830
Hydroxyproline	73	Phenylalanine	8,600
Serine	81	Tyrosine	6,080
Threonine	97	Tryptophan	20,400
Glutamic acid	151	Histidine·HCl	5,200
Aspartic acid	136	Valine	97

The results expressed in Figures 17-3 and 17-4 and Table 17-2 have been employed to calculate tentatively the average contribution to the molecular absorption coefficient of each peptide by each peptide bond (3) (Table 17-3).

TABLE 17-3
Molecular Absorption Coefficients (E mol.) of Cystine Peptides and Other Compounds at 205 mμ^a (3)

Compound	E mol.	Peptide Bond Coefficient at 205 mμ
Cyclo-L-cystinyl[b]	11,200	3,600
L-Cystinyl-L-cystine[b]	11,200	3,600
L-Cystinyl-D-cystine	12,600	4,300
D-Cystinyl-L-cystine	12,600	4,300
L-Cystinyldiglycine	8,200	3,050
Glycyl-L-methionine	3,200	1,500
Glycylglycine	1,100	1,000
L-Cystine	2,000	–
L-Methionine	1,650	–
L-Homocystine	1,350	–
Glycine	45	–

[a] In 0.01N HCl.
[b] Cf. ref. (15).

The molecular absorption coefficient of D-cystine is the same as that of L-cystine. The values of the peptides of cystine are higher than those for the simpler peptides, and they suggest that the magnitude of the peptide bond coefficient may depend not only on the nature of the constituent amino acids in the peptide, but also on the relative position of these amino acids in regard to each other.

SPECTROPHOTOMETRY

Although optical isomers possess identical spectra in the ultraviolet, it is of interest to note (Figure 17–3) that diastereomers may be distinguished by this criterion. Thus the spectra of L-cystinyl-D-cystine and of D-cystinyl-L-cystine are identical, but different from that of L-cystinyl-L-cystine (3).

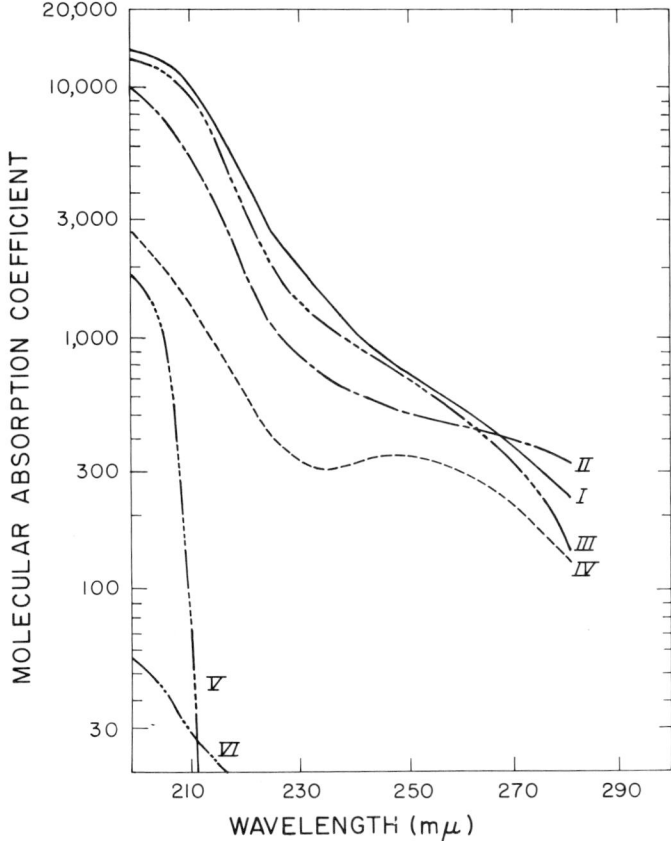

Figure 17–3. Absorption curves in 0.01N HCl of (I) L-cystinyl-D-cystine and D-cystinyl-L-cystine; (II) L-cystinyldiglycine; (III) cyclo-L-cystinyl and L-cystinyl-L-cystine; (IV) L-cystine; (V) glycylglycine; and (VI) glycine. Otey, M. C., and Greenstein, J. P., *Arch. Biochem. Biophys.*, **53**, 501 (1954).

Of equal interest is the fact that the two compounds, cyclo-L-cystinyl and L-cystinyl-L-cystine, monomer and dimer respectively (15), possess identical spectra (3). Studies on the absorption of various diastereomeric peptides, such as L-tyrosyl-L-tyrosine and L-tyrosyl-D-tyrosine, may prove of great interest in this connection.

Superimposed upon the specific absorption of tyrosine, phenylalanine, tryptophan, and cystine as components of peptides is that of the peptide bond. A still more vivid illustration of this phenomenon is afforded by the use of an unsaturated or so-called dehydropeptide bond whose contribution to the absorption in the ultraviolet is much greater than that of the normal

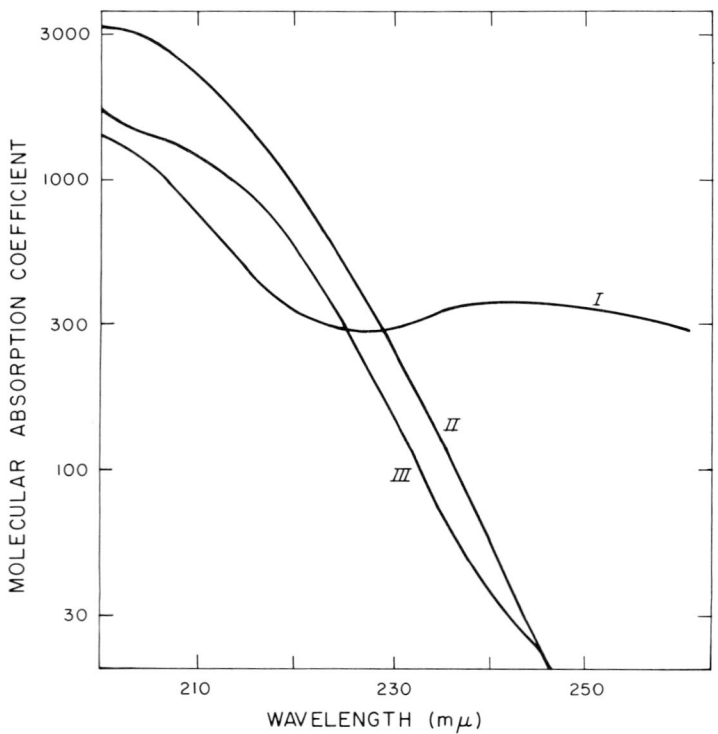

Figure 17–4. Absorption curves in 0.01N HCl of (I) L-homocystine; (II) glycyl-L-methionine; and (III) L-methionine. Otey, M. C., and Greenstein, J. P., *Arch. Biochem. Biophys.*, **53**, 501 (1954).

peptide bond (Section 10–9). Thus such compounds as acetyldehydrophenylalanine (N-acetyl-α-amino-β-phenylacrylic acid),

$$CH_3CONHC(=CHC_6H_5)COOH$$

(Figure 10–4) (16), or acetyldehydrotyrosine (Figure 10–5) (17) possess a double bond which is conjugated with the aromatic ring system and produces a marked enhancement of absorption of ultraviolet light by the entire molecule (16). As noted in Figures 10–4 and 10–5, not only is there a considerably greater absorption observed for these compounds as compared with that for the corresponding saturated acetylamino acids, acetylphenylalanine and acetyltyrosine, but also in both sets of curves the maximum is shifted toward longer wavelengths. The enhancement of absorption by the dehydropeptide bond is exhibited not only where aromatic amino acids are concerned but occurs also in the case of the N-acylated aliphatic dehydroamino acids as well (18–20) (Figure 10-3).

The problem of whether the amino acids in solution retain the characteristics of the crystalline state has enlisted the interest of many investigators. Spectral studies have contributed considerably to this problem, and in Table 17-4 are given the results of the study by Ley and Arends (9) on the absorption spectra over a relatively short wavelength range of glycine in water and in the crystalline state. It will be noted that the spectra are nearly identical, and thus the dipolar ion form is characteristic of the amino acid both in the solid state and in solution.

TABLE 17-4

Ultraviolet Light Absorption of Glycine in Water Solution and in the Crystalline Form (9)

Glycine in Water		Glycine in Crystalline Form							
$\log E$	λ	$\log E^a$	λ	$\log E^b$	λ	$\log E^c$	λ	$\log E^d$	λ
−0.81	241.6	−0.643	241.1	−0.473	238.3	−0.190	234.8	+0.048	235.8
−0.51	238.5	−0.560	239.3	−0.390	237.5	−0.016	233.3	+0.141	231.3
−0.39	237.1	−0.432	238.0	−0.263	235.4	+0.020	232.5	+0.268	230.5
±0.00	232.7	−0.135	233.5	+0.034	231.6	+0.318	229.0	+0.565	225.0
+0.60	225.6								

$^a d = 0.1078$ cm. $^b d = 0.0730$ cm. $^c d = 0.0380$ cm. $^d d = 0.0215$ cm.

2. Infrared Absorption Spectra. The infrared absorption spectra of α-amino acids have been the subject of a large number of investigations. The literature up to 1952 has been considered by G. B. B. M. Sutherland in an excellent review (21). References to later work in this field are to be found in the annual surveys of infrared spectra by Gore (cf. 22), and in the excellent book by Bellamy (23). Most of these studies were conducted on amino acids in the solid state, although Gore, Barnes, and Peterson (24) have demonstrated the usefulness of aqueous phase infrared methods, and Lacher, Croy, Kianpour, and Park (25) have suggested the use of antimony trichloride as a solvent for obtaining the infrared absorption spectra of amino acids. Of considerable value in the interpretation of the ionic state of the amino acids, and of the assignment of characteristic frequencies to the —NH_3^+ and —COO^- groups involved, has been the work of Edsall on the Raman spectra of the amino acids and related compounds in aqueous solution (26) (see below). As a result of these various spectroscopic studies it may be accepted that (a) the α-amino acids in the solid state or at their isoelectric points in aqueous solution exist almost exclusively as dipolar ions, and (b) as a consequence of this dipolar ion structure many amino acids possess a characteristic absorption frequency at about 6.3 μ which is related to the —COO⁻ group, as well as a relatively weak absorption at about 4.7 μ which may be attributed to NH frequencies in the —NH$_3^+$ ion (27, 28).

Beyond these basic assignments it has been difficult to interpret further the seemingly complex infrared spectra of the amino acids. This may be due in part to lack of systemization in the choice of the compounds used for spectral studies. In many cases the groups of amino acids selected have included those of the L- as well as those of the DL-configuration, although there is considerable evidence at hand that the infrared spectra in the solid state of an amino acid in these two optical forms may not in many instances be comparable (29–32).

The solid state infrared spectra of the optically pure (>99.9%) individual L and D isomers of some 50 α-amino acids and their derivatives have been examined in a comprehensive study (33) between 2 μ and 15 μ. The experimental procedure was briefly as follows. An approximately 1% mixture of the dried amino acid with KBr was ground to pass a 200-mesh screen, and an aliquot thereof transferred to an evacuable die. After evacuation at very low pressure, the mixture was pressed for 2 minutes at 14,000 lb. per sq. in. The window so prepared was placed in the sample beam of the spectrometer, and a similar window lacking the amino acid placed in the reference beam. In every case the spectrum of an L-amino acid was indistinguishable over this wavelength range from that of its corresponding D-antipode. Table 17-5 lists and characterizes the spectral absorption bands in the 2-μ to 8-μ region, which is that in which the specific vibrational frequencies of the α-amino acids as a class would be expected to appear. In this table, the compounds are categorized into eight general groups based essentially upon obvious structural considerations (33).

The general structure of the α-amino acids may be represented by RCH(NH$_3^+$)COO⁻. Group I compounds in Table 17-5 represent a homologous series of straight-chain α-amino acids which as a whole constitute a prototype of this class of compounds. An analogous homologous straight-chain series in which an ω-OH group, an ω-COOH group, and an ω-NH$_2$ group are substituted form the substance, respectively, of groups IV, VI, and VII. Group II is composed of compounds in which R consists of various branched hydrocarbon chains, and group III is composed of compounds in which aromatic or corresponding alicyclic rings are substituted on the β-carbon atom of the α-amino acid. Group V consists of the alicyclic α-amino acids, and group VIII consists of a miscellaneous group of α-amino acids all of which contain sulfur.

Inspection of Table 17-5 reveals first of all a marked similarity in the infrared spectra of many of the amino acids in the region of 6.3 μ to 7.5 μ. Within this range six absorption peaks appear to be shared in common with most of the compounds studied, namely, 6.3 μ, 6.6 μ, 6.9 μ, 7.1 μ, 7.3 μ, and 7.5 μ. The bands at 6.3 μ and 7.1 μ have been related, respectively, to the antisymmetrical and symmetrical stretching vibrations of the ionized carboxyl group of the dipolar ions, at 6.6 μ to an N-H deformation motion of the α-amino group; the 6.9-μ and 7.3-μ bands are, respectively, related to antisymmetrical and symmetrical CH_3 stretching and possibly CH_2 deformation motions, and finally the 7.5-μ band may be considered to be related to a CH_2 wagging motion.

The apparent exceptions to this uniformity in spectra include threonine, proline, allohydroxyproline, and alloaminotricarballylic acid in which the 6.3-μ band is not observed; isovaline, leucine, serine, homoserine, hydroxyproline, and allohydroxyproline, in which the 6.6-μ band is not observed; and valine, phenylalanine, allothreonine, hydroxyproline, aspartic acid, glutamic acid, aminoadipic acid, alloaminotricarballylic acid, β-aminoalanine, ornithine, and lysine, in whose spectra the 6.9-μ band is not apparent. None of the amino acids studied lacks the 7.1-μ band. In the spectrum of glycine, however, the 7.3-μ band, and in that of alanine, the 7.5-μ band, is not apparent. Other absorption bands shared by many but not all the amino acids are the 3.3-μ and 3.9-μ peaks which are provisionally assigned to the N-H and C-H stretching motions, and the 4.7-μ peak which is tentatively assigned to an N-H stretching vibration in the —NH_3^+ group of the dipolar ion form of the amino acid. Perhaps one of the most striking differences between Group I amino acids and most of those in other groups is the nearly complete absence of the 6.2-μ band in the former.

COMPOUNDS IN GROUP I. This homologous series of straight-chain α-amino-α-carboxylic acids all possess five absorption peaks in common, namely, at 4.7 μ (due to some motion of the charged α-amino group), 6.3 μ (antisymmetric stretch of —COO^-), 6.6 μ (amino acid II band, or N—H deformation), 6.9 μ (—CH_2 or —CH_3 deformation), and 7.1 μ (symmetric stretch of —COO^-). All but aminocaprylic acid possess a band at 3.9 μ, all but glycine possess a band at 7.3 μ, and all but alanine possess a band at 7.5 μ. The lack of the 7.3-μ peak in the spectrum of glycine may be due to the shortness of the skeletal chain and the absence of a free methyl group. In the case of alanine, the N-H deformation at 6.6 μ appears to be very weak, the antisymmetrical carboxylate vibration is split into two bands, absorbing at 6.15 μ and 6.25 μ, while the absorbance of the CH_3 bending motion is the most marked of any compound in this group. As the number of methylene groups in the chain increases, the absorbance at 7.3 μ tends to diminish. The hydrogenic N-H stretching motion at 4.7 μ is relatively

TABLE

Absorption Spectra in the Infrared

			2–5 μ					
Group I								
Glycine	3.17MS	3.45sh	3.50MB	3.73sh		3.90WS	4.75WB	
Alanine		3.30SS		3.73SB		3.90MS	4.77WB	
α-Aminobutyric acid			3.50SB			3.85sh	4.73WB	
Norvaline		3.40SB				3.87sh	4.73WB	
Norleucine		3.37SB		3.65sh		3.90sh	4.71WB	
α-Aminoheptylic acid		3.40SB				3.90sh	4.73WB	
α-Aminocaprylic acid		3.36MS		3.68MB			4.73WB	
α-Aminononylic acid		3.43SS	3.52sh			3.90sh	4.73WB	
α-Aminodecylic acid			3.57SB			3.90sh	4.75WB	
α-Aminoundecylic acid			3.57SB			3.90sh	4.73WB	
α-Aminododecylic acid			3.57SB			3.90sh	4.73WB	
Group II								
Valine		3.38SB		3.75SB		3.92sh	4.79MS	
Isovaline	2.97SS [3.18sh]	3.32SB		3.80SB		4.02SB	4.97WB	
Leucine		3.39SB		3.75MB		3.93MB	4.75WB	
Isoleucine		3.44SB				3.90sh	4.77WB	
Alloisoleucine		3.44SB				3.90WS	4.78WB	
t-Leucine			3.48SB			3.88WS	4.87WB	
Group III								
α-Aminocyclohexylacetic acid		3.37SB					4.77WB	
α-Aminocyclohexyl-propionic acid	2.98MS	3.27SB	3.60sh			3.92sh	4.77WB	
α-Aminophenylacetic acid			3.47SB			3.90vw	4.82WB	
Phenylalanine		3.33SS					4.90MB	
Tyrosine	3.16sh	3.25SB	3.38sh	3.75SB		3.90sh	4.85WB	
Tryptophan	2.96MS	3.34MS				4.00MB	4.85WB	5.98MS
Group IV								
Serine	2.95MS	3.35SB		3.80WB		3.90sh	4.92WB	
Homoserine	3.15MS	3.40SS		3.70WB		3.90sh	4.80WB	
Homoserine lactone·HCl		3.40SB	3.52sh					5.10WB	5.63SS
Pentahomoserine	3.05sh [3.15sh]	3.37SB		3.63sh			4.73WB	
Hexahomoserine	3.06MS	3.40MB		3.66MB			4.73WB	
Phenylserine	2.83MS [3.15SB]	3.33sh				3.95WB		5.13WB
Allophenylserine	3.00sh	3.30SB						5.00WB
Threonine	3.20SB	3.40SB					4.90WB	
Allothreonine		3.30SB					4.90WS	

17–5 (33)

in the 2-μ to 8-μ Region[a,b,c]

		5–7 μ					7–8 μ		
6.15SS	6.23SB 6.28SS 6.33SB		6.60SB 6.65WB 6.63SS	6.93WS 6.88MS 6.90WS [6.85MS]	7.08SS 7.08SS 7.10SS	7.35SS 7.37MS	7.50SS 7.55SS	.7.65SS 7.67WS	
	6.33SB 6.32SB 6.33SS 6.33SS 6.33SS 6.34SS		6.63SS 6.62MB 6.63MS 6.62SS 6.62MS 6.62SS	6.92WS 6.92WS 6.93MS 6.93WS 6.93WS 6.94MS [6.84vw]	7.10SS 7.10SS 7.10SS 7.10SS 7.10MS 7.13SS	7.42MS 7.39MS 7.40WS 7.38WS 7.38WB 7.39MS	7.57WS 7.55SS 7.57MS 7.58MS 7.57MS 7.58SS	7.74WS 7.83WS	7.93vw 8.02vw
	6.34SS 6.35SS		6.64SS 6.63SS	6.94MS 6.94MS	7.12SS 7.12SS	7.37MB 7.37MB	7.57SS 7.57SS		
6.20sh	6.35SS		6.67SS		7.02WS [7.18MS]	7.40WS	7.53SS	7.87WS	
6.09sh	6.35SB			6.95MB [6.85sh]	7.11SB	7.28MS	7.45MS	7.75SS	
6.20sh 6.20sh	6.34SB 6.32SB		6.62MS 6.60SS	6.95WS 6.84WS	7.10SS 7.06MS [7.16SS]	7.35MB 7.40MS	7.45sh 7.52MS	7.61MS 7.64WS	7.72MS 7.86vw [7.96vw]
6.20sh	6.32SB		6.65SS	6.85WS	7.03MS [7.18SS]	7.39MS	7.60SS	7.80vw	7.96vw
	6.26SB	6.45sh [6.53sh]	6.76MB	6.83sh	7.12SS [7.18sh]	7.30WS	7.45SS	7.73SS	7.98vw
6.22sh	6.33SS		6.65SS	6.93vw	7.07MS [7.20MS]	7.42MS	7.50vw	7.62MS	7.87vw
	6.33SB		6.66MS	6.94WS	7.10SS	7.30WB [7.37sh]	7.50MS [7.67WS]	7.76vw	7.98vw
6.23SS	6.32sh	6.45sh	6.63SS	6.90vw	7.14MS	7.40WS		7.70vw	7.89vw
6.17MS 6.22SS	6.30SS 6.30SS		6.66SS 6.62MS	6.95vw	7.10SS 7.06MS	7.34MS	7.50WS 7.50SS	7.65MS	7.73sh 7.90sh [8.03SS]
	6.28SS			6.90vw	7.07SS	7.36SS	7.60vw		7.12vw
6.21sh	6.25SB 6.34SB 6.28WB	6.50sh	6.66MS	6.81MS 6.82vw	7.08MS 7.10SS 7.18MS	7.22sh 7.26WS 7.33MS	7.46MS 7.46SS	7.67MS 7.72MS 7.67WS	8.00MS 8.25SS
	6.35SS		6.57SS	6.94WS	7.12SS	7.40MS	7.55MS		7.86WS
6.00SS	6.36SS 6.25SB [6.32sh]	6.52sh	6.65SS 6.62SB [6.67sh]	6.96MS 6.90MS	7.14SS 7.18SS	7.42MS 7.40SS	7.59MS		8.05WB
6.20SB 6.14SS	6.32sh	6.52sh	6.70WS 6.77SS	6.90WS 6.87SS	7.11SS 7.05SS	7.40WS 7.43SS [7.28sh]	7.60WS	7.65SS	7.85WS 8.00MS
6.10SS	6.27vw		6.80SS		7.07MS	7.35WS	7.50WS	7.75WS	7.93WS

1700 CHEMISTRY OF THE AMINO ACIDS

TABLE 17-5

		2–5 μ					
Group V							
Proline		3.33MB [3.38sh]		3.65vw			
Hydroxyproline	3.10SS	3.23MS	3.47MB	3.76MB	3.93MB [4.12vw]		
Allohydroxyproline	3.17SS		3.45MB		3.90MB		
Group VI							
Aspartic acid		3.34sh	3.43SB			4.85WB	5.25WB	5.93SS
Glutamic acid		3.32SS		3.70sh			5.20MB	
α-Aminoadipic acid		3.37SB		3.70vw	4.00vw			
Succinic acid		3.40SB		3.85sh	3.98sh			5.80SS 5.92SS
Tricarballylic acid		3.27SB						5.72sh 5.83SB 5.90sh
Allo-α-aminotricar-ballylic acid		3.26SB	3.44vw	3.85vw			5.25WB	5.80 5.92 SB
α-Aminotricarballylic acid	3.09SS	3.27SB	3.42sh					5.76SB
Allopyrrolidonedi-carboxylic acid	2.87MS [3.14WS]		3.50MB		4.00vw			5.80SS
Pyrrolidonedicarboxylic acid	3.15MS				4.02vw		5.75SS	5.86MS
Isocitric acid lactone	3.00SB						5.60SS	5.80SS
Alloisocitric acid lactone	3.00SB						5.63SS	5.83SS
Group VII							
α,β-Diaminopropionic acid·HCl		3.30SB					5.08WB	
α,γ-Diaminobutyric acid·HCl	3.20SS	3.40SB			4.00WS	4.97WB		
Ornithine·2HCl		3.30SB						
Lysine·HCl			3.50SB			4.80WB		5.73SS
Arginine·HCl	3.07SS	3.27SS	3.50SB			4.77WB		5.95SS
Citrulline	3.05SS	3.17sh	3.34SB	3.45sh	3.90sh	4.78WB		5.95SS
Histidine		3.40SB		3.62sh				
Group VIII							
Methionine			3.50SB		3.95MB	4.76MB		
Ethionine		3.40SB		3.75sh	3.90MB	4.75WB		
Cystine			3.47SB		3.90sh	4.80WB		
Homocystine		3.50SB	3.57sh	3.75sh	3.90sh	4.75WB		
Cysteine·HCl			3.46SB		3.90sh	4.80WB		
S-Benzylcysteine	3.20sh		3.55SB		3.90MB	4.94WB		
S-Benzylhomocysteine	3.18sh		3.50SB	3.70sh	3.90MB	4.80WB		

[a] Succinic and tricarballylic acids have been included for comparison.
[b] The bracketed numbers are so placed because of spatial limitations and are not to be regarded as
[c] W = weak intensity, S = sharp band, sh = shoulder, M = medium intensity, B = broad band,

SPECTROPHOTOMETRY

(*continued*)

5–7 μ					7–8 μ				
6.18SS	6.43SS	6.55sh		6.92MS	7.13sh	7.29SB	7.57WS	7.75MS	7.98WS
6.10MS	6.31SB				7.01WS [7.15MS]	7.37WS	7.58MS	7.80WS	7.96MS
6.13SS		6.42MS		6.97MS	7.05sh	7.23MS	7.53MS	7.63vw [7.70vw]	7.93MS
6.06MS	6.25MB		6.65SS		7.03SS	7.42MS	7.57SB		8.01SS
6.07SS	6.30vw		6.60SS		7.04MB	7.38SS		7.62MS	7.94SS
6.00SS [6.07SS]	6.33SB		6.67SB		7.04MB	7.33MS [7.40WS]	7.55SS	7.73SS	8.00MS
					7.06SS			7.66SS	
				6.98SS		7.47WS		7.73MS	8.05SS
6.17WS		6.47vw	6.55MB		7.04sh [7.12SB]	7.37MS	7.54MS	7.80SB	
6.16WS	6.30MS		6.63SS	6.90vw	7.10SB	7.40vw		7.66MB	7.80vw
6.09SS						7.25MS	7.57WS		8.00SS
6.02SS				6.94MS	7.12MS	7.32MS	7.45MS	7.62WS [7.78vw]	7.87vw [8.13SS]
6.12sh					7.07MB		7.50WS	7.67WS	8.00MS
6.12vw					7.05MB	7.36WS	7.47WS	7.80MS	
	6.23SS	6.47MS	6.77SS		7.02MS	7.22SS	7.45SS	7.75MS	
	6.27SS	6.60vw	6.73MS	6.92WS	7.11sh	7.24MS [7.37MS]	7.50vw	7.60MS	7.90WS
	6.25MS		6.68SS		7.02vw		7.48WS		8.00MS
	6.35SB	6.62SB			7.03SS		7.45vw	7.60vw	
6.08SS	6.37SS	6.60SS	6.85MS		7.08SS	7.37MS	7.55MS	7.77vw	7.90vw
	6.25SB	6.55SS	6.65MS [6.77vw]	6.90MS	7.07SS	7.40MS	7.55MS	7.73WS	8.00vw
6.11SS	6.27WS	6.57WS	6.67sh	6.84SB	7.06SS	7.43SS	7.60MS	7.84MS	7.98SS
6.15sh	6.33SB		6.63SS	6.90WS	7.09SS	7.40MS	7.58MS	7.85vw	8.04MS
6.20sh	6.33SB		6.65MS	6.92vw	7.10SS	7.40MS	7.57MS	7.90WS	8.07WS
6.16MS	6.33SS		6.74SB	6.88sh	7.10SS	7.24MS	7.47MS	7.72MS	7.89vw
	6.34SS		6.64MS	6.88MS 6.95sh	7.13MS	7.27sh	7.48WS	7.61WS	7.82WS
	6.33SS		6.63MS	6.85sh	7.13SS				
6.18sh	6.31SB	6.42sh	6.70SS	6.88vw 6.95vw	7.08MS 7.17MS	7.40MS	7.46sh	7.58MS	7.83MS
6.18sh	6.35SB	6.40sh	6.65SB	6.87WS	7.02MS 7.11MS	7.40MS	7.59MS	7.85WS	8.00MS

special designations.
vw = very weak band, S = strong intensity.

weak for all the compounds of this group. Of all the amino acids in group I, only glycine possesses a band below 3.3 μ, namely, at 3.1 μ. However, the latter band occurs in the spectra of amino acids in other groups. The apparent lack of regularity in the bands in the 2.0-μ to 3.9-μ region may be a reflection of the strong hydrogen bonding of amino acids in the solid state, and the consequent perturbation of the O-H and N-H stretching frequencies. The resulting shift in many instances toward absorbance at longer wavelengths makes it very difficult to differentiate between the O-H, N-H, and C-H stretching motions. The metal complexes of glycine still retain the 6.2-μ and 7.1-μ bands of the free amino acid (33a); the spectra of the red and violet isomers of cobalt triglycinate are not greatly different, although the spectra of complexes of various metals with glycine are quite diverse.

COMPOUNDS IN GROUP II. These branched-chain, monoaminomonocarboxylic acids, like those in group I, possess the 4.7-μ, 6.3-μ, and 7.1-μ peaks in common. In addition, they all possess the 3.9-μ, 7.3-μ, and 7.5-μ peaks in common, as well as, with the exception of *tert*-leucine, the 3.3-μ and 6.2-μ bands and, with the exception of isovaline, the 6.6-μ band. The amino acids in this category possess a branched-chain residue on the α-carbon atom (isovaline), on the β-carbon atom (valine, isoleucine, alloisoleucine, *tert*-leucine), or on the γ-carbon atom (leucine). Of all these compounds, the spectrum of leucine most closely resembles that of the amino acids in group I, a reflection, no doubt, of the relative distance along the chain of the branched methyl group from the amino and carboxyl radicals. *tert*-Leucine possesses three methyl groups on the β-carbon atom, and this crowding apparently produces a marked interaction with the N-H bending motions of the α-amino groups so that the characteristic frequency is no longer resolved as a single absorption band but is shifted into the region of carboxylate ion absorption to produce a strong, broad, poorly resolved band. The spectrum of *tert*-leucine shows other characteristics which may be related to the unusual structure of this compound; thus a splitting of the symmetrical stretching frequency of the carboxylate ion seems to occur, producing two absorption bands at 7.12 μ and 7.18 μ. The symmetrical CH$_3$ stretching frequency appears at 7.29 μ, the C-H twisting motion is very strong and sharp at 7.45 μ, and the C-H deformation or CH$_3$ antisymmetrical stretching frequency splits into two poorly resolved bands at 6.67 μ and 6.85 μ. The absence of the N-H deformation frequency in the spectrum of isovaline, and its shift in position and attenuation in *tert*-leucine must be a function of either van der Waals repulsive forces or steric conflict, or a combination of both. The spectrum of isovaline in the 3-μ region is further distinguished by the possession of bands at 2.97 μ and 3.18 μ, that of *tert*-leucine in the 6-μ region by bands at 6.45 μ and 6.53 μ. Peaks in the former region are not encountered in number except in the amino acids of group IV (the ω-hydroxy compounds) and group VI (the ω-amino compounds), and in the latter region except for the compounds of group IV. The spectra of valine and of the isoleucines resemble each other, as might be expected; the presence of a sharp and discrete band at 6.84 μ for the latter is the distinguishing difference between the two in the 2.0-μ to 7.5-μ region.

COMPOUNDS IN GROUPS IV, VI, and VII. These amino acids constitute respectively the ω-OH, ω-COOH, and ω-NH$_2$ substituted straight-chain α-amino acids. The electronegative groups act upon the N-H stretching vibration of the —NH$_3^+$ group with a resulting shift in its absorption to longer wavelengths as they approach the α-amino group. Thus, in serine, homoserine, δ-hydroxynorvaline, and ε-hydroxynorleucine, this vibration absorbs respectively at 4.92 μ, 4.80 μ, 4.73 μ, and 4.73 μ; in aspartic acid at 4.85 μ and 5.25 μ, and in aminoadipic acid at 5.20 μ; and in β-aminoalanine at 5.08 μ, in γ-aminobutyrine at 4.97 μ, and in lysine at 4.80 μ. As the number of methylene groups between the α-amino group and the electronegative group increases, the degree of interaction and magnitude of the wavelength shift decreases.

All the amino acids of groups IV, VI, and VII (with the exception of lysine) possess the 3.3-μ band in common. The ω-OH amino acids in addition possess absorption peaks below 3.3 μ except allothreonine. The lactone of homoserine, unlike the free amino acid, does not absorb below 3.3 μ but does possess an extra band at 3.52 μ. Furthermore, the lactone does not absorb at 3.7 μ nor at 3.9 μ, nor does its N-H motion absorb at 4.7 μ but instead is shifted toward longer wavelengths in the region of 5.1 μ. This lactone is an internal ester, and the loss of the 3-μ OH-vibration frequency is not surprising. A shift in the N-H 4.7-μ region to that of 5 μ is also apparent in the spectra of the phenylserines, an effect not entirely due to interference by the β-ring substituent inasmuch as all the compounds in group III absorb normally in the 4.7-μ region. In group VII, arginine and citrulline have bands below 3.3 μ. The strong sharp absorption bands at 3.0 μ in these compounds is tentatively assigned to the N-H stretching frequency of the NH$_2$ group in the ureido and guanidino radicals.

An interesting group of compounds in which absorption peaks occur at less than 3.3 μ consists of aminotricarballylic acid and of the pyrrolidone forms of this compound and of its allostereomer, as well as of the corresponding lactones of the isocitric acids derived therefrom (group VI). The pyrrolidones and lactones do not absorb at 3.3 μ nor at 4.7 μ, 6.3 μ, or 6.6 μ. The former group but not the latter absorb at 4.0 μ and 6.9 μ.

Although the 4.7-μ N–H stretching frequency band occurs as such in most of the compounds of group VI and group VII, or else is recognizably shifted to longer wavelengths, most of the compounds in group VI apparently are lacking in this peak. Thus glutamic acid has no band in this region, nor has aminotricarballylic acid or the corresponding pyrrolidones and lactones. The aminotricarballylic acids and their pyrrolidones and lactones as well as aspartic acid, and the unsubstituted succinic and tricarballylic acids, all have instead sharp bands at 5.9 μ which are probably related to the vibrational frequencies of an un-ionized carboxyl group. The 5.9-μ band, related to the $\gamma(C\!=\!N)$ or $\gamma(C\!=\!O)$ frequency, occurs also in the spectra of arginine and of citrulline. Ornithine possesses no band in the 4.7-μ region. The sharp band at 5.73 μ may represent un-ionized —COOH, in view of the fact that this compound was studied as the dihydrochloride, unlike the other diamino acids, which were studied as the mononhydrochlorides.

The polycarboxylic acids may be expected to contain not only ionized but also un-ionized carboxyl groups. The latter absorb at 5.76 μ, 5.80 μ, 5.92 μ, 6.00 μ, and 6.07 μ. One or more of these bands is to be found in the spectra of the compounds in group VI. All these compounds when examined in D_2O exhibit three strong, sharp absorption peaks at 5.83 $\pm$ 0.03 μ, at 6.19 $\pm$ 0.04 μ, and at 7.00 $\pm$ 1.0 μ. The 5.83-μ band is due to the $\gamma(C\!=\!O)$ of the un-ionized carboxyl group, and the other two bands, respectively, to the antisymmetrical and symmetrical $\gamma(C\!=\!O)$ of the carboxylate ion.

Ornithine and lysine possess a 6.6-μ band related to the $\delta(N\text{-}H)$ frequency. With β-aminoalanine, wherein the two amino groups are closest in structure, this band is seemingly replaced by two bands at 6.47 μ and 6.77 μ, and, if this is so, the splitting of the band in this region may well result from the inductive interaction of the two adjacent amino groups. In γ-aminobutyrine the influence on the $\delta(N\text{-}H)$ motion is not so marked; two absorption bands are present at 6.60 μ and 6.73 μ, but the peak at 6.60 μ is very weak. The spectrum of histidine also suggests a similar inductive effect, for there is a strong, broad absorption band at 6.84 μ with a weak shoulder at 6.67 μ. This band and shoulder are tentatively assigned to an N-H deformation motion.

In the region above 6μ, ε-hydroxynorleucine exhibits a spectrum which for all practical purposes is nearly identical with that of the prototypical amino acids in group I. The symmetrical and antisymmetrical stretching frequencies of the ionized carboxyl absorb at 7.14 μ and 6.36 μ, respectively, the N-H deformation motion at 6.56 μ and the C-H bending at 6.96 μ. As the ω-OH group approaches the α-carbon configuration, as in δ-hydroxynorvaline, homoserine, and serine, there is a progressive shift toward the shorter wavelength in the 6.96-μ, 7.14-μ, 7.42-μ, and 7.59-μ bands of ε-hydroxynorleucine. Even more dramatically, the N-H deformation motion at 6.65 μ in ε-hydroxynorleucine is shifted to 6.57 μ in δ-hydroxynorvaline, then to 6.50 μ in homoserine, and seemingly disappears altogether in serine. Thus, again, as the functional groups in a homologous series of amino acids approach each other spatially, some type of interaction occurs which results in a progressively increasing perturbation of the N-H deformation motion.

COMPOUNDS IN GROUP III. The compounds in this group are characterized by having phenyl or cyclohexyl groups on the α-carbon atom of glycine (aminophenylacetic acid or aminocyclohexylacetic acid) or on the β-carbon atom of alanine (phenylalanine or aminocyclohexylpropionic acid), and p-hydroxyphenyl or indole rings on the β-carbon atom of alanine (tyrosine or tryptophan). Comparison of corresponding phenyl and cyclohexylamino acids reveals that aminophenylacetic acid differs from aminocyclohexylacetic acid in lacking the 3.3-μ and 7.5-μ bands, and in possessing a 6.45-μ band; all other bands are shared in common. On the other hand, the differences between phenylalanine and aminocyclohexylpropionic acid are due to the lack in the spectrum of the former of the 3.9-μ, the 6.9-μ, and 7.4-μ bands, and the possession of a 6.17-μ band. No unique effect seems to be produced on the spectrum by converting a phenyl to a cyclohexyl group. Tryptophan differs considerably in its spectrum from that of the other members of this group in possessing a 5.98-μ band which appears in the spectra only of the compounds in groups VI and VII, and in lacking the 6.2-μ and 6.6-μ bands. Phenylalanine, tyrosine, and aminophenylacetic acid absorb strongly at 6.2 μ, a region to which vibrations of the phenyl radical have been assigned. It must be pointed out, however, that aminocyclohexylacetic acid also absorbs in this region, and that tryptophan does not.

COMPOUNDS IN GROUP V. These compounds all have a basic imino nitrogen bond in a five-membered hydrocarbon ring. It is of interest therefore to scrutinize particularly those regions of the spectrum assigned to N-H motions, and it is significant therefore to note that the 4.7-μ region is completely transparent for all three compounds in this group, and the 6.6-μ band is present only in the spectrum of proline. The 7.1-μ, 7.3-μ, and 7.5-μ bands are shared by all three. The 3.1-μ band, present in the hydroxyprolines but not in the spectrum of proline probably reflects the presence of the γ-OH group in the former.

COMPOUNDS IN GROUP VIII. The spectra of cystine and cysteine·HCl are indistinguishable from the 3-μ to the 6-μ regions. At higher wavelengths the spectra diverge, for the latter compound does not possess the 6.1-μ, 7.3-μ, and 7.5-μ bands characteristic of the former. The 6.1-μ band should be missing, for it is close to that characteristic of the ionized carboxyl group which is absent in cysteine·HCl. From 3.9 μ to higher wavelengths, i.e., 7.5 μ, the spectra of methionine and ethionine, of cystine and homocystine, and of S-benzylcysteine and S-benzylhomocysteine are nearly identical. The presence of the sulfur atom does not appear to induce any striking effect on the spectra of the compounds in this group. All the compounds, like most of those in groups I and II, possess a weak absorption band at about 3.9 μ.

3. Infrared Spectra of Diastereomeric Amino Acids. The diastereomeric amino acids possess two centers of asymmetry, and, for the greater part, the spectra of corresponding diastereomers are quite distinct. Considered in this connection are the following pairs of diastereomers (in which the α-center is always L): isoleucine-alloisoleucine, threonine-allothreonine, hydroxyproline-allohydroxyproline, phenylserine-allophenylserine, α-aminotricarballylic acid–allo-α-aminotricarballylic acid, and O-methylthreonine-allo-O-methylthreonine. In addition, there are octopine-allooctopine and cystathionine-allocystathionine, in which the configuration of the shorter branch is derived from D-alanine and L-serine, respectively, the configurational designation of the whole compound by definition (cf. Chapter 2), being that of the shorter branch. A simultaneous change in the configuration of both asymmetric centers of all of these compounds leads of course to the respective optical antipodes, and the spectra of the antipodes of each of these compounds are identical (33).

Another class of amino acids is also distinguished by the possession of two asymmetric centers, and also by a center of symmetry. The compounds considered in this category are cystine–*meso*-cystine and α,ε-diaminopimelic acid–*meso*-α,ε-diaminopimelic acid. The configurations of the two centers of the normal or natural member of each of these pairs are both L, whereas of those for the respective *meso*-forms one is L and the other is D. The former are therefore optically active, the latter, by virtue of internal compensation, are optically inactive.

ISOLEUCINE-ALLOISOLEUCINE (33). Of all the diastereomeric pairs studied, the spectra of isoleucine and alloisoleucine most closely resemble each other. From 2 μ to 8 μ, the spectra of these two compounds are practically identical, and this striking similarity in the region of the fundamental stretching frequencies of their solid state spectra can only be interpreted as indicating that the difference in spatial configuration about the respective β-center of asymmetry must produce little if any change in the vibrating electrical charge coupled with each nuclear vibration. It is of interest in this connection that the optical rotatory power of isoleucine and alloisoleucine is very nearly the same, a condition which holds for no other pair of diastereomeric amino acids studied. The first marked difference in the spectra of isoleucine and alloisoleucine appears in the 8-μ region, and from here to 15 μ the spectra of these compounds are sufficiently different to permit their use for analytical purposes.

THREONINE-ALLOTHREONINE (33). The infrared spectra of these two isomers reveal several differences. Thus threonine lacks the 6.3-μ band

and allothreonine lacks the 6.9-μ band. On the other hand, threonine possesses a strong band at 3.2 μ which is not observed in the spectrum of allothreonine. Indeed, allothreonine is the only hydroxyamino acid studied in whose spectrum this band is not observed. Both compounds, however, absorb in the 3.3-μ region. Beyond 8 μ, there are a larger number of discrete bands in the spectrum of allothreonine than in that of threonine.

HYDROXYPROLINE-ALLOHYDROXYPROLINE (33). In the L-form of hydroxyproline the hydroxyl group of the γ-asymmetric center is *trans* to the α-carboxyl group. In the 3.0-μ region, the spectra of this pair show differences of some magnitude. The allo isomer absorbs at 3.17 μ, assigned to O-H and N-H stretching motions, and the wavelength at which this band appears suggests considerable perturbation of these vibrations. In the spectrum of hydroxyproline there are two strong, sharp bands in this region at 3.10 μ and 3.23 μ also assigned to N-H and O-H stretching motions. The 3.7-μ and 6.3-μ bands found in the spectrum of hydroxyproline are not observed at these positions in that of allohydroxyproline. These bands refer, respectively, to N-H and C-H and to antisymmetrical —COO$^-$ vibrations. The O-H deformation motion in hydroxyproline absorbs at 9.47 μ; the corresponding vibration in the allo isomer absorbs some 0.13 μ toward the shorter wavelength. The 6.9-μ band (C-H bending motion) is not seen in the spectrum of hydroxyproline, but there are two bands in the 7.1-μ spectral region of this compound. Beyond 8 μ, the spectra of the two diastereomers differ very considerably.

PHENYLSERINE-ALLOPHENYLSERINE (33). Phenylserine has three bands in the 3-μ spectral region, allophenylserine has two. The former compound also has two bands in the 6.3-μ region and 6.6-μ region, instead of only one in each region for the latter compound. Allophenylserine is lacking the 3.95-μ band which is present in phenylserine. There seems little doubt that in the 2-μ to 7.5-μ region, phenylserine possesses more bands than does its allo diastereomer, and this difference also holds for the spectra beyond 8 μ as well.

AMINOTRICARBALLYLIC ACID-ALLOAMINOTRICARBALLYLIC ACID (33). The optical configurations at the β-carbon atoms of these compounds is not known exactly at the present time (cf. Chapter 3). These α-amino acids possess three carboxyl groups on adjacent carbon atoms, and they may be considered from one point of view as β-carboxylated glutamic acids. There are marked differences in the spectra of aminotricarballylic and alloaminotricarballylic acids, the latter showing many more discrete bands than the former over the entire spectral range studied. The allo isomer possesses two resolved absorption bands at 5.8 μ, its diastereomer only one band, all of which are assigned to the motions of the un-ionized carboxyl group or groups. It may be suggested therefrom that the spatial positions of the carboxyl groups in aminotricarballylic acid relative to each other are so oriented that perturbation of their carbonyl stretching frequencies does not occur. The antisymmetrical $\gamma(C{=}O)$ vibration at 6.3 μ occurs in the spectrum of aminotricarballylic acid, and not in that of its allo isomer unless it is assumed that it is shifted toward the lower wavelength at 6.17 μ owing to perturbation of this vibration. Neither diastereomer possesses the 4.7-μ band characteristic of N-H vibration, although it is possible that in the spectrum of the allo form this band has been shifted to 5.25 μ. Both diastereomers readily and quantitatively form the corresponding pyrrolidonedicarboxylic acid in aqueous solution, but the allo form accomplishes this much more rapidly.

PYRROLIDONEDICARBOXYLIC ACID DERIVATIVES OF AMINOTRICARBALLYLIC ACID–ALLOAMINOTRICARBALLYLIC ACID (33). In these compounds, the α-amino nitrogen of the amino acid becomes an amide nitrogen owing to ring closure with the γ-carboxyl group. The spectrum of the derivative of aminotricarballylic acid has two bands in the un-ionized —COOH region at 5.8 μ, that of the allo form but one. This is the converse of the finding for the free amino acids. Neither compound shows the presence of bands characteristic of N-H motion in —NH_3^+, and neither shows a band at 6.3 μ.

LACTONE DERIVATIVES OF ISOCITRIC ACID–ALLOISOCITRIC ACID (33). The optically active isocitric acids were prepared from the isomers of aminotricarballylic acid without change in configuration and were isolated as the lactones (34). They differ from the corresponding pyrrolidonedicarboxylic acids in possessing an oxygen in the ring instead of nitrogen, and hence are internal esters rather than internal amides. The spectra of the pair of diastereomeric lactones show a surprising degree of similarity in the 2-μ to 7-μ region. Only at 7.36 μ, a band possessed by the lactone of alloisocitric acid but not by its diastereomer, is there a visible difference in this spectral range between the two. Beyond 8 μ the spectra are quite dissimilar, that of the isocitric acid lactone being rather ill-defined.

The sharp band in the 14-μ region, arising in part from a C-H rocking vibration (35), and later suggested by Blout and Linsley as due also in part to the N-H grouping (36), occurs in all the amino acids studied. There is no evidence of this peak in the spectrum of alloisocitric acid lactone, while in that of its diastereomer it occurs as a broad band at about 14.3 μ.

O-METHYLTHREONINE–O-METHYLALLOTHREONINE (37). Although the spectra of both compounds possess a strong band at 3.5 μ and a weak band at 4 μ, the characteristic 4.7-μ band of O-methylallothreonine appears to be shifted to 5.0 μ in the spectrum of O-methylthreonine. The 3.2-μ band present in the spectrum of threonine appears as a shoulder on the stronger band at 3.5 μ of O-methylthreonine, whilst the 3.2-μ band lacking in the spectrum of allothreonine is also lacking in the spectrum of O-methylallothreonine. The remainder of the spectra of the two O-methylated diastereomers of threonine, from 6 μ on, is quite dissimilar.

OCTOPINE-ALLOOCTOPINE (38). The two diastereomers possess bands at 3.0 μ and 3.2 μ, but beyond this region the spectra are entirely unlike each other. The natural octopine isomer with a D-configuration on the alanine moiety and an L-configuration on the arginine moiety, is here compared with that diastereomer with an L-configuration for both portions.

CYSTATHIONINE-ALLOCYSTATHIONINE (39, 40). The spectra of these two compounds are quite dissimilar. The former possesses peaks at 2.8 μ, 3.3 μ, 3.8 μ, 5.0 μ, 6.2 μ, 6.4 μ, and 7.1 μ, the latter at 2.9 μ, 3.4 μ, 3.7 μ, 4.8 μ, 6.1 μ, 6.25 μ, 6.4 μ, 6.7 μ, 7.0 μ, 7.2 μ, and 7.4 μ. The fingerprint region for this pair of compounds, as in the case of all the diastereomeric pairs, is quite different for each member of the pair.

CYSTINE–*meso*-CYSTINE (41). The spectra were obtained upon samples of L-, D-, and *meso*-cystine secured by the specific enzymic resolution of a mixture of pure diacetyl-DL-cystine and diacetyl-*meso*-cystine. No trace of tyrosine or other possible contaminant arising from natural sources was present. The experimental results indicated that the spectra of L-, D-, and *meso*-cystine were practically indistinguishable. These results are quite different from those reported some years ago by Wright (29), who layered the amino acids in a thin film on a KBr plate and placed the resulting arrangement in the radiation path; the data obtained indicated that the spectra of L-cystine and of *meso*-cystine were quite different. The reason for the disagreement in the results obtained by the two groups of investigators is not apparent and is all the more puzzling in view of the fact that the spectra of L-cystine alone as obtained by the two groups are also not in agreement. It is not implausible to conceive the possibility that solid state spectra are reproducible only when determined under identical experimental conditions. This has been rather interestingly shown in the recent work of Bak and Christensen (42), who prepared KBr windows with glycine by three different procedures and (a) obtained certain spectral lines with intensities which depended on the procedure employed to prepare the disks, and (b) obtained at certain levels of glycine new spectral lines not demonstrated at other levels of the amino acid. These phenomena may, however, contribute to only part of the story.

α,ε-DIAMINOPIMELIC ACID–*meso*-α,ε-DIAMINOPIMELIC ACID (43). The spectrum of the *meso*-form possesses a number of sharp bands in the region of 6 to 8 μ, in contrast with the more diffuse spectrum of the L-form within this range. From 8 to 15 μ the spectra of the two compounds are entirely dissimilar.

Related to the diastereomeric amino acids are the diastereomeric peptides studied by Ellenbogen (44) and others (3). Discussion of these interesting compounds and of the higher peptides from the standpoint of infrared spectroscopy is deferred to a later time when more information will have been acquired.

4. Infrared Spectra of Corresponding Optically Active and Racemic Amino Acids. The early studies by Wright (29) over the wavelength range of 3 μ to 24 μ demonstrated that although L- and D-isomers of the amino acids, as well as mechanical mixtures of both, possessed identical spectra, that of the DL-amino acid, crystallized from solution, might possess a quite different spectrum. This was shown to be true in the cases of cystine, alanine, valine, leucine, and phenylalanine; glutamic acid, however, whether L or DL, possessed the same spectrum. Other examples of spectral differences of optical isomers and racemates in the solid state occur for the tartrates (45), for substituted dicarboxylic acids (46), and for acetylleucine and acetylisoleucine (30).

More recently, Brockmann and Musso (32) have shown that the spectra of L- and of DL-alanine differ relatively little, whereas the spectra of L- and of DL-serine differ very considerably, and they have related this difference in behavior to the crystal lattice energy of the compounds concerned. Thus L- and DL-alanine possess nearly the same solubility in water, whereas L-serine is very much more soluble than is DL-serine. This emphasis on crystal forces might serve as an attractive hypothesis were it not for the following facts. The solubility of DL-glutamic acid in water is considerably greater than that of L-glutamic acid (Table 5–21), but according to Wright (29) the spectra are identical. The solubility of L-isoleucine is less than that of L-alloisoleucine (Table 5–21), but the spectra are identical (33). The solubility of DL-cystine and of *meso*-cystine in water have been reported to be nearly the same (Table 5–21); the spectra of these two compounds have been reported to be unlike (29) and alike (41). In view of these incompatible data, it might appear to be of value to limit investigation of the problem to the L- and DL-forms of a homologous series of the simplest amino acids, namely those based on the aliphatic straight-chain series (31).

The spectrum of the racemic form of alanine from 2 to 15 μ differs very little from that of its optically active L-form (Figure 17–5) (31). The spectrum of the former shows an adequately resolved peak at 9.73 μ which is absent in the active isomer, and in the 6-μ region the amino acid I band at 6.07 μ appears more intense and more adequately resolved from the 6.27-μ frequency assigned to the antisymmetric (COO$^-$) peak. At all other frequency regions the spectra appear to be nearly identical. As the comparison is

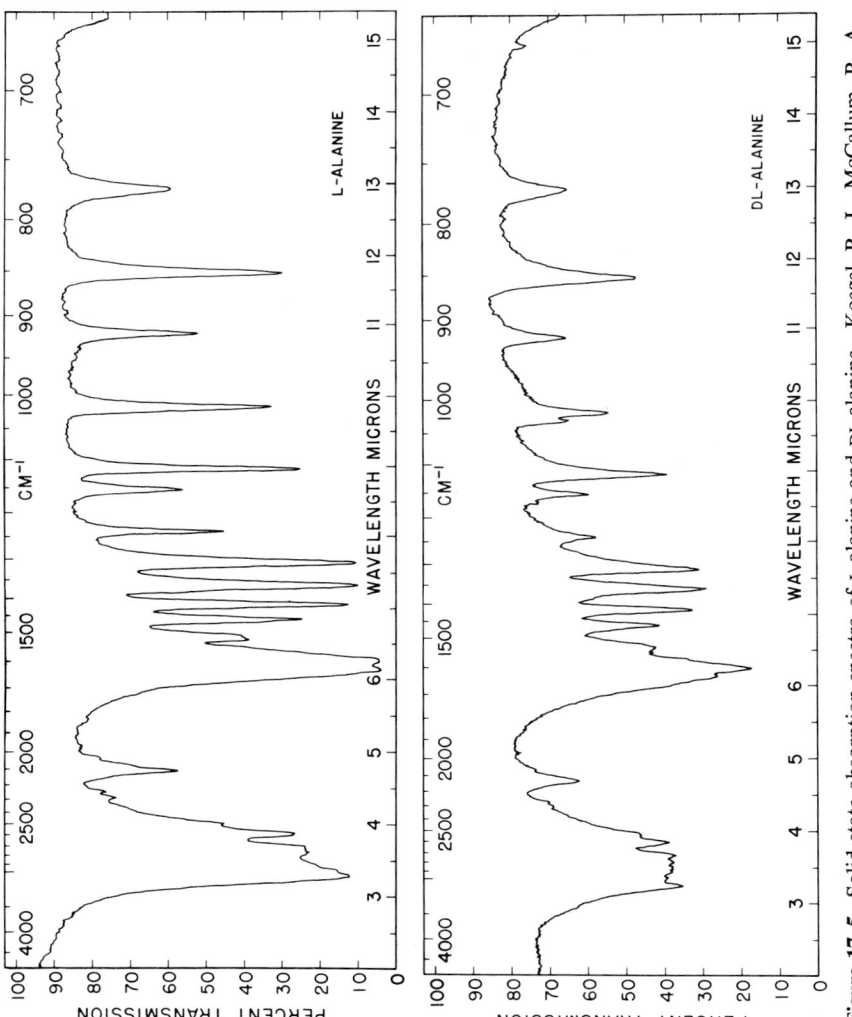

Figure 17-5. Solid state absorption spectra of L-alanine and DL-alanine. Koegel, R. J., McCallum, R. A., Greenstein, J. P., Winitz, M., and Birnbaum, S. M., *Ann. N.Y. Acad. Sci,* **69,** 94 (1957).

extended to L- and DL-forms of the homologous aliphatic α-amino acids, i.e., butyrine, norvaline, norleucine, etc., the spectra for each pair show small differences, if any, in the 2.5-μ–6.0-μ region, but from 6 to 15 μ the appearance of the spectrum for the L-form is quite different from that for the DL-form. This may be illustrated by the spectra for L- and for DL-norleucine (Figure 17-6). The spectrum of the racemate seems to be characterized by (a) a sharp, intense band at 6.03 μ, (b) a striking difference in the intensity of the amino acid II peak (6.6 μ) relative to the antisymmetric (COO$^-$) band at 6.33 μ, and (c) distinctive differences at those spectral frequencies known to correspond to the bending motions of the methyl and methylene groups.

With increasing chain length starting with DL-norleucine, the spectra of the DL straight-chain α-amino acids are distinguished in the 9.0-μ to 15.0-μ region by an increase in the intensity of the absorption near 9.3 μ and 14.3 μ. Corresponding peaks in the L-forms tend to decrease in intensity until in the spectrum of α-amino-n-octanoic acid there is little or no absorption at these frequences. The differences in the solid state spectra of the pairs of L- and DL-forms of certain amino acids in certain spectral regions emphasize the necessity of comparing the spectra of structures which are not only chemically and optically pure but also configurationally similar; failure to recognize these limitations may be responsible in part for the current ambiguity in group-frequency assignments (31). The frequency assignment and relative intensities of the amino acid I and II bands are a case in point, for it is generally agreed that all α-amino acids in the polar form exhibit two characteristic absorption peaks in the range 6.02 to 6.67 μ, in addition to the antisymmetric (COO$^-$) band at 6.33 μ (cf. 23). The first of these peaks at 6.06–6.21 μ, the amino acid I band, is usually of low intensity or else appears as a shoulder on the high-frequency side of the antisymmetric (COO$^-$) band at 6.33 μ. The second of these peaks, at 6.45–6.74 μ, the so-called amino acid II band, is usually more intense. There has been generally more agreement in the literature on the occurrence of the latter than of the former amino acid band, and it has been suggested (23) that the observational differences arose either from the inherently low intensity of the amino acid I band or else were associated with differences in the optical forms examined. The data accumulated in the homologous series of aliphatic α-amino acids alluded to above appear to favor the latter explanation (31). Thus, in the spectrum of the L-form, the amino acid I band appears as an adequately resolved shoulder on the high-frequency side of the antisymmetric (COO$^-$) peak at 6.30 μ, and the amino acid II band, the intensity of which approximates that of the antisymmetric (COO$^-$) peak, absorbs at 6.60 μ. In the spectrum of the racemic amino acid, however, the amino acid II band still absorbs near 6.60 μ, but its intensity relative to the antisymmetric (COO$^-$) peak undergoes a striking decrease. The

SPECTROPHOTOMETRY

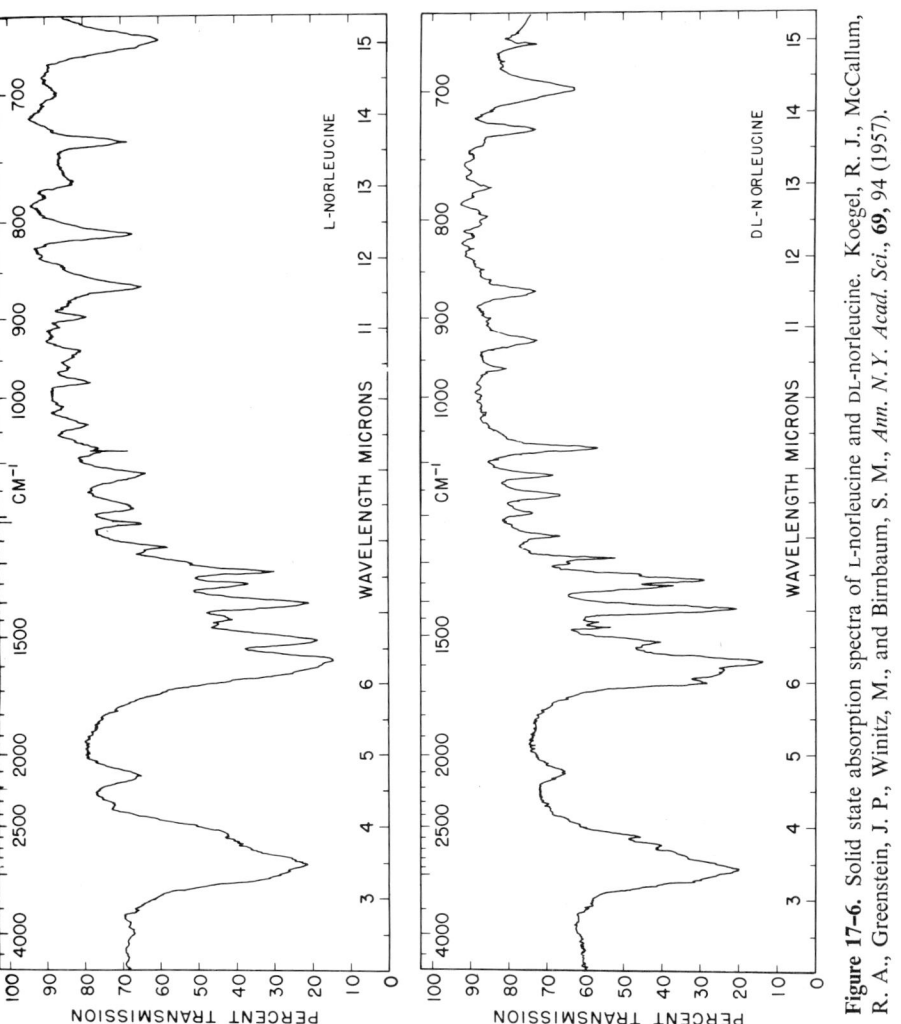

Figure 17-6. Solid state absorption spectra of L-norleucine and DL-norleucine. Koegel, R. J., McCallum, R. A., Greenstein, J. P., Winitz, M., and Birnbaum, S. M., *Ann. N.Y. Acad. Sci.*, **69**, 94 (1957).

amino acid I band appears to be still present as a shoulder on the high-frequency side of the antisymmetric (COO$^-$) band; however, a new, sharp, and resolved peak is now observed near 6.03 μ, and it has been suggested (31) that the appearance of this new peak in the spectrum of the racemate explains the extended range described by Bellamy (23) for the amino acid I band. In any event, it is of interest to note that the frequency of the peak intensity of the antisymmetric (COO$^-$) band is virtually the same in the spectra of both L- and DL-forms (31).

SPECTRA OF THE AMINO ACID HYDROCHLORIDES. As noted above, the bands at 6.3 and 7.1 μ have been attributed, respectively, to the antisymmetrical and symmetrical stretching vibrations of the ionized carboxyl group. These bands should therefore disappear in the spectra of the hydrochloride salts of the amino acids, and the bands characteristic of the unionized carboxyl, namely, at 5.76, 5.80, 5.92, 6.00, and 6.07 μ, should appear wholly or in part. For L-serine and its hydrochloride, this is indeed true (32), and the relation holds for many other pairs of similar compounds. Indeed, the spectra of L-serine and of DL-serine, which are quite divergent in the 6-μ to 7-μ region, are quite similar in this region when the comparison is made on the basis of the hydrochloride salts of the two forms (32). In the methylamino acids, the spectra of the hydrochlorides appear to retain the 7.1-μ —COO$^-$ band, and whether this band is inherent in the hydrochlorides of such substances, or whether its presence is due to contamination by some free amino acid, remains to be determined (47).

The solid state spectrum of betaine reveals a strong band at 6.12 μ which is that of the ionized carboxyl group, and hence characteristic of the known dipolar ion structure of this compound (47).

5. Aqueous Phase Infrared Spectroscopy. By the use of silver chloride windows throughout the rock salt and potassium bromide regions, Gore, Barnes, and Peterson (24) were able to obtain a series of amino acid spectra in aqueous solution. As is known, liquid water (H$_2$O) possesses strong absorption bands at 3.0 μ, 6.1 μ, and 12.5 μ. In D$_2$O, however, the O-H stretching vibration at 3.0 μ is shifted to 4.0 μ, and the 6.1-μ band is shifted to 8.2 μ. It is therefore possible, by the use of both kinds of aqueous solvents, to study the complete rock salt infrared region of the spectrum of the soluble amino acids (24). A particularly lucid experimental approach to this problem has been described by Lenormant (48).

The C-H stretching and bending vibrations near 3.4 μ and 7.3 μ of the salts of carboxylic acids are readily revealed in aqueous solutions, as are the asymmetric and symmetric stretching vibrations of the ionized carboxyl group at 6.4 μ and 7.1 μ. When deuterium chloride (prepared by treating PCl$_3$ with D$_2$O) in D$_2$O is employed as solvent, the carbonyl band at 6.4 μ considerably diminishes, and a new band near 5.8 μ makes its appearance.

SPECTROPHOTOMETRY

This new band can be attributed to the production in solution of un-ionized, only slightly bonded, carboxyl radicals (24).

Crystalline glycine possesses a band at 6.2 μ for the carbonyl vibration, which may be said to be a characteristic of its dipolar ion structure. In aqueous solution, or in the presence of NaOH in aqueous solution, this band is obscured by the strong water bending vibration. When HCl is added, however, this band diminishes in intensity, and new bands at 5.8 μ (as in the carboxylic acids) and at 8.0 μ make their appearance.

In D_2O solution the 6.1-μ water band is shifted to 8.2 μ, and the carbonyl absorption by glycine, whether in D_2O solution alone or in the presence as well of NaOD (by reaction of sodium in D_2O), is thus laid bare at 6.2 μ. When DCl is added to the D_2O solution of glycine, this carbonyl band disappears and two new bands, one at 5.8 μ (un-ionized carboxyl) and the other at 7.9 μ, make their appearance. The latter band corresponds with that at 8.0 μ found in the HCl spectrum of glycine, and may be associated with the C-OH bending vibration or the C-O stretching vibration (24). The uncharged —NH_2 group possesses a characteristic frequency at 3.0 μ (49); that of the ionized NH_3^+ group is at about 3.3 μ to 3.4 μ.

The equilibria involved together with the characteristic frequencies may be summarized as follows:

$$NH_3^+RCOOH \underset{DCl}{\overset{HCl}{\rightleftharpoons}} NH_3^+RCOO^- \underset{NaOD}{\overset{NaOH}{\rightleftharpoons}} NH_2RCOO^-$$

Cation $\rightleftharpoons$ Dipolar ion $\rightleftharpoons$ Anion

5.8 μ (un-ionized carboxyl) 6.2 μ (ionized carboxyl) 6.2 μ (ionized carboxyl)
3.3 μ (ionized amino)   3.3 μ (ionized amino)   3.0 μ (un-ionized amino)
                               7.1 μ (ionized carboxyl) 7.1 μ (ionized carboxyl)

In D_2O solution, the polycarboxylic acids exhibit the characteristic frequencies of both ionized (6.2 μ the antisymmetric and 7.1 μ the symmetric) and un-ionized (at 5.8 μ) carboxyl groups (33).

Many of the data in aqueous solutions were, as might be anticipated, consistent with the earlier studies by Edsall on Raman spectra. It would be highly desirable to extend the present studies on aqueous phase methods using both infrared and Raman techniques since quantitative data are so much more readily secured than with the usual procedures with solids.

ANALYTICAL PROCEDURE. Darmon, Sutherland, and Tristram (30) developed an ingenious procedure to estimate by means of infrared spectroscopy the ratio of leucine to isoleucine in protein hydrolysates. They acetylated the mixture of amino acids in the hydrolysate by means of acetic anhydride and NaOH, and fractionated the acetyl amino acids by absorption on silica gel columns. Only the center portion of the "leucine" band was collected by elution, and this portion consisted of nearly all of the leucine and isoleucine of the protein. Absorption curves were obtained for pure acetyl-L-leucine and acetyl-L-isoleucine, and two bands in these spectra were chosen for analysis, bands which were sufficiently close that they could be studied under identical spectroscopic conditions such as slit-width, but far enough apart to afford accuracy of the results. The band at 14.01 μ was chosen from the spectrum of acetyl-L-leucine and that at 13.58 μ from the spectrum of acetyl-L-isoleucine. With these standards, the leucine : isoleucine ratio could be determined on the basis of Beer's law, the results yielded being in fairly good agreement with those obtained by other methods. The possible error evoked by some degree of racemization of the constituent amino acids with consequent spectral differences between L- and DL-forms was recognized by these authors (30); their spectra of the acetyl-DL-amino acids were quite different from those of the corresponding L-compounds.

6. Raman Spectra. These spectra are due to vibrational frequencies characteristic of organic molecules capable of scattering incident monochromatic light. A mercury arc with appropriate filters is generally employed to excite the Raman spectra, and the diffused light is observed at right angles to the incident beam. Aqueous solutions are readily employable. Water, however, yields a strong Raman line in the region of 2.8 to 3.1 μ, which would tend to obscure frequencies due to N-H vibration; another strong band due to water appears at 6.1 μ (50). These values correspond to frequencies of infrared absorption bands, and indeed infrared and Raman spectra are closely related (cf. Table 17-6).

The development of this subject, in so far as it concerns amino acids, peptides, and related compounds, is very largely due to Edsall (26; 50–53), and his studies were perhaps the first which unequivocally revealed the dipolar character of the neutral amino acids. Thus he demonstrated that amino acid cations, containing the un-ionized carboxyl group, all possessed a strong line at 5.8 μ which was not present in the neutral, dipolar amino acid, and which vanished on ionization of the carboxyl group. On the other hand, ionization of the carboxyl group gave rise to strong Raman frequencies near 7.1 μ (50), a characteristic of the isoelectric amino acid (Section 4-8).

Un-ionized primary amines show strong frequencies at about 3 μ, these vibrations appearing to arise chiefly from N-H in the —NH$_2$ group. The Raman bands of water partially overlap these frequencies but may be distinguished by the sharp and intense character of the N-H frequencies as contrasted with the broad and diffuse nature of the water lines (26). Amino acids in aqueous alkaline solution show strong frequencies near 3 μ, characteristic of the uncharged —NH$_2$ group; no such lines are present in the Raman spectrum of the isoelectric amino acids (51). The charged —NH$_3^+$ group possesses a Raman line at about 3.3 μ, and closely related lines appear in the spectrum of isoelectric glycine crystals (51). These —NH$_3^+$ lines are relatively weak and diffuse as compared with the sharper and more intense frequencies characteristic of the uncharged —NH$_2$ group.

TABLE 17-6
Comparison of Spectra of Glycine
(Data in terms of μ)

Isoelectric Crystal		Isoelectric in H$_2$O		In HCl		
Raman	Infrared	Raman	Infrared	Raman	Infrared	Assignments
–	3.17	–	–	–	–	–
3.33	–	3.31	–	3.32	–	–
3.37	3.45	3.36	–	3.38	3.42	Ionized amino
–	3.90	–	–	–	–	–
–	4.75	–	–	–	–	–
–	–	–	–	5.73	5.78	Un-ionized carboxyl
–	–	–	–	6.60	6.67	–
–	6.23	6.14	6.18	–	–	Ionized carboxyl
–	6.93	6.71	6.67	6.96	6.89	–
7.12	7.08	7.08	7.10	–	–	Ionized carboxyl
7.56	7.50	7.52	7.56	7.60	7.52	—CH$_2$
8.99	9.00	8.91	8.89	7.94	8.00	–
9.68	9.70	9.68	9.60	9.01	8.90	–
–	11.00	–	–	9.53	9.53	–
11.22	11.20	11.15	11.10	–	10.66	–
–	–	–	–	11.46	11.40	–

When the hydrogen of the —NH$_2$ group is replaced by deuterium, the characteristic frequencies are considerably depressed, e.g., from about 3 μ to 4.1 μ (52). The ratio is close to 1.37. A similar ratio holds for the comparison of the characteristic frequencies of the —NH$_3^+$ and —ND$_3^+$ groups, e.g., from 3.3 μ for hydrazine·HCl to 4.6 μ for deuterated hydrazine·HCl (52). The principal deformation frequencies of the —NH$_3^+$ and —NH$_2$ groups appear to be near 6.2 μ, those of the —ND$_3^+$ and —ND$_2$ groups near 8.3 μ (26), again a ratio close to 1.3.

SPECTRA OF THE VARIOUS AMINO ACIDS. Between 2 μ and 8 μ, the infrared and Raman spectra of the amino acids which reveal essentially the frequencies of the groups common to all these compounds are naturally very much alike (cf. Table 17-5 and (33)), and only as the spectral region is extended to longer wavelengths do marked differences among the individual amino acids begin to emerge. Where two amino acids differ in the possession of β-substituted groups, new characteristic bands for these groups may make their appearance even in the 2-μ to 8-μ region. Thus it might have been expected that the infrared spectrum of cysteine·HCl would reveal a mercaptan group frequency at about 3.90 μ which would not have been present in the spectrum, for example, of cystine. As it turns out, this band, which is also characteristic of C-H stretching vibrations, is found not only in the cysteine·HCl and cystine spectra, but also in the spectra of a good many other amino acids as well (Table 17-5), and thus the mercaptan frequency is obscured. A clearer picture is afforded by the Raman spectra of cysteine·HCl and cystine·2HCl which were obtained by Edsall, Otvos, and Rich (53) (Table 17-7).

TABLE 17-7
Raman Spectra of Cysteine·HCl and Cystine·2HCl (53)

Cysteine·HCl	Cystine·2HCl	Assignments
μ	μ	
3.24	–	–
3.32	–	–
3.38	3.38	Ionized amino
3.88	–	Mercaptan
5.73	5.73	Un-ionized carboxyl
6.07	–	–
7.00	7.02	–
7.34	–	–
7.55	–	–
7.87	–	–
8.19	8.22	–
8.70	–	–
9.26	9.32	–
10.00	10.39	–
10.66	11.29	–
11.54	12.13	–
12.54	13.15	–
12.82	13.74	–
–	14.24	–
14.62	14.99	C—S bond
16.31	–	–
19.01	–	–
–	19.84	Disulfide

As the authors pointed out, the spectrum relating to cystine·2HCl was not complete (53), but it is clear from the table that the characteristic frequencies of amino, mercaptan, carboxyl, and disulfide groups are well represented. At the longer wavelengths beyond 9 μ, the spectra of cysteine·HCl and of cystine·2HCl have apparently little in common except the C—S bond frequency at 14.6 μ to 15.0 μ.

7. Spectral Changes and Ionization.

The ionization of an amino acid may be represented as follows:

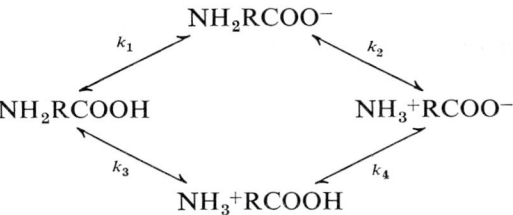

where

$$k_1 = [H^+][NH_2RCOO^-]/[NH_2RCOOH]$$

$$k_2 = [H^+][NH_2RCOO^-]/[NH_3^+RCOO^-]$$

$$k_3 = [H^+][NH_2RCOOH]/[NH_3^+RCOOH]$$

and

$$k_4 = [H^+][NH_3^+RCOO^-]/[NH_3^+RCOOH]$$

The individual or *microscopic ionization* constants are defined by k. When the amino acid is actually titrated with acid or alkali, the pH meter does not measure the ionization of any particular group or groups, but only the mean number of hydrogen ions present at the moment of measurement. The *macroscopic* or experimental ionization constants for the amino acid are defined as $K_1 = [H^+][NH_3^+RCOO^- + NH_2RCOOH]/[NH_3^+RCOOH]$, and $K_2 = [H^+][NH_2RCOO^-]/[NH_2RCOOH + NH_3^+RCOO^-]$, and the relations between the two kinds of constants are therefore $K_1 = k_3 + k_4$ and $1/K_2 = 1/k_1 + 1/k_2$, whereby $K_1K_2 = k_2k_4 = k_1k_3$. Since K_1 and K_2 are known from experiment, if one of the microscopic constants could be independently apprehended, the values for the other three microscopic constants would follow from the relations just cited. This problem was originally solved by Ebert, (54) who equated k_3 to the experimentally determined ionization constant K_e of the amino acid ester, on the assumption that the effect of a —COOEt group on the ionization of the amino group was similar to that of a —COOH group. For the monoaminomonocarboxylic acids, with K_1 and K_2 values which were widely separated, k_3 was small compared with k_4, k_1 was small compared with k_2, and [NH_2RCOOH] negligible compared with [NH_3^+RCOO^-] (see Section 4–2 and Table 4–2). From this it follows that $K_1 = k_4$ and $K_2 = k_2$, and K_1 therefore refers to the ionization of the carboxyl group of the cation, NH_3^+RCOOH, and K_2 to the ionization of the amino group of the dipolar ion, NH_3^+RCOO^-.

The same kind of reasoning could be applied to the amino acids containing three ionizable groups and hence three macroscopic and eight microscopic constants. By the use of the half-esters, Neuberger determined the relations among these constants for glutamic acid, and could assign the experimental constants K_1, K_2, and K_3 to the ionization of the α-carboxyl, γ-carboxyl, and α-amino groups, respectively (55). In the instance of such trivalent amino acids as cysteine and tyrosine, the problem of assignment is more difficult. For cysteine, the experimental constants at 25° are $K_1 = 10^{-1.71}$, $K_2 = 10^{-8.33}$, and $K_3 = 10^{-10.78}$, and, for tyrosine at 25°, $K_1 = 10^{-2.20}$, $K_2 = 10^{-9.11}$, and $K_3 = 10^{-10.07}$ (Table 4–11). There is little doubt that K_1 for both compounds is related to the ionization of the carboxyl group in the cation, $NH_3^+R(COOH)(OH$ or $SH)$. On the other hand, it is difficult to ascertain from the experimental values of K_2 and K_3 alone which of these constants represents the ionization of the amino group on the one hand, and which the ionization of phenol or mercaptan on the other. Only a determination of the corresponding microscopic constants can be of help in this connection, and two procedures have generally been followed. In these procedures, only the ionization occurring at pH values above 7, at which K_2 and K_3 occur, is considered, so that in all the microscopic forms the carboxyl group is invariably COO$^-$, and the remainder of the cysteine or tyrosine molecule is essentially a dibasic acid involving the ionization only of NH_3^+ and SH in cysteine, and of NH_3^+ and OH in tyrosine. Treatment of the equilibria among the microscopic forms is therefore similar to that given above, SH or OH being substituted for COOH, S$^-$ or O$^-$ for COO$^-$, and K_2 and K_3 for K_1 and K_2, respectively.

The first approach was that of chemical substitution as employed earlier by Ebert. For cysteine (Section 4–16), the experimental ionization constant of S-ethylcysteine, $10^{-8.60}$, was assumed to be representative of k_3, and the experimental ionization constant of cysteine betaine, $10^{-8.65}$, was assumed to be representative of k_4. On the basis of the values for K_2, K_3, k_3, and k_4, and of the relations cited above, it follows that $k_2 = 10^{-10.46}$ and $k_1 = 10^{-10.51}$. For tyrosine (56), the experimental ionization constant of O-methyltyrosine, $10^{-9.27}$, was assumed to be representative of k_3, and the experimental ionization constant of tyrosine betaine, $10^{-9.75}$, was assumed to be representative of k_4; again, the derived values of k_2 and k_1 are $10^{-9.43}$ and $10^{-9.91}$, respectively. All these values of k are "apparent" in the sense that they have been derived by the employment of K_2 and K_3 data obtained at a single finite salt concentration level.

The second approach was by the use of spectral measurements, in the ultraviolet region, of alkaline solutions of cysteine (57) and of tyrosine (56). In such solutions, the absorption is chiefly due to S$^-$ or O$^-$, and this absorption was measured in the former instance at 230–240 mμ, and in the latter at 300 mμ (cf. Table 17–1). The hydrogen ion concentration at the point of half the maximum absorption in these instances could be considered to be related to the ionization of SH or OH groups, respectively (see Figure 4–13). There are two problems which make interpretation of this relatively simple phenomenon rather difficult. The first of these stems from the fact that the absorption of not one but two forms is being measured, i.e., NH_2RS^- and $NH_3^+RS^-$ for cysteine, and NH_2RO^- and $NH_3^+RO^-$ for tyrosine. All four microscopic constants and not just one are therefore involved. The second problem arises from the question whether the molecular extinction coefficients of the two ionized forms of each amino acid are equal or not; in the absence of reliable information it was assumed that such extinction values were essentially equal or at least of the same order of magnitude.

The calculation of the microscopic constants from the absorption data for cystine was accomplished algebraically by Benesch and Benesch (57) as follows:

$$\frac{[\text{Forms with S}^-]}{[\text{Maximum absorbing forms}]}$$

$$= \frac{[NH_2RS^-] + [NH_3^+RS^-]}{[NH_2RS^-] + [NH_3^+RS^-] + [NH_2RSH] + [NH_3^+RSH]}$$

$$= \frac{k_4/k_3 + k_1/[H^+]}{[H^+]/k_3 + k_4/k_3 + k_1/[H^+] + 1}$$

Values of k_4, k_3, and k_1 were obtained by substituting the experimental values for the relation of [Forms with S$^-$]/[Maximum absorbing forms] to [H$^+$], determined by absorption measurements, into three simultaneous equations; the value of k_2 could then be derived from those of the other three constants by the relations given earlier. By these means the values turned out to be $k_1 = 10^{-10.03}$, $k_2 = 10^{-10.36}$, $k_3 = 10^{-8.86}$, and $k_4 = 10^{-8.53}$. From these data it does not seem quite possible to assign the experimental K_2 and K_3 data for cysteine to NH_3^+ or SH groups, although it is probable that the SH group ionizes well before the NH_3^+ group.

For tyrosine, Edsall and his associates calculated the microscopic constants from the absorption data as follows (56) (where E is the molar absorption coefficient):

$$\frac{[\text{Forms with O}^-]}{[\text{Maximum absorbing forms}]}$$

$$= \alpha = \frac{E \text{ (at a known } p\text{H)} - E_0}{\epsilon \text{ (maximum at highest alkalinity)} - E_0}$$

$$= \frac{k_4/[H^+] + k_4k_2/[H^+]^2}{1 + (k_4 + k_3)/[H^+] + k_4k_2/[H^+]^2} = \frac{k_4/[H^+] + K_2K_3/[H^+]^2}{1 + K_2/[H^+] + K_2K_3/[H^+]^2}$$

A function F may be defined as

$$F = \frac{[H^+]\alpha}{1 - \alpha} = \frac{k_4[H^+] + k_4k_2}{[H^+] + k_3} = \frac{k_4[H^+] + k_3k_1}{[H^+] + k_3}$$

The form of F is apparently determined by k_4/k_1 and k_3/k_4. In logarithmic form,

$$pF = pH - \log \frac{\alpha}{1-\alpha} = -\log \frac{k_4[H^+] + k_3 k_1}{[H^+] + k_3}$$

and a plot of pF against α or against pH should extrapolate to pk_4 when $\alpha = 0$ or $[H^+] \to \infty$, and to pk_1 when $\alpha = 1$ or $[H^+] \to 0$. When such plots have been made and the values of k_4 and k_1 obtained by extrapolation, it is possible to solve for k_3 from the plot of pF versus α, reading off from the curve the value of pF corresponding to $\alpha = 0.5$. At this point $pF = pH$, and hence

$$k_3 = \frac{[H^+](k_4 - [H^+])}{([H^+] - k_1)}$$

where $\alpha = 0.5$; k_1, k_3, and k_4 now being known, it is possible to solve for k_2 from the relation $k_2 k_4 = k_1 k_3$. Values of the microscopic constants for tyrosine were found (56) to be $k_1 = 10^{-10.04}$, $k_2 = 10^{-9.69}$, $k_3 = 10^{-9.28}$, and $k_4 = 10^{-9.63}$. Although in Chapter 4 it was assumed that the K_2 and K_3 values for tyrosine represented the NH_3^+ and OH^- ionization, respectively, it is clear that this was only an approximation, and that the ionization of the two groups overlaps over a considerable region of $[H^+]$.

REFERENCES

1. Kober, P. A., *J. Biol. Chem.*, **22**, 433 (1915).
2. Beaven, G. H., and Holiday, E. K., *Advances in Protein Chem.*, **7**, 319 (1952).
3. Otey, M. C., and Greenstein, J. P., *Arch. Biochem. Biophys.*, **53**, 501 (1954).
4. Stenström, W., and Reinhard, M., *J. Biol. Chem.*, **66**, 819 (1925).
5. Crammer, J. L., and Neuberger, A., *Biochem. J.*, **37**, 302 (1943).
6. Fromageot, C., and Schnek, G., *Biochem. Biophys. Acta*, **6**, 113 (1950).
7. Holiday, E. R., *Biochem. J.*, **30**, 1795 (1936).
8. Holiday, E. R., and Ogston, A. G., *Biochem. J.*, **32**, 1166 (1938).
9. Ley, H., and Arends, B., *Z. physik. Chem.*, **B17**, 177 (1932).
10. Ward, F. W., *Biochem. J.*, **17**, 891 (1923).
11. Goldfarb, A. R., Saidel, L. J., and Mosovich, E., *J. Biol. Chem.*, **193**, 402 (1951); Saidel, L. J., and Lieberman, H., *Arch. Biochem. Biophys.*, **76**, 401 (1958).
12. Ham, J. S., and Platt, J. R., *J. Chem. Phys.*, **20**, 335 (1952).
13. Goldfarb, A. R., *J. Biol. Chem.*, **201**, 317 (1953).
14. Saidel, L. J., Goldfarb, A. R., and Waldman, S., *J. Biol. Chem.*, **197**, 285 (1952).
15. Wade, R., Winitz, M., and Greenstein, J. P., *J. Am. Chem. Soc.*, **78**, 373 (1956).
16. Greenstein, J. P., *Advances in Enzymol.*, **8**, 117 (1948).
17. Fruton, J. S., Simmonds, S., and Smith, V. A., *J. Biol. Chem.*, **169**, 267 (1947).
18. Carter, C. E., and Greenstein, J. P., *J. Natl. Cancer Inst.*, **7**, 51, 433 (1946–1947).
19. Levintow, L., Fu, S.-C J., Price, V. E., and Greenstein, J. P., *J. Biol. Chem.*, **184**, 633 (1950).
20. Meister, A., and Greenstein, J. P., *J. Biol. Chem.*, **195**, 849 (1952).

21. Sutherland, G. B. B. M., *Advances in Protein Chem.*, **7**, 291 (1952).
22. Gore, R. C., *Anal. Chem.*, **26**, 11 (1954).
23. Bellamy, L. J., *The Infra-Red Spectra of Complex Molecules*, John Wiley and Sons, New York, 1954.
24. Gore, R. C., Barnes, R. B., and Peterson, R., *Anal. Chem.*, **21**, 382 (1949).
25. Lacher, J. R., Croy, V. D., Kianpour, A., and Park, J. D., *J. Phys. Chem.*, **58**, 206 (1954).
26. Edsall, J. T., *Cold Spring Harbor Symposia Quant. Biol.*, **6**, 40 (1938).
27. Thompson, H. W., Nicholson, D. L., and Short, L. N., *Discussions Faraday Soc.*, No. 9, 222 (1950).
28. Klotz, I. M., and Gruen, D. M., *J. Phys. & Colloid Chem.*, **52**, 961 (1948).
29. Wright, N., *J. Biol. Chem.*, **120**, 641 (1937); **127**, 137 (1939).
30. Darmon, S. E., Sutherland, G. B. B. M., and Tristram, G. R., *Biochem. J.*, **42**, 508 (1948).
31. Koegel, R. J., McCallum, R. A., Greenstein, J. P., Winitz, M., and Birnbaum, S. M., *Ann. N. Y. Acad. Sci.*, **69**, 94 (1957).
32. Brockmann, H., and Musso, H., *Chem. Ber.*, **89**, 241 (1956).
33. Koegel, R. J., Greenstein, J. P., Winitz, M., Birnbaum, S. M., and McCallum, R. A., *J. Am. Chem. Soc.*, **77**, 5708 (1955).
33a. Saraceno, A. J., Nakagawa, I., Mizushima, S., Curran, C., and Quagliano, J. V., *J. Am. Chem. Soc.*, **80**, 5018 (1958).
34. Greenstein, J. P., Izumiya, N., Winitz, M., and Birnbaum, S. M., *J. Am. Chem. Soc.*, **77**, 707 (1955).
35. Sheppard, N., and Sutherland, G. B. B. M., *Nature*, **159**, 739 (1947).
36. Blout, E. R., and Linsley, S. G., *J. Am. Chem. Soc.*, **74**, 1946 (1952).
37. Koegel, R. J., personal communication.
38. Izumiya, N., Wade, R., Winitz, M., Otey, M. C., Birnbaum, S. M., Koegel, R. J., and Greenstein, J. P., *J. Am. Chem. Soc.*, **79**, 652 (1957).
39. Downey, P. F., and Black, S., *J. Biol. Chem.*, **228**, 171 (1957).
40. Blackburn, S., and Schöberl, A., *Z. physiol. Chem.*, **305**, 105 (1956).
41. Marshall, R., Winitz, M., Birnbaum, S. M., and Greenstein, J. P., *J. Am. Chem. Soc.*, **79**, 4538 (1957).
42. Bak, B., and Christensen, D., *Acta Chem. Scand.*, **10**, 692 (1956).
43. Wade, R., Birnbaum, S. M., Winitz, M., Koegel, R. J., and Greenstein, J. P., *J. Am. Chem. Soc.*, **79**, 648 (1957).
44. Ellenbogen, E., *J. Am. Chem. Soc.*, **78**, 363 (1956).
45. Duval, C., and Lecomte, J., *J. Chem. Phys.*, **18**, 117 (1950).
46. Rosenberg, A., and Schotte, L., *Acta Chem. Scand.*, **8**, 867 (1951).
47. Leifer, A., and Lippincott, E. R., *J. Am. Chem. Soc.*, **79**, 5098 (1957).
48. Lenormant, H., *J. chim. phys.*, **49**, 635 (1952).
49. Freymann, M., Freymann, R., and Rumpf, P., *J. phys. radium*, [7] **7**, 30 (1936).
50. Edsall, J. T., *J. Chem. Phys.*, **4**, 1 (1936).
51. Edsall, J. T., *J. Chem. Phys.*, **5**, 225 (1937).
52. Edsall, J. T., and Scheinberg, H., *J. Chem. Phys.*, **8**, 520 (1940).
53. Edsall, J. T., Otvos, J. W., and Rich, A., *J. Am. Chem. Soc.*, **72**, 474 (1950); see also Garfinkel, D., and Edsall, J. T., *ibid.*, **80**, 3823 (1958).
54. Ebert, L., *Z. physik. Chem.*, **121**, 385 (1926).
55. Neuberger, A., *Biochem. J.*, **30**, 2085 (1936).
56. Edsall, J. T., Martin, R. B., and Hollingworth, B. R., *Proc. Natl. Acad. Sci. (U. S.)*, **44**, 505 (1958); see also Martin, R. B., Edsall, J. T., Wetlaufer, D. B., and Hollingworth, B. R., *J. Biol. Chem.*, **233**, 1429 (1958).
57. Benesch, R. E., and Benesch, R., *J. Am. Chem. Soc.*, **77**, 5877 (1955).

chapter 18

Optical Rotation

1. General Aspects. The theoretical and practical aspects of this subject have been ably reviewed by Shriner, Adams, and Marvel (1), by Heller (2), and by Bates (3). An illuminating discussion of optical rotatory power is to be found in the 1930 Discussion held by the Faraday Society under the chairmanship of T. M. Lowry (4).

For pure compounds, the specific optical activity is defined as

$$[\alpha]_\lambda \text{ at temperature } T \text{ and wavelength } \lambda = \frac{\alpha}{1 \cdot d}$$

where α is the degrees of rotation observed in a tube 1 dcm. in length for a pure compound whose density is d.

For compounds in solution, the specific optical activity is defined as

$$[\alpha]_\lambda \text{ at temperature } T \text{ and wavelength } \lambda = \frac{\alpha}{1 \cdot g \cdot d} \text{ or } \frac{\alpha}{1 \cdot c}$$

where α is the degrees of rotation observed in a tube 1 dcm. in length for a solution containing g grams of solute per 100 grams of a relatively concentrated solution of density d, or where c is the grams of solute per 100 ml. of relatively dilute solution wherein the density is very close to unity.

Molecular rotations are frequently employed, and these are generally defined as

$$[M]_\lambda \text{ at temperature } T = [\alpha]_\lambda \cdot \text{molecular weight divided by 100}$$

Measurements of optical rotation of the amino acids have been employed for four general purposes, namely, (a) as an indication of the optical purity of an amino acid sample, assuming the existence and prior measurements of an unexceptional reference standard; (b) to characterize uniquely a new amino acid in terms of a particular physical constant; (c) to help identify an otherwise unknown amino acid by the magnitude of the optical rotation, and to identify it further as its L- or D-isomer by virtue of the sign of rotation, again with the implication of the possession of a pure reference standard compound; and (d) with the assistance of certain empirical optical rotatory relations to determine whether an amino acid is of the L- or D-configuration (e.g., configurational analysis). Purpose (d) is considered in some detail in Chapter 2.

The optical rotation values generally given in the literature have an empirical quality, and the accepted values are those agreed upon by the majority of investigators. These values are a function of the nature of the solvent, of the concentration of solute, of temperature, of wavelength, and in many cases of the concentration of acid and alkali employed (Section 2-9). As a rule, only a single rotation value of a given compound is described, and that under quite arbitrarily selected conditions. This creates no special problems provided that subsequent identifications are made under the same conditions for the same compound. A uniform procedure in this area is as difficult to achieve as in any other, and the weight of time and precedence lies heavy on innovation. Thus the D-line of sodium derived from the fusion of a bead of sodium carbonate on a platinum wire was early adopted as a cheap source of relatively monochromatic radiation, and, probably because of the considerable literature which followed, subsequent recommendations for the use of purer lines nearer the violet end of the mercury arc spectrum yielding higher orders of magnitude of rotation values with resulting higher accuracy met with relatively little response until quite recently. As an example, at the same concentration in N HCl, the rotation of 3:4-dihydroxyphenyl-L-alanine is about 10% greater at 546 mμ than at 589 mμ (5). The dependence of optical rotation on wavelength has been described in detail in Section 2-9.

The more common solvents employed have been water and dilute HCl solutions. Aqueous alkali has occasionally been used as a solvent, but the destructive effect which alkaline solutions produce on glass has discouraged the more frequent application of this medium. Polarimeter tubes now manufactured are composed entirely of glass, and if etching or scratching of the endplates occurs the entire tube must be discarded. With the older types of polarimeter tubes in which removable and exchangeable glass endplates are tightly held over the solutions by metal screw flanges with rubber washers, any leakage, no matter how small, of strongly acid solutions results in contamination of the solution with metal halides.

Many amino acids have higher specific rotations in glacial acetic acid than in aqueous hydrochloric acid (6; cf. 7 and 8) (Section 2-9), but in most cases the lower solubility in glacial acetic acid reduces the advantages of using this solvent. No racemization occurs in this solvent even on warming, except in the case of α-phenylglycine, where the loss of optical activity is complete (6). Several amino acids are very soluble in aqueous solvents, and at higher concentrations a correspondingly larger angular rotation can be achieved; in such solutions, however, the density factor must be taken into consideration (see equations above), and where HCl or NaOH is to be present care must be taken that these reagents are in considerable excess. Under the same conditions, a 4-dcm. polarimeter tube will give twice the angular reading of a 2-dcm. tube, and four times the angular reading of a 1-dcm. tube, but a larger volume will usually be required, and the construction of the longer tube, including the alignment of the endplates must necessarily be more precise. Temperature control is often of importance in the measurement of the rotation values of certain amino acids in solution, e.g., tyrosine, cystine, etc. (Section 2-9), and polarimeter tubes provided with jackets through which solvents at maintained temperatures can circulate are available on the market. Inasmuch as the heat exchange under these conditions (between a moving and a stationary liquid) is quite slow, and a considerable period of time must necessarily elapse before a condition of temperature equilibrium between circulating and stationary phases can take place, the use of such controls is rarely attempted in the course of routine measurements. More often the polarimetric assembly is established in rooms held at constant temperature, in which the solvents employed are also maintained together with the necessary gravimetric equipment required for composing the solutions, so that the entire operation can be conducted at a single temperature. This luxurious device, although desirable, is not common, and not quite so crucial as to warrant the expense save for purposes of polarimetry research.

The light source for optical rotation measurements in the time of Biot and Pasteur was derived from a strong lamp which yielded a whole spectrum of the visible range of "white light." For more accurate and reproducible measurements, in view of the fact that the rotation varied considerably with the wavelength, it was found necessary to employ monochromatic radiation, and, since the eye was the indicator, this radiation had perforce to be in the visible region of the spectrum. Three experimental devices came to mind in this connection, namely, (a) the use of monochromatic filters with white light as a source, (b) the use of prisms capable of transmitting light within a narrow wavelength band, with white light as a source, and (c) light itself arising from a monochromatic radiation source. The use of (a) and (b), however, was accompanied by a considerable loss in intensity, and so much light was lost in traversing the polarimeter tube that the limit of sensitivity of the eye was reached. More transparent filters were accompanied by broader bands of light transmitted which no longer deserved the designation of monochromatic. To register the weak, monochromatic radiation which came through the polarimeter tube a more sensitive indicator than the eye was needed, and this was found in the photoelectric cell. With this device, it has been possible to develop the polarimeter so as to obtain optical rotation measurements at specified wavelengths not only over the visible portion of the spectrum (using various light sources, including the mercury arc), but also, with the aid of the quartz prism and a hydrogen emission source, over a portion of the ultraviolet. These admirable instruments yield information of value, but they are primarily research instruments of a somewhat cranky and temperamental disposition, which require frequent attention. They cannot be set aside for the occasional measurement, whilst even during active operation the unstable zero setting demands constant correction. These technical problems are not insurmountable, and they yield to patient and affectionate care. This leaves (c) as the visual polarimetric standby, in which the intense 589-mμ emission line of sodium vapor has served most frequently as the nearly monochromatic light source; data obtained with this device are in complete accord with those obtained by photoelectric devices using standard filters or prisms.

2. Mineral Acid to Amino Acid Ratios. With optically active ionic compounds, such as the amino acids, the magnitude of the optical rotation

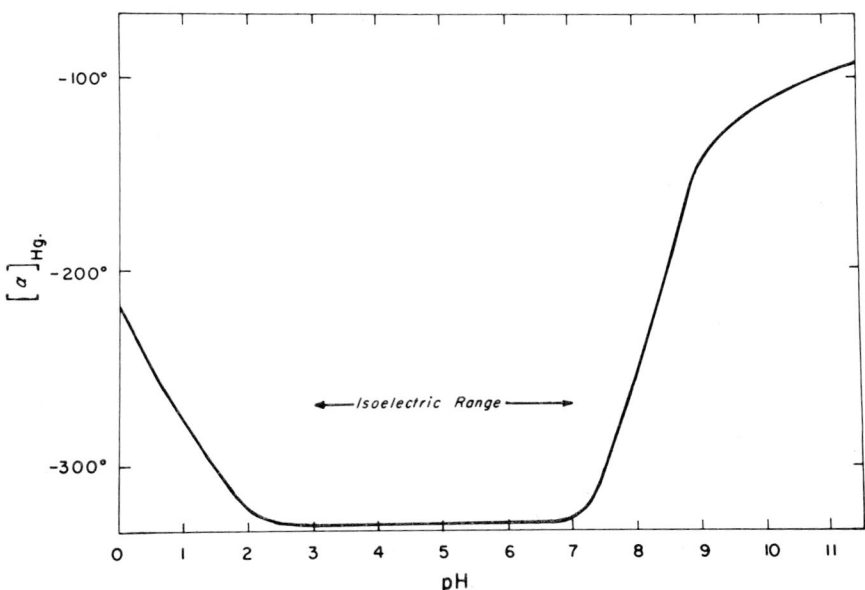

Figure 18-1. Effect of pH on the $[\alpha]_{Hg}$ of L-cystine. Toennies, G., Lavine, T. F., and Bennett, M. A., *J. Biol. Chem.*, **112**, 493 (1935–36).

is a function of the degree of ionization up to a constant and limiting value (Figure 18–1) (9). The use of this property for the determination of optical configuration has been described in Section 2-9, and for the determination of ionization constants in Section 4–1. The phenomenon itself was probably first observed by Schulze in 1885 (10), when he found that 1 gram of L-tyrosine dissolved in 4% HCl to a final volume of 20 ml. possessed an $[\alpha]_D$ value of $-15.6°$, whereas, when the acid concentration was 21% instead of 4%, the $[\alpha]_D$ value was $-8.5°$. In either case, the concentration of the L-tyrosine was $0.28M$, the more dilute acid being $1.1M$, and the more concentrated acid being $5.5M$, so that the ratio of moles of mineral acid to moles of

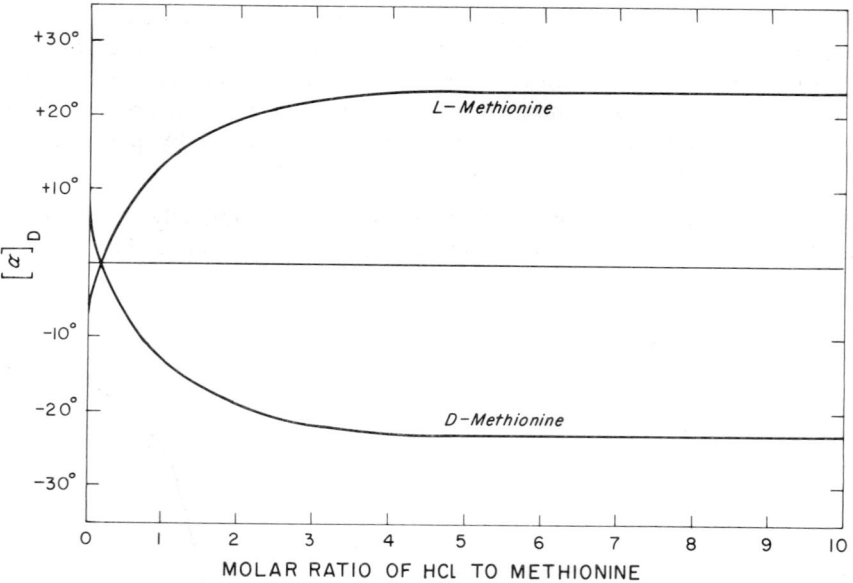

Figure 18–2. Effect of different molar ratios of HCl to amino acid on the specific rotation of L- and D-methionine. Spies, J. R., *J. Biol. Chem.*, **182**, 439 (1950).

amino acid in the former case was 4 : 1, and in the latter 20 : 1. Table 18–1 (11–14) and Figure 18–2, taken from the precise work of Spies (15), illustrate the phenomenon further. The maximum rotation is not reached at a 1 : 1 ratio of mineral acid to amino acid, but only when this ratio is increased to a value which is probably different for each amino acid. Beyond this optimal ratio, the magnitude of the optical rotation may decrease.

The free amino acid in aqueous solution possesses a certain optical rotation value. As mineral acid is progressively added to the solution, the optical rotation value will be the sum of the rotations due to the newly formed cation halide and the remaining free amino acid. At the equivalence point, i.e., when the molarities of mineral acid and amino acid are equal, there is still present some free amino acid which is due to hydrolysis of the amino acid salt; if this is indeed so, increasing dilution of solutions of amino acid

TABLE 18-1
Optical Rotation as a Function of the Molar Ratio of HCl to Amino Acid (AA)

L-Serine (11)		S-Benzyl-L-cysteine (11)		L-Lysine·2HCl (12)		L-Cystine·2HCl (13)		Seleno-L-cystine (14)	
[HCl]/AA[a]	$[\alpha]_D$	[HCl]/AA[b]	$[\alpha]_D$	[HCl]/AA·2HCl	$[\alpha]_D$	[HCl]/AA·2HCl[c]	$[\alpha]_D$	[HCl]/AA[d]	$[\alpha]_D$
0	−7.0°	21.4	−1.7°	0	+16.3°	7.8	−265°	3.3	−183°
0.525	+1.8	41.7	−5.0	1	+17.2	32.8	−237	66.7	−162
0.787	+6.3	62.5	−9.0	2	+17.3	70.5	−230		
1.05	+9.0	83.4	−12.4	4	+17.0	120.6	−225		
1.31	+11.5	103.7	−13.6	8	+17.2	289.0	−205		
1.58	+13.0					570.0	−195		
2.63	+14.8					851.5	−192		
5.25	+14.5					1132.5	−190		
11.8	+13.8					1413.8	−185		
23.6	+13.3								

[a] Concentration of L-serine always 2%.
[b] Concentration of S-benzyl-L-cysteine always 1%.
[c] Concentration of L-cystine·2HCl always 0.05%.
[d] Concentration of seleno-L-cystine always 1%. The L-compound was prepared from L-serine by the Fischer-Raske procedure (Chapter 24).

halides with water should result in a trend of the optical rotation values toward that characteristic of the free amino acid as the halide salts are progressively hydrolyzed. Table 18-2, taken from the work of Anslow and King (16), shows this phenomenon vividly. Hence increase in the concentration of mineral acid by repressing hydrolysis of the amino acid salt and compelling all amino acid present to become amino acid halide results in an increase in rotation (Figure 18-2 and Table 18-1). However, still

TABLE 18-2

Optical Rotation of L-Glutamic Acid Hydrochloride as a Function of Its Molar Concentration in Water (15)

Molarity[a]	$[\alpha]_{5461}$
0.55	+28.63°
0.27	+27.45
0.14	+26.85
0.07	+26.28
0.035	+23.54
0.027	+22.87
0.014	+20.59

[a] Mineral acid: amino acid ratio always 1 : 1 in terms of equivalence.

further increase in the concentration of mineral acid will repress the ionization of the amino acid halide salt and cause a decrease in the rotation values. The maximum value of the optical rotation will therefore be that characteristic of the maximum ionization of the amino acid cation halide.

3. Influence of the Disulfide Bond on Optical Rotation.

Of all the α-amino acids, L-cystine possesses the highest order of magnitude of molecular rotation in HCl solution, the $[M]_D$ value being $-557.4°$ (6; 17-24). Table 18-3 lists the values of $[M]_D$ for cystine and for several related compounds. The abnormally high rotation for cystine has been related to the proximity of the disulfide bond to the asymmetric carbon atom (25); thus a number of optically active disulfide acids of the type $[HO_2CCHR(CH_2)_nS-]_2$, where $n = 0$ or 1, have been found to have quite high rotation values. That there is apparently some element of truth in this viewpoint follows from a comparison of the $[M]_D$ value of L-homocystine in which the disulfide bond is further removed from the asymmetric center with that of the isomeric L-β-homocystine in which, as in L-cystine, the disulfide bond is next to the asymmetric center (Table 18-3); the value of $[M]_D$ for the former is considerably less than that for the latter. That the disulfide bond exerts some augmenting influence on the neighboring asymmetric center follows as well on inspection of the data for the peptides of L-cystine with glycine (Table 18-3), although in these peptides the $[M]_D$ values are lower than that of

L-cystine alone. In the dipeptides of cystine, L-cystinyl-L-cystine, and L-cystinyl-D-cystine, high values of $[M]_D$ are noted in the table, that for the latter being considerably greater than for the former; the monomeric compound, cyclo-L-cystinyl, however, possibly because of its antiparallel configuration (cf. 24), possesses a relatively low $[M]_D$ value. In a quite interesting discussion, Fieser (26) suggested that the high rotation of cystine might be due to its existence as an endocyclic ring structure, in which the α-amino and α-carboxyl groups might be joined through hydrogen bonds. In cystinylcystine, and particularly in the diketopiperazine of cystine (Table 18–3), such ring forms actually exist and, as shown by the latter compound, possess quite high rotatory values.

TABLE 18–3

Molar Rotation ($[M]_D$) Values of Cystine and Related Compounds at 20–24°

Compound	$[M]_D$[a]	Reference
L-Cystine	−557.4°[b]	(6)
L-Homocystine	+209.2[b]	(17)
L-β-Homocystine	−702.2[b]	(18)
Diglycyl-L-cystine	−382.3[b]	(19)
L-Cystinyldiglycine	−304.4[b]	(20)
L-Cystinyldiglycylglycine	−257.4[b]	(21)
Anhydro-L-cystinyl-L-cystine	+1276.1[c]	(22)
Cyclo-L-cystinyl	−67.2[b]	(23)(24)
L-Cystinyl-L-cystine	−266.4[b]	(23)(24)
L-Cystinyl-D-cystine	−843.6[b]	(23)

[a] $[M]_D = [α]_D \cdot$ Molecular weight/100.
[b] In N HCl.
[c] In water.

4. Procedure for Optical Rotation Measurements. The polarimeter tube is carefully washed with distilled water, alcohol, and ether, and dried by drawing clean air through it, the endplates being wiped clean with soft tissue. The tube is filled with solvent, care being taken that no bubbles of air have been entrapped in the length of the tube or near the endplates, closed with the ground-glass stoppers, and placed in the polarimeter in a position which experience has shown will permit the entire field to be visible when the light source is turned on. This position is carefully noted, as is also the relative facing of the tube in the polarimeter (i.e., which end faces the light source). The light source (sodium vapor lamp) is turned on, and the assembly allowed to stand for 30 minutes to 1 hour for the liquid to reach temperature equilibrium and for the lamp to attain its maximum intensity. Lights in the room are extinguished, or a dark hood is drawn over the head and shoulders of the observer in order to prevent the entrance of stray light, and readings are taken on the polarimeter. The analyzer is deliberately turned so that the fields are quite mismatched, and the eyepiece so focused as to obtain the clearest possible image. The extent of focusing is generally unique for each individual, and must be held constant as long as that individual is the observer. After the close focus has been achieved, the analyzer is turned until in the observer's judgment the fields of analyzer and polarizer match (i.e., the same intensity of light comes through each half-field). The first reading is usually only tentative and is best discarded. Adjustment of the analyzer until the separate fields just match in light transmission intensity is carried on by several consecutive readings; the analyzer is thrown off each time in opposite directions, and thus the match is approached alternately from the high side and from the low side. When three or more consecutive readings agree within 0.02°, the readings may be averaged and ended for the observer. It is wise at this point to request a colleague to take an independent set of readings, with focus set to his eye before he undertakes the readings. If a third person is present, it is not amiss to request his services in this connection as well. The final, agreed-upon reading serves as the zero point of the instrument. The tube is removed and dried as before.

The amino acid to be tested is dried to constant weight *in vacuo* and generally at a temperature of boiling ethanol. It is then accurately weighed, transferred to a calibrated volumetric flask, made up in a concentration of 1 to 2%, and *well shaken*. The solution must be completely transparent at this stage, for if even barely turbid it will be difficult to view in the polarimeter. This is particularly acute if the light must pass through a 4- or even a 2-dcm. tube. A check on the transparency of the solution may be made by viewing an object (perhaps a clock) across the room through the tube. If any difficulty is experienced in viewing the object, the endplates must be thoroughly cleaned, and if the haziness still persists the solution is discarded, the tube cleaned, and the compound recrystallized in the presence of a little charcoal. The final, acceptably clear solution is returned to the cleaned and dried polarimeter tube and the tube placed within the polarimeter in the same setting and direction as used before. The solution is allowed to reach temperature equilibrium, which may be ascertained in part by the fact that the entire field is illuminated. With solutions of amino acids in glacial acetic acid it frequently takes close to an hour before this point is reached, the illuminated field only rising gradually to fill the eyepiece, like a rising full moon. When this occurs, the readings are made as described above, beginning with the proper focus, and enlisting the independent observations of any cooperative colleagues. The final, agreed-upon reading is corrected for the zero reading of the instrument obtained previously with the pure solvent. Thus, if the zero reading is $-0.03°$ and the reading of the test solution is $+0.82°$, the final determination would be $+0.85°$; similarly, if the zero reading is $+0.03°$, the final reading would be $+0.79°$. Polarimetric readings should not be attempted under conditions of visual fatigue, nor continued too long lest such fatigue develop. Readings are taken as long as a critical attitude can be maintained; beyond a certain number of such readings, which varies from one individual to another, fatigue and impatience emerge, and the readings diminish in objectivity and value. Excessive care with its undertone of timidity and unsureness may lead to no better results than may undue haste or carelessness. Visual polarimetry, because of its dependence upon precise personal judgment, is probably an anachronism in an age of automatic recording systems, and perhaps for this reason it is a nice test of the investigator's self-confidence and professional attitude.

REFERENCES

1. Shriner, R. L., Adams, R., and Marvel, C. S., in *Organic Chemistry*, Vol. I, John Wiley and Sons, New York, p. 214, 1942.
2. Heller, W., in *Physical Methods of Organic Chemistry*, Vol. I, Part II, 2nd ed., Interscience Publishers, New York, p. 1491, 1949.
3. Bates, F. J., "Polarimetry, Saccharimetry, and the Sugars," *Nat. Bur. Standards Circ.*, **C440**, (1942).
4. "Optical Rotatory Power," Faraday Society General Discussion, 1930.
5. Harington, C. R., and Randall, S. S., *Biochem. J.*, **25**, 1029 (1931).
6. Greenstein, J. P., Birnbaum, S. M., and Otey, M. C., *J. Biol. Chem.*, **204**, 307 (1953).
7. von Przylecki, St. J., and Kasprzyk, K., *Biochem. Z.*, **289**, 243 (1936–37).
8. Thomas, D. W., and Niemann, C., *J. Biol. Chem.*, **175**, 241 (1948).
9. Toennies, G., Lavine, T. F., and Bennett, M. A., *J. Biol. Chem.*, **112**, 493 (1935–36).
10. Schulze, E., *Z. physiol. Chem.*, **9**, 63 (1885).
11. Data by Dr. Robin Marshall (serine) and by Dr. Ted Otani (S-benzylcysteine) from this Laboratory.
12. Lawrow, D., *Z. physiol. Chem.*, **28**, 388 (1899).
13. Andrews, J. C., *J. Biol. Chem.*, **65**, 147 (1925).
14. Fredga, A., *Svensk Kem. Tidskr.*, **48**, 160 (1936); **49**, 124 (1937).
15. Spies, J. R., *J. Biol. Chem.*, **182**, 439 (1950).
16. Anslow, W. K., and King, H., *Biochem. J.*, **21**, 1168 (1927).
17. du Vigneaud, V., and Patterson, W. I., *J. Biol. Chem.*, **109**, 97 (1935).
18. Balenovic, K., Jambresic, I., Gaspert, B., and Cerar, D., *Rec. trav. chim.*, **75**, 1252 (1956).
19. Greenstein, J. P., *J. Biol. Chem.*, **128**, 241 (1939).
20. Loring, H. S., and du Vigneaud, V., *J. Biol. Chem.*, **111**, 385 (1935).
21. Greenstein, J. P., *J. Biol. Chem.*, **124**, 255 (1938).
22. Greenstein, J. P., *J. Biol. Chem.*, **118**, 321 (1937).
23. Izumiya, N., and Greenstein, J. P., *Arch. Biochem. Biophys.*, **52**, 203 (1954).
24. Wade, R., Winitz, M., and Greenstein, J. P., *J. Am. Chem. Soc.*, **78**, 373 (1956).
25. Fredga, A., *Acta Chem. Scand.*, **4**, 1307 (1950).
26. Fieser, L., *Rec. trav. chim.*, **69**, 410 (1950).

chapter 19

Determination of Optical and Steric Purity

1. General Considerations. Like virtue or honor, the purity of a chemical substance is not absolute but possesses a value relative to a set of standards. In the highly individualistic realm of biochemical investigation, these standards vary widely, are largely a personal matter, and are, all too often, lightly regarded. A tolerance for biochemicals of dubious antecedents may spring from haste, an undue confidence in the label of the manufacturer, an unfamiliarity with the exacting requirements of a good training in synthetic and analytic organic chemistry, and a comforting but often deceptive assurance that, since the chemical in question is to be administered to the conglomeration of chemicals which is the whole animal, or the tissue homogenate, or the bacterial culture, a little more impurity cannot do any harm. The ice is often quite thin. Another factor sometimes involved in problems of the use of so-called fine chemicals is that of financial cost, as illustrated by the following statement in the foreword of a recent publication on chemical standards: "The consumers of fine chemicals require a quality which has proved satisfactory to them and does not require extremes which in practice are attainable only at disproportionate financial expense." Inasmuch as the investigator may expend a "disproportionate" amount of his own time in handling materials short of the highest purity, it may be assumed that his time has no financial value.

The criteria of purity of the amino acids involve considerations of analytic, optical, and—in the special case of amino acids with two centers of optical asymmetry—steric individuality. It is not unusual to equate synthetic amino acids with a high order of analytic purity in terms of content of carbon, hydrogen, nitrogen (and in some cases sulfur). Although the analytic data for these elements may be within the acceptable 1–2 % allowance, they may, however, represent mixtures of isomers. Thus in 1900 Emil Fischer (1) explained certain bizarre data involving synthetic tyrosine as due to the presence of a contaminating isomer arising in the course of the preparation of this amino acid from an unrecognized mixture of isomeric starting materials. Again, when fusel oil was used as a source of isoamyl alcohol for the preparation of the necessary aldehyde for the Strecker synthesis of leucine, it was found necessary to fractionate this alcohol carefully from the accompanying d-amyl alcohol, or the resulting DL-leucine would otherwise be contaminated with an L-isoleucine + D-alloisoleucine mixture (cf. 2) (Section 30–1 and 30–4). Indeed, some samples of commercially available DL-leucine tested in this Laboratory were found to contain as much as 20% of isoleucine—but the C, H, and N analyses approached closely to the theoretical.

Evidence from elemental analysis, although indispensable, is not by itself a sufficient guarantee of chemical individuality. Where racemic amino acids are sought as starting materials for the preparation of the optical isomers by resolution, an unequivocal synthesis leading to a single chemical individual must be employed. In some cases, the L-amino acids which are readily isolated from protein hydrolysates or other natural sources may be converted by racemization into their DL-forms; this procedure appears to be preferable for such compounds as glutamic acid, leucine, and tyrosine, where the monetary advantage of using the natural materials reinforces the argument, as well as for such amino acids as arginine, histidine, and proline. Recommended syntheses and racemization procedures for the various amino acids are described in Part VI.

Methods of synthesis of amino acids with two centers of asymmetry usually lead to mixtures of two racemic diastereomers, and not infrequently preparations on the market of "DL-isoleucine," "DL-threonine," or "DL-allothreonine" are actually such diastereomeric mixtures of unknown, or at least unstated, composition. For such amino acids as cystine or α,ε-diaminopimelic acid, methods of synthesis lead to a mixture of a racemic and an internally compensated or *meso* form, again in unknown proportion. Methods of recognizing and resolving such mixtures are given in detail in Part VI for each of the amino acids in this category. For purposes of comparison at this time illustrative examples are briefly described in Table 19–1 (3–12).

Final determination of the chemical individuality of a racemic amino acid, whether it contains one center of asymmetry or two, is best effected by the methods of paper (cf. 3) and column chromatography (cf. 4, 13) (Chapter 15). Except for such unusual instances involving diaminopimelic acid (14), histidine (15), and certain of the aromatic-substituted amino acids (16) which are partially resolved into their optical isomers on paper under particular conditions, the compounds should yield a single ninhydrin-reactive spot on the paper chromatograms, and a well-defined and symmetrical peak on elution from ion exchange resins. Paper chromatography is rarely capable

TABLE 19-1
Determinations of the Steric Composition of Diastereomeric Mixtures

Mixtures	Procedure	Products
DL-Isoleucine + DL-alloisoleucine[a]	Treatment with D-amino acid oxidase (3)	Mixture of enantiomorphic 2:4-dinitrophenylhydrazones of the corresponding α-keto acids[c]
DL-Isoleucine + DL-alloisoleucine	Elution from Dowex-50 resin (4)	Two separate peaks
DL-Threonine + DL-allothreonine[b]	Elution from Dowex-50 resin (5)	Two separate peaks
L-Hydroxyproline + D-allohydroxyproline	Treatment with D-amino acid oxidase (6)	Consumption of 0.5 mole of oxygen per mole of D-amino acid
L-Hydroxyproline + D-allohydroxyproline	Elution from Dowex-50 resin	Two separate peaks
β-Phenyl-L-serine + allo-β-phenyl-L-serine	Treatment with L-amino acid oxidase (7)	Mixture of enantiomorphic mandelic acids
D-Hydroxylysine + D-allohydroxylysine	Elution from Dowex-50 resin (4)	Two separate peaks
DL-α-Aminotricarballylic acid + DL-allo-α-aminotricarballylic acid	Conversion with HNO_2 to isocitric acid followed by treatment with isocitric acid dehydrogenase (8)	Oxalosuccinic acid from L-α-aminotricarballylic acid moiety

[a] Inasmuch as only L-isoleucine of the four isomers present will support the growth of *Lactobacillus arabinosus*, the relative ratio of isoleucine to alloisoleucine can be determined by microbiological procedures (9–11).

[b] Inasmuch as only L-threonine of the four isomers present will support the growth of *Streptococcus faecalis*, the relative ratio of threonine to allothreonine can be determined by the usual microbiological procedures (5).

[c] The *l*-isomer is derived from D-isoleucine, the *d*-isomer from D-alloisoleucine. If L-amino acid oxidase is employed to obtain the α-keto acids (12), the *d*-isomer would be derived from L-isoleucine and the *l*-isomer from L-alloisoleucine.

DETERMINATION OF OPTICAL AND STERIC PURITY

of distinguishing optical isomers or diastereomers, and recourse must be sought in techniques of column chromatography, microbiology, or enzymology. Moreover, paper chromatography reveals only ninhydrin-reactive material, and hence is of limited applicability.

The pure racemate subjected to available resolution procedures yields the L- and D-isomers, and the subsequent problem relates to the optical purity of the isomers so obtained, i.e., the degree of success of the resolution procedure in separating the isomers completely. With relatively non-specific resolving agents, such as the alkaloids, the effectiveness of which depends on marked differences in solubility between the diastereomeric salts formed, this degree of success can only be apprehended when the isomers are finally isolated and characterized. On the other hand, when optically specific enzymes, such as renal acylase I, are employed (17) as the resolving agents, it is possible to follow the course of the asymmetric hydrolysis of the N-acylated DL-amino acids quantitatively by means of manometric measurements of ninhydrin-developed carbon dioxide; a maximum of 50% hydrolysis indicates termination of the reaction and assurance of the optical specificity of the resolving enzyme. However, these data may not reflect as high an order of accuracy as may be desired. The manometric measurement of ninhydrin-developed carbon dioxide in solutions of pure amino acids is no better than 0.2 to 0.3% (18, 19) (Chapter 12). In enzymic digests, this error may be as much as ±1%. Thus either of the isomers could be contaminated by as much as 1% of the other without detection by the manometric criterion.

The customary criterion of optical purity, namely that of optical rotation, is usually not sufficiently sensitive to reveal this amount of contamination. A simple example will suffice to show this. If the specific optical rotation of L-methionine for a 2.00% solution in $2N$ HCl is accepted as $+23.0°$, the angular rotation in a 2-dcm. tube will be $+0.92°$. If the L-methionine contained 1% of the D-form, the angular rotation would be expected to be $+0.90°$, and the specific optical rotation $+22.5°$. Even with a good polarimeter and careful observations, it would be difficult to accept the differences between these readings as significant. There is no "theoretical value" for an optical rotation, but only one on which most observers agree. The area of agreement, however, may be several per cent wide. It is therefore difficult to determine whether the spread in values in the literature for the rotation of the amino acids is due to individual experimental variations or to contamination of the isomers by their respective optical enanntimorphs. Moreover, the optical rotation value as measured is more or less dependent upon the concentration of the solution, the concentration of acid or alkali added, the wavelength, and the temperature, and no systematic standardization of experimental conditions has yet been agreed upon (except for the nearly universal use of the D-line of sodium as the light source) (6) (Chapter 18).

2. The Use of Oxidases and Decarboxylases. A more sensitive criterion of optical purity, first suggested by Zeller (20), and provided that all other criteria have been met, is the use of optically specific amino acid oxidases and decarboxylases, the action of which can be measured in the ordinary respirometer with an accuracy of at least 1 part in 1000 (21). The use of these enzymes possesses a further advantage in identifying the respective isomers as L or D if the method of resolution had not already done so. Thus the resolution of an amino acid which does not occur in nature, and for which no standard of reference is available, may yield through the action of an optically specific resolving agent, such as renal acylase I, isomers which are identifiable thereby as L and as D (17; 22). If, however, such an amino acid is resolved by an unspecific agent, such as one of the alkaloids, the isomers may not be sterically identifiable. For this identification the oxidases may in certain instances be quite suitable, and Table 20-16 in Chapter 20 lists the relative susceptibility of the L- and D-isomers to these enzymes.

The technique employed for optical purity determinations as routinely carried out in this Laboratory is as follows (21): 1000 micromoles of the isomer to be tested is placed in each of four Warburg vessels, and to two of these flasks 1 micromole of the optical enantiomorph (in the form of an aliquot of a larger volume) is added. To these four flasks, as well as to two others which serve as enzyme blanks, 1.5–2.5 ml. buffer solution is added: these involve $0.1M$ sodium pyrophosphate at pH 8.1 with D-amino acid oxidase, $0.1M$ "tris" buffer at pH 7.2 with L-amino acid oxidase, and $0.1M$ acetate buffer at pH 4.9 (or see Chapter 20 for optimal pH of specific decarboxylase) with the decarboxylase preparations. For studies with the L-amino acid oxidase, 25 units of crystalline catalase are added to the main compartment of the vessels; there is usually enough catalase present in the crude D-amino acid oxidase preparation that none need be added (see Chapter 20). In the side arm of all six vessels, 0.3–0.4 ml. of the enzyme solutions are added. These aqueous solutions contain hog kidney D-amino acid oxidase, snake venom L-amino acid oxidase, or L-specific bacterial decarboxylase (Chapter 20) at near saturation levels. The flasks are tipped after a 10- to 15-minute equilibrium period and read at intervals until gas evolution or consumption is complete (15 to 120 minutes). Ten micromoles of an optically pure, completely susceptible amino acid consumes 112 μl. of oxygen gas or evolves 224 μl. of carbon dioxide gas, under standard conditions.

This method is obviously applicable only where 1 micromole of added susceptible isomer is readily and quantitatively oxidized or decarboxylated in the presence of the 1000-fold amount of the resistant enantiomorph. As a rule, a considerable amount of the enzyme is employed. The criteria of purity adopted demand (a) that the 1000 micromoles alone of the L-isomer tested with D-amino acid oxidase must consume less than 1 microatom of oxygen, but in the presence of the added 1 micromole of the D-isomer an increment amounting to 1 microatom of oxygen must be consumed, and (b) that the 1000 micromoles alone of the D-isomer tested with L-amino acid oxidase or decarboxylase must, respectively, consume less than 1 microatom of oxygen or evolve less than 1 micromole of carbon dioxide, but that, in the presence of the added 1 micromole of the L-isomer, an increment amounting to 1 microatom of oxygen must be consumed or 1 micromole of carbon dioxide evolved. The isomers which conform to these criteria may be described as possessing an optical purity greater than 99.9%. In the cases of L-alanine and L-serine, it is possible to test 10,000 micromoles of these isomers at a time, and to detect successfully by means of the hog kidney D-amino acid oxidase preparation 1 micromole of the added D-optical enantiomorph; samples of these isomers prepared as described below may be stated to possess an optical purity >99.99% (21). If the Warburg vessels are suitably designed, there is little reason to doubt that the purity determinations may be carried to still greater degrees of sensitivity, and possible enantiomorphic contaminations studied at levels of 0.01% or less. Table 19–2 lists the isomers for which the optical purity criteria are or are not applicable at the present time (17, 21, 23).

The isomers whose optical purity could not be tested by the enzymic procedures described are those whose enantiomorphs are not oxidized by the stated oxidases at the 1-micromole level. However, when these enantiomorphs are studied at higher levels, e.g., 10 micromoles, many of them are oxidized wholly or in part (6). These include the L-isomers of allothreonine, β-phenylserine, γ-aminobutyrine, decyline, undecyline, and dodecyline, which are susceptible to *Crotalus adamanteus* L-amino acid oxidase, as well as the D-isomers of aspartic acid, glutamic acid, histidine, ornithine, threonine, γ-aminobutyrine, decyline, and undecyline, which are susceptible to the action of hog kidney D-amino acid oxidase. At best, however, to use the 10 micromole concentration of substrate in the presence of the 1000 micromoles of isomer whose purity was to be tested would be to lower the criterion of purity of the latter to the 1% level. It is of course true that an increase in the amount of the tested isomer to 10,000 micromoles would, in the presence of 10 micromoles of the susceptible enantiomorph, restore the criterion of purity to the 0.1% level, and 10,000 micromoles of such quite soluble amino acids as L-alanine and L-serine have been employed for the purpose of ascertaining their optical purity at the 0.01% level (21). To use this amount of the less soluble amino acids would be hazardous, and would require the design of larger respirometers than those ordinarily employed. In any event, it is desirable to adhere to the criterion stated, that an amino acid isomer is not considered optically pure unless it contains less than 0.1% of its enantiomorph.

The search for oxidases from other sources, which might be more active toward isomerides ordinarily resistant to *Crotalus adamanteus* venom or hog kidney, would extend the application of the purity criterion to these substances. Thus *Crotalus terrificus* possesses an appreciable action

TABLE 19-2
Applicability of Criterion of >99.9% Optical Purity by the Use of Certain Oxidases and Decarboxylases (17, 21, 25)

| Amino Acid Isomers which Can Be Tested || Amino Acid Isomers which Cannot Be Tested ||
L-Isomer[a]	D-Isomer[b]	L-Isomer[a]	D-Isomer[b]
Alanine	Alanine[c]	α-Aminoadipic acid	β-Aminoalanine
β-Aminoalanine	α-Aminoadipic acid	γ-Aminobutyrine	γ-Aminobutyrine
S-Benzylcysteine	Arginine[d]	Aspartic acid	Decyline
S-Benzylhomocysteine	Aspartic acid[e]	Decyline	Dodecyline
Butyrine	S-Benzylcysteine	Dodecyline	Hydroxyproline
Capryline	S-Benzylhomocysteine	Glutamic acid	Allohydroxyproline
β-Cyclohexylalanine	Butyrine	Histidine	Isovaline
α-Cyclohexylglycine	Capryline	Isovaline	tert-Leucine
Cystine	β-Cyclohexylalanine	tert-Leucine	β-Phenylserine
Ethionine	α-Cyclohexylglycine	Lysine	Proline
Heptyline	Cystine	Ornithine	Serine
Homoserine	Ethionine	β-Phenylserine	Threonine
ε-Hydroxynorleucine	Glutamic acid[e]	Allo-β-phenylserine	Allothreonine
δ-Hydroxynorvaline	Heptyline	Threonine	Undecyline
Hydroxyproline	Histidine	Undecyline	
Allohydroxyproline	Homoserine		
Isoleucine	ε-Hydroxynorleucine		
Alloisoleucine	δ-Hydroxynorvaline		
Leucine	Isoleucine		
Methionine	Alloisoleucine		
Nonyline	Leucine		
Norleucine	Lysine[f]		
Norvaline	Methionine		
Phenylalanine	Nonyline		
α-Phenylglycine	Norleucine		
Proline	Norvaline		
Serine	Ornithine[g]		
Allothreonine	Phenylalanine		
Tryptophan	α-Phenylglycine		
Tyrosine	Allo-β-phenylserine		
Valine	Tryptophan		
	Tyrosine		
	Valine		

[a] Enzyme employed is hog kidney D-amino acid oxidase.
[b] Unless otherwise noted, the enzyme employed is *Crotalus adamanteus* L-amino acid oxidase.
[c] *Bothrops jararaca* L-amino acid oxidase is used.
[d] *E. coli* 7020 L-arginine decarboxylase is used.
[e] *C. welchii* SR 12 decarboxylase is used.
[f] *B. cadaveris* 6578 L-lysine decarboxylase is used.
[g] *C. septicum* P-III L-ornithine decarboxylase plus added pyridoxal phosphate is used.

toward L-threonine (24) and *Neurospora crassa* toward L-α-aminoadipic acid (25) and L-diaminopimelic acid (26); again, sheep kidney possesses a definite action toward D-histidine (25). These results, however, were obtained with substrate concentrations far above the 1-micromole level, and whether these oxidases would be effective at this level remains for future investigation.

When still higher substrate concentrations are employed, e.g., 50 micromoles, all other conditions remaining the same, the following rates of oxidation are obtained (6): L-isoleucine 117, L-alloisoleucine 14, L-threonine 0.2,

L-allothreonine 3.7, β-amino-L-alanine 0.5, and L-serine 0.5, in terms of micromoles of oxygen absorbed per hour per milligram of nitrogen. Thus in all cases the absolute magnitude of the oxidative rates is increased with increasing substrate concentration, and in the case of the isoleucine diastereomers the ratio of the oxidative rates of L-isoleucine to L-alloisoleucine, instead of being about 90 : 1 with 10 micromoles of each substrate is now about 8 : 1. When phosphate buffer is used in place of the tris-(hydroxymethyl)aminomethane buffer at pH 7.2, the following rates with 50 micromoles each of the amino acids are obtained: L-isoleucine 46 and L-alloisoleucine 14. In the presence of phosphate as contrasted with the tris buffer, a considerable inhibition in the oxidative rate of L-isoleucine is observed, whereas the oxidative rate of L-alloisoleucine is unchanged.

A lesser effect is noted on increasing the substrate concentrations to 50 micromoles in the presence of the D-amino acid oxidase preparation. Under these conditions, the oxidative rates are: D-isoleucine 13.5, D-alloisoleucine 8.7, D-α-aminoadipic acid 0.6, D-threonine 0.6, and D-allothreonine 4.5. Again, the rates for the diastereomers of isoleucine are closer in value at the higher substrate concentration, and a small but definite oxidative rate is noted with D-α-aminoadipic acid and D-threonine (6).

These data are not useful at the present time for optical purity determinations, but they are given to illustrate the capacities of the oxidases and potentialities for their possible future employment in these and similar studies.

Although the L- and D-isomers of the α,ω-diamino acids, with the exception of β-amino-D-alanine, are weakly susceptible to the action of the stated respective L- and D-amino acid oxidases, their ω-acyl derivatives are quite readily oxidized (27–29) (Chapter 20). To test the purity of the free amino acids it might only be necessary to convert them into the corresponding ω-acetyl derivatives by acetylating their copper chelates in alkaline solutions with acetic anhydride (cf. 30); removal of the copper with H_2S yields the free ω-acetyl amino acid, which can subsequently be tested with the appropriate oxidase according to the procedure cited. If the isolation of the ω-acetyl amino acid is accompanied by a fractionation of the optically active compound from any accompanying racemic contamination, the value of this procedure will naturally be diminished.

The amino acid oxidases are optically specific but, with rare exceptions, are not chemically specific. Thus they are used in the present instance to detect the presence of one or the other optical form in an amino acid, but it need not necessarily be the optical isomeride of that particular amino acid which is revealed by the test; it may be any susceptible amino acid contaminant of favorable optical configuration. If any doubt exists about the nature of the isomer studied, a paper chromatogram may be employed to identify the compound, and then a similar chromatogram, undeveloped with ninhydrin and freed of solvent, is sprayed with either a D-amino acid oxidase or an L-amino acid oxidase solution (cf. 31). After incubation for several hours the chromatogram is dried and sprayed with ninhydrin. A decrease in ninhydrin color indicates the optical nature of the isomer. On the other hand, the presence of a foreign and resistant isomeride would go undetected, while the presence of little more than traces of a foreign amino acid contaminant of the same optical configuration as that of the amino acid to be tested would likewise go undetected by these methods. All these possibilities of foreign or undetectable contaminants owe their origin to the use of impure starting materials for the resolution. Great care must therefore be taken to be certain of the chemical and steric purity of the starting materials before the resolution procedure is begun.

The optical purity of amino acids used as starting materials for peptide synthesis obviously constitutes an important factor in the optical homogeneity of the final products, and this problem has been considered in Chapter 10 (see Table 10–31) (32).

3. Criteria of Purity Suggested by the National Research Council. The Committee on Biological Chemistry of the Division of Chemistry and Chemical Technology, National Research Council, undertook a program of supplying to biochemists pertinent information concerning commercially available reagents used in biochemical research. Subcommittees consisting of academic and industrial representatives were established to cover the principal areas of biochemistry. Among these subcommittees was one on amino acids, of which the writers were members. The preface to the recommendations of the subcommittee on amino acids may be summarized in the following.

The subcommittee on amino acids has selected for consideration those amino acids which for the most part are readily available on the commercial market. Of these compounds some are racemic, and some are optically active and in the natural, L-form. Most of the latter compounds have been isolated from the hydrolysates of various proteins, the remainder by some form of resolution of the synthetic, racemic forms.

The manufacturers of amino acids have performed an outstanding service in furnishing materials to the biochemical field in volume and at relatively low cost. Each year sees a lowering of costs with consequent gain to the consumer. In general, the quality of the amino acids sold has been high, and for this the manufacturers deserve added credit. What constitutes an adequate standard of purity, however, is in the long run the responsibility of the purchaser, and in this responsibility he has a relatively easy task. Of all biochemicals on the market, the amino acids are probably the easiest to purify for they are, for the most part, readily and rapidly crystallizable either from water or from water-ethanol mixtures. For this reason, the subcommittee has described for each of the amino acids the appropriate solvent required. The general procedure is to bring the solvent to the boiling

DETERMINATION OF OPTICAL AND STERIC PURITY

temperature and to pour it over the solid amino acid in an extra-large Erlenmeyer flask. Enough of the hot solvent is added to bring most of the amino acid into solution. The mixture is then placed on the hot plate and brought to the boil. If the remainder of the solid does not go into solution, more of the hot solvent is added to the boiling mixture until practically all of the solid is dissolved. At this point, a solid charcoal preparation (Norit or Darco) is carefully added (if added too quickly frothing will occur) to about 1 gram of charcoal for every 100 grams of amino acid, and the mixture is boiled carefully for 2 to 5 minutes. At the end of this period of time, the mixture is filtered through *two* layers of filter paper (usually Whatman No. 4) in a hot water funnel. The hot filtrate is either allowed to chill directly (proline, tryptophan, etc.), or else is treated slowly and with careful stirring with a hot liquid reagent to some specified volume, such as hot ethanol (alanine, arginine, etc.) or hot dilute NH_4OH to neutrality (cystine) and then chilled. In all cases, the amino acid is obtained in crystalline form within a few hours, filtered off with suction, and washed successively with ethanol and ether, and dried. The recoveries are generally better than 80%. The recrystallization procedure as described should remove all traces of color from the commercial preparations (tryptophan may require two crystallizations to accomplish this purpose), and practically all traces of salts, heavy metals, proteins, more soluble compounds and adventitious impurities, and frequently, although not invariably, traces of the racemate from the corresponding optically active form. The more meticulous investigator might like to perform two or more recrystallizations of a given amino acid preparation before he is completely satisfied.

It might be asked whether the manufacturer goes through these or similar simple crystallization procedures. The answer is that he often does, but the consumer rarely if ever knows. The safest assumption for the consumer, therefore, is to accept the fact that most manufacturers are furnishing him with a conscientiously prepared product, which may not yet be of the highest purity. He may therefore (a) accept the product at face value and use it directly, (b) check it by the criteria described below and use it directly, or (c) purify it further by recrystallization and by other procedures, and check its properties, before using it. These are matters for the consumer to decide, on the basis of his own judgment of his needs and facilities.

Analytical and Identification Procedures

A. Melting Point

When heated to certain temperatures, the amino acids or their salts will in general decompose over a range of degrees, and hence this criterion has little value as a means either of identification or as a method of determining purity.

B. Loss of Weight on Drying

Only proline of the amino acids described is inclined to be hygroscopic, and this compound should be maintained in a dry atmosphere. Unless otherwise specified, the general procedure for determining volatile contaminants (normally water) is the following, described in section 29.6 ("Vacuum Drying—Official") of the *Official Methods of Analysis of the Association of Official Agricultural Chemists*, AOAC, 8th ed., Washington, D.C., 1955, p. 532. Dry 2–5 grams of a representative sample (powdered, if necessary), in a flat dish (Ni, Pt, or Al) with tight-fitting cover, 2 hours at not over 70°C. (preferably 60°C.), under reduced pressure (not exceeding 50 mm. of Hg). Remove the dish from the oven, cover, cool in a desiccator, and weigh. Redry 1 hour and repeat process until change in weight between successive dryings at 1-hour intervals is not more than 2 mg. Unless it is otherwise indicated, the pure amino acids should not lose more than 0.5% of their weight.

C. Elemental Analyses

These are performed by standard procedures. The tolerated limit for C is <1% relative, for N <3% relative, for ash <0.1% and for van Slyke manometric ninhydrin-CO_2 <2% relative.

D. Optical Rotation

The specific optical rotations are determined on samples previously dried to constant weight at 78° and 1 mm. pressure and dissolved in 1–2% solutions at 24–28°. The values are given from the relation: specific rotation = (observed rotation in degrees × 100)/(grams of amino acid per 100 ml. of solution × length of the polarimeter tube in decimeters). The D-line of sodium is used. Readings should be taken in a darkened room, preferably by two or more individuals. The method is not of the highest accuracy, and the results are simply those agreed upon by the majority of observers. There can well be an allowance of ±2% in such readings.

E. Paper Chromatography

Solvents (see table on facing page)
1. 88% phenol: H_2O = 100 : 20 v/v. Add 15 mg. per cent of 8-hydroxyquinoline. Run in the presence of 100 ml. of $2N$ NH_4OH.
2. 1-Butanol: acetic acid: H_2O = 450 : 50 : 125 v/v.
3a. 2-Butanol: 3.3% aq. NH_3 = 150 : 60 v/v; 3.3% aq. NH_3 is prepared by diluting 65 ml. of $14.8N$ NH_4OH to 500 ml. with H_2O.
3b. 2-Butanol: 3% aq. NH_3 = 150 : 50 v/v (1 : 6 aq. NH_4OH atmosphere).
A. Solvent 1 followed by solvent 2.
B. Solvent 1 followed by solvent 3.
C. Solvent 2 followed by solvent 3.

Color Reagents

Ninhydrin: 0.25% in acetone.
Isatin: 0.40% in acetone.

Specific Reagents

Sakaguchi. α-Naphthol:hypobromite reagent. Dissolve 0.01% α-naphthol in ethanol containing 5% urea. Add KOH to 5% just before spraying. Air-dry a few minutes, and spray lightly with 0.8 ml. of Br_2 in 100 ml. of 5% KOH.

Nitroprusside. Reagent 1: Sodium nitroprusside (1.5 g.) is dissolved in 5 ml. of $2N$ H_2SO_4. Then 95 ml. of methanol and 10 ml. of 28% ammonia are added. The solution is filtered and stored in the refrigerator. Reagent 2: Two grams of NaCN is dissolved in 5 ml. of water and diluted to 100 ml. with methanol. These solutions are always freshly prepared.

PAPER CHROMATOGRAPHY

(cf. Block, R. J., Durrum, E. L., and Zweig, G., *A Manual of Paper Chromatography and Paper Electrophoresis*, Academic Press, New York, 1955)

Amino Acid	Solvents 1 Dimen.	Solvents 2 Dimen.	Color Reagents	Specific Reagents
Alanine	2	A and B	Ninhydrin	
Arginine	2	A and B	Ninhydrin	Sakaguchi (red color)
Aspartic acid	1	A and B	Ninhydrin	
Asparagine		A and B		
Cysteine	2		Ninhydrin	Nitroprusside (red color)
Cystine	2		Ninhydrin	Nitroprusside + NaCN (red color)
Diiodotyrosine	3	C	Ninhydrin	$Ce(HSO_4)_4$ + $NaAsO_2$
Glutamic acid	1	A and B	Ninhydrin	
Glutamine		A and B	Ninhydrin	
Glycine	1	A and B	Ninhydrin	
Histidine	2	A and B	Ninhydrin	Pauly (red color)
Hydroxyproline	2	A and B	Ninhydrin and Isatin	Isatin and Ehrlich
Hydroxylysine	2	A and B		HIO_4 + Nessler
Isoleucine	3	B	Ninhydrin	
Leucine	3	B	Ninhydrin	
Lysine	2	A and B	Ninhydrin	
Methionine	2	A and B	Ninhydrin	Platinic iodide
Monoiodotyrosine	3	C	Ninhydrin	$Ce(HSO_4)_4$ + $NaAsO_2$
Phenylalanine	2		Ninhydrin	
Proline	2		Ninhydrin and Isatin	
Serine	1	A and B	Ninhydrin	Nessler and HIO_4
Threonine	1	A and B	Ninhydrin	Nessler and HIO_4
Thyroxine	3	C	Ninhydrin	$Ce(HSO_4)_4$ + $NaAsO_2$
Triiodothyronine	3	C	Ninhydrin	$Ce(HSO_4)_4$ + $NaAsO_2$
Tryptophan	3	A and B	Ninhydrin	Ehrlich
Tyrosine	2	A and B	Ninhydrin	Pauly (orange color)
Valine	3	A and B	Ninhydrin	

Pauly. 1% sulfanilamide in 10% v/v HCl; 5% $NaNO_2$; half-saturated Na_2CO_3. Place 5 ml. of sulfanilamide and 5 ml. of $NaNO_2$ in a 100-ml. separatory funnel. Shake for 1 min. Then add 50 ml. of *n*-butanol. Shake for 1 min. and let stand for 4 min. Decant the butanol layer, and spray or dip the chromatogram. Dry the sheet in a current of air and then dip into Na_2CO_3 solution. Imidazoles give a deep cherry-red color.

Ehrlich. Prepare fresh a mixture of 1 g. of *p*-dimethylaminobenzaldehyde, 90 ml. of acetone, and 10 ml. of concentrated HCl.

Platinic iodide. Add in the following order 4 ml. of $0.002M$ $PtCl_6^{2-}$, 0.25 ml. of N KI, 0.4 ml. of $2N$ HCl, and 76 ml. of acetone. The dried chromatograms are dipped into this reagent. Cystine, cysteine, methionine, and some other reducing substances give a white spot on a red-purple background.

Nessler. The paper is sprayed with Nessler's reagent almost saturated with $NaIO_4$. Serine and threonine liberate ammonia and thus give yellow spots.

Ceric sulfate. Sodium arsenite. (See directions for Iodo Compounds below.)

Isatin. Spray with 0.40% isatin in acetone; after drying in air, the chromatogram is heated for 10 min. in an H_2O-saturated oven at 70–76°C. Proline and hydroxyproline give blue colors; cystine and tyrosine often also give blue colors. Glutamic and aspartic acids give pink spots which turn blue on standing. The other amino acids give pink spots which fade. Pipecolic acid (piperidine-2-carboxylic acid) also gives a blue color with isatin.

Qualitative Detection of Iodo Compounds on Paper Chromatograms

Reagents
A. 10% ceric sulfate $(Ce(HSO_4)_4)$ w/v in 10% H_2SO_4 v/v.
B. 5% sodium arsenite $(NaAsO_2)$ w/v.
C. 0.05% methylene blue.
D. Ammonia (sp. gr. 0.90).

Procedure: After development of the chromatogram in its appropriate solvent, the papers are dried thoroughly in an atmosphere free of phenol. The paper is then sprayed lightly on both sides with a mixture of Reagents A and B in the proportions of 2 and 3 parts respectively. (*Note:* use reagent immediately after mixing.) The paper is dried in an air stream (fan) for 5 min. It is then sprayed lightly with Reagent C, dried for 5 min., and then subjected to NH_3 vapors in an aquarium. The completion of the neutralization can be detected by a change in the background color from pale purple to bright yellow. The chromatogram is again dried.

Results: The iodo compounds appear as bright blue spots against a yellow background. The minimum amount detectable is in the order of 0.1 to 0.2 μg. of iodine.

F. Infrared Spectroscopy

Infrared spectra can be used for the identification of amino acids and are also useful in specific cases for the determination of small amounts of impurities that are difficult to detect by paper chromatography. Examples (with the appropriate absorption bands of the impurity) are DL-leucine (11.78μ) in L-isoleucine with D-alloisoleucine, L-isoleucine with D-alloisoleucine (12.48μ) in DL-leucine, and DL-allothreonine (9.95μ or 11.99μ) in DL-threonine. Minimum detectable amounts are about 0.5% in the leucine-isoleucine pairs and about 2% in the allothreonine in threonine.

G. Ultraviolet Absorption (Tyrosine and Tryptophan)

These acids possess characteristic absorption maxima in the ultraviolet region. The molecular extinction coefficients for tyrosine in acid are 1340 at 274.5 mμ and 8200 at 223.0 mμ, both of which are maxima, and 170 at 245.0 mμ, which represents a minimum in the curve for this region; the corresponding values in alkaline solution are 2330 at 293.5 mμ and 11,050 at 240.0 mμ for the maxima and 1000 at 269.5 for the minimum. For tryptophan in either acid or alkaline solution, the maxima are 4550 and 5550 at 287.5 mμ and 278.0 mμ, respectively, and the minimum 1930 at 242.0 mμ.

H. D-Amino Acid Oxidase

Most of the amino acids isolated from proteins can be obtained in the pure L-form. L-Cystine, however, is a notable exception, for it is often not only contaminated by L-tyrosine (removable by the charcoal treatment in the recrystallization procedures), but also by D- and *meso*-cystine as a result of some racemization by the boiling HCl used in the hydrolysis of the original protein. Experience in several laboratories has shown commercially available L-cystine to possess anywhere between 5 and 15% D-cystine. The presence of the D-isomer in samples not only of L-cystine, but also of the L-isomers of hydroxyproline, proline, leucine, phenylalanine, tyrosine, and tryptophan, can be determined by the use of D-amino acid oxidase. The technique employed is described in Section 19–2.

I. Recrystallization of Amino Acids (in the main from Dunn, M. S., and Rockland, L. B., *Advances in Protein Chem.*, 3, 296 (1947))

Amino Acid	Solvent 1	Ml./g. Amino Acid		Solvent 2	Ml./g. Amino Acid	Wash Fluid
DL-Alanine	Water	3.0	95% ethanol	6.0	95% ethanol
L-Arginine·HCl	0.4N HCl	0.5	95% ethanol	1.0	80–95% ethanol
DL-Aspartic acid	Water	9.5	95% ethanol	20.0	Ice water
L-Asparagine·H$_2$O	Water				95% ethanol
L-Cysteine	H$_2$S-water				95% ethanol
L-Cystine	1.5N HCl	18.0	0.6N NH$_4$OH to pH 5		Hot water
L-Diiodotyrosine	Water				95% ethanol
L-Glutamic acid	Water (80°)	12.0			50–100% methanol
Glycine	Water	2.3	95% ethanol	1.0	35–95% ethanol
L-Histidine·HCl·H$_2$O	0.2N HCl	1.0			75–95% ethanol
L-Hydroxyproline	50% methanol 50% ethanol	3.1			Methanol
L-Isoleucine + D-alloisoleucine	Water				95% ethanol
L-Leucine	Water	24.0	95% ethanol	24.0	50–95% ethanol
DL-Leucine	Water	30.0			25–100% methanol
L-Lysine·HCl	Water	1.0	95% ethanol	4.0	60–95% ethanol
DL-Methionine	Water	9.0	95% ethanol	9.0	50–95% ethanol
L-Phenylalanine	Water				95% ethanol
DL-Phenylalanine	Water	23.0	95% ethanol	15.0	95% ethanol
L-Proline	Abs. ethanol	15.0			Abs. ethanol
DL-Serine	Water	13.0	95% ethanol	4.5	30–95% ethanol
DL-Threonine	Water	2.5	95% ethanol	20.0	95% ethanol
L-Tryptophan	65% ethanol	42.0			95% ethanol
L-Tyrosine	Water	200.0			Ice water
DL-Tyrosine	Water	220.0			Ice water
DL-Valine	Water	7.0	95% ethanol	7.0	50–95% ethanol

4. A Brief Recapitulation. In many instances of biological investigation, the use of racemic amino acids has led to ambiguous interpretations of the results. This has been emphasized in several places in Chapter 3 and need not be repeated here. The use of racemic amino acids for the synthesis of peptides, leading to epimeric mixtures of unknown composition, has been deplored in many quarters, and has been discussed at some length in Section 10-7. The more careful investigator has at this time carefully avoided the employment of the racemic amino acids except for such studies in which the optical configuration of the amino acids plays no role whatever. For most studies in the biological and synthetic organic chemical fields, therefore, there is now an increasing emphasis on the use of optically active amino acids. Here, however, is where the problem of optical purity enters. Thus, in the synthesis of peptides by the use of optically active amino acids, the optical purity of the peptide obtained may well be a reflection of the optical purity of the starting amino acids; if recrystallization toward the impurity rather than away from it occurs, the proportion of the unwanted antipodes in the original amino acids becomes even greater in the final synthetic peptide. This subject has been discussed in Section 10-25; cf. Table 10-31. The problem of determining the growth-promoting capacities in living organisms of ostensibly D-amino acids when these compounds contain appreciable amounts of the much more effective L-isomers has long been familiar (Chapter 3).

The question that ultimately emerges is: how pure is pure? A pragmatic answer might be: a state in which any possible impurity present does not interfere with the reaction, chemical or biological, under investigation. Lack of interference cannot, however, always be predicted, and the very knowledge that interference is present cannot be definitely known unless material of the highest possible purity is examined side by side with that of lesser purity; therefore, if clean material must necessarily be run as a control, it might as well be employed in the first place. For many investigations, the presence of less than 1% of the D-isomer in a preparation of an L-amino acid is considered quite harmless. However, when a 2-gram sample of L-phenylalanine containing as little as 0.6% of the D-antipode was given to human subjects, more than half of the phenylalanine excreted in the urine during the following hour was D in configuration (33); essentially similar results were obtained when 5 to 10 gram samples of L-phenylalanine containing about 0.1% of the D-form were administered. Little ambiguity arose in these studies because the concentration of urinary phenylalanine determined by means of paper chromatography was checked by the subsequent use of the exclusively L-directed phenylalanine decarboxylase (33); the sole employment of the optically indifferent chromatographic technique would obviously have led to results much too high if the presence of the relatively small amount of D-phenylalanine in the sample of L-phenylalanine originally administered had been considered too negligible to merit any concern. The highly optically specific concentrating mechanisms of the kidney, in this instance, provided an interesting answer to the question in the first sentence of this paragraph.

REFERENCES

1. Fischer, E., *Ber.*, **33**, 3638 (1900).
2. Hegsted, D. M., and Wardwell, E. D., *J. Biol. Chem.*, **153**, 167 (1944).
3. Greenstein, J. P., Levintow, L., Baker, C. G., and White, J., *J. Biol. Chem.*, **188**, 647 (1951).
4. Piez, K. A., *J. Biol. Chem.*, **207**, 77 (1954).
5. Shulgin, A. T., Lien, O. G., Gal, E. M., and Greenberg, D. M., *J. Am. Chem. Soc.*, **74**, 2427 (1952).
6. Greenstein, J. P., Birnbaum, S. M., and Otey, M. C., *J. Biol. Chem.*, **204**, 307 (1953).
7. Fones, W. S., *Arch. Biochem. Biophys.*, **36**, 486 (1952).
8. Greenstein, J. P., Izumiya, N., Winitz, M., and Birnbaum, S. M., *J. Am. Chem. Soc.*, **77**, 707 (1955).
9. Hegsted, D. M., *J. Biol. Chem.*, **157**, 741 (1945).
10. Hood, D. W., and Lyman, C. M., *J. Biol. Chem.*, **186**, 195 (1950).
11. Meister, A., *J. Biol. Chem.*, **195**, 813 (1952).
12. Meister, A., *J. Biol. Chem.*, **190**, 269 (1951).
13. Moore, S., and Stein, W. H., *J. Biol. Chem.*, **211**, 893, 907 (1954).
14. Rhuland, L. E., Work, E., Denman, R. F., and Hoare, D. S., *J. Am. Chem. Soc.*, **77**, 4844 (1955).
15. Weichert, R., *Acta Chem. Scand.*, **9**, 547 (1955).
16. Dalgliesh, C. E., *J. Chem. Soc.*, **1952**, 3940.
17. Birnbaum, S. M., Levintow, L., Kingsley, R. B., and Greenstein, J. P., *J. Biol. Chem.*, **194**, 455 (1952).
18. Van Slyke, D. D., Dillon, R. T., MacFadyen, D. A., and Hamilton, P., *J. Biol. Chem.*, **141**, 627 (1941).
19. Dunn, M. S., and Rockland, L. B., *Advances in Protein Chem.*, **3**, 296 (1947).
20. Zeller, E. A., *Advances in Enzymol.*, **8**, 459 (1948).
21. Meister, A., Levintow, L., Kingsley, R. B., and Greenstein, J. P., *J. Biol. Chem.*, **192**, 535 (1951).
22. Birnbaum, S. M., Fu, S.-C. J., and Greenstein, J. P., *J. Biol. Chem.*, **203**, 333 (1953).
23. Birnbaum, S. M., and Greenstein, J. P., *Arch. Biochem. Biophys.*, **39**, 108 (1952).
24. Winitz, M., Bloch-Frankenthal, L., Izumiya, N., Birnbaum, S. M., Baker, C. G., and Greenstein, J. P., *J. Am. Chem. Soc.*, **78**, 2423 (1956).
25. Bender, A. E., and Krebs, H. A., *Biochem. J.*, **46**, 210 (1950).
26. Work, E., *Biochim. Biophys. Acta*, **17**, 410 (1955).
27. Neuberger, A., and Sanger, F., *Biochem. J.*, **38**, 119 (1944).
28. Zeller, E. A., and Maritz, A., *Helv. Chim. Acta*, **28**, 365 (1945).
29. Fu, S.-C. J., Rao, K. R., Birnbaum, S. M., and Greenstein, J. P., *J. Biol. Chem.*, **199**, 267 (1952).
30. Neuberger, A., and Sanger, F., *Biochem. J.*, **37**, 515 (1943).
31. Synge, R. L. M., *Biochem. J.*, **44**, 542 (1949).
32. Greenstein, J. P., *Advances in Protein Chem.*, **9**, 121 (1954).
33. Gartler, S. M., and Tashian, R. E., *Science*, **126**, 75 (1957).

PART V

Enzymes in Amino Acid Technology

chapter 20

Enzymes Involved in the Determination, Characterization, and Preparation of the Amino Acids

1. Introduction. Included in this chapter are those enzymes which have been applied to practical problems associated with the optical resolution of the α-amino acids and their derivatives, to the subsequent determination of the optical purity of the isomers so obtained, and to the determination of specific amino acids, together with such characteristics of these enzymes as may illuminate, and assist in the solution of, the practical problems mentioned. The background for these approaches is described in Chapters 2, 9, 10, and 19. The enzymes listed and their uses are as follows:

Renal acylase I—acts on α-N-acylated L-amino acids with aliphatic side chains, hydrolyzing the N-acyl binding—used for the resolution of DL-amino acids.

Renal acylase II—acts on N-acylated L-aspartic acid, hydrolyzing the N-acyl binding—used for the resolution of DL-aspartic acid.

Pancreatic carboxypeptidase—acts on N-chloroacetylated L-amino acids with a β-aromatic group on the side chain, hydrolyzing the N-chloroacetyl binding—used for the resolution of DL-tyrosine and DL-tryptophan, and for the determination of the C-terminal amino acid residue in polypeptide chains (Chapter 16).

Renal D-amino acid oxidase—oxidizes only D-amino acids—used for the determination of the optical purity of L-amino acid preparations, and for the preparation of L-amino acids from the racemate.

Snake venom L-amino acid oxidase—oxidizes only L-amino acids—used for the determination of the optical purity of D-amino acid preparations, and for the preparation of D-amino acids from the racemate.

Bacterial decarboxylases specific for L-lysine, L-glutamic acid, L-aspartic acid, L-tyrosine, L-histidine, L-ornithine, and L-arginine—used for the specific determination of these amino acids through measurement of the carbon dioxide evolved, for the determination of the optical purity of their D-antipodes, and for the preparation of the D-isomers from the racemate.

Hepatic arginase—specific for L-arginine, used to prepare L-ornithine therefrom, to prepare D-arginine from the racemate, and to test for the presence of L-arginine in mixtures.

Renal aminopeptidase (solubilized particulates)—used for the determination of the optical purity of the amino acid residues in peptides, prior to the subsequent employment of either L- or D-amino acid oxidase (Section 10-49).

2. Mammalian Tissue Acylases. In 1881, Schmiedeberg (1) observed the presence of a catalytic function in aqueous extracts of kidney which possessed the capacity of hydrolyzing hippuric acid into benzoic acid and glycine. He stated at the time "Es konnte dann leicht festgestellt werden, dass diese Spaltung nicht von einer vitalen Funktion des unverändterten Gewebes, sondern von einer nach Art der ungeformten Fermente oder Enzyme wirkenden Substanz abhängig ist . . .," and he continued with perhaps some understandable enthusiasm " . . . welche bei den Stoffwechselvorgängen in den Geweben eine grosse Rolle zu spielen scheint und deshalb den Namen Histozym erhalten mag."[51] That homologs of hippuric acid could also be enzymically hydrolyzed by extracts of a number of tissues was subsequently shown by Smorodinzev (2), who made as well the important observation that, although benzoyl-L-butyrine was appreciably hydrolyzed by extracts of muscle, benzoyl-D-butyrine was unaffected. A further observation by this author indicated that N-benzoylated β-amino acids were not attacked by this enzyme, which suggested that the action of the enzyme was directed exclusively toward N-substituted α-amino acids. That the enzyme would hydrolyze other N-acylated α-amino acids, such as acetylglycine, was shown by Nawa (3) and Mori (4; cf. 5 and 6). The enzyme has been given several designations, such as the restricted one of hippuricase, without reference to the homogeneity of the tissue fraction involved. The designation "acylase" (cf. 2), as referring to the catalytic activity of a tissue fraction concerned with the hydrolysis of N-acylated α-amino acids, appears to be more suitable. Such designation would apparently include the enzyme associated with pancreatic tissue, which also hydrolyzes N-acylated α-amino acids, and which has long been known under the name of carboxypeptidase. The distinction between "acylase" and "carboxypeptidase" has been chiefly drawn on the basis that the preferred substrate for the former enzyme is an

N-acylated α-amino acid with an aliphatic side chain, in contrast with the preferred substrate for the latter enzyme, which is an N-acylated α-amino acid with an aromatic group on the side chain. Other distinctions between the two categories of enzymes are described below.

3. Preparation and Properties of Renal Acylase I (7).

Two and one half kilograms of fresh-frozen hog kidney is thawed, defatted, and homogenized in the Waring Blendor with 2 volumes of ice water. Fibrous material is removed by straining through cheese-cloth, and the homogenate is centrifuged for 20 min. at 1600 × g to remove cellular débris. The specific activity of the supernatant suspension when tested against acetyl-L-methionine as substrate is about 800 micromoles of the substrate hydrolyzed per hour per milligram of total nitrogen, and the total activity is equal to 18 moles per hour. The homogenate is then chilled to 0° in an ice bath and the pH adjusted to 4.7–5.0 by the addition of a predetermined amount of $2N$ HCl. The resulting thick suspension must be *immediately* centrifuged at 0° and at about 2700 × g for a period of 20 min. The clear red supernatant is decanted and is quickly adjusted to a pH of about 6.5 by the addition of a predetermined volume of $2N$ NaOH. The specific activity at this stage is about 2300 micromoles substrate hydrolyzed per hour per mg. N and the total activity about 15 moles per hour. This supernatant is treated with 266 g. of solid ammonium sulfate per liter and, if necessary, the pH is adjusted to 6.0–6.2. The resulting precipitate which contains most of the acylase I activity can be separated either in the Sharples supercentrifuge or in the International or Spinco refrigerated centrifuge. When the latter instruments are employed it is convenient to allow the precipitate to settle overnight in the cold room, and to siphon or decant off as much of the supernatant as possible before centrifuging. The clear red supernatant fraction obtained at this point is suitable for the preparation of acylase II (see below).

The dark precipitate is suspended in about 40 ml. of ice water, dialyzed overnight against running tap water for complete removal of ammonium ions, and the heavy precipitate which forms during the dialysis is centrifuged off and discarded. Most of the acylase I remains in the clear, almost black, supernatant fluid, the specific activity of which averages around 12,000 micromoles substrate hydrolyzed per hour per mg. N, with a total activity of 11 moles per hour. *This solution can be lyophilized to yield the preparation referred to as "crude acylase," which has been employed to advantage in the resolution of racemic acetylcystine (Section 24), for it is more stable than acylase I in the presence of this substrate* (8). The activity of this "crude" preparation is roughly one-half that of acylase I.

For many purposes, however, where color and excess protein might be disadvantageous, the material is further fractionated by means of acetone. The dark-colored solution is diluted to 200 ml. with distilled water and is adjusted to pH 5.9–6.0 with dilute acetic acid. Chilled acetone (0.4 volume) is slowly added while the mixture is maintained at a temperature just above freezing in an alcohol bath at −10° to −15°. The resulting precipitate is centrifuged off at −8° in the refrigerated centrifuge and discarded, and the clear straw-colored supernatant is again returned to the cold bath and treated as before with 0.6 volume of distilled acetone (based upon the volume of the original aqueous solution). After centrifugation at $-8°$, the active precipitate is dissolved in a small amount of ice water, if necessary any insoluble material is removed by centrifuging, and the light pink-colored supernatant is quick-frozen and lyophilized. The final product should weigh about 2 g. with a nitrogen content of 16%; its specific activity is about 20,000–30,000 micromoles acetyl-L-methionine hydrolyzed per hour per mg. N with a total activity of 9 moles per hour or about 50% of that of the original extract. The increase in specific activity over that of the crude homogenate is therefore 20- to 40-fold. This increase is very nearly the same for most susceptible N-acylated amino acids tested.

Table 20–1 indicates the extent of purification of the enzyme over the homogenate (9). The 20 to 40-fold concentration of specific activity (column 4 of the table) is applicable to all the chloroacetyl derivatives except those of aspartic acid, tyrosine, and tryptophan, which may be hydrolyzed by enzymes in the homogenate other than acylase I. The comparable glycyl derivatives of the L-amino acids are hydrolyzed by acylase I at generally lower rates (column 6).

That the maximum acylase activity is found in kidney follows from the data given in Table 20–2. Approximately similar ratios (column 5) for the two substrates suggest the similar nature of the activity of the enzyme in the various tissues studied, whilst the atypical value for the tumor in column 6 suggests a different distribution from normal of acylase I and acylase II activity in this neoplastic tissue.

ASSAY OF ACYLASE I. The method of choice for the determination of acylase I activity involves the use of the very susceptible substrate N-acetyl-L-methionine, and the detection of the liberated amino acid by means of the ninhydrin-CO_2 analytical procedure of Van Slyke (Chapter 12). Two tubes, each containing 1 ml. of $0.1M$ phosphate buffer at pH 7.0 and 1 ml. of suitably diluted enzyme solution in $0.01M$ buffer, are warmed to 37°. To one tube, 1 ml. of neutralized $0.025M$ acetyl-L-methionine is added. Both tubes are incubated for a measured period of time at the expiration of which 3 ml. of saturated picric acid solution is added to each. One milliliter of substrate solution is then added to the control mixture, and suitable aliquots are taken from each for ninhydrin-CO_2 analysis. Where the possibility of crystallization of the liberated amino acid exists, one half the amounts of the above reagents can be added to and incubated directly in the ninhydrin-CO_2 reaction vessels. The hydrolytic action catalyzed by acylase I follows zero-order kinetics up to at least 40% cleavage of the total available L-substrate under these conditions. Thus, from any point obtained below 40% hydrolysis, the number of micromoles of substrate hydrolyzed per hour per milligram of enzyme N may be designated as the initial reaction rate. The substrate itself, and in fact all similar N-acylamino acids studied, experience no detectable non-enzymic hydrolysis under the conditions described.

pH-ACTIVITY OPTIMUM. The pH at which acylase I acts most rapidly is within the range 7.0 to 7.5 (9). This pH range is readily maintained with

TABLE 20-1 (9)
Initial Hydrolytic Rates with Hog Kidney Preparations[a]

L-Amino Acid	Rates of Chloroacetyl Derivatives with			Rates of Glycyl Derivatives with			Chloroacetyl:Glycyl with Acylase I
	Homogenate	Acylase I	Acylase I:Homogenate	Homogenate	Acylase I	Acylase I:Homogenate	
1	2	3	4	5	6	7	8
Alanine	440	14,800	34	1,090	645	0.6	23
α-Aminobutyric acid	975	33,600	34	2,380	2,960	1.2	12
Valine	140	4,970	35	2,720	380	0.1	13
Norvaline	1,200	40,500	33	2,850	6,930	2.4	6
Leucine	630	16,500	27	2,690	1,040	0.4	16
Isoleucine	36	1,010	28	2,630	132	0.05	8
Alloisoleucine	29	950	33	2,740	88	0.03	11
Norleucine	830	30,400	36	3,340	5,600	1.7	6
Methionine	2,600	88,000	34	3,180	15,000	4.7	6
Serine	455	11,600	26	620	505	0.8	23
Threonine	38	720	19	1,370	91	0.07	8
Aspartic acid	32	4	0.1	45	4	0.1	1
Asparagine	8	129	16	1,120	54	0.05	3
Glutamic acid	480	12,700	27	310	490	1.6	26
Phenylalanine	30	460	15	2,180	106	0.05	4
Tyrosine	10	33	3	450	48	0.1	0.7
Tryptophan	3	12	4	1,530	122	0.08	0.1
Glycine[b]	54	2,640	48	110	88	0.8	30

[a] In terms of micromoles of substrate hydrolyzed at 38° per hr. per mg. of protein N. All studies conducted in phosphate buffer at pH 7.0 and final concentration of 0.03M.
[b] Obviously not an L-amino acid, but included because of its natural occurrence.

TABLE 20-2

Rates of Hydrolysis of Acylamino Acids by Rat Tissues
(Data by Dr. Robin Marshall)

	Rate of Hydrolysis[a]			Ratios of Rates of Hydrolysis	
Tissue Homogenate	Acetyl-L-methionine	Acetyl-L-alanine	Acetyl-L-aspartic Acid	Acetyl-L-methionine: Acetyl-L-alanine	Acetyl-L-methionine: Acetyl-L-aspartic Acid
1	2	3	4	5	6
Kidney	44	17	1.2	2.6	36
Liver	5.4	3.4	0.2	1.6	33
Brain	4.8	1.8	0.2	2.8	24
Heart	1.2	0.6	v.s.[b]	–	–
Lungs	1.2	0.6	v.s.[b]	–	–
Muscle	0.6	0.2	0[c]	–	–
Spleen	0[c]	0[c]	0[c]	–	–
Pancreas	0[c]	0[c]	0[c]	–	–
Walker tumor 256	2.4	1.5	0.3	1.6	8

[a] Rates in terms of micromoles of substrate hydrolyzed per hour per milligram of protein nitrogen at 37°.
[b] Very small—some hydrolysis but too small to measure accurately.
[c] No hydrolysis in 3 hrs. with protein nitrogen concentrations of 1–5 mg. per ml. Digests consisted of 1 ml. of $0.1M$ phosphate buffer at pH 7, 1 ml. of homogenate, and 1 ml. of $0.05M$ neutralized substrate solution.

phosphate buffers, although the neutralized N-acylated amino acid (with dilute NaOH) in the absence of any added buffer salt is hydrolyzed at nearly the same rate as in the presence of the buffer. The hydrolytic reaction in unbuffered solutions is accompanied by a change in pH of no more than a few tenths of a unit, except where such substrates as α,β-dichloroacetyl-β-aminoalanine (Chapter 44) and chloroacetylserine (Chapter 36) tend at pH 7 or higher to split off part of the chlorine of the chloroacetyl moiety as HCl, thereby lowering the pH appreciably, and ultimately bringing the reaction to a halt.

STABILITY OF ACYLASE I. A sample of lyophilized acylase I may be placed in a tightly stoppered dry test tube and heated for 48 hours at 37°, and at the end of this period its activity against acetyl-L-methionine will be found to have not perceptibly changed. In routine storage at 5° the dry enzyme is apparently stable for months. In phosphate buffer solution at pH 7 this activity remains unchanged after heating for 1 hour at 60° (7); the enzyme treated in this way, however, loses its stability after dialysis and lyophilization. In solution at pH values of 5.0 or below, the enzyme is rapidly and irreversibly denatured (Table 20-3), the proportionate loss in activity toward chloroacetylalanine and toward glycylalanine being the same (8). Acylase I in concentrated solution (10 mg. N per ml.) is little affected by overnight dialysis against distilled or tap water or 0.005M

TABLE 20-3

Acid Denaturation of Acylase I[a] (8)

Period of Incubation at pH 4.7, min.	Rates of Hydrolysis[b] of Chloroacetyl -L-alanine	Glycyl-L-alanine	Ratio, Chloroacetyl / Glycyl
0	13,500	525	26
20	8,270	282	29
40	6,350	228	28
60	4,970	159	31

[a] Acylase I dissolved in acetate buffer at pH 4.7 to 1 mg. of N per ml. and maintained at 37°; 1 ml. is removed at the times indicated and added to 9 ml. of phosphate buffer at pH 7.0. The activity of this enzyme solution is then measured against the substrates designated.

[b] The rate of hydrolysis is in micromoles of substrate hydrolyzed at 38° per hour per mg. of protein N.

NaCl. In dilute solution (1 mg. N per ml.), however, as noted by Dr. Robin Marshall, a loss in activity of some 80% of the original is thereby incurred.

SPECTROPHOTOMETRY. At 238 mμ the absorption by acetylmethionine is appreciably greater than that of methionine (cf. Section 17–1), a phenomenon based on the properties of the —CONH— bond in the low wavelength region of the ultraviolet. This difference between amino acid and acetylamino acid was exploited by Mitz and Schlueter (9a) as the basis of a method of differential spectrophotometry for following the hydrolytic action of acylase I. Thus, a solution of L-methionine was placed in one of two matching cuvettes, and a solution containing an equivalent concentration of acetyl-L-methionine in the other. The decrease in optical density per unit time following the addition of the appropriate amount of a solution of acylase I to the solution containing the acetyl-L-methionine, as related to the molar extinction coefficient of acetyl-L-methionine at the same wavelength, gave up to 40% hydrolysis of the substrate a measure via zero-order kinetics of the activity of the enzyme.

PRESENCE OF OTHER ENZYMES. Kidney tissue contains a large number of enzyme systems, and it would not be unexpected that the active acylase fraction might contain as inadvertent contaminants traces or more of several of these systems. Although the acylase I preparation described above is substantially free of histidase and arginase activity, thus allowing the preparation of the L-isomers of histidine and of arginine in good yield (10), there appears to be appreciable D-amino acid oxidase activity present. One such preparation of acylase I (7) oxidized D-methionine at a rate of 4 micromoles per hour per mg. N. Such contamination, although it could conceivably complicate the calculation of rates of hydrolysis of susceptible acyl-D-amino acids, can exert only a beneficial influence, if any, on the course of a resolution by tending to oxidize any susceptible D-amino acid produced. The absence of chemically undetectable amounts of enzymic cofactors such as biotin, the flavins, etc., from a relatively crude protein preparation cannot, of course, be taken for granted. Contamination of the resolution products with these materials can, however, be usually avoided by careful recrystallization of the amino acids in the presence of appreciable amounts of charcoal.

STRUCTURAL REQUIREMENTS OF THE SUBSTRATE. The primary requirements for the substrates of acylase I are (a) a free terminal α-carboxyl group, and (b) a susceptible α-N-acyl radical. For the same α-amino acid residue, the susceptibility of various acyl radicals differs quite widely, generally in the order: trifluoroacetyl > chloroacetyl > propionyl $\simeq$ acetyl > formyl > benzoyl (11, 12). The N-carbobenzoxy derivatives of all amino acids tested, with the exception of that of glutamic acid (13), are completely resistant to acylase I. With the same acyl radical, the most susceptible substrates are those of the aliphatic straight-chain series with maximum susceptibility at C_5 (Figure 42–1), and among the least susceptible are those with substituents on the β-carbon of the aromatic type (Table 9–6 and Table 20–1). A hydrogen atom on the α-carbon of the amino acid residue is desirable for ready susceptibility of the substrate, but it is not an absolute requirement, inasmuch as chloroacetylisovaline (14) and chloroacetyl-α-amino-α-methyl-n-valeric acid (15) are hydrolyzed, albeit slowly. However, a hydrogen atom is required on the peptide nitrogen, for such compounds as chloroacetyl-N-methylalanine (15) and chloroacetylproline (7) are practically completely resistant to acylase I.

Acylase I does not affect the binding of N-acyl groups other than those on the α-carbon atom, and hence may be employed with racemic α,ω-diacyldiamino acids to yield the ω-acyl diamino acid with a free α-amino group (cf. Section 32–4). Moreover, acylase I preparations are free of ε-lysine acylase (see below) and hence the yield of ε-acetyllysine by the action of acylase I on α,ε-diacetyllysine is not diminished as it would be were both enzymes present together.

When the amino acid residue is aspartic acid, the susceptibility of the N-acylated substrate to acylase I is considerably less than it is toward still another fraction of the hog kidney homogenate to which the designation of acylase II has been given (Table 20–4) (7). The latter enzyme is therefore the one employed in the resolution of aspartic acid (Section 23–4). The generally low susceptibility to acylase I of the N-acylated aromatic amino acids as compared with the aliphatic group rather strikingly distinguishes this kidney enzyme from pancreatic carboxypeptidase. Although N-acylated racemic tyrosine has been successfully resolved by the use of acylase I, and N-acylated racemic phenylalanine is quite easily resolved by this

TABLE 20–4
Initial Hydrolytic Rates with Hog Kidney Acylases I and II (7)[a]

	Rates with		
Substrate	Homogenate	Acylase I	Acylase II
Chloroacetyl-L-glutamic acid	480	12,700	6
Glycyl-L-glutamic acid	310	490	3
Chloroacetyl-L-aspartic acid	32	4	142
Glycyl-L-aspartic acid	45	4	2
Chloroacetyl-L-asparagine	8	129	0.3
Glycyl-L-asparagine	1,120	54	19
Acetyl-DL-aspartic acid	11	5	27
Chloroacetyl-DL-serine	455	11,600	3
Chloroacetyl-DL-leucine	630	16,500	7

[a] Digests as in Table 20–2 except racemic substrates added as 0.05M solutions. Rate definition as in Table 20–2.

enzyme, the resolution of N-acylated DL-tryptophan has never been successfully accomplished where this biocatalyst has been concerned. All three are easily resolved as their N-chloroacetyl derivatives by pancreatic carboxypeptidase (7, 16; cf. 17). The activity ratios of renal acylase I to the homogenate for these aromatic-substituted substrates (cf. Table 20–1) suggest that there may be still a third acylase system in the homogenate which is more directly involved with such substrates than is acylase I, and to which the tentative designation of acylase III has been given.

EFFECTS OF SUBSTRATE CONCENTRATION. As in the case of many other enzymes, the activity of acylase I in the presence of increasing amounts of substrate increases to a maximal value. Table 20–5 describes the Michaelis-Menten constants for acylase I with different substrates (18). At the maximum rate of hydrolysis it is doubtful whether in all cases the enzymic cleavage of the N-acylated L-amino acid will go to completion, and indeed in the cases of N-acetyl-L-alanine and N-acetyl-L-methionine there is evidence that in the presence of high substrate:enzyme ratios the cleavage does not go to completion (7) (Chapter 9). Under the conditions given in Table 9–6, the enzymic rates are less than optimal, but the hydrolytic reactions go to completion, a necessary feature for any practical resolution procedure.

The rates of hydrolysis given in Table 9–6 serve as rough guides in the determination of the amount of acylase I or other enzyme to be used in the resolution of a given substrate, as well as the approximate time required for complete digestion of the L-moiety of the substrate. Thus, for the resolution of

TABLE 20–5
Michaelis-Menten Constants (18)

Substrate	Acylase I Maximum Rate, V	Acylase I $K_s \times 10^3$, moles/liter	Acylase IA[b] Maximum Rate, V	Acylase IA[b] $K_s \times 10^3$, moles/liter
Acetylglycine	6,480	40.8	6,410	9.4
Acetyl-L-alanine	15,500	25.6	15,600	7.1
Acetyl-L-butyrine	20,700	8.3	19,900	5.0
Acetyl-L-norvaline	26,900	3.0	25,500	1.0
Acetyl-L-norleucine	22,300	2.0	19,000	v.s.[a]
Acetyl-L-heptyline	14,700	1.3	16,200	v.s.[a]
Acetyl-L-capryline	2,690	v.s.[a]	3,300	v.s.[a]
Acetyl-L-methionine	30,700	3.7	32,800	1.8
Acetyl-L-leucine	19,500	12.8	25,700	5.6
Acetyl-L-valine	10,200	30.6	12,500	13.2
Acetyl-L-isoleucine	1,820	17.8	3,770	15.1
Acetyl-L-alloisoleucine	–	–	3,970	13.9
Acetyl-L-aspartic acid	44.5	409	142	178
Acetyl-L-glutamic acid	17,900	63.1	17,800	28.8
Acetyl-L-arginine	–	–	2,120	27.6
Acetyl-D-alanine	6.1	34.4	–	–
Acetyl-D-methionine	62.0	77.8	–	–

[a] Very small.
[b] Complex of acylase I with Co^{2+}.

one mole of acetyl-DL-methionine by means of acylase I, reference to Table 9–6 reveals that the hydrolysis of the L-moiety of this substrate under the conditions given proceeds at a rate of approximately 25,000 micromoles per hour per mg. N. One mole of the racemic compound contains 500,000 micromoles of the susceptible L-isomer, whereupon

$$\frac{500,000}{25,000} = 20 \text{ mg. N per hour}$$

That is to say, 20 mg. of enzyme nitrogen (about 120 mg. of the dry acylase I powder) should complete the asymmetric hydrolysis in about one hour of incubation at 37°. For purposes of economy, the amount of enzyme can be decreased, and the estimated incubation time proportionately lengthened. The data in Table 9–6 were obtained with relatively low substrate concentrations (0.008M of the susceptible L-isomer). The resolutions actually performed, however, as described in Volume 3 (Part VI), have almost invariably been conducted with that amount of enzyme calculated as above and sufficient to complete the hydrolysis within one hour but with a substrate concentration (L-isomer) of $0.05M$. Under these conditions, the hydrolytic rates are not appreciably larger than those described in Table 9–6, and in every case the enzymic cleavage of the N-acylated L-amino acid goes to completion.

OPTICAL SPECIFICITY (cf. Chapter 2). It is clear that a certain range of ratio of substrate to acylase I must be present in order that the hydrolysis of the susceptible L-isomer approach 100%. A change in this ratio in favor of the substrate while keeping the enzyme level constant will result in a higher initial rate of cleavage of the N-acyl-L-moiety, but the hydrolysis will stop short of the 100% mark. Again, a change in this ratio in favor of the enzyme while the substrate level is kept constant will result in a complete hydrolysis of the N-acyl-L-amino acid, but, if the optical antipode is also present as in a racemate, some of the N-acyl-D-amino acid may also be hydrolyzed (7). This is shown in Table 20–6, which describes conditions

TABLE 20–6

Effect of Excess Acylase I on Certain Acylated DL-Amino Acids (7)

Compound[a]	Total Amino Acids Liberated, micromoles	D-Amino Acid Liberated, micromoles
Acetyl-DL-methionine	193	43
Chloroacetyl-DL-alanine	213	63
Chloroacetyl-DL-norvaline	154	4
Chloroacetyl-DL-leucine	160	10

[a] 300 micromoles in digest containing 1 mg. of acylase I nitrogen. Incubation period 42 hr. at 38°. Total amino acid determined by ninhydrin-CO_2 method, D-amino acids estimated with D-amino acid oxidase.

under which N-acyl-DL-amino acids, treated with that amount of acylase I calculated to hydrolyze the L-component in about *one minute*, were, however, allowed to incubate with the enzyme for nearly *two days*. Indeed, the incubation of acetyl-D-methionine (7) and of acetyl-D-alanine (18) with a very large amount of acylase I at pH 7.0 and at 37° for several days resulted in the subsequent isolation in nearly quantitative yield of the respective D-amino acids, in which no trace of the L-antipode was present.

The enzymic hydrolysis of the acyl-D-amino acid moiety of the corresponding racemate, even under these conditions, is inhibited by the presence of the free L-amino acid liberated rapidly from the acyl-L-amino acid moiety by the large proportion of acylase I present (7) (Table 20–7). This is an

TABLE 20-7

Inhibition of Hydrolysis of Acetyl-D-methionine by L-Methionine (7)[a]

Compound	D-Methionine Liberated, micromoles
Acetyl-D-methionine[b]	103
Acetyl-DL-methionine[c]	26
Acetyl-D-methionine[b] + L-methionine[b]	23
Acetyl-D-methionine + sodium acetate[b]	90

[a] Digests consisted of 1 ml. of 0.1M phosphate buffer at pH 7.0, 1 ml. of acylase I (1 mg. N per ml.), and 1 ml. of neutralized substrate solution. Incubation time, 24 hr. at 38°C. D-Methionine was assayed with the aid of the D-amino acid oxidase of hog kidney.

[b] 150 micromoles.

[c] 300 micromoles.

obviously fortunate circumstance from the standpoint of the optical specificity requirements in an enzymic resolution procedure. It is not inconceivable (cf. 7) that, even in digests with acylase I and N-acyl-DL-amino acids in which the proportion of enzyme to substrate is that followed in Table 9-6, and whereby optically pure L- and D-amino acid isomers are ultimately obtained, some possibility of hydrolysis of the D-moiety of the racemic substrate is present; that no measurable contamination of the L-amino acid by its D-antipode is observed may be due (a) to the inhibition of the hydrolysis of the N-acyl-D-amino acid by the free L-amino acid present (as in Table 20-7), (b) to the oxidative destruction of what little free D-amino acid might be liberated by the D-amino acid oxidase present in the acylase I preparation, and (c) to the final crystallization of the L-amino acid which may conceivably cleanly separate the relatively insoluble pure L-form from traces of the more soluble DL-form.

An interesting aspect of the problem of the optical specificity of acylase I springs from a consideration of the relative susceptibility of the optically isomeric N-trifluoroacetyl derivatives to the action of this enzyme. Whereas, under the experimental conditions involved in the resolution with the aid of acylase I of the N-acetyl- and N-chloroacetyl derivatives of the DL-amino acids (Table 9-6 and the Resolution sections in Volume 3) little or no enzymic hydrolysis of the D-moiety of the substrates seems to occur and the final products are optically pure (Chapter 19), certain of the analogous N-trifluoroacetyl derivatives are appreciably hydrolyzed whether the amino acid residue is L or D in configuration (12) (Table 20-8). This lack of optical specificity on the part of acylase I toward N-trifluoroacetyl-D-amino acids is, however, restricted to the derivatives of the straight-chain D-amino acids, those of the branched-chain variety, i.e., valine and leucine, and of phenylalanine, being as resistant to the enzyme as are the comparable N-acetyl or N-chloroacetyl derivatives (Table 20-8). The results given in this table

TABLE 20-8
Hydrolysis of Optically Active Trifluoroacetylamino Acids by Acylase I (12)[a]

Trifluoroacetyl Derivative of	Rate with Pure L-Isomer	Rate with Pure D-Isomer	Ratio, L/D
Alanine	16,000	200	80
Butyrine	48,400	60	805
Norvaline	21,500	145	148
Norleucine	19,500	315	62
Valine	16,400	0	–
Leucine	57,000	<1	–
Methionine	15,700	5,200	3
Phenylalanine	11,000	3	3,670

[a] Rate and composition of digests as in Table 20–2.

might suggest the presence of a D-acylase in the otherwise strongly L-directed acylase I preparation; this possibility, however, was removed by two pieces of evidence, namely (a) the finding that trifluoroacetyl-DL-methionine at twice the concentration employed for either of the isomeric derivatives was hydrolyzed at the same rate as that of the L-isomer alone, and (b) the observation that the progressive acid denaturation of acylase I resulted in a parallel loss of hydrolytic activity toward trifluoroacetyl-L-norleucine and trifluoroacetyl-D-norleucine (12).

EFFECT OF Co^{2+}. The addition of cobalt salts to an acylase I digest at a final concentration of about $1 \times 10^{-3}M$ results in the acceleration of the hydrolysis of those N-acylated amino acids ordinarily less readily hydrolyzed by this enzyme (9, 18; cf. 19) (Table 20–9); hydrolysis of the more susceptible substrates is generally inhibited by this concentration of cobalt salt. The interaction of cobalt with the enzyme-substrate system appears to be instantaneous (18). It would appear to be advantageous to employ cobalt ion as an activator for resolution digests involving relatively resistant substrates inasmuch as the requirement for substantial amounts of acylase I for the reaction would thereby be lessened. This turned out to be true in the case of the resolution of acetylisoleucine (Chapter 30–4), for the additional and quite important reason that the acetyl-D-alloisoleucine moiety of the racemate was not appreciably attacked by acylase I whether Co^{2+} was present or not. A striking example was found in the resolution of N-chloroacetyl-γ-hydroxy-DL-glutamic acid (20), for in this case the hydrolytic action of acylase I on the substrate was increased ten-fold (Chapter 53). As noted from Table 20–9, however, the enzymic hydrolysis of acetyl-D-alanine is strongly accelerated by cobalt ion, to an extent proportionately greater than that of the corresponding L-antipode, so that the risk of resolving

TABLE 20-9
Effect of Added Co^{2+} on the Hydrolytic Rate of Acylase I[a] (18)

Substrate	Rate without Added Co^{2+}	$1 \times 10^{-4}M$	$1 \times 10^{-3}M$	$1 \times 10^{-2}M$	$4 \times 10^{-1}M$
Acetyl-L-alanine	5,800	+12	+60	+25	−9
Acetyl-D-alanine	2.0	+350	+440	+270	+20
Acetyl-L-methionine	25,800	−7	−19	−26	−62
Acetyl-D-methionine	10.9	+28	+80	+20	−21
Acetyl-L-isoleucine	970	+124	+240	+280	+82
Acetyl-L-aspartic acid	3.7	+200	+280	+290	+128
Acetyl-L-glutamic acid	3,690	+30	+70	+27	−6
Acetyl-L-arginine	1,110	−5	−36	−66	−78
Acetyl-L-histidine	740	+11	+31	−44	−75

Per Cent Increase or Decrease in Rate on Addition of Co^{2+} at Concentrations of

[a] Digests composed of 1 ml. of veronal acetate buffer at pH 7, 1 ml. of neutralized 0.05M substrate, and 1 ml. of enzyme solution. Rates in terms of micromoles per hour per mg. N.

acetyl-DL-alanine by acylase I in the presence of cobalt, from the standpoint of the possibility of appreciable hydrolysis of the D-moiety, even though the inhibitory, free L-amino acid is present, might be too great.

A new type of acylase I, referred to as acylase IA, has been prepared as follows (18). When acylase I is mixed with cobalt acetate (1×10^{-4} to $1 \times 10^{-1}M$) in neutral veronal buffer and the mixture subsequently exhaustively dialyzed against several changes of distilled water, about 65% of the protein remains soluble. Lyophilization of the soluble portion yields enzymically active products with a cobalt content which may reach a maximum value of 0.26%, and which appear to be activated forms of acylase I. Although the maximum rates of hydrolysis by acylase I and by acylase IA are not greatly different (Table 20–5), the K_s values for acylase IA are uniformly lower, indicating an increased affinity of acylase IA for each of the substrates studied (18).

EQUILIBRIUM. Acylase I has been further concentrated in activity by Orekhovich and his associates in Moscow through electrophoresis on a starch block (20a); the molecular weight found for this electrophoretically homogeneous preparation was 119,000. In accord with the results obtained in the writers' Laboratory (see discussion above on Effects of Substrate Concentration, and Chapters 9 and 21), the hydrolytic action of the acylase prepared by Orekhovich et al. on acylated amino acids *in concentrated solutions* did not go to completion. The Soviet workers went on to demonstrate that the action of acylase I could be essentially reversible by the following procedure: a solution 0.5M in acetyl-L-alanine and 2.0M in sodium acetate, with added enzyme, yielded at equilibrium the same amounts of acetyl-L-alanine (0.103M) and L-alanine (0.397M) as did an acylase digest initially 0.5M in L-alanine and 2.5M in sodium acetate, under the same conditions. The equilibrium constant at pH 7.2 and at 38° calculated from these data was 0.108. Under the same conditions L-leucine could also be acetylated; less synthesis, however, was achieved when the more bulky acyl radicals such as valeryl or trichloroacetyl were employed.

4. Renal Acylase II (7). A second fraction of the hog kidney homogenate contains most of the activity against N-acylaspartic acids. The enzyme involved, which apparently has a relative specificity for those L-aspartic acid derivatives in which both carboxyl groups are free and the acyl group is other than an α-amino acid, has been designated acylase II (7). It has been successfully employed for the resolution of DL-aspartic acid as either its acetyl or its chloroacetyl derivative (Section 23–4). The activity of the enzyme is not appreciably affected by either Co^{2+} or Mn^{2+}. Initial hydrolytic rates of this preparation, as compared with those of acylase I and the whole hog kidney homogenate on the same substrates, have been listed in Table 20–4.

Preparation of acylase II. The procedure given below yields a voluminous preparation of very easily soluble protein. Attempts further to purify acylase II from this material by alcohol or acetone fractionation or by adsorbents have not so far been successful. The potency of the enzyme is progressively diminished upon storage at 5°, and it is essential that it be used within 2 to 3 weeks after its preparation or else prepared afresh.

The red supernatant solution obtained after the separation of acylase I by ammonium sulfate is treated with an additional 150 g. of ammonium sulfate per liter and is allowed to stand for several hours in the cold. The resulting precipitate is then separated either in the Sharples refrigerated supercentrifuge or, less satisfactorily, in the International centrifuge at 2600 × g for 60 min. The supernatant solution is discarded and the precipitate, dissolved in a minimum of ice water, is dialyzed free of ammonium salt and subsequently lyophilized. From 12 to 14 g. of a fluffy pink-colored protein material is thus obtained.

Assay method. Acylase II activity is measured in the same manner as acylase I. The substrate must be one of the neutralized N-acylaspartic acids, and since the ninhydrin-CO_2 method is employed it should be recalled that 1 micromole of aspartic acid yields 2 micromoles of carbon dioxide gas (Chapter 12).

5. Pancreatic Carboxypeptidase. The substrate specificity of pancreatic carboxypeptidase of concern in problems involved in the resolution of amino acids resembles that of renal acylase in some respects and differs from it in others. The most important resemblance lies in the fact that both enzymes require the presence of a free α-carboxyl group on the terminal residue adjacent to the susceptible peptide linkage. In addition, the presence of a free α-amino group on the N-acyl residue is usually inhibitory for both enzymes (Tables 20-1 and 20-10), whilst the presence of a residue of the D-configuration confers on the substrate a relative resistance to the action of either enzyme. For both enzymes, the chloroacetyl derivatives of the amino acids are more susceptible than are the corresponding acetyl derivatives, the ratio of the susceptibilities of the two derivatives being about 4:1 in the case of renal acylase I, and about 100:1 in the case of pancreatic carboxypeptidase. Data pertinent to these considerations are described in Table 20-10 for crystalline pancreatic carboxypeptidase acting on several N-acylated derivatives of L-phenylalanine (21).

TABLE 20-10

Susceptibility of Acylated L-Phenylalanine with Optically Active and Other Acyl Groups to Crystalline Pancreatic Carboxypeptidase according to First-Order Kinetics (21)

Derivative of L-Phenylalanine	First-Order Velocity Constant
L-Chloropropionyl[a]	0.264
D-Chloropropionyl[a]	0.224
L-Alanyl[b]	0.047
D-Alanyl[b]	0.018
Carbobenzoxy-L-alanyl	71.0
Carbobenzoxy-D-alanyl	0.265
Acetyl	0.034
Chloroacetyl	4.13
Propionyl	0.105
Glycyl[b]	0.020

[a] Corresponding data for the derivatives of L-tyrosine are 0.304 and 0.214.

[b] The hydrolysis of these compounds followed zero-order kinetics under the present conditions; the rates, however, have been approximated in terms of a first-order reaction for purposes of comparison with other data in the table. Digests were composed of 1 ml. of $0.1M$ veronal buffer at pH 7.45, 1 ml. of $0.025M$ neutralized substrate, and 1 ml. of suitably diluted enzyme; incubation temperature, 37°.

As noted above, renal acylase I acts more readily on N-acylated aliphatic amino acids, whereas pancreatic carboxypeptidase acts more readily on N-acylated amino acids containing aromatic substituents on the β-carbon atom. In the particular case of the diastereomeric β-phenylserines, renal acylase I is ineffective toward either N-acetyl or N-chloroacetyl derivatives (22). Interestingly enough, crystalline pancreatic carboxypeptidase is also relatively ineffective toward these same substrates. However, the pancreatic enzyme acts quite rapidly on the N-trifluoroacetyl derivatives of the diastereomeric phenylserines (22) (Table 20-11), and, unlike the optically unspecific behavior of renal acylase I toward such N-trifluoroacetylated racemic amino acids (cf. Table 20-8), the action of the pancreatic enzyme is exclusively

L-directed. Hence the phenylserines are easily resolved as the N-trifluoroacetyl derivative by this enzyme (Chapter 51).

As shown by Hofmann and Bergmann (23), the chloroacetic acid liberated by the hydrolytic action of pancreatic carboxypeptidase on N-chloroacetyl amino acids tends to inhibit the crystalline enzyme. This is obviously a serious handicap in the enzymic resolution procedure, and to avoid this a less pure preparation of the enzyme has been found to be a more suitable agent. For the purpose of resolving tyrosine, tryptophan, and phenylalanine as the corresponding chloroacetyl derivatives, the crude, intermediate preparation

TABLE 20-11

Rates of Hydrolysis of N-Acyl Derivatives of the Diastereomeric Phenylserines by Crystalline Pancreatic Carboxypeptidase (22)

N-Acyl Group	Hydrolysis Rate of the N-Acyl Derivative of[a]	
	threo-β-Phenyl-DL-serine	erythro-β-Phenyl-DL-serine
Acetyl	0	0
Chloroacetyl	5	5
Trifluoroacetyl	1100	800

[a] As micromoles hydrolyzed per hour per mg. protein N. Digests consisted of 1 ml. of enzyme solution, 1 ml. of water, and 1 ml. of $0.025M$ neutralized racemic substrate at 37°.

of carboxypeptidase from frozen beef pancreas, which is sufficiently active and quite stable, is entirely adequate (16). The use of this "crude pancreatic carboxypeptidase," although of lower specific activity but of greater stability than the crystalline variety, is analogous to the use of the "crude acylase" described above which was found to be more suitable in the resolution of N-acylated derivatives of cystine than the more purified form of this renal enzyme, acylase I. For end-group analysis (Chapter 16), the crystalline variety of the pancreatic enzyme is the more suitable, for it is substantially free of adherent amino acids.

"*Crude pancreatic carboxypeptidase*" (24). Frozen beef pancreas is ground and stirred with 3 times its weight of 2% sodium chloride. Twenty per cent of its weight of toluene is added, and the mixture is allowed to stand overnight at room temperature. The next morning, fat and toluene are skimmed off and the suspension is filtered through cheese-cloth. Five normal acetic acid is added to this filtrate until the reaction is acid to bromocresol green, and the resulting acid solution is filtered in the cold on a Büchner funnel with the aid of Standard Super Cel. Ammonium sulfate in the amount of 390 g. per l. is added to the clear filtrate, and the resulting precipitate is filtered or centrifuged off, taken up in a little water, and dialyzed overnight against cold running water in the shaking dialyzer whereby the enzymically active euglobulin comes out of solution. The salt-free protein suspension is then centrifuged, the supernatant fluid is discarded, and the precipitate, which is the crude enzyme, is suspended in water and lyophilized. Solution of the enzyme for resolution purposes is readily accomplished by suspending the protein in water and adding a concentrated LiCl solution dropwise and with stirring until a homogeneous aqueous phase results. The assay of activity is conducted as described above for acylase I, except that in the present instance chloroacetyl-L-phenylalanine is used as substrate. The activity of the "crude" enzyme is roughly one-fourth that of the crystalline form, the value of which for several N-chloroacetyl aromatic amino acids ranges from 1000 to 2000 micromoles of substrate hydrolyzed per hour per mg. N at 37°.

Although Anson described two methods for the extraction of carboxypeptidase from beef pancreas, namely, saline extraction (above), and the collection of the exudate of thawing pancreas at 5°, the latter procedure is almost universally used in the preparation of the crystalline enzyme. Neurath (25) has described an excellent method for this purpose. Crystalline carboxypeptidase has long been available on the commercial market.

6. Acylases in Microorganisms. Probably the first description of acylase activity was that reported by Van Tieghem in 1864 (26) in a paper transmitted by Pasteur to the Academy of Sciences in Paris. In this study, the urine of herbivorous animals was allowed to stand for some time, and the fate of the hippuric acid, a natural constituent of the urine from this source, carefully followed. It was found that "... pendant la fermentation de l'urine, l'acide hippurique se transforme en acide benzoique ... et en glycollammine ... avec assimilation de l'eau ..."[52] These results, due to the hydrolytic capacity of certain "ferments" in the urine, contributed their share toward the concept of the nearly universal occurrence of microorganisms in living forms then engrossing the attention of Pasteur. As the various microorganisms were subsequently sorted out and individually identified, their chemical as well as morphologic differentiation became of theoretical interest, and in the hands of Neuberg, for instance, of considerable practical significance. If the historical development of the subject is restricted to the catalytic hydrolysis of hippuric acid, it may be noted that Shibata in 1904 (27) observed that the mold *Aspergillus niger* acted readily on this substrate; this observation was confirmed somewhat later by Dox (28) with a variety of molds, many of significance in the manufacture of cheese, and bearing such interesting designations as *Aspergillus fumigatus, Penicillium roqueforti,* and *Penicillium camemberti.* Among the earliest uses of bacteria in the present connection was that described in 1922 by Ayers and Rupp (29), who distinguished the hemolytic streptococci of human association, which had no effect on hippuric acid, from those of bovine association, which could readily hydrolyze this compound. Later studies by Gilbert and Frobisher (30) demonstrated that the possession or lack of possession of hippuricase activity by various bacterial strains might serve as a means of identifying them, an approach whose validity was substantially confirmed by Reis and Swensson (31).

These early investigations, of which few were systematic, led to little of practical significance, and it was not until Neuberg and his colleagues undertook a highly skillful series of studies on the wealth of enzymes in Japanese Takadiastase that the value of plant hippuricase assumed some meaning. Among the enzymes from this source was one which Neuberg and Linhardt (32) observed to hydrolyze specifically the L-moiety of benzoyl-DL-alanine to yield benzoic acid, L-alanine, and benzoyl-D-alanine. The optically asymmetric character of the enzyme involved suggested to these authors that this enzyme might be employed as a means of resolving racemic amino acids via their N-acyl derivatives, a suggestion adopted and successfully applied to the resolution of alanine by Hoppert in Neuberg's laboratory one year later (33) (see Chapter 19). This accomplishment lay apparently unnoticed for a quarter of a century, and it was not until 1950 that Neuberg and Mandl (34), in a resumption of this work, described the susceptibility of a variety of N-acylated α-amino acids to a host of commercially available mold extracts, and applied the asymmetric hydrolytic procedure to the resolution of acetyl-DL-tryptophan. This substrate was buffered in water with solid calcium carbonate and allowed to incubate for 11 days with "Orthozym." The calcium was removed as oxalate, the acetyl-D-tryptophan extracted into acetone from the dried filtrate and hydrolyzed with dilute mineral acid to yield D-tryptophan, whilst the residual L-tryptophan was purified through the copper salt.

From 1950 on, two developments in the field of the amino acid acylases were carried on more or less simultaneously, both with the aim of achieving a ready and general applicability to the resolution of racemic amino acids via their α-N-acyl derivatives. One, developed in the writers' Laboratory, involved the use of hog kidney as an enzyme source (see early sections in this chapter, Chapter 9, and the sections on Resolution in Volume 3), the other, carried on almost exclusively by Far Eastern workers, involved the use of purified mold, yeast, and bacterial preparations.

Michi and her associates in Tokyo (35, 36) examined the acylase activity of a number of strains of *Aspergillus* and *Penicillium*, and decided to employ *Penicillium vinaceous* as the best source of the enzyme. The mold was cultivated on moist wheat bran in the presence of solid calcium carbonate to maintain a neutral pH, the enzyme precipitated first with ammonium sulfate, then with Rivanol (6:9-diamino-2-ethoxyacridine lactate), and, finally, again with ammonium sulfate. The purified enzyme was stable only in the pH range 5.5–7.5, hydrolyzed with greater rapidity the N-acylated aromatic amino acids than the corresponding N-acylated aliphatic amino acids, and acted exclusively on the L-moiety of susceptible N-acylated DL-amino acids. Thirty grams of acetyl-DL-phenylalanine yielded, with 70 mg. of the acylase within 2 days of incubation at 38°, 10 g. of pure L-phenylalanine and 11.5 g. of pure acetyl-D-phenylalanine. Essentially similar results were obtained in the resolution of 20 g. of acetyl-DL-methionine by 70 mg. of the purified enzyme in less than 2 days of digestion (pH set at neutrality by the presence of excess solid $CaCO_3$).

TABLE 20-12

Relative Hydrolytic Rates for the Acylases of *Aspergillus oryzae* and of Yeast (37-39)

Amino Acid Residue (L-configuration)	Aspergillus[a] Acetyl Derivative	Aspergillus[a] Chloroacetyl Derivative	Yeast (Brewer's)[b] Acetyl Derivative	Yeast (Brewer's)[b] Chloroacetyl Derivative
Alanine	73	144	72	305
Aspartic acid	10	10	7	37
ε-Benzoyllysine	83	158	29	52
Glutamic acid	37	53	21	42
Leucine	31	46	21	227
Methionine	100	180	100	274
Phenylalanine	145	215	20	165
Tryptophan	74	63	8	13
Tyrosine	–	226	–	208

[a] Relative to hydrolysis of acetyl-L-methionine = 100. Rate of hydrolysis of this substrate given as 16 micromoles per hour per milligram of solids. Digests consisted of 1 ml. of enzyme solution, 1 ml. of phosphate buffer at pH levels around neutrality, and 1 ml. of neutralized 0.05M racemic substrate; incubated for 2 hr. at 37°.

[b] Relative to hydrolysis of acetyl-L-methionine = 100. Rate of hydrolysis of this substrate given as 86 micromoles per hour per mg. N. Digests consisted of 1 ml. of enzyme solution, 1 ml. of phosphate buffer at pH 6–7, and 1 ml. of neutralized 0.025M susceptible substrate.

Chibata and his colleagues (37, 38) in Osaka investigated the acylase activity of *Aspergillus oryzae* and employed this mold as the source of the subsequently purified enzyme. In this instance, the mold was grown on wheat bran, and the enzyme isolated after being consecutively precipitated with ammonium sulfate and cold acetone. From 340 g. of dried wheat bran about 950 mg. of an acylase preparation was obtained which hydrolyzed acetyl-L-methionine at a rate of about 16 micromoles per hour per milligram of solids. The activity of this preparation toward the susceptible L-moiety of a variety of acetylamino acids and of chloroacetylamino acids is described in Table 20–12. Included in this table are data by Chibata and Ishikawa (39) on the susceptibility of the same substrates to a purified acylase from brewer's yeast. The enzyme was extracted from this source by successive liquefaction with chloroform and precipitation with ammonium sulfate, and represented approximately a ten-fold increase in specific activity. With both mold and yeast acylases, as with renal acylase I, the chloroacetylamino acids are more rapidly hydrolyzed than are the corresponding acetylamino acids. Even more rapidly hydrolyzed by mold acylase than the chloroacetylamino acids are the corresponding formyl derivatives. The enzyme preparation with which this observation (40) was made had been isolated from *Aspergillus flavus-oryzae* by grinding the cells, extracting with water, precipitating the enzyme with chilled acetone and subsequently with ammonium sulfate, adsorbing the enzyme from the dialyzed solution onto a calcium phosphate gel, eluting with dilute ammonium sulfate, and precipitating again on addition of more of the sulfate salt. The increase in specific activity was about 200-fold. The enzyme so obtained, like other mold acylases, was generally more active toward the N-acylated derivatives of the aromatic amino acids than toward those of the aliphatic amino acids, and in this respect bore a closer resemblance to pancreatic carboxypeptidase than to renal aclyase; however, the susceptibility of the acetylamino acids to the mold acylase was considerably greater than that characteristic of pancreatic carboxypeptidase.

The plant enzymes thus far considered are generally weaker in specific activity than are the animal tissue acylases. Thus the yeast enzyme activity of 235 micromoles of chloroacetyl-L-methionine hydrolyzed per hour per mg. N may be compared with the corresponding value of 100,000 for renal acylase I. The plant enzymes are, however, of sufficient activity to be employable for amino acid resolutions on a relatively large scale, and their nearly absolute optical specificity toward the L-moiety of the N-acetylated racemic substrates should assure the production of L- and D-amino acid isomers of high optical purity. Their very special advantage over the animal acylases lies in the fact that acetyl-L-tryptophan is a susceptible substrate, as first shown by Neuberg and Mandl. Neither renal acylase I nor pancreatic carboxypeptidase possesses appreciable activity toward this compound, although the latter enzyme acts quite readily on the chloroacetyl derivative of L-tryptophan. In many efficient syntheses of tryptophan, the penultimate product is acetyltryptophan (Section 39-3), and a resolution of the amino acid at this stage would provide considerable saving in time and material over that involving a removal of the acetyl group by alkaline hydrolysis, followed by a chloroacetylation of the free tryptophan, and then by a resolution of the chloroacetyltryptophan. This factor and that of the financial economy associated with the acquisition and development of plant products are the important advantages in the use of the mold or yeast acylases.

Illustrative procedure for the isolation of yeast acylase (39). One kilogram of brewer's yeast is liquified with 100 ml. of chloroform. One liter of water is added, and the mixture maintained for 1 hr. at 10° with occasional stirring, centrifuged, and the supernatant solution discarded. To the separated precipitate, 50 ml. of chloroform and 1 l. of 0.4 saturated aqueous ammonium sulfate at pH 6.0 are added, and for further autolysis the mixture is allowed to stand for 96 hr. at 10° with maintenance of the pH at 6.0. Centrifugation gives a clear supernatant solution (about 1 l.) which is treated at pH 6.0 with solid ammonium sulfate to 0.75 saturation. The resulting precipitate is collected and dissolved in 500 ml. of 0.03M phosphate buffer at pH 6.0, and the solution treated gradually with solid ammonium sulfate. The precipitate obtained up to 0.45 saturation is centrifuged off, the supernatant solution brought to 0.7 saturation with more sulfate salt, and the resulting precipitate collected at the centrifuge. The supernatant solution is discarded. Dissolution of the precipitate in 0.03M phosphate buffer at pH 6.0 is followed by dialysis against cold water, the precipitate formed during this period (2 days) is removed by centrifugation, and to the supernatant solution at $-5°$ (about 260 ml.) there is added chilled acetone to 33% by volume. The resulting precipitate is collected by centrifuging, taken up in 0.03M phosphate buffer at pH 6.0, the solution cleared by centrifuging and lyophilized. The white powder so obtained weighs 4–5 g., and the yield of total activity is about 60% that of the first extract.

A resumption of the earlier interest in bacterial acylases resulted in the observation of relatively low activity in *Escherichia coli* (41, 42). Thus an active fraction isolated from a wild strain of *E. coli* by cold ethanol precipitation of the phosphate buffer (pH 7.0) extract possessed the ability to hydrolyze acetyl-L-methionine at a rate of 7 micromoles per hour per mg. N (42), a rate about one-half that of *Aspergillus* acylase, one-fourteenth that of yeast acylase (Table 20–12), and one-three-thousandth that of renal acylase I. Of more theoretical interest has been the finding of Kameda, Toyoura, and Kimura (43) of the simultaneous presence of L- and D-acylases in a strain of *Pseudomonas* sp., KT 83. The crude extracts of this organism appeared to possess the ability to hydrolyze both benzoyl-L-phenylalanine and benzoyl-D-phenylalanine at significant rates. Fractionation of the two activities toward these isomeric substrates was conducted as follows. The aqueous extract of several grams of the dried organism was treated with protamine sulfate whereby a protein-protamine complex was precipitated, while some protein remained behind in solution. Dialysis of the insoluble complex first against sodium chloride solution and then against water resulted in removal of the protamine. This was followed by the finding that the protein itself possessed acylase activity almost completely restricted to the hydrolysis of the L-isomer of benzoylphenylalanine. The soluble protein left behind in the crude extract after the insoluble protein-protamine complex had been removed was fractionated by the addition of ammonium sulfate to yield at 50 to 60% saturation of the salt an active protein component which, after dialysis against water to remove the salt, possessed an acylase activity almost completely restricted to the D-isomer of benzoylphenylalanine. Neither L- nor D-acylase activity was entirely pure, but the separation yielded evidence of a completely valid character. Table 20–13 contains the data pertinent to this somewhat dramatic accomplishment (43). To lend further emphasis to the achievement, the authors undertook the resolution of 1.4 g. of benzoyl-DL-phenylalanine via 15 mg. of the partially purified D-acylase preparation (43). The digest after completion of the enzymic reaction within 20 hours at 37° contained D-phenylalanine (which was subsequently isolated in the pure state in 80% yield) and benzoyl-L-phenylalanine (m.p. 139–140°, $[\alpha]_D^{15} = +14\cdot9°$ in N NaOH) which, after acid hydrolysis and subsequent neutralization, gave pure L-phenylalanine in 84% over-all yield.

Further efforts by Kameda and his associates in the Antibiotics Laboratory at Kanazawa on the acylase activity in *Pseudomonas* led to a brilliant series of studies on the susceptibility of various substrates to the bacterial enzyme, and on the practical application of this susceptibility to the resolution of a number of N-acylated racemic amino acids. The basic problem of these investigators was essentially bacteriological and not chemical in nature, for the hydrolytic and separation procedures involved in the resolution of the amino acids were already known. The bacteriological problem involved the discovery and cultivation of suitable strains of the soil bacterium, *Pseudomonas*, which would hydrolyze acylated amino acids not only relatively rapidly but also strictly asymmetrically. As could be inferred (Table 20–13), the crude extract of the KT 83 strain of *Pseudomonas*, because of its possession of both L- and D-acylase entities, would be unsuitable for purposes of asymmetric resolution of acylated racemic amino acids. Only when the D-acylase entity had been separated from the L-directed fraction could resolution be attempted (see above) with either purified fraction. However, it is interesting to note that the crude extract or related crude preparations,

TABLE 20–13
Fractionation of L- and D-Acylase Activity in Extracts of *Pseudomonas* sp., KT 83 (43)[a]

Source	Specific Activity against Benzoyl-D-phenylalanine	Specific Activity against Benzoyl-L-phenylalanine	Total Activity against Benzoyl-D-phenylalanine	Total Activity against Benzoyl-L-phenylalanine
Crude extract	2.3	11.5	1035	5175
Partially-purified L-acylase	1.0	23.0	120	2760
Partially-purified D-acylase	32.0	<0.03	520	0.5

[a] Activity expressed as micromoles of substrate hydrolyzed per milligram of protein at 38°. Digests consisted of 0.5 ml. enzyme solution, 0.5 ml. H$_2$O, and 1 ml. neutralized 0.05M substrate.

e.g., acetone-dried powders, of the KT 83 strain of *Pseudomonas* possessed a purely L-directed ε-lysine acylase (44). This enzyme had earlier been observed to occur in the rat kidney, from which source it was isolated and purified from no more than traces of acylase I (45). The renal ε-lysine acylase acted on ε-acylated L-lysine but not on δ-acylated L-ornithine, more rapidly on ε-chloroacetyl- than on ε-acetyllysine, and not at all on ε-acylated D-lysine. Its optimal pH was found to be about 7.0 in phosphate buffer. The *Pseudomonas* preparation was also, as noted, exclusively L-directed, and in view of this property was employed by Kameda and his associates (44) to resolve ε-benzoyl-DL-lysine. This substrate, incubated at pH 7.2 with a crude mass of the KT 83 strain of *Pseudomonas*, yielded after 3 days at 37° L-lysine, benzoic acid, and ε-benzoyl-D-lysine ($[\alpha]_D$ at $18° = -19.5°$ in $5N$ HCl) in satisfactory amount. The enzyme in this organism is relatively weak, for it was necessary, in order to accomplish fully the resolution within the period of time mentioned, to employ a larger weight in bacteria (on a wet weight basis, to be sure) than of substrate.

Illustrative procedure for the preparation of bacterial and renal ε-lysine acylases. The bacterial ε-lysine acylase is readily prepared by grinding the cells with alumina-extracting the mass with water, centrifuging clear, and adding chilled acetone to the cooled supernatant at 5° (44); the powder so obtained contains most of the activity of the organisms. The renal ε-acylase is most readily isolated as follows (45). Rat kidneys are homogenized in a Blendor in the presence of 2–3 times their weight of cold water, and the homogenate centrifuged at $40,000 \times g$. The nearly clear supernatant is treated with 0.25 volume of calcium phosphate gel, and the suspension adjusted to pH 7.0 with dilute NaOH and centrifuged clear. After the precipitate is washed with water, it is eluted with $0.1M$ phosphate buffer at pH 7.2, and the eluate treated with 0.8 of its volume of saturated (25°) ammonium sulfate solution. After 10 min., the precipitate is centrifuged down, taken up in cold water, dialyzed against cold running tap water, and lyophilized. A nearly white, stable powder with a specific activity of 16 micromoles of ε-acetyl-L-lysine hydrolyzed per hour per mg. N is obtained, representing about a 100-fold increase in activity over that of the original homogenate. Inasmuch as the release of the ε-N-acyl group from ε-N-acyl-L-lysine leads to free lysine, the progress of the enzymic hydrolysis is most readily followed by a determination of the L-lysine so freed via the specific action of lysine decarboxylase (see Section 20–10 below).

The KT 83 strain, as noted, possessed a limited if interesting set of properties. If the *Pseudomonas* acylase was to be employed on a more general scale of amino acid resolution, it was evident that a new strain of the organism with a more sharply defined and single optical specificity toward α-N-acyl amino acids would have to be sought. This strain was ultimately secured from the soil in the region of Kanazawa, cultivated, and designated KT 84. With this strain of *Pseudomonas*, Kameda and associates accomplished through acylase action (Chapter 9) the resolution of the following α-N-acylated racemic amino acids, the pertinent N-α-acyl radical being given in parentheses: phenylalanine and α-phenylglycine (benzoyl and chloroacetyl) (46), *threo-* and *erythro-β*-phenylserines (benzoyl and N-dichloroacetyl) (47), ε-benzoyllysine (formyl, acetyl, chloroacetyl, and benzoyl) (48), leucine and valine (benzoyl) (49), glutamic and aspartic acids (benzoyl) (50), methionine and cystine (benzoyl) (51), and serine, threonine, allothreonine, α,γ-diaminobutyric acid, and ornithine (benzoyl or α,ω-dibenzoyl) (52). The yields of the optical isomers in each case, i.e., free L-amino acid and N-acyl-D-amino acid, were satisfactory except that of L-threonine, which was quite low and strongly contaminated with glycine, suggesting the presence of threonine aldolase in the microbial preparation. In most cases the N-acyl radical of choice for the racemic amino acid was benzoyl. Although N-benzoyl-L-amino acids are among the substrates least susceptible to the action of renal acylase I, they are among the most susceptible to the action of the *Pseudomonas* acylase. Thus the rates of hydrolysis by crude, cell-free extracts of the KT 84 strain, expressed as micromoles of substrate hydrolyzed per hour per mg. N at 37°, were, for the following α-N-acylated derivatives of ε-benzoyl-L-lysine (48): formyl 0, acetyl 3, chloroacetyl 25, N-dichloroacetyl 150, benzoyl 148, benzyl 0, cinnamoyl 13, *o*-nitrobenzoyl 0, *m*-nitrobenzoyl 268, *p*-nitrobenzoyl 250, and *p*-aminobenzoyl 20. The digests in this study were similar to those described in Table 20–13.

The acetyl derivative of DL-alloisoleucine was hydrolyzed far too slowly for practical purposes by the acylase of either the KT 83 or the KT 84 strain and hence to resolve this amino acid still another strain had to be found. Such a new strain of *Pseudomonas*, designated KT 85, was found to be successful in hydrolyzing the substrate asymmetrically and fairly rapidly to L-alloisoleucine and acetyl-D-alloisoleucine (53). For the resolution of tryptophan in the form of its N-acetyl derivative, none of the KT strains available was sufficiently active to hydrolyze the L-moiety of the N-acetyl-DL-tryptophan at a reasonable rate. Kameda and his associates (54) with "0.2 g. of a soil sample taken from a bamboo thicket at Hiraguri village in Kanazawa" were ultimately able to achieve this aim with a *Pseudomonas* strain isolated from this source which would readily hydrolyze acetyl-DL-tryptophan to pure L-tryptophan and pure acetyl-D-tryptophan. The strain was designated KT 104 and was developed as follows. The soil sample taken as described was inoculated into 10 ml. of a culture medium at 25° composed of 200 mg. of N-benzoylanthranilic acid, 100 mg. of ammonium chloride, 100 mg. of dipotassium phosphate, 50 mg. of magnesium sulfate, 1 mg. of calcium chloride, and 0.5 mg. of ferric chloride in 100 ml. of solution brought to *p*H 7.0 by addition of NaOH solution. The resulting culture was transferred three times to fresh media of this composition, the organism required being apparently able to exist in a medium containing benzoylanthranilic acid as the sole source of carbon, and ammonia as the sole source of nitrogen, for at least three generations. The bacteria were then grown in bouillon, the cells harvested by centrifugation, washed with water, and suspended with vigorous stirring for 5 minutes in excess of acetone at $-5°$. The resulting solid was filtered and washed successively with cold acetone and then cold ether, and finally gently rubbed until the solvent evaporated and a white, dry powder remained. About 6 g. of acetyl-DL-tryptophan at pH 7 required approximately 0.8 g. of the powder to hydrolyze completely the L-moiety of this substrate in 1–2 days at 37°. Although not generally stated, the method of following the enzymic hydrolysis of the α-N-acylated L-amino acids involved a titration with standard alkali in 90% alcohol in the presence of thymolphthalein (see Chapters 4 and 12). The N-benzoylated racemic amino acids employed as substrates for the bacterial resolution procedures described have been collected in Table 10–49.

7. Renal Amidase. There is present in mammalian kidney one or more enzymes capable of effecting the hydrolysis of α-amino acid amides to the corresponding α-amino acids and ammonia. The specificity and other characteristics of a preparation from hog kidney of one of these enzymes, to which the designation leucine aminopeptidase has been given, was studied extensively by Smith and his associates (55–58). The enzyme is strikingly activated by Mn^{2+}. A summary of part of the data on the susceptibility to this enzyme of a variety of amino acid amides is given in Table 20–14. The range of susceptible substrates is rather broad and goes beyond that

TABLE 20–14

Hydrolysis of α-Amino Acid Amides by Leucine Aminopeptidase (58)[a]

Substrate (L-form)	Relative Rate (L-leucine amide = 100)	Substrate (L-form)	Relative Rate (L-leucine amide = 100)
Leucine amide	100	Lysine amide	7
Norleucine amide	101	Arginine amide	7
Norvaline amide	84	Alanine amide	3
α-Aminocaprylamide	75	Aspartic acid diamide	3
α-Amino-n-butyramide	36	Isoglutamine	2
Phenylalanine amide	26	Serine amide	0.8
Tryptophan amide	24	Proline amide	0.7
Isoleucine amide	20	Hydroxyproline amide	0.6
Histidine amide	19	Glycine amide	0.1
Valine amide	17	$tert$-Leucine amide	0.1
Tyrosine amide	16	D-Leucine amide	0.0
Alloisoleucine amide	7		

[a] Hydrolysis conducted in the presence of Mn^{2+}. Rate of hydrolysis for L-leucine amide in terms of zero-order proteolytic coefficient, 14,000, which is the per cent hydrolysis per minute divided by the enzyme level in mg. protein N per ml. of digest.

implied by the restricted designation of the enzyme to derivatives of leucine (cf. 58).

In the course of the program on the resolution of amino acids via the asymmetric action of the renal acylases on α-N-acylated amino acids undertaken in the writers' Laboratory, it soon became apparent that certain representatives of this class of compounds were completely or nearly completely resistant to the action of the acylases (59). It was therefore necessary in these cases to seek an alternative procedure which would maintain the advantages basic to the acylase procedure but necessarily involve other types of substrates susceptible to an enzyme other than acylase. This alternative procedure was found in the use of the α-amino acid amides which were asymmetrically hydrolyzed by a renal amidase to the (generally) water-soluble, ethanol-insoluble, L-amino acid, and the corresponding ethanol-soluble D-amino acid amide. Because of their greatly different solubility properties, these products might be expected to be readily separable (Chapter 9). The amidase itself employed for the purpose stated was a crude fraction of hog kidney aqueous homogenate the specific activity of which had been increased over that of the homogenate (L-leucine amide as substrate) some 16-fold (60). Manganese ions provided a potent activator of the enzyme whose optimal pH level of activity was about 8.0. This system was applied to the resolution of the amides of the following racemic amino acids: proline (61), *tert*-leucine (60), diaminopimelic acid (DL- and *meso*-) (62, 63), and S-benzylpenicillamine (8). What relation the amidase employed in these resolutions bears to leucine aminopeptidase, other than that both are isolated from the same source, is not entirely clear in view of the fact that neither preparation is quite pure, and the activity of each has been described in different terms. Leucine aminopeptidase has recently been successfully employed by Tanaka and Izumiya (64) for the resolution of the amides of racemic phenylalanine and α-amino-γ-phenylbutyric acid; in the course of this work the authors reported that, depending on the concentration of substrate, the susceptibility of the amide of aminophenylbutyric acid to the enzyme was equal to or greater than that of leucine amide.

Preparation of hog kidney amidase (60). Fresh-frozen hog kidney is thawed, stripped of fat, and 1 kg. of the diced material is homogenized in the Waring Blendor with 2 l. of ice-cold water. The homogenate is strained through cheesecloth and centrifuged for 20 min. at 1200 × g to remove cellular débris. The specific activity of the supernatant against L-leucine amide is 200 micromoles of the substrate hydrolyzed per hour per mg. N. For the next step, a portion of the supernatant that can be handled in a single operation of the centrifuge is measured out, chilled in an ice-salt bath to nearly 0°, and treated with 2N HCl very carefully and with gentle stirring until a pH of 5.0 is reached. The thick suspension which appears is immediately centrifuged down at 3600 × g for 30 min. at 0°, discarded, and the clear, red-colored supernatant without delay brought to pH 6.5 by the careful addition of 2N NaOH. At this stage the specific activity is 370 micromoles of substrate hydrolyzed per hour per mg. N.

When the entire homogenate has been so treated, the combined supernatants (at pH 6.5) are treated with solid ammonium sulfate in the amount of 350 g. per l. After 30–60 min. of standing at 5°, the precipitate is removed by centrifugation in a Spinco batch bowl at 20,000 r.p.m. for 20 min., and to the supernatant an additional 220 g. of ammonium sulfate is supplied per liter. The protein which emerges from the solution on standing at 5° for 1 or 2 hr. is highly active as an amidase. It is centrifuged at 5° as above, the supernatant discarded, the precipitate taken up in cold water, and the resulting solution dialyzed for several hours against running tap water. The clear, deep-red solution remaining in the sack is quickly frozen and lyophilized. The red powder so obtained is very soluble in water, stable on storage at 5°, with a specific activity of 1800 micromoles of L-leucine amide hydrolyzed per hour per mg. N, and with relatively little loss of the total activity originally present in the first tissue homogenate.

Three grams of the lyophilized enzyme powder is dissolved in 480 ml. of water, a few drops of M sodium acetate solution added to raise the pH to 7.0, and 120 ml. of a calcium phosphate gel (20 mg. solids per ml.) is added and mixed. The resulting suspension is centrifuged and the fluid discarded. For elution, 100 ml. of $0.1M$ phosphate buffer at pH 7.0 is thoroughly stirred with the gel, and the whole centrifuged. Most of the activity is found in the extract, which is dialyzed free of phosphate and subsequently lyophilized to yield a light, yellowish white powder. Half the amount of the dried protein is lost as a result of this adsorption step, but the specific activity rises to 3200–3400 micromoles of L-leucine amide hydrolyzed per hour per mg. N. The susceptibility of several amino acid amides to this preparation is depicted in Table 20-15.

TABLE 20–15

Initial Hydrolytic Rates with Hog Kidney Amidase[a,b]

Amide	Rate[c]
L-Leucine amide	3200
D-Leucine amide	0
Acetyl-L-leucinamide	0
L-Alanine amide	128
L-Phenylalanine amide	1950
Glycyl-L-phenylalanine amide	493
L-Proline amide	7
L-tert-Leucine amide	12
Diaminopimelic acid diamide (DL + meso)	75
DL-Serine amide	56
S-Benzyl-DL-penicillamine amide	5

[a] Digests composed of 0.7 ml. of $0.2M$ "tris" buffer at pH 8.0, 1 ml. of enzyme solution, 1 ml. of $0.05M$ racemic, or $0.025M$ optically active substrate, and 0.3 ml. of $0.1M$ MnCl$_2$.

[b] These data are from the writers' Laboratory, for the most part hitherto unpublished.

[c] In terms of micromoles per hour per mg. N., the rate being determined by measurement of the ammonia evolved from the substrates.

ASSAY METHOD. The rate at which either product of the amidase reaction appears, i.e., amino acid or ammonia, can be taken as a measure of the activity of the enzyme. Where both products have been measured simultaneously at selected time intervals, the amino acid by the manometric ninhydrin-CO_2 procedure (Chapter 12), and the ammonia by the aeration-titration procedure described below, the expected 1:1 relation is observed (61).

Two mixtures are prepared in 20 x 150 mm. test tubes, each containing 0.7 ml. of 0.2M "tris" buffer at pH 8.0, 0.3 ml. of 0.1M manganese chloride, and 1.0 ml. of suitably diluted enzyme preparation in water. To one of the mixtures 1 ml. of neutralized 0.025M L-leucine amide is added, and both are incubated at 37° for a known period of time. At the end of this time period, 0.4 ml. of N acetic acid is added to both mixtures to stop amidase activity, then 1 ml. of the substrate solution is added to the mixture (control) previously lacking it. The mixtures are placed in a boiling water bath for 10 min., and then set aside to cool and to await the determination of either free amino acid or liberated ammonia. Independent determinations, under the same conditions, of mixtures of buffer, activator, and substrate incubated at 37° for the same period of time must also be made to assure the absence of any non-enzymic hydrolysis of the substrate; all amino acid amides so far investigated, however, have been found to be completely stable.

For the determination of ammonia, the digestion tubes are set up in a train with receivers of the same dimensions, each of which contains a trapping solution of 2 ml. of 2% boric acid to which bromocresol green and methyl red in 5:1 ratio have been added. All tubes are fitted for aeration, with a No. 2 two-hole rubber stopper carrying a 5-mm. glass tubing inlet reaching to the bottom of the tube and an outlet tube of the same dimension protruding no more than 5 mm. below the stopper. The tubes are connected in series by short lengths of rubber tubing. In the presence of manganese ions in strongly alkaline solutions exposed to oxygen, many amino acid amides appear to undergo appreciable hydrolysis. Consequently the ammonia distillation is accomplished by sweeping the train through with nitrogen rather than with air. Starting with the tube adjacent to the nitrogen source, one or two drops of caprylic alcohol and 1 ml. of saturated potassium carbonate are added to each digestion tube, and the stopper is inserted immediately. The alkali is added down the side of the tube carefully so as not to disturb the mixture and thereby liberate ammonia prematurely, and the stopper is inserted with some care for the same reason. When the entire train is connected, the nitrogen gas is admitted at a rate sufficient to carry the ammonia over into the receivers, but not so vigorous as to cause droplets of the alkaline solution to be carried over as well. As the boric acid-indicator mixture adsorbs ammonia, the color changes from the initial pink to a bluish green. After 60 min. of distillation the tubes are disconnected, the tube farthest from the nitrogen source being first. The inlet tubes of the receivers are rinsed down with water, and the contents of each diluted to about 8–10 ml. by addition of water, and titrated with 0.005–0.01N HCl delivered by means of an ultramicro burette. The pink-colored endpoint is compared with the color of 2 ml. of the original 2% boric acid-indicator trapping mixture diluted to 8–10 ml. with water.

The ammonia released from the alkalinized digestion mixtures can also be trapped in 2% sulfuric acid solution, and measured colorimetrically by the addition to the receiver, brought to exactly 9 ml. volume with water, of 1 ml. of Nessler's reagent. Comparison of the density of the color obtained thereby with that secured in the same manner with standard solutions of ammonium sulfate permits a determination of the ammonia trapped by the procedure described.

Inasmuch as the degree of hydrolysis up to 30 to 40% of the total is directly proportional to the period of incubation of the enzymic mixture, the activity can be expressed within this limitation in terms of a zero-order reaction, i.e. in terms of micromoles of substrate hydrolyzed per hour per milligram of protein N.

8. Renal D-Amino Acid Oxidase. The properties and distribution in mammalian tissues of an enzyme which catalyzes the oxidation of a large number of D-amino acids was described by Krebs in 1933 (65) and again in 1935 (66). The most active tissue in respect to this phenomenon was found to be in the kidney. Not long after, Warburg and Christian (67) succeeded in purifying the enzyme and identifying it as a flavoprotein, capable of removing two hydrogen atoms from the susceptible amino acid and subsequently transferring them to molecular oxygen to form hydrogen peroxide (cf. 68). One of the two hydrogen atoms so transferred comes from the α-amino group, the other from combination with the α-carbon atom, leaving as residue an unstable α-imino acid. The existence of the α-imino acid, originally suggested by Knoop (69), has never been experimentally demonstrated, but the following facts may be cited in its support: (a) the appearance among the products of the oxidase reaction of hydrogen peroxide (in the absence of catalase activity), (b) the complete resistance to the oxidase of α-methylamino acids which possess a free α-amino group but lack a hydrogen on the α-carbon atom, and of amino acids in which both amino hydrogen atoms are substituted by alkyl groups, and (c) the appearance among the products of the reaction of equivalent amounts of ammonia and the corresponding α-keto acid (again in the absence of catalase) which could readily be conceived as arising from the spontaneous hydrolysis of an unstable α-imino acid. The reactions which appear to be involved are

$$RCH(NH_2)CO_2H + \text{oxidase (FAD)} \longrightarrow [RC(=NH)CO_2H] + \text{oxidase (FAD-H}_2)$$

where FAD refers to flavin adenine dinucleotide, and the hypothetical α-imino acid is represented in brackets.

$$[RC(=NH)CO_2H] \xrightarrow{H_2O} RC(=O)CO_2H + NH_3$$

$$\text{Oxidase (FAD-H}_2) + O_2 \longrightarrow \text{oxidase (FAD)} + H_2O_2$$

In the absence of catalase, the hydrogen peroxide so formed reacts with the α-keto acid by a decarboxylation mechanism to produce carbon dioxide and a fatty acid with one carbon atom less than the keto acid:

$$RC(=O)CO_2H + H_2O_2 \rightarrow RCO_2H + CO_2$$

so that the over-all reaction of the oxidase—*in the absence of catalase*—is expressed as

$$RCH(NH_2)CO_2H + O_2 \rightarrow RCO_2H + CO_2 + NH_3$$

Renal tissue possesses a high catalase activity, and it is quite difficult to purify D-amino acid oxidase preparations from this peroxide-splitting catalyst. However, on addition of cyanide, the catalase contaminant is completely inhibited without affecting the amino acid oxidase appreciably. *In the presence of catalase*, the hydrogen peroxide formed by the oxidase reaction is decomposed to water and molecular oxygen, i.e., $H_2O_2 \rightarrow H_2O + \frac{1}{2}O_2$, and the over-all reaction under these conditions is then expressed as

$$RCH(NH_2)CO_2H + \tfrac{1}{2}O_2 \rightarrow RC(=O)CO_2H + NH_3$$

These reactions hold for all the susceptible D-amino acids studied (19; cf. 70), except for the D-isomers of proline, hydroxyproline, and pipecolic acid whose oxidation is not accompanied by the release of ammonia. Thus the oxidation of D-proline by crude D-amino acid oxidase leads initially to Δ'-pyrroline-2-carboxylic acid (which is essentially an α-imino acid as envisaged by Knoop, see above) which then is hydrated to form α-keto-δ-amino-*n*-valeric acid; the last-mentioned compound is also the end product of the oxidation of D-ornithine by D-amino acid oxidase (71). The reactions involving the oxidation of D-proline are

```
CH₂—CH₂           CH₂—CH₂
|    |      ½O₂   |    |       H₂O
CH₂  CHCO₂H  —→  CH₂  CCO₂H  —→  CH₂(NH₂)CH₂CH₂C(=O)CO₂H
 \  /              \ //
  NH                N
D-Proline    Δ'-Pyrroline-2-carboxylic acid    α-Keto-δ-amino-n-valeric acid
```

With D-pipecolic acid, the initial oxidation product is Δ'-piperidine-2-carboxylic acid. In the case of the enzymic oxidation of the D-diastereomers of hydroxyproline, it was found by Radhakrishnan and Meister (72) that the end product was 2-pyrrolecarboxylic acid, formed very probably by way of the intermediate α-keto-γ-hydroxy-δ-amino-*n*-valeric acid as follows:

```
HO—CH——CH₂           ⎡HO—CH—CH₂  ⎤           CH——CH
    |    |      ½O₂  ⎢    |    |  ⎥  −2H₂O   ||    ||
   CH₂  CHCO₂H  —→   ⎢   CH₂  C—CO₂H⎥  —→    CH    CCO₂H
     \  /            ⎢         ||  ⎥          \   /
      NH             ⎣    NH₂   O  ⎦           NH
D-Hydroxyproline      α-Keto-γ-hydroxy-δ-     2-Pyrrolecarboxylic
                      amino-n-valeric acid        acid
```

In vivo studies led to substantially the same conclusion (73).

In Table 20–16 are gathered data of the effect of D-amino acid oxidase isolated in crude form from hog kidney, and containing adherent catalase, on a series of pure D-amino acids (19). A summary of the requirements for the action of this enzyme follows: (a) a D-configuration on the α-carbon atom (cf. Chapter 2); (b) the presence of a free α-carboxyl group; (c) the presence of a free amino group which can be either primary or secondary, but not tertiary; and (d) the presence of a hydrogen atom on the α-carbon (e.g., D-isovaline is completely resistant). With the straight-chain aliphatic amino acids, the oxidative rate decreases on passing from the C_3- to the C_4- and C_5-amino acids, rises progressively to the C_6- and C_7-amino acids, and thereafter progressively diminishes to D-α-aminododecylic acid which, under the conditions employed, is apparently inert (Figure 42–1). These results are compatible with the earlier data by Bender and Krebs (70) obtained through the use of sheep kidney D-amino acid oxidase and a variety of DL-amino acids.

As a rule, the presence of additional polar groups in ω-positions on potential substrates tends to diminish the action of the enzyme. Thus D-glutamic acid is much less susceptible than is D-norvaline, and D-lysine is practically resistant whereas D-norleucine is very susceptible (Table 20–16). However, masking of the ε-amino group of D-lysine by acylation serves to raise the susceptibility to enzymic oxidation (74–76) (Table 20–16).

D-Amino acid oxidase tested with D-alanine shows a sharp optimum activity at pH 8.8 (71). However, the greater stability of the enzyme at more nearly neutral reactions makes the working range of pH 8.0–8.3 preferable. The nature of the buffer also appears to influence the stability of the enzyme, pyrophosphate being more favorable in this respect than either veronal acetate or tris(hydroxymethyl)aminomethane at the same pH. It is possible that the higher activity of the enzyme in pyrophosphate-containing solutions may be ascribed to the removal of inhibitory heavy metals ordinarily present in the crude preparations of the enzyme.

The oxidase attains maximal activity toward D-valine at about $0.02M$ concentration of the substrate. When diastereomeric amino acids are employed as substrates, the effect of concentration of the substrate may be different for each diastereomer (Chapter 2). Thus, according to Table 20–16, the rate of oxidation of D-isoleucine under the stated conditions was more than double that of D-alloisoleucine. On increasing the substrate concentration, everything else being kept constant, the rate of oxidation of the former compound remained the same but that of the latter very considerably increased (19). Again, on increasing the substrate concentration, the enzymic oxidation of the D-isomer of threonine and of allothreonine increased, that of the latter more than that of the former, e.g., to 0.6 for D-threonine, and to 4.5 for D-allothreonine (19). The D-forms of isoleucine and of alloisoleucine yield on oxidation the corresponding optically active α-keto-β-methyl-n-valeric

TABLE 20-16
Enzymic Oxidation of Optically Active Amino Acids (19)

Amino Acid	Oxidation[a] of L-Isomer by Rattlesnake Venom[c]	Oxidation[b] of D-Isomer by Hog Kidney Preparation[d]
Alanine	0.9	10.5
Butyrine	49	7.1
Norvaline	181	6.7
Norleucine	192	13.6
Heptyline	142	14.6
Capryline	102	6.1
Nonyline	61	4.0
Decyline	35	1.0
Undecyline	13	0.2
Dodecyline	1.0	0
Valine	9.0	9.9
Isovaline	0	0
Leucine	225	7.8
Isoleucine	71	14.8
Alloisoleucine	0.8	5.9
tert-Leucine	0	0
Serine	0	2.8
Homoserine	8.0	3.2
Pentahomoserine	53.0	1.8
Hexahomoserine	201	3.2
Threonine	0	0.3
Allothreonine	0.9	2.6
Methionine	243	15.6
Ethionine	242	8.5
Cystine	63	1.4
Homocystine	84	0.9
S-Benzylcysteine	155	3.5
S-Benzylhomocysteine	108	8.3
Aspartic acid	0.1	4.6
Glutamic acid	0.2	0.3
α-Aminoadipic acid	17	0[e]
β-Aminoalanine	0.1	2.7
γ-Aminobutyrine	0.2	0.7
Ornithine	0.3	1.6
Lysine	0.4	0
β-Acetylaminoalanine	0.9	—
γ-Chloroacetylaminobutyrine	37.7	—
δ-Chloroacetylornithine	51.5	—

TABLE 20–16 (continued)

Amino Acid	Oxidation[a] of L-Isomer by Rattlesnake Venom[c]	Oxidation[b] of D-Isomer by Hog Kidney Preparation[d]
ε-Chloroacetyllysine	58.3	–
ε-Acetyllysine	65.1	2.4 calc.[f]
δ-Acetylornithine	–	0.8 calc.[f]
Histidine	35	0.8
Arginine	18	1.0
Citrulline	98	0.9
Phenylalanine	185	9.6
Tyrosine	185	11.1
Tryptophan	199	3.0
Aminophenylacetic acid	5	4.0
Aminocyclohexylacetic acid	4.0	7.5
Aminocyclohexylpropionic acid	92	4.4
β-Phenylserine (threo)	0.7	0
β-Phenylserine (erythro)	140	0
Proline	0	20.3
Hydroxyproline	0	5.0
Allohydroxyproline	0	6.1
Pipecolic acid[g]	0	3.0

[a] Ten micromoles of substrate at pH 7.2 (5 micromoles in the case of cystine and homocystine), dissolved or suspended in 2 ml. of $0.1M$ tris(hydroxymethyl)aminomethane buffer at pH 7.2, and 0.1 ml. of catalase solution containing approximately 0.6 unit were placed in the main compartment of the Warburg vessel. The side arm contained 0.3 ml. of the enzyme solution and the center well, KOH. Temperature, 37°; gas phase, air. Rates in terms of micromoles of oxygen consumed per hour per mg. N.

[b] As above, except that pH 8.2 pyrophosphate buffer at $0.05M$ was used, and the enzyme solution was in 0.4 ml. volume. Rates as above. Catalase present as contaminant of the preparation of D-amino acid oxidase.

[c] *Crotalus adamanteus.*

[d] Preparation described in text.

[e] A five-fold increase in substrate concentration resulted in a rate of 0.6 in the terms given above.

[f] From data of Neuberger and Sanger (74).

[g] From data by Dr. J. R. Parikh in the writers' Laboratory.

acids (77, 78) (see Chapter 3), an indication that α,β-unsaturation of the substrate is not involved in the enzymic oxidation mechanism. This is further borne out by the fact that D-aminophenylacetic acid, which does not possess a hydrogen on the β-carbon atom, is readily oxidized by renal D-amino acid oxidase (Table 20–16) (cf. 79). D-Lysine is inert to D-amino acid oxidase, and is also inhibitory to the action of this enzyme toward more susceptible substrates (79a).

The oxidation of a susceptible D-amino acid by D-amino acid oxidase is not inhibited by the presence of a very considerable excess of the corresponding L-antipode, which permits thereby the ready use of this enzyme to detect very small amounts of susceptible D-amino acids as impurities in preparations of L-amino acids (Chapter 19). The enzyme is, however, inhibited by benzoic acid, and by various compounds containing double bonds (80, 81). Although the oxidase is not inhibited by amino acids containing an aromatic nucleus, it is strongly inhibited by such α-keto acids and fatty acids as contain an aromatic group or some type of ring form with double bonds, and thus the oxidation of the D-isomers of tyrosine, tryptophan, phenylalanine, and hydroxyproline is inhibited by the products of the reaction. In these cases, the oxidative reaction is brought to completion with difficulty if at all. For the preparation of the pure L-isomers of these compounds by the action of D-amino acid oxidase on the respective racemates (Chapters 9 and 19), it is evidently necessary to overcome this inhibition and permit the oxidation of the D-isomer to go to completion. This was accomplished in the cases of phenylalanine and of hydroxyproline by carrying on the oxidation in the presence of cyanide (82). The employment of this ion, by inhibiting the catalase present in the oxidase, permitted the accumulated hydrogen peroxide, in the oxidation of D-phenylalanine, to produce the less toxic phenylacetic acid from the more toxic phenylpyruvic acid, and, in the oxidation of D-hydroxyproline, to produce the non-toxic β-hydroxy-γ-aminobutyric acid (from the intermediate α-keto-γ-hydroxy-δ-n-valeric acid—see above) instead of the highly toxic 2-pyrrolecarboxylic acid (72). (Under the same conditions, the oxidation of D-proline would lead to the innocuous γ-aminobutyric acid). In this manner, optically pure L-phenylalanine (Section 34–4) and L-hydroxyproline (Section 29–4) were prepared by the action of the oxidase on the respective racemates. The same treatment, i.e., cyanide addition, failed to yield optically pure L-tyrosine, the products of the enzymic oxidation being much too inhibitory (82).

Figure 20–1, from Parikh et al. (82), illustrates the comparative inhibitory effects of 2-pyrrolecarboxylic acid and of β-phenylpyruvic acid on the oxidation of DL-alanine by hog kidney D-amino acid oxidase. From the data, the K_s value of DL-alanine is of the order of 3.5×10^{-3} mole per liter, whilst the K_i values for the inhibitors are 9.9×10^{-6} and 6.3×10^{-4} mole per liter, respectively. It appears that the 2-pyrrolecarboxylic acid is bound to the enzyme about 1000 times more strongly, the phenylpyruvic acid about 10 times more strongly, than is the substrate (82).

PREPARATION OF D-AMINO ACID OXIDASE. A highly active and relatively pure D-amino acid oxidase preparation without appreciable catalase activity can be obtained from sheep kidney by the method of Negelein and Brömel (83, 84). Such preparations have been found to oxidize 25 micromoles of D-proline at 37° and at pH 8.3 at a rate of 1000–2000 microliters of oxygen absorbed per hour per milligram of protein (84), or roughly 700 micromoles of oxygen consumed per hour per milligram of nitrogen.

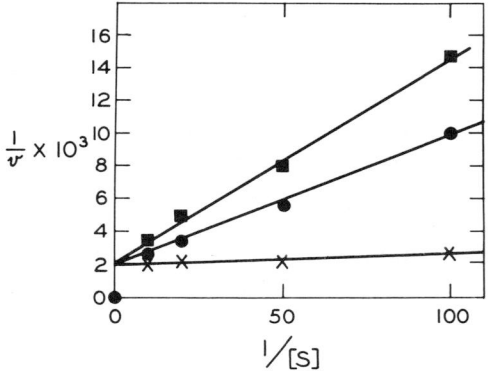

Figure 20–1. Effect of $1 \times 10^{-4}M$ 2-pyrrolecarboxylic acid (●) and of $10^{-2}M$ phenylpyruvic acid (■) on the oxidation at 37° of DL-alanine by hog renal D-amino acid oxidase. Reaction without inhibitor represented by crosses: $v = \mu l$. of O_2 consumed per hour, [S] = molar concentration of susceptible D-isomer of substrate at 2×10^{-1}, 4×10^{-2}, and $2 \times 10^{-2}M$. Parikh, J. R., Greenstein, J. P., Winitz, M., and Birnbaum, S. M., *J. Am. Chem. Soc.*, **80**, 953 (1958).

For less exacting requirements, a cruder but still satisfactory preparation of D-amino acid oxidases can be obtained from hog kidney, which contains catalase in varying but usually excessive amounts, and which oxidizes 10 micromoles of D-proline at a rate of 20 micromoles of oxygen consumed per hour per milligram of nitrogen (Table 20–16). The procedure herein described leads to a water-soluble powder which can be stored for months at 5° without serious loss of activity, and which, when dissolved in pyrophosphate buffer at pH 8.2 and at 37°, absorbs very little oxygen.

Illustrative procedure for the preparation of D-amino acid oxidase from hog kidney. Fresh-frozen hog kidney is thawed, defatted, cut into small pieces, and homogenized in a Waring Blendor for 1 min. with 10 volumes of cold acetone. The resulting suspension is filtered with suction over Whatman No. 4 paper. The filter cake is blended with 5 volumes of cold acetone and again filtered. After the filter cake is washed with cold ethyl ether, the solvents are removed in a vacuum desiccator. When the cake is thoroughly dry, it is extracted with twice its weight of water in the Blendor and the extract either filtered or centrifuged clear. The extraction is repeated and the combined supernatant solutions are quick-frozen and lyophilized. About 18 g. of a light easily soluble powder is thus obtained from

600 g. of defatted kidney. It is this preparation whose effect on various D-amino acids is described in Table 20–16.

D- or DL-Alanine is usually employed as the standard substrate for the assay of mammalian D-amino acid oxidase activity. The most frequently employed procedure involves the manometric determination of the oxygen consumed during the reaction. Ten micromoles of the substrate (20 micromoles if the racemic modification is employed) dissolved in 2 ml. of $0.05M$ sodium pyrophosphate buffer at pH 8.2 is placed in the main compartment of a Warburg vessel. The center well contains filter paper soaked in 20% KOH. The appropriately diluted enzyme solution in 0.4 ml. volume is placed in the side arm. The gas phase is usually air. After equilibrium at 37°, the enzyme is tipped in and manometric readings at 5-min. intervals are recorded. Reaction rates expressed in micromoles of substrate consumed per hour per milligram of protein nitrogen can be determined from the initial linear relation between time and oxygen uptake. The readings are corrected for enzyme blanks run simultaneously, buffer being used only in the main compartment, with all other components of the mixture present. One micromole of the optically pure D-amino acid consumes at 37° (and in the presence of the oxidase and of catalase) 1 microatom of oxygen gas. The manometer reading of this volume, multiplied by the calibration factor of the system to bring to standard conditions, is 11.2 μl. Ten micromoles of the optically pure substrate will therefore consume 112 μl. of oxygen gas with the formation of ammonia and the corresponding α-keto acid.

9. L-Amino Acid Oxidase. This enzyme, if it occurs at all in mammalian tissues, is very weakly active. On the other hand, as first shown by Zeller (85), it is present to an astonishingly high level in the venoms of a number of species of snakes. The enzyme acts exclusively on L-amino acids, and exerts no measurable effect on any D-amino acid known. The oxidation mechanism appears to be identical with that described above for D-amino acid oxidase. Thus the mixture of venom L-amino acid oxidase and susceptible L-amino acid absorbs one molecule of oxygen gas with the production of ammonia, the corresponding α-keto acid, and hydrogen peroxide; inasmuch as the venoms generally lack catalase, the peroxide acts upon the α-keto acid with the formation of carbon dioxide and a fatty acid with one carbon atom less than the keto acid. If the α-keto acid is to be saved, catalase must be added to the reaction mixture, whereby not one molecule but one atom of oxygen is consumed in the oxidative reaction (79).

Singer and Kearney (86) have isolated and purified the enzyme from the venom of the moccasin, and have shown that, like D-amino acid oxidase, the prosthetic group of the enzyme is flavin adenine dinucleotide. In accord with this observation is the finding (85) that the activity of the L-amino acid oxidase parallels the intensity of the yellow color of the venom or purified fraction thereof; thus a white venom sample of *Vipera aspis* exhibited a Q_{O_2} value (L-leucine as substrate, where Q_{O_2} is described in terms of microliters of oxygen absorbed per hour per milligram of venom) of about 3, whereas a yellow-colored venom from the same species possessed a Q_{O_2} value, under the same conditions, of about 600. That the venoms vary widely in activity according to the species of snake was observed by Zeller (85), and is illustrated in part by Table 20–17 taken from data by Singer and Kearney (86), and by Table 20–18 constructed by Dr. W. K. Paik in the writers' Laboratory.

TABLE 20–17

Oxidation of L-Leucine by Various Snake Venoms (86)

Source of Enzyme	Family	$Q_{O_2}^{a,b}$
Crotalus viridis	Crotalidae	777
Crotalus horridus	Crotalidae	227
Crotalus adamanteus	Crotalidae	743
Crotalus atrox	Crotalidae	416
Crotalus terrificus	Crotalidae	296
Sistrurus catenatus	Crotalidae	524
Agkistrodon piscivorus	Crotalidae	630
Agkistrodon mokasen	Crotalidae	234
Naja naja	Elapidae	132
Naja flava	Elapidae	56
Micrurus fulvius	Elapidae	158
Bungarus coeruleus	Elapidae	193
Echis cantenatus	Viperidae	236
Vipera russelli	Viperidae	600

[a] Digests consisted of 0.7 mg. of dried venom in 3 ml. of 0.01M tris(hydroxymethyl)aminomethane buffer at pH 7.2 which was 7 × 10⁻³M with respect to L-leucine. $T = 38°$.
[b] Q_{O_2} = μl. of O_2 uptake per hour per mg. of dried venom.

The susceptibility of various L-amino acids to the action of the L-amino acid oxidase present in the crude venom of *Crotalus adamanteus* is described in Tables 20–16 (19), 20–18, and 2–33. The substrate requirements include (a) an L-configuration at the α-carbon atom, and (b) a free primary α-amino group; e.g., L-proline, L-hydroxyproline, and L-pipecolic acid are completely resistant to L-amino acid oxidase. ω-Acylation of L-α,ω-diamino acids, again, confers an increase in susceptibility to the oxidase over that characteristic of the corresponding free diamino acids under the same conditions (Table 20–16) (75, 87), and this property, for example, has been employed as a preparative method for obtaining pure D-lysine from the reaction of *Crotalus adamanteus* L-amino acid oxidase on ε-carbobenzoxy-DL-lysine (Section 32–4). Although free L-lysine and L-ornithine are oxidized relatively slowly by most venoms, reference to Table 20–18 indicates that these compounds are quite rapidly oxidized by the venom of *Naja hanna*; even γ-amino-L-butyrine and β-amino-L-alanine are not inconsiderably oxidized by the L-amino acid oxidase of this venom. L-Glutamine and L-asparagine, in

TABLE 20-18
Rates of Oxidation of Some of the Less Susceptible Amino Acids by Snake Venoms
(Data of Dr. W. K. Paik)[a]

Venom Employed	L-Serine	L-Allo-threonine	β-Amino-L-alanine	γ-Amino-L-butyrine	L-Ornithine	L-Lysine	Allo-γ-hydroxy-DL-glutamic Acid	γ-Hydroxy-DL-glutamic Acid	L-Leucine[b]
Bothrops atrox	0.2	1.1	0.5	0.2	0.9	2.7	0	0	92.8
Bothrops jararaca	0	0.8	0	0	0.3	0.3	0	0	19.8
Bungarus fasciatus	0	0	0	0	0	0	1.1	11.3	8.4
Bungarus candidus	0	0	0	0	0	0	2.1	12.0	9.3
Naja naja	0	0	0	0	0	0	0	0	9.7
Naja flava	0	0	0	0	0	0	0	0	8.5
Naja hanna	0.1	1.4	0.9	1.3	13.8	13.3	0	0	108.1
Agkistrodon piscivorus	0	0.6	0	0	0.2	0.3	0.2	0.2	124.0
Agkistrodon contortrix	0.1	0.9	0	0	0.3	0.3	0.0	0	99.2
Vipera russelli	0	0.4	0	0	1.1	2.6	0	0	83.1
Crotalus adamanteus	0.1	1.6	0.3	0.2	0.5	0.6	0.2	0.1	168.8
Crotalus d. terrificus	0.2	1.1	0.2	0.1	0.4	0.4	0	0	214.0
Crotalus viridis	0	0.5	0	0	0.9	0.5	0.3	0.3	—
Crotalus d. durissus	0.4	3.8	0.4	0.3	0.9	0.7	—	—	—
Crotalus basilicus	0	0.5	0	0	0.2	0	—	—	—

[a] In terms of micromoles of O_2 consumed per milligram of venom nitrogen per hour. Digests consisted of 0.3 ml. of a 1:20 dilution of catalase, 1.2 ml. of $0.1M$ pH 7.2 "tris" buffer, 1 ml. of substrate in buffer (10 micromoles of L-amino acid or 20 micromoles of DL-amino acid per milliliter), and 0.5 ml. of buffer containing 30 mg. of venom from side arm. Center well contained 0.2 ml. of 20% KOH. $T = 37°C$. Gas phase = air. L-Threonine, L-proline, L-hydroxyproline, and DL-α-aminotricarballylic acid were completely resistant to all venoms employed. Data from the writers' Laboratory.

[b] As above, except that 3 mg. of venom per vessel was used.

which the ω-carboxyl group is blocked by an amide substituted, are much more susceptible to enzymic oxidation than are the corresponding free aminodicarboxylic acids (79). γ-Hydroxy-L-glutamic acid, although resistant to most venoms, is readily oxidized by *Bungarus* venom (Table 20–18). The susceptibility toward *Crotalus adamanteus* of the homologous straight-chain amino acids shows a regular progression with chain length, with a maximum at C_6 (Figure 42–1).

The enzyme has been quite useful in the determination of the optical configuration at the β-center of L-amino acids with two centers of optical asymmetry. Thus Fones converted the L-forms of β-phenylserine and allo-β-phenylserine by means of oxidation through *Crotalus adamanteus* venom to the corresponding pure D- and L-mandelic acids (88). A more extended discussion of this field of investigation is given in Chapter 2, and only a brief reference to the data on the diastereomeric isoleucines may be mentioned here. According to the data in Table 20–16, the ratio of the oxidative rates of L-isoleucine to L-alloisoleucine is about 90:1. When the concentration of these substrates was increased five-fold, this ratio became nearer 8:1, owing to the greatly augmented rate of oxidation of the allo stereomer (19). The results in Table 20–16 were obtained in the presence of "tris" buffer. When phosphate buffer was used at the same pH in place of the "tris" buffer, a very considerable reduction in the rate of oxidation of L-isoleucine occurred, whereas the rate of oxidation of the L-alloisoleucine stereomer remained unchanged, the ratio of the two rates being in this instance close to 3:1 (19). The inhibition of the oxidation of L-amino acids by certain venoms in the presence of phosphate ions was first reported by Singer and Kearney (86), and this property, unrecognized by many of the early workers in this field, has rendered much of their kinetic measurements difficult to interpret. The optimum activity for most of the snake venom L-amino acid oxidases which have been studied lies between 7.2 and 7.5, the pH being preferably established by means of tris(hydroxymethyl)amino methane buffers. Under these conditions, the venom is quite stable and may be employed several times. It is more active in oxygen than in air.

The L-amino acid oxidase of snake venoms is not inhibited by large quantities of D-amino acids, and hence is suitable for the determination of the presence of very small amounts of susceptible L-amino acids as possible contaminants of D-amino acid preparations obtained by resolution of the corresponding racemates (Chapter 19). The enzyme is also not inhibited by the products of the oxidation, including the α-keto acids derived from phenylalanine, tyrosine, and tryptophan, and in this respect it differs sharply from renal D-amino acid oxidase (see above). Inasmuch as the reaction on susceptible substrates almost invariably goes to completion, the preparation, therefore, of the optically pure D-isomers of phenylalanine, tyrosine, and tryptophan by the action of crude *Crotalus adamanteus* L-amino acid oxidase on the corresponding racemates is readily accomplished (82) (Chapter 9).

For the practical use of snake venom L-amino acid oxidase in the determination of the optical purity of D-amino acids (Chapter 19) or in the preparation of D-amino acids from the corresponding racemates (Chapter 9), the crude venoms are usually sufficiently active and stable to be employed directly. A short dialysis of aqueous solutions of the venom for 4–5 hours duration against cold water, followed by centrifugation and lyophilization of the supernatant solution, yields a preparation with no loss of activity, and free of small, contaminating, compounds which would otherwise contribute appreciably to the blank values. The standard substrate for the oxidase is either L-leucine or L-methionine, and the assay procedure is similar to that described above for D-amino acid oxidase except that (a) a "tris" buffer at pH 7.2 and at $0.1M$ is employed, and (b) 0.1 ml. of a catalase solution containing approximately 6 units is added from the side arm of the flask. The substrate concentration is 10 micromoles of the L-form in 2 ml. of the buffer, to which 0.3 ml. of the venom in "tris" buffer is added from the side arm, simultaneously with the catalase solution. Rates of oxidation proportional to enzyme activity can be calculated in terms of micromoles of substrate oxidized per hour per milligram of venom nitrogen from the initial linear relation between period of incubation (shaking) at 38° and oxygen consumption; the blank value is usually negligible.

10. Amino Acid Decarboxylases of Bacterial Origin. In contrast with such enzymes as the acylases, amidases, peptidases, and oxidases which act upon amino acids or amino acid derivatives as a class of compounds, there exist in nature several enzymes which act exclusively on specific amino acids and occasionally on amino acids closely resembling them. Included in this category are such representatives as hepatic arginase, hepatic histidase, hepatic cysteine desulfhydrase, hepatic glutamic acid dehydrogenase, renal aspartic acid oxidase, renal glutaminase, and hepatic threonine aldolase. These systems are characterized by the limitation of their action to certain chemical structures in susceptible substrates, and contain in their designations the particular name of these substrates; they share with the systems of more general application a dependence on a specific optical configuration in such substrates, and thus all the specific enzymes referred to, with the possible exception of aspartic acid oxidase, are exclusively L-directed.

Of particular interest in the characterization and identification of certain individual amino acids is the group of bacterial decarboxylases, of which six were early recognized to act upon individual and sharply limited substrates. These are the separate systems which act on the L-isomers of lysine, arginine, ornithine, glutamic acid, histidine, and tyrosine, and which are known as lysine decarboxylase, arginine decarboxylase, etc., respectively; their separation, description, and identifying characteristics are almost wholly based upon the outstanding efforts of Gale and his associates from 1940 to 1946 (cf. 89, 90). The fundamental reaction which all the amino acid decarboxylases demonstrate in common is

$$RCH(NH_2)CO_2H \rightarrow RCH_2NH_2 + CO_2$$

It is clear that the progress of the reaction can be followed by measuring the rate of appearance either of carbon dioxide (in acid media) or of amine. In most cases a manometric determination of the evolution of carbon dioxide is the simpler. However, the tyrosine decarboxylase from *Streptococcus faecalis* can also decarboxylate phenylalanine, as well as 3:4-dihydroxyphenylalanine, and if, for example, this enzyme is used to measure the level of tyrosine in a mixture containing either or both of the other susceptible amino acids mentioned, it would be necessary to follow the reaction by a determination of the specific amine formed (91, 92). A similar problem might be expected to arise because lysine decarboxylase also acts upon δ-hydroxylysine (93), and glutamic acid decarboxylase can also act upon β-hydroxyglutamic acid (94). It is of interest in this brief allusion to the minor lack of exact specificity of some of the bacterial decarboxylases to note that lysine decarboxylase is ineffective toward L-ornithine or toward α-N-methyl-, ε-N-methyl-, α-N-acetyl-, or ε-N-acetyl-L-lysine, whilst ornithine decarboxylase is ineffective toward L-lysine; tyrosine decarboxylase will not affect either O-methyl- or N-methyl-L-tyrosine, histidine decarboxylase is inert to α-N-acetyl-L-histidine and L-thiolhistidine, and glutamic acid decarboxylase is ineffective toward N-methylglutamic acid, α-ketoglutaric acid, N-methylglutamic acid, and glutathione. A similar example may be selected from the array of mammalian decarboxylases which demonstrates that renal 5-hydroxytryptophan decarboxylase is completely ineffective toward either L- or D-tryptophan (95). The reactions of the six bacterial decarboxylases developed by Gale and his associates are summarized in Table 20–19. To them are added the L-aspartic acid-β-decarboxylase system of Meister, Sober, and Tice (96) (Section 23–2) and the *meso*-α,ε-diaminopimelic acid decarboxylase prepared by Work and her associates (97) (Section 45–2).

Listed in Table 20–19 are the richest bacterial sources for the enzymes referred to. Exact proof for the presence of a specific decarboxylase for a single amino acid can only be demonstrated by isolation and identification of the amine formed by the enzymic reaction (98). No one organism possesses all the decarboxylases, and some bacteria possess none of them. The number of decarboxylases coexisting within any one bacterium may range from 0 to a maximum of 5. Gale (89) reported, for example, that, of 151 strains of *Escherichia coli* investigated, 114 possessed arginine decarboxylase; 142, lysine decarboxylase; 130, glutamic acid decarboxylase; 14, histidine

ENZYMES IN AMINO ACID TECHNOLOGY

decarboxylase; 6, tyrosine decarboxylase; and a few, ornithine decarboxylase. At full growth of the cells and under optimal conditions (pH 4–5), the activity of the arginine, lysine, and glutamic acid enzymes were, in most cases, of the same order (Q_{CO_2} approximately 200, where Q refers to microliters of carbon dioxide released at 30° per hour per milligram of dried cells), and of a much lower order in the other amino acid decarboxylases. No one enzyme ever appears to occur in constant association with any other.

TABLE 20-19
Bacterial Decarboxylase Reactions

Substrate	Reaction Products	Bacterial source
L-Lysine	CO_2 + α,δ-diaminopentane (putrescine)	*Bacterium cadaveris*
L-Arginine	CO_2 + α-amino-γ'-guanidobutane (agmatine)	*Escherichia coli*
L-Ornithine	CO_2 + α,γ-diaminobutane (cadaverine)	*Clostridium septicum* (PIII)
L-Glutamic acid	CO_2 + γ-aminobutyric acid (via α-decarboxylation)	*Clostridium welchii* SR 12
L-Histidine	CO_2 + β-aminoethylimidazole (histamine)	*Clostridium welchii* (type A)
L-Tyrosine	CO_2 + p-β-aminoethylphenol (tyramine)	*Streptococcus faecalis*
L-Aspartic acid	CO_2 + L-alanine (via β-decarboxylation)	*Clostridium welchii* SR 12
meso-α,ε-Diaminopimelic acid	CO_2 + L-lysine	*Aerobacter aerogenes*

Of 10 strains of *Clostridium welchii* (type A) examined, 9 possessed only histidine and glutamic acid decarboxylases, while strain SR 12 of this organism apparently possessed only the decarboxylase for glutamic acid. Four strains of *Clostridium septicum* all possessed ornithine decarboxylase exclusively, two strains of *Clostridium bifermentans* possessed only glutamic acid decarboxylase, one of two strains of *Clostridium fallax* possessed histidine decarboxylase, whilst *Clostridium aerofoetidum* had both tyrosine and glutamic acid decarboxylases. Many other strains of *Clostridia*, e.g., *sporogenes* and *tetani*, possess none of these enzymes. Of the *Streptococci*, 500 strains of *faecalis* possessed tyrosine decarboxylase to variable degrees, and no other known amino acid decarboxylase. The distribution among the different bacteria of the various enzymes was probably the first clue that these decarboxylases were individual entities. It is evident that, in order to possess a preparation with an exclusive decarboxylase activity toward a single substrate, it is necessary (a) to start with an organism which possesses such a single activity, or (b) to prepare a cell-free extract from an organism preferably with no more than two separate activities and by fractionation procedures destroy or completely remove all but one of them.

The presence of the decarboxylases in bacteria is frequently a result of adaptation during growth on media containing amino acids susceptible to the action of these enzymes. Thus, the *E. coli* organism grown in a glucose

TABLE 20-20

Adaptive Formation of Amino Acid Decarboxylases in *Escherichia coli*[a] (89, 98)

Addition to Salt-Glucose Medium of 1%

Decarboxylase for	None	Lysine	Arginine	Ornithine	Glutamate	Histidine	Tyrosine	Casein Hydrolysate
L-Lysine	4	210	—	4	—	—	—	194
L-Arginine	0	—	27	—	—	—	—	330
L-Ornithine	3	—	—	225	—	—	—	145
L-Glutamic acid	45	—	—	—	88	—	—	100
L-Histidine	0	—	—	—	—	7	—	18
L-Tyrosine	0	—	—	—	—	—	60	63

[a] The numerical data relate to values of Q_{CO_2} at 30° and pH 4–5, which represent decarboxylase activity in terms of microliters carbon dioxide evolved per hour per milligram dried cells.
[b] Medium composed only of inorganic salts including ammonium phosphate and pure amino acid where stated.

medium containing all the L-amino acids, as in a digest of casein, is found to possess the decarboxylases for the L-form of lysine, arginine, ornithine, glutamic acid, histidine, and tyrosine. If, however, the organism is grown on a simpler medium containing only ammonium phosphate and other salts together with glucose and L-glutamic acid, it will be found to possess only glutamic acid decarboxylase with no more than a trace of lysine decarboxylase. Only when the appropriate L-amino acid is introduced into the simple medium will the corresponding decarboxylase appear (Table 20-20) (89, cf. 98). The bacteria are grown in the media at a pH close to 5.0, and generally at temperatures of 20-26°. Formation of the enzymes themselves occurs at the later stage of growth, and reaches an optimum at about the time that active cell division ceases. The data in Table 20-20 indicate that the specific activity of the decarboxylases grown in the chemically defined media each supplemented by a single pure L-amino acid is, with the exception of arginine decarboxylase, of the same order of magnitude as that obtained in the casein hydrolysate medium containing all the protein-bound amino acids.

GENERAL PROCEDURE FOR GROWING BACTERIAL CELLS WITH ACTIVE DECARBOXYLASE ACTIVITY. The method employed by Gale and his associates involved the use of a casein digest–glucose mixture as the medium for the growth of all the bacteria investigated. Casein was suspended in water, sodium bicarbonate added until the pH of the suspension was 7.8, and an active preparation of trypsin added. After digestion of the mixture at 38° for about 3 weeks, the pH being kept at 7.8 throughout, the mixture was filtered, the filtrate brought to pH 5.5, heated, cooled, and filtered again. The clear filtrate was autoclaved, brought to pH 7.5, and diluted with sufficient sterile water to bring the concentration of total solids to about 3%. Glucose was then added to a concentration of 2%, and the final mixture, supplemented on occasion with yeast extract or minced heart muscle, was employed as the growth medium.

The medium, usually about 15 liters in volume, was inoculated with the individual type of organism (see Chapter 14), and the incubation permitted to continue at a definite temperature for a particular length of time. During the growth of the organisms the carbohydrate undergoes fermentation, producing an acidic reaction which is highly favorable for the development of the decarboxylases within the dividing cells (98). For most of the bacterial types studied, a pH of about 5 was optimal for bacterial growth. A more acid pH than 5 would come close to the limit of acid tolerance of most organisms. Growth at a pH of 7 or higher results in lack of decarboxylase development in the cells and, instead, a development of specific deaminases for amino acids, such as alanine deaminase and serine deaminase (99). The decarboxylases develop therefore in an acidic medium, at temperatures usually within the range 20–26°, and at a maximum rate shortly before active cell division ceases (100). At the end of the selected incubation period the cells are harvested in the Sharples supercentrifuge and washed once with cold water. Their further fate is an individual matter depending upon the bacterial type employed and upon the purpose desired.

The use of a crude casein digest–glucose mixture for the growth of a bacterial type presumed to develop a single amino acid decarboxylase is almost a contradiction in terms, for the dividing cells are obviously exposed to, and have the opportunity of adapting to, all the amino acids present in the digest. The crude casein employed for the digest was apparently sufficiently contaminated with B-vitamins to supply the co-factors required in the early studies on bacterial growth, these co-factors being later augmented by adding the crude yeast and muscle preparations alluded to (103). The use of the purified B-vitamins by Bellamy and Gunsalus (104, 105) demonstrated the high requirement for these co-factors in bacterial growth, and led to the observation that pyridoxal phosphate was the specific co-enzyme for certain of the amino acid decarboxylases (106), in particular L-tyrosine decarboxylase. Reliance upon crude protein hydrolysates and unreproducible vitamin sources as growth media for bacteria has little to recommend it, in view of the availability of pure amino acids and of individual vitamins at the present time. It would appear desirable to return, enriched by the pure compounds now on hand, to the early procedure of Gale (98) (Table 20–20) in which individual amino acids were employed in chemically defined media, and which at that time (1940) was reluctantly abandoned "owing to shortage of amino acids." Until such time as this intelligent approach is resumed, a description of the preparation of the amino acid decarboxylases must necessarily follow the quite empirical path generally employed up to now.

L-Lysine Decarboxylase. *Illustrative procedure for the preparation of* L-*lysine decarboxylase* (101, 102). *Bacillus cadaveris*, ATCC No. 9760 or NCTC No. 6578, is grown for a period of 24 hr. at 25° and collected as described. The washed cells are mixed with a little water to form a thick cream which is poured rapidly and with stirring at room temperature into five times its volume of acetone. The resulting coagulum is allowed to settle, and the supernatant solution siphoned off and discarded. Filtration of the residual mass is accomplished with gentle suction, and just before the residue is dry it is stirred with fresh acetone and again submitted to gentle suction. The process is repeated with dry ether and the dried filter cake crumbled and spread thinly on filter paper to dry out spontaneously in the air. When dried, the preparation is stored in a desiccator in the cold. The *B. cadaveris* organism has initially a strong lysine decarboxylase and a weak arginine decarboxylase; no other L-amino acid is decarboxylated. On standing for about 1 week, the acetone-dried preparation loses practically all of this weak arginine decarboxylase activity without significant loss of the lysine decarboxylase activity. The acetone powder can be safely stored in a desiccator for at least 4 weeks without serious loss of lysine decarboxylase activity. It is of interest to note that the lysine decarboxylase activity of the freshly prepared acetone-dried powder is higher by about 20% than that of the freshly harvested cells from which it was derived (102). To extract the enzyme from the powder, the latter is stirred for 2 hr. at 27° in a 0.03M phosphate buffer at pH 8.0 in a ratio of 1 ml. of buffer for each 20 mg. of powder, and then centrifuged clear. Most of the activity passes into solution in this way (102), and since it is unstable in this form the extract must be employed without undue delay.

Escherichia coli 86 also possesses a strong lysine decarboxylase activity, accompanied, however, by moderate to weak decarboxylases for arginine, histidine, and ornithine. When treated as above, it was found (102) that the acetone treatment destroyed the activity toward ornithine but the other three remained. To the phosphate buffer extract obtained as described in the paragraph above, ethanol was added to 20%, then acid was added until the pH decreased to 5.5–6.0. This manipulation resulted in destruction of the arginine and histidine decarboxylase activities leaving the lysine decarboxylase activity virtually intact.

The extract of the acetone powder of either the *cadaveris* or *coli* source demonstrates optimal lysine decarboxylase activity at pH 6.0, in contrast with the optimal activity of the washed cells which occurs at pH 5.0 (102). An assay of the activity consists of mixing 2 ml. of 0.2M phosphate buffer at pH 6.0 and 0.5 ml. of enzyme solution in the main cup of a Warburg flask. The flask is immersed in a bath at 30°, and after temperature equilibrium is established 0.5 ml. of 0.06M L-lysine dihydrochloride is added from the side arm. The rate of evolution of carbon dioxide which ensues yields a measure of the activity of the decarboxylase per unit mass of enzyme. The activity measure was originally expressed as $Q_{CO_2}^C$, or microliters of carbon dioxide evolved per hour per milligram of carbon in the enzyme preparation (102), but this curious reference to enzyme carbon was subsequently abandoned and no longer is in use. At pH 6.0, some carbon dioxide remains in solution, and for a more precise measurement of rate of enzymic reaction it is advisable to employ a flask with a second side arm which contains 0.5 ml. of 4N H$_2$SO$_4$; at the termination of the initial period of the reaction the acid is tipped in and the total carbon dioxide evolved is measured—for this period of reaction! This procedure obviously provides only a single measurement of the reaction rate, for the enzyme is inactivated by the acid.

The decarboxylase has been employed for the following purposes: (a) to prepare D-lysine after its prolonged incubation with DL-lysine until no more carbon dioxide was evolved from the L-isomer (a feasible procedure inasmuch as this enzyme, like the other decarboxylases, carries the reaction practically to completion) (107); (b) to determine the possible contamination by very small amounts of L-lysine in preparations of D-lysine secured by resolution of the racemate (inasmuch as the enzyme is not inhibited in its action on L-lysine by large excesses of the enantiomorph) (108) (Chapter 19); (c) to follow the reaction of ε-lysine acylase on ε-acetyl-L-lysine by the decarboxylation of the L-lysine which appears as a product (inasmuch as ε-acetyl-L-lysine is inert to the enzyme) (109); (d) to identify L-lysine as the product of the reaction of diaminopimelic acid decarboxylase on *meso*-diaminopimelic acid (97); and (e) to determine the amount of L-lysine in amino acid mixtures and biological mixtures (101). The preparation of the D-moieties of racemic amino acids by metabolic decarboxylation of the L-isomers is a classic procedure, originating with Schulze and Bosshard in 1886 (110) by the use of the mold *Penicillium glaucum*, and continuing through the extensive studies of F. Ehrlich with yeast (cf. 111). The studies of Neuberger and Sanger (107) on the preparation of D-lysine from the racemate were, however, among the first in which a purified enzyme of known optical and structural specificity was employed.

L-ARGININE DECARBOXYLASE (112). This enzyme is found in *Escherichia coli*, the NCTC No. 86 strain possessing, in addition, the decarboxylases for ornithine, histidine, and lysine (113). When the washed cells are treated with acetone exactly as described above for the preparation of L-lysine decarboxylase, the decarboxylase for L-ornithine is destroyed, but the activities toward histidine and lysine remain. Washed cell preparations of *E. coli* act optimally on L-arginine at pH 4.0 to form carbon dioxide and agmatine, and are very weakly active at pH 5.5. The L-ornithine decarboxylase of such preparations, on the other hand, has an optimal effect on its substrate at pH 5.5. Thus, if washed cell suspensions of *E. coli* No. 86 and *Streptococcus faecalis* (which contains an arginase activity but no decarboxylase other than that effective on L-tyrosine) are mixed and incubated at pH 5.5 with L-arginine, little or no agmatine is formed, whereas nearly the equivalent amount of putrescine makes its appearance (114).

In 1946, Gale discovered a strain of *E. coli* which was active only against arginine (112), and which received the designations NCTC No. 7020 and ATCC No. 10787. It was grown, collected, and submitted to acetone treatment exactly as described above for the preparation of the acetone-dried powder from *B. cadaveris* with lysine decarboxylase activity, except that in the present instance the acetone was chilled. The L-arginine decarboxylase activity in the powder is preserved for several weeks. It can be extracted from the powder as described above for the similar extraction of lysine decarboxylase from the *Bacillus cadaveris* acetone powder. In solution, the cell-free enzyme possesses an optimal activity at pH 5.2 and is relatively unstable. It is assayed against L-arginine monohydrochloride in a citrate buffer at this pH as described above, except that no acid tip is necessary, and the rate of evolution of carbon dioxide can be read off the manometer continuously.

L-ORNITHINE DECARBOXYLASE (101, 113). This enzyme is the only known amino acid decarboxylase found in *Clostridium septicum* (PIII), NCTC No. 547 or ATCC No. 12464. It is ordinarily quite unstable, and should be used on the day of preparation or very shortly thereafter. The cells are grown, harvested in the Sharples supercentrifuge, and washed once with water as described for the two preparations given above (lysine and arginine decarboxylases), except that in this instance macerated heart muscle is added to the casein digest–glucose medium, and growth of the organisms is maintained for 16 hr. at 37°. Before the centrifugation step, the medium is cleared of heart muscle débris by filtration through cheese-cloth. The cells are not subjected to acetone treatment, for in such an event the enzyme is immediately destroyed. The packed cells therefore, after the water wash, are suspended in water, pyridoxal phosphate is added to stabilize the enzyme (113, 115, 116), and the cell suspension employed directly for the specific detection of L-ornithine. The pH at which optimal activity of such suspensions occurs is at 5.0–5.5 (101, 113). Assay of the activity of the cell suspensions is conducted in the Warburg respirometers as above, at pH 5.0 in acetate buffer, and in the presence of a large amount of added pyridoxal phosphate. Use has been made of this enzyme in washed cell suspensions to determine the presence or absence of L-ornithine in protein hydrolysates (101), and in the D-ornithine preparations obtained by resolution of the racemic amino acid (7).

L-HISTIDINE DECARBOXYLASE (117). *Clostridium welchii* Type A organisms were found by Gale (101, 118) to possess a decarboxylase strongly active toward histidine and a decarboxylase weakly active toward glutamic acid. The bacteria, designated *Cl. welchii* (Type A) BW 21, NCTC No. 6785 and ATCC No. 10783, are grown as described above for *Clostridium septicum*, the source of L-ornithine decarboxylase (117), the culture filtered through cheese-cloth, and the packed cells washed once with water. The histidine decarboxylase is stable to subsequent acetone treatment, and this step is conducted as described above for the preparation of L-lysine decarboxylase from *Bacillus cadaveris*. Another advantage of the acetone treatment is that the weak L-glutamic acid decarboxylase of the *Cl. welchii* Type A organism is thereby destroyed. A cell-free extract is prepared from the acetone-dried powder by suspending the latter in $0.05M$ borate buffer at pH 8.5 (40 mg. per ml.), incubating the suspension for 15 hours at 37°, and centrifuging clear. Assay of L-histidine decarboxylase activity in this extract is conducted in acetate buffer at pH 4.5 at a temperature of 30°. Two milliliters of the acetate buffer is mixed with 0.5 ml. of $0.03M$ L-histidine solution in the Warburg flask, the mixture brought to temperature, and 0.5 ml. of the enzyme solution, previously brought carefully to pH 4.5 by addition of dilute acid, is added from the side arm. The flask is shaken in the bath for 2 minutes, and the carbon dioxide evolved in the succeeding 5 minutes is recorded for the determination of enzyme rate. The limitation on the assay of enzyme potency is imposed because the course of the gas evolution is not linear beyond the period of time described (117). It is of interest to note (a) that the washed cells of the organism possess optimal activity toward L-histidine at pH 2.5 (117), and (b) that, as usual, acetone-drying results in an increase in the specific L-histidine decarboxylase activity. In the form of the acetone-dried powder, the preparation maintains its activity for several weeks at 5°. The enzyme has been successfully employed to determine the level of L-histidine in protein hydrolysates (101).

L-TYROSINE DECARBOXYLASE (98, 119). Of 16 L-amino acids of protein origin, only L-tyrosine served as a substrate for the decarboxylase activity of various strains of *Streptococcus faecalis*. The capacity of the organism also to decarboxylate certain related L-amino acids not of protein derivation, such as 3:4-dihydroxyphenylalanine (119, 120) has been alluded to above. Other substrates for the enzyme are the 2:5-, 3:5-, and 2:4-dihydroxyphenylalanines (120), *m*-hydroxyphenylalanine (121), and the diastereomeric ring-hydroxylated phenylserines (122, 123). The amines, arterenol, noradrenalin, etc., formed by enzymic decarboxylation of the last-mentioned compounds, are of considerable physiologic interest (Chapter 51).

Illustrative procedure for the preparation of tyrosine decarboxylase. The organism generally employed is *S. faecalis*, designated NCTC No. 6783. It is grown in the casein digest–glucose medium supplemented with a little yeast extract at 37° for 16 hr., and the cells are collected by centrifugation and washed with water. The thick slurry of cells is chilled and poured with stirring into 10 volumes of chilled acetone, and subsequently filtered and dried as described above for the acetone-dried powder of *Bacillus cadaveris* (lysine decarboxylase). The acetone-dried powder of *S. faecalis* preserves its activity toward L-tyrosine for several months. In order to obtain a cell-free preparation, the powder is suspended in 0.02M phosphate buffer at pH 5.5 (20 mg. powder per ml.) and the suspension allowed to stand with occasional stirring for 21 hr. at 37°. As is usual among the bacterial preparations discussed, the activity in the extract is much less stable than it had been in the acetone-dried powder.

L-Tyrosine decarboxylase possesses an optimal activity, whether in the washed cells or in the extract from the acetone powder, at pH 5.0 (119). It is assayed as described above for L-lysine decarboxylase except that the buffer employed is 0.2M acetate at pH 5.5, and 5–10 micromoles of pyridoxal phosphate is added to the reaction mixture (119). The enzyme has been employed for the quantitative determination of L-tyrosine in protein hydrolysates (101).

GLUTAMIC ACID–ASPARTIC ACID DECARBOXYLASES (96, 101, 124). In his earlier studies Gale had observed that various *coliform* and *clostridial* organisms possessed the ability to decarboxylate L-glutamic acid as well as certain other L-amino acids (101). Somewhat later (124) he observed that the washed cells of *Clostridium welchii* SR 12 would apparently decarboxylate only L-glutamic acid and L-glutamine (125) of all the L-amino acids tested. Krebs subsequently repeated these experiments with L-glutamine and observed that evolution of ammonia preceded that of carbon dioxide (126). It was apparent that the *Clostridium* possessed strong glutaminase activity, and on the basis of this finding Krebs developed an elegant procedure for the simultaneous determination of L-glutamine and L-glutamic acid in biological mixtures. Thus incubation of *Cl. welchii* SR 12 with a mixture of L-glutamic acid and L-glutamine produced at the termination of the reaction one equivalent of ammonia and two equivalents of carbon dioxide, one equivalent of carbon dioxide being evolved by decarboxylation of the deamidated glutamine, and the other from the original glutamic acid. Two equivalents of γ-aminobutyric acid were simultaneously formed. The amount of ammonia was a measure of the glutamine originally present. This value in molar quantities subtracted from the moles of carbon dioxide produced yielded a measure of the glutamic acid originally present. The organism seemingly had no effect on L-asparagine or L-aspartic acid (89, 126).

However, the capacity of *Cl. welchii* to decarboxylate L-aspartic acid, albeit slowly, was subsequently reported by Müller and Leuthardt (127), who also noted that the evolution of carbon dioxide was accelerated by addition to the reaction medium of α-ketoglutaric acid. It appeared to these authors quite reasonable to assume that a transamination from aspartic acid to the α-keto acid occurred with the formation of glutamic acid which was subsequently decarboxylated by the organism. If this were indeed the case, there should have been γ-aminobutyric acid remaining after completion of the reaction. In experiments carried on simultaneously and independently by Meister and his associates (96), the absence of γ-aminobutyric acid from the reaction mixture was proved with the aid of paper chromatography, and it was evident that the reaction took a course other than that of transamination from aspartate to α-ketoglutarate.

In the course of studies by Meister, Sober, and Tice (96) on aspartic-glutamic transaminase in which *Cl. welchii* was used to determine the amount of glutamic acid present, one of the control flasks containing L-aspartic acid, α-ketoglutaric acid, and the organism showed an unexpectedly high evolution of carbon dioxide. Further study of this phenomenon revealed that the source of the carbon dioxide was the L-aspartic acid, which was decarboxylated by the activity of the organism to yield L-alanine in addition to the gas. Even in the absence of the α-keto acid, there was a definite if quite slow enzymic decarboxylation of L-aspartic acid, which was completely inhibited by addition of semicarbazide to the reaction medium, and markedly accelerated by the addition of α-keto acids or of pyridoxal phosphate (96). It was therefore possible to assay one or the other aminodicarboxylic acid in the presence of a mixture of both (Section 25–2). Of some interest was the fact that the enzymic decarboxylation of L-glutamic acid involved the α-carboxyl group, whereas that of L-aspartic acid involved the β-carboxyl group. The reaction mixture was devoid of β-alanine, which would have been the product of the α-decarboxylation of aspartic acid.

$$\underset{\text{L-Glutamic acid}}{\underset{|}{\overset{NH_2CHCO_2H}{CH_2CH_2CO_2H}}} \xrightarrow{-CO_2} \underset{\text{γ-Aminobutyric acid}}{\underset{|}{\overset{NH_2CH_2}{CH_2CH_2CO_2H}}}$$

$$\underset{\text{L-Aspartic acid}}{\underset{|}{\overset{NH_2CHCO_2H}{CH_2CO_2H}}} \xrightarrow{-CO_2} \underset{\text{L-Alanine}}{\underset{|}{\overset{NH_2CHCO_2H}{CH_3}}}$$

Preparation of the glutamic acid–aspartic acid decarboxylase of Clostridium welchii (96). The culture originally employed by Gale was *Cl. welchii* SR 12, NCTC No. 6784. The same strain is also available as *Clostridium perfringens (welchii)*, ATCC No. 8009. The organism is grown in a medium containing 0.5% yeast extract (Difco), 1.5% casein hydrolysate (N-Z-Case, Sheffield), 0.25% sodium chloride, 0.005% L-cystine, and 2% glucose. The cultures are incubated for 12 to 18 hr. at 37°, the cells harvested by centrifugation, washed twice with 0.85% sodium chloride, suspended in water, and lyophilized immediately (drying with acetone destroys the activity (113)), and stored at 5°. Such preparations retain their enzymic activity for at least 6 months. With glutamic acid as substrate the rate of decarboxylation is about 90 μl. of carbon dioxide released per hour per mg. of dried cells, whereas with aspartic acid (in the absence of accelerators) the rate is about 9 in the same units. If DL-aspartic acid to 2% is added to the medium at the time of inoculation of the bacteria, the cells ultimately obtained in the manner described possess 20% more activity in decarboxylating L-aspartic acid than that given (96).

The optimum pH for the decarboxylation of aspartic acid with added pyruvate is 5.5 in acetate buffer (96), whilst that for the decarboxylation of glutamic acid under the same conditions is about 4.0. The pH level employed by Meister and his associates for the determination of glutamic and aspartic acids in the same sample was set at 4.9, or somewhere between the two extremes. For the purpose of determining the activity of each enzyme separately, 1 ml. of lyophilized cell suspension in 0.2M acetate buffer is placed in the main compartment of a Warburg flask. For the assay of aspartic acid decarboxylase, 0.2 ml. of the buffer containing 0.5 micromole of sodium pyruvate is added, and 0.3 ml. of the buffer containing 10 micromoles of L-aspartic acid is placed in the side arm. For the assay of glutamic acid decarboxylase a more dilute lyophilized cell suspension is used, the 0.2 ml. of buffer added does not contain pyruvate, and the side arm contains 10 micromoles of L-glutamic acid in 0.3 ml. of the buffer. The flasks are equilibrated at 37° for 15 minutes, the substrate solution tipped in, and the evolution of carbon dioxide followed at intervals of time. Rate values so obtained are proportional to the enzyme concentration. The *Cl. welchii* SR 12 cells have been used to determine the possible presence of traces of the L-isomers of glutamic and aspartic acids in preparations of the D-forms obtained by resolution of the respective racemates (108).

For large-scale decarboxylations, Camien, McClure, and Dunn (128) abandoned the use of buffers and brought the initial reaction mixtures to the desired pH by addition of either dilute acid or dilute alkali. As the reaction proceeded, the mixture became more alkaline, and standard acid was added to maintain the initial pH, the acid added being a measure both of the rate of the reaction (in the early stages) and of the end point (when the pH no longer changed) (see Chapter 14).

An active L-glutamic acid decarboxylase has also been obtained from *Escherichia coli* ATCC No. 4157, which contains as well a still more active L-lysine decarboxylase (115). The organism was grown in a medium consisting of 1% pepticase (casein hydrolysate), 0.1% yeast extract, 0.25% dipotassium phosphate, and 1% cerelose, for a period of 15 hours at 25° when growth apparently ceased. After 24 hours longer, the cells were harvested by centrifugation, washed with saline, suspended in a little water, and dried *in vacuo*. The drying process apparently destroyed the lysine decarboxylase activity, for the resulting powder was devoid of this activity while retaining nearly all of the activity characteristic of the washed cells toward glutamic acid. The action of this preparation on DL-glutamic acid resulted in conversion of the L-moiety to γ-aminobutyric acid, and at completion of the reaction pure D-glutamic acid could be isolated (128) (Section 25–4). A cell-free preparation of glutamic acid decarboxylase was obtained (115) by incubating the dried *E. coli* cells for 2 hours at 37° in 0.02M phosphate buffer at pH 7.0 and subsequently removing the cell débris by centrifugation; the enzyme under these conditions, however, rapidly loses activity.

Still another *E. coli* preparation with glutamic acid decarboxylase activity was that developed by Najjar and Fischer (129). The strain was ATCC No. 11246, and it possessed decarboxylases active against glutamic acid, histidine, lysine, and arginine. Unlike the enzyme in *C. welchii* (113), the glutamic acid decarboxylase activity of this strain of *E. coli* is stable toward acetone treatment, and a purification procedure could be established on the basis of this observation.

Illustrative procedure for the preparation of glutamic acid decarboxylase. The *E. coli* organisms are grown on 3% trypticase soy broth for 18 hr. at 37°, collected by centrifugation, washed, suspended in a little water, and treated with 9 volumes of pure acetone. After filtration and drying as above, the resulting powder is found to have lost the capacity to decarboxylate histidine. The lysine and arginine decarboxylases in the acetone-dried powder are destroyed by an autolysis of the material in a 2% suspension in water at 55° for 4–7 days. The powder is centrifuged, the supernatant discarded, and the residue mixed with a little water and treated again with 9 volumes of acetone. After filtration and drying, this second powder is found to contain only glutamic acid decarboxylase activity, functioning optimally at pH 5.3 in 0.1M acetate buffer.

DIAMINOPIMELIC ACID DECARBOXYLASE (97). Another bacterial decarboxylase, which when acting on an amino acid substrate yields an amino acid as a product, is diaminopimelic acid decarboxylase. This enzyme acts upon *meso*-α,ε-diaminopimelic acid with the result that carbon dioxide and L-lysine are formed (97). The richest and most convenient source of the enzyme at the present time is *Aerobacter aerogenes*. The strain employed contains as well a still more active L-lysine decarboxylase, so that the final products of the incubation of washed or dried cells of *Aero. aerogenes* with diaminopimelic acid is cadaverine and two moles of carbon dioxide.

$$HO_2CCH(NH_2)(CH_2)_3CH(NH_2)CO_2H \xrightarrow{-CO_2} HO_2CCH(NH_2)(CH_2)_3CH_2NH_2$$
$$\alpha,\varepsilon\text{-Diaminopimelic acid} \qquad\qquad\qquad\qquad\qquad \text{L-Lysine}$$

$$NH_2CH_2(CH_2)_3CH_2NH_2 \xleftarrow{-CO}$$
$$\text{Cadaverine}$$

Illustrative procedure for the preparation of diaminopimelic acid decarboxylase (97). Strain 1 of *Aero. aerogenes* (Medical Research Council Unit for Chemical Microbiology, Cambridge) is inoculated into a broth consisting of 5 g. proteose peptone (Difco), 2 g. yeast extract (Marmite), 1 g. Oxoid Lablemco, 5 g. sodium chloride, and 5 g. glucose (autoclaved separately), all in 1 l. of water. A slow stream of air is introduced, and the organisms are allowed to grow for 24 hr. at 25°. The cells are collected by centrifugation, washed with water, dried with acetone as described above for lysine decarboxylase (*Bacillus cadaveris*), and stored at −10° in a desiccator.

Inasmuch as the lysine decarboxylase of *Aero. aerogenes* is very much more active than is the diaminopimelic acid decarboxylase, the latter is rate-limiting, and a determination of the rate of evolution of the two moles of carbon dioxide from one mole of diaminopimelic acid will yield a measure of the activity of the diaminopimelic acid decarboxylase. The optimum pH for the decarboxylation of diaminopimelic acid by the dried cells is 6.8; added L-lysine is also quantitatively converted into cadaverine with evolution of one mole of carbon dioxide, indicating that the lysine decarboxylase of this organism is quite active at pH 6.8. D-Lysine is unreactive in this system, and it would appear that the decarboxylation of *meso*-diaminopimelic acid, in order to yield the susceptible L-lysine, must take place at the carboxyl group on the carbon atom with a D-configuration (see Chapters 32 and 45). This implies that diaminopimelic acid decarboxylase, unlike all the other bacterial decarboxylases described above, which are uniformly L-directed and completely inert to the D-isomers of the susceptible amino acids, must be D-directed at least in part. The last-mentioned reservation is introduced because both L- and D-diaminopimelic acid are inert to the enzyme, and thus although the enzyme attacks the susceptible *meso* substrate at the D-center it requires also that the other center of optical asymmetry in the molecule be L in configuration (130).

The decarboxylase activity is measured with about 40 mg. of dried cells suspended in 2 ml. of $0.1M$ phosphate buffer at pH 6.8 supplemented with 10 μg. of pyridoxal phosphate in 0.1 ml. of solution. From the side arm, 0.5 ml. of $0.025M$ *meso*-diaminopimelic acid in the buffer is added when temperature equilibrium (at 37°) is reached, and the evolution of carbon dioxide followed manometrically. At pH 6.8 there is considerable retention of carbon dioxide, and in order to obtain a quantitative measure of the gas evolved it is necessary to add acid (0.2 ml. of $8N$ H_2SO_4) from a second side arm of the flask.

11. Arginase. This enzyme, which degrades L-arginine to L-ornithine and urea, is highly specific for this substrate and is found chiefly in the hepatic tissue of all urea-forming animals. Its first practical application was

$$NH_2C(=NH)NH(CH_2)_3CH(NH_2)CO_2H \rightarrow NH_2(CH_2)_3CH(NH_2)CO_2H + NH_2CONH_2$$
L-Arginine   L-Ornithine   Urea

revealed in 1906 when Riesser incubated DL-arginine with a crude liver preparation for several days, and subsequently isolated almost equivalent amounts of L-ornithine and D-arginine (131). The enzyme is thus highly suited to the production of optically pure L-ornithine (Chapter 44). As a specific reagent for L-arginine, it shares with all other optically specific enzymes the limitation that the unsusceptible enantiomorph, if present in a mixture to be analyzed, would be completely missed. Inasmuch as the products of the enzymic reaction are L-ornithine and urea, it is possible to follow its course by the rate of appearance of either or both of these products. The measurement of L-ornithine, chromatographically or by the action of L-ornithine decarboxylase, is not distinguished by rapidity or ease of manipulation. The measurement of urea is best accomplished by the use of an excess of a second enzyme, urease; this enzyme reacting quantitatively on the urea converts it to two moles of ammonia and one mole of carbon dioxide, either or both of which can be determined by precise methods. Tedious though it may be, the procedure involving the successive use of arginase and urease is quite effective in the determination of L-arginine.

Preparation of arginase. A crude but active preparation may be made as follows (132). A weighed quantity of minced fresh calf liver is blended with an equal quantity of cold water containing manganous acetate to a final concentration of $0.001M$ for a period of 10 min., and filtered through cheese-cloth into a large flask. The flask is transferred to a water bath at 65°, and the contents constantly swirled until a uniform temperature of 58° is reached. After 5 min. at this temperature, the coagulated mass is cooled and filtered by gravity in the cold. To the clear, red filtrate 5N NaOH is very carefully added with gentle agitation to bring the pH to 7.0, and the whole then lyophilized to a powder. This powder is practically completely soluble in water, and retains its activity for several weeks when kept in a vacuum desiccator at 5°.

The urease employed is an acetone-dried powder obtained by mixing commercial jackbean meal with the five-fold amount of water for several hours, removing the insoluble material by centrifugation, and pouring the supernatant solution with stirring into 10 volumes of chilled acetone. The precipitate which separates is filtered, dried, dissolved in a little water, and dialyzed first against water and then against $0.001M$ phosphate at pH 6.5. The contents of the dialysis sack are centrifuged clear, and lyophilized to yield a highly active urease powder, free of the canavanine and arginine originally present in the crude jackbean meal.

For the assay of arginase activity, a mixture of 1 ml. of a solution of the arginase powder, 1 ml. of secondary phosphate, and 1 ml. of a $0.01M$ solution of L-arginine·HCl is incubated at 38° for a period of time, at the end of which the reaction is terminated by the addition of N H_2SO_4 to a pH of 2.5. A blank is prepared at this stage by adding the substrate to the already acidified enzyme. Sample and blank are treated with bromothymol blue indicator and titrated to pH 6.8 (slight green color) with a solution of secondary phosphate. One milliliter of a 10% solution of the urease powder is now added, the mixture allowed to stand for 30 min. at 38°, and the ammonia formed is determined as described in the section above on amidase (Section 20-7). For each mole of L-arginine degraded, two moles of ammonia are formed.

12. Aminopeptidase. The ability of the kidney whole homogenate to hydrolyze completely the dipeptide glycyl-DL-alanine (cf. Figure 9–1) indicated the presence in this tissue of an enzyme, or enzymes, capable of effecting the hydrolysis of a peptide bond involving a D-amino acid. Subsequent fractionation experiments on the kidney homogenate, employing optically pure substrates, led to the following conclusions: (a) the soluble fraction of the tissue homogenate hydrolyzed glycyl-L-alanine at a very rapid rate, but affected glycyl-D-alanine little if at all, whereas (b) the particulate fraction of the tissue homogenate hydrolyzed both glycyl-L-alanine and glycyl-D-alanine at not greatly different rates (133). Data on a variety of glycyl-L- and glycyl-D-amino acids in Table 20–21 illustrate these findings. All results were obtained under identical experimental conditions, and the optimal conditions may not have been the same for each member of an enantiomorphic pair of substrates. The enzyme in (b) responsible for this phenomenon was found to require the presence of a free α-amino group on the acyl residue, and hence received the designation aminopeptidase (133). It is clear that the employment of glycyl-D-alanine as a typical substrate for this enzyme would be appropriate, inasmuch as the use of the antipodal glycyl-L-alanine would involve not only the particulate enzyme but the soluble, exclusively L-directed peptidase as well. It is also clear that whereas the acylases (see above) are inhibited by the presence of a free α-amino group on the acyl residue, and cannot readily attack the bond involving a C-terminal residue of the D-configuration, the present aminopeptidase requires the presence of a free α-amino group on the acyl residue and readily attacks the peptide bond involving a C-terminal residue whether L or D in configuration. Both categories of enzymes, however, require the presence of a free α-carboxyl group on the C-terminal residue, and in this respect these enzymes are different from the basic requirement of the amidase described above.

TABLE 20–21

Initial Rates of Hydrolysis of Corresponding Glycyl-L- and Glycyl-D-amino Acids by Renal Aminopeptidase and by Hog Kidney Homogenates[a] (133)

Terminal Residue of N-Glycylamino Acids	L-Peptides Rate with Peptidase	D-Peptides Rate with Homogenate	D-Peptides Rate with Peptidase	Ratio
Alanine	128,000	200	300,000	1,500
Butyrine	120,000	62	137,000	2,200
Valine	19,600	13	25,000	1,900
Norvaline	237,000	160	182,000	1,200
Isovaline	91,500	21	56,000	2,600
Leucine	227,000	64	132,000	2,100
Norleucine	206,000	156	215,000	1,400
Isoleucine	4,300	5	9,600	1,920
Alloisoleucine	12,800	10	52,000	5,200
Methionine	350,000	156	251,000	1,600
Phenylalanine	222,000	55	108,000	1,960
Tyrosine	188,000	35	86,000	2,400
Tryptophan	142,000	36	66,500	1,900
Serine	128,000	64	154,000	2,400
Threonine	42,500	4	7,100	1,800
Aspartic acid	32,500	15	39,500	2,620
Glutamic acid	23,000	—	—	—
Lysine	78,000	—	—	—

[a] In terms of micromoles of substrate hydrolyzed per hour per milligram of protein N at 37°. Digests consisted of 1 ml. of borate buffer at pH 8, 1 ml. of enzyme solution, and 1 ml. of $0.05M$ neutral substrate solution. The enzyme preparation had stood for 60 days at 5° in the lyophilized state prior to the present studies.

Still another aspect of the specificity of these enzymes is of interest, and this involves the effect of the optical configuration of the acyl residue. Thus, in the case of the acylases, L-chloropropionyl-L-alanine is hydrolyzed at practically the same rate as is D-chloropropionyl-L-alanine (21) and the optical configuration of the acyl residue is thus of relatively little importance. In the case of aminopeptidase however, the configuration of the N-terminal residue is rather crucial, for L-alanyl-D-alanine is hydrolyzed some 80 times faster than is D-alanyl-D-alanine, and L-alanylglycine some 2000 times faster than D-alanylglycine (133). Where the possibility of steric hindrance exists on the N-terminal residue, as in isoleucyl or valyl peptides, the rates of hydrolysis by aminopeptidase are reduced, and in such cases as D-valyl-D-valine, D-valyl-L-valine, or D-alloisoleucyl-D-alanine, the rates may fall very nearly to zero; however, L-alloisoleucyl-D-alanine is readily hydrolyzed (134), and as shown in the writers' Laboratory by Dr. W. K. Paik, the rates of hydrolysis by aminopeptidase of L-valyl-D-valine and of L-valyl-L-valine, although low, are nevertheless easily measurable, and nearly equal in value.

The susceptible substrates for aminopeptidase are hydrolyzed by this enzyme to completion, and the resulting free L- and D-amino acids, if in turn susceptible to L- and D-amino acid oxidases, can be quantitatively determined by these enzymes (Section 10–49). No racemase activity of the aminopeptidase preparation is evident. On the basis of these phenomena, a method for determining the optical purity of peptides susceptible to aminopeptidase action, and whose amino acid moieties are, when freed, susceptible to amino acid oxidases, can be developed. Such a method is described in Section 10–49.

Preparation of renal aminopeptidase (133). The peptidase was concentrated in its activity toward the substrate glycyl-D-alanine. The purification procedure was unusual in that it involved so few fractionation steps. Essentially, the kidney particulate fraction was freed from soluble proteins, and the enzyme solubilized by treatment with *n*-butanol in a modification of a procedure described by Morton (135). After dialysis and removal of the insoluble residue, a single ammonium sulfate fractionation was sufficient to yield a preparation with an initial specific activity at least 600 times that of the crude homogenate.

Step 1. Four kilos of fresh, frozen hog kidneys are thawed, defatted, and homogenized in a Waring Blendor with 2 volumes of ice water. The homogenate is strained through cheese-cloth and centrifuged at 1200 × *g* for 20 min. to remove cellular débris. The specific activity at this stage in terms of micromoles of substrate hydrolyzed per hour per milligram of total N is 150 to 250. The total activity is about 15×10^6 micromoles per hr.

Step 2. The supernatant fluid is chilled to 0° in a cold bath, brought to *p*H 5 by the careful addition of 2*N* hydrochloric acid, and the resulting thick suspension immediately centrifuged at 0° and 3000 × *g* for 30 min. The supernatant fluid is discarded. The sediment is washed from the tubes with an equal volume of Sörensen's 0.066*M* phosphate buffer at *p*H 7. The last traces of protein in the centrifuge tubes are removed with a similar volume of 0.1*M* potassium chloride solution and added to the first washings. The lumpy suspension is briefly homogenized in the Blendor and frozen solid at −10°. After thawing, the suspension is again taken to *p*H 5 with 2*N* hydrochloric acid, and the centrifuging, followed by transfer of the sediment with phosphate buffer and potassium chloride solutions, repeated. Brief homogenization yields a suspension with a specific activity in the range 200 to 300, and total activity of 8×10^6.

Step 3. Cold acetone is added to the suspension and stirred at pH 7 and 0° to a concentration of 70% (v/v). Several large Büchner funnels are layered thinly with Hyflo Super-Cel on No. 4 Whatman paper and set up in a room at 5°. After standing for 1 hr. at 5° after the acetone treatment, the aggregated suspension is poured slowly on the funnels without disturbing the Hyflo layer. After a few minutes of filtration by gravity, the filtrate is clear. When the acetone solution has nearly completely filtered through, the residue on the funnel is washed with $0.2M$ potassium chloride solution added very carefully and slowly from a large reservoir. Inasmuch as the rate of filtration declines fairly rapidly, it is expedient to wash the sediment from the filter paper with a jet of distilled water to homogenize the lumpy suspension, and to set up the filters once more with a fresh layer of Hyflo. After the first day's filtration, water is used as the wash fluid in place of the potassium chloride solution. The washing and filtration are carried on for several days, entailing a daily relayering. After each relayering, the filtrate becomes clear in a few minutes of flow. The filtrates are checked daily for the presence of protein, and at least two further filtrations are carried out even after no protein is detectable (precipitation with 10% trichloroacetic acid being used).

It must be stressed at this point that the filtration procedure must exhaustively remove all traces of soluble protein. Otherwise, the final preparation is generally of low activity, and thus far no fractionation procedure has been found which will raise the activity level at this final stage. Throughout the filtration procedure described, the specific activity remains practically constant in the range 200 to 300, while the total activity decreases to about 6×10^6.

Step 4. The filter cake, with Hyflo included, is finally washed off the filter paper and homogenized for a brief period with 8 to 10 l. of water in the Blendor. n-Butanol, chilled to 0°, is added to a concentration of 20% by volume with rapid stirring. The suspension is mechanically shaken for 1 hr. at 5° and dialyzed for 18 hr. against cold running tap water to remove the butanol. $2N$ Hydrochloric acid is then added at 0° to pH 5, and the mixture centrifuged at $3000 \times g$ for 30 min. at 0°. The sediment is discarded. The supernatant fluid, taken to pH 7 with $2N$ sodium hydroxide, has a specific activity of 22,000, and total activity of 5 to 6×10^6. Thus the extraction increases the specific activity some 100-fold without substantial decrease in the total activity.

Step 5. The volume of the preparation at this stage is usually about 10 l., and it is found convenient to reduce this volume by placing the solution in cellophane bags in front of a powerful fan. The evaporation is continued until the volume is about 500 ml. A small amount of insoluble material which appears is centrifuged and discarded.

Step 6. Solid ammonium sulfate is added at pH 7 to 50% saturation (35.3 gm. per 100 ml. at 0°), and after standing for 1 hr. the precipitate is discarded after centrifugation at $3000 \times g$ for 45 min. at 0°. To the supernatant fluid solid ammonium sulfate is added to 75% saturation, and, after further standing, the suspension is centrifuged at $3000 \times g$ for 1 hr. The sediment is taken up in a small volume of water and dialyzed for several hours. The specific activity of the freshly prepared enzyme is usually in the range 120,000 to 140,000, and the total activity about 4 × 10⁶. Lyophilization yields a white powder weighing about 200 mg. and having a nitrogen content of 10.8%. The enzyme is completely soluble in water. Since the preparation is to be used in the hydrolysis of peptides containing D-amino acids, it is necessary to determine whether it contains appreciable D-amino acid oxidase activity; with DL-methionine as the test substrate, the oxidase activity is found to be zero.

The aminopeptidase prepared according to the above procedure possesses the unique property of actually increasing in specific activity upon storage at 5° either in the lyophilized state or in aqueous solution (133). Thus a freshly prepared enzyme with an initial specific activity (against glycyl-D-alanine) of 128,800 micromoles per hour per milligram of nitrogen rose to 240,000 in 5 weeks, to 260,000 in 7 weeks, to 285,000 in 8.5 weeks, to 336,000 in 11 weeks, and to 365,000 in 12 weeks. Prolonged dialysis of either freshly prepared or aged enzyme against distilled water failed to alter the activity in any way. After about 60 days of storage, the rate of increase in specific activity generally falls off, so that no useful purpose is served by aging the product much longer.

The substrate generally employed in the determination of the activity of preparations of this enzyme is glycyl-D-alanine; the use of this substrate eliminates the effect of any contamination by the powerful, soluble, and optically specific L-peptidases which are universally present in tissue extracts. One milliliter of $0.1M$ borate buffer at pH 8.0 and 1 ml. of suitably diluted enzyme solution are placed in each of two test tubes. The tubes are then placed in a water bath at 37° and, after temperature equilibrium is attained, 1 ml. of $0.05M$ substrate solution is added to the assay tube. After an appropriate incubation period (30 min.), 3 ml. of saturated picric acid is added to both tubes and 1 ml. of the substrate to the blank. Ninhydrin-CO_2 determinations on aliquots of the acidified digests indicate the degree of hydrolysis of the peptide (2 micromoles of CO_2 per micromole of peptide cleaved). The hydrolytic rate is proportional to the enzyme concentration and is linear with time up to the point where 30% of the total substrate is hydrolyzed. Thus, from any value below that point, the specific activity of the preparation can be calculated in terms of micromoles hydrolyzed per hour per milligram of protein N.

REFERENCES

1. Schmiedeberg, O., *Arch. exptl. Pathol. Pharmakol.*, **14**, 379 (1881).
2. Smorodinzev, I. A., *Z. physiol. Chem.*, **124**, 123 (1923).
3. Nawa, K., *J. Biochem.* (*Tokyo*), **28**, 237 (1938).
4. Mori, T., *J. Biochem.* (*Toyko*), **29**, 225 (1939).
5. So, T., *J. Biochem.* (*Toyko*), **12**, 107 (1930).
6. Akizuki, H., *J. Biochem.* (*Toyko*), **25**, 43 (1937).
7. Birnbaum, S. M., Levintow, L., Kingsley, R. B., and Greenstein, J. P., *J. Biol. Chem.*, **194**, 455 (1952).

8. Marshall, R., Winitz, M., Birnbaum, S. M., and Greenstein, J. P., *J. Am. Chem. Soc.*, **79**, 4538 (1957).
9. Rao, K. R., Birnbaum, S. M., Kingsley, R. B., and Greenstein, J. P., *J. Biol. Chem.*, **198**, 507 (1952); see also Greenstein, J. P., Price, V. E., and Leuthardt, F. M., *ibid.*, **175**, 953 (1948).
9a. Mitz, M. A., and Schlueter, R. J., *Biochim. Biophys. Acta*, **27**, 168 (1958).
10. Birnbaum, S. M., and Greenstein, J. P., *Arch. Biochem. Biophys.*, **39**, 108 (1952).
11. Fodor, P. J., Price, V. E., and Greenstein, J. P., *J. Biol. Chem.*, **178**, 503 (1949); **182**, 467 (1950).
12. Fones, W. S., and Lee, M., *J. Biol. Chem.*, **201**, 847 (1953); **210**, 227 (1954).
13. Levintow, L., Greenstein, J. P., and Kingsley, R. B., *Arch. Biochem. Biophys.*, **31**, 77 (1951).
14. Baker, C. G., Fu, S.-C. J., Birnbaum, S. M., Sober, H. A., and Greenstein, J. P., *J. Am. Chem. Soc.*, **74**, 4701 (1952).
15. Fu, S.-C. J., and Birnbaum, S. M., *J. Am. Chem. Soc.*, **75**, 918 (1953).
16. Gilbert, J. B., Price, V. E., and Greenstein, J. P., *J. Biol. Chem.*, **180**, 473 (1949).
17. Crowe, B. F., and Nord, F. F., *J. Org. Chem.*, **15**, 688 (1950).
18. Marshall, R., Birnbaum, S. M., and Greenstein, J. P., *J. Am. Chem. Soc.*, **78**, 4636 (1956).
19. Greenstein, J. P., Birnbaum, S. M., and Otey, M. C., *J. Biol. Chem.*, **204**, 307 (1953).
20. Benoiton, L., Winitz, M., Birnbaum, S. M., and Greenstein, J. P., *J. Am. Chem. Soc.*, **79**, 6129 (1957).
20a. Personal communication from Dr. V. N. Orekhovich; cf. Cheng-Wu, C., and Orekhovich, V. N., *Biokhimiya*, **22**, 838 (1957); p. 787 in English translation.
21. Fu, S.-C. J., Birnbaum, S. M., and Greenstein, J. P., *J. Am. Chem. Soc.*, **76**, 6054 (1954).
22. Fones, W. S., *J. Biol. Chem.*, **204**, 323 (1953).
23. Hofmann, K., and Bergmann, M., *J. Biol. Chem.*, **134**, 225 (1940).
24. Anson, M. L., *J. Gen. Physiol.*, **20**, 663, 777, 781 (1937).
25. Neurath, H., in *Methods in Enzymology*, Vol. 2, Colowick, S., and Kaplan, N. O., eds., Academic Press, New York, 1955.
26. Van Tieghem (no initial given), *Compt. rend.*, **58**, 210 (1864).
27. Shibata, K., *Beitr. Physiol. Pathol.*, **5**, 384 (1940).
28. Dox, A. W., *J. Biol. Chem.*, **6**, 461 (1910); see also Dox, A. W., and Neidig, R. E., *Z. physiol. Chem.*, **85**, 68 (1913).
29. Ayers, S. H., and Rupp, P., *J. Infectious Diseases*, **30**, 388 (1922).
30. Gilbert, I., and Frobisher, M., *Bull. Johns Hopkins Hosp.*, **47**, 55 (1930).
31. Reis, I., and Swensson, A., *Compt. rend. soc. biol.*, **107**, 647 (1931).
32. Neuberg, C., and Linhardt, K., *Biochem. Z.*, **147**, 372 (1924).
33. Hoppert, C., *Biochem. Z.*, **149**, 510 (1925).
34. Neuberg, C., and Mandl, I., *Enzymologia*, **14**, 128 (1950).
35. Michi, K., and Nonake, H., *J. Agr. Chem. Soc. Japan*, **19**, 153 (1955).
36. Michi, K., and Tsuda, H., *J. Agr. Chem. Soc. Japan*, **21**, 18 (1957).
37. Chibata, I., Yamada, S., and Yamada, S., *Bull. Agr. Chem. Soc. Japan*, **20**, 174 (1956).
38. Chibata, I., Ishikawa, T., and Yamada, S., *Bull. Agr. Chem. Soc. Japan*, **21**, 305 (1957).
39. Chibata, I., and Ishikawa, T., *Bull. Agr. Chem. Soc. Japan*, **22**, 218 (1958).
40. Borkar, P. S., "Studies on Amino Acid Acylase of Fungi," Ph. D. Thesis, University of Poona, 1957; by permission of the University authorities.
41. Vogel, H. J., and Bonner, D. M., *J. Biol. Chem.*, **218**, 97 (1956).
42. Chibata, I., Kisumi, M., and Yamada, S., *Bull. Agr. Chem. Soc. Japan*, **22**, 24 (1958).
43. Kameda, Y., Toyoura, E., and Kimura, Y., *Nature*, **181**, 1225 (1958).

44. Kameda, Y., Toyoura, E., Kimura, Y., and Matsui, K., *Chem. Pharm. Bull.*, **6**, 394 (1958).
45. Paik, W. K., Bloch-Frankenthal, L., Birnbaum, S. M., Winitz, M., and Greenstein, J. P., *Arch. Biochem. Biophys.*, **69**, 56 (1957).
46. Kameda, Y., Toyoura, E., Kimura, Y., Matsui, K., and Hotta, Y., *Yakugaku Zasshi*, **78**, 748 (1948).
47. Kameda, Y., Toyoura, E., Kimura, Y., Matsui, K., and Kawasaki, T., *Yakugaku Zasshi*, **78**, 754 (1948).
48. Kameda, Y., Toyoura, E., Kimura, Y., Matsui, K., and Saito, H., *Yakugaku Zasshi*, **78**, 759 (1948).
49. Kameda, Y., Toyoura, E., Kimura, Y., Kanaya, Y., and Noda, K., *Yakugaku Zasshi*, **78**, 763 (1958).
50. Kameda, Y., Toyoura, E., Kimura, Y., Kanaya, Y., and Yoshimura, K., *Yakugaku Zasshi*, **78**, 765 (1958).
51. Kameda, Y., Toyoura, E., Kimura, Y., Kanaya, Y., Ishikawa, J., and Yoshimura, K., *Yakugaku Zasshi*, **78**, 767 (1958).
52. Kameda, Y., Toyoura, E., Matsui, K., Kimura, Y., Kanaya, Y., Nakatani, A., Saito, H., and Kawase, K., *Yakagaku Zasshi*, **78**, 769 (1958).
53. Kameda, Y., Toyoura, E., and Matsui, K., *Chem. Pharm. Bull.*, **6**, 441 (1958).
54. Kameda, Y., Toyoura, E., Kimura, Y., and Okino, B., *Chem. Pharm. Bull.*, **6**, 395 (1958).
55. Smith, E. L., and Polglase, W. J., *J. Biol. Chem.*, **180**, 1209 (1949).
56. Smith, E. L., Spackman, D. H., and Polglase, W. J., *J. Biol. Chem.*, **199**, 801 (1952).
57. Spackman, D. H., Smith, E. L., and Brown, D. M., *J. Biol. Chem.*, **212**, 255 (1955).
58. Smith, E. L., and Spackman, D. H., *J. Biol. Chem.*, **212**, 271 (1955).
59. Greenstein, J. P., *Advances in Protein Chem.*, **9**, 121 (1954).
60. Izumiya, N., Fu, S.-C. J., Birnbaum, S. M., and Greenstein, J. P., *J. Biol. Chem.*, **205**, 221 (1953).
61. Hamer, D., and Greenstein, J. P., *J. Biol. Chem.*, **193**, 81 (1951).
62. Work, E., Birnbaum, S. M., Winitz, M., and Greenstein, J. P., *J. Am. Chem. Soc.*, **77**, 1916 (1955).
63. Wade, R., Birnbaum, S. M., Winitz, M., Koegel, R. J., and Greenstein, J. P., *J. Am. Chem. Soc.*, **79**, 648 (1957).
64. Tanaka, A., and Izumiya, N., *Bull. Chem. Soc. Japan*, **31**, 529 (1958).
65. Krebs, H. A., *Z. physiol. Chem.*, **217**, 191 (1933).
66. Krebs, H. A., *Biochem. J.*, **29**, 1620 (1935).
67. Warburg, O., and Christian, W., *Biochem. Z.*, **296**, 294 (1938); **298**, 150 (1938).
68. Straub, F. B., *Biochem. J.*, **33**, 787 (1939).
69. Knoop, F., *Z. physiol. Chem.*, **67**, 489 (1910).
70. Bender, A. E., and Krebs, H. A., *Biochem. J.*, **46**, 210 (1950).
71. Krebs, H. A., *Enzymologia*, **7**, 53 (1939).
72. Radhakrishnan, A. N., and Meister, A., *J. Biol. Chem.*, **226**, 559 (1957).
73. Letellier, G., and Bouthillier, L. P., *Can. J. Biochem. Physiol.*, **34**, 1123 (1956).
74. Neuberger, A., and Sanger, F., *Biochem. J.*, **38**, 119 (1944).
75. Fu, S.-C. J., Rao, K. R., Birnbaum, S. M., and Greenstein, J. P., *J. Biol. Chem.*, **199**, 207 (1952).
76. Meister, A., *J. Biol. Chem.*, **206**, 577 (1954).
77. Greenstein, J. P., Levintow, L., Baker, C. G., and White, J., *J. Biol. Chem.*, **188**, 647 (1951).
78. Meister, A., Nature, **168**, 1119 (1951); also, *J. Biol. Chem.*, **190**, 269 (1951).
79. Meister, A., *Biochemistry of the Amino Acids*, Academic Press, New York, pp. 152–156, 1957.

79a. Murachi, T., and Tashiro, M., *Biochim. Biophys. Acta*, **29**, 645 (1958).
80. Hellerman, L., Lindsay, A., and Bovarnick, M. R., *J. Biol. Chem.*, **163**, 553 (1946).
81. Frisell, W. R., Lowe, H. J., and Hellerman, L., *J. Biol. Chem.*, **223**, 75 (1956).
82. Parikh, J. R., Greenstein, J. P., Winitz, M., and Birnbaum, S. M., *J. Am. Chem. Soc.*, **80**, 953 (1958).
83. Negelein, E., and Brömel, H., *Biochem. Z.*, **300**, 225 (1939).
84. Radhakrishnan, A. N., and Meister, A., *J. Biol. Chem.*, **233**, 444 (1958).
85. Zeller, E. A., *Advances in Enzymol.*, **8**, 459 (1948).
86. Singer, T. P., and Kearney, E. B., *Arch. Biochem.*, **29**, 190 (1950).
87. Zeller, E. A., and Maritz, A., *Helv. Chim. Acta*, **27**, 1888 (1944); **28**, 365 (1945).
88. Fones, W. S., *Arch. Biochem. Biophys.*, **36**, 486 (1952).
89. Gale, E. F., *Advances in Enzymol.*, **6**, 1 (1946).
90. Gale, E. F., *The Chemical Activities of Bacteria*, University Tutorial Press, Foxton near Cambridge, 3rd ed., 1951.
91. McGilvery, R. W., and Cohen, P. P., *J. Biol. Chem.*, **174**, 813 (1948).
92. Udenfriend, S., and Cooper, J., *J. Biol. Chem.*, **203**, 953 (1953).
93. Linstedt, S., *Acta Chem. Scand.*, **5**, 486 (1951).
94. Umbreit, W. W., and Heneage, P., *J. Biol. Chem.*, **201**, 15 (1953).
95. Clark, C. T., Weissbach, H., and Udenfriend, S., *J. Biol. Chem.*, **210**, 139 (1954).
96. Meister, A., Sober, H. A., and Tice, S. V., *J. Biol. Chem.*, **189**, 577, 591 (1951).
97. Dewey, D. L., Hoare, D. S., and Work, E., *Biochem. J.*, **58**, 523 (1954).
98. Gale, E. F., *Biochem. J.*, **34**, 392 (1940).
99. Gale, E. F., and Epps, H. M. R., *Biochem. J.*, **36**, 600 (1942).
100. Gale, E. F., *Biochem. J.*, **35**, 64 (1941).
101. Gale, E. F., *Biochem. J.*, **39**, 46 (1945).
102. Gale, E. F., and Epps, H. M. R., *Biochem. J.*, **38**, 232, 250 (1944).
103. Gale, E. F., *Biochem. J.*, **34**, 846 (1940).
104. Bellamy, W. D., and Gunsalus, I. C., *J. Bacteriol.*, **48**, 191 (1944).
105. Gunsalus, I. C., and Bellamy, W. D., *J. Biol. Chem.*, **155**, 557 (1944).
106. Gunsalus, I. C., Bellamy, W. D., and Umbreit, W. W., *J. Biol. Chem.*, **155**, 685 (1944).
107. Neuberger, A., and Sanger, F., *Biochem. J.*, **38**, 125 (1944).
108. Meister, A., Levintow, L., Kingsley, R. B., and Greenstein, J. P., *J. Biol. Chem.*, **192**, 535 (1951).
109. Paik, W. K., Bloch-Frankenthal, L., Birnbaum, S. M., Winitz, M., and Greenstein, J. P., *Arch. Biochem. Biophys.*, **69**, 56 (1957).
110. Schulze, E., and Bosshard, E., *Z. physiol. Chem.*, **10**, 134 (1886).
111. Ehrlich, F., *Biochem. Z.*, **63**, 379 (1914).
112. Gale, E. F., *Nature*, **157**, 265 (1946).
113. Taylor, E. S., and Gale, E. F., *Biochem. J.*, **39**, 52 (1945).
114. Gale, E. F., *Biochem. J.*, **34**, 853 (1940).
115. Umbreit, W. W., and Gunsalus, I. C., *J. Biol. Chem.*, **159**, 333 (1945).
116. Geiger, E., *Proc. Soc. Exptl. Biol. Med.*, **55**, 11 (1944).
117. Epps, H. M. R., *Biochem. J.*, **39**, 42 (1945).
118. Gale, E. F., *Biochem. J.*, **35**, 66 (1941).
119. Epps, H. M. R., *Biochem. J.*, **38**, 242 (1943).
120. Sourkes, T., Keneage, P., and Trano, Y., *Arch. Biochem. Biophys.*, **40**, 185 (1952).
121. Sloane-Stanley, G. H., *Biochem. J.*, **44**, 373 (1949).
122. Blaschko, H., *Biochim. Biophys. Acta*, **4**, 130 (1950).
123. Drell, W., *J. Am. Chem. Soc.*, **77**, 5429 (1955).
124. Gale, E. F., *Biochem. J.*, **41**, vi (1947).
125. Gale, E. F., *J. Gen. Microbiol.*, **1**, 53 (1947).
126. Krebs, H. A., *Biochem. J.*, **43**, 51 (1948).

127. Müller, A. F., and Leuthardt, F., *Helv. Chim. Acta*, **33,** 268 (1950).
128. Camien, M. N., McClure, L. E., and Dunn, M. S., *Arch. Biochem. Biophys.*, **28,** 220 (1950).
129. Najjar, V. A., and Fischer, J., *J. Biol. Chem.*, **206,** 215 (1954).
130. Antia, M., Hoare, D. S., and Work, E., *Biochem. J.*, **65,** 448 (1957).
131. Riesser, O., *Z. physiol. Chem.*, **49,** 210 (1906).
132. Hunter, A., and Dauphinee, J. A., *J. Biol. Chem.*, **85,** 627 (1930).
133. Robinson, D. S., Birnbaum, S. M., and Greenstein, J. P., *J. Biol. Chem.*, **202,** 1 (1953).
134. Winitz, M., Bloch-Frankenthal, L., Izumiya, N., Birnbaum, S. M., Baker, C. G., and Greenstein, J. P., *J. Am. Chem. Soc.*, **78,** 2423 (1956).
135. Morton, R. K., *Nature*, **166,** 1092 (1950).

Translations of Foreign Quotations

⁴⁰ I have proposed the name polypeptide for the products which arise through the amide-type linkage of amino acids, and whose simplest representative is the derivative of glycine, the so-called glycylglycine, $NH_2CH_2CO-NHCH_2CO_2H$. They will be distinguished as di-, tri-, tetrapeptides, etc., according to the number of their component amino acids. This designation is patterned after the nomenclature of the carbohydrates, on the one hand, and it utilizes the old word peptone, on the other, since I have anticipated from the beginning, and have been confirmed in this conviction by all subsequent observations, that these synthetic products are very closely related to the natural peptones; in other words, the peptones are essentially a hitherto inseparable mixture of polypeptides.

⁴¹ [All] are amorphous, difficulty characterizable substances about whose structure just as little can be said as about the degree of their relationship with natural proteins. If one wishes to obtain dependable results in this difficult area, a method must first be found which permits placing molecules of various amino acids consecutively, and with definitive intermediate stages, in an anhydride-like series.

⁴² Such synthesis [polymerization] . . . is to be compared to a traveler who hurries through a country in an express train and afterwards scarcely can remember anything about it, whereas the situation appears entirely different if the synthesis is compelled to proceed stepwise and the molecule built up step by step. . . . This is comparable to the pedestrian who seeks his way step by step with careful attentiveness and who must examine many roads until he has found the right one. On his long troublesome travels, not only does he learn to recognize completely the geography and topography of the country, but also he becomes intimate with the tongue and culture of its inhabitants. When he finally has reached his goal, he is able to locate himself properly in every corner of the country, and this will be possible for other people also if he writes a book about it.

⁴³ These and similar compounds are closer to the free polypeptides than the benzoyl derivatives of Curtius, since they incorporate only a carboxyl group as the foreign constituent. But the hope to be able to split this off as carbonic acid in order to obtain the free polypeptides, following the behavior of carbamic acid and similar substances, must await adoption of another means.

⁴⁴ The action of diazomethane on hippuryl chloride takes a course different from

the reaction of diazomethane with most other acid chlorides. Diazomethane acts here to remove hydrogen chloride.

45 Communications Concerning Lactone-Like Acylated Amino Acids.

46 The behavior of the carboxyanhydride of glycine toward water is worthy of note. At 0°, it dissolves therein without perceptible change; evolution of carbon dioxide occurs only upon warming to about 15°, while pure glycine is found in the solution.

47 Accordingly, the process wherefrom hippurylglycine results proceeds in a way that initially hippuric acid and silver chloride form from the action of benzoyl chloride on silver glycinate. Benzoyl chloride further acts on the former in such a way that benzoic acid and hippuryl chloride arise, whereupon the latter finally reacts with the second molecule of silver glycinate, hippurylglycine and silver chloride being produced.

48 . . . because they form a natural bridge between the carbohydrates and the simple amino acids. . . .

49 Whereas cautious professional colleagues fear that a rational study of this class of compounds [proteins], because of their complicated structure and their highly inconvenient physical characteristics, would today still uncover insurmountable difficulties, other optimistically endowed observers, among which I will count myself, are inclined to the view that an attempt should at least be made to besiege this virgin fortress with all the expedients of the present; because only through this hazardous affair can the limitations of the ability of our methods be ascertained.

50 . . . the numerous hydroxyl groups of the hydroxyamino acids are by no means neutral in the protein molecule—they could through intramolecular anhydride formation be transformed into ester or ether groups. . . .

51 It could be easily established, then, that this cleavage is dependent not upon a vital function of the unchanged tissue, but upon a substance acting in the manner of a crude ferment or enzyme . . . which apparently plays a significant role in the metabolic processes in the tissues and therefore could receive the designation of histozyme.

52 . . . during the fermentation of urine, hippuric acid is transformed into benzoic acid . . . and glycine . . . with the assimilation of water. . . .

Date Due